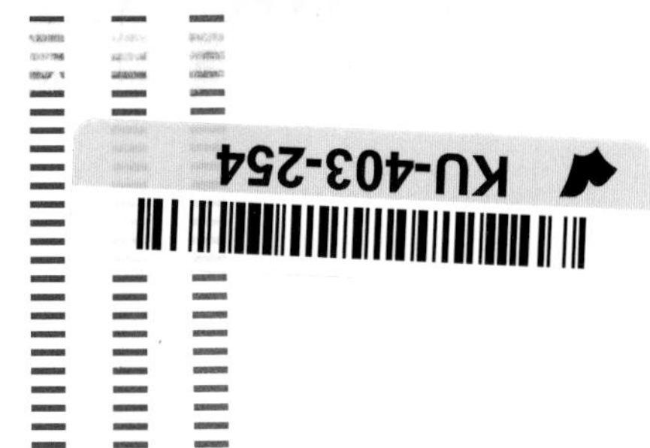

EUROPEAN UNION

OFFICIAL DIRECTORY OF THE EUROPEAN UNION

2009

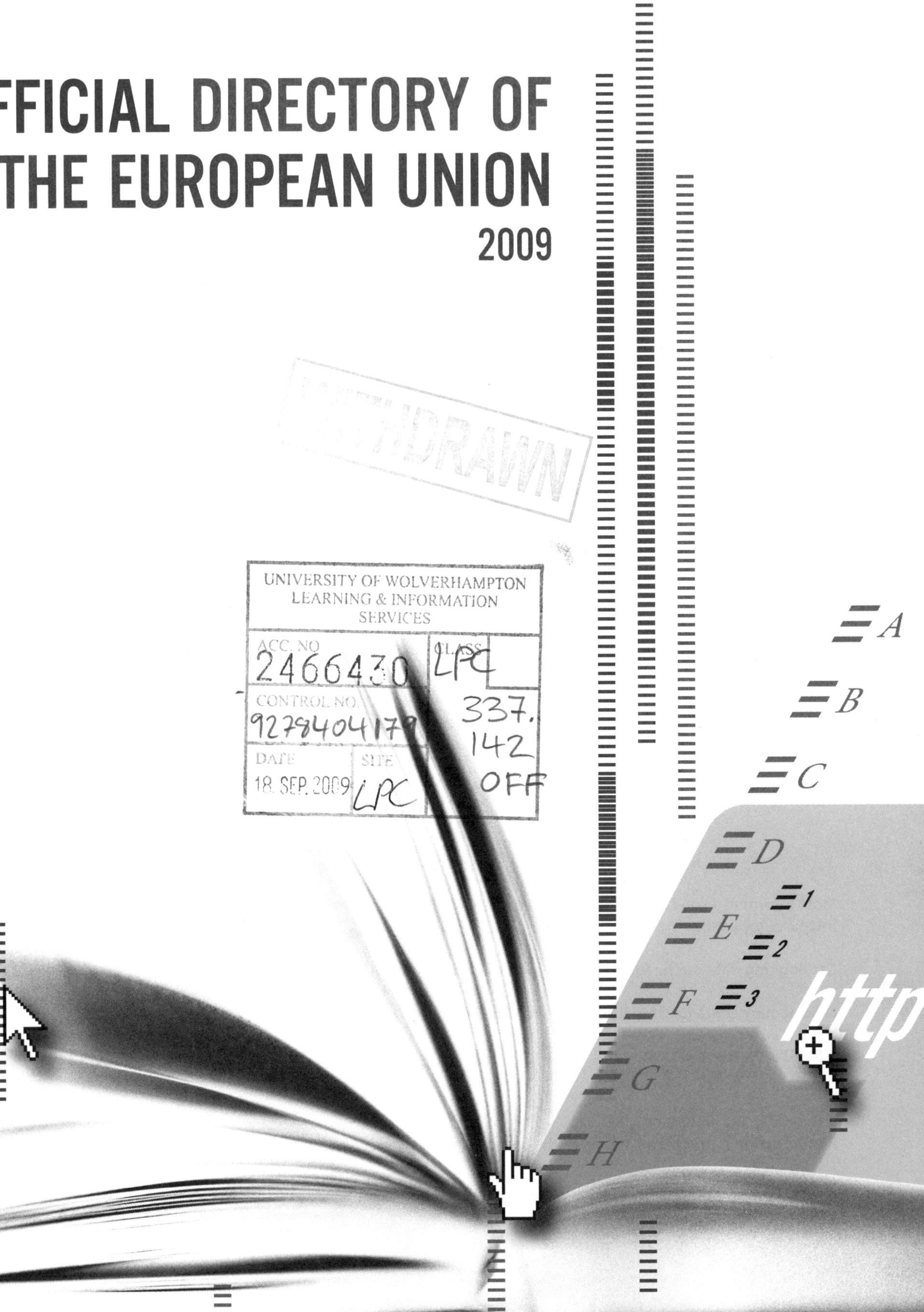

Note to the reader

This publication appears once a year in three languages: English, French and German.

It contains the organisation charts of the institutions, bodies and agencies of the European Union. An identical electronic version, updated every week, can be consulted on the site **http://whoiswho.europa.eu**

The personal data in this directory are provided by the institutions, agencies and bodies.

The data are presented following the established order where there is one, otherwise by alphabetical order, barring errors or omissions.

If you detect any errors, please report them to:
whoiswho@publications.europa.eu

Because of the number and the complexity of the titles of posts in all the various language versions, we are unable to systematically provide their feminine/masculine variants. We have therefore opted for a single title, which should be regarded as neutral.

Updated in January 1, 2009

Europe Direct is a service to help you find answers to your questions about the European Union

Freephone number (*):
00 800 6 7 8 9 10 11

(*) Certain mobile telephone operators do not allow access to 00 800 numbers or these calls may be billed.

More information on the European Union is available on the Internet (http://europa.eu).

Cataloguing data can be found at the end of this publication.

Luxembourg: Office for Official Publications of the European Communities, 2009

ISBN 978-92-78-40601-1
doi 10.2830/22439

Printed in Luxembourg

PRINTED ON WHITE CHLORINE-FREE PAPER

CONTENTS

SECTION 1

SECTION 2

SECTION 3

Useful information

Community institutions, bodies and agencies

General index of names

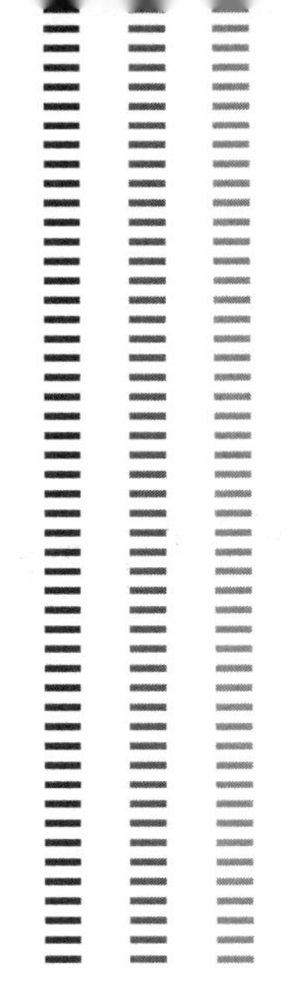

INTRODUCING THE INSTITUTIONS OF THE EUROPEAN UNION

The European Union (EU) is not a federation like the United States. Nor is it simply an organisation for cooperation between governments, like the United Nations. It is, in fact, unique. The countries that make up the EU (its Member States) pool their sovereignty in order to gain a strength and world influence that none of them could have on their own.

Pooling sovereignty means, in practice, that the Member States delegate some of their decision-making powers to shared institutions they have created, so that decisions on specific matters of joint interest can be made democratically at European level.

THE EU INSTITUTIONS

The EU's decision-making process, in general, and the co-decision procedure, in particular, involve three main institutions:

— the European Parliament, which represents the EU's citizens and is directly elected by them;

— the Council of the European Union, which represents the individual Member States;

— the European Commission, which seeks to uphold the interests of the Union as a whole.

This 'institutional triangle' produces the policies and laws (directives, regulations and decisions) that apply throughout the EU. In principle, it is the Commission that proposes new EU laws but it is the Parliament and the Council that adopt them.

Two other institutions have a vital part to play: the Court of Justice upholds the rule of European law, and the Court of Auditors checks the financing of the Union's activities.

These institutions were set up under the Treaties, which are the foundation of everything the EU does. The Treaties are agreed by the Member States' presidents and prime ministers and ratified by their parliaments. They lay down the rules and procedures that the EU institutions must follow.

In addition to its institutions, the EU has a number of other bodies that play specialised roles.

The European Ombudsman investigates complaints alleging maladministration on the part of the institutions and bodies of the European Union.

The European Data Protection Supervisor is an independent supervisory authority devoted to protecting personal data and privacy and promoting good practice in the EU institutions and bodies.

Financial bodies

— The European Central Bank is responsible for European monetary policy.

— The European Investment Bank finances EU investment projects.

— The European Investment Fund provides guarantees and venture capital to help small and medium-sized enterprises (SMEs).

Advisory bodies

— The European Economic and Social Committee represents civil society and the two sides of industry.

— The Committee of the Regions represents regional and local authorities.

Interinstitutional bodies

— The Office for Official Publications of the European Communities publishes, prints and distributes information about the EU and its activities.

— The European Communities Personnel Selection Office recruits staff for the EU institutions and other bodies.

— The core mission of the European Administrative School (EAS) is to provide training and development opportunities to groups of staff in the EU institutions at various crucial stages of their career development:

Decentralised agencies

— Within the EU's 'Community domain' — the 'first pillar' of the European Union — 23 specialised agencies (Community agencies) handle specific technical, scientific or management tasks.

— Under the common foreign and security policy (CFSP) — the 'second pillar' of the EU — agencies have been set up to carry out very specific technical, scientific and management tasks within the framework of the CFSP.

— For police and judicial cooperation in criminal matters — the 'third pillar' of the EU — another group of agencies has been set up to help the EU Member States cooperate in the fight against organised international crime.

— Executive agencies are organisations established in accordance with Council Regulation (EC) No 58/2003 (OJ L 11, 16.1.2003) with a view to being entrusted with certain tasks relating to the management of one or more Community programmes. These agencies are set up for a fixed period. Their location has to be at the seat of the European Commission (Brussels or Luxembourg).

THE EUROPEAN COUNCIL

The European Council is the highest ruling organ of the European Union. It has the role of providing political impetus for the Union and defining general political guidelines. Alongside its function as arbiter in the event of internal crises, the European Council is the initiator of new policies in all matters pertaining to the Union.

As regards its procedures and arrangements for its operation, the European Council generally meets four times a year. Each Member State is represented by its Head of State or Government, assisted by the minister for foreign affairs and, in some cases, the minister for finance. The European Commission is represented by its President, assisted by a member of the college. The President of the European Parliament is invited to address each meeting.

THE EUROPEAN PARLIAMENT

The European Parliament consists of representatives of the peoples of the Member States of the European Union. At present, 495 million Europeans from 27 countries participate in the process of European integration via their representatives, the 785 Members of the European Parliament. The Members are elected by the citizens of the Union in each Member State to serve a five-year term of office.

Legitimised by direct universal suffrage since 1979, the European Parliament, the most striking symbol of the EU's unity and democratic basis, has secured ever-increasing influence and powers whenever the Treaties were updated. With the Treaty of Maastricht (1992), the Treaty of Amsterdam (1997), the Treaty of Nice (2000) and the forthcoming Treaty of Lisbon, the European Parliament has progressed from being a mere consultative assembly to becoming a co-legislator exercising powers similar to those of national parliaments, by way of the 'co-decision' procedure. The European Parliament is the only Community institution whose meetings and deliberations are open to the public.

Composition and organisation

The Treaties lay down the following number of MEPs per Member State (figures for the period 2007–09): 99 for Germany, 78 for France, Italy and the United Kingdom, 54 for Poland and Spain, 35 for Romania, 27 for the Netherlands, 24 for Belgium, the Czech Republic, Greece, Hungary and Portugal, 19 for Sweden, 18 for Bulgaria and Austria, 14 for Denmark, Finland and Slovakia, 13 for Ireland and Lithuania, 9 for Latvia, 7 for Slovenia, 6 for Cyprus, Estonia and Luxembourg and 5 for Malta.

In the chamber, the Members do not sit in national delegations but on the basis of the political group to which they belong. At present, there are seven political groups in the European Parliament, as well as a number of 'non-attached Members'. The political groups accommodate Members of more than 100 national political parties.

The President is the representative of Parliament as an institution. He or she is responsible for the institution's external relations and chairs plenary sittings of the House and meetings of the Bureau and of the Conference of Presidents. At interinstitutional level, the President speaks at every European Council (where the Heads of State or Government meet), makes the annual budget of the European Union enforceable and signs legislative acts adopted in the context of co-decision.

The European Parliament's governing bodies are the following:

— The Conference of Presidents, which consists of the President of Parliament and the chairpersons of the political groups, is the institution's political body responsible for questions concerning relations with the other bodies and institutions of the Union, the national parliaments of the Member States, third countries and international organisations. It decides on how Parliament's work is organised, draws up the agenda of part-sessions and establishes the calendar of work of the parliamentary bodies and the powers and responsibilities and the number of members of the parliamentary committees and delegations.

— The Bureau, which is the institution's executive body, is responsible, in particular, for Parliament's preliminary draft budget and for financial, organisational and administrative matters concerning the Members, Parliament's internal organisation, its Secretariat and bodies. In addition to the President and the 14 Vice-Presidents, it also includes six Quaestors who have an advisory role and are responsible for the administrative and financial tasks directly concerning Members. Members of the Bureau are elected by the plenary session for a term of office of two and a half years.

— The Conference of Committee Chairmen, which consists of the chairmen of Parliament's standing or temporary committees, makes recommendations to the Conference of Presidents about the work of the committees and the drafting of the agenda of part-sessions.

— The Conference of Delegation Chairmen, which consists of the chairmen of all standing interparliamentary delegations, makes recommendations about the work of the delegations.

Role and powers

Like all parliaments, the European Parliament exercises three fundamental powers:

— legislative power,

— budgetary power,

— power to monitor the executive.

Legislative power

Since the entry into force of the Treaty of Amsterdam, the standard legislative procedure followed is the co-decision procedure, which places the European Parliament and the Council on an equal footing. It culminates in the adoption of joint acts of the Council and of the European Parliament. Thanks to the co-decision procedure, a large number of European Parliament amendments find their way into Community legislation. What is more, under the co-decision procedure, no legislation may now be adopted without the formal agreement of the European Parliament and of the Council of the European Union.

Co-decision currently constitutes one of Parliament's most significant powers. In particular, the procedure covers the free movement of workers, the establishment of the single market, transport, research and technological development, the environment, consumer protection, education, culture and health. Nevertheless, there are also important fields, such as taxation or the fixing of farm prices, where Parliament merely delivers an opinion on draft legislation.

Budgetary power

The budgetary authority has two arms: the European Parliament and the Council. Accordingly, it is for Parliament to adopt the budget of the Union each year, in December, at the end of the procedure laid down by the Treaties. In this way, the European Parliament indicates its political priorities. The budget, which provides the Union with the financial resources it requires for its activities in the following year, does not enter into force until it has been signed by the President of the European Parliament. That signature makes the budget officially binding.

The European Parliament has the final say as regards certain items of expenditure such as those for the regions (ERDF), for combating unemployment, especially unemployment among women and young people (ESF), and expenditure on cultural and educational programmes (Erasmus and Socrates, for example), which it can increase up to a ceiling determined jointly with the Council and the Commission. On the other hand, as regards the bulk of spending on agriculture, Parliament may table amendments, but the Council has the final say.

Should Parliament and the Council fail to reach agreement on the total amount of the budget after two readings of the draft budget, which are held between May and December, Parliament has the right to reject the entire budget, and the procedure has to go back to square one.

Power to monitor the executive

Once Parliament has adopted the budget, it also monitors the proper use of taxpayers' money through its Committee on Budgetary Control. In practical terms, it continuously monitors the management of funds, pursues an ongoing programme to improve the prevention, detection and punishment of fraud and carries out an assessment of the impact of expenditure financed by the Union budget. Parliament makes an annual assessment of the political management of the European Commission before granting it 'discharge' in respect of the implementation of the budget, in particular on the basis of reports from the Court of Auditors. In 1999, the European Parliament refused to grant discharge in respect of the implementation of the 1996 budget on the grounds of mismanagement and lack of transparency.

Parliament exercises democratic scrutiny over all Community activities. Apart from the Commission, insofar as the Council of Ministers, the European Council and the bodies responsible for political cooperation report on their activities to Parliament in the relevant debates, Parliament may be said to scrutinise their activities as well. The European Parliament may also set up committees of inquiry. By the same token, it was in response to a European Parliament initiative that the European Anti-Fraud Office (OLAF) was set up to investigate fraud against the Union's financial interests.

Parliament and the other institutions

The European Parliament plays an essential role in the procedure to appoint the Commission. Once it has ratified the appointment of the President of the Commission, the European Parliament organises hearings of the nominee Commissioners and, subsequently, elects the Commission by means of a vote of confidence.

That right comes in addition to Parliament's right to adopt a motion of censure on the Commission. This is a genuine political weapon for the European Parliament, since the adoption of a motion of censure requires the Commission to resign *en bloc*. To date, the European Parliament has never adopted a motion of censure. However, in March 1999, following a report on mismanagement in the Commission drawn up by a Committee of Wise Men at the European Parliament's behest, the Commission took the option of resigning before being subject to a formal motion of censure by Parliament.

In more general terms, Parliament scrutinises the activities of the Commission by considering a large number of monthly or annual reports which the Commission is required to submit to it (for example, the annual general report and the monthly reports on the implementation of the budget).

Members of the European Parliament may also table oral or written questions to the Commission or the Council. During part-sessions, 'Question time' provides for a series of questions on topical subjects from Members of the European Parliament with answers from Members of the Commission. Under these arrangements more than 5 000 questions are tabled by Members every year.

The extension of the powers conferred on Parliament as regards budgetary and legislative matters has increased Parliament's influence on the Council. In particular, the co-decision procedure has helped to secure a better balance in legislative powers between the Council and the European Parliament.

The European Parliament and the common foreign and security policy (CFSP)

Beginning in the early 1970s, European political cooperation culminated in a genuine joint approach by the Member States to foreign policy. The Treaty on European Union acknowledges the need to integrate a measure of common security into the foreign policy pursued jointly. The common foreign and security policy is considered to be the second pillar of the EU Treaty. In principle, it covers all the fields of international policy involving the Union's interests and constitutes the natural extension of Union activity.

The Council Presidency consults the European Parliament on the major aspects and fundamental options of the common foreign and security policy and ensures that due account is taken of the European Parliament's opinions. The European Parliament is kept regularly informed by the Council Presidency and by the Commission about trends in the Union's foreign and security policy. It will hear at regular intervals the report by the Union's High Representative for the common foreign and security policy, an office created by the Treaty of Amsterdam, the holder of which was appointed for the very first time by the Cologne European Council.

The European Parliament tables questions or makes recommendations to the Council.

The important powers in the field of external relations conferred on the European Parliament make it a genuine international forum.

The European Parliament has an opportunity to target and support the European Union's development cooperation programmes with virtually every developing country in the world through its Committee on Development and Cooperation and the ACP–EU Joint Assembly.

Moreover, Parliament's input is also guaranteed in the dialogue between the European Union and the countries of the Mediterranean (the Barcelona process), by way of Parliament's delegation to the Euromed parliamentary assembly.

Since 2006, Parliament has also been contributing to the work of the Eurolat parliamentary assembly, in the context of the EU's relations with the countries of Latin America.

More generally, the assent of the European Parliament is required for the accession of new Member States, for association agreements with third countries and for the conclusion of other international agreements.

Since it attaches great importance to the protection of human rights, it uses that power to require third countries, where appropriate, to improve their human rights record.

The European Parliament and cooperation in the fields of justice and home affairs

The European Parliament attaches great importance to the implementation of policies involving matters of common interest in the policies on asylum and immigration, and combating drugs, fraud and international crime.

Parliament is regularly consulted and informed about cooperation between the bodies responsible for justice and home affairs in the Member States of the Union. It tables questions or makes recommendations to the Council. Every year, it holds a debate on the progress achieved in those areas.

The European Parliament and democratic scrutiny of economic and monetary union

With regard to the European Central Bank, a major role is conferred on Parliament in the context of economic and monetary union.

The bank enjoys total independence as regards monetary policy. It alone is entitled to fix short-term interest rates and use the other monetary instruments required to maintain the stability of the euro.

Nevertheless, that operational independence of the ECB is counterbalanced by its obligation to report back to the European Parliament. Parliament has incorporated some very specific provisions in its rules of procedure to govern its role in the appointment of the President of the ECB and of the Vice-President and other executive board members. The latter, after being heard in committee, must secure the approval of the European Parliament before they may be appointed by the Council.

Each year, the President of the ECB is required to report to the European Parliament meeting in plenary session. Furthermore, the President of the ECB and other executive board members appear at regular intervals before the European Parliament's appropriate committee. Either party may ask for that procedure to be initiated; at all events, at least four such meetings are held every year.

Seat and administration

In accordance with the decision taken in Edinburgh by the representatives of the governments of the Member States on 12 December 1992, 'The European Parliament shall have its seat in Strasbourg where the 12 periods of monthly plenary sessions, including the budget session, shall be held. The periods of additional plenary sessions shall be held in Brussels.'

The parliamentary committees and the political groups also meet in Brussels. In all, 1821 officials and other servants employed in the Parliament's Secretariat are assigned to Luxembourg, with a further 1255 in Brussels, 53 in Strasbourg and 110 in the external offices.

THE COUNCIL OF THE EUROPEAN UNION

The Council of the European Union is a Community institution composed of one representative of each Member State at ministerial level, authorised to commit the government of that Member State.

Under the Treaty establishing the European Community, the main responsibilities of the Council are the following:

— the Council, together with Parliament, is the Community's legislative body; for a wide range of Community issues, it exercises that legislative power in co-decision with the European Parliament (see below);

— the Council coordinates the general economic policies of the Member States;

— the Council concludes, on behalf of the Community, international agreements between the latter and one or more States or international organisations;

— the Council and the European Parliament constitute the budgetary authority that adopts the Community budget.

Under the Treaty on European Union:

— the Council takes the decisions necessary for defining and implementing the common foreign and security policy, on the basis of general guidelines established by the European Council;

— the Council coordinates the activities of Member States and adopts measures in the field of police and judicial cooperation in criminal matters.

The Council meets when convened by its President on his own initiative or at the request of one of its members or of the Commission. The Council's seat is in Brussels at 175, rue de la Loi.

During the months of April, June and October, the Council holds its meetings in Luxembourg. The Council meets in different compositions depending on the matters to be dealt with, namely:

1. General affairs and external relations

2. Economic and financial affairs

3. Justice and home affairs

4. Employment, social policy, health and consumer affairs

5. Competitiveness (internal market, industry and research)

6. Transport, telecommunications and energy

7. Agriculture and fisheries

8. Environment

9. Education, youth and culture.

Where the Council acts alone as legislator, the right of initiative lies with the European Commission, which submits a proposal to the Council. The proposal is examined within the Council, which consults the European Parliament, and it may be amended before adoption. In the acts which it adopts, the Council may confer implementing powers on the Commission.

In most cases, the European Parliament takes part in the legislative process and acts are adopted jointly by the Parliament and the Council under the co-decision procedure. The European Community's budget is also drawn up jointly by the European Parliament and the Council.

The Treaties lay down that, depending on the case, the Council acts by a simple majority of its members, by a qualified majority or unanimously. In the Community sphere, a large proportion of legislative decisions are taken by qualified majority.

In the framework of the Treaty establishing the European Community, Council acts may take the form of regulations, directives, decisions, recommendations or opinions. The Council may also adopt conclusions of a political nature or other types of acts such as declarations or resolutions.

With regard to cooperation in justice and home affairs, Council acts may take the form of framework decisions, decisions and conventions, and the general voting rule is unanimity.

As regards the common foreign and security policy (CFSP) and the European security and defence policy (ESDP), the Council takes the decisions necessary for defining and implementing these policies on the basis of the general guidelines adopted by the European Council if need be.

The Council's work is prepared by the Permanent Representatives Committee (Coreper), consisting of the permanent representatives of the Member States of the European Union and of their deputies, which meets every week. This Committee also oversees and coordinates the work of committees and working parties made up of civil servants from the Member States who prepare at the technical level the matters to be discussed by Coreper and the Council.

Council website: http://www.consilium.europa.eu/

THE EUROPEAN COMMISSION

Up until 31 October 2004, the European Commission had two Members from Germany, Spain, France, Italy and the United Kingdom and one Member from each of the other European Union countries. Since then, after a brief interim phase corresponding to the enlargement of the Union to 27 Member States, it has had one Member from each of these countries. In 1995, the Commission's term of office was raised from four to five years, bringing it into line with the European Parliament. According to the Treaty of Nice, the President of the Commission is nominated by the Council, meeting at the level of Heads of State or Government. This nomination must be approved by Parliament. The Council and the nominee for President then adopt, by common agreement, the list of Commission Members, in accordance with the proposals made by each Member State. Once the composition of the Commission has been approved by the Parliament, the President and the other Members of the Commission are appointed by the Council.

In carrying out their duties, Members of the Commission are obliged to be completely independent of their national governments and of any other body and to act only in the interests of the European Union. Only Parliament has the right to pass a motion of censure against it; in this case, the Members of the Commission are obliged to resign collectively. Each Member of the Commission has special responsibility for one or more policy areas as allocated by the President, but decisions are taken jointly, by simple majority, on the basis of collective responsibility.

At the start of its term of office, the Commission presents the European Parliament with the strategic objectives that it intends to pursue during the five years of this term of office. Then, under its annual programming cycle, it adopts its annual policy strategy as well as a legislative and work programme for the year in question.

As regards its responsibilities, the Commission is first and foremost the guardian of the Treaties. In this capacity, it sees to it that Treaty provisions and European Union decisions are correctly applied. It can initiate infringement proceedings against any Member State and may, if necessary, refer matters to the Court of Justice. It can also impose fines on individuals or companies, notably when they act in breach of the European Union's competition rules.

The Commission is also the catalyst of the European Union. It has the sole right of initiative in the field of European Community legislation, and it can exert its influence at any stage of the process preceding the adoption of a new legislative act, including by amending its initial proposal. In the area of intergovernmental cooperation, the Commission has the same rights as the individual Member States with regard to the submission of proposals.

In its role as catalyst, in addition to presenting reports on the application of legislation in general (for example, competition law) or specific legislation (for example, this or that directive) or on the implementation of operational activities (for example, development cooperation), the Commission also produces many guideline and discussion documents. These generally take the form of communications, but also, more sporadically, the form of Green Papers, aimed at launching a wide debate on a given subject, or White Papers, advocating a series of measures for implementing a policy.

Finally, the Commission is the European Union's executive body. This involves issuing rules for the implementation of certain Treaty articles and administering budget appropriations earmarked for Community operations. A large part of this budget is allocated to one or other of the main funds aimed at financing Community policies such as agricultural policy, social policy, regional policy or development aid to certain non-member countries.

In carrying out its duties, the Commission is often required to seek the opinion of committees made up of representatives from the Member States. More generally, it holds extensive consultations so that the parties affected by a given legislative act can have their say in its preparation. An evaluation of the economic, environmental and social impact of the proposed legislative initiative is, furthermore, generally drawn up and published at the same time as the proposal. Finally, the principles of subsidiarity and proportionality should be respected, which means that the Commission should not propose to legislate unless it is more effective to do it at Community level and only to the extent necessary to achieve the desired objectives. The Commission should not legislate if it is more effective to legislate at national, regional or local level.

The Commission met 43 times in 2008. It presented 413 proposals for directives, regulations and decisions and seven recommendations for adoption by the Council or by Parliament and the Council together. It also presented 394 communications (including the communications according to Article 251, 2nd paragraph, 2nd line of the EC Treaty EC concerning the Council common position) and reports, as well as four Green Papers and one White Paper.

In November 2008, the Commission had 23008 permanent administrative posts and 1879 temporary administrative posts. Besides, 5759 contractual agents, 516 temporary staff, 2102 service providers and 1124 detached national experts work in the services of the Commission.

THE COURT OF JUSTICE OF THE EUROPEAN COMMUNITIES (COURT OF JUSTICE, COURT OF FIRST INSTANCE AND CIVIL SERVICE TRIBUNAL)

Composition

The Court of Justice of the European Communities, which has its seat in Luxembourg, is composed of the Court of Justice of the European Communities and the Court of First Instance of the European Communities, to which has been added the Civil Service Tribunal of the European Union.

The Court of Justice consists of 27 judges (one judge per Member State) and is assisted by eight advocates-general. The judges and advocates-general are appointed by common accord of the governments of the Member States for a renewable term of six years. They are chosen from jurists whose independence is beyond doubt, and who possess the qualifications required for appointment to the highest judicial offices in their respective countries, or are of recognised competence.

The Court of First Instance, established in 1988, consists of at least one judge per Member State (currently 27 judges). They are appointed by common accord of the governments of the Member States for a renewable term of six years, from persons whose independence is beyond doubt and who possess the ability required for appointment to high judicial office.

The European Union Civil Service Tribunal — a judicial panel the creation of which was made possible by the Treaty of Nice — was created in November 2004. It consists of seven judges appointed by the Council for a renewable period of six years, following a call for candidacies and notice of a committee comprising seven persons chosen from among former members of the Court of Justice and the Court of First Instance and lawyers of recognised competence.

Jurisdiction

It is the role of the Court of Justice, and of the Court of First Instance likewise, to ensure that the law is observed in the interpretation and application of the Treaties establishing the European Communities and of the provisions laid down by the competent Community institutions.

The Court of Justice, whose opinion may also be sought by the Member States and the institutions, possesses extensive jurisdiction. It has, inter alia, jurisdiction:

- to give a preliminary ruling, at the request of national courts, on the interpretation of the Treaties and also on the validity and interpretation of acts adopted by the institutions;
- to give a decision, where the matter is brought before it by the Commission or a Member State, on the failure of a Member State to fulfil one of its obligations under the Treaties. The Member State is required to take the measures necessary to comply with the Court's judgment and, if it fails to do so, the case may again be brought before the Court which may order that Member State to pay a lump sum or penalty payment;
- to hear and determine actions for annulment and actions for a declaration of failure to act brought by a Member State against Parliament and/or the Council (except in respect of certain acts of the Council) or brought by one institution against another;
- to decide appeals against decisions of the Court of First Instance.

The Court of First Instance has jurisdiction to hear and determine at first instance:

- direct actions brought by natural or legal persons against acts of the Community institutions (of which they are the addressees or which are of direct and individual concern to them) or against a failure by those institutions to act;
- actions brought by the Member States against the Commission;
- actions brought by the Member States against the Council concerning acts adopted in the sphere of State aid, measures to protect trade (dumping) and acts in respect of which it exercises implementing powers;
- actions seeking damages for loss caused by the Community institutions or their agents;
- actions based on contracts entered into by the Communities that provide expressly for the Court of First Instance to have jurisdiction;
- actions relating to the Community trade mark.

An appeal limited to points of law may be brought, within a period of two months, against decisions given by the Court of First Instance.

Disputes between the Communities and their agents are entrusted to the Civil Service Tribunal. It is possible to lodge an appeal limited to points of law before the Court of First Instance against a decision of the Civil Service Tribunal. The decision on appeal by the Court of First Instance may, exceptionally, be reviewed by the Court of Justice.

Volume of litigation

Between 1952 and 2007, 15068 cases were brought before the Court of Justice, of which 14337 have been settled and in which 7557 judgments have been delivered, and of which 8129 were direct actions and 6030 requests for a preliminary ruling. Between 1952 and 2007 the Court of Justice gave 18 opinions.

Between 1989 and 2007, 6778 cases were brought before the Court of First Instance. During the same period, 5 624 cases were settled and 2 087 judgments delivered.

Between 2005 and 2007, 435 cases were brought before the Civil Service Tribunal. During that period, 200 cases were settled and 87 judgments delivered.

THE EUROPEAN COURT OF AUDITORS

The European Court of Auditors is the institution of the European Union established by the Treaty to carry out the audit of European Union finances. As the European Union's external auditor it contributes to improving European Union financial management and acts as the independent guardian of the financial interests of the citizens of the Union.

The Court was created in 1975, started work in 1977 and has its offices in Luxembourg. The Treaty of Maastricht of 7 February 1992 made the European Court of Auditors an institution of the European Communities. The Treaty of Amsterdam of 2 October 1997 recognised the Court of Auditors as an institution of the European Union and thus formally enlarged the Court's audit scope to include the second and third pillars of the Union.

Governance and organisation

Structure

The Court of Auditors operates as a collegiate body of 27 Members, one from each Member State. All audit reports and opinions are adopted by the college. It also takes decisions concerning the Court's organisation and administration.

The Court organises itself around five audit groups, to which Members are assigned. There are four sectorial groups, covering different parts of the budget (preservation and management of natural resources; structural policies, transport, research and energy; external actions; own resources, banking activities, administrative expenditure, Community institutions and bodies and internal policies). Each group is chaired by a dean, elected by the Members of the group from amongst their number for a renewable two-year term.

A fifth audit group (CEAD or 'coordination, communication, evaluation, assurance and development') is responsible for 'horizontal' matters such as the coordination of the statement of assurance, quality assurance, the development of the Court's audit methodology and communication of the Court's work and output.

An Administrative Committee, composed of Members representing all audit groups, prepares all administrative matters for a formal decision by the Court.

The Members

The Members of the Court are appointed by the Council, after consultation of the European Parliament, following nomination by their respective Member States. Members are appointed for a renewable term of six years. They are required to perform their duties in complete independence and in the general interest of the European Union. Apart from being part of the college, taking the final decisions on audits and opinions as well as on broader strategic and administrative issues, each Member is responsible for his or her own audit tasks.

The President

The European Court of Auditors is headed by a President who is elected for a renewable term of three years by the Members from amongst their number. His or her role is that of *primus inter pares* — first amongst equals. He or she chairs the Court meetings, ensures that Court decisions are implemented and that the institution and its activities are soundly managed.

The President represents the Court in its external relations, in particular with the discharge authority, the other EU institutions and the supreme audit institutions of the Member and beneficiary States.

Role

As the external auditor of the EU, the European Court of Auditors checks that EU funds are correctly accounted for and spent in compliance with rules and legislation with due consideration for achieving best value for money, irrespective of where the funds are spent.

The results of the Court's work are used by the Commission, the Parliament and the Council as well as by Member States, to improve financial management of the EU budget.

The Court's work provides an important basis for the annual discharge procedure whereby the Parliament, basing its decision on recommendations from the Council, decides whether the Commission has met its responsibility for the execution of the previous year's budget.

Despite its name, the Court has no judicial powers. The European Court of Auditors informs OLAF, the European Anti-Fraud Office, of cases of irregularity or suspected fraud detected in the course of its audit work.

In the areas of the budget where management is shared, Member States cooperate with the Commission in setting up supervisory and control systems — internal control — to ensure that funds are spent properly and in accordance with the rules. Internal control thus has an EU as well as a national dimension. In addition to the work done by the Court, many national audit institutions audit European funds that are managed and spent by national administrations.

Audit work

The Court carries out three different types of audits: financial, compliance and performance. These address the three following questions.

- Do the accounts present fairly, in all material respects, the financial position, results and cash flow for the year, in accordance with the applicable financial reporting framework? (*Financial audit.*)
- Are activities, financial transactions and information, in all material respects, in compliance with the legal and regulatory frameworks which govern them? (*Compliance audit.*)
- Is the financial management sound, i.e. are the funds used kept to a minimum (economy), are the results achieved with the least possible resources (efficiency) and have objectives been met (effectiveness)? (*Performance audit.*)

Most of the Court's financial and compliance audit is carried out in the context of its annual statement of assurance which is presented in the annual report on the implementation of the EU budget. The EC Treaty requires the Court to give such a statement — or opinion — on the reliability of the accounts and the legality and regularity of underlying transactions. The annual statement of assurance is generally known by its French acronym DAS *(declaration d'assurance)*.

Audit reports and opinions

The results of the Court's financial and compliance audits are mainly published in annual reports on the general EU budget and on the European Development Funds (EDFs), as well as in specific reports on the Union's agencies. The results of its performance audits are published in special reports over the year.

The Court also contributes to improving the financial management of EU funds by providing opinions on proposals or financial management issues. These opinions are required as part of the process of adopting financial legislation, or can be delivered at the request of one or other of the EU institutions. The Court of Auditors may also produce opinions on its own initiative.

ADVISORY BODIES

The European Economic and Social Committee (EESC)

The European Economic and Social Committee is a consultative body set up by the Treaties of Rome in 1957. Its main task is to advise the three major institutions (the European Parliament, the Council of the European Union and the European Commission).

It is mandatory for the Committee to be consulted on those issues stipulated in the Treaties and in all cases where the institutions deem it appropriate. In addition, the Committee can itself take the initiative to issue opinions — around 15 % of its opinions are own-initiative opinions — or to draft information reports. The other institutions can also ask it to produce an exploratory opinion in areas of particular importance. Currently, the Committee produces around 180 opinions a year on a wide range of subjects.

In addition to its consultative role, the EESC has two other complementary roles. These consist of:

- involving civil society organisations more in the European venture;
- boosting the role of civil society organisations in non-member countries, such as the countries applying for EU membership, the Euro-Med countries bordering the Mediterranean, the African, Caribbean and Pacific (ACP) countries, the Mercosur countries (Latin America), and India, amongst others.

To this end, the Committee is developing a structured dialogue with representatives of civil society organisations in these countries and regions and endeavouring to promote the creation of consultative structures in them.

The members of the Committee

The Committee is made up of 344 members split into three groups. Traditionally the 'Employers' and the 'Employees' groups represent the employers and trade union organisations, while the 'Various Interests' group' includes 'various other economic and social components of organised civil society' including representatives of bodies acting on behalf of craftsmen, farmers, SMEs and the professions.

Nevertheless, the Committee's membership is not static. It changes with each renewal of the Committee so as to reflect changes in civil society in the Member States. Representatives of consumer bodies, associations promoting the rights of disabled people and combating exclusion, family associations, environmental protection bodies have also, over the years, contributed to the wealth of experience represented in the Committee since its establishment.

The Committee as a 'bridge' between Europe and civil society

Because they belong to civil society organisations in the Member States, EESC members directly represent the many different interests of civil society organisations in their activities. They thus bring to bear the expertise for which they were appointed.

The Committee of the Regions of the European Union

The Committee of the Regions, which was created by the Treaty on European Union, currently has 344 full members and an equal number of alternates, appointed for a four-year term by the Council of the European Union following a proposal from the Member States. The Treaty of Nice, adopted in December 2000, set the maximum number of members of the Committee of the Regions at 350 to take into account future enlargements of the Union.

Since the Treaty of Nice entered into force, the members of the Committee of the Regions must hold a regional or a local authority electoral mandate or be politically accountable to an elected regional or local assembly. Furthermore, they are now appointed by the Council on the basis of a qualified majority vote and no longer unanimously.

The members of the Committee fulfil a twofold function on behalf of the EU's citizens: firstly, by defending their immediate interests in the Community policymaking process and, secondly, by communicating to them all the European Union activities that have an impact on the day-to-day running of their regional or local authorities.

The members of the Committee of the Regions, who live and work in the region or town where they were elected and assume political responsibilities within regional or local authorities, are well acquainted with the concerns of the citizens they represent. At the meetings of the Committee of the Regions, they can therefore act as the representatives of their localities or regions, whose workings they understand perfectly, and then explain the Community policies to their fellow citizens on their return.

Since the Amsterdam Treaty entered into force in 1999, the European Commission and the Council consult the Committee on a wide range of Community issues that are important to local and regional authorities:

- transport policy;
- employment policy guidelines;
- incentives to promote cooperation between Member States in the employment field and to support their employment measures;
- social provisions;
- implementing decisions concerning the European Social Fund;
- support measures in the field of education and youth;
- vocational training;
- support measures in the cultural field;
- support measures in the health sector;
- definition of guidelines and actions for the construction and expansion of trans-European networks;
- specific structural policy actions outside the scope of the Structural Funds;
- definition of the tasks, objectives, organisation and general rules of the Structural Funds, and setting-up of the Cohesion Fund;
- implementing decisions concerning the European Regional Development Fund;
- environment policy.

Furthermore, the Committee of the Regions may now be consulted by the European Parliament on matters of mutual interest. The Committee has also forged extremely close and complementary ties with the European Parliament.

The Committee of the Regions is a direct link between the European Union and its citizens and issues opinions on its own initiative on draft European legislation and other initiatives likely to have repercussions at regional or local level. Moreover, in accordance with the White Paper on European governance, published in July 2001 by the Commission, which concluded that citizens should participate more in the process of drawing up Community policies, a cooperation protocol between the Commission and the Committee of the Regions was signed at the end of September 2001, strengthening the Committee's involvement in the debates through 'outlook and impact reports'. The Commission requests outlook reports on topics it considers important and before it takes any decision, enabling the Committee of the Regions to intervene before a decision is made. Only the President of the Commission or a member of the college is entitled to request such reports from the Committee. The Commission can also ask the Committee of the Regions for an impact report which evaluates the regional or local effect of a policy.

The Committee holds five plenary sessions per year, at which around 60 opinions are adopted. These opinions are drawn up by six specialised commissions, which deal with all aspects of Community policy (territorial cohesion, economic and social policy, sustainable development, culture and education, external relations and constitutional affairs).

These opinions address the concerns and expectations of the regions and cities on specific issues and contribute to applying the principle of subsidiarity, whereby decisions should be taken as close to the citizen as possible.

Another of the CoR's priorities is the promotion of economic, social and territorial cohesion within the European Union. Reducing disparities, with the aid of the Structural and Cohesion Funds, essentially fosters balanced development throughout the Community, the creation of jobs and the protection of the environment. The cohesion policy ensures solidarity between all regions and citizens.

Maintaining the cohesion policy in a Europe of 27 Member States, in which economic, social and territorial disparities are widening, is crucial for the Committee of the Regions. The Committee of the Regions thus covered this issue in numerous opinions until a new regional cohesion policy for 2007–13 was developed, incorporating Community funding of EUR 308 billion.

The Committee of the Regions has also invested heavily in the second phase of the Lisbon strategy. It has been able to stimulate mobilisation and the involvement of regional and local authorities, both of which had been neglected in the past by this Community policy designed to increase growth and employment.

The consultative role of the Committee of the Regions in the Community legislative process has been enhanced by a series of communication and forum initiatives within regions and cities (and their networks). Of these, it is particularly worth noting the organisation of 'Open days', the European Week of Regions and Cities, which brings together thousands of regional policy decision-makers and stakeholders every autumn in Brussels.

FINANCIAL BODIES

The European Investment Bank (EIB)

The European Investment Bank (EIB) is the European Union's financing institution. Its shareholders are the 27 Member States of the Union, which have jointly subscribed its capital. The EIB's Board of Governors is composed of the finance ministers of these States.

The EIB's role is to provide long-term loans in support of projects in a number of regions and various fields, furthering one or more of the European Union's objectives.

Within the European Union, the EIB's current operational priorities are focused on investment that:

— promotes, as a priority objective, economic and social cohesion in the EU-27 (two thirds of financing is targeted at assisted areas);

— supports innovation under its 'Innovation 2010' initiative (for research, development and innovation, human capital formation, and information and communications technology networks) to help implement the Lisbon strategy (European Council, March 2000);

— develops the trans-European networks (TENs) — major transport, energy and telecommunications infrastructure networks — in particular as part of the 'action for growth' initiative (European Council, December 2003);

— protects the natural and urban environments (about 35 % of lending);

— assists investment by SMEs through medium- and long-term EIB global loans to financial intermediaries.

In the partner countries, the Bank participates in implementing the Union's development aid and cooperation policies. It operates mainly in:

— the enlargement countries in eastern and southern Europe;

— the non-member Mediterranean countries by helping to attain the objectives of the Facility for Euro-Mediterranean Investment and Partnership (FEMIP) with a view to facilitating the establishment of a customs union by 2010;

— Russia and the eastern neighbours;

— the African, Caribbean and Pacific (ACP) States, South Africa, and the overseas countries and territories (OCTs);

— Asia and Latin America, where it supports certain types of projects of mutual interest to the Union and the countries concerned;

The EIB, the largest international non-sovereign lender and borrower, raises the resources it needs to finance its lending activities by borrowing on the capital markets, primarily via public bond issues. By virtue of its top credit rating (AAA), it can obtain the keenest terms on the market. As a not-for-profit institution, the EIB passes on this advantage in the terms it offers to the beneficiaries of its loans in both the public and private sectors.

The EIB has close working relations with the other EU institutions, in particular the European Parliament, the European Council and the European Commission. The European Investment Fund is a subsidiary of the EIB.

European Investment Fund

The European Investment Fund (EIF) was created in 1994 and is the European Union's specialised vehicle to support innovation and small- and medium-sized enterprises (SMEs). It operates across the EU, the candidate and EFTA countries and its headquarters are located in Luxembourg.

The EIF has a tripartite shareholder structure. The European Investment Bank (EIB) is the primary shareholder, holding 64 % of shares; the EIF forms part of the EIB Group. The European Community has a 27 % shareholding and 31 public and private banks and financial institutions hold 9 % of shares. The EIF has an authorised capital of EUR 3 000 million, of which EUR 2 865 million is subscribed.

The EIF has the status of a multilateral development bank and has a 20 % BIS weighting and a 0 % proposed BIS-II weighting.

Its long-term risk rating is AAA, Aaa and AAA by Standard and Poor's, Moody's and Fitch respectively.

Activity is focused on the complementary instruments of SME portfolio guarantees and venture capital. These are provided using either the EIF's own funds or monies available within the framework of mandates entrusted to it by the EIB and the European Commission. Funds are also managed by the EIF for other third parties.

The EIF provides portfolio guarantees to a wide range of counterparties, namely banks, leasing companies, guarantee institutions, mutual guarantee funds and special purpose vehicles.

In the context of securitisation transactions, intermediaries may obtain an EIF portfolio guarantee which enables banks and leasing companies to transfer their credit risk to the capital markets, achieving capital relief and freeing up capacity for new SME loans or leases. In the context the EC 'Competitiveness and Innovation Framework Programme' (CIP 2007–13), the EIF provides guarantees or counter-guarantees covering up to 50 % of the credit risk in relation to a portfolio of SME loans or leases.

The EIF acts as a fund-of-funds and participates in venture capital and private equity funds that invest primarily in early to mid-stage SMEs. It also provides funding for business expansion and innovation. Through its unique strategy framework, the EIF contributes to the pursuit of European Community objectives whilst acting as a commercially minded investor seeking a risk-commensurate return on its investments. It invests both in country-specific and in multi-country funds and contributes to the development of a balanced private equity market. Based on its broad, pan-European experience, the EIF promotes EU best-industry practice for terms and conditions, fund governance and structure. The EC CIP programme also covers venture capital through the High Growth and Innovative SME Facility (GIF). The GIF supports innovative SMEs throughout their life cycle and provides important leverage for the supply of equity to these companies.

The GIF also incorporates increased eco-innovation financing, an area where EIF is further developing its activities.

Finally, the EIF's advisory services provide strategic and technical financial advice for a fee to public and private counterparts.

The Joint European Resources for Micro to Medium Enterprises (Jeremie) initiative was launched at the end of 2005 by the Regional Policy DG of the European Commission and by the EIF, with the objective of improving SMEs' access to finance in regional development areas. In 2006 and 2007, the EIF team responsible for managing Jeremie and the national and regional authorities responsible for the programmes evaluated, in conjunction with the national institutions, the disparities between the supply and the demand for finance for SMEs and agreed on operational action plans to implement. As the initiative is now in its implementation phase, EIF will elaborate financing mechanisms in close cooperation with financial institutions such as the EIB, other international financial institutions and national and regional banks, including several EIF shareholders.

The European Central Bank

Background

Since 1 January 1999 the European Central Bank (ECB) has been responsible for conducting monetary policy for the euro area, which comprises the 16 European Union countries that have introduced the euro. The euro area came into being when responsibility for monetary policy was transferred from the national central banks of 11 EU Member States to the ECB in January 1999. Greece joined as the 12th member two years later. Slovenia adopted the euro in 2007, Cyprus and Malta in 2008, Slovakia in 2009.

The creation of the euro area and a new supranational institution, the ECB, was a milestone in a long and complex process of European integration. The legal basis for the single monetary policy is the EC Treaty and the Statute of the European System of Central Banks and of the European Central Bank. The Statute established both the ECB and the European System of Central Banks (ESCB) as from 1 June 1998. The ESCB comprises the ECB and the national central banks (NCBs) of all EU Member States (Article 107(1) of the EC Treaty) whether they have adopted the euro or not. Within the ESCB, the Eurosystem comprises the ECB and the NCBs of those countries that have adopted the euro. The Eurosystem and the ESCB will co-exist as long as there are EU Member States outside the euro area.

Composition

ESCB: the European Central Bank and the NCBs of all EU Member States.

Eurosystem: the European Central Bank and the NCBs of Belgium, Germany, Ireland, Greece, Spain, France, Italy, Cyprus, Luxembourg, Malta, the Netherlands, Austria, Portugal, Slovakia, Slovenia and Finland.

Objectives

- The primary objective of the ESCB shall be to maintain price stability.
- Without prejudice to the objective of price stability, the ESCB shall support the general economic policies in the Community with a view to contributing to the achievement of the objectives of the Community.

Tasks

According to the EC Treaty (Article 105, 2nd paragraph), the basic tasks are:

- definition and implementation of monetary policy for the euro-area;
- conduct of foreign exchange operations;
- holding and management of the official foreign reserves of the euro-area countries (portfolio management);
- promotion of the smooth operation of payment systems.

Further tasks

- Banknotes: the ECB has the exclusive right to authorise the issuance of banknotes within the euro area.
- Statistics: in cooperation with the NCBs, the ECB collects statistical information necessary for fulfilling its tasks, either from national authorities or directly from economic agents.
- Financial stability supervision: the Eurosystem contributes to the smooth conduct of policies pursued by the authorities in charge related to the prudential supervision of credit institutions and the stability of the financial system.
- International and European cooperation: the ECB maintains working relations with relevant institutions, bodies and forums both within the EU and internationally in respect of tasks entrusted to the Eurosystem.

Decision-making

The decision-making bodies of the ECB are the Governing Council, the Executive Board and, as long as there are EU Member States which have not yet adopted the euro, the General Council.

The Governing Council

The Governing Council comprises all the members of the Executive Board and the governors and presidents of the NCBs of the EU Member States which have adopted the euro. It is responsible for formulating the monetary policy for the euro area, including decisions relating to monetary objectives, key interest rates, the supply of reserves in the Eurosystem, as well as the establishment of guidelines for the implementation of those decisions.

The Executive Board

The Executive Board comprises the President, the Vice-President and four other members, all chosen from among persons of recognised standing and professional experience in monetary or banking matters. All members are appointed by common accord of the Heads of State or Government of the euro-area countries. The Executive Board prepares Governing Council meetings, is responsible for the implementation of the monetary policy for the euro area, in accordance with the guidelines specified and decisions taken by the Governing Council. In so doing, it gives the necessary instructions to the euro-area NCBs; the Executive Board also manages the day-to-day business of the ECB and exercises certain powers delegated to it by the Governing Council. These include some of a regulatory nature.

The General Council

The General Council comprises the President and the Vice-President and the governors and presidents of the NCBs of all EU Member States. It can be regarded as a transitional body and carries out the tasks taken over from the European Monetary Institute which the ECB is required to perform in Stage III of economic and monetary union (EMU) on account of the fact that not all EU Member States have adopted the euro yet.

Organisation

At the ECB headquarters (Frankfurt am Main), there are some 1 375 staff members (as per the ECB annual report 2007), recruited from all 27 EU countries, fulfilling their tasks assigned to certain business areas: administration, banknotes, communications, counsel to the Executive Board, ECB permanent representation in Washington DC, economics, financial stability and supervision, human resources, budget and organisation, information systems, internal audit, international and European relations, legal services, market operations, payments and market infrastructure, research, secretariat and language services or statistics.

Corporate governance

In addition to the decision-making bodies, the corporate governance of the ECB encompasses a number of external and internal control layers, as well as rules concerning public access to ECB documents. The Statute of the ESCB provides for two layers, namely the external auditor, which is appointed to audit the annual accounts of the ECB (Article 27.1 of the Statute of the ESCB), and the European Court of Auditors, which examines the operational efficiency of the management of the ECB (Article 27.2). The annual report of the European Court of Auditors, together with the ECB's reply, is published in the *Official Journal of the European Union* and on the ECB's website.

OTHER BODIES

The European Ombudsman

The European Ombudsman investigates complaints about maladministration in the institutions and bodies of the European Union. The Ombudsman is completely independent and impartial. The current Ombudsman is Mr P. Nikiforos Diamandouros, who took office on 1 April 2003.

The Ombudsman investigates cases of maladministration (poor or failed administration). Maladministration occurs if an institution fails to act in accordance with the law, fails to respect the principles of good administration, or violates human rights. Some examples are:

- administrative irregularities,
- unfairness,
- discrimination,
- abuse of power,
- failure to reply,
- refusal of information,
- unnecessary delay.

The Ombudsman usually conducts inquiries on the basis of complaints but can also launch inquiries on his own initiative.

The Ombudsman cannot investigate:

- complaints against national, regional or local authorities in the Member States, even when the complaints are about EU matters; examples of such authorities are government departments, State agencies and local councils;
- the activities of national courts or ombudsmen; the European Ombudsman is not an appeals body for decisions taken by these entities;
- complaints against businesses or private individuals.

If you are a citizen of a Member State of the Union or reside in a Member State, you can make a complaint to the European Ombudsman. Businesses, associations or other bodies with a registered office in the Union may also complain to the Ombudsman.

Complaints can be lodged by post, fax or e-mail. A complaint guide and form is available from the Ombudsman's office and can be downloaded from the Ombudsman's website.

European Data Protection Supervisor

The EDPS is an independent supervisory authority devoted to protecting personal data and privacy and promoting good practice in the EU institutions and bodies. It does so by:

- monitoring the EU administration's processing of personal data;
- advising on policies and legislation that affect privacy;
- cooperating with similar authorities to ensure consistent data protection.

The EDPS

Peter Hustinx and Joaquin Bayo Delgado were appointed European Data Protection Supervisor (EDPS) and Assistant Supervisor for a five-year term, as of January 2004. Their mission is to make sure that the fundamental right to protection of personal data is respected by the EU institutions and bodies. A data protection culture needs to be developed in practice. This work towards good administration takes several forms.

Supervision

The supervisory task is to ensure that the EU institutions and bodies process personal data of EU staff and others lawfully. The EDPS oversees Regulation (EC) No 45/2001 on data protection, which is based on two main principles.

1. The responsible data controller needs to respect a number of obligations. For instance, personal data can only be processed for a specific and legitimate reason which must be stated when the data are collected.
2. The person whose data are processed — the data subject — enjoys a number of enforceable rights. This includes, for instance, the right to be informed about the processing and the right to correct data.

Every institution or body should have an internal data protection officer. The DPO keeps a register of processing operations and notifies systems with specific risks to the EDPS. The EDPS prior checks whether or not those systems comply with data protection requirements. The EDPS also deals with complaints and conducts inquiries.

Consultation

The EDPS advises the European Commission, the European Parliament and the Council on proposals for new legislation and a wide range of other issues with data protection impact. In essence, the consultative task is to analyse how policies affect the privacy rights of the citizens. This assessment helps to enable proper political discussions on how new legislation can be effective with due respect and adequate safeguards for citizens' freedoms. The advice makes it possible for the legislators in Europe to adopt better legislation that is in line with European values.

Cooperation

The EDPS cooperates with other data protection authorities in order to promote consistent data protection throughout Europe. Data protection laws are built on common principles. Moreover, for an increasing number of European databases, supervision is shared between different data protection authorities (such as the Eurodac database). The central platform for cooperation with national supervisory authorities is the Article 29 Working Party.

OFFICIAL DIRECTORY
OF THE EUROPEAN UNION

Useful information

information

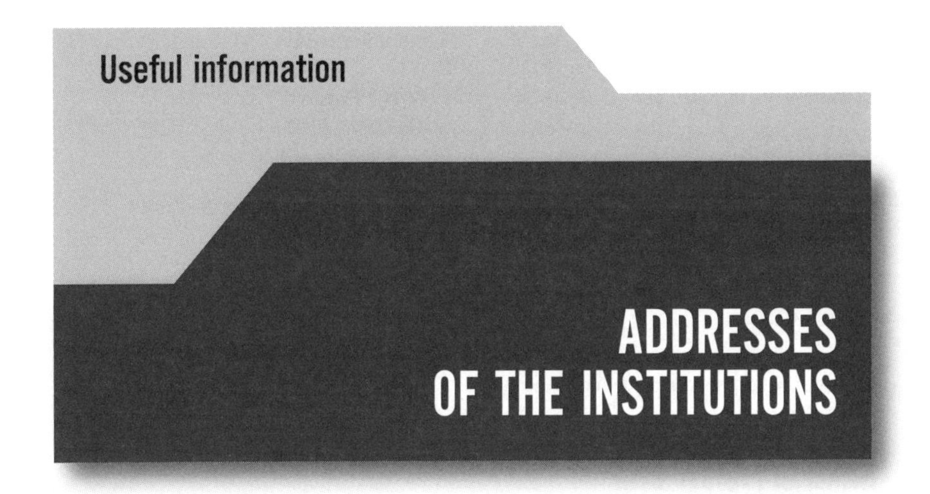

EUROPEAN PARLIAMENT

Strasbourg

Allée du Printemps
BP 1024
67070 Strasbourg Cedex
FRANCE
Tel. +33 3881-74001 / 3881 + extension
Telex 890129 / 890139
Fax +33 388256501

Luxembourg

Plateau du Kirchberg
BP 1601
2929 Luxembourg
LUXEMBOURG
Tel. +352 4300-1 / 4300 + extension
Telex 2894
Fax +352 4300-29494/29393/29292

Brussels

Rue Wiertz
BP 1047
1047 Bruxelles
BELGIQUE
Wiertzstraat
Postbus 1047
1047 Brussel
BELGIË
Tel. +32 22842111 / 2284 + extension
Telex 26999
Fax +32 22846974 / 22306933
Website:
http://www.europarl.europa.eu

The addresses of the European Parliament's Information Offices can be found in the corresponding chapter of the Directorate-General 4 – Information.

COUNCIL OF THE EUROPEAN UNION

Brussels

Rue de la Loi 175
1048 Bruxelles
BELGIQUE
Wetstraat 175
1048 Brussel
BELGIË
Tel. +32 22816111 / 2281 + extension
Fax +32 22816934

Luxembourg

Centre de conférences
Kirchberg
2929 Luxembourg
LUXEMBOURG
Tel. +352 4302-1 / 4302 + extension

Geneva

64, rue du Grand-Pré
CH-1202 Genève
Tel. +41 229197400
Fax +41 229197499

New York

222 East 41st Street, Floor 20
New York, N.Y. 10017 USA
Tel. +1-212 2928600
Fax +1-212 6816266 / 6816267
Website:
http://www.consilium.europa.eu

EUROPEAN COMMISSION

Brussels

Rue de la Loi 200
1049 Bruxelles
BELGIQUE
Wetstraat 200
1049 Brussel
BELGIË
Tel. +32 22991111 / 229 + extension
Telex 21877 COMEU B
Fax +32 22950138 / 22950139

Luxembourg

Bâtiment Jean Monnet
Rue Alcide De Gasperi
2920 Luxembourg
LUXEMBOURG
Tel. +352 4301-1 / 4301 + extension
Telex 3423 / 3446 / 3476 COMEUR LU
Fax +352 436124 / 4301-35049
Website: **http://ec.europa.eu**

COURT OF JUSTICE OF THE EUROPEAN COMMUNITIES

Luxembourg

Boulevard Konrad Adenauer
2925 Luxembourg
LUXEMBOURG
Tel. +352 4303-1 (standard) / 4303 + extension
Telex 2771 CJINFO LU
Fax +352 4303-2600

Registry, Court of Justice
Telex 2510 CURIA LU
Fax +352 433766

Registry, Court of First Instance
Fax +352 4303-2100

Registry, Civil Service Tribunal
Fax +352 4303-4453
Website: **http://curia.europa.eu**

EUROPEAN COURT OF AUDITORS

Luxembourg

12, rue Alcide De Gasperi
1615 Luxembourg
LUXEMBOURG
Tel. +352 4398-1 / 4398 + extension
Fax +352 439342
Website: **http://eca.europa.eu**
E-mail: **euraud@eca.europa.eu**

Brussels (sub-office)

Bâtiment Eastman
Rue Belliard 135
1040 Bruxelles
BELGIQUE
Belliardstraat 135
1040 Brussel
BELGIË
Tel. +32 22305090
Fax +32 22306483

EUROPEAN ECONOMIC AND SOCIAL COMMITTEE

Brussels

Rue Belliard 99
1040 Bruxelles
BELGIQUE
Belliardstraat 99
1040 Brussel
BELGIË
Tel. +32 25469011 / 2546 + extension
Fax +32 25134893
Website: **http://eesc.europa.eu**

COMMITTEE OF THE REGIONS OF THE EUROPEAN UNION

Brussels

Rue Belliard 101
1040 Bruxelles
BELGIQUE
Belliardstraat 101
1040 Brussel
BELGIË
Tel. +32 22822211 / 2282 + extension
Fax +32 22822325
Website: **http://www.cor.europa.eu**

EUROPEAN CENTRAL BANK

Frankfurt am Main

Eurotower
Kaiserstrasse 29
60311 Frankfurt am Main
DEUTSCHLAND
Tel. +49 6913440
Fax +49 6913446000
E-mail: **info@ecb.europa.eu**
Website: **http://www.ecb.europa.eu**

EUROPEAN INVESTMENT BANK

Luxembourg

98-100, boulevard Konrad Adenauer
2950 Luxembourg
LUXEMBOURG
Tel. +352 43791
Fax +352 437704
E-mail: **info@bei.org**

EXTERNAL OFFICES:

Austria

Mattiellistraße 2-4
1040 Wien
ÖSTERREICH
Tel. +43 15053676
Fax +43 15053674

Belgium

Rue de la Loi 227/Wetstraat 227
1040 Bruxelles/Brussel
BELGIQUE/BELGIË
Tel. +32 22350070
Fax +32 22305827

Finland

Fabianinkatu 34
PL 517
FI-00101 Helsinki
SUOMI/FINLAND
Tel. +358 106180830
Fax +358 92785229

France

21 rue des Pyramides
75001 Paris
FRANCE
Tel. +33 155047455
Fax +33 142616302

Germany

Lennéstraße 11
10785 Berlin
DEUTSCHLAND
Tel. +49 3059004790
Fax +49 3059004799

Greece

1, Herodou Attikou Vas. Sofias Ave
10674 Athina
GREECE
Tel. +30 2106824517
Fax +30 2106824520

Italy

Via Sardegna 38
00187 Roma
ITALIA
Tel. +39 0647191
Fax +39 0642873438

Poland

Plac Piłsudskiego 1
00-078 Warszawa
POLSKA
Tel. +48 223100500
Fax +48 223100501

Portugal

Avenida da Liberdade, 190-4° A
1250-147 Lisboa
PORTUGAL
Tel. +351 213428989
Fax +351 213470487

Romania

Str. Jules Michelet 18-20
010463 Bucureşti, Sector 1
ROMÂNIA
Tel. +40 212086400
Fax +40 213179090

Spain

Calle José Ortega y Gasset, 29, 5°
28006 Madrid
ESPAÑA
Tel. +34 914311340
Fax +34 914311383

United Kingdom

2 Royal Exchange Buildings
London EC3V 3LF
UNITED KINGDOM
Tel. +44 2073759660
Fax +44 2073759699

Carib

1 boulevard du Général-de-Gaulle
97200 Fort-de-France
FRANCE
Tel. +596 596747310
Fax +596 596561833

Egypt

6 Boulos Hanna Street
Dokki, 12311 Giza
ÉGYPTE
Tel. +20 2 33366583
Fax +20 2 33366584

Kenya

Africa Re Centre, 5th floor
Hospital Road, PO Box 40193
00100 Nairobi
KENYA
Tel. +254 20 2735260
Fax +254 20 2713278

Morocco

Riad Business Center,
Aile sud, Immeuble S3, 4 étage
Boulevard Er-Riad
Rabat
MAROC
Tel. +212 37565460
Fax +212 37565393

Pacific

Level 32, ABN AMRO Tower
88 Phillip Street
Sydney NSW 2000
AUSTRALIA
Tel. +61 2 82110536
Fax +61 2 82110538

Senegal

3, rue du Docteur Roux
BP 6935, Dakar-Plateau
SÉNÉGAL
Tel. +221 338894300
Fax +221 338429712

South Africa

5 Greenpark Estates
27 George Storrar Drive
Groenkloof 0181, Tshwane
PRETORIA
Tel. +27 12 4250460
Fax +27 12 4250470

Tunisia

70, avenue Mohamed V
1002 Tunis
TUNISIE
Tel. +216 71280222
Fax +216 71280998

Turkey

Büyükdere Cd. No: 185
Kanyon Ofis Binasi Kat: 6
TR-34394 Levent
Istanbul
TURQUIE
Tel. +90 212 31976045
Fax +90 212 3197600

EUROPEAN INVESTMENT FUND

Luxembourg

43, avenue J. F. Kennedy
2968 Luxembourg
LUXEMBOURG
Tel. +352 4266881
Fax +352 426688200
Website: **http://www.eif.org**
E-mail: **info@eif.org**

EUROPEAN OMBUDSMAN

Strasbourg

1 avenue du Président-Robert-Schuman
CS 30403
67001 Strasbourg Cedex
FRANCE
Tel. +33 388172313
Fax +33 388179062
Website:
http://www.ombudsman.europa.eu

EUROPEAN DATA PROTECTION SUPERVISOR

Offices:

Wiertz 60
Bâtiment MON 63
1047 Bruxelles/Brussel
BELGIQUE/BELGIË
Tel. +32 22831900
Fax +32 22831950
Website: **http://www.edps.europa.eu**

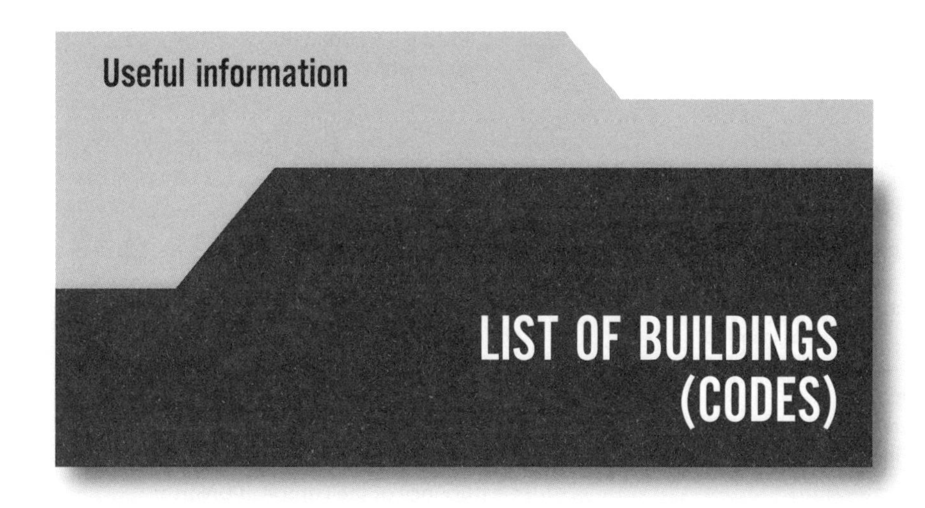

BRUSSELS

Code	Page	Address
A-73	XXXII	Building Rue Archimède 73/Archimedestraat 73
AN-88	XXXII	SCAN Complex Rue d'Arlon 88/Aarlenstraat 88
ASP	XXXII	Altiero Spinelli Building European Parliament Rue Wiertz 60/Wiertzstraat 60
ATR	XXXII	Atrium Building European Parliament Rue d'Ardenne 2/Ardennenstraat 2
B28	XXXII	Belliard 28 Building Rue Belliard 28/Belliardstraat 28
B68	XXXII	Building CoR/EESC Rue Belliard 68/Belliardstraat 68
B-100	XXXII	Building Rue Belliard 100/Belliardstraat 100
B-135	XXXII	Building European Court of Auditors Rue Belliard 135/Belliardstraat 135
B-232	XXXII	Belliard 232 Building Rue Belliard 232/Belliardstraat 232
BERL	XXXII	Berlaymont Complex Rue de la Loi 200/Wetstraat 200
BRE-2	XXXII	Breydel 2 Building Avenue d'Auderghem 19/Oudergemselaan 19
BREY	XXXII	Breydel 45 Building Avenue d'Auderghem 45/Oudergemselaan 45
BU-1	XXXIII	Beaulieu 1 Building Avenue de Beaulieu 1/Beaulieustraat 1
BU-5	XXXIII	Beaulieu 5 Building Avenue de Beaulieu 5/Beaulieustraat 5
BU-9	XXXIII	Beaulieu 9 Building Avenue de Beaulieu 9/Beaulieustraat 9
BU-24	XXXIII	Croissant Building Avenue de Beaulieu 24/Beaulieustraat 24
BU-25	XXXIII	Beaulieu 25 Building Avenue de Beaulieu 25/Beaulieustraat 25
BU-29	XXXIII	Beaulieu 29 Building Avenue de Beaulieu 29/Beaulieustraat 29
BU-31	XXXIII	Beaulieu 31 Building Avenue de Beaulieu 31/Beaulieustraat 31
BU-33	XXXIII	Beaulieu 33 Building Avenue de Beaulieu 33/Beaulieustraat 33
BvS	XXXII	CoR/EESC Building Rue Montoyer 92-102/Montoyerstraat 92-102
C-80	XXXII	Cortenberg 80 Building Avenue de Cortenberg 80/Kortenberglaan 80
C-107	XXXII	Cortenberg 107 Building Avenue de Cortenberg 107/Kortenberglaan 107
CCAB	XXXII	A. Borschette Centre Rue Froissart 36/Froissartstraat 36

Code	Page	Address
CDMA	XXXII	Champ de Mars Building Rue de Champ de Mars 21/Marsveldstraat 21
CHAR	XXXII	Charlemagne Building Rue de la Loi 170/Wetstraat 170-
CLOV	XXXII	Clovis Crèche Boulevard Clovis 75-79/Clovislaan 75-79
CO	XXXII	Cortenberg – Council of the European Union Avenue de Cortenberg 150/Kortenberglaan 150
CSM-1	XXXII	Cour Saint-Michel Building Cour Saint-Michel, rue Père de Deken/ Sint-Michiels Warande, Pater de Dekenstraat
CSM-2	XXXII	Cour Saint-Michel Building Cour Saint-Michel, avenue de Tervuren 41/ Sint-Michiels Warande, Tervurenlaan 41
DAIL	XXXII	Crèche – Council of the European Union Avenue de la Brabançonne 100
DAV-1	XXXI XXXIII	Logistics Building Avenue du Bourget 1-3/Bourgetlaan 1-3
DEM-24	XXXII	Demot 24 Building Rue Demot 24/Demotstraat 24
DEM-28	XXXII	Demot 28 Building Rue Demot 28/Demotstraat 28
EAS	XXXII	Eastman Building European Court of Auditors, Ombudsman Rue Belliard 135/Belliardstraat 135
F-101	XXXII	Froissart 101 Building Rue Froissart 101/Froissartstraat 101
FO	XXXII	Frère Orban Building Square Frère Orban 10/Frère Orban-square 10
G-1	XXXIII	Genève 1 Astrid Complex Rue de Genève 1/Genèvestraat 1
G-6	XXXIII	Genève 6 Building Rue de Genève 6-8/Genèvestraat 6-8
G-12	XXXIII	Genève 12 Building Rue de Genève 12/Genèvestraat 12
GUIM	XXXII	Adminfo Building Rue Guimard 10/Guimardstraat 10
HTWG	XXXI XXXIII	Houtweg Houtweg 23
J-27	XXXII	Joseph II 27 Building Rue Joseph II 27/Josef II-straat 27
J-30	XXXII	Joseph II 30 Building Rue Joseph II 30/Josef II-straat 30
J-54	XXXII	Joseph II 54 Building Rue Joseph II 54/Josef II-straat 54
J-70	XXXII	Joseph II 70 Building Rue Joseph II 70/Josef II-straat 70
J-79	XXXII	Joseph II 79 Building Rue Joseph II 79/Josef II-straat 79
J-99	XXXII	Joseph II 99 Building Rue Joseph II 99/Josef II-straat 99
JDE	XXXII	CoR/EESC Building Rue Belliard 99-101/Belliardstraat 99-101
JL	XXXII	Justus Lipsius Building Council of the European Union Rue de la Loi 175/Wetstraat 175
KORT	XXXI XXXIII	Archives Building Industriepark Guldendelle Vinkstraat 2, B-3070 Kortenberg
L-41	XXXII	Loi 41 Building Rue de la Loi 41/Wetstraat 41
L-46	XXXII	Loi 46 Building Rue de la Loi 56/Wetstraat 56
L-86	XXXII	Loi 86 Building Rue de la Loi 86/Wetstraat 86
L-102	XXXII	Loi 102 Building Rue de la Loi 102/Wetstraat 102
L-130	XXXII	Loi 130 Building Rue de la Loi 130/Wetstraat 130 Rue Joseph II 121/Josef II-straat 121
L-145	XXXII	Lex Building Rue de la Loi 145/ Wetstraat 145
LX 40	XXXII	Luxembourg 40 Building Rue du Luxembourg 40/ Luxemburgstraat 40
LX-46	XXXII	Luxembourg 46 Building Rue du Luxembourg 46/Luxemburgstraat 46
MADO	XXXII	Madou Building Place Madou 1/Madouplein 1
MO-34	XXXII	Montoyer 34 Building Rue Montoyer 34/Montoyerstraat 34
MO-51	XXXII	Montoyer 51 Building Rue Montoyer 51/Montoyerstraat 51
MO-59	XXXII	Montoyer 59 Building Rue Montoyer 59/Montoyerstraat 59
N-105	XXXII	Building Avenue des Nerviens 105/Nerviërslaan 105
OVER	XXXI XXXIII	Building Dennenboslaan 54, B-3090 Overijse

Code	Page	Address
PALM	XXXII	Palmerston Crèche Avenue Palmerston 6-14/Palmerstonlaan 6-14
PHS	XXXII	Paul-Henri Spaak Building European Parliament Rue Wiertz 47/Wiertzstraat 47
REM	XXXII	CoR/EESC Building Rue Belliard 93/Belliardstraat 93
RMD	XXXII	Remard Building Rue Belliard 89/Belliardstraat 89
RP-14	XXXII	InfEuropa Schuman 14 Rue Archimède 1/Archimedesstraat 1
SC-11	XXXII	Science 11 Building Rue de la Science 11/Wetenschapsstraat 11
SC-15	XXXII	Science 15 Building Rue de la Science 15/Wetenschapsstraat 15
SC-27	XXXII	Scan Complex Rue de la Science 27/Wetenschapsstraat 27
SC-29	XXXII	Scan Complex Rue de la Science 29/Wetenschapsstraat 29 (SCAN) see AN88 + SC27 + SC29
SDME	XXXII	Building Square de Meeûs 8/de Meeûs-square 8
SPA2	XXXII	SPA2 Building Rue de Spa 2/Spastraat 2
SPA3	XXXII	SPA3 Building Rue de Spa 3/Spastraat 3
TRE	XXXII	CoR/EESC Building Rue de Trèves 74/Trierstraat 74
VMA	XXXII	CoR/EESC Building Rue van Maerlant 2/van Maerlantstraat 2
VM-18	XXXII	Van Maerlant 18 Building Rue van Maerlant 18/van Maerlantstraat 18
WAY	XXXII	Wayenberg Building Rue Wayenberg 9/Wayenbergstraat 9
WIE	XXXII	Wiertz Building Rue Wiertz 30-50/Wiertzstraat 30-50
WILS	XXXII	Wilson Kindergarten Rue Wilson 16/Wilsonstraat 16

LUXEMBOURG

Code	Page	Address
A-NE	XXXV	'North-East' Annex Building Plateau du Kirchberg, place de l'Europe
AN	XXXV	Cour de Justice — Anneau plateau du Kirchberg, rue Fort Niedergrünewald
ADG	XXXV	Alcide De Gasperi Building Plateau du Kirchberg, place de l'Europe
BECH	XXXV	Bech Building 5, rue Alphonse Weicker
BEI	XXXV	European Investment Bank 98-100, boulevard Konrad Adenauer
C	XXXV	Building C/Court of Justice Plateau du Kirchberg, boulevard Konrad Adenauer
CPE-1	XXXV	Centre polyvalent de la petite enfance 1, rue Albert Borschette
CPE-2	XXXV	Centre polyvalent de la petite enfance (crèche) Rue Albert Borschette
CPE-3	XXXV	Centre polyvalent de la petite enfance (new building) Rue Albert Borschette
DRB	XXXIV	Drosbach Building Drosbach, 12, rue G. Kroll
ECA-K1/K2	XXXV	European Court of Auditors 12, rue Alcide De Gasperi
ECA-K7	XXXV	European Court of Auditors T Building Plateau du Kirchberg, boulevard Konrad Adenauer
ECA-K8	XXXV	European Court of Auditors Services administratifs et bureau d'accueil du personnel 6, circuit de la Foire internationale
ECA-K9	XXXV	Cour des comptes européenne, Traduction 26, rue Edward Steichen
ERA	XXXV	Erasmus Building /Court of Justice Plateau du Kirchberg, rue Fort Niedergrünewald
EUFO	XXXIV	Euroforum Building Zone d'activités de la Cloche d'or, 12, rue Robert Stumper
FEI	XXXV	European Investment Fund 96, boulevard Konrad Adenauer
FISR	XXXIV	Fischer Building 135, rue Adolphe Fischer
HEI	XXXIV	Building (Foyer européen) 10-12, rue Heine
GAL	XXXV	Court of Justice – Gallery Plateau du Kirchberg, rue Fort Niedergrünewald

Code	Page	Address
GASP	XXXIV	Distribution Centre of the Publications Office 3, rue Émile Bian, Gasperich
GEOS	XXXV	Building GEOS/Court of Justice 22-24, rue Edward Steichen
GOL	XXXIV	Goldbell Building 21, rue Eugène Ruppert, Gasperich
HTC	XXXIV	Hitec Building 11, rue E. Ruppert, Gasperich
JFK	XXXV	JFK Building 43, avenue John F. Kennedy
JMO	XXXV	Jean Monnet Building Rue Alcide De Gasperi
KAD	XXXV	Konrad Adenauer Building Plateau du Kirchberg, rue Alcide De Gasperi
KIRC	XXXV	European School Kirchberg 23, boulevard Konrad Adenauer
MER	XXXIV	Publications Office 2, rue Mercier
PA	XXXV	Court of Justice — Palace Plateau du Kirchberg, rue Fort Niedergrünewald
SCH	XXXV	Schuman Building Plateau du Kirchberg, place de l'Europe
SEN	XXXIV	Senningerberg Building Zone Bredwues
T	XXXV	Building T Court of Justice Plateau du Kirchberg, 90, boulevard Konrad Adenauer
TFP	XXXV	Court of Justice, Allegro Building - TFP Plateau du Kirchberg, 35 A avenue John F. Kennedy
Th M.	XXXV	Court of Justice Thomas More Building Plateau du Kirchberg, boulevard Konrad Adenauer
TOA	XXXV	European Parliament Tower A Plateau du Kirchberg, 10, avenue John F. Kennedy
TOA	XXXV	Court of Justice, Tour A Building Plateau du Kirchberg, rue Fort Niedergrünewald
TOB	XXXV	European Parliament Tower B Plateau du Kirchberg, 11, avenue John F. Kennedy
TOB	XXXV	Court of Justice, Tour B Building Plateau du Kirchberg, rue Fort Niedergrünewald
WAG	XXXV	Wagner Building Plateau du Kirchberg, rue Alcide De Gasperi

STRASBOURG

Code	Page	Address
IPE3	XXXVI	IPE3 Building Allée Spach
LOW	XXXVI	Louise Weiss Building Allée du Printemps
SDM	XXXVI	Salvador De Madariaga Building Rue du Général-Uhrich
WIC	XXXVI	Winston Churchill Building 1, avenue du Président-Robert-Schuman

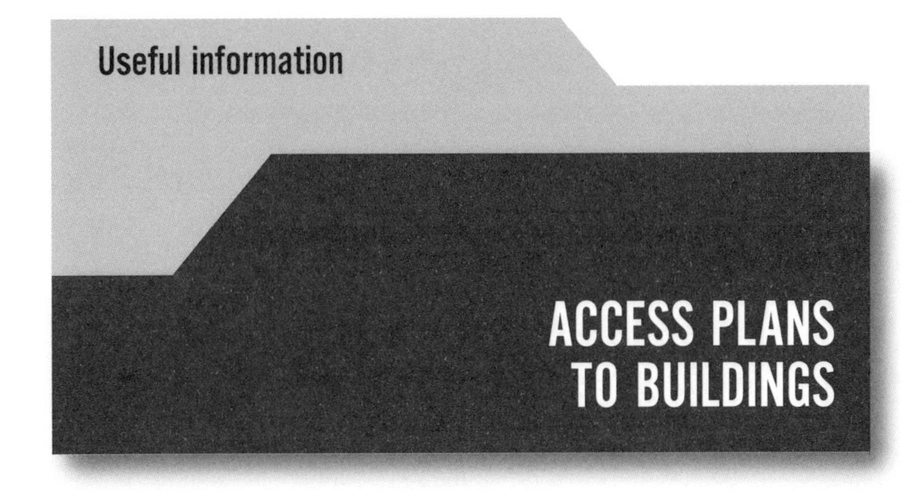
Useful information
ACCESS PLANS
TO BUILDINGS

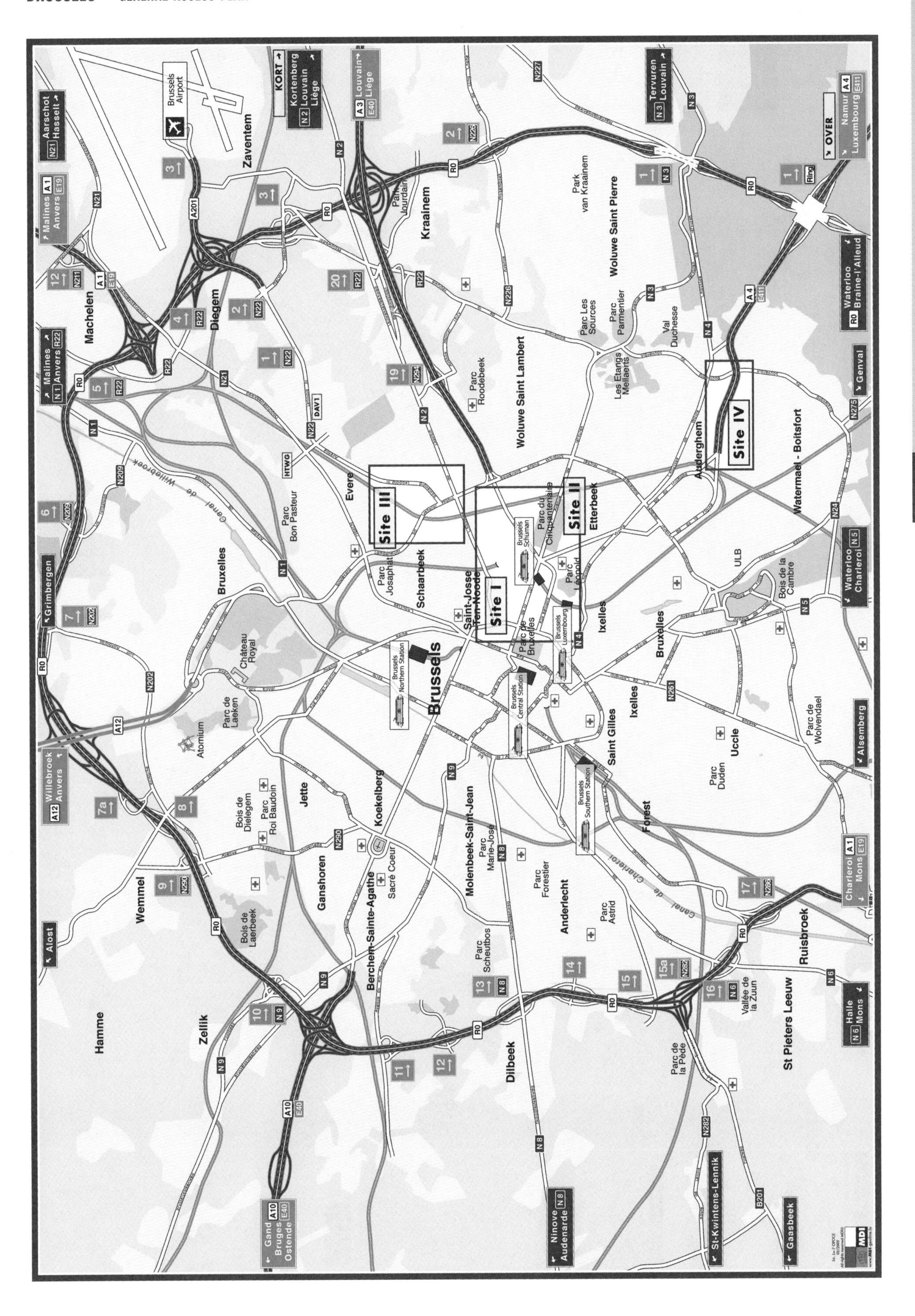

ACCESS PLANS TO BUILDINGS

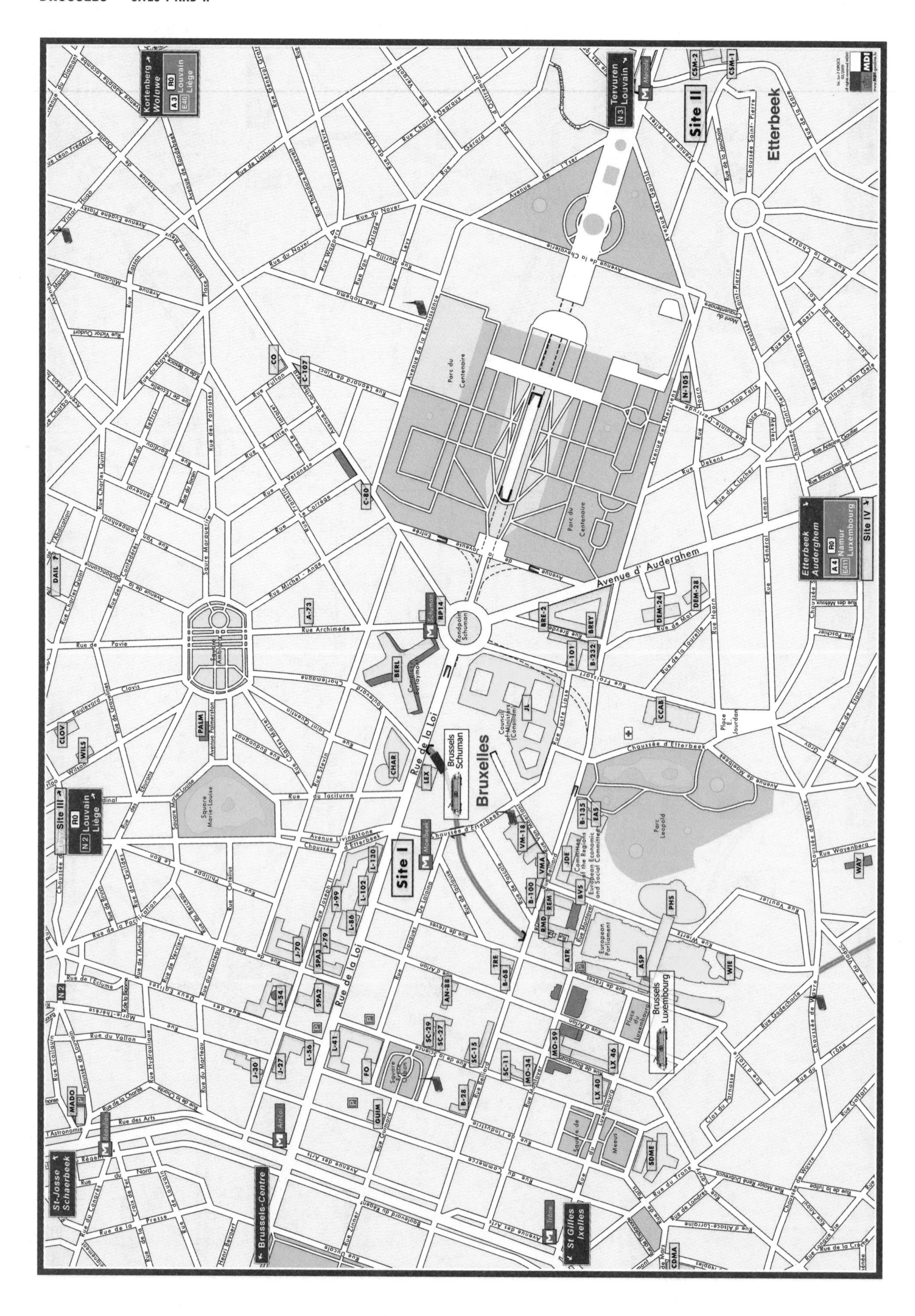

Site I
Site II
Site III
Site IV
Bruxelles
Etterbeek
Brussels Schuman
Brussels Luxembourg
Brussels-Centre
St-Josse Schaerbeek
St Gilles Ixelles
Kortenberg Woluwe
A 3 R0 E40 Louvain Liège
Tervuren Louvain N 3
N 2 R0 Louvain Liège
Etterbeek Auderghem
A 4 R0 E411 Namur Luxembourg
Parc du Cinquantenaire
Parc Leopold
Square Ambiorix
Square Marie-Louise
Rondpoint Schuman
European Parliament
Council of Ministers (Consilium)
Committee of the Regions European Economic and Social Committee
Place du Luxembourg
Square Frère Orban
Square de Meeus
Place E. Jourdan
Avenue d' Auderghem
Rue de la Loi
Rue Belliard
Chaussée d'Etterbeek
Avenue de Cortenbergh
Rue Archimède
Rue Joseph II
Rue du Trône
Rue des Arts
Boulevard du Régent
Rue de Trèves
Rue Froissart
Rue Wiertz
Chaussée de Wavre
Avenue des Nerviens
Avenue de la Renaissance
Avenue de Tervueren
Avenue des Celtes
Chaussée Saint-Pierre
Rue Stévin
Rue Charlemagne
Avenue Livingstone
Rue du Taciturne
Rue de la Science
Rue d'Arlon
Rue du Luxembourg
Rue de l'Industrie
Rue du Commerce
Rue Guimard
Rue Montoyer
Rue Ducale
Rue du Marteau
Rue de la Pacification
Rue des Confédérés
Rue de Pavie
Avenue Palmerston
Rue Michel-Ange
Rue du Noyer
Rue des Patriotes
Rue de Linthout
Rue Gérard
Rue Charles Degroux
Rue Général Leman
Rue Hoorn
Rue Gray
Rue Vautier
Rue Wayenberg
CSM-1
CSM-2
N-105
C-107
C-80
CO
DAIL
A-73
RP14
BERL
PALM
CLOV
WILS
CHAR
LEX
JL
BRE-2
BREY
F-101
B-232
DEM-24
DEM-28
CCAB
B-135
EAS
VM-18
VMA
JDE
B-100
REM
RMD
BVS
PHS
ATR
ASP
WIE
WAY
TRE
B-68
J-99
L-102
L-130
L-86
J-70
J-79
SPA3
SPA2
J-54
AN-88
SC-29
SC-27
SC-15
SC-11
MO-34
MO-59
LX 46
LX 40
L-41
L-56
J-27
J-30
FO
B-28
GUIM
MADO
SDME
CDMA

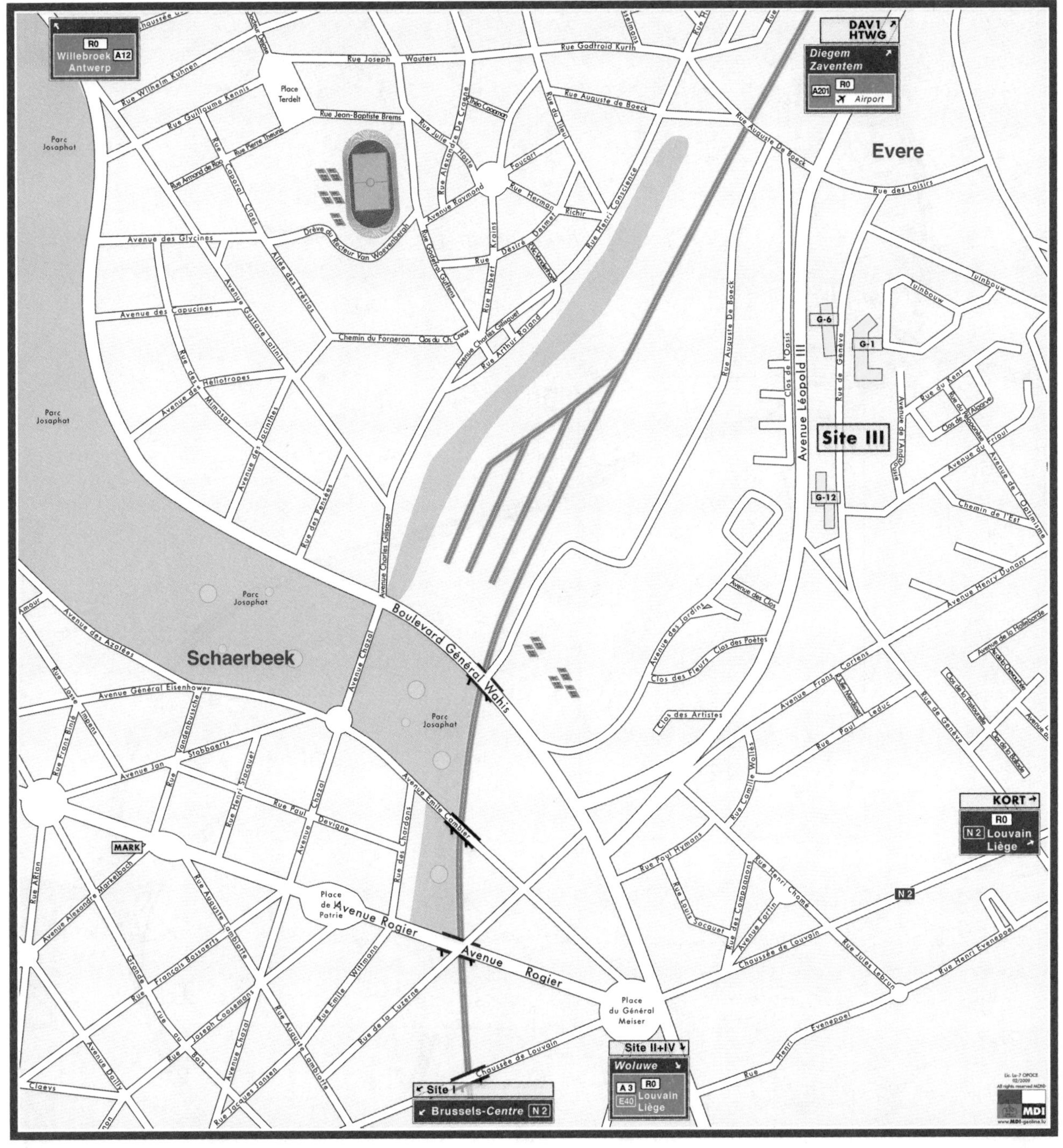

R0
Willebroek A12
Antwerp
DAV1
HTWG
Diegem
Zaventem
R0
A201 Airport
Evere
Site III
G-6
G-1
G-12
Avenue Léopold III
Schaerbeek
Parc Josaphat
Boulevard Général Wahis
Avenue Rogier
Place du Général Meiser
Place de la Patrie
Place Terdelt
KORT
R0
N2 Louvain
Liège
MARK
N2
Site II+IV
Woluwe
A3 R0
E40 Louvain
Liège
Site I
Brussels-Centre N2
MDI

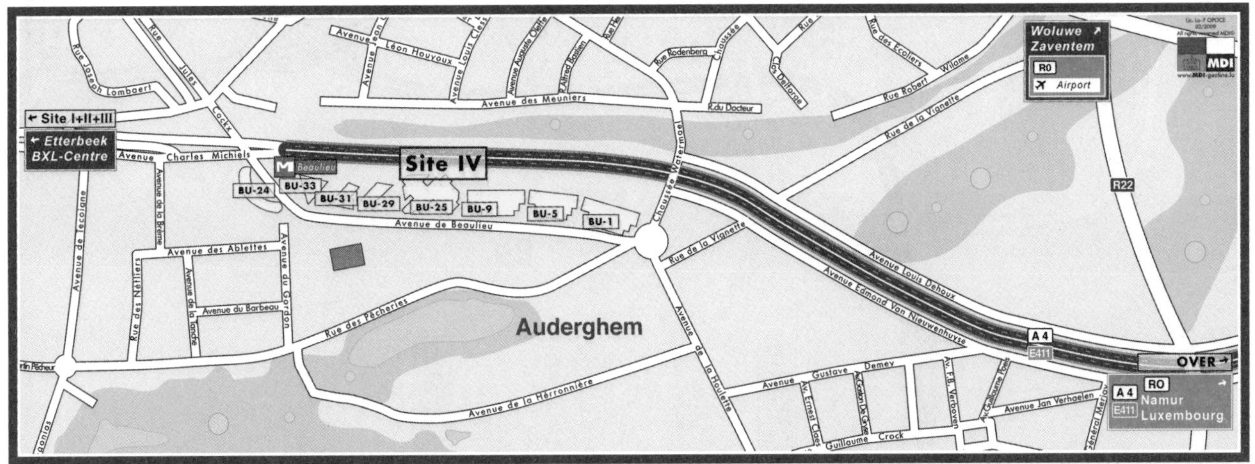

Woluwe
Zaventem
R0
Airport
Site I+II+III
Etterbeek
BXL-Centre
Beaulieu
Site IV
BU-24
BU-33
BU-31
BU-29
BU-25
BU-9
BU-5
BU-1
Avenue de Beaulieu
Auderghem
Avenue Louis Dehoux
Avenue Edmond Van Nieuwenhuyse
R22
A4
E411
OVER
A4 R0
E411 Namur
Luxembourg
MDI

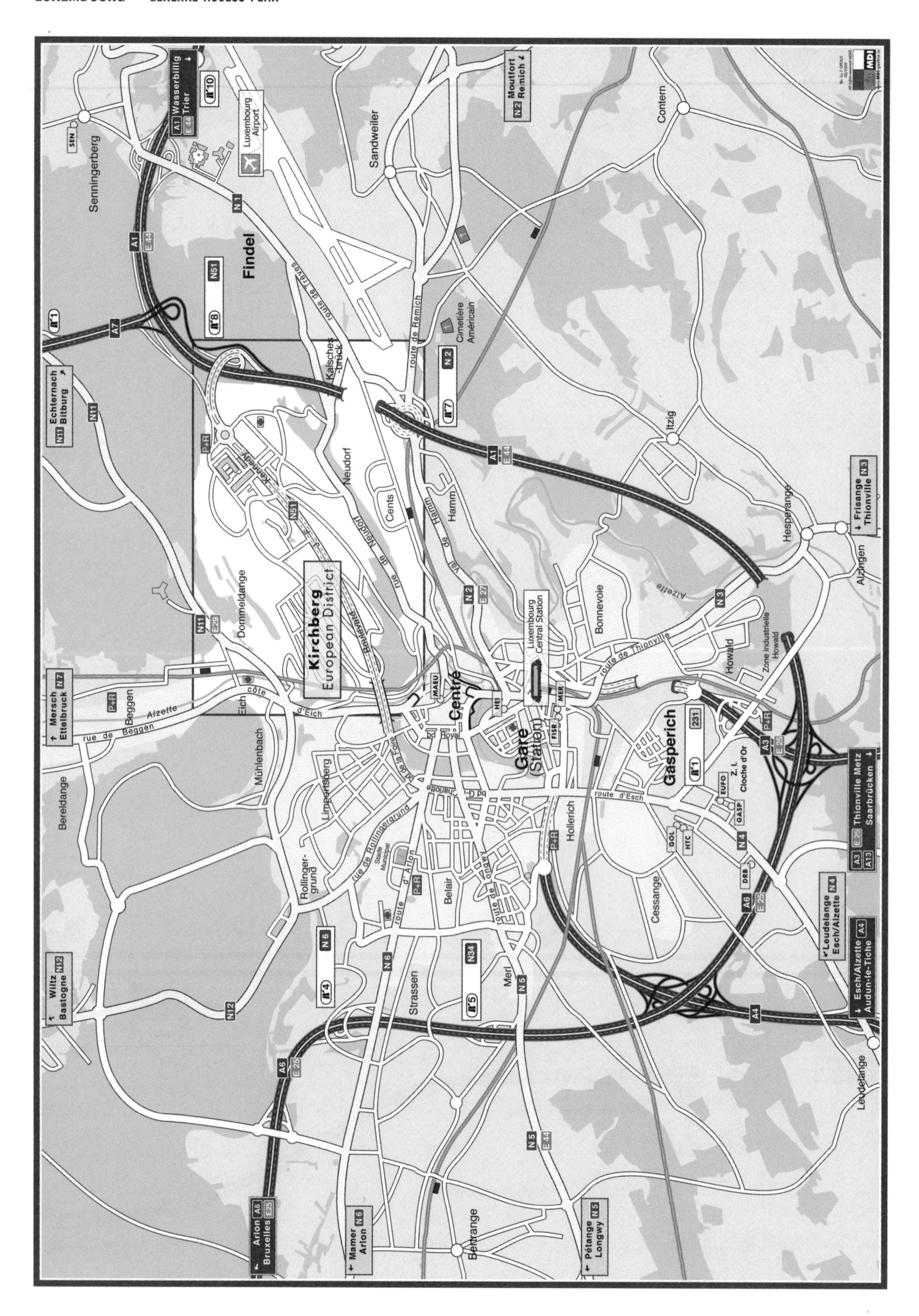
Kirchberg
European District
Findel
Luxembourg Airport
Senningerberg
Sandweiler
Contern
Itzig
Hesperange
Alzingen
Howald
Zone industrielle Howald
Gasperich
Z. I. Cloche d'Or
Cessange
Hollerich
Bonnevoie
Luxembourg Central Station
Gare (Station)
Centre
Limpertsberg
Rollingergrund
Belair
Merl
Strassen
Bertrange
Leudelange
Mühlenbach
Beggen
Bereldange
Dommeldange
Neudorf
Cents
Hamm
Cimetière Américain
Kalsches-brück
A1 Wasserbillig
E44 Trier
N11 Echternach Bitburg
N7 Mersch Ettelbruck
N12 Wiltz Bastogne
A6 E25 Arlon Bruxelles
N6 Mamer Arlon
N5 Pétange Longwy
A4 Esch/Alzette Audun-le-Tiche
N4 Leudelange Esch/Alzette
A3 E25 A13 Thionville Metz Saarbrücken
N3 Frisange Thionville
N2 Moutfort Remich
route de Trèves
route de Remich
rue de Neudorf
val de Hamm
route de Thionville
route d'Esch
route d'Arlon
route de Longwy
rue de Rollingergrund
rue de Beggen
bd Royal
Alzette
Stade Municipal
P+R
MDI

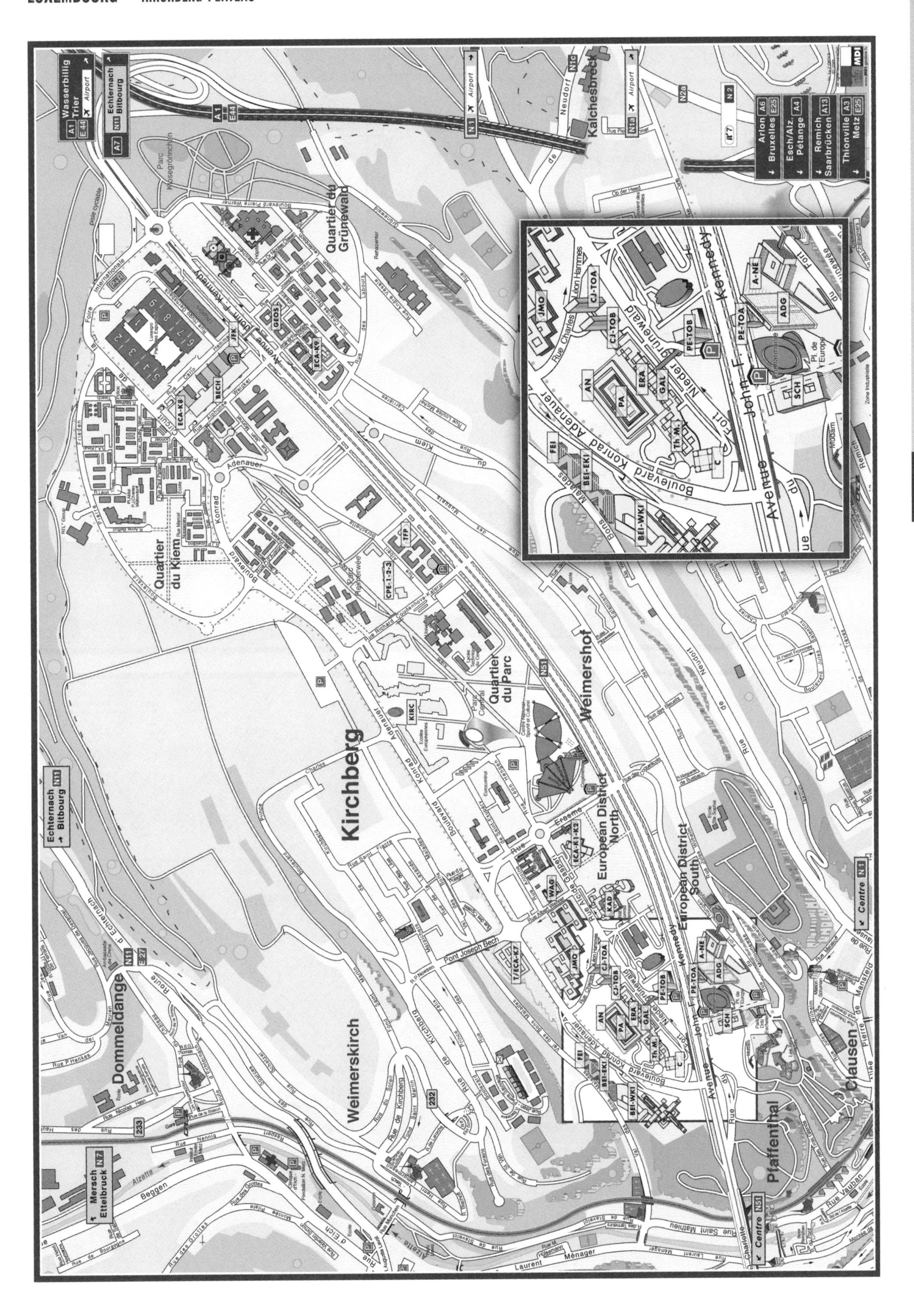
Kirchberg
Quartier du Kiem
Quartier du Grünewald
Quartier du Parc
European District North
European District South
Weimershof
Weimerskirch
Dommeldange
Pfaffenthal
Clausen
Kalchesbreck
Parc Klosegrönnchen
Avenue John F. Kennedy
Boulevard Konrad Adenauer
Pont Joseph Bech
Echternach Bitbourg
Wasserbillig Trier Airport
Mersch Ettelbruck
Arlon Bruxelles
Esch/Alz. Pétange
Remich Saarbrücken
Thionville Metz
Centre
KIRC
JFK
BECH
GEOS
TFP
CPE-1-2-3
JMO
CJ-TOA
CJ-TOB
PE-TOB
PE-TOA
A-NE
ADG
SCH
AN
PA
ERA
GAL
Th.M.
C
FEI
BEI-EKI
BEI-WKI
WAG
KAD
ECA-K1-K2
T/ECA-K7
ECA-K8
ECA-K9

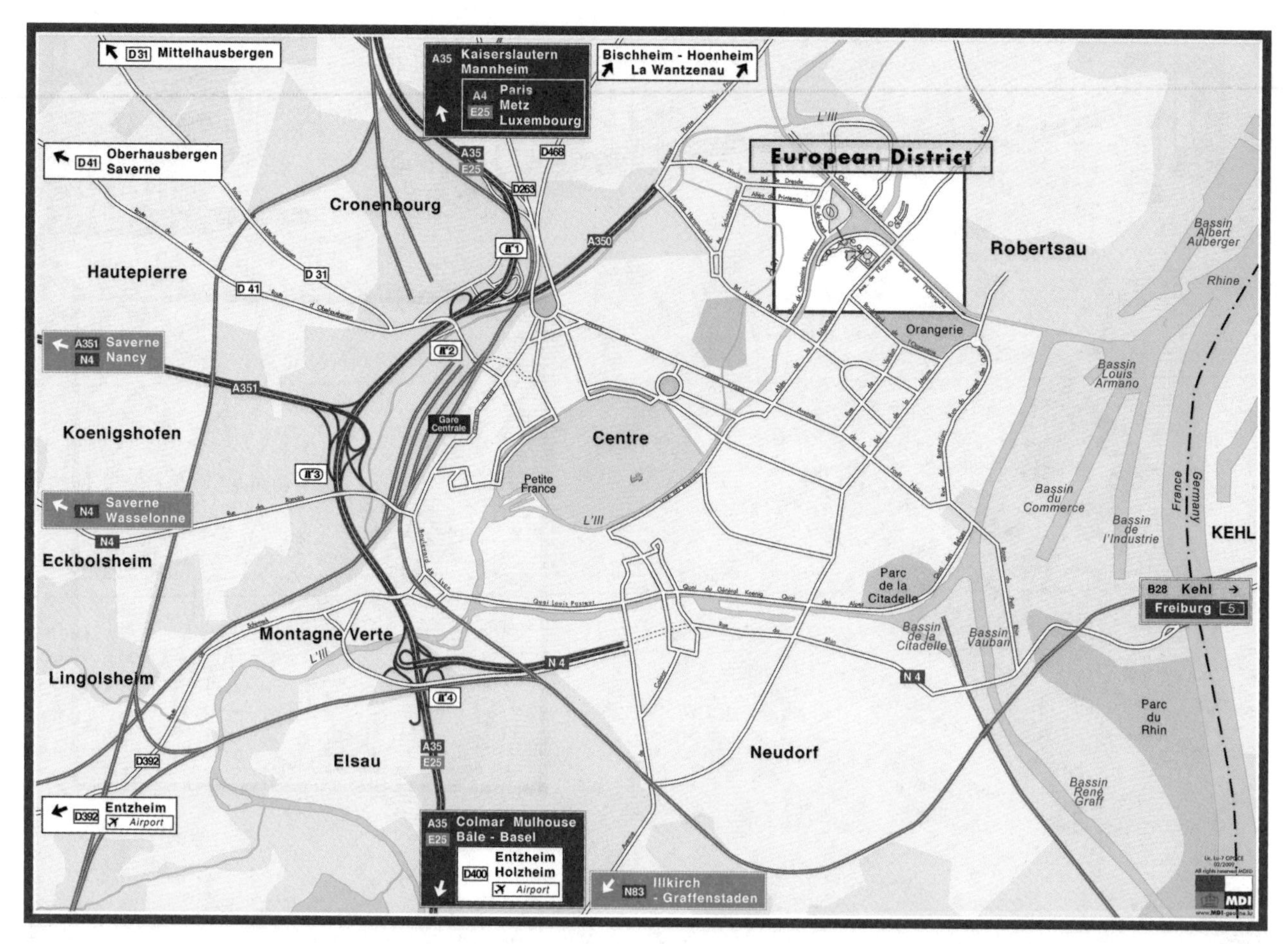

D31 Mittelhausbergen
A35 Kaiserslautern Mannheim
A4 E25 Paris Metz Luxembourg
Bischheim - Hoenheim
La Wantzenau
D41 Oberhausbergen Saverne
European District
Cronenbourg
Hautepierre
Robertsau
Bassin Albert Auberger
Rhine
A351 N4 Saverne Nancy
Orangerie
Bassin Louis Armand
Koenigshofen
Centre
Petite France
Gare Centrale
N4 Saverne Wasselonne
Eckbolsheim
Bassin du Commerce
Bassin de l'Industrie
France
Germany
KEHL
Parc de la Citadelle
B28 Kehl
Freiburg
Montagne Verte
Bassin de la Citadelle
Bassin Vauban
Lingolsheim
Parc du Rhin
Elsau
Neudorf
Bassin René Graff
D392 Entzheim Airport
A35 E25 Colmar Mulhouse Bâle - Basel
D400 Entzheim Holzheim Airport
N83 Illkirch - Graffenstaden
MDI

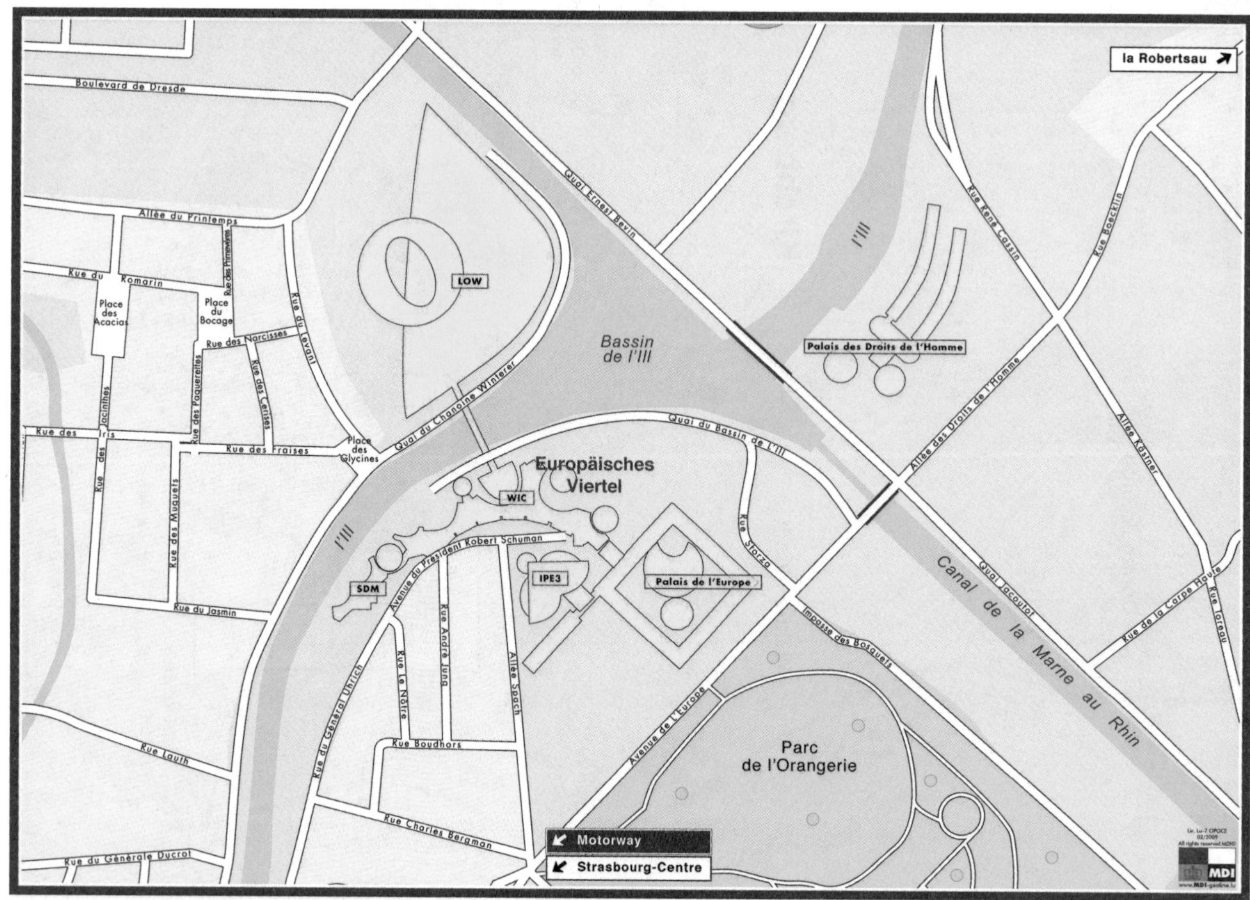

la Robertsau
Boulevard de Dresde
Allée du Printemps
Quai Ernest Bevin
LOW
Rue du Komarin
Place des Acacias
Place du Bocage
Rue des Narcisses
Rue du Levant
Palais des Droits de l'Homme
Bassin de l'Ill
l'Ill
Rue des Iris
Rue des Fraises
Place des Glycines
Quai du Chanoine Winterer
Quai du Bassin de l'Ill
Allée des Droits de l'Homme
Europäisches Viertel
WIC
SDM
IPE3
Palais de l'Europe
Avenue du Président Robert Schuman
Rue Sforza
Rue du Jasmin
Rue des Muguets
Canal de la Marne au Rhin
Quai Jacoutot
Rue de la Carpe Haute
Impasse des Bosquets
Avenue de l'Europe
Rue Boudhors
Rue Lauth
Parc de l'Orangerie
Rue du Général Ulrich
Rue Charles Bergman
Motorway
Strasbourg-Centre
Rue du Générale Ducrot
MDI

Useful information

LIST OF THE MEMBERS OF THE EDITORIAL COMMITTEE OF THE OFFICIAL DIRECTORY OF THE EUROPEAN UNION

Information or proposals

OFFICE FOR OFFICIAL PUBLICATIONS OF THE EUROPEAN COMMUNITIES

Crossmedia Unit
2, rue Mercier
2985 Luxembourg
LUXEMBOURG
Fax +352 2929-44637

If you detect errors, please submit them to: **whoiswho@publications.europa.eu.**

MODIFICATIONS IN THE DATA

For modifications to the data, please contact the person responsible in the relevant institution.

EUROPEAN PARLIAMENT

Mr Carlo MULLER
European Parliament, DG ITEC
Tel. +352 4300-24031
Fax +352 4300-22848
E-mail: **idea@europarl.europa.eu**

COUNCIL OF THE EUROPEAN UNION

General Secretariat of the Council of the European Union
DG F Publications
Office 00-HN-80
Rue de la Loi 175
1048 Bruxelles
BELGIQUE
Tel. +32 22815415
Fax +32 22818375
E-mail: **annuaire.interinstitutionnel@consilium.europa.eu**

EUROPEAN COMMISSION

The collection of data is coordinated by the Personnel and Administration DG, Directorate A—Staff and Careers: Organisation chart and management staff.

For modifications to the data, please contact the Head of the Human Resources Unit of the relevant Commission DG or Service.

In order to contact the European Commission, consult this webpage: **http://ec.europa.eu/contact/index_en.htm**

COURT OF JUSTICE

Mr Juan Carlos GONZÁLEZ
Information Service
2925 Luxembourg
LUXEMBOURG
Tel. +352 4303-2623
Fax +352 4303-2005
E-mail:
juan-carlos.gonzalez@curia.europa.eu

EUROPEAN COURT OF AUDITORS

Mr Roberto GABELLA CARENA
Communication and reports
12, rue Alcide De Gasperi
1615 Luxembourg
LUXEMBOURG
Tel. +352 4398-45797
Fax +352 4398-46233
E-mail: **euraud@eca.europa.eu**

ECONOMIC AND SOCIAL COMMITTEE OF THE EUROPEAN COMMUNITIES

For modifications to the data, please contact the Greffe Unit: _GreffeCESE@eesc.europa.eu

In order to contact the Economic and Social Committee, consult this webpage: **http://www.eesc.europa.eu/**

COMMITTEE OF THE REGIONS

Ms Monika WEYMANN
Rue Belliard 101
1040 Bruxelles
BELGIQUE
Tel. +32 22822509
Fax +32 22822119
E-mail:
monika.weymann@cor.europa.eu

EUROPEAN CENTRAL BANK

Mr Wiktor KZYŻANOWSKI
Press and Information Division
Kaiserstr. 29
60311 Frankfurt am Main
DEUTSCHLAND
Tel. +49 6913447455
Fax +49 6913447404
E-mail: **info@ecb.europa.eu**

EUROPEAN INVESTMENT BANK

Mr Marc BELLO
Publications and electronic media Unit
98-100, boulevard Konrad Adenauer
2950 Luxembourg
LUXEMBOURG
Tel. +352 437983119
Fax +352 437963188
E-mail: **m.bello@bei.org**

EUROPEAN INVESTMENT FUND

Ms Delphine MUNRO
43, avenue J. F. Kennedy
2968 Luxembourg
LUXEMBOURG
Tel. +352 426688-237
Fax +352 426688-302
E-mail: **d.munro@eif.org**

EUROPEAN OMBUDSMAN

Mr Alessandro DEL BON
Head of the Unit Administration
and Personnel
Office of the European Ombudsman
1, avenue du Président-Robert-Schuman
CS 30403
67001 Strasbourg Cedex
FRANCE
Tel. +33 388172382
Fax +33 388179062
E-mail: **alessandro.delbon@ombudsman.europa.eu**

EUROPEAN DATA PROTECTION SUPERVISOR

Ms Anne-Françoise REYNDERS
Personnel, Budget, Administration Unit
Rue Wiertz 60
1047 Bruxelles
BELGIQUE
Tel. +32 22831930
Fax +32 22841039
E-mail: **francoise.reynders@edps.europa.eu**

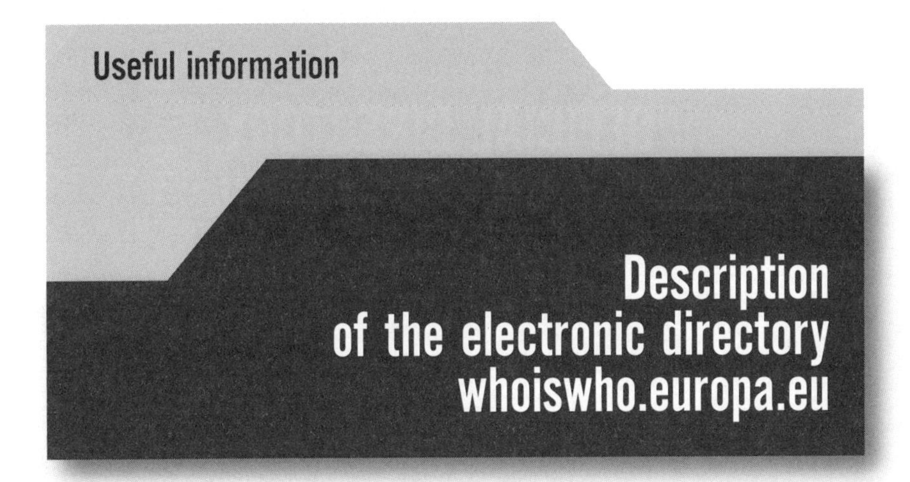

Whoiswho enables you to consult the directory online in three ways:

- — search by organisational entities (directorate or department),
- — search by persons,
- — hierarchical search.

The Whoiswho website is updated every day. The site is available in 23 languages.

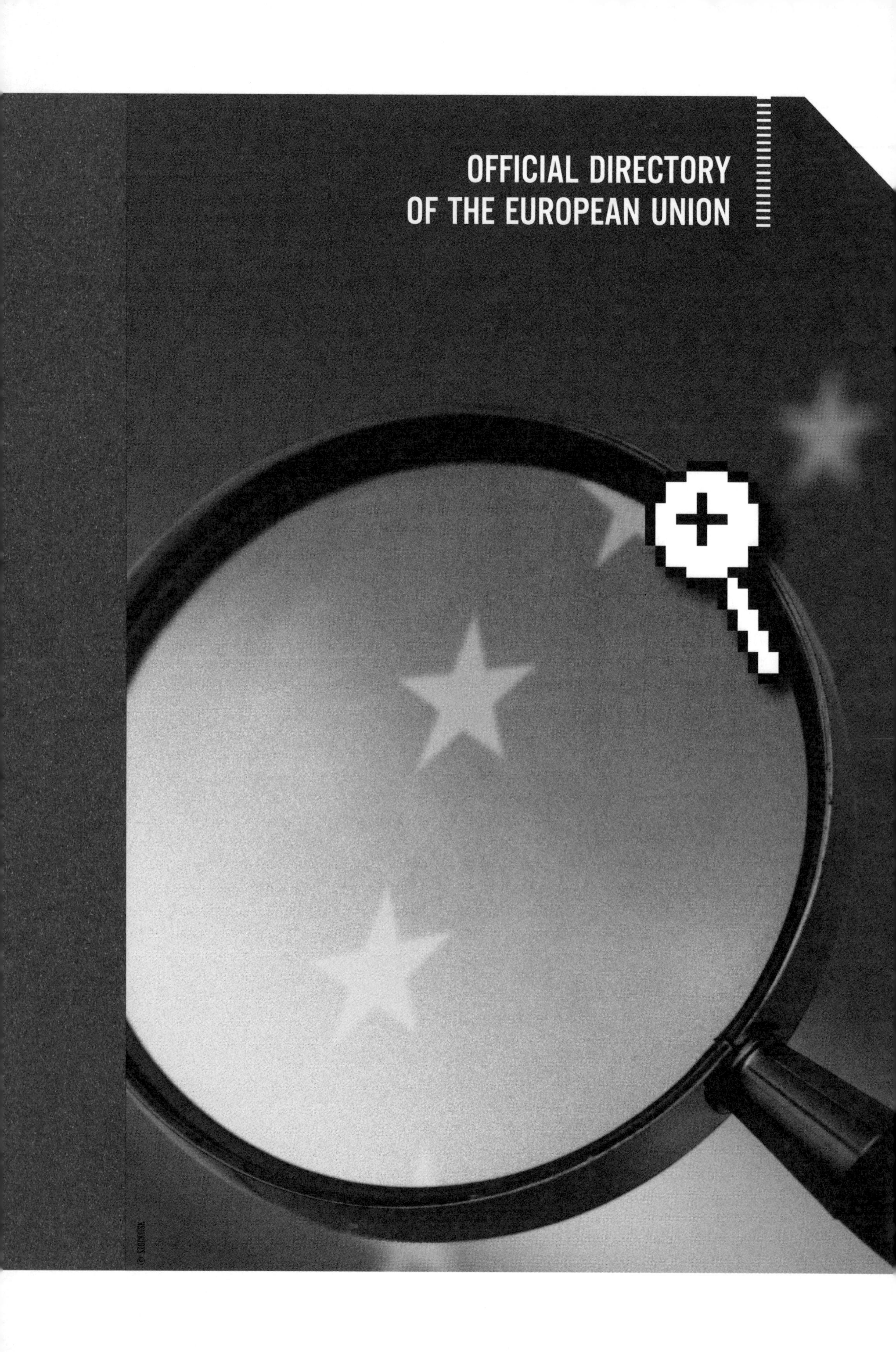
OFFICIAL DIRECTORY
OF THE EUROPEAN UNION

Community institutions, bodies and agencies

Community institutions, bodies and agencies

Community institutions, bodies and agencies

EUROPEAN PARLIAMENT

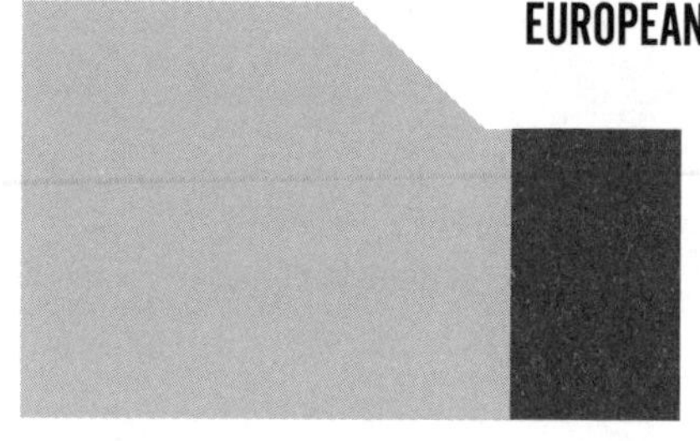

Governing bodies

PARLIAMENT'S BUREAU

Mr Hans-Gert PÖTTERING
President

Mr Adam BIELAN
Vice-President

Mr Luigi COCILOVO
Vice-President

Mrs Rodi KRATSA-TSAGAROPOULOU
Vice-President

Mr Edward McMILLAN-SCOTT
Vice-President

Mr Miguel Angel MARTÍNEZ MARTÍNEZ
Vice-President

Mr Mario MAURO
Vice-President

Mrs Luisa MORGANTINI
Vice-President

Mr Gérard ONESTA
Vice-President

Mrs Mechtild ROTHE
Vice-President

Mrs Martine ROURE
Vice-President

Mr Manuel António dos SANTOS
Vice-President

Mr Marek SIWIEC
Vice-President

Mr Alejo VIDAL-QUADRAS
Vice-President

Mrs Diana WALLIS
Vice-President

Mrs Mia DE VITS
Quaestor

Mr Szabolcs FAZAKAS
Quaestor

Mr Ingo FRIEDRICH
Quaestor

Mrs Astrid LULLING
Quaestor

Mr Jan MULDER
Quaestor

Mr James NICHOLSON
Quaestor

QUAESTORS

Mrs Mia DE VITS
Member

Mr Szabolcs FAZAKAS
Member

Mr Ingo FRIEDRICH
Member

Mrs Astrid LULLING
Member

Mr Jan MULDER
Member

Mr James NICHOLSON
Member

CONFERENCE OF PRESIDENTS

Mr Hans-Gert PÖTTERING
President

Mrs Irena BELOHORSKÁ
Member

Mr Daniel COHN-BENDIT
Member

Mr Brian CROWLEY
Member

Mr Joseph DAUL
Member

Mr Nigel FARAGE
Member

Mrs Monica FRASSONI
Member

Mrs Cristiana MUSCARDINI
Member

Mr Martin SCHULZ
Member

Mr Graham WATSON
Member

Mr Francis WURTZ
Member

CONFERENCE OF DELEGATION CHAIRMEN

Mr Raimon OBIOLS i GERMÀ
Chairman

Mrs Angelika BEER
Member

Mr Josep BORRELL FONTELLES
Member

Mr Giusto CATANIA
Member

Mr Giles CHICHESTER
Member

Mr Jonathan EVANS
Member

Mr Robert EVANS
Member

Mrs Neena GILL
Member

Mrs Jana HYBÁŠKOVÁ
Member

Mrs Marie Anne ISLER BÉGUIN
Member

Mr Carlos José ITURGAIZ ANGULO
Member

Mr Georg JARZEMBOWSKI
Member

Mrs Ona JUKNEVIČIENĖ
Member

Mrs Glenys KINNOCK
Member

Mr Joost LAGENDIJK
Member

Mr Alain LIPIETZ
Member

Mrs Pia Elda LOCATELLI
Member

Mrs Erika MANN
Member

Mrs Marianne MIKKO
Member

Mr Hartmut NASSAUER
Member

Mr Seán Ó NEACHTAIN
Member

Mrs Ria OOMEN-RUIJTEN
Member

Mrs Doris PACK
Member

Mrs Béatrice PATRIE
Member

Mr Hubert PIRKER
Member

Mr Guido PODESTÀ
Member

Mr Hans-Gert PÖTTERING
Member

Mr Vittorio PRODI
Member

Mr Jacek PROTASIEWICZ
Member

Mrs Bilyana Ilieva RAEVA
Member

Mr José Ignacio SALAFRANCA SÁNCHEZ-NEYRA
Member

Mr Jacek SARYUSZ-WOLSKI
Member

Mr Pál SCHMITT
Member

Mr Adrian SEVERIN
Member

Mr Sérgio SOUSA PINTO
Member

Mr Dirk STERCKX
Member

Mr Antonios TRAKATELLIS
Member

Mr Kyriacos TRIANTAPHYLLIDES
Member

CONFERENCE OF COMMITTEE CHAIRMEN

Mr Gerardo GALEOTE
Chairman

Mr Jan ANDERSSON
Member

Mrs Katerina BATZELI
Member

Mrs Pervenche BERÈS
Member

Mr Reimer BÖGE
Member

Mr Herbert BÖSCH
Member

Mr Josep BORRELL FONTELLES
Member

Mr Paolo COSTA
Member

Mr Gérard DEPREZ
Member

Mrs Hélène FLAUTRE
Member

Mr Giuseppe GARGANI
Member

Mr Jo LEINEN
Member

Mr Marcin LIBICKI
Member

Mrs Arlene McCARTHY
Member

Mr Helmuth MARKOV
Member

Mr Philippe MORILLON
Member

Mrs Angelika NIEBLER
Member

Mr Miroslav OUZKÝ
Member

Mr Neil PARISH
Member

Mr Guido SACCONI
Member

Mr Jacek SARYUSZ-WOLSKI
Member

Mr Karl von WOGAU
Member

Mrs Anna ZÁBORSKÁ
Member

Political groups

GROUP OF THE EUROPEAN PEOPLE'S PARTY (CHRISTIAN DEMOCRATS) AND EUROPEAN DEMOCRATS

Mr Joseph DAUL
Chairman
Tel. +32 228-45525 (Brussels)
Fax +32 228-49525 (Brussels)
Tel. +33 3881-75525 (Strasbourg)
Fax +33 3881-79525 (Strasbourg)
E-mail: joseph.daul@europarl.europa.eu
Website: http://president.epp-ed.eu

Mr Vito BONSIGNORE
Vice-Chairman
Tel. +32 228-45382 (Brussels)
Fax +32 228-49382 (Brussels)
Tel. +33 3881-75382 (Strasbourg)
Fax +33 3881-79382 (Strasbourg)
Website: http://www.vitobonsignore.eu

Mr Gunnar HÖKMARK
Vice-Chairman
Tel. +32 228-45822 (Brussels)
Fax +32 228-49822 (Brussels)
Tel. +33 3881-75822 (Strasbourg)
Fax +33 3881-79822 (Strasbourg)
Website: http://www.gunnar.moderat.se

Mr Othmar KARAS
Vice-Chairman
Tel. +32 228-45627 (Brussels)
Fax +32 228-49627 (Brussels)
Tel. +33 3881-75627 (Strasbourg)
Fax +33 3881-79627 (Strasbourg)
E-mail: othmar.karas@europarl.europa.eu
Website: http://www.othmar-karas.at

Mr Marian-Jean MARINESCU
Vice-Chairman
Tel. +32 228-45416 (Brussels)
Fax +32 228-49416 (Brussels)
Tel. +33 3881-75416 (Strasbourg)
Fax +33 3881-79416 (Strasbourg)
E-mail: adsc@adcx.ro
Website: http://www.marian-jean-marinescu.oltenia.ro

Mr Jaime MAYOR OREJA
Vice-Chairman
Tel. +32 228-45601 (Brussels)
Fax +32 228-49601 (Brussels)
Tel. +33 3881-75601 (Strasbourg)
Fax +33 3881-79601 (Strasbourg)
E-mail: jaime.mayororeja@europarl.europa.eu

Mr Hartmut NASSAUER
Vice-Chairman
Tel. +32 228-45361 (Brussels)
Fax +32 228-49361 (Brussels)
Tel. +33 3881-75361 (Strasbourg)
Fax +33 3881-79361 (Strasbourg)
E-mail: hartmut.nassauer@europarl.europa.eu

Mr João de Deus PINHEIRO
Vice-Chairman
Tel. +32 228-45374 (Brussels)
Fax +32 228-49374 (Brussels)
Tel. +33 3881-75374 (Strasbourg)
Fax +33 3881-79374 (Strasbourg)
Website: http://www.joaodeuspinheiro.org

Mr Struan STEVENSON
Vice-Chairman
Tel. +32 228-45710 (Brussels)
Fax +32 228-49710 (Brussels)
Tel. +33 3881-75710 (Strasbourg)
Fax +33 3881-79710 (Strasbourg)
E-mail: struanmep@aol.com
Website: http://www.scottishtorymeps.org.uk

Mr József SZÁJER
Vice-Chairman
Tel. +32 228-45871 (Brussels)
Fax +32 228-49871 (Brussels)
Tel. +33 3881-75871 (Strasbourg)
Fax +33 3881-79871 (Strasbourg)
E-mail: jozsef.szajer@europarl.europa.eu
Website: http://www.szajer.eppfrakcio.hu

Mrs Marianne THYSSEN
Vice-Chairwoman
Tel. +32 228-45918 (Brussels)
Fax +32 228-49918 (Brussels)
Tel. +33 3881-75918 (Strasbourg)
Fax +33 3881-79918 (Strasbourg)
E-mail: marianne.thyssen@europarl.europa.eu
Website: http://www.mariannethyssen.be

Mrs Laima Liucija ANDRIKIENĖ
Member of the Bureau
Tel. +32 228-45858 (Brussels)
Fax +32 228-49858 (Brussels)
Tel. +33 3881-75858 (Strasbourg)
Fax +33 3881-79858 (Strasbourg)
Website: http://www.laimaandrikiene.lt

Sir Robert ATKINS
Member of the Bureau
Tel. +32 228-45373 (Brussels)
Fax +32 228-49373 (Brussels)
Tel. +33 3881-75373 (Strasbourg)
Fax +33 3881-79373 (Strasbourg)
E-mail: ratsmep@sir-robertatkins.org
Website: http://www.sir-robertatkins.org

Mr Reimer BÖGE
Member of the Bureau
Tel. +32 228-45326 (Brussels)
Fax +32 228-49326 (Brussels)
Tel. +33 3881-75326 (Strasbourg)
Fax +33 3881-79326 (Strasbourg)
Website: http://www.reimerboege.de

Mr John BOWIS
Member of the Bureau
Tel. +32 228-45780 (Brussels)
Fax +32 228-49780 (Brussels)
Tel. +33 3881-75780 (Strasbourg)
Fax +33 3881-79780 (Strasbourg)
Website: http://www.johnbowis.com

Mr Iles BRAGHETTO
Member of the Bureau
Tel. +32 228-45489 (Brussels)
Fax +32 228-49489 (Brussels)
Tel. +33 3881-75489 (Strasbourg)
Fax +33 3881-79489 (Strasbourg)
Website: http://www.braghettoiles.it

Mr Mihael BREJC
Member of the Bureau
Tel. +32 228-45636 (Brussels)
Fax +32 228-49636 (Brussels)
Tel. +33 3881-75636 (Strasbourg)
Fax +33 3881-79636 (Strasbourg)
Website: http://www.mihabrejc.si

Mr Elmar BROK
Member of the Bureau
Tel. +32 228-45323 (Brussels)
Fax +32 228-49323 (Brussels)
Tel. +33 3881-75323 (Strasbourg)
Fax +33 3881-79323 (Strasbourg)
Website: http://www.elmarbrok.de

Mr Philip BUSHILL-MATTHEWS
Member of the Bureau
Tel. +32 228-45114 (Brussels)
Fax +32 228-49114 (Brussels)
Tel. +33 3881-75114 (Strasbourg)
Fax +33 3881-79114 (Strasbourg)

Mr Simon BUSUTTIL
Member of the Bureau
Tel. +32 228-45686 (Brussels)
Fax +32 228-49686 (Brussels)
Tel. +33 3881-75686 (Strasbourg)
Fax +33 3881-79686 (Strasbourg)
Website: http://www.simonbusuttil.eu

Mr Martin CALLANAN
Member of the Bureau
Tel. +32 228-45701 (Brussels)
Fax +32 228-49701 (Brussels)
Tel. +33 3881-75701 (Strasbourg)
Fax +33 3881-79701 (Strasbourg)

Mrs Charlotte CEDERSCHIÖLD
Member of the Bureau
Tel. +32 228-45823 (Brussels)
Fax +32 228-49823 (Brussels)
Tel. +33 3881-75823 (Strasbourg)
Fax +33 3881-79823 (Strasbourg)
E-mail: charlotte.cederschiold@europarl.europa.eu
Website: http://www.charlotte.moderat.se

Mr Giles CHICHESTER
Member of the Bureau
Tel. +32 228-45296 (Brussels)
Fax +32 228-49296 (Brussels)
Tel. +33 3881-75296 (Strasbourg)
Fax +33 3881-79296 (Strasbourg)
Website: http://www.gileschichestermep.org.uk

Mr Carlos COELHO
Member of the Bureau
Tel. +32 228-45551 (Brussels)
Fax +32 228-49551 (Brussels)
Tel. +33 3881-75551 (Strasbourg)
Fax +33 3881-79551 (Strasbourg)
E-mail: carlos.coelho@europarl.europa.eu
Website: http://www.carloscoelho.eu

Mr Panayiotis DEMETRIOU
Member of the Bureau
Tel. +32 228-45558 (Brussels)
Fax +32 228-49558 (Brussels)
Tel. +33 3881-75558 (Strasbourg)
Fax +33 3881-79558 (Strasbourg)
E-mail: panayiotis.demetriou@europarl.europa.eu

Mr Nirj DEVA
Member of the Bureau
Tel. +32 228-45245 (Brussels)
Fax +32 228-49245 (Brussels)
Tel. +33 3881-75245 (Strasbourg)
Fax +33 3881-79245 (Strasbourg)

Mr Valdis DOMBROVSKIS
Member of the Bureau
Tel. +32 228-45335 (Brussels)
Fax +32 228-49335 (Brussels)
Tel. +33 3881-75335 (Strasbourg)
Fax +33 3881-79335 (Strasbourg)
Website: http://www.valdisdombrovskis.lv

Mrs Avril DOYLE
Member of the Bureau
Tel. +32 228-45784 (Brussels)
Fax +32 228-49784 (Brussels)
Tel. +33 3881-75784 (Strasbourg)
Fax +33 3881-79784 (Strasbourg)
E-mail: avril.doyle@europarl.europa.eu
Website: http://www.avrildoyle.eu

Mr Michl EBNER
Member of the Bureau
Tel. +32 228-45460 (Brussels)
Fax +32 228-49460 (Brussels)
Tel. +33 3881-75460 (Strasbourg)
Fax +33 3881-79460 (Strasbourg)
E-mail: michl.ebner@europarl.europa.eu

Mr Christian EHLER
Member of the Bureau
Tel. +32 228-45325 (Brussels)
Fax +32 228-49325 (Brussels)
Tel. +33 3881-75325 (Strasbourg)
Fax +33 3881-79325 (Strasbourg)
E-mail: wahlkreisbuero@christian-ehler.de
Website: http://www.christian-ehler.de

Mr Markus FERBER
Member of the Bureau
Tel. +32 228-45230 (Brussels)
Fax +32 228-49230 (Brussels)
Tel. +33 3881-75230 (Strasbourg)
Fax +33 3881-79230 (Strasbourg)
E-mail: markus.ferber@europarl.europa.eu
Website: http://www.markus-ferber.de

Mr Karl-Heinz FLORENZ
Member of the Bureau
Tel. +32 228-45320 (Brussels)
Fax +32 228-49320 (Brussels)
Tel. +33 3881-75320 (Strasbourg)
Fax +33 3881-79320 (Strasbourg)
E-mail: karl-heinz.florenz@europarl.europa.eu
Website: http://www.karl-heinz-florenz.de

Mrs Carmen FRAGA ESTÉVEZ
Member of the Bureau
Tel. +32 228-45239 (Brussels)
Fax +32 228-49239 (Brussels)
Tel. +33 3881-75239 (Strasbourg)
Fax +33 3881-79239 (Strasbourg)

Mr Gerardo GALEOTE
Member of the Bureau
Tel. +32 228-45892 (Brussels)
Fax +32 228-49892 (Brussels)
Tel. +33 3881-75892 (Strasbourg)
Fax +33 3881-79892 (Strasbourg)

Mr Giuseppe GARGANI
Member of the Bureau
Tel. +32 228-45168 (Brussels)
Fax +32 228-49168 (Brussels)
Tel. +33 3881-75168 (Strasbourg)
Fax +33 3881-79168 (Strasbourg)

Mr Salvador GARRIGA POLLEDO
Member of the Bureau
Tel. +32 228-45303 (Brussels)
Fax +32 228-49303 (Brussels)
Tel. +33 3881-75303 (Strasbourg)
Fax +33 3881-79303 (Strasbourg)

Mr Jas GAWRONSKI
Member of the Bureau
Tel. +32 228-45292 (Brussels)
Fax +32 228-49292 (Brussels)
Tel. +33 3881-75292 (Strasbourg)
Fax +33 3881-79292 (Strasbourg)
E-mail: jas.gawronski@europarl.europa.eu

Mr Lutz GOEPEL
Member of the Bureau
Tel. +32 228-45760 (Brussels)
Fax +32 228-49760 (Brussels)
Tel. +33 3881-75760 (Strasbourg)
Fax +33 3881-79760 (Strasbourg)
Website: http://www.cdu-csu-ep.de

Mrs Ingeborg GRÄSSLE
Member of the Bureau
Tel. +32 228-45868 (Brussels)
Fax +32 228-49868 (Brussels)
Tel. +33 3881-75868 (Strasbourg)
Fax +33 3881-79868 (Strasbourg)

Mr Luis de GRANDES PASCUAL
Member of the Bureau
Tel. +32 228-45512 (Brussels)
Fax +32 228-49512 (Brussels)
Tel. +33 3881-75512 (Strasbourg)
Fax +33 3881-79512 (Strasbourg)
E-mail: luis.degrandespascual@europarl.europa.eu

Mr Mathieu GROSCH
Member of the Bureau
Tel. +32 228-45229 (Brussels)
Fax +32 228-49229 (Brussels)
Tel. +33 3881-75229 (Strasbourg)
Fax +33 3881-79229 (Strasbourg)
Website: http://www.grosch.be

Mr Malcolm HARBOUR
Member of the Bureau
Tel. +32 228-45132 (Brussels)
Fax +32 228-49132 (Brussels)
Tel. +33 3881-75132 (Strasbourg)
Fax +33 3881-79132 (Strasbourg)
Website: http://www.torymeps.com

Ville ITÄLÄ
Member of the Bureau
Tel. +32 228-45647 (Brussels)
Fax +32 228-49647 (Brussels)
Tel. +33 3881-75647 (Strasbourg)
Fax +33 3881-79647 (Strasbourg)
Website: http://www.villeitala.net

Mr Georg JARZEMBOWSKI
Member of the Bureau
Tel. +32 228-45306 (Brussels)
Fax +32 228-49306 (Brussels)
Tel. +33 3881-75306 (Strasbourg)
Fax +33 3881-79306 (Strasbourg)
Website: http://www.gjarzembowski.de

Mrs Elisabeth JEGGLE
Member of the Bureau
Tel. +32 228-45351 (Brussels)
Fax +32 228-49351 (Brussels)
Tel. +33 3881-75351 (Strasbourg)
Fax +33 3881-79351 (Strasbourg)
E-mail: elisabeth.jeggle@europarl.europa.eu
Website: http://www.eurojeggle.de

Mrs Rumiana JELEVA
Member of the Bureau
Tel. +32 228-45662 (Brussels)
Fax +32 228-49662 (Brussels)
Tel. +33 3881-75662 (Strasbourg)
Fax +33 3881-79662 (Strasbourg)
E-mail: rumiana.jeleva@europarl.europa.eu
Website: http://www.rumiana-jeleva.eu

Mr Tunne KELAM
Member of the Bureau
Tel. +32 228-45279 (Brussels)
Fax +32 228-49279 (Brussels)
Tel. +33 3881-75279 (Strasbourg)
Fax +33 3881-79279 (Strasbourg)
E-mail: tunne.kelam@europarl.europa.eu
Website: http://www.kelam.ee

Mr Timothy KIRKHOPE
Member of the Bureau
Tel. +32 228-45321 (Brussels)
Fax +32 228-49321 (Brussels)
Tel. +33 3881-75321 (Strasbourg)
Fax +33 3881-79321 (Strasbourg)
Website: http://www.kirkhope.org.uk

Mrs Rodi KRATSA-TSAGAROPOULOU
Member of the Bureau
Tel. +32 228-45308 (Brussels)
Fax +32 228-49308 (Brussels)
Tel. +33 3881-75308 (Strasbourg)
Fax +33 3881-79308 (Strasbourg)
E-mail: rodi.kratsa-tsagaropoulou@europarl.europa.eu

Mr Alain LAMASSOURE
Member of the Bureau
Tel. +32 228-45706 (Brussels)
Fax +32 228-49706 (Brussels)
Tel. +33 3881-75706 (Strasbourg)
Fax +33 3881-79706 (Strasbourg)
Website: http://www.alainlamassoure.com

Mr Vytautas LANDSBERGIS
Member of the Bureau
Tel. +32 228-45550 (Brussels)
Fax +32 228-49550 (Brussels)
Tel. +33 3881-75550 (Strasbourg)
Fax +33 3881-79550 (Strasbourg)

Mr Werner LANGEN
Member of the Bureau
Tel. +32 228-45385 (Brussels)
Fax +32 228-49385 (Brussels)
Tel. +33 3881-75385 (Strasbourg)
Fax +33 3881-79385 (Strasbourg)
Website: http://www.euinfo.de

Mr Klaus-Heiner LEHNE
Member of the Bureau
Tel. +32 228-45047 (Brussels)
Fax +32 228-49047 (Brussels)
Tel. +33 3881-75047 (Strasbourg)
Fax +33 3881-79047 (Strasbourg)
E-mail: klaus-heiner.lehne@europarl.europa.eu

Mr Antonio LÓPEZ-ISTÚRIZ WHITE
Member of the Bureau
Tel. +32 228-45713 (Brussels)
Fax +32 228-49713 (Brussels)
Tel. +33 3881-75713 (Strasbourg)
Fax +33 3881-79713 (Strasbourg)

Mr Edward McMILLAN-SCOTT
Member of the Bureau
Tel. +32 228-45959 (Brussels)
Fax +32 228-49959 (Brussels)
Tel. +33 3881-75959 (Strasbourg)
Fax +33 3881-79959 (Strasbourg)
E-mail: edward.mcmillan-scott@europarl.europa.eu
Website: http://www.emcmillanscott.com

Mrs Maria MARTENS
Member of the Bureau
Tel. +32 228-45857 (Brussels)
Fax +32 228-49857 (Brussels)
Tel. +33 3881-75857 (Strasbourg)
Fax +33 3881-79857 (Strasbourg)
E-mail: maria.martens@europarl.europa.eu
Website: http://www.mariamartens.nl

Mr Mario MAURO
Member of the Bureau
Tel. +32 228-45387 (Brussels)
Fax +32 228-49387 (Brussels)
Tel. +33 3881-75387 (Strasbourg)
Fax +33 3881-79387 (Strasbourg)

Mr Íñigo MÉNDEZ DE VIGO
Member of the Bureau
Tel. +32 228-45755 (Brussels)
Fax +32 228-49755 (Brussels)
Tel. +33 3881-75755 (Strasbourg)
Fax +33 3881-79755 (Strasbourg)
E-mail: inigo.mendezdevigo@europarl.europa.eu

Mrs Angelika NIEBLER
Member of the Bureau
Tel. +32 228-45390 (Brussels)
Fax +32 228-49390 (Brussels)
Tel. +33 3881-75390 (Strasbourg)
Fax +33 3881-79390 (Strasbourg)
Website: http://www.angelika-niebler.de

Mr Lambert van NISTELROOIJ
Member of the Bureau
Tel. +32 228-45434 (Brussels)
Fax +32 228-49434 (Brussels)
Tel. +33 3881-75434 (Strasbourg)
Fax +33 3881-79434 (Strasbourg)
E-mail: lnist@home.nl
Website: http://www.lambertvannistelrooij.eu

Mr Jan OLBRYCHT
Member of the Bureau
Tel. +32 228-45511 (Brussels)
Fax +32 228-49511 (Brussels)
Tel. +33 3881-75511 (Strasbourg)
Fax +33 3881-79511 (Strasbourg)
Website: http://www.janolbrycht.pl

Mr Miroslav OUZKÝ
Member of the Bureau
Tel. +32 228-45810 (Brussels)
Fax +32 228-49810 (Brussels)
Tel. +33 3881-75810 (Strasbourg)
Fax +33 3881-79810 (Strasbourg)
E-mail: miroslav@ouzky.cz
Website: http://www.ouzky.cz

Mrs Doris PACK
Member of the Bureau
Tel. +32 228-45310 (Brussels)
Fax +32 228-49310 (Brussels)
Tel. +33 3881-75310 (Strasbourg)
Fax +33 3881-79310 (Strasbourg)
E-mail: doris.pack@europarl.europa.eu
Website: http://www.dorispack.de

Mr Neil PARISH
Member of the Bureau
Tel. +32 228-45392 (Brussels)
Fax +32 228-49392 (Brussels)
Tel. +33 3881-75392 (Strasbourg)
Fax +33 3881-79392 (Strasbourg)
E-mail: neil.parish@europarl.europa.eu

Mr Hans-Gert PÖTTERING
Member of the Bureau
Tel. +32 228-45769 (Brussels)
Fax +32 228-49769 (Brussels)
Tel. +33 3881-75769 (Strasbourg)
Fax +33 3881-79769 (Strasbourg)
E-mail: hans-gert.poettering@europarl.europa.eu
Website: http://www.cdu-lkos.de/poettering

Mr José Javier POMÉS RUIZ
Member of the Bureau
Tel. +32 228-45899 (Brussels)
Fax +32 228-49899 (Brussels)
Tel. +33 3881-75899 (Strasbourg)
Fax +33 3881-79899 (Strasbourg)

Mr Luís QUEIRÓ
Member of the Bureau
Tel. +32 228-45227 (Brussels)
Fax +32 228-49227 (Brussels)
Tel. +33 3881-75227 (Strasbourg)
Fax +33 3881-79227 (Strasbourg)

Mr Reinhard RACK
Member of the Bureau
Tel. +32 228-45773 (Brussels)
Fax +32 228-49773 (Brussels)
Tel. +33 3881-75773 (Strasbourg)
Fax +33 3881-79773 (Strasbourg)
E-mail: reinhard.rack@europarl.europa.eu

Mr Christian ROVSING
Member of the Bureau
Tel. +32 228-45243 (Brussels)
Fax +32 228-49243 (Brussels)
Tel. +33 3881-75243 (Strasbourg)
Fax +33 3881-79243 (Strasbourg)
E-mail: cfr@cfr.dk

Mr José Ignacio SALAFRANCA SÁNCHEZ-NEYRA
Member of the Bureau
Tel. +32 228-45603 (Brussels)
Fax +32 228-49603 (Brussels)
Tel. +33 3881-75603 (Strasbourg)
Fax +33 3881-79603 (Strasbourg)
E-mail: joseignacio.salafranca@europarl.europa.eu
Website: http://www.salafranca.net

Mrs Amalia SARTORI
Member of the Bureau
Tel. +32 228-45556 (Brussels)
Fax +32 228-49556 (Brussels)
Tel. +33 3881-75556 (Strasbourg)
Fax +33 3881-79556 (Strasbourg)
E-mail: amalia.sartori@europarl.europa.eu
Website: http://www.amaliasartori.it

Mr Jacek SARYUSZ-WOLSKI
Member of the Bureau
Tel. +32 228-45371 (Brussels)
Fax +32 228-49371 (Brussels)
Tel. +33 3881-75371 (Strasbourg)
Fax +33 3881-79371 (Strasbourg)
Website: http://www.saryusz-wolski.pl

Mr Pál SCHMITT
Member of the Bureau
Tel. +32 228-45544 (Brussels)
Fax +32 228-49544 (Brussels)
Tel. +33 3881-75544 (Strasbourg)
Fax +33 3881-79544 (Strasbourg)
E-mail: pal.schmitt@europarl.europa.eu

Mr Jean SPAUTZ
Member of the Bureau
Tel. +32 228-45737 (Brussels)
Fax +32 228-49737 (Brussels)
Tel. +33 3881-75737 (Strasbourg)
Fax +33 3881-79737 (Strasbourg)
E-mail: jean.spautz@europarl.europa.eu

Mr Peter ŠŤASTNÝ
Member of the Bureau
Tel. +32 228-45683 (Brussels)
Fax +32 228-49683 (Brussels)
Tel. +33 3881-75683 (Strasbourg)
Fax +33 3881-79683 (Strasbourg)

Mr Theodor Dumitru STOLOJAN
Member of the Bureau
Tel. +32 228-45670 (Brussels)
Fax +32 228-49670 (Brussels)
Tel. +33 3881-75670 (Strasbourg)
Fax +33 3881-79670 (Strasbourg)

Mr Robert STURDY
Member of the Bureau
Tel. +32 228-45294 (Brussels)
Fax +32 228-49294 (Brussels)
Tel. +33 3881-75294 (Strasbourg)
Fax +33 3881-79294 (Strasbourg)

Mrs Margie SUDRE
Member of the Bureau
Tel. +32 228-45473 (Brussels)
Fax +32 228-49473 (Brussels)
Tel. +33 3881-75473 (Strasbourg)
Fax +33 3881-79473 (Strasbourg)

Mr David SUMBERG
Member of the Bureau
Tel. +32 228-45372 (Brussels)
Fax +32 228-49372 (Brussels)
Tel. +33 3881-75372 (Strasbourg)
Fax +33 3881-79372 (Strasbourg)

Mr László SURJÁN
Member of the Bureau
Tel. +32 228-45835 (Brussels)
Fax +32 228-49835 (Brussels)
Tel. +33 3881-75835 (Strasbourg)
Fax +33 3881-79835 (Strasbourg)
E-mail: laszlo.surjan@europarl.europa.eu

Mr Antonios TRAKATELLIS
Member of the Bureau
Tel. +32 228-45762 (Brussels)
Fax +32 228-49762 (Brussels)
Tel. +33 3881-75762 (Strasbourg)
Fax +33 3881-79762 (Strasbourg)
E-mail: antonios.trakatellis@europarl.europa.eu
Website: http://www.atrakatellis.gr

Mr Ioannis VARVITSIOTIS
Member of the Bureau
Tel. +32 228-45680 (Brussels)
Fax +32 228-49680 (Brussels)
Tel. +33 3881-75680 (Strasbourg)
Fax +33 3881-79680 (Strasbourg)
E-mail: ioannis.varvitsiotis@europarl.europa.eu

Mr Alejo VIDAL-QUADRAS
Member of the Bureau
Tel. +32 228-45322 (Brussels)
Fax +32 228-49322 (Brussels)
Tel. +33 3881-75322 (Strasbourg)
Fax +33 3881-79322 (Strasbourg)
E-mail: alejo.vidal-quadras@europarl.europa.eu

Mr Manfred WEBER
Member of the Bureau
Tel. +32 228-45890 (Brussels)
Fax +32 228-49890 (Brussels)
Tel. +33 3881-75890 (Strasbourg)
Fax +33 3881-79890 (Strasbourg)
E-mail: info@weber-manfred.de
Website: http://www.weber-manfred.de

Mr Karl von WOGAU
Member of the Bureau
Tel. +32 228-45301 (Brussels)
Fax +32 228-49301 (Brussels)
Tel. +33 3881-75301 (Strasbourg)
Fax +33 3881-79301 (Strasbourg)
Website: http://www.wogau.de

Mrs Anna ZÁBORSKÁ
Member of the Bureau
Tel. +32 228-45923 (Brussels)
Fax +32 228-49923 (Brussels)
Tel. +33 3881-75923 (Strasbourg)
Fax +33 3881-79923 (Strasbourg)
Website: http://www.zaborska.sk

Mr Jan ZAHRADIL
Member of the Bureau
Tel. +32 228-45666 (Brussels)
Fax +32 228-49666 (Brussels)
Tel. +33 3881-75666 (Strasbourg)
Fax +33 3881-79666 (Strasbourg)

Mr Stefano ZAPPALA'
Member of the Bureau
Tel. +32 228-45208 (Brussels)
Fax +32 228-49208 (Brussels)
Tel. +33 3881-75208 (Strasbourg)
Fax +33 3881-79208 (Strasbourg)
E-mail: stefano.zappala@europarl.europa.eu
Website: http://www.zappalaonline.org

Mr Josef ZIELENIEC
Member of the Bureau
Tel. +32 228-45540 (Brussels)
Fax +32 228-49540 (Brussels)
Tel. +33 3881-75540 (Strasbourg)
Fax +33 3881-79540 (Strasbourg)
Website: http://www.zieleniec.cz

Mr Gabriele ALBERTINI
Member
Tel. +32 228-45366 (Brussels)
Fax +32 228-49366 (Brussels)
Tel. +33 3881-75366 (Strasbourg)
Fax +33 3881-79366 (Strasbourg)

Mr Emmanouil ANGELAKAS
Member
Tel. +32 228-45242 (Brussels)
Fax +32 228-49242 (Brussels)
Tel. +33 3881-75242 (Strasbourg)
Fax +33 3881-79242 (Strasbourg)
E-mail: emmanouil.angelakas@europarl.europa.eu
Website: http://www.angelakas.gr

Mr Alfredo ANTONIOZZI
Member
Tel. +32 228-45516 (Brussels)
Fax +32 228-49516 (Brussels)
Tel. +33 3881-75516 (Strasbourg)
Fax +33 3881-79516 (Strasbourg)

Mr Richard James ASHWORTH
Member
Tel. +32 228-45309 (Brussels)
Fax +32 228-49309 (Brussels)
Tel. +33 3881-75309 (Strasbourg)
Fax +33 3881-79309 (Strasbourg)
E-mail: richardjames.ashworth@europarl.europa.eu

Mr Jean-Pierre AUDY
Member
Tel. +32 228-45126 (Brussels)
Fax +32 228-49126 (Brussels)
Tel. +33 3881-75126 (Strasbourg)
Fax +33 3881-79126 (Strasbourg)
Website: http://www.jeanpierreaudy.com

Mrs Pilar AYUSO
Member
Tel. +32 228-45398 (Brussels)
Fax +32 228-49398 (Brussels)
Tel. +33 3881-75398 (Strasbourg)
Fax +33 3881-79398 (Strasbourg)

Mrs Etelka BARSI-PATAKY
Member
Tel. +32 228-45582 (Brussels)
Fax +32 228-49582 (Brussels)
Tel. +33 3881-75582 (Strasbourg)
Fax +33 3881-79582 (Strasbourg)

Mr Paolo BARTOLOZZI
Member
Tel. +32 228-45396 (Brussels)
Fax +32 228-49396 (Brussels)
Tel. +33 3881-75396 (Strasbourg)
Fax +33 3881-79396 (Strasbourg)
Website: http://www.paolobartolozzi.it

Edit BAUER
Member
Tel. +32 228-45673 (Brussels)
Fax +32 228-49673 (Brussels)
Tel. +33 3881-75673 (Strasbourg)
Fax +33 3881-79673 (Strasbourg)
Website: http://www.editbauer.sk

Mr Christopher BEAZLEY
Member
Tel. +32 228-45226 (Brussels)
Fax +32 228-49226 (Brussels)
Tel. +33 3881-75226 (Strasbourg)
Fax +33 3881-79226 (Strasbourg)

Mr Zsolt László BECSEY
Member
Tel. +32 228-45888 (Brussels)
Fax +32 228-49888 (Brussels)
Tel. +33 3881-75888 (Strasbourg)
Fax +33 3881-79888 (Strasbourg)
Website: http://www.becseyzsolt.hu

Mr Ivo BELET
Member
Tel. +32 228-45623 (Brussels)
Fax +32 228-49623 (Brussels)
Tel. +33 3881-75623 (Strasbourg)
Fax +33 3881-79623 (Strasbourg)
E-mail: ivo.belet@europarl.europa.eu
Website: http://www.ivobelet.be

Mr Rolf BEREND
Member
Tel. +32 228-45413 (Brussels)
Fax +32 228-49413 (Brussels)
Tel. +33 3881-75413 (Strasbourg)
Fax +33 3881-79413 (Strasbourg)
Website: http://www.cdu-csu-ep.de

Mr Sebastian Valentin BODU
Member
Tel. +32 228-45634 (Brussels)
Fax +32 228-49634 (Brussels)
Tel. +33 3881-75634 (Strasbourg)
Fax +33 3881-79634 (Strasbourg)

Mr Philip BRADBOURN
Member
Tel. +32 228-45407 (Brussels)
Fax +32 228-49407 (Brussels)
Tel. +33 3881-75407 (Strasbourg)
Fax +33 3881-79407 (Strasbourg)
E-mail: philip.bradbourn@europarl.europa.eu

Mrs Frieda BREPOELS
Member
Tel. +32 228-45862 (Brussels)
Fax +32 228-49862 (Brussels)
Tel. +33 3881-75862 (Strasbourg)
Fax +33 3881-79862 (Strasbourg)
Website: http://www.friedabrepoels.be

Mr Jan BŘEZINA
Member
Tel. +32 228-45484 (Brussels)
Fax +32 228-49484 (Brussels)
Tel. +33 3881-75484 (Strasbourg)
Fax +33 3881-79484 (Strasbourg)
E-mail: brezina@janbrezina.cz
Website: http://www.janbrezina.cz

Mr Nicodim BULZESC
Member
Tel. +32 228-45622 (Brussels)
Fax +32 228-49622 (Brussels)
Tel. +33 3881-75622 (Strasbourg)
Fax +33 3881-79622 (Strasbourg)
E-mail: nicodim.bulzesc@europarl.europa.eu
Website: http://www.nicodim-bulzesc.eu

Mr Colm BURKE
Member
Tel. +32 228-45417 (Brussels)
Fax +32 228-49417 (Brussels)
Tel. +33 3881-75417 (Strasbourg)
Fax +33 3881-79417 (Strasbourg)
E-mail: colmburke@colmburke.eu

Mr Jerzy BUZEK
Member
Tel. +32 228-45631 (Brussels)
Fax +32 228-49631 (Brussels)
Tel. +33 3881-75631 (Strasbourg)
Fax +33 3881-79631 (Strasbourg)

Mr Milan CABRNOCH
Member
Tel. +32 228-45378 (Brussels)
Fax +32 228-49378 (Brussels)
Tel. +33 3881-75378 (Strasbourg)
Fax +33 3881-79378 (Strasbourg)
Website: http://www.cabrnoch.cz

Mrs Maddalena CALIA
Member
Tel. +32 228-45866 (Brussels)
Fax +32 228-49866 (Brussels)
Tel. +33 3881-75866 (Strasbourg)
Fax +33 3881-79866 (Strasbourg)

Mr Giorgio CAROLLO
Member
Tel. +32 228-45178 (Brussels)
Fax +32 228-49178 (Brussels)
Tel. +33 3881-75178 (Strasbourg)
Fax +33 3881-79178 (Strasbourg)

Mr David CASA
Member
Tel. +32 228-45445 (Brussels)
Fax +32 228-49445 (Brussels)
Tel. +33 3881-75445 (Strasbourg)
Fax +33 3881-79445 (Strasbourg)

Mr Carlo CASINI
Member
Tel. +32 228-45330 (Brussels)
Fax +32 228-49330 (Brussels)
Tel. +33 3881-75330 (Strasbourg)
Fax +33 3881-79330 (Strasbourg)
E-mail: carlo.casini@europarl.europa.eu
Website: http://www.carlocasini.it

Mr Daniel CASPARY
Member
Tel. +32 228-45978 (Brussels)
Fax +32 228-49978 (Brussels)
Tel. +33 3881-75978 (Strasbourg)
Fax +33 3881-79978 (Strasbourg)
E-mail: daniel@caspary.de
Website: http://www.caspary.de

Mrs Pilar del CASTILLO VERA
Member
Tel. +32 228-45982 (Brussels)
Fax +32 228-49982 (Brussels)
Tel. +33 3881-75982 (Strasbourg)
Fax +33 3881-79982 (Strasbourg)
E-mail: pilar.delcastillo@europarl.europa.eu

Mr Călin Cătălin CHIRIŢĂ
Member
Tel. +32 228-45799 (Brussels)
Fax +32 228-49799 (Brussels)
Tel. +33 3881-75799 (Strasbourg)
Fax +33 3881-79799 (Strasbourg)
E-mail: calincatalin.chirita@europarl.europa.eu

Mr Zdzisław Kazimierz CHMIELEWSKI
Member
Tel. +32 228-45329 (Brussels)
Fax +32 228-49329 (Brussels)
Tel. +33 3881-75329 (Strasbourg)
Fax +33 3881-79329 (Strasbourg)

Mr Dragoş Florin DAVID
Member
Tel. +32 228-45651 (Brussels)
Fax +32 228-49651 (Brussels)
Tel. +33 3881-75651 (Strasbourg)
Fax +33 3881-79651 (Strasbourg)
E-mail: dragosflorin.david@europarl.europa.eu

Mr Antonio DE BLASIO
Member
Tel. +32 228-45702 (Brussels)
Fax +32 228-49702 (Brussels)
Tel. +33 3881-75702 (Strasbourg)
Fax +33 3881-79702 (Strasbourg)

Mr Jean-Luc DEHAENE
Member
Tel. +32 228-45867 (Brussels)
Fax +32 228-49867 (Brussels)
Tel. +33 3881-75867 (Strasbourg)
Fax +33 3881-79867 (Strasbourg)
Website: http://www.dehaene.be

Mrs Marie-Hélène DESCAMPS
Member
Tel. +32 228-45730 (Brussels)
Fax +32 228-49730 (Brussels)
Tel. +33 3881-75730 (Strasbourg)
Fax +33 3881-79730 (Strasbourg)
E-mail: marie-helene.descamps@europarl.europa.eu

Mr Albert DESS
Member
Tel. +32 228-45231 (Brussels)
Fax +32 228-49231 (Brussels)
Tel. +33 3881-75231 (Strasbourg)
Fax +33 3881-79231 (Strasbourg)
E-mail: albert.dess@europarl.europa.eu
Website: http://www.albert-dess.de

Mrs Christine DE VEYRAC
Member
Tel. +32 228-45739 (Brussels)
Fax +32 228-49739 (Brussels)
Tel. +33 3881-75739 (Strasbourg)
Fax +33 3881-79739 (Strasbourg)
Website: http://www.christinedeveyrac.fr

Mr Agustín DÍAZ DE MERA GARCÍA CONSUEGRA
Member
Tel. +32 228-45624 (Brussels)
Fax +32 228-49624 (Brussels)
Tel. +33 3881-75624 (Strasbourg)
Fax +33 3881-79624 (Strasbourg)

Mr Giorgos DIMITRAKOPOULOS
Member
Tel. +32 228-45941 (Brussels)
Fax +32 228-49941 (Brussels)
Tel. +33 3881-75941 (Strasbourg)
Fax +33 3881-79941 (Strasbourg)
E-mail: giorgos.dimitrakopoulos@europarl.europa.eu

Mr Bert DOORN
Member
Tel. +32 228-45543 (Brussels)
Fax +32 228-49543 (Brussels)
Tel. +33 3881-75543 (Strasbourg)
Fax +33 3881-79543 (Strasbourg)

Mr Den DOVER
Member
Tel. +32 228-45787 (Brussels)
Fax +32 228-49787 (Brussels)
Tel. +33 3881-75787 (Strasbourg)
Fax +33 3881-79787 (Strasbourg)
E-mail: den.dover@europarl.europa.eu
Website: http://www.dendovermep.co.uk

Mr Petr DUCHOŇ
Member
Tel. +32 228-45375 (Brussels)
Fax +32 228-49375 (Brussels)
Tel. +33 3881-75375 (Strasbourg)
Fax +33 3881-79375 (Strasbourg)
Website: http://www.petrduchon.eu

Árpád DUKA-ZÓLYOMI
Member
Tel. +32 228-45238 (Brussels)
Fax +32 228-49238 (Brussels)
Tel. +33 3881-75238 (Strasbourg)
Fax +33 3881-79238 (Strasbourg)

Mr Constantin DUMITRIU
Member
Tel. +32 228-45617 (Brussels)
Fax +32 228-49617 (Brussels)
Tel. +33 3881-75617 (Strasbourg)
Fax +33 3881-79617 (Strasbourg)
Website: http://www.constantindumitriu.eu

Mr James ELLES
Member
Tel. +32 228-45951 (Brussels)
Fax +32 228-49951 (Brussels)
Tel. +33 3881-75951 (Strasbourg)
Fax +33 3881-79951 (Strasbourg)
Website: http://www.jameselles.com

Mrs Maria da Assunção ESTEVES
Member
Tel. +32 228-45566 (Brussels)
Fax +32 228-49566 (Brussels)
Tel. +33 3881-75566 (Strasbourg)
Fax +33 3881-79566 (Strasbourg)
E-mail: assuncao.esteves@europarl.europa.eu
Website: http://www.assuncaoesteves.org

Mr Jonathan EVANS
Member
Tel. +32 228-45528 (Brussels)
Fax +32 228-49528 (Brussels)
Tel. +33 3881-75528 (Strasbourg)
Fax +33 3881-79528 (Strasbourg)

Mr Hynek FAJMON
Member
Tel. +32 228-45806 (Brussels)
Fax +32 228-49806 (Brussels)
Tel. +33 3881-75806 (Strasbourg)
Fax +33 3881-79806 (Strasbourg)
E-mail: hynek.fajmon@europarl.europa.eu
Website: http://www.hynek-fajmon.cz

Mr Carlo FATUZZO
Member
Tel. +32 228-45219 (Brussels)
Fax +32 228-49219 (Brussels)
Tel. +33 3881-75219 (Strasbourg)
Fax +33 3881-79219 (Strasbourg)
E-mail: carlo.fatuzzo@europarl.europa.eu

Mr Fernando FERNÁNDEZ MARTÍN
Member
Tel. +32 228-45605 (Brussels)
Fax +32 228-49605 (Brussels)
Tel. +33 3881-75605 (Strasbourg)
Fax +33 3881-79605 (Strasbourg)

Mr Christofer FJELLNER
Member
Tel. +32 228-45536 (Brussels)
Fax +32 228-49536 (Brussels)
Tel. +33 3881-75536 (Strasbourg)
Fax +33 3881-79536 (Strasbourg)

Mrs Nicole FONTAINE
Member
Tel. +32 228-45225 (Brussels)
Fax +32 228-49225 (Brussels)
Tel. +33 3881-75225 (Strasbourg)
Fax +33 3881-79225 (Strasbourg)

Mrs Brigitte FOURÉ
Member
Tel. +32 228-45876 (Brussels)
Fax +32 228-49876 (Brussels)
Tel. +33 3881-75876 (Strasbourg)
Fax +33 3881-79876 (Strasbourg)
E-mail: brigitte.foure@europarl.europa.eu
Website: http://www.brigittefoure.com

Mr Duarte FREITAS
Member
Tel. +32 228-45790 (Brussels)
Fax +32 228-49790 (Brussels)
Tel. +33 3881-75790 (Strasbourg)
Fax +33 3881-79790 (Strasbourg)
Website: http://www.duarte-freitas.org

Mr Ingo FRIEDRICH
Member
Tel. +32 228-45324 (Brussels)
Fax +32 228-49324 (Brussels)
Tel. +33 3881-75324 (Strasbourg)
Fax +33 3881-79324 (Strasbourg)
Website: http://www.ingo-friedrich.de

Mr Daniel Petru FUNERIU
Member
Tel. +32 228-45577 (Brussels)
Fax +32 228-49577 (Brussels)
Tel. +33 3881-75577 (Strasbourg)
Fax +33 3881-79577 (Strasbourg)

Mrs Urszula GACEK
Member
Tel. +32 228-45733 (Brussels)
Fax +32 228-49733 (Brussels)
Tel. +33 3881-75733 (Strasbourg)
Fax +33 3881-79733 (Strasbourg)
E-mail: biuro@urszulagacek.pl
Website: http://www.urszulagacek.pl

Mr Michael GAHLER
Member
Tel. +32 228-45977 (Brussels)
Fax +32 228-49977 (Brussels)
Tel. +33 3881-75977 (Strasbourg)
Fax +33 3881-79977 (Strasbourg)
Website: http://www.michael-gahler.de

Mrs Kinga GÁL
Member
Tel. +32 228-45599 (Brussels)
Fax +32 228-49599 (Brussels)
Tel. +33 3881-75599 (Strasbourg)
Fax +33 3881-79599 (Strasbourg)
Website: http://www.galkinga.hu

Mr Milan GAĽA
Member
Tel. +32 228-45643 (Brussels)
Fax +32 228-49643 (Brussels)
Tel. +33 3881-75643 (Strasbourg)
Fax +33 3881-79643 (Strasbourg)
Website: http://www.milangala.sk

Mr José Manuel GARCÍA-MARGALLO Y MARFIL
Member
Tel. +32 228-45904 (Brussels)
Fax +32 228-49904 (Brussels)
Tel. +33 3881-75904 (Strasbourg)
Fax +33 3881-79904 (Strasbourg)

Mrs Elisabetta GARDINI
Member
Tel. +32 228-45393 (Brussels)
Fax +32 228-49393 (Brussels)
Tel. +33 3881-75393 (Strasbourg)
Fax +33 3881-79393 (Strasbourg)

Mr Patrick GAUBERT
Member
Tel. +32 228-45156 (Brussels)
Fax +32 228-49156 (Brussels)
Tel. +33 3881-75156 (Strasbourg)
Fax +33 3881-79156 (Strasbourg)
Website: http://www.patrickgaubert.eu

Mr Jean-Paul GAUZÈS
Member
Tel. +32 228-45700 (Brussels)
Fax +32 228-49700 (Brussels)
Tel. +33 3881-75700 (Strasbourg)
Fax +33 3881-79700 (Strasbourg)

Mr Roland GEWALT
Member
Tel. +32 228-45442 (Brussels)
Fax +32 228-49442 (Brussels)
Tel. +33 3881-75442 (Strasbourg)
Fax +33 3881-79442 (Strasbourg)

Mr Ioannis GKLAVAKIS
Member
Tel. +32 228-45409 (Brussels)
Fax +32 228-49409 (Brussels)
Tel. +33 3881-75409 (Strasbourg)
Fax +33 3881-79409 (Strasbourg)
Website: http://www.gklavakis.gr

Mr Béla GLATTFELDER
Member
Tel. +32 228-45889 (Brussels)
Fax +32 228-49889 (Brussels)
Tel. +33 3881-75889 (Strasbourg)
Fax +33 3881-79889 (Strasbourg)

Mr Alfred GOMOLKA
Member
Tel. +32 228-45307 (Brussels)
Fax +32 228-49307 (Brussels)
Tel. +33 3881-75307 (Strasbourg)
Fax +33 3881-79307 (Strasbourg)
Website: http://www.cdu-csu-ep.de

Mr Vasco GRAÇA MOURA
Member
Tel. +32 228-45369 (Brussels)
Fax +32 228-49369 (Brussels)
Tel. +33 3881-75369 (Strasbourg)
Fax +33 3881-79369 (Strasbourg)

Mrs Françoise GROSSETÊTE
Member
Tel. +32 228-45952 (Brussels)
Fax +32 228-49952 (Brussels)
Tel. +33 3881-75952 (Strasbourg)
Fax +33 3881-79952 (Strasbourg)
E-mail: francoise.grossetete@europarl.europa.eu
Website: http://www.francoise-grossetete.eu

Mr Ambroise GUELLEC
Member
Tel. +32 228-45520 (Brussels)
Fax +32 228-49520 (Brussels)
Tel. +33 3881-75520 (Strasbourg)
Fax +33 3881-79520 (Strasbourg)
Website: http://www.ambroiseguellec.com

Mrs Cristina GUTIÉRREZ-CORTINES
Member
Tel. +32 228-45594 (Brussels)
Fax +32 228-49594 (Brussels)
Tel. +33 3881-75594 (Strasbourg)
Fax +33 3881-79594 (Strasbourg)
E-mail: cristina.gutierrez-cortines@europarl.europa.eu

Mr András GYÜRK
Member
Tel. +32 228-45727 (Brussels)
Fax +32 228-49727 (Brussels)
Tel. +33 3881-75727 (Strasbourg)
Fax +33 3881-79727 (Strasbourg)

Mrs Małgorzata HANDZLIK
Member
Tel. +32 228-45319 (Brussels)
Fax +32 228-49319 (Brussels)
Tel. +33 3881-75319 (Strasbourg)
Fax +33 3881-79319 (Strasbourg)

Mr Christopher HEATON-HARRIS
Member
Tel. +32 228-45523 (Brussels)
Fax +32 228-49523 (Brussels)
Tel. +33 3881-75523 (Strasbourg)
Fax +33 3881-79523 (Strasbourg)

Mrs Erna HENNICOT-SCHOEPGES
Member
Tel. +32 228-45836 (Brussels)
Fax +32 228-49836 (Brussels)
Tel. +33 3881-75836 (Strasbourg)
Fax +33 3881-79836 (Strasbourg)
E-mail: erna.hennicot-schoepges@europarl.europa.eu
Website: http://www.ehennicotschoepges.lu

Mrs Esther HERRANZ GARCÍA
Member
Tel. +32 228-45274 (Brussels)
Fax +32 228-49274 (Brussels)
Tel. +33 3881-75274 (Strasbourg)
Fax +33 3881-79274 (Strasbourg)
E-mail: esther.herranzgarcia@europarl.europa.eu
Website: http://www.eherranz.net

Mr Luis HERRERO-TEJEDOR
Member
Tel. +32 228-45644 (Brussels)
Fax +32 228-49644 (Brussels)
Tel. +33 3881-75644 (Strasbourg)
Fax +33 3881-79644 (Strasbourg)

Mrs Ruth HIERONYMI
Member
Tel. +32 228-45859 (Brussels)
Fax +32 228-49859 (Brussels)
Tel. +33 3881-75859 (Strasbourg)
Fax +33 3881-79859 (Strasbourg)
Website: http://www.hieronymi.de

Mr Jim HIGGINS
Member
Tel. +32 228-45843 (Brussels)
Fax +32 228-49843 (Brussels)
Tel. +33 3881-75843 (Strasbourg)
Fax +33 3881-79843 (Strasbourg)
E-mail: jim.higgins@europarl.europa.eu

Mr Krzysztof HOŁOWCZYC
Member
Tel. +32 228-45729 (Brussels)
Fax +32 228-49729 (Brussels)
Tel. +33 3881-75729 (Strasbourg)
Fax +33 3881-79729 (Strasbourg)
E-mail: krzysztof.holowczyc@europarl.europa.eu
Website: http://www.holowczyc.eu

Mr Karsten Friedrich HOPPENSTEDT
Member
Tel. +32 228-45660 (Brussels)
Fax +32 228-49660 (Brussels)
Tel. +33 3881-75660 (Strasbourg)
Fax +33 3881-79660 (Strasbourg)

Mr Ján HUDACKÝ
Member
Tel. +32 228-45286 (Brussels)
Fax +32 228-49286 (Brussels)
Tel. +33 3881-75286 (Strasbourg)
Fax +33 3881-79286 (Strasbourg)
E-mail: jan.hudacky@europarl.europa.eu
Website: http://www.hudacky.sk

Mrs Jana HYBÁŠKOVÁ
Member
Tel. +32 228-45519 (Brussels)
Fax +32 228-49519 (Brussels)
Tel. +33 3881-75519 (Strasbourg)
Fax +33 3881-79519 (Strasbourg)
E-mail: jana.hybaskova@europarl.europa.eu
Website: http://www.hybaskova.cz

Mrs Anna IBRISAGIC
Member
Tel. +32 228-45775 (Brussels)
Fax +32 228-49775 (Brussels)
Tel. +33 3881-75775 (Strasbourg)
Fax +33 3881-79775 (Strasbourg)
E-mail: anna.ibrisagic@europarl.europa.eu
Website: http://www.ibrisagic.net

Mr Carlos José ITURGAIZ ANGULO
Member
Tel. +32 228-45965 (Brussels)
Fax +32 228-49965 (Brussels)
Tel. +33 3881-75965 (Strasbourg)
Fax +33 3881-79965 (Strasbourg)

Mrs Caroline JACKSON
Member
Tel. +32 228-45255 (Brussels)
Fax +32 228-49255 (Brussels)
Tel. +33 3881-75255 (Strasbourg)
Fax +33 3881-79255 (Strasbourg)
E-mail: caroline.jackson@europarl.europa.eu
Website: http://www.carolinejackson-mep.org.uk

Mr Stanisław JAŁOWIECKI
Member
Tel. +32 228-45973 (Brussels)
Fax +32 228-49973 (Brussels)
Tel. +33 3881-75973 (Strasbourg)
Fax +33 3881-79973 (Strasbourg)
Website: http://www.jalowiecki.pl

Mrs Lívia JÁRÓKA
Member
Tel. +32 228-45218 (Brussels)
Fax +32 228-49218 (Brussels)
Tel. +33 3881-75218 (Strasbourg)
Fax +33 3881-79218 (Strasbourg)
Website: http://www.jarokalivia.hu

Mrs Romana JORDAN CIZELJ
Member
Tel. +32 228-45280 (Brussels)
Fax +32 228-49280 (Brussels)
Tel. +33 3881-75280 (Strasbourg)
Fax +33 3881-79280 (Strasbourg)
E-mail: romana.jordancizelj@europarl.europa.eu
Website: http://www.rjordancizelj.si

Mr Filip KACZMAREK
Member
Tel. +32 228-45317 (Brussels)
Fax +32 228-49317 (Brussels)
Tel. +33 3881-75317 (Strasbourg)
Fax +33 3881-79317 (Strasbourg)
Website: http://www.filipkaczmarek.pl

Mr Syed KAMALL
Member
Tel. +32 228-45792 (Brussels)
Fax +32 228-49792 (Brussels)
Tel. +33 3881-75792 (Strasbourg)
Fax +33 3881-79792 (Strasbourg)
Website: http://www.syedkamall.com

Mr Sajjad KARIM
Member
Tel. +32 228-45640 (Brussels)
Fax +32 228-49640 (Brussels)
Tel. +33 3881-75640 (Strasbourg)
Fax +33 3881-79640 (Strasbourg)
E-mail: sajjad.karim@europarl.europa.eu
Website: http://www.sajjadkarim.org.uk

Mr Ioannis KASOULIDES
Member
Tel. +32 228-45155 (Brussels)
Fax +32 228-49155 (Brussels)
Tel. +33 3881-75155 (Strasbourg)
Fax +33 3881-79155 (Strasbourg)
Website: http://www.kasoulides.com

Mr Martin KASTLER
Member
Tel. +32 228-45538 (Brussels)
Fax +32 228-49538 (Brussels)
Tel. +33 3881-75538 (Strasbourg)
Fax +33 3881-79538 (Strasbourg)

Mrs Ewa KLAMT
Member
Tel. +32 228-45971 (Brussels)
Fax +32 228-49971 (Brussels)
Tel. +33 3881-75971 (Strasbourg)
Fax +33 3881-79971 (Strasbourg)
Website: http://www.cdu-csu-ep.de

Mrs Christa KLASS
Member
Tel. +32 228-45313 (Brussels)
Fax +32 228-49313 (Brussels)
Tel. +33 3881-75313 (Strasbourg)
Fax +33 3881-79313 (Strasbourg)

Mr Dieter-Lebrecht KOCH
Member
Tel. +32 228-45761 (Brussels)
Fax +32 228-49761 (Brussels)
Tel. +33 3881-75761 (Strasbourg)
Fax +33 3881-79761 (Strasbourg)
E-mail: dieter-lebrecht.koch@europarl.europa.eu
Website: http://www.europaabgeordneter.de

Mr Christoph KONRAD
Member
Tel. +32 228-45333 (Brussels)
Fax +32 228-49333 (Brussels)
Tel. +33 3881-75333 (Strasbourg)
Fax +33 3881-79333 (Strasbourg)
E-mail: berlin@dr-christoph-konrad.de

Eija-Riitta KORHOLA
Member
Tel. +32 228-45472 (Brussels)
Fax +32 228-49472 (Brussels)
Tel. +33 3881-75472 (Strasbourg)
Fax +33 3881-79472 (Strasbourg)
E-mail: eija-riitta.korhola@europarl.europa.eu
Website: http://www.korhola.com

Mr Aldis KUŠĶIS
Member
Tel. +32 228-45410 (Brussels)
Fax +32 228-49410 (Brussels)
Tel. +33 3881-75410 (Strasbourg)
Fax +33 3881-79410 (Strasbourg)
E-mail: aldis.kuskis@europarl.europa.eu
Website: http://www.kuskis.lv

Mrs Esther de LANGE
Member
Tel. +32 228-45954 (Brussels)
Fax +32 228-49954 (Brussels)
Tel. +33 3881-75954 (Strasbourg)
Fax +33 3881-79954 (Strasbourg)
E-mail: esther.delange@europarl.europa.eu
Website: http://www.estherdelange.nl

Mr Raymond LANGENDRIES
Member
Tel. +32 228-45615 (Brussels)
Fax +32 228-49615 (Brussels)
Tel. +33 3881-75615 (Strasbourg)
Fax +33 3881-79615 (Strasbourg)
E-mail: raymond.langendries@europarl.europa.eu

Mr Kurt Joachim LAUK
Member
Tel. +32 228-45772 (Brussels)
Fax +32 228-49772 (Brussels)
Tel. +33 3881-75772 (Strasbourg)
Fax +33 3881-79772 (Strasbourg)
E-mail: info@prof-lauk.de

Mr Kurt LECHNER
Member
Tel. +32 228-45826 (Brussels)
Fax +32 228-49826 (Brussels)
Tel. +33 3881-75826 (Strasbourg)
Fax +33 3881-79826 (Strasbourg)
E-mail: kurt.lechner@europarl.europa.eu

Mr Janusz LEWANDOWSKI
Member
Tel. +32 228-45742 (Brussels)
Fax +32 228-49742 (Brussels)
Tel. +33 3881-75742 (Strasbourg)
Fax +33 3881-79742 (Strasbourg)
E-mail: janusz.lewandowski@europarl.europa.eu
Website: http://www.januszlewandowski.pl

Mr Peter LIESE
Member
Tel. +32 228-45981 (Brussels)
Fax +32 228-49981 (Brussels)
Tel. +33 3881-75981 (Strasbourg)
Fax +33 3881-79981 (Strasbourg)
E-mail: info@peter-liese.de

Mrs Eleonora LO CURTO
Member
Tel. +32 228-45597 (Brussels)
Fax +32 228-49597 (Brussels)
Tel. +33 3881-75597 (Strasbourg)
Fax +33 3881-79597 (Strasbourg)
E-mail: oneleonoralocurto@libero.it

Mrs Astrid LULLING
Member
Tel. +32 228-45386 (Brussels)
Fax +32 228-49386 (Brussels)
Tel. +33 3881-75386 (Strasbourg)
Fax +33 3881-79386 (Strasbourg)
E-mail: astrid.lulling@europarl.europa.eu

Mr Florencio LUQUE AGUILAR
Member
Tel. +32 228-45949 (Brussels)
Fax +32 228-49949 (Brussels)
Tel. +33 3881-75949 (Strasbourg)
Fax +33 3881-79949 (Strasbourg)

Mrs Mairead McGUINNESS
Member
Tel. +32 228-45214 (Brussels)
Fax +32 228-49214 (Brussels)
Tel. +33 3881-75214 (Strasbourg)
Fax +33 3881-79214 (Strasbourg)
Website: http://www.maireadmcguinness.ie

Mr Thomas MANN
Member
Tel. +32 228-45318 (Brussels)
Fax +32 228-49318 (Brussels)
Tel. +33 3881-75318 (Strasbourg)
Fax +33 3881-79318 (Strasbourg)
E-mail: thomas.mann@europarl.europa.eu
Website: http://www.mann-europa.de

Mr Adrian MANOLE
Member
Tel. +32 228-45663 (Brussels)
Fax +32 228-49663 (Brussels)
Tel. +33 3881-75663 (Strasbourg)
Fax +33 3881-79663 (Strasbourg)
E-mail: alcorexpert@yahoo.com

Mr Sérgio MARQUES
Member
Tel. +32 228-45404 (Brussels)
Fax +32 228-49404 (Brussels)
Tel. +33 3881-75404 (Strasbourg)
Fax +33 3881-79404 (Strasbourg)

Mrs Véronique MATHIEU
Member
Tel. +32 228-45220 (Brussels)
Fax +32 228-49220 (Brussels)
Tel. +33 3881-75220 (Strasbourg)
Fax +33 3881-79220 (Strasbourg)
E-mail: mathieuve@wanadoo.fr
Website: http://www.veronique-mathieu.net

Mr Yiannakis MATSIS
Member
Tel. +32 228-45128 (Brussels)
Fax +32 228-49128 (Brussels)
Tel. +33 3881-75128 (Strasbourg)
Fax +33 3881-79128 (Strasbourg)

Mr Iosif MATULA
Member
Tel. +32 228-45589 (Brussels)
Fax +32 228-49589 (Brussels)
Tel. +33 3881-75589 (Strasbourg)
Fax +33 3881-79589 (Strasbourg)
E-mail: matulaiosif@yahoo.com

Mr Manolis MAVROMMATIS
Member
Tel. +32 228-45334 (Brussels)
Fax +32 228-49334 (Brussels)
Tel. +33 3881-75334 (Strasbourg)
Fax +33 3881-79334 (Strasbourg)

Mr Hans-Peter MAYER
Member
Tel. +32 228-45994 (Brussels)
Fax +32 228-49994 (Brussels)
Tel. +33 3881-75994 (Strasbourg)
Fax +33 3881-79994 (Strasbourg)
Website: http://www.cdu-csu-ep.de

Mr Miroslav MIKOLÁŠIK
Member
Tel. +32 228-45289 (Brussels)
Fax +32 228-49289 (Brussels)
Tel. +33 3881-75289 (Strasbourg)
Fax +33 3881-79289 (Strasbourg)
E-mail: miroslav.mikolasik@europarl.europa.eu
Website: http://www.mikolasik.sk

Mr Francisco José MILLÁN MON
Member
Tel. +32 228-45430 (Brussels)
Fax +32 228-49430 (Brussels)
Tel. +33 3881-75430 (Strasbourg)
Fax +33 3881-79430 (Strasbourg)

Mr Gay MITCHELL
Member
Tel. +32 228-45228 (Brussels)
Fax +32 228-49228 (Brussels)
Tel. +33 3881-75228 (Strasbourg)
Fax +33 3881-79228 (Strasbourg)

Mr Nickolay MLADENOV
Member
Tel. +32 228-45717 (Brussels)
Fax +32 228-49717 (Brussels)
Tel. +33 3881-75717 (Strasbourg)
Fax +33 3881-79717 (Strasbourg)
E-mail: nickolay.mladenov@europarl.europa.eu
Website: http://www.nmladenov.eu

Mrs Elisabeth MORIN
Member
Tel. +32 228-45630 (Brussels)
Fax +32 228-49630 (Brussels)
Tel. +33 3881-75630 (Strasbourg)
Fax +33 3881-79630 (Strasbourg)
Website: http://www.elisabethmorin.eu

Mr Juan Andrés NARANJO ESCOBAR
Member
Tel. +32 228-45268 (Brussels)
Fax +32 228-49268 (Brussels)
Tel. +33 3881-75268 (Strasbourg)
Fax +33 3881-79268 (Strasbourg)
Website: http://www.juannaranjo.net

Mr Alexandru NAZARE
Member
Tel. +32 228-45656 (Brussels)
Fax +32 228-49656 (Brussels)
Tel. +33 3881-75656 (Strasbourg)
Fax +33 3881-79656 (Strasbourg)

Mr James NICHOLSON
Member
Tel. +32 228-45933 (Brussels)
Fax +32 228-49933 (Brussels)
Tel. +33 3881-75933 (Strasbourg)
Fax +33 3881-79933 (Strasbourg)

Mr Rareş-Lucian NICULESCU
Member
Tel. +32 228-45590 (Brussels)
Fax +32 228-49590 (Brussels)
Tel. +33 3881-75590 (Strasbourg)
Fax +33 3881-79590 (Strasbourg)

Mrs Ljudmila NOVAK
Member
Tel. +32 228-45395 (Brussels)
Fax +32 228-49395 (Brussels)
Tel. +33 3881-75395 (Strasbourg)
Fax +33 3881-79395 (Strasbourg)
Website: http://www.ljudmilanovak.org

Mr Péter OLAJOS
Member
Tel. +32 228-45315 (Brussels)
Fax +32 228-49315 (Brussels)
Tel. +33 3881-75315 (Strasbourg)
Fax +33 3881-79315 (Strasbourg)
Website: http://www.olajospeter.hu

Mrs Ria OOMEN-RUIJTEN
Member
Tel. +32 228-45863 (Brussels)
Fax +32 228-49863 (Brussels)
Tel. +33 3881-75863 (Strasbourg)
Fax +33 3881-79863 (Strasbourg)
E-mail: ria.oomen-ruijten@europarl.europa.eu

Mr Csaba ŐRY
Member
Tel. +32 228-45833 (Brussels)
Fax +32 228-49833 (Brussels)
Tel. +33 3881-75833 (Strasbourg)
Fax +33 3881-79833 (Strasbourg)

Mrs Marie PANAYOTOPOULOS-CASSIOTOU
Member
Tel. +32 228-45447 (Brussels)
Fax +32 228-49447 (Brussels)
Tel. +33 3881-75447 (Strasbourg)
Fax +33 3881-79447 (Strasbourg)
E-mail: marie.panayotopoulos-cassiotou@europarl.europa.eu
Website: http://mpanayotopouloscassiotou.blogspot.com

Mr Georgios PAPASTAMKOS
Member
Tel. +32 228-45448 (Brussels)
Fax +32 228-49448 (Brussels)
Tel. +33 3881-75448 (Strasbourg)
Fax +33 3881-79448 (Strasbourg)
E-mail: georgios.papastamkos@europarl.europa.eu
Website: http://www.papastamkos.gr

Mr Aldo PATRICIELLO
Member
Tel. +32 228-45418 (Brussels)
Fax +32 228-49418 (Brussels)
Tel. +33 3881-75418 (Strasbourg)
Fax +33 3881-79418 (Strasbourg)
E-mail: aldo@patriciello.it
Website: http://www.udc-italia.it

Mr Alojz PETERLE
Member
Tel. +32 228-45638 (Brussels)
Fax +32 228-49638 (Brussels)
Tel. +33 3881-75638 (Strasbourg)
Fax +33 3881-79638 (Strasbourg)
E-mail: alojz.peterle@europarl.europa.eu
Website: http://www.peterle.si

Mrs Maria PETRE
Member
Tel. +32 228-45657 (Brussels)
Fax +32 228-49657 (Brussels)
Tel. +33 3881-75657 (Strasbourg)
Fax +33 3881-79657 (Strasbourg)
E-mail: maria.petre@europarl.europa.eu
Website: http://mariapetre.eu

Mr Markus PIEPER
Member
Tel. +32 228-45305 (Brussels)
Fax +32 228-49305 (Brussels)
Tel. +33 3881-75305 (Strasbourg)
Fax +33 3881-79305 (Strasbourg)
Website: http://www.markus-pieper.eu

Sirpa PIETIKÄINEN
Member
Tel. +32 228-45264 (Brussels)
Fax +32 228-49264 (Brussels)
Tel. +33 3881-75264 (Strasbourg)
Fax +33 3881-79264 (Strasbourg)

Mr Rihards PĪKS
Member
Tel. +32 228-45293 (Brussels)
Fax +32 228-49293 (Brussels)
Tel. +33 3881-75293 (Strasbourg)
Fax +33 3881-79293 (Strasbourg)

Mr Hubert PIRKER
Member
Tel. +32 228-45766 (Brussels)
Fax +32 228-49766 (Brussels)
Tel. +33 3881-75766 (Strasbourg)
Fax +33 3881-79766 (Strasbourg)
Website: http://www.hubert-pirker.at

Mrs Zita PLEŠTINSKÁ
Member
Tel. +32 228-45204 (Brussels)
Fax +32 228-49204 (Brussels)
Tel. +33 3881-75204 (Strasbourg)
Fax +33 3881-79204 (Strasbourg)
Website: http://www.plestinska.sk

Mr Guido PODESTÀ
Member
Tel. +32 228-45340 (Brussels)
Fax +32 228-49340 (Brussels)
Tel. +33 3881-75340 (Strasbourg)
Fax +33 3881-79340 (Strasbourg)
E-mail: guido.podesta@europarl.europa.eu

Mr Nicolae Vlad POPA
Member
Tel. +32 228-45576 (Brussels)
Fax +32 228-49576 (Brussels)
Tel. +33 3881-75576 (Strasbourg)
Fax +33 3881-79576 (Strasbourg)

Mr Horst POSDORF
Member
Tel. +32 228-45567 (Brussels)
Fax +32 228-49567 (Brussels)
Tel. +33 3881-75567 (Strasbourg)
Fax +33 3881-79567 (Strasbourg)
Website: http://www.horst-posdorf.de

Mr Bernd POSSELT
Member
Tel. +32 228-45232 (Brussels)
Fax +32 228-49232 (Brussels)
Tel. +33 3881-75232 (Strasbourg)
Fax +33 3881-79232 (Strasbourg)
E-mail: mail@bernd-posselt.de
Website: http://www.bernd-posselt.de

Mr Jacek PROTASIEWICZ
Member
Tel. +32 228-45743 (Brussels)
Fax +32 228-49743 (Brussels)
Tel. +33 3881-75743 (Strasbourg)
Fax +33 3881-79743 (Strasbourg)
Website: http://protasiewicz.pl

Mr John PURVIS
Member
Tel. +32 228-45684 (Brussels)
Fax +32 228-49684 (Brussels)
Tel. +33 3881-75684 (Strasbourg)
Fax +33 3881-79684 (Strasbourg)
E-mail: john.purvis@europarl.europa.eu
Website: http://www.scottishtorymeps.org.uk

Mrs Godelieve QUISTHOUDT-ROWOHL
Member
Tel. +32 228-45338 (Brussels)
Fax +32 228-49338 (Brussels)
Tel. +33 3881-75338 (Strasbourg)
Fax +33 3881-79338 (Strasbourg)
Website: http://www.cdu-csu-ep.de

Mr Herbert REUL
Member
Tel. +32 228-45244 (Brussels)
Fax +32 228-49244 (Brussels)
Tel. +33 3881-75244 (Strasbourg)
Fax +33 3881-79244 (Strasbourg)

Mr José RIBEIRO E CASTRO
Member
Tel. +32 228-45783 (Brussels)
Fax +32 228-49783 (Brussels)
Tel. +33 3881-75783 (Strasbourg)
Fax +33 3881-79783 (Strasbourg)
E-mail: jose.ribeiroecastro@europarl.europa.eu

Mrs Zuzana ROITHOVÁ
Member
Tel. +32 228-45485 (Brussels)
Fax +32 228-49485 (Brussels)
Tel. +33 3881-75485 (Strasbourg)
Fax +33 3881-79485 (Strasbourg)
E-mail: zuzana.roithova@europarl.europa.eu
Website: http://www.roithova.cz

Mr Paul RÜBIG
Member
Tel. +32 228-45749 (Brussels)
Fax +32 228-49749 (Brussels)
Tel. +33 3881-75749 (Strasbourg)
Fax +33 3881-79749 (Strasbourg)
E-mail: paul.ruebig@europarl.europa.eu
Website: http://www.ruebig.at

Mr Flaviu Călin RUS
Member
Tel. +32 228-45658 (Brussels)
Fax +32 228-49658 (Brussels)
Tel. +33 3881-75658 (Strasbourg)
Fax +33 3881-79658 (Strasbourg)

Mrs Tokia SAÏFI
Member
Tel. +32 228-45562 (Brussels)
Fax +32 228-49562 (Brussels)
Tel. +33 3881-75562 (Strasbourg)
Fax +33 3881-79562 (Strasbourg)
Website: http://www.tokia-saifi.com

Mr Sebastiano SANZARELLO
Member
Tel. +32 228-45433 (Brussels)
Fax +32 228-49433 (Brussels)
Tel. +33 3881-75433 (Strasbourg)
Fax +33 3881-79433 (Strasbourg)

Mr Salvador Domingo SANZ PALACIO
Member
Tel. +32 228-45427 (Brussels)
Fax +32 228-49427 (Brussels)
Tel. +33 3881-75427 (Strasbourg)
Fax +33 3881-79427 (Strasbourg)

Mrs Agnes SCHIERHUBER
Member
Tel. +32 228-45741 (Brussels)
Fax +32 228-49741 (Brussels)
Tel. +33 3881-75741 (Strasbourg)
Fax +33 3881-79741 (Strasbourg)
E-mail: agnes.schierhuber@europarl.europa.eu
Website: http://www.agnes-schierhuber.at

Mr Margaritis SCHINAS
Member
Tel. +32 228-45192 (Brussels)
Fax +32 228-49192 (Brussels)
Tel. +33 3881-75192 (Strasbourg)
Fax +33 3881-79192 (Strasbourg)
E-mail: margaritis.schinas@europarl.europa.eu
Website: http://www.mschinas.gr

Mr Horst SCHNELLHARDT
Member
Tel. +32 228-45618 (Brussels)
Fax +32 228-49618 (Brussels)
Tel. +33 3881-75618 (Strasbourg)
Fax +33 3881-79618 (Strasbourg)

Mr György SCHÖPFLIN
Member
Tel. +32 228-45884 (Brussels)
Fax +32 228-49884 (Brussels)
Tel. +33 3881-75884 (Strasbourg)
Fax +33 3881-79884 (Strasbourg)

Mr Jürgen SCHRÖDER
Member
Tel. +32 228-45560 (Brussels)
Fax +32 228-49560 (Brussels)
Tel. +33 3881-75560 (Strasbourg)
Fax +33 3881-79560 (Strasbourg)
E-mail: juergen.schroeder@europarl.europa.eu
Website: http://www.cdu-csu-ep.de

Mr Andreas SCHWAB
Member
Tel. +32 228-45938 (Brussels)
Fax +32 228-49938 (Brussels)
Tel. +33 3881-75938 (Strasbourg)
Fax +33 3881-79938 (Strasbourg)
E-mail: andreas.schwab@europarl.europa.eu
Website: http://www.andreas-schwab.de

Mr Richard SEEBER
Member
Tel. +32 228-45468 (Brussels)
Fax +32 228-49468 (Brussels)
Tel. +33 3881-75468 (Strasbourg)
Fax +33 3881-79468 (Strasbourg)
E-mail: richard.seeber@europarl.europa.eu
Website: http://www.richard-seeber.at

Mr Czesław Adam SIEKIERSKI
Member
Tel. +32 228-45793 (Brussels)
Fax +32 228-49793 (Brussels)
Tel. +33 3881-75793 (Strasbourg)
Fax +33 3881-79793 (Strasbourg)
E-mail: czeslaw.siekierski@europarl.europa.eu
Website: http://www.siekierski.pl

Eva-Riitta SIITONEN
Member
Tel. +32 228-45894 (Brussels)
Fax +32 228-49894 (Brussels)
Tel. +33 3881-75894 (Strasbourg)
Fax +33 3881-79894 (Strasbourg)
Website: http://www.eva-riitta.fi

Mr José Albino SILVA PENEDA
Member
Tel. +32 228-45381 (Brussels)
Fax +32 228-49381 (Brussels)
Tel. +33 3881-75381 (Strasbourg)
Fax +33 3881-79381 (Strasbourg)
Website: http://www.silvapeneda.org

Mrs Nina ŠKOTTOVÁ
Member
Tel. +32 228-45358 (Brussels)
Fax +32 228-49358 (Brussels)
Tel. +33 3881-75358 (Strasbourg)
Fax +33 3881-79358 (Strasbourg)
E-mail: ris.olonz.ods@volny.cz

Mr Csaba SÓGOR
Member
Tel. +32 228-45389 (Brussels)
Fax +32 228-49389 (Brussels)
Tel. +33 3881-75389 (Strasbourg)
Fax +33 3881-79389 (Strasbourg)

Mrs Renate SOMMER
Member
Tel. +32 228-45383 (Brussels)
Fax +32 228-49383 (Brussels)
Tel. +33 3881-75383 (Strasbourg)
Fax +33 3881-79383 (Strasbourg)
E-mail: renate.sommer@europarl.europa.eu

Mr Bogusław SONIK
Member
Tel. +32 228-45690 (Brussels)
Fax +32 228-49690 (Brussels)
Tel. +33 3881-75690 (Strasbourg)
Fax +33 3881-79690 (Strasbourg)

Mrs Gabriele STAUNER
Member
Tel. +32 228-45711 (Brussels)
Fax +32 228-49711 (Brussels)
Tel. +33 3881-75711 (Strasbourg)
Fax +33 3881-79711 (Strasbourg)
E-mail: info@stauner.de
Website: http://www.stauner.de

Mrs Petya STAVREVA
Member
Tel. +32 228-45678 (Brussels)
Fax +32 228-49678 (Brussels)
Tel. +33 3881-75678 (Strasbourg)
Fax +33 3881-79678 (Strasbourg)
E-mail: petya.stavreva@europarl.europa.eu
Website: http://www.petyastavreva.eu

Mr Ivo STREJČEK
Member
Tel. +32 228-45667 (Brussels)
Fax +32 228-49667 (Brussels)
Tel. +33 3881-75667 (Strasbourg)
Fax +33 3881-79667 (Strasbourg)

Dr Charles TANNOCK
Member
Tel. +32 228-45870 (Brussels)
Fax +32 228-49870 (Brussels)
Tel. +33 3881-75870 (Strasbourg)
Fax +33 3881-79870 (Strasbourg)
Website: http://www.charlestannock.com

Mr Jacques TOUBON
Member
Tel. +32 228-45166 (Brussels)
Fax +32 228-49166 (Brussels)
Tel. +33 3881-75166 (Strasbourg)
Fax +33 3881-79166 (Strasbourg)
Website: http://jacquestoubon.over-blog.com

Mr Thomas ULMER
Member
Tel. +32 228-45314 (Brussels)
Fax +32 228-49314 (Brussels)
Tel. +33 3881-75314 (Strasbourg)
Fax +33 3881-79314 (Strasbourg)
E-mail: doculmer@aol.com
Website: http://www.thomas-ulmer.de

Mr Vladimir URUTCHEV
Member
Tel. +32 228-45145 (Brussels)
Fax +32 228-49145 (Brussels)
Tel. +33 3881-75145 (Strasbourg)
Fax +33 3881-79145 (Strasbourg)
E-mail: vladimir.urutchev@europarl.europa.eu

Mr Nikolaos VAKALIS
Member
Tel. +32 228-45937 (Brussels)
Fax +32 228-49937 (Brussels)
Tel. +33 3881-75937 (Strasbourg)
Fax +33 3881-79937 (Strasbourg)
Website: http://www.nvakalis.gr

Mr Geoffrey VAN ORDEN
Member
Tel. +32 228-45332 (Brussels)
Fax +32 228-49332 (Brussels)
Tel. +33 3881-75332 (Strasbourg)
Fax +33 3881-79332 (Strasbourg)

Mr Daniel VARELA SUANZES-CARPEGNA
Member
Tel. +32 228-45950 (Brussels)
Fax +32 228-49950 (Brussels)
Tel. +33 3881-75950 (Strasbourg)
Fax +33 3881-79950 (Strasbourg)

Ari VATANEN
Member
Tel. +32 228-45995 (Brussels)
Fax +32 228-49995 (Brussels)
Tel. +33 3881-75995 (Strasbourg)
Fax +33 3881-79995 (Strasbourg)
E-mail: ari.vatanen@europarl.europa.eu

Mr Armando VENETO
Member
Tel. +32 228-45302 (Brussels)
Fax +32 228-49302 (Brussels)
Tel. +33 3881-75302 (Strasbourg)
Fax +33 3881-79302 (Strasbourg)

Mr Riccardo VENTRE
Member
Tel. +32 228-45461 (Brussels)
Fax +32 228-49461 (Brussels)
Tel. +33 3881-75461 (Strasbourg)
Fax +33 3881-79461 (Strasbourg)
E-mail: riccardo.ventre@europarl.europa.eu
Website: http://www.riccardoventre.com

Mr Marcello VERNOLA
Member
Tel. +32 228-45304 (Brussels)
Fax +32 228-49304 (Brussels)
Tel. +33 3881-75304 (Strasbourg)
Fax +33 3881-79304 (Strasbourg)
E-mail: marcello.vernola@europarl.europa.eu
Website: http://www.marcellovernola.it

Mr Cornelis VISSER
Member
Tel. +32 228-45509 (Brussels)
Fax +32 228-49509 (Brussels)
Tel. +33 3881-75509 (Strasbourg)
Fax +33 3881-79509 (Strasbourg)
E-mail: cornelis.visser@europarl.europa.eu

Mr Oldřich VLASÁK
Member
Tel. +32 228-45357 (Brussels)
Fax +32 228-49357 (Brussels)
Tel. +33 3881-75357 (Strasbourg)
Fax +33 3881-79357 (Strasbourg)
E-mail: oldrich.vlasak@europarl.europa.eu

Mrs Dominique VLASTO
Member
Tel. +32 228-45161 (Brussels)
Fax +32 228-49161 (Brussels)
Tel. +33 3881-75161 (Strasbourg)
Fax +33 3881-79161 (Strasbourg)

Mrs Anja WEISGERBER
Member
Tel. +32 228-45337 (Brussels)
Fax +32 228-49337 (Brussels)
Tel. +33 3881-75337 (Strasbourg)
Fax +33 3881-79337 (Strasbourg)
Website: http://www.anja-weisgerber.de

Mr Rainer WIELAND
Member
Tel. +32 228-45545 (Brussels)
Fax +32 228-49545 (Brussels)
Tel. +33 3881-75545 (Strasbourg)
Fax +33 3881-79545 (Strasbourg)
E-mail: rainer.wieland@europarl.europa.eu
Website: http://www.mdep.de

Mr Anders WIJKMAN
Member
Tel. +32 228-45401 (Brussels)
Fax +32 228-49401 (Brussels)
Tel. +33 3881-75401 (Strasbourg)
Fax +33 3881-79401 (Strasbourg)
Website: http://www.wijkman.nu

Mr Iuliu WINKLER
Member
Tel. +32 228-45406 (Brussels)
Fax +32 228-49406 (Brussels)
Tel. +33 3881-75406 (Strasbourg)
Fax +33 3881-79406 (Strasbourg)
Website: http://www.iuliuwinkler.ro

Mr Lars WOHLIN
Member
Tel. +32 228-45679 (Brussels)
Fax +32 228-49679 (Brussels)
Tel. +33 3881-75679 (Strasbourg)
Fax +33 3881-79679 (Strasbourg)
E-mail: lars.wohlin@europarl.europa.eu

Mrs Corien WORTMANN-KOOL
Member
Tel. +32 228-45570 (Brussels)
Fax +32 228-49570 (Brussels)
Tel. +33 3881-75570 (Strasbourg)
Fax +33 3881-79570 (Strasbourg)
Website: http://www.corienwortmann.nl

Mr Zbigniew ZALESKI
Member
Tel. +32 228-45481 (Brussels)
Fax +32 228-49481 (Brussels)
Tel. +33 3881-75481 (Strasbourg)
Fax +33 3881-79481 (Strasbourg)
E-mail: zbigniew.zaleski@europarl.europa.eu
Website: http://www.zbigniewzaleski.pl

Mrs Iva ZANICCHI
Member
Tel. +32 228-45422 (Brussels)
Fax +32 228-49422 (Brussels)
Tel. +33 3881-75422 (Strasbourg)
Fax +33 3881-79422 (Strasbourg)

Mr Tomáš ZATLOUKAL
Member
Tel. +32 228-45534 (Brussels)
Fax +32 228-49534 (Brussels)
Tel. +33 3881-75534 (Strasbourg)
Fax +33 3881-79534 (Strasbourg)
E-mail: tomas.zatloukal@europarl.europa.eu
Website: http://www.tomaszatloukal.cz

Mrs Dushana ZDRAVKOVA
Member
Tel. +32 228-45672 (Brussels)
Fax +32 228-49672 (Brussels)
Tel. +33 3881-75672 (Strasbourg)
Fax +33 3881-79672 (Strasbourg)
E-mail: dushana@yahoo.com

Mr Marian ZLOTEA
Member
Tel. +32 228-45852 (Brussels)
Fax +32 228-49852 (Brussels)
Tel. +33 3881-75852 (Strasbourg)
Fax +33 3881-79852 (Strasbourg)
Website: http://www.zlotea.ro

Mr Jaroslav ZVĚŘINA
Member
Tel. +32 228-45483 (Brussels)
Fax +32 228-49483 (Brussels)
Tel. +33 3881-75483 (Strasbourg)
Fax +33 3881-79483 (Strasbourg)
E-mail: jaroslav.zverina@europarl.europa.eu
Website: http://www.zverina.cz

Mr Tadeusz ZWIEFKA
Member
Tel. +32 228-45258 (Brussels)
Fax +32 228-49258 (Brussels)
Tel. +33 3881-75258 (Strasbourg)
Fax +33 3881-79258 (Strasbourg)

SOCIALIST GROUP IN THE EUROPEAN PARLIAMENT

Mr Martin SCHULZ
Chairman
Tel. +32 228-45503 (Brussels)
Fax +32 228-49503 (Brussels)
Tel. +33 3881-75503 (Strasbourg)
Fax +33 3881-79503 (Strasbourg)

Mr Harlem DÉSIR
Vice-Chairman
Tel. +32 228-45853 (Brussels)
Fax +32 228-49853 (Brussels)
Tel. +33 3881-75853 (Strasbourg)
Fax +33 3881-79853 (Strasbourg)
E-mail: harlem.desir@free.fr

Mrs Bárbara DÜHRKOP DÜHRKOP
Vice-Chairwoman
Tel. +32 228-45478 (Brussels)
Fax +32 228-49478 (Brussels)
Tel. +33 3881-75478 (Strasbourg)
Fax +33 3881-79478 (Strasbourg)
E-mail: barbara.duhrkop@europarl.europa.eu
Website: http://www.psoe-pe.org

Mr Robert GOEBBELS
Vice-Chairman
Tel. +32 228-45648 (Brussels)
Fax +32 228-49648 (Brussels)
Tel. +33 3881-75648 (Strasbourg)
Fax +33 3881-79648 (Strasbourg)
E-mail: robert.goebbels@europarl.europa.eu

Mrs Linda McAVAN
Vice-Chairwoman
Tel. +32 228-45438 (Brussels)
Fax +32 228-49438 (Brussels)
Tel. +33 3881-75438 (Strasbourg)
Fax +33 3881-79438 (Strasbourg)
E-mail: linda.mcavan@europarl.europa.eu

Mrs Pasqualina NAPOLETANO
Vice-Chairwoman
Tel. +32 228-45130 (Brussels)
Fax +32 228-49130 (Brussels)
Tel. +33 3881-75130 (Strasbourg)
Fax +33 3881-79130 (Strasbourg)
E-mail: pasqualina.napoletano@europarl.europa.eu
Website: http://www.pasqualinanapoletano.it

Mr Hannes SWOBODA
Vice-Chairman
Tel. +32 228-45716 (Brussels)
Fax +32 228-49716 (Brussels)
Tel. +33 3881-9516 (Strasbourg)
Fax +33 3881-9716 (Strasbourg)
E-mail: hannes.swoboda@spoe.at
Website: http://www.hannes-swoboda.at

Mr Kristian VIGENIN
Vice-Chairman
Tel. +32 228-45694 (Brussels)
Fax +32 228-49694 (Brussels)
Tel. +33 3881-75694 (Strasbourg)
Fax +33 3881-79694 (Strasbourg)
E-mail: kristian.vigenin@europarl.europa.eu
Website: http://www.vigenin.eu

Mr Jan Marinus WIERSMA
Vice-Chairman
Tel. +32 228-45435 (Brussels)
Fax +32 228-49435 (Brussels)
Tel. +33 3881-75435 (Strasbourg)
Fax +33 3881-79435 (Strasbourg)
E-mail: janmarinus.wiersma@europarl.europa.eu
Website: http://www.wiersma.pvda.nl

Mrs Magda KÓSÁNÉ KOVÁCS
Treasurer
Tel. +32 228-45831 (Brussels)
Fax +32 228-49831 (Brussels)
Tel. +33 3881-75831 (Strasbourg)
Fax +33 3881-79831 (Strasbourg)

Mr Jan ANDERSSON
Member
Tel. +32 228-45554 (Brussels)
Fax +32 228-49554 (Brussels)
Tel. +33 3881-75554 (Strasbourg)
Fax +33 3881-79554 (Strasbourg)
E-mail: jan.andersson@europarl.europa.eu
Website: http://www.socialdemokraterna.se

Mr Rapisardo ANTINUCCI
Member
Tel. +32 228-45587 (Brussels)
Fax +32 228-49587 (Brussels)
Tel. +33 3881-75587 (Strasbourg)
Fax +33 3881-79587 (Strasbourg)
E-mail: rapisardo.antinucci@partitosocialista.it

Mr Kader ARIF
Member
Tel. +32 228-45170 (Brussels)
Fax +32 228-49170 (Brussels)
Tel. +33 3881-75170 (Strasbourg)
Fax +33 3881-79170 (Strasbourg)

Mr Stavros ARNAOUTAKIS
Member
Tel. +32 228-45568 (Brussels)
Fax +32 228-49568 (Brussels)
Tel. +33 3881-75568 (Strasbourg)
Fax +33 3881-79568 (Strasbourg)

Mr Francisco ASSIS
Member
Tel. +32 228-45770 (Brussels)
Fax +32 228-49770 (Brussels)
Tel. +33 3881-75770 (Strasbourg)
Fax +33 3881-79770 (Strasbourg)

Mr John ATTARD-MONTALTO
Member
Tel. +32 228-45116 (Brussels)
Fax +32 228-49116 (Brussels)
Tel. +33 3881-75116 (Strasbourg)
Fax +33 3881-79116 (Strasbourg)
E-mail: john.attard-montalto@europarl.europa.eu
Website: http://www.johnattardmontalto.com

Mrs Inés AYALA SENDER
Member
Tel. +32 228-45508 (Brussels)
Fax +32 228-49508 (Brussels)
Tel. +33 3881-75508 (Strasbourg)
Fax +33 3881-79508 (Strasbourg)
E-mail: ines.ayalasender@europarl.europa.eu
Website: http://www.psoe-pe.org

Mrs Maria BADIA i CUTCHET
Member
Tel. +32 228-45682 (Brussels)
Fax +32 228-49682 (Brussels)
Tel. +33 3881-75682 (Strasbourg)
Fax +33 3881-79682 (Strasbourg)
E-mail: maria.badiaicutchet-assistant@europarl.europa.eu
Website: http://www.psoe-pe.org

Mr Enrique BARÓN CRESPO
Member
Tel. +32 228-45490 (Brussels)
Fax +32 228-49490 (Brussels)
Tel. +33 3881-75490 (Strasbourg)
Fax +33 3881-79490 (Strasbourg)
Website: http://www.psoe-pe.org

Mr Alessandro BATTILOCCHIO
Member
Tel. +32 228-45496 (Brussels)
Fax +32 228-49496 (Brussels)
Tel. +33 3881-75496 (Strasbourg)
Fax +33 3881-79496 (Strasbourg)
E-mail: alessandro.battilocchio@europarl.europa.eu
Website: http://www.battilocchio.com

Mrs Katerina BATZELI
Member
Tel. +32 228-45362 (Brussels)
Fax +32 228-49362 (Brussels)
Tel. +33 3881-75362 (Strasbourg)
Fax +33 3881-79362 (Strasbourg)
E-mail: katerina.batzeli@europarl.europa.eu
Website: http://www.kbatzeli.gr

Mr Glenn BEDINGFIELD
Member
Tel. +32 228-45376 (Brussels)
Fax +32 228-49376 (Brussels)
Tel. +33 3881-75376 (Strasbourg)
Fax +33 3881-79376 (Strasbourg)
Website: http://www.glennbedingfield.com

Mrs Monika BEŇOVÁ
Member
Tel. +32 228-45160 (Brussels)
Fax +32 228-49160 (Brussels)
Tel. +33 3881-75160 (Strasbourg)
Fax +33 3881-79160 (Strasbourg)
E-mail: asistent.benova@strana-smer.sk
Website: http://www.strana-smer.sk

Mrs Pervenche BERÈS
Member
Tel. +32 228-45777 (Brussels)
Fax +32 228-49777 (Brussels)
Tel. +33 3881-75777 (Strasbourg)
Fax +33 3881-79777 (Strasbourg)
E-mail: pervenche.beres@europarl.europa.eu
Website: http://www.pervenche-beres.fr

Mrs Maria BERGER
Member
Tel. +32 228-45397 (Brussels)
Fax +32 228-49397 (Brussels)
Tel. +33 3881-75397 (Strasbourg)
Fax +33 3881-79397 (Strasbourg)
E-mail: maria.berger@europarl.europa.eu

Mr Giovanni BERLINGUER
Member
Tel. +32 228-45107 (Brussels)
Fax +32 228-49107 (Brussels)
Tel. +33 3881-75107 (Strasbourg)
Fax +33 3881-79107 (Strasbourg)
Website: http://www.delegazionepse.it

Mr Thijs BERMAN
Member
Tel. +32 228-45479 (Brussels)
Fax +32 228-49479 (Brussels)
Tel. +33 3881-75479 (Strasbourg)
Fax +33 3881-79479 (Strasbourg)
E-mail: thijs.berman@europarl.europa.eu

Mr Herbert BÖSCH
Member
Tel. +32 228-45677 (Brussels)
Fax +32 228-49677 (Brussels)
Tel. +33 3881-75677 (Strasbourg)
Fax +33 3881-79677 (Strasbourg)
E-mail: herbert.boesch@europarl.europa.eu
Website: http://www.herbertboesch.at

Mr Guy BONO
Member
Tel. +32 228-45424 (Brussels)
Fax +32 228-49424 (Brussels)
Tel. +33 3881-75424 (Strasbourg)
Fax +33 3881-79424 (Strasbourg)

Mr Josep BORRELL FONTELLES
Member
Tel. +32 228-45341 (Brussels)
Fax +32 228-49341 (Brussels)
Tel. +33 3881-75341 (Strasbourg)
Fax +33 3881-79341 (Strasbourg)
Website: http://www.psoe-pe.org

Mr Victor BOŞTINARU
Member
Tel. +32 228-45832 (Brussels)
Fax +32 228-49832 (Brussels)
Tel. +33 3881-75832 (Strasbourg)
Fax +33 3881-79832 (Strasbourg)
E-mail: victor.bostinaru@europarl.europa.eu

Mr Costas BOTOPOULOS
Member
Tel. +32 228-45290 (Brussels)
Fax +32 228-49290 (Brussels)
Tel. +33 3881-75292 (Strasbourg)
Fax +33 3881-79292 (Strasbourg)
Website: http://www.botopoulos.gr

Mrs Catherine BOURSIER
Member
Tel. +32 228-45158 (Brussels)
Fax +32 228-49158 (Brussels)
Tel. +33 3881-75158 (Strasbourg)
Fax +33 3881-79158 (Strasbourg)

Mrs Emine BOZKURT
Member
Tel. +32 228-45940 (Brussels)
Fax +32 228-49940 (Brussels)
Tel. +33 3881-75940 (Strasbourg)
Fax +33 3881-79940 (Strasbourg)

Mr Wolfgang BULFON
Member
Tel. +32 228-45721 (Brussels)
Fax +32 228-49721 (Brussels)
Tel. +33 3881-75721 (Strasbourg)
Fax +33 3881-79721 (Strasbourg)
E-mail: wolfgang.bulfon@spoe.at

Mr Udo BULLMANN
Member
Tel. +32 228-45342 (Brussels)
Fax +32 228-49342 (Brussels)
Tel. +33 3881-75342 (Strasbourg)
Fax +33 3881-79342 (Strasbourg)

Mrs Ieke van den BURG
Member
Tel. +32 228-45394 (Brussels)
Fax +32 228-49394 (Brussels)
Tel. +33 3881-75394 (Strasbourg)
Fax +33 3881-79394 (Strasbourg)
E-mail: ieke.vandenburg@europarl.europa.eu
Website: http://iekevandenburg.pvda.nl

Mr Philippe BUSQUIN
Member
Tel. +32 228-45514 (Brussels)
Fax +32 228-49514 (Brussels)
Tel. +33 3881-75514 (Strasbourg)
Fax +33 3881-79514 (Strasbourg)

Mr Luis Manuel CAPOULAS SANTOS
Member
Tel. +32 228-45991 (Brussels)
Fax +32 228-49991 (Brussels)
Tel. +33 3881-75991 (Strasbourg)
Fax +33 3881-79991 (Strasbourg)

Mrs Marie-Arlette CARLOTTI
Member
Tel. +32 228-45789 (Brussels)
Fax +32 228-49789 (Brussels)
Tel. +33 3881-75789 (Strasbourg)
Fax +33 3881-79789 (Strasbourg)

Mr Carlos CARNERO GONZÁLEZ
Member
Tel. +32 228-45969 (Brussels)
Fax +32 228-49969 (Brussels)
Tel. +33 3881-75969 (Strasbourg)
Fax +33 3881-79969 (Strasbourg)
E-mail: carlos.carnerogonzalez@europarl.europa.eu

Mr Paulo CASACA
Member
Tel. +32 228-45336 (Brussels)
Fax +32 228-49336 (Brussels)
Tel. +33 3881-75336 (Strasbourg)
Fax +33 3881-79336 (Strasbourg)
Website: http://www.paulocasaca.net

Mr Michael CASHMAN
Member
Tel. +32 228-45759 (Brussels)
Fax +32 228-49759 (Brussels)
Tel. +33 3881-75759 (Strasbourg)
Fax +33 3881-79759 (Strasbourg)
Website: http://www.michaelcashmanmep.org.uk

Mrs Françoise CASTEX
Member
Tel. +32 228-45129 (Brussels)
Fax +32 228-49129 (Brussels)
Tel. +33 3881-75129 (Strasbourg)
Fax +33 3881-79129 (Strasbourg)
E-mail: francoise.castex@europarl.europa.eu
Website: http://www.francoisecastex.org

Mr Alejandro CERCAS
Member
Tel. +32 228-45455 (Brussels)
Fax +32 228-49455 (Brussels)
Tel. +33 3881-75455 (Strasbourg)
Fax +33 3881-79455 (Strasbourg)
E-mail: alejandro.cercas@europarl.europa.eu
Website: http://www.psoe-pe.org

Mr Giulietto CHIESA
Member
Tel. +32 228-45602 (Brussels)
Fax +32 228-49602 (Brussels)
Tel. +33 3881-75602 (Strasbourg)
Fax +33 3881-79602 (Strasbourg)

Mr Ole CHRISTENSEN
Member
Tel. +32 228-45464 (Brussels)
Fax +32 228-49464 (Brussels)
Tel. +33 3881-75464 (Strasbourg)
Fax +33 3881-79464 (Strasbourg)
E-mail: ole.christensen@europarl.europa.eu
Website: http://www.oleeu.dk

Mr Richard CORBETT
Member
Tel. +32 228-45504 (Brussels)
Fax +32 228-49504 (Brussels)
Tel. +33 3881-75504 (Strasbourg)
Fax +33 3881-79504 (Strasbourg)
Website: http://www.richardcorbett.org.uk

Mrs Dorette CORBEY
Member
Tel. +32 228-45236 (Brussels)
Fax +32 228-49236 (Brussels)
Tel. +33 3881-75236 (Strasbourg)
Fax +33 3881-79236 (Strasbourg)
Website: http://www.corbey.nl

Mrs Giovanna CORDA
Member
Tel. +32 228-45740 (Brussels)
Fax +32 228-49740 (Brussels)
Tel. +33 3881-75740 (Strasbourg)
Fax +33 3881-79740 (Strasbourg)
Website: http://www.giovanna-corda.be

Mr Jean Louis COTTIGNY
Member
Tel. +32 228-45703 (Brussels)
Fax +32 228-49703 (Brussels)
Tel. +33 3881-75703 (Strasbourg)
Fax +33 3881-79703 (Strasbourg)

Mr Jan CREMERS
Member
Tel. +32 228-45992 (Brussels)
Fax +32 228-49992 (Brussels)
Tel. +33 3881-75992 (Strasbourg)
Fax +33 3881-79992 (Strasbourg)
E-mail: jan.cremers@europarl.europa.eu
Website: http://www.jancremers.pvda.nl

Mrs Corina CREŢU
Member
Tel. +32 228-45844 (Brussels)
Fax +32 228-49844 (Brussels)
Tel. +33 3881-75844 (Strasbourg)
Fax +33 3881-79844 (Strasbourg)
E-mail: cretucorina@yahoo.com
Website: http://www.corina-cretu.ro

Mrs Gabriela CREŢU
Member
Tel. +32 228-45812 (Brussels)
Fax +32 228-49812 (Brussels)
Tel. +33 3881-75812 (Strasbourg)
Fax +33 3881-79812 (Strasbourg)
E-mail: gabriela.cretu@europarl.europa.eu
Website: http://www.gabrielacretu.ro

Mrs Véronique DE KEYSER
Member
Tel. +32 228-45774 (Brussels)
Fax +32 228-49774 (Brussels)
Tel. +33 3881-75774 (Strasbourg)
Fax +33 3881-79774 (Strasbourg)
E-mail: veronique.dekeyser@europarl.europa.eu
Website: http://www.vdekeyser.be

Mr Gianni DE MICHELIS
Member
Tel. +32 228-45454 (Brussels)
Fax +32 228-49454 (Brussels)
Tel. +33 3881-75454 (Strasbourg)
Fax +33 3881-79454 (Strasbourg)

Mr Jean-Paul DENANOT
Member
Tel. +32 228-45432 (Brussels)
Fax +32 228-49432 (Brussels)
Tel. +33 3881-75432 (Strasbourg)
Fax +33 3881-79432 (Strasbourg)
E-mail: jp-denanot@cr-limousin.fr

Mr Proinsias DE ROSSA
Member
Tel. +32 228-45681 (Brussels)
Fax +32 228-49681 (Brussels)
Tel. +33 3881-75681 (Strasbourg)
Fax +33 3881-79681 (Strasbourg)
E-mail: proinsias.derossa@europarl.europa.eu
Website: http://www.derossa.com

Mrs Mia DE VITS
Member
Tel. +32 228-45715 (Brussels)
Fax +32 228-49715 (Brussels)
Tel. +33 3881-75715 (Strasbourg)
Fax +33 3881-79715 (Strasbourg)
E-mail: mia.devits@europarl.europa.eu

Mrs Alexandra DOBOLYI
Member
Tel. +32 228-45370 (Brussels)
Fax +32 228-49370 (Brussels)
Tel. +33 3881-75370 (Strasbourg)
Fax +33 3881-79370 (Strasbourg)

Mrs Brigitte DOUAY
Member
Tel. +32 228-45786 (Brussels)
Fax +32 228-49786 (Brussels)
Tel. +33 3881-75786 (Strasbourg)
Fax +33 3881-79786 (Strasbourg)
E-mail: brigitte.douay@europarl.europa.eu

Mr Saïd EL KHADRAOUI
Member
Tel. +32 228-45564 (Brussels)
Fax +32 228-49564 (Brussels)
Tel. +33 3881-75564 (Strasbourg)
Fax +33 3881-79564 (Strasbourg)
E-mail: said.elkhadraoui@europarl.europa.eu
Website: http://www.websaid.be

Mrs Edite ESTRELA
Member
Tel. +32 228-45515 (Brussels)
Fax +32 228-49515 (Brussels)
Tel. +33 3881-75515 (Strasbourg)
Fax +33 3881-79515 (Strasbourg)

Mr Harald ETTL
Member
Tel. +32 228-45726 (Brussels)
Fax +32 228-49726 (Brussels)
Tel. +33 3881-75726 (Strasbourg)
Fax +33 3881-79726 (Strasbourg)
E-mail: harald.ettl@europarl.europa.eu
Website: http://www.harald-ettl.at

Mr Robert EVANS
Member
Tel. +32 228-45298 (Brussels)
Fax +32 228-49298 (Brussels)
Tel. +33 3881-75298 (Strasbourg)
Fax +33 3881-79298 (Strasbourg)
E-mail: robertevansmep@btclick.com
Website: http://www.robertevansmep.net

Mr Göran FÄRM
Member
Tel. +32 228-45262 (Brussels)
Fax +32 228-49262 (Brussels)
Tel. +33 3881-75262 (Strasbourg)
Fax +33 3881-79262 (Strasbourg)
E-mail: goran.farm@europarl.europa.eu
Website: http://goranfarm.nu

Mr Richard FALBR
Member
Tel. +32 228-45470 (Brussels)
Fax +32 228-49470 (Brussels)
Tel. +33 3881-75470 (Strasbourg)
Fax +33 3881-79470 (Strasbourg)
E-mail: richard.falbr@europarl.europa.eu
Website: http://falbr.cz

Mr Claudio FAVA
Member
Tel. +32 228-45203 (Brussels)
Fax +32 228-49203 (Brussels)
Tel. +33 3881-75203 (Strasbourg)
Fax +33 3881-79203 (Strasbourg)

Mr Szabolcs FAZAKAS
Member
Tel. +32 228-45818 (Brussels)
Fax +32 228-49818 (Brussels)
Tel. +33 3881-75818 (Strasbourg)
Fax +33 3881-79818 (Strasbourg)
E-mail: szabolcs.fazakas@parlament.hu

Mr Emanuel Jardim FERNANDES
Member
Tel. +32 228-45649 (Brussels)
Fax +32 228-49649 (Brussels)
Tel. +33 3881-75649 (Strasbourg)
Fax +33 3881-79649 (Strasbourg)

Mrs Anne FERREIRA
Member
Tel. +32 228-45193 (Brussels)
Fax +32 228-49193 (Brussels)
Tel. +33 3881-75193 (Strasbourg)
Fax +33 3881-79193 (Strasbourg)
E-mail: anne.ferreira@europarl.europa.eu

Mrs Elisa FERREIRA
Member
Tel. +32 228-45164 (Brussels)
Fax +32 228-49164 (Brussels)
Tel. +33 3881-75164 (Strasbourg)
Fax +33 3881-79164 (Strasbourg)
E-mail: elisa.ferreira@europarl.europa.eu
Website: http://www.elisaferreira.net

Mr Glyn FORD
Member
Tel. +32 228-45518 (Brussels)
Fax +32 228-49518 (Brussels)
Tel. +33 3881-75518 (Strasbourg)
Fax +33 3881-79518 (Strasbourg)
E-mail: glyn.ford@europarl.europa.eu
Website: http://www.glynford.eu

Mr Juan FRAILE CANTÓN
Member
Tel. +32 228-45893 (Brussels)
Fax +32 228-49893 (Brussels)
Tel. +33 3881-75893 (Strasbourg)
Fax +33 3881-79893 (Strasbourg)

Mr Armando FRANÇA
Member
Tel. +32 228-45768 (Brussels)
Fax +32 228-49768 (Brussels)
Tel. +33 3881-75768 (Strasbourg)
Fax +33 3881-79768 (Strasbourg)
E-mail: armando.franca@europarl.europa.eu
Website: http://www.armandofranca.eu

Mr Vicente Miguel GARCÉS RAMÓN
Member
Tel. +32 228-45864 (Brussels)
Fax +32 228-49864 (Brussels)
Tel. +33 3881-75864 (Strasbourg)
Fax +33 3881-79864 (Strasbourg)

Mrs Iratxe GARCÍA PÉREZ
Member
Tel. +32 228-45646 (Brussels)
Fax +32 228-49646 (Brussels)
Tel. +33 3881-75646 (Strasbourg)
Fax +33 3881-79646 (Strasbourg)
Website: http://www.psoe-pe.org

Mrs Evelyne GEBHARDT
Member
Tel. +32 228-45466 (Brussels)
Fax +32 228-49466 (Brussels)
Tel. +33 3881-75466 (Strasbourg)
Fax +33 3881-79466 (Strasbourg)
E-mail: evelyne.gebhardt@europarl.europa.eu

Mrs Lidia Joanna GERINGER de OEDENBERG
Member
Tel. +32 228-45809 (Brussels)
Fax +32 228-49809 (Brussels)
Tel. +33 3881-75809 (Strasbourg)
Fax +33 3881-79809 (Strasbourg)
Website: http://www.lgeringer.pl

Mr Adam GIEREK
Member
Tel. +32 228-45781 (Brussels)
Fax +32 228-49781 (Brussels)
Tel. +33 3881-75781 (Strasbourg)
Fax +33 3881-79781 (Strasbourg)
Website: http://www.gierek.com.pl

Mrs Neena GILL
Member
Tel. +32 228-45125 (Brussels)
Fax +32 228-49125 (Brussels)
Tel. +33 3881-75125 (Strasbourg)
Fax +33 3881-79125 (Strasbourg)

Mrs Monica GIUNTINI
Member
Tel. +32 228-45174 (Brussels)
Fax +32 228-49174 (Brussels)
Tel. +33 3881-75174 (Strasbourg)
Fax +33 3881-79174 (Strasbourg)
Website: http://www.monicagiuntini.eu

Mr Norbert GLANTE
Member
Tel. +32 228-45356 (Brussels)
Fax +32 228-49356 (Brussels)
Tel. +33 3881-75356 (Strasbourg)
Fax +33 3881-79356 (Strasbourg)
Website: http://www.glante.eu

Mr Bogdan GOLIK
Member
Tel. +32 228-45197 (Brussels)
Fax +32 228-49197 (Brussels)
Tel. +33 3881-75197 (Strasbourg)
Fax +33 3881-79197 (Strasbourg)

Mrs Ana Maria GOMES
Member
Tel. +32 228-45824 (Brussels)
Fax +32 228-49824 (Brussels)
Tel. +33 3881-75824 (Strasbourg)
Fax +33 3881-79824 (Strasbourg)

Mrs Donata GOTTARDI
Member
Tel. +32 228-45881 (Brussels)
Fax +32 228-49881 (Brussels)
Tel. +33 3881-75881 (Strasbourg)
Fax +33 3881-79881 (Strasbourg)
Website: http://www.donatagottardi.net

Mrs Genowefa GRABOWSKA
Member
Tel. +32 228-45260 (Brussels)
Fax +32 228-49260 (Brussels)
Tel. +33 3881-75260 (Strasbourg)
Fax +33 3881-79260 (Strasbourg)
Website: http://www.grabowska.org.pl

Mr Martí GRAU i SEGÚ
Member
Tel. +32 228-45440 (Brussels)
Fax +32 228-49440 (Brussels)
Tel. +33 3881-75440 (Strasbourg)
Fax +33 3881-79440 (Strasbourg)
E-mail: marti.grauisegu@europarl.europa.eu

Mr Louis GRECH
Member
Tel. +32 228-45235 (Brussels)
Fax +32 228-49235 (Brussels)
Tel. +33 3881-75235 (Strasbourg)
Fax +33 3881-79235 (Strasbourg)
E-mail: louis.grech@europarl.europa.eu

Mrs Lissy GRÖNER
Member
Tel. +32 228-45412 (Brussels)
Fax +32 228-49412 (Brussels)
Tel. +33 3881-75412 (Strasbourg)
Fax +33 3881-79412 (Strasbourg)
E-mail: lissy.groener@europarl.europa.eu
Website: http://www.lissy-groener.de

Mr Matthias GROOTE
Member
Tel. +32 228-45431 (Brussels)
Fax +32 228-49431 (Brussels)
Tel. +33 3881-75431 (Strasbourg)
Fax +33 3881-79431 (Strasbourg)
E-mail: info@matthias-groote.de
Website: http://www.matthias-groote.eu

Mrs Zita GURMAI
Member
Tel. +32 228-45819 (Brussels)
Fax +32 228-49819 (Brussels)
Tel. +33 3881-75819 (Strasbourg)
Fax +33 3881-79819 (Strasbourg)
E-mail: zita.gurmai@europarl.europa.eu
Website: http://www.gurmai.hu

Mrs Catherine GUY-QUINT
Member
Tel. +32 228-45931 (Brussels)
Fax +32 228-49931 (Brussels)
Tel. +33 3881-75931 (Strasbourg)
Fax +33 3881-79931 (Strasbourg)
E-mail: c.guyquint@wanadoo.fr
Website: http://www.catherine-guy-quint.org

Mr Klaus HÄNSCH
Member
Tel. +32 228-45467 (Brussels)
Fax +32 228-49467 (Brussels)
Tel. +33 3881-75467 (Strasbourg)
Fax +33 3881-79467 (Strasbourg)
Website: http://www.klaus-haensch.de

Mr Benoît HAMON
Member
Tel. +32 228-45476 (Brussels)
Fax +32 228-49476 (Brussels)
Tel. +33 3881-75476 (Strasbourg)
Fax +33 3881-79476 (Strasbourg)
E-mail: benoit.hamon@europarl.europa.eu

Mr Gábor HARANGOZÓ
Member
Tel. +32 228-45873 (Brussels)
Fax +32 228-49873 (Brussels)
Tel. +33 3881-75873 (Strasbourg)
Fax +33 3881-79873 (Strasbourg)

Mr Joel HASSE FERREIRA
Member
Tel. +32 228-45399 (Brussels)
Fax +32 228-49399 (Brussels)
Tel. +33 3881-75399 (Strasbourg)
Fax +33 3881-79399 (Strasbourg)

Mrs Jutta HAUG
Member
Tel. +32 228-45595 (Brussels)
Fax +32 228-49595 (Brussels)
Tel. +33 3881-75595 (Strasbourg)
Fax +33 3881-79595 (Strasbourg)
Website: http://www.jutta-haug.de

Mrs Anna HEDH
Member
Tel. +32 228-45527 (Brussels)
Fax +32 228-49527 (Brussels)
Tel. +33 3881-75527 (Strasbourg)
Fax +33 3881-79527 (Strasbourg)
E-mail: anna.hedh@europarl.europa.eu

Mr Gyula HEGYI
Member
Tel. +32 228-45829 (Brussels)
Fax +32 228-49829 (Brussels)
Tel. +33 3881-75829 (Strasbourg)
Fax +33 3881-79829 (Strasbourg)
Website: http://www.hegyigyula.hu

Mrs Edit HERCZOG
Member
Tel. +32 228-45596 (Brussels)
Fax +32 228-49596 (Brussels)
Tel. +33 3881-75596 (Strasbourg)
Fax +33 3881-79596 (Strasbourg)
E-mail: edit.herczog@europarl.europa.eu
Website: http://www.herczogedit.hu

Mrs Mary HONEYBALL
Member
Tel. +32 228-45209 (Brussels)
Fax +32 228-49209 (Brussels)
Tel. +33 3881-75209 (Strasbourg)
Fax +33 3881-79209 (Strasbourg)
E-mail: mary.honeyball@europarl.europa.eu

Mr Richard HOWITT
Member
Tel. +32 228-45477 (Brussels)
Fax +32 228-49477 (Brussels)
Tel. +33 3881-75477 (Strasbourg)
Fax +33 3881-79477 (Strasbourg)
E-mail: richard.howitt@geo2.poptel.org.uk
Website: http://www.richardhowittmep.com

Mr Stephen HUGHES
Member
Tel. +32 228-45408 (Brussels)
Fax +32 228-49408 (Brussels)
Tel. +33 3881-75408 (Strasbourg)
Fax +33 3881-79408 (Strasbourg)
Website: http://www.stephenhughesmep.org

Mr Alain HUTCHINSON
Member
Tel. +32 228-45451 (Brussels)
Fax +32 228-49451 (Brussels)
Tel. +33 3881-75451 (Strasbourg)
Fax +33 3881-79451 (Strasbourg)
E-mail: alain.hutchinson@europarl.europa.eu
Website: http://www.alainhutchinson.be

Mrs Iliana Malinova IOTOVA
Member
Tel. +32 228-45708 (Brussels)
Fax +32 228-49708 (Brussels)
Tel. +33 3881-75708 (Strasbourg)
Fax +33 3881-79708 (Strasbourg)
E-mail: ilianamalinova.iotova@europarl.europa.eu

Mrs Lily JACOBS
Member
Tel. +32 228-45669 (Brussels)
Fax +32 228-49669 (Brussels)
Tel. +33 3881-75669 (Strasbourg)
Fax +33 3881-79669 (Strasbourg)
E-mail: lily.jacobs@europarl.europa.eu

Mrs Karin JÖNS
Member
Tel. +32 228-45535 (Brussels)
Fax +32 228-49535 (Brussels)
Tel. +33 3881-75535 (Strasbourg)
Fax +33 3881-79535 (Strasbourg)
E-mail: karin.joens@europarl.europa.eu
Website: http://www.joens.de

Mr Dan JØRGENSEN
Member
Tel. +32 228-45771 (Brussels)
Fax +32 228-49771 (Brussels)
Tel. +33 3881-75771 (Strasbourg)
Fax +33 3881-79771 (Strasbourg)
Website: http://www.danj.dk

Mr Aurelio JURI
Member
Tel. +32 228-45240 (Brussels)
Fax +32 228-49240 (Brussels)
Tel. +33 3881-75240 (Strasbourg)
Fax +33 3881-79240 (Strasbourg)
E-mail: aurelio.juri@gmail.com

Mr Heinz KINDERMANN
Member
Tel. +32 228-45060 (Brussels)
Fax +32 228-49060 (Brussels)
Tel. +33 3881-75060 (Strasbourg)
Fax +33 3881-79060 (Strasbourg)

Mrs Glenys KINNOCK
Member
Tel. +32 228-45402 (Brussels)
Fax +32 228-49402 (Brussels)
Tel. +33 3881-75402 (Strasbourg)
Fax +33 3881-79402 (Strasbourg)

Mr Evgeni KIRILOV
Member
Tel. +32 228-45750 (Brussels)
Fax +32 228-49750 (Brussels)
Tel. +33 3881-75750 (Strasbourg)
Fax +33 3881-79750 (Strasbourg)
E-mail: evgeni.kirilov@europarl.europa.eu
Website: http://www.evgenikirilov.eu

Mrs Maria Eleni KOPPA
Member
Tel. +32 228-45343 (Brussels)
Fax +32 228-49343 (Brussels)
Tel. +33 3881-75343 (Strasbourg)
Fax +33 3881-79343 (Strasbourg)

Mr Miloš KOTEREC
Member
Tel. +32 228-45175 (Brussels)
Fax +32 228-49175 (Brussels)
Tel. +33 3881-75175 (Strasbourg)
Fax +33 3881-79175 (Strasbourg)
E-mail: milos.koterec@europarl.europa.eu

Mrs Constanze Angela KREHL
Member
Tel. +32 228-45134 (Brussels)
Fax +32 228-49134 (Brussels)
Tel. +33 3881-75134 (Strasbourg)
Fax +33 3881-79134 (Strasbourg)

Mr Wolfgang KREISSL-DÖRFLER
Member
Tel. +32 228-45110 (Brussels)
Fax +32 228-49110 (Brussels)
Tel. +33 3881-75110 (Strasbourg)
Fax +33 3881-79110 (Strasbourg)
E-mail: europa@kreissl-doerfler.de
Website: http://www.kreissl-doerfler.de

Mr Helmut KUHNE
Member
Tel. +32 228-45428 (Brussels)
Fax +32 228-49428 (Brussels)
Tel. +33 3881-75428 (Strasbourg)
Fax +33 3881-79428 (Strasbourg)
E-mail: helmut.kuhne@europarl.europa.eu
Website: http://www.helmut-kuhne.de

Mr André LAIGNEL
Member
Tel. +32 228-45935 (Brussels)
Fax +32 228-49935 (Brussels)
Tel. +33 3881-75935 (Strasbourg)
Fax +33 3881-79935 (Strasbourg)
E-mail: andre.laignel@europarl.europa.eu
Website: http://www.andre-laignel.fr

Mr Stavros LAMBRINIDIS
Member
Tel. +32 228-45529 (Brussels)
Fax +32 228-49529 (Brussels)
Tel. +33 3881-75529 (Strasbourg)
Fax +33 3881-79529 (Strasbourg)
E-mail: stala@politicalforum.gr

Mr Vincenzo LAVARRA
Member
Tel. +32 228-45162 (Brussels)
Fax +32 228-49162 (Brussels)
Tel. +33 3881-75162 (Strasbourg)
Fax +33 3881-79162 (Strasbourg)
Website: http://www.delegazionepse.it

Mr Stéphane LE FOLL
Member
Tel. +32 228-45495 (Brussels)
Fax +32 228-49495 (Brussels)
Tel. +33 3881-75495 (Strasbourg)
Fax +33 3881-79495 (Strasbourg)

Mrs Roselyne LEFRANÇOIS
Member
Tel. +32 228-45360 (Brussels)
Fax +32 228-49360 (Brussels)
Tel. +33 3881-75360 (Strasbourg)
Fax +33 3881-79360 (Strasbourg)

Lasse LEHTINEN
Member
Tel. +32 228-45189 (Brussels)
Fax +32 228-49189 (Brussels)
Tel. +33 3881-75189 (Strasbourg)
Fax +33 3881-79189 (Strasbourg)
E-mail: riitta.aarrevuo@brutto.inet.fi
Website: http://www.lasselehtinen.net

Mr Jörg LEICHTFRIED
Member
Tel. +32 228-45436 (Brussels)
Fax +32 228-49436 (Brussels)
Tel. +33 3881-75436 (Strasbourg)
Fax +33 3881-79436 (Strasbourg)
Website: http://www.joerg-leichtfried.at

Mr Jo LEINEN
Member
Tel. +32 228-45842 (Brussels)
Fax +32 228-49842 (Brussels)
Tel. +33 3881-75842 (Strasbourg)
Fax +33 3881-79842 (Strasbourg)
E-mail: jo.leinen@europarl.europa.eu
Website: http://www.joleinen.de

Mrs Katalin LÉVAI
Member
Tel. +32 228-45834 (Brussels)
Fax +32 228-49834 (Brussels)
Tel. +33 3881-75834 (Strasbourg)
Fax +33 3881-79834 (Strasbourg)

Mr Bogusław LIBERADZKI
Member
Tel. +32 228-45423 (Brussels)
Fax +32 228-49423 (Brussels)
Tel. +33 3881-75423 (Strasbourg)
Fax +33 3881-79423 (Strasbourg)

Mrs Marie-Noëlle LIENEMANN
Member
Tel. +32 228-45102 (Brussels)
Fax +32 228-49102 (Brussels)
Tel. +33 3881-75102 (Strasbourg)
Fax +33 3881-79102 (Strasbourg)
E-mail: mn.lienemann@nordpasdecalais.fr

Mrs Pia Elda LOCATELLI
Member
Tel. +32 228-45443 (Brussels)
Fax +32 228-49443 (Brussels)
Tel. +33 3881-75443 (Strasbourg)
Fax +33 3881-79443 (Strasbourg)
Website: http://www.delegazionepse.it

Mrs Marusya Ivanova LYUBCHEVA
Member
Tel. +32 228-45753 (Brussels)
Fax +32 228-49753 (Brussels)
Tel. +33 3881-75753 (Strasbourg)
Fax +33 3881-79753 (Strasbourg)
E-mail: marusyaivanova.lyubcheva@europarl.europa.eu
Website: http://www.bs-ml.eu

Mrs Arlene McCARTHY
Member
Tel. +32 228-45501 (Brussels)
Fax +32 228-49501 (Brussels)
Tel. +33 3881-75501 (Strasbourg)
Fax +33 3881-79501 (Strasbourg)
Website: http://www.arlenemccarthy.labour.co.uk

Mrs Jamila MADEIRA
Member
Tel. +32 228-45898 (Brussels)
Fax +32 228-49898 (Brussels)
Tel. +33 3881-75898 (Strasbourg)
Fax +33 3881-79898 (Strasbourg)

Mr Vladimír MAŇKA
Member
Tel. +32 228-45449 (Brussels)
Fax +32 228-49449 (Brussels)
Tel. +33 3881-75449 (Strasbourg)
Fax +33 3881-79449 (Strasbourg)
E-mail: vladimir.manka@europarl.europa.eu
Website: http://www.europoslanec.sk

Mrs Erika MANN
Member
Tel. +32 228-45191 (Brussels)
Fax +32 228-49191 (Brussels)
Tel. +33 3881-75191 (Strasbourg)
Fax +33 3881-79191 (Strasbourg)
Website: http://www.erikamann.com

Mrs Catiuscia MARINI
Member
Tel. +32 228-45388 (Brussels)
Fax +32 228-49388 (Brussels)
Tel. +33 3881-75388 (Strasbourg)
Fax +33 3881-79388 (Strasbourg)
Website: http://www.catiusciamarini.eu

Mr David MARTIN
Member
Tel. +32 228-45539 (Brussels)
Fax +32 228-49539 (Brussels)
Tel. +33 3881-75539 (Strasbourg)
Fax +33 3881-79539 (Strasbourg)

Mr Miguel Angel MARTÍNEZ MARTÍNEZ
Member
Tel. +32 228-45269 (Brussels)
Fax +32 228-49269 (Brussels)
Tel. +33 3881-75269 (Strasbourg)
Fax +33 3881-79269 (Strasbourg)
E-mail: miguelangel.martinez@europarl.europa.eu
Website: http://www.psoe-pe.org

Mr Antonio MASIP HIDALGO
Member
Tel. +32 228-45474 (Brussels)
Fax +32 228-49474 (Brussels)
Tel. +33 3881-75474 (Strasbourg)
Fax +33 3881-79474 (Strasbourg)
Website: http://www.antoniomasipeuropa.blogspot.com

Mrs Maria MATSOUKA
Member
Tel. +32 228-45522 (Brussels)
Fax +32 228-49522 (Brussels)
Tel. +33 3881-75522 (Strasbourg)
Fax +33 3881-79522 (Strasbourg)
E-mail: maria.matsouka@europarl.europa.eu
Website: http://www.marymatsouka.gr

Mr Manuel MEDINA ORTEGA
Member
Tel. +32 228-45882 (Brussels)
Fax +32 228-49882 (Brussels)
Tel. +33 3881-75882 (Strasbourg)
Fax +33 3881-79882 (Strasbourg)
E-mail: manuel.medinaortega@europarl.europa.eu
Website: http://www.psoe-pe.org

Mr Emilio MENÉNDEZ del VALLE
Member
Tel. +32 228-45752 (Brussels)
Fax +32 228-49752 (Brussels)
Tel. +33 3881-75752 (Strasbourg)
Fax +33 3881-79752 (Strasbourg)
Website: http://www.psoe-pe.org

Mrs Rosa MIGUÉLEZ RAMOS
Member
Tel. +32 228-45532 (Brussels)
Fax +32 228-49532 (Brussels)
Tel. +33 3881-75532 (Strasbourg)
Fax +33 3881-79532 (Strasbourg)
E-mail: rosa.miguelezramos@europarl.europa.eu

Mrs Marianne MIKKO
Member
Tel. +32 228-45122 (Brussels)
Fax +32 228-49122 (Brussels)
Tel. +33 3881-75122 (Strasbourg)
Fax +33 3881-79122 (Strasbourg)

Mr Claude MORAES
Member
Tel. +32 228-45553 (Brussels)
Fax +32 228-49553 (Brussels)
Tel. +33 3881-75553 (Strasbourg)
Fax +33 3881-79553 (Strasbourg)
E-mail: claude.moraes@europarl.europa.eu
Website: http://www.claudemoraes.net

Mr Javier MORENO SÁNCHEZ
Member
Tel. +32 228-45165 (Brussels)
Fax +32 228-49165 (Brussels)
Tel. +33 3881-75165 (Strasbourg)
Fax +33 3881-79165 (Strasbourg)
E-mail: javier.morenosanchez@europarl.europa.eu
Website: http://www.psoe-pe.org

Mrs Eluned MORGAN
Member
Tel. +32 228-45457 (Brussels)
Fax +32 228-49457 (Brussels)
Tel. +33 3881-75457 (Strasbourg)
Fax +33 3881-79457 (Strasbourg)
E-mail: eluned.morgan@europarl.europa.eu

Riitta MYLLER
Member
Tel. +32 228-45738 (Brussels)
Fax +32 228-49738 (Brussels)
Tel. +33 3881-75738 (Strasbourg)
Fax +33 3881-79738 (Strasbourg)
E-mail: riitta.myller@europarl.europa.eu
Website: http://www.riittamyller.net

Mrs Catherine NERIS
Member
Tel. +32 228-45745 (Brussels)
Fax +32 228-49745 (Brussels)
Tel. +33 3881-75745 (Strasbourg)
Fax +33 3881-79745 (Strasbourg)

Mr Raimon OBIOLS i GERMÀ
Member
Tel. +32 228-45592 (Brussels)
Fax +32 228-49592 (Brussels)
Tel. +33 3881-75592 (Strasbourg)
Fax +33 3881-79592 (Strasbourg)
E-mail: robiols@psc.es

Mr Vural ÖGER
Member
Tel. +32 228-45411 (Brussels)
Fax +32 228-49411 (Brussels)
Tel. +33 3881-75411 (Strasbourg)
Fax +33 3881-79411 (Strasbourg)
E-mail: vural.oeger@europarl.europa.eu
Website: http://www.vural-oeger.de

Reino PAASILINNA
Member
Tel. +32 228-45734 (Brussels)
Fax +32 228-49734 (Brussels)
Tel. +33 3881-75734 (Strasbourg)
Fax +33 3881-79734 (Strasbourg)
Website: http://www.rpaasilinna.net

Mrs Maria Grazia PAGANO
Member
Tel. +32 228-45910 (Brussels)
Fax +32 228-49910 (Brussels)
Tel. +33 3881-75910 (Strasbourg)
Fax +33 3881-79910 (Strasbourg)

Mr Justas Vincas PALECKIS
Member
Tel. +32 228-45921 (Brussels)
Fax +32 228-49921 (Brussels)
Tel. +33 3881-75921 (Strasbourg)
Fax +33 3881-79921 (Strasbourg)
Website: http://www.paleckis.lt

Mr Pier Antonio PANZERI
Member
Tel. +32 228-45349 (Brussels)
Fax +32 228-49349 (Brussels)
Tel. +33 3881-75349 (Strasbourg)
Fax +33 3881-79349 (Strasbourg)
Website: http://www.delegazionepse.it

Mr Atanas PAPARIZOV
Member
Tel. +32 228-45699 (Brussels)
Fax +32 228-49699 (Brussels)
Tel. +33 3881-75699 (Strasbourg)
Fax +33 3881-79699 (Strasbourg)
E-mail: atanas.paparizov@europarl.europa.eu
Website: http://www.paparizov.eu

Mr Ioan Mircea PAŞCU
Member
Tel. +32 228-45813 (Brussels)
Fax +32 228-49813 (Brussels)
Tel. +33 3881-75813 (Strasbourg)
Fax +33 3881-79813 (Strasbourg)
E-mail: msatmareanu@yahoo.com

Mrs Béatrice PATRIE
Member
Tel. +32 228-45883 (Brussels)
Fax +32 228-49883 (Brussels)
Tel. +33 3881-75883 (Strasbourg)
Fax +33 3881-79883 (Strasbourg)
E-mail: aquitaine@beatrice-patrie.org
Website: http://www.beatrice-patrie.org

Mr Vincent PEILLON
Member
Tel. +32 228-45312 (Brussels)
Fax +32 228-49312 (Brussels)
Tel. +33 3881-75312 (Strasbourg)
Fax +33 3881-79312 (Strasbourg)
E-mail: vincent.peillon@europarl.europa.eu
Website: http://www.vincent-peillon.fr

Mr Józef PINIOR
Member
Tel. +32 228-45875 (Brussels)
Fax +32 228-49875 (Brussels)
Tel. +33 3881-75875 (Strasbourg)
Fax +33 3881-79875 (Strasbourg)

Mr Gianni PITTELLA
Member
Tel. +32 228-45159 (Brussels)
Fax +32 228-49159 (Brussels)
Tel. +33 3881-75159 (Strasbourg)
Fax +33 3881-79159 (Strasbourg)
E-mail: gianni.pittella@europarl.europa.eu
Website: http://www.giannipittella.org

Mrs Francisca PLEGUEZUELOS AGUILAR
Member
Tel. +32 228-45897 (Brussels)
Fax +32 228-49897 (Brussels)
Tel. +33 3881-75897 (Strasbourg)
Fax +33 3881-79897 (Strasbourg)
E-mail: francisca.pleguezuelosaguilar@europarl.europa.eu
Website: http://www.psoe-pe.org

Mrs Rovana PLUMB
Member
Tel. +32 228-45803 (Brussels)
Fax +32 228-49803 (Brussels)
Tel. +33 3881-75803 (Strasbourg)
Fax +33 3881-79803 (Strasbourg)
E-mail: rovana.plumb@europarl.europa.eu

Mrs Anni PODIMATA
Member
Tel. +32 228-45202 (Brussels)
Fax +32 228-49202 (Brussels)
Tel. +33 3881-75202 (Strasbourg)
Fax +33 3881-79202 (Strasbourg)
E-mail: anni.podimata@europarl.europa.eu

Mr Bernard POIGNANT
Member
Tel. +32 228-45405 (Brussels)
Fax +32 228-49405 (Brussels)
Tel. +33 3881-75405 (Strasbourg)
Fax +33 3881-79405 (Strasbourg)
E-mail: bernard.poignant@europarl.europa.eu
Website: http://www.europinion.org/index.php5

Mrs Christa PRETS
Member
Tel. +32 228-45591 (Brussels)
Fax +32 228-49591 (Brussels)
Tel. +33 3881-75591 (Strasbourg)
Fax +33 3881-79591 (Strasbourg)
E-mail: christa.prets@europarl.europa.eu

Mr Pierre PRIBETICH
Member
Tel. +32 228-45993 (Brussels)
Fax +32 228-49993 (Brussels)
Tel. +33 3881-75993 (Strasbourg)
Fax +33 3881-79993 (Strasbourg)
E-mail: pierre.pribetich@europarl.europa.eu
Website: http://www.pierre-pribetich.eu

Mr Bernhard RAPKAY
Member
Tel. +32 228-45593 (Brussels)
Fax +32 228-49593 (Brussels)
Tel. +33 3881-75593 (Strasbourg)
Fax +33 3881-79593 (Strasbourg)
Website: http://www.rapkay.de

Mr Poul Nyrup RASMUSSEN
Member
Tel. +32 228-45463 (Brussels)
Fax +32 228-49463 (Brussels)
Tel. +33 3881-75463 (Strasbourg)
Fax +33 3881-79463 (Strasbourg)
Website: http://www.nyrup.dk

Mrs Teresa RIERA MADURELL
Member
Tel. +32 228-45415 (Brussels)
Fax +32 228-49415 (Brussels)
Tel. +33 3881-75415 (Strasbourg)
Fax +33 3881-79415 (Strasbourg)
E-mail: teresa.rieramadurell@europarl.europa.eu
Website: http://www.psoe-pe.org

Mr Michel ROCARD
Member
Tel. +32 228-45785 (Brussels)
Fax +32 228-49785 (Brussels)
Tel. +33 3881-75785 (Strasbourg)
Fax +33 3881-79785 (Strasbourg)

Mrs Ulrike RODUST
Member
Tel. +32 228-45502 (Brussels)
Fax +32 228-49502 (Brussels)
Tel. +33 3881-75502 (Strasbourg)
Fax +33 3881-79502 (Strasbourg)
Website: http://www.ulrike-rodust.de

Mr Dariusz ROSATI
Member
Tel. +32 228-45182 (Brussels)
Fax +32 228-49182 (Brussels)
Tel. +33 3881-75182 (Strasbourg)
Fax +33 3881-79182 (Strasbourg)
E-mail: dariusz.rosati@europarl.europa.eu
Website: http://www.rosati.pl

Mrs Dagmar ROTH-BEHRENDT
Member
Tel. +32 228-45453 (Brussels)
Fax +32 228-49453 (Brussels)
Tel. +33 3881-75453 (Strasbourg)
Fax +33 3881-79453 (Strasbourg)
E-mail: dagmar.roth-behrendt@europarl.europa.eu
Website: http://www.dagmarrothbehrendt.de

Mrs Mechtild ROTHE
Member
Tel. +32 228-45414 (Brussels)
Fax +32 228-49414 (Brussels)
Tel. +33 3881-75414 (Strasbourg)
Fax +33 3881-79414 (Strasbourg)

Mr Libor ROUČEK
Member
Tel. +32 228-45259 (Brussels)
Fax +32 228-49259 (Brussels)
Tel. +33 3881-75259 (Strasbourg)
Fax +33 3881-79259 (Strasbourg)
E-mail: libor.roucek@europarl.europa.eu
Website: http://www.liborroucek.cz

Mrs Martine ROURE
Member
Tel. +32 228-45138 (Brussels)
Fax +32 228-49138 (Brussels)
Tel. +33 3881-75138 (Strasbourg)
Fax +33 3881-79138 (Strasbourg)

Mr Guido SACCONI
Member
Tel. +32 228-45776 (Brussels)
Fax +32 228-49776 (Brussels)
Tel. +33 3881-75776 (Strasbourg)
Fax +33 3881-79776 (Strasbourg)
E-mail: guido.sacconi@europarl.europa.eu
Website: http://www.toscanaeuropa.it

Mr Aloyzas SAKALAS
Member
Tel. +32 228-45542 (Brussels)
Fax +32 228-49542 (Brussels)
Tel. +33 3881-75542 (Strasbourg)
Fax +33 3881-79542 (Strasbourg)

Mrs Katrin SAKS
Member
Tel. +32 228-45148 (Brussels)
Fax +32 228-49148 (Brussels)
Tel. +33 3881-75148 (Strasbourg)
Fax +33 3881-79148 (Strasbourg)
E-mail: katrin.saks@europarl.europa.eu

Mrs María Isabel SALINAS GARCÍA
Member
Tel. +32 228-45348 (Brussels)
Fax +32 228-49348 (Brussels)
Tel. +33 3881-75348 (Strasbourg)
Fax +33 3881-79348 (Strasbourg)
Website: http://www.psoe-pe.org

Mr Antolín SÁNCHEZ PRESEDO
Member
Tel. +32 228-45471 (Brussels)
Fax +32 228-49471 (Brussels)
Tel. +33 3881-75471 (Strasbourg)
Fax +33 3881-79471 (Strasbourg)
Website: http://www.psoe-pe.org

Mr Manuel António dos SANTOS
Member
Tel. +32 228-45869 (Brussels)
Fax +32 228-49869 (Brussels)
Tel. +33 3881-75869 (Strasbourg)
Fax +33 3881-79869 (Strasbourg)
E-mail: manuel.dossantos@europarl.europa.eu
Website: http://www.mdossantos.com

Mrs Daciana Octavia SÂRBU
Member
Tel. +32 228-45805 (Brussels)
Fax +32 228-49805 (Brussels)
Tel. +33 3881-75805 (Strasbourg)
Fax +33 3881-79805 (Strasbourg)
E-mail: dacianaoctavia.sarbu@europarl.europa.eu
Website: http://www.dacianasarbu.ro

Mr Gilles SAVARY
Member
Tel. +32 228-45420 (Brussels)
Fax +32 228-49420 (Brussels)
Tel. +33 3881-75420 (Strasbourg)
Fax +33 3881-79420 (Strasbourg)
E-mail: gilles.savary@europarl.europa.eu

Mrs Christel SCHALDEMOSE
Member
Tel. +32 228-45491 (Brussels)
Fax +32 228-49491 (Brussels)
Tel. +33 3881-75491 (Strasbourg)
Fax +33 3881-79491 (Strasbourg)
E-mail: christel.schaldemose@europarl.europa.eu
Website: http://www.christels.dk

Mr Pierre SCHAPIRA
Member
Tel. +32 228-45791 (Brussels)
Fax +32 228-49791 (Brussels)
Tel. +33 3881-75791 (Strasbourg)
Fax +33 3881-79791 (Strasbourg)
E-mail: pierre.schapira@mairie-paris.fr

Mrs Inger SEGELSTRÖM
Member
Tel. +32 228-45199 (Brussels)
Fax +32 228-49199 (Brussels)
Tel. +33 3881-75199 (Strasbourg)
Fax +33 3881-79199 (Strasbourg)

Mr Adrian SEVERIN
Member
Tel. +32 228-45811 (Brussels)
Fax +32 228-49811 (Brussels)
Tel. +33 3881-75811 (Strasbourg)
Fax +33 3881-79811 (Strasbourg)

Mr Brian SIMPSON
Member
Tel. +32 228-45510 (Brussels)
Fax +32 228-49510 (Brussels)
Tel. +33 3881-75510 (Strasbourg)
Fax +33 3881-79510 (Strasbourg)
E-mail: briansimpson.labour@virgin.net
Website: http://www.briansimpsonmep.co.uk

Mr Marek SIWIEC
Member
Tel. +32 228-45653 (Brussels)
Fax +32 228-49653 (Brussels)
Tel. +33 3881-75653 (Strasbourg)
Fax +33 3881-79653 (Strasbourg)
Website: http://www.mareksiwiec.pl

Mr Peter SKINNER
Member
Tel. +32 228-45458 (Brussels)
Fax +32 228-49458 (Brussels)
Tel. +33 3881-75458 (Strasbourg)
Fax +33 3881-79458 (Strasbourg)
E-mail: peter.skinner@europarl.europa.eu

Mrs María SORNOSA MARTÍNEZ
Member
Tel. +32 228-45974 (Brussels)
Fax +32 228-49974 (Brussels)
Tel. +33 3881-75974 (Strasbourg)
Fax +33 3881-79974 (Strasbourg)
Website: http://www.psoe-pe.org

Mr Sérgio SOUSA PINTO
Member
Tel. +32 228-45486 (Brussels)
Fax +32 228-49486 (Brussels)
Tel. +33 3881-75486 (Strasbourg)
Fax +33 3881-79486 (Strasbourg)
E-mail: sergio.sousapinto@europarl.europa.eu

Mrs Catherine STIHLER
Member
Tel. +32 228-45462 (Brussels)
Fax +32 228-49462 (Brussels)
Tel. +33 3881-75462 (Strasbourg)
Fax +33 3881-79462 (Strasbourg)
E-mail: cstihlermep@btconnect.com
Website: http://www.cstihlermep.com

Mr Ulrich STOCKMANN
Member
Tel. +32 228-45687 (Brussels)
Fax +32 228-49687 (Brussels)
Tel. +33 3881-75687 (Strasbourg)
Fax +33 3881-79687 (Strasbourg)
Website: http://www.ulrich-stockmann.de

Mr Andrzej Jan SZEJNA
Member
Tel. +32 228-45652 (Brussels)
Fax +32 228-49652 (Brussels)
Tel. +33 3881-75652 (Strasbourg)
Fax +33 3881-79652 (Strasbourg)
E-mail: andrzejjan.szejna@europarl.europa.eu

Mr Csaba Sándor TABAJDI
Member
Tel. +32 228-45821 (Brussels)
Fax +32 228-49821 (Brussels)
Tel. +33 3881-75821 (Strasbourg)
Fax +33 3881-79821 (Strasbourg)
Website: http://www.tabajdi.hu

Mr Andres TARAND
Member
Tel. +32 228-45429 (Brussels)
Fax +32 228-49429 (Brussels)
Tel. +33 3881-75429 (Strasbourg)
Fax +33 3881-79429 (Strasbourg)
E-mail: andres.tarand@europarl.europa.eu

Mr Michel TEYCHENNÉ
Member
Tel. +32 228-45421 (Brussels)
Fax +32 228-49421 (Brussels)
Tel. +33 3881-75421 (Strasbourg)
Fax +33 3881-79421 (Strasbourg)
Website: http://www.michelteychenne.net

Mrs Britta THOMSEN
Member
Tel. +32 228-45452 (Brussels)
Fax +32 228-49452 (Brussels)
Tel. +33 3881-75452 (Strasbourg)
Fax +33 3881-79452 (Strasbourg)

Mrs Silvia-Adriana ȚICĂU
Member
Tel. +32 228-45838 (Brussels)
Fax +32 228-49838 (Brussels)
Tel. +33 3881-75838 (Strasbourg)
Fax +33 3881-79838 (Strasbourg)

Mr Gary TITLEY
Member
Tel. +32 228-45212 (Brussels)
Fax +32 228-49212 (Brussels)
Tel. +33 3881-75212 (Strasbourg)
Fax +33 3881-79212 (Strasbourg)
E-mail: gary.titley@europarl.europa.eu
Website: http://www.garytitley.com

Mrs Catherine TRAUTMANN
Member
Tel. +32 228-45425 (Brussels)
Fax +32 228-49425 (Brussels)
Tel. +33 3881-75425 (Strasbourg)
Fax +33 3881-79425 (Strasbourg)

Mrs Evangelia TZAMPAZI
Member
Tel. +32 228-45345 (Brussels)
Fax +32 228-49345 (Brussels)
Tel. +33 3881-75345 (Strasbourg)
Fax +33 3881-79345 (Strasbourg)

Mrs Anne VAN LANCKER
Member
Tel. +32 228-45494 (Brussels)
Fax +32 228-49494 (Brussels)
Tel. +33 3881-75494 (Strasbourg)
Fax +33 3881-79494 (Strasbourg)
E-mail: anne.vanlancker@europarl.europa.eu
Website: http://www.annevanlancker.be

Mr Yannick VAUGRENARD
Member
Tel. +32 228-45113 (Brussels)
Fax +32 228-49113 (Brussels)
Tel. +33 3881-75113 (Strasbourg)
Fax +33 3881-79113 (Strasbourg)

Mrs Bernadette VERGNAUD
Member
Tel. +32 228-45210 (Brussels)
Fax +32 228-49210 (Brussels)
Tel. +33 3881-75210 (Strasbourg)
Fax +33 3881-79210 (Strasbourg)
E-mail: bernadette.vergnaud@europarl.europa.eu
Website: http://www.bernadette-vergnaud.fr

Mr Ralf WALTER
Member
Tel. +32 228-45426 (Brussels)
Fax +32 228-49426 (Brussels)
Tel. +33 3881-75426 (Strasbourg)
Fax +33 3881-79426 (Strasbourg)

Mr Henri WEBER
Member
Tel. +32 228-45788 (Brussels)
Fax +32 228-49788 (Brussels)
Tel. +33 3881-75788 (Strasbourg)
Fax +33 3881-79788 (Strasbourg)
E-mail: henri.weber@europarl.europa.eu

Mrs Barbara WEILER
Member
Tel. +32 228-45439 (Brussels)
Fax +32 228-49439 (Brussels)
Tel. +33 3881-75439 (Strasbourg)
Fax +33 3881-79439 (Strasbourg)
Website: http://www.barbara-weiler.de

Mrs Åsa WESTLUND
Member
Tel. +32 228-45586 (Brussels)
Fax +32 228-49586 (Brussels)
Tel. +33 3881-75586 (Strasbourg)
Fax +33 3881-79586 (Strasbourg)
E-mail: asa.westlund@europarl.europa.eu
Website: http://www.asawestlund.se

Mrs Glenis WILLMOTT
Member
Tel. +32 228-45459 (Brussels)
Fax +32 228-49459 (Brussels)
Tel. +33 3881-75459 (Strasbourg)
Fax +33 3881-79459 (Strasbourg)
Website: http://www.gleniswillmott.org.uk

Mr Luis YAÑEZ-BARNUEVO GARCÍA
Member
Tel. +32 228-45718 (Brussels)
Fax +32 228-49718 (Brussels)
Tel. +33 3881-75718 (Strasbourg)
Fax +33 3881-79718 (Strasbourg)
Website: http://www.psoe-pe.org

Mr Mauro ZANI
Member
Tel. +32 228-45526 (Brussels)
Fax +32 228-49526 (Brussels)
Tel. +33 3881-75526 (Strasbourg)
Fax +33 3881-79526 (Strasbourg)
E-mail: mauro.zani@europarl.europa.eu

GROUP OF THE ALLIANCE OF LIBERALS AND DEMOCRATS FOR EUROPE

Mr Graham WATSON
Chairman
Tel. +32 228-45626 (Brussels)
Fax +32 228-49626 (Brussels)
Tel. +33 3881-75626 (Strasbourg)
Fax +33 3881-79626 (Strasbourg)
E-mail: graham.watson@europarl.europa.eu

Mrs Marielle DE SARNEZ
Vice-Chairwoman
Tel. +32 228-45297 (Brussels)
Fax +32 228-49297 (Brussels)
Tel. +33 3881-75297 (Strasbourg)
Fax +33 3881-79297 (Strasbourg)

Mrs Silvana KOCH-MEHRIN
Vice-Chairwoman
Tel. +32 228-45112 (Brussels)
Fax +32 228-49112 (Brussels)
Tel. +33 3881-75112 (Strasbourg)
Fax +33 3881-79112 (Strasbourg)
E-mail: silvana.koch-mehrin@europarl.europa.eu
Website: http://www.koch-mehrin.de

Mrs Karin RIIS-JØRGENSEN
Vice-Chairwoman
Tel. +32 228-45794 (Brussels)
Fax +32 228-49794 (Brussels)
Tel. +33 3881-75794 (Strasbourg)
Fax +33 3881-79794 (Strasbourg)
Website: http://www.karinriis.dk

Mr Gianluca SUSTA
Vice-Chairman
Tel. +32 228-45565 (Brussels)
Fax +32 228-49565 (Brussels)
Tel. +33 3881-75565 (Strasbourg)
Fax +33 3881-79565 (Strasbourg)
E-mail: gianluca.susta@europarl.europa.eu
Website: http://www.gianlucasusta.it

Mrs Adina-Ioana VĂLEAN
Vice-Chairwoman
Tel. +32 228-45861 (Brussels)
Fax +32 228-49861 (Brussels)
Tel. +33 3881-75861 (Strasbourg)
Fax +33 3881-79861 (Strasbourg)
Website: http://www.valean.eu

Mr Georgs ANDREJEVS
Member of the Bureau
Tel. +32 228-45548 (Brussels)
Fax +32 228-49548 (Brussels)
Tel. +33 3881-75548 (Strasbourg)
Fax +33 3881-79548 (Strasbourg)
Website: http://www.andrejevs.eu

Mr Šarūnas BIRUTIS
Member of the Bureau
Tel. +32 228-45671 (Brussels)
Fax +32 228-49671 (Brussels)
Tel. +33 3881-75671 (Strasbourg)
Fax +33 3881-79671 (Strasbourg)
Website: http://www.birutis.lt

Mr Marco CAPPATO
Member of the Bureau
Tel. +32 228-45288 (Brussels)
Fax +32 228-49288 (Brussels)
Tel. +33 3881-75288 (Strasbourg)
Fax +33 3881-79288 (Strasbourg)
Website: http://www.marcocappato.it

Mr Jean-Marie CAVADA
Member of the Bureau
Tel. +32 228-45367 (Brussels)
Fax +32 228-49367 (Brussels)
Tel. +33 3881-75367 (Strasbourg)
Fax +33 3881-79367 (Strasbourg)
E-mail: jean-marie.cavada@europarl.europa.eu
Website: http://www.jeanmariecavada.eu

Mr Luigi COCILOVO
Member of the Bureau
Tel. +32 228-45854 (Brussels)
Fax +32 228-49854 (Brussels)
Tel. +33 3881-75854 (Strasbourg)
Fax +33 3881-79854 (Strasbourg)
Website: http://www.luigicocilovo.ilcannocchiale.it

Mr Paolo COSTA
Member of the Bureau
Tel. +32 228-45537 (Brussels)
Fax +32 228-49537 (Brussels)
Tel. +33 3881-75537 (Strasbourg)
Fax +33 3881-79537 (Strasbourg)
E-mail: info@paolocostaonline.it
Website: http://www.paolocostaonline.it

Mr Gérard DEPREZ
Member of the Bureau
Tel. +32 228-45223 (Brussels)
Fax +32 228-49223 (Brussels)
Tel. +33 3881-75223 (Strasbourg)
Fax +33 3881-79223 (Strasbourg)
E-mail: gerard.deprez@europarl.europa.eu
Website: http://www.gdeprez.be

Mr Beniamino DONNICI
Member of the Bureau
Tel. +32 228-45249 (Brussels)
Fax +32 228-49249 (Brussels)
Tel. +33 3881-75249 (Strasbourg)
Fax +33 3881-79249 (Strasbourg)
E-mail: beniaminodonnici@virgilio.it
Website: http://www.beniaminodonnici.it

Mr Andrew DUFF
Member of the Bureau
Tel. +32 228-45998 (Brussels)
Fax +32 228-49998 (Brussels)
Tel. +33 3881-75998 (Strasbourg)
Fax +33 3881-79998 (Strasbourg)
E-mail: andrew.duff@europarl.europa.eu
Website: http://www.andrewduffmep.org

Mrs Lena EK
Member of the Bureau
Tel. +32 228-45714 (Brussels)
Fax +32 228-49714 (Brussels)
Tel. +33 3881-75714 (Strasbourg)
Fax +33 3881-79714 (Strasbourg)

Mr Eugenijus GENTVILAS
Member of the Bureau
Tel. +32 228-45493 (Brussels)
Fax +32 228-49493 (Brussels)
Tel. +33 3881-75493 (Strasbourg)
Fax +33 3881-79493 (Strasbourg)
Website: http://www.gentvilas.lt

Mr Ignasi GUARDANS CAMBÓ
Member of the Bureau
Tel. +32 228-45608 (Brussels)
Fax +32 228-49608 (Brussels)
Tel. +33 3881-75608 (Strasbourg)
Fax +33 3881-79608 (Strasbourg)
E-mail: ignasi.guardans@europarl.europa.eu
Website: http://www.ignasiguardans.cat

Mrs Marian HARKIN
Member of the Bureau
Tel. +32 228-45797 (Brussels)
Fax +32 228-49797 (Brussels)
Tel. +33 3881-75797 (Strasbourg)
Fax +33 3881-79797 (Strasbourg)
E-mail: marian.harkin@europarl.europa.eu

Mrs Filiz Hakaeva HYUSMENOVA
Member of the Bureau
Tel. +32 228-45903 (Brussels)
Fax +32 228-49903 (Brussels)
Tel. +33 3881-75903 (Strasbourg)
Fax +33 3881-79903 (Strasbourg)
E-mail: filizhakaeva.hyusmenova@europarl.
europa.eu

Mrs Sophia in 't VELD
Member of the Bureau
Tel. +32 228-45796 (Brussels)
Fax +32 228-49796 (Brussels)
Tel. +33 3881-75796 (Strasbourg)
Fax +33 3881-79796 (Strasbourg)
Website: http://www.sophieintveld.eu

Mr Jelko KACIN
Member of the Bureau
Tel. +32 228-45748 (Brussels)
Fax +32 228-49748 (Brussels)
Tel. +33 3881-75748 (Strasbourg)
Fax +33 3881-79748 (Strasbourg)
Website: http://www.kacin.si

Henrik LAX
Member of the Bureau
Tel. +32 228-45828 (Brussels)
Fax +32 228-49828 (Brussels)
Tel. +33 3881-75828 (Strasbourg)
Fax +33 3881-79828 (Strasbourg)
E-mail: henrik.lax@europarl.europa.eu
Website: http://www.henriklax.nu

Mr Johannes LEBECH
Member of the Bureau
Tel. +32 228-45916 (Brussels)
Fax +32 228-49916 (Brussels)
Tel. +33 3881-75916 (Strasbourg)
Fax +33 3881-79916 (Strasbourg)
E-mail: johannes.lebech@europarl.europa.eu
Website: http://www.johanneslebech.dk

Mr Jules MAATEN
Member of the Bureau
Tel. +32 228-45606 (Brussels)
Fax +32 228-49606 (Brussels)
Tel. +33 3881-75606 (Strasbourg)
Fax +33 3881-79606 (Strasbourg)

Mr Marios MATSAKIS
Member of the Bureau
Tel. +32 228-45816 (Brussels)
Fax +32 228-49816 (Brussels)
Tel. +33 3881-75816 (Strasbourg)
Fax +33 3881-79816 (Strasbourg)

Mr Philippe MORILLON
Member of the Bureau
Tel. +32 228-45506 (Brussels)
Fax +32 228-49506 (Brussels)
Tel. +33 3881-75506 (Strasbourg)
Fax +33 3881-79506 (Strasbourg)

Mr Josu ORTUONDO LARREA
Member of the Bureau
Tel. +32 228-45267 (Brussels)
Fax +32 228-49267 (Brussels)
Tel. +33 3881-75267 (Strasbourg)
Fax +33 3881-79267 (Strasbourg)
E-mail: josu.ortuondolarrea@europarl.europa.eu

Mrs Siiri OVIIR
Member of the Bureau
Tel. +32 228-45815 (Brussels)
Fax +32 228-49815 (Brussels)
Tel. +33 3881-75815 (Strasbourg)
Fax +33 3881-79815 (Strasbourg)
Website: http://www.siirioviir.ee

Mrs Lydie POLFER
Member of the Bureau
Tel. +32 228-45621 (Brussels)
Fax +32 228-49621 (Brussels)
Tel. +33 3881-75621 (Strasbourg)
Fax +33 3881-79621 (Strasbourg)

Mrs Bilyana Ilieva RAEVA
Member of the Bureau
Tel. +32 228-45922 (Brussels)
Fax +32 228-49922 (Brussels)
Tel. +33 3881-75922 (Strasbourg)
Fax +33 3881-79922 (Strasbourg)
E-mail: bilyana.raeva@europarl.europa.eu

Mrs Karin RESETARITS
Member of the Bureau
Tel. +32 228-45513 (Brussels)
Fax +32 228-49513 (Brussels)
Tel. +33 3881-75513 (Strasbourg)
Fax +33 3881-79513 (Strasbourg)
Website: http://www.karinresetarits.at

Mrs Frédérique RIES
Member of the Bureau
Tel. +32 228-45549 (Brussels)
Fax +32 228-49549 (Brussels)
Tel. +33 3881-75549 (Strasbourg)
Fax +33 3881-79549 (Strasbourg)
E-mail: frederique.ries@europarl.europa.eu
Website: http://www.frederiqueries.be

Mr Toomas SAVI
Member of the Bureau
Tel. +32 228-45814 (Brussels)
Fax +32 228-49814 (Brussels)
Tel. +33 3881-75814 (Strasbourg)
Fax +33 3881-79814 (Strasbourg)
E-mail: toomas.savi@europarl.europa.eu

Mr Olle SCHMIDT
Member of the Bureau
Tel. +32 228-45541 (Brussels)
Fax +32 228-49541 (Brussels)
Tel. +33 3881-75541 (Strasbourg)
Fax +33 3881-79541 (Strasbourg)
E-mail: olle.schmidt@europarl.europa.eu
Website: http://www.folkpartiet.se/Schmidt

Mr Dirk STERCKX
Member of the Bureau
Tel. +32 228-45111 (Brussels)
Fax +32 228-49111 (Brussels)
Tel. +33 3881-75111 (Strasbourg)
Fax +33 3881-79111 (Strasbourg)
E-mail: dirk.sterckx@europarl.europa.eu
Website: http://www.dirksterckx.be

Mr István SZENT-IVÁNYI
Member of the Bureau
Tel. +32 228-45578 (Brussels)
Fax +32 228-49578 (Brussels)
Tel. +33 3881-75578 (Strasbourg)
Fax +33 3881-79578 (Strasbourg)

Kyösti VIRRANKOSKI
Member of the Bureau
Tel. +32 228-45847 (Brussels)
Fax +32 228-49847 (Brussels)
Tel. +33 3881-75847 (Strasbourg)
Fax +33 3881-79847 (Strasbourg)
E-mail: kyosti.virrankoski@europarl.europa.eu
Website: http://www.virrankoski.net

Mrs Diana WALLIS
Member of the Bureau
Tel. +32 228-45201 (Brussels)
Fax +32 228-49201 (Brussels)
Tel. +33 3881-75201 (Strasbourg)
Fax +33 3881-79201 (Strasbourg)
Website: http://www.dianawallismep.org.uk

Mr Alexander ALVARO
Member
Tel. +32 228-45328 (Brussels)
Fax +32 228-49328 (Brussels)
Tel. +33 3881-75328 (Strasbourg)
Fax +33 3881-79328 (Strasbourg)
E-mail: alexander.alvaro@europarl.europa.eu
Website: http://www.alexander-alvaro.de

Mrs Elspeth ATTWOOLL
Member
Tel. +32 228-45795 (Brussels)
Fax +32 228-49795 (Brussels)
Tel. +33 3881-75795 (Strasbourg)
Fax +33 3881-79795 (Strasbourg)
E-mail: elspeth.attwooll@europarl.europa.eu

Mrs Mariela Velichkova BAEVA
Member
Tel. +32 228-45917 (Brussels)
Fax +32 228-49917 (Brussels)
Tel. +33 3881-75917 (Strasbourg)
Fax +33 3881-79917 (Strasbourg)
E-mail: marielavelichkova.baeva@europarl.europa.eu

Mr Jean Marie BEAUPUY
Member
Tel. +32 228-45354 (Brussels)
Fax +32 228-49354 (Brussels)
Tel. +33 3881-75354 (Strasbourg)
Fax +33 3881-79354 (Strasbourg)
Website: http://www.jeanmarie-beaupuy.eu

Mrs Sharon BOWLES
Member
Tel. +32 228-45221 (Brussels)
Fax +32 228-49221 (Brussels)
Tel. +33 3881-75221 (Strasbourg)
Fax +33 3881-79221 (Strasbourg)
E-mail: sharon.bowles@europarl.europa.eu
Website: http://www.sharonbowles.org.uk

Mrs Danutė BUDREIKAITĖ
Member
Tel. +32 228-45635 (Brussels)
Fax +32 228-49635 (Brussels)
Tel. +33 3881-75635 (Strasbourg)
Fax +33 3881-79635 (Strasbourg)

Mr Niels BUSK
Member
Tel. +32 228-45365 (Brussels)
Fax +32 228-49365 (Brussels)
Tel. +33 3881-75365 (Strasbourg)
Fax +33 3881-79365 (Strasbourg)
E-mail: niels.busk@europarl.europa.eu
Website: http://www.nielsbusk.dk

Mr Cristian Silviu BUŞOI
Member
Tel. +32 228-45732 (Brussels)
Fax +32 228-49732 (Brussels)
Tel. +33 3881-75732 (Strasbourg)
Fax +33 3881-79732 (Strasbourg)
E-mail: cristiansilviu.busoi@europarl.europa.eu
Website: http://www.cristibusoi.ro

Mr Jorgo CHATZIMARKAKIS
Member
Tel. +32 228-45149 (Brussels)
Fax +32 228-49149 (Brussels)
Tel. +33 3881-75149 (Strasbourg)
Fax +33 3881-79149 (Strasbourg)
Website: http://www.chatzi.de

Mr Fabio CIANI
Member
Tel. +32 228-45109 (Brussels)
Fax +32 228-49109 (Brussels)
Tel. +33 3881-75109 (Strasbourg)
Fax +33 3881-79109 (Strasbourg)

Mr Thierry CORNILLET
Member
Tel. +32 228-45579 (Brussels)
Fax +32 228-49579 (Brussels)
Tel. +33 3881-75579 (Strasbourg)
Fax +33 3881-79579 (Strasbourg)

Mr Magor Imre CSIBI
Member
Tel. +32 228-45845 (Brussels)
Fax +32 228-49845 (Brussels)
Tel. +33 3881-75845 (Strasbourg)
Fax +33 3881-79845 (Strasbourg)
E-mail: magorimre.csibi@europarl.europa.eu
Website: http://www.magorcsibi.ro

Mr Marek Aleksander CZARNECKI
Member
Tel. +32 228-45194 (Brussels)
Fax +32 228-49194 (Brussels)
Tel. +33 3881-75194 (Strasbourg)
Fax +33 3881-79194 (Strasbourg)
E-mail: marekaleksander.czarnecki@europarl.europa.eu
Website: http://www.marek-czarnecki.pl

Mr Daniel DĂIANU
Member
Tel. +32 228-45891 (Brussels)
Fax +32 228-49891 (Brussels)
Tel. +33 3881-75891 (Strasbourg)
Fax +33 3881-79891 (Strasbourg)
Website: http://www.daniel-daianu.eu

Mr Chris DAVIES
Member
Tel. +32 228-45353 (Brussels)
Fax +32 228-49353 (Brussels)
Tel. +33 3881-75353 (Strasbourg)
Fax +33 3881-79353 (Strasbourg)

Mr Arūnas DEGUTIS
Member
Tel. +32 228-45604 (Brussels)
Fax +32 228-49604 (Brussels)
Tel. +33 3881-75604 (Strasbourg)
Fax +33 3881-79604 (Strasbourg)
Website: http://www.arunasdegutis.lt

Mrs Jolanta DIČKUTĖ
Member
Tel. +32 228-45632 (Brussels)
Fax +32 228-49632 (Brussels)
Tel. +33 3881-75632 (Strasbourg)
Fax +33 3881-79632 (Strasbourg)
Website: http://www.dickute.lt

Mrs Mojca DRČAR MURKO
Member
Tel. +32 228-45368 (Brussels)
Fax +32 228-49368 (Brussels)
Tel. +33 3881-75368 (Strasbourg)
Fax +33 3881-79368 (Strasbourg)
E-mail: mojca.drcarmurko@europarl.europa.eu
Website: http://www.drcar-murko.si

Mr Antoine DUQUESNE
Member
Tel. +32 228-45216 (Brussels)
Fax +32 228-49216 (Brussels)
Tel. +33 3881-75216 (Strasbourg)
Fax +33 3881-79216 (Strasbourg)
E-mail: antoine.duquesne@europarl.europa.eu
Website: http://www.antoine-duquesne.be

Mr Francesco FERRARI
Member
Tel. +32 228-45331 (Brussels)
Fax +32 228-49331 (Brussels)
Tel. +33 3881-75331 (Strasbourg)
Fax +33 3881-79331 (Strasbourg)

Mrs Janelly FOURTOU
Member
Tel. +32 228-45150 (Brussels)
Fax +32 228-49150 (Brussels)
Tel. +33 3881-75150 (Strasbourg)
Fax +33 3881-79150 (Strasbourg)
E-mail: janelly.fourtou@europarl.europa.eu

Mrs Claire GIBAULT
Member
Tel. +32 228-45613 (Brussels)
Fax +32 228-49613 (Brussels)
Tel. +33 3881-75613 (Strasbourg)
Fax +33 3881-79613 (Strasbourg)
E-mail: claire.gibault@europarl.europa.eu
Website: http://www.claire-gibault.eu

Mrs Nathalie GRIESBECK
Member
Tel. +32 228-45391 (Brussels)
Fax +32 228-49391 (Brussels)
Tel. +33 3881-75391 (Strasbourg)
Fax +33 3881-79391 (Strasbourg)
E-mail: nathalie.griesbeck@europarl.europa.eu
Website: http://www.nathalie-griesbeck.fr

Mrs Fiona HALL
Member
Tel. +32 228-45561 (Brussels)
Fax +32 228-49561 (Brussels)
Tel. +33 3881-75561 (Strasbourg)
Fax +33 3881-79561 (Strasbourg)
Website: http://www.fionahall.org.uk

Mrs Jeanine HENNIS-PLASSCHAERT
Member
Tel. +32 228-45817 (Brussels)
Fax +32 228-49817 (Brussels)
Tel. +33 3881-75817 (Strasbourg)
Fax +33 3881-79817 (Strasbourg)

Anneli JÄÄTTEENMÄKI
Member
Tel. +32 228-45614 (Brussels)
Fax +32 228-49614 (Brussels)
Tel. +33 3881-75614 (Strasbourg)
Fax +33 3881-79614 (Strasbourg)
Website: http://www.annelijaatteenmaki.net

Mrs Anne E. JENSEN
Member
Tel. +32 228-45798 (Brussels)
Fax +32 228-49798 (Brussels)
Tel. +33 3881-75798 (Strasbourg)
Fax +33 3881-79798 (Strasbourg)
E-mail: annee.jensen@europarl.europa.eu
Website: http://www.anne-e.dk

Mrs Ona JUKNEVIČIENĖ
Member
Tel. +32 228-45830 (Brussels)
Fax +32 228-49830 (Brussels)
Tel. +33 3881-75830 (Strasbourg)
Fax +33 3881-79830 (Strasbourg)

Mr Metin KAZAK
Member
Tel. +32 228-45924 (Brussels)
Fax +32 228-49924 (Brussels)
Tel. +33 3881-75924 (Strasbourg)
Fax +33 3881-79924 (Strasbourg)
E-mail: metinhusein.kazak@europarl.europa.eu

Mr Wolf KLINZ
Member
Tel. +32 228-45641 (Brussels)
Fax +32 228-49641 (Brussels)
Tel. +33 3881-75641 (Strasbourg)
Fax +33 3881-79641 (Strasbourg)
Website: http://www.wolf-klinz.de

Mr Holger KRAHMER
Member
Tel. +32 228-45344 (Brussels)
Fax +32 228-49344 (Brussels)
Tel. +33 3881-75344 (Strasbourg)
Fax +33 3881-79344 (Strasbourg)
Website: http://www.holger-krahmer.de

Mr Jan Jerzy KUŁAKOWSKI
Member
Tel. +32 228-45848 (Brussels)
Fax +32 228-49848 (Brussels)
Tel. +33 3881-75848 (Strasbourg)
Fax +33 3881-79848 (Strasbourg)
E-mail: biuro@jankulakowski.pl
Website: http://www.jankulakowski.pl

Alexander Graf LAMBSDORFF
Member
Tel. +32 228-45118 (Brussels)
Fax +32 228-49118 (Brussels)
Tel. +33 3881-75118 (Strasbourg)
Fax +33 3881-79118 (Strasbourg)

Mrs Anne LAPERROUZE
Member
Tel. +32 228-45450 (Brussels)
Fax +32 228-49450 (Brussels)
Tel. +33 3881-75450 (Strasbourg)
Fax +33 3881-79450 (Strasbourg)
Website: http://www.anne-laperrouze.eu

Mr Bernard LEHIDEUX
Member
Tel. +32 228-45547 (Brussels)
Fax +32 228-49547 (Brussels)
Tel. +33 3881-75547 (Strasbourg)
Fax +33 3881-79547 (Strasbourg)

Mr Andrea LOSCO
Member
Tel. +32 228-45585 (Brussels)
Fax +32 228-49585 (Brussels)
Tel. +33 3881-75585 (Strasbourg)
Fax +33 3881-79585 (Strasbourg)
Website: http://www.andrealosco.it

Baroness Sarah LUDFORD
Member
Tel. +32 228-45104 (Brussels)
Fax +32 228-49104 (Brussels)
Tel. +33 3881-75104 (Strasbourg)
Fax +33 3881-79104 (Strasbourg)
E-mail: sarah.ludford@europarl.europa.eu
Website: http://www.sarahludfordmep.org.uk

Mrs Elizabeth LYNNE
Member
Tel. +32 228-45521 (Brussels)
Fax +32 228-49521 (Brussels)
Tel. +33 3881-75521 (Strasbourg)
Fax +33 3881-79521 (Strasbourg)
E-mail: elizabeth.lynne@europarl.europa.eu
Website: http://www.lizlynne.org.uk

Mr Toine MANDERS
Member
Tel. +32 228-45629 (Brussels)
Fax +32 228-49629 (Brussels)
Tel. +33 3881-75629 (Strasbourg)
Fax +33 3881-79629 (Strasbourg)
E-mail: toine.manders@europarl.europa.eu
Website: http://www.toinemanders.nl

Mrs Ramona Nicole MĂNESCU
Member
Tel. +32 228-45865 (Brussels)
Fax +32 228-49865 (Brussels)
Tel. +33 3881-75865 (Strasbourg)
Fax +33 3881-79865 (Strasbourg)
E-mail: ramonanicole.manescu@europarl.europa.eu
Website: http://www.ramonamanescu.ro/blog

Mrs Viktória MOHÁCSI
Member
Tel. +32 228-45628 (Brussels)
Fax +32 228-49628 (Brussels)
Tel. +33 3881-75628 (Strasbourg)
Fax +33 3881-79628 (Strasbourg)

Mr Jan MULDER
Member
Tel. +32 228-45607 (Brussels)
Fax +32 228-49607 (Brussels)
Tel. +33 3881-75607 (Strasbourg)
Fax +33 3881-79607 (Strasbourg)
E-mail: jan.mulder@europarl.europa.eu
Website: http://www.jan-mulder.eu

Mr Bill NEWTON DUNN
Member
Tel. +32 228-45712 (Brussels)
Fax +32 228-49712 (Brussels)
Tel. +33 3881-75712 (Strasbourg)
Fax +33 3881-79712 (Strasbourg)
E-mail: bill.newtondunn@europarl.europa.eu
Website: http://www.newton-dunn.com

Mrs Annemie NEYTS-UYTTEBROECK
Member
Tel. +32 228-45661 (Brussels)
Fax +32 228-49661 (Brussels)
Tel. +33 3881-75661 (Strasbourg)
Fax +33 3881-79661 (Strasbourg)
Website: http://www.annemie.eu

Baroness NICHOLSON OF WINTERBOURNE
Member
Tel. +32 228-45625 (Brussels)
Fax +32 228-49625 (Brussels)
Tel. +33 3881-75625 (Strasbourg)
Fax +33 3881-79625 (Strasbourg)
E-mail: emma.nicholson@europarl.europa.eu
Website: http://www.emmanicholson.info

Mr Janusz ONYSZKIEWICZ
Member
Tel. +32 228-45872 (Brussels)
Fax +32 228-49872 (Brussels)
Tel. +33 3881-75872 (Strasbourg)
Fax +33 3881-79872 (Strasbourg)
Website: http://www.januszonyszkiewicz.pl

Mr Vladko Todorov PANAYOTOV
Member
Tel. +32 228-45384 (Brussels)
Fax +32 228-49384 (Brussels)
Tel. +33 3881-75384 (Strasbourg)
Fax +33 3881-79384 (Strasbourg)

Mr Marco PANNELLA
Member
Tel. +32 228-45120 (Brussels)
Fax +32 228-49120 (Brussels)
Tel. +33 3881-75120 (Strasbourg)
Fax +33 3881-79120 (Strasbourg)
E-mail: marco.pannella@europarl.europa.eu

Mr Paweł Bartłomiej PISKORSKI
Member
Tel. +32 228-45531 (Brussels)
Fax +32 228-49531 (Brussels)
Tel. +33 3881-75531 (Strasbourg)
Fax +33 3881-79531 (Strasbourg)
E-mail: pawelbartlomiej.piskorski@europarl.europa.eu

Mr Samuli POHJAMO
Member
Tel. +32 228-45850 (Brussels)
Fax +32 228-49850 (Brussels)
Tel. +33 3881-75850 (Strasbourg)
Fax +33 3881-79850 (Strasbourg)
E-mail: samuli.pohjamo@europarl.europa.eu
Website: http://www.samulipohjamo.fi

Mr Vittorio PRODI
Member
Tel. +32 228-45581 (Brussels)
Fax +32 228-49581 (Brussels)
Tel. +33 3881-75581 (Strasbourg)
Fax +33 3881-79581 (Strasbourg)
Website: http://www.vittorioprodi.it

Mrs Maria ROBSAHM
Member
Tel. +32 228-45620 (Brussels)
Fax +32 228-49620 (Brussels)
Tel. +33 3881-75620 (Strasbourg)
Fax +33 3881-79620 (Strasbourg)
Website: http://www.mariacarlshamre.se

Mr Willem SCHUTH
Member
Tel. +32 228-45291 (Brussels)
Fax +32 228-49291 (Brussels)
Tel. +33 3881-75291 (Strasbourg)
Fax +33 3881-79291 (Strasbourg)
Website: http://www.willem-schuth.de

Mrs Grażyna STANISZEWSKA
Member
Tel. +32 228-45849 (Brussels)
Fax +32 228-49849 (Brussels)
Tel. +33 3881-75849 (Strasbourg)
Fax +33 3881-79849 (Strasbourg)
Website: http://www.staniszewska.pl

Mrs Margarita STARKEVIČIŪTĖ
Member
Tel. +32 228-45610 (Brussels)
Fax +32 228-49610 (Brussels)
Tel. +33 3881-75610 (Strasbourg)
Fax +33 3881-79610 (Strasbourg)
Website: http://www.starkeviciute.lt

Hannu TAKKULA
Member
Tel. +32 228-45851 (Brussels)
Fax +32 228-49851 (Brussels)
Tel. +33 3881-75851 (Strasbourg)
Fax +33 3881-79851 (Strasbourg)
E-mail: hannu.takkula@europarl.europa.eu

Mrs Patrizia TOIA
Member
Tel. +32 228-45127 (Brussels)
Fax +32 228-49127 (Brussels)
Tel. +33 3881-75127 (Strasbourg)
Fax +33 3881-79127 (Strasbourg)
E-mail: patrizia.toia@europarl.europa.eu
Website: http://www.patriziatoia.eu

Mr Johan VAN HECKE
Member
Tel. +32 228-45190 (Brussels)
Fax +32 228-49190 (Brussels)
Tel. +33 3881-75190 (Strasbourg)
Fax +33 3881-79190 (Strasbourg)
E-mail: johan.vanhecke@europarl.europa.eu
Website: http://www.johanvanhecke.be

Mr Donato Tommaso VERALDI
Member
Tel. +32 228-45856 (Brussels)
Fax +32 228-49856 (Brussels)
Tel. +33 3881-75856 (Strasbourg)
Fax +33 3881-79856 (Strasbourg)
E-mail: donatotommaso.veraldi@europarl.europa.eu

Mrs Renate WEBER
Member
Tel. +32 228-45846 (Brussels)
Fax +32 228-49846 (Brussels)
Tel. +33 3881-75846 (Strasbourg)
Fax +33 3881-79846 (Strasbourg)
E-mail: renate.weber@europarl.europa.eu
Website: http://www.renateweber.eu

Andrzej WIELOWIEYSKI
Member
Tel. +32 228-45841 (Brussels)
Fax +32 228-49841 (Brussels)
Tel. +33 3881-75841 (Strasbourg)
Fax +33 3881-79841 (Strasbourg)

GROUP OF THE GREENS/EUROPEAN FREE ALLIANCE

Mr Daniel COHN-BENDIT
Co-president
Tel. +32 228-45498 (Brussels)
Fax +32 228-49498 (Brussels)
Tel. +33 3881-75498 (Strasbourg)
Fax +33 3881-79498 (Strasbourg)
E-mail: daniel.cohn-bendit@europarl.europa.eu
Website: http://www.cohn-bendit.de

Mrs Monica FRASSONI
Co-president
Tel. +32 228-45932 (Brussels)
Fax +32 228-49932 (Brussels)
Tel. +33 3881-75932 (Strasbourg)
Fax +33 3881-79932 (Strasbourg)
E-mail: monica.frassoni@europarl.europa.eu
Website: http://www.monicafrassoni.it

Mrs Marie-Hélène AUBERT
Vice-Chairwoman
Tel. +32 228-45475 (Brussels)
Fax +32 228-49475 (Brussels)
Tel. +33 3881-75475 (Strasbourg)
Fax +33 3881-79475 (Strasbourg)

Mrs Rebecca HARMS
Vice-Chairwoman
Tel. +32 228-45695 (Brussels)
Fax +32 228-49695 (Brussels)
Tel. +33 3881-75695 (Strasbourg)
Fax +33 3881-79695 (Strasbourg)
Website: http://www.rebecca-harms.de

Mr Ian HUDGHTON
Vice-Chairman
Tel. +32 228-45499 (Brussels)
Fax +32 228-49499 (Brussels)
Tel. +33 3881-75499 (Strasbourg)
Fax +33 3881-79499 (Strasbourg)
E-mail: ian.hudghton@europarl.europa.eu
Website: http://www.hudghtonmep.com

Mr Pierre JONCKHEER
Vice-Chairman
Tel. +32 228-45896 (Brussels)
Fax +32 228-49896 (Brussels)
Tel. +33 3881-75896 (Strasbourg)
Fax +33 3881-79896 (Strasbourg)
Website: http://www.pierrejonckheer.be

Mrs Eva LICHTENBERGER
Vice-Chairwoman
Tel. +32 228-45139 (Brussels)
Fax +32 228-49139 (Brussels)
Tel. +33 3881-75139 (Strasbourg)
Fax +33 3881-79139 (Strasbourg)
E-mail: eva.lichtenberger@gruene.at

Mr Claude TURMES
Vice-Chairman
Tel. +32 228-45246 (Brussels)
Fax +32 228-49246 (Brussels)
Tel. +33 3881-75246 (Strasbourg)
Fax +33 3881-79246 (Strasbourg)

Mrs Margrete AUKEN
Member
Tel. +32 228-45327 (Brussels)
Fax +32 228-49327 (Brussels)
Tel. +33 3881-75327 (Strasbourg)
Fax +33 3881-79327 (Strasbourg)
E-mail: margrete.auken@europarl.europa.eu
Website: http://www.auken.dk

Mrs Angelika BEER
Member
Tel. +32 228-45135 (Brussels)
Fax +32 228-49135 (Brussels)
Tel. +33 3881-75135 (Strasbourg)
Fax +33 3881-79135 (Strasbourg)

Mr Jean-Luc BENNAHMIAS
Member
Tel. +32 228-45574 (Brussels)
Fax +32 228-49574 (Brussels)
Tel. +33 3881-75574 (Strasbourg)
Fax +33 3881-79574 (Strasbourg)
E-mail: jean-luc.bennahmias@europarl.europa.eu

Mrs Hiltrud BREYER
Member
Tel. +32 228-45287 (Brussels)
Fax +32 228-49287 (Brussels)
Tel. +33 3881-75287 (Strasbourg)
Fax +33 3881-79287 (Strasbourg)
E-mail: hiltrud.breyer@europarl.europa.eu
Website: http://www.hiltrud-breyer.eu

Mr Paul van BUITENEN
Member
Tel. +32 228-45972 (Brussels)
Fax +32 228-49972 (Brussels)
Tel. +33 3881-75972 (Strasbourg)
Fax +33 3881-79972 (Strasbourg)
Website: http://www.paulvanbuitenen.nl

Mrs Kathalijne Maria BUITENWEG
Member
Tel. +32 228-45266 (Brussels)
Fax +32 228-49266 (Brussels)
Tel. +33 3881-75266 (Strasbourg)
Fax +33 3881-79266 (Strasbourg)
E-mail: kathalijnemaria.buitenweg@europarl.europa.eu
Website: http://www.groenlinks.nl/europa

Mr Michael CRAMER
Member
Tel. +32 228-45779 (Brussels)
Fax +32 228-49779 (Brussels)
Tel. +33 3881-75779 (Strasbourg)
Fax +33 3881-79779 (Strasbourg)
Website: http://www.michael-cramer.eu

Mrs Jill EVANS
Member
Tel. +32 228-45103 (Brussels)
Fax +32 228-49103 (Brussels)
Tel. +33 3881-75103 (Strasbourg)
Fax +33 3881-79103 (Strasbourg)

Mrs Hélène FLAUTRE
Member
Tel. +32 228-45364 (Brussels)
Fax +32 228-49364 (Brussels)
Tel. +33 3881-75364 (Strasbourg)
Fax +33 3881-79364 (Strasbourg)
Website: http://www.flautre.net

Mr Friedrich-Wilhelm GRAEFE zu BARINGDORF
Member
Tel. +32 228-45154 (Brussels)
Fax +32 228-49154 (Brussels)
Tel. +33 3881-75154 (Strasbourg)
Fax +33 3881-79154 (Strasbourg)

Mrs Elly de GROEN-KOUWENHOVEN
Member
Tel. +32 228-45480 (Brussels)
Fax +32 228-49480 (Brussels)
Tel. +33 3881-75480 (Strasbourg)
Fax +33 3881-79480 (Strasbourg)

Mr David HAMMERSTEIN
Member
Tel. +32 228-45754 (Brussels)
Fax +32 228-49754 (Brussels)
Tel. +33 3881-75754 (Strasbourg)
Fax +33 3881-79754 (Strasbourg)
Website: http://www.davidhammerstein.org

Satu HASSI
Member
Tel. +32 228-45437 (Brussels)
Fax +32 228-49437 (Brussels)
Tel. +33 3881-75437 (Strasbourg)
Fax +33 3881-79437 (Strasbourg)
Website: http://www.satuhassi.net

Mr Milan HORÁČEK
Member
Tel. +32 228-45196 (Brussels)
Fax +32 228-49196 (Brussels)
Tel. +33 3881-75196 (Strasbourg)
Fax +33 3881-79196 (Strasbourg)
E-mail: milan.horacek@europarl.europa.eu
Website: http://www.milan-horacek.de

Mr Mikel IRUJO AMEZAGA
Member
Tel. +32 228-45299 (Brussels)
Fax +32 228-49299 (Brussels)
Tel. +33 3881-75299 (Strasbourg)
Fax +33 3881-79299 (Strasbourg)

Mrs Marie Anne ISLER BÉGUIN
Member
Tel. +32 228-45572 (Brussels)
Fax +32 228-49572 (Brussels)
Tel. +33 3881-75572 (Strasbourg)
Fax +33 3881-79572 (Strasbourg)
E-mail: marieanne.islerbeguin@europarl.europa.eu
Website: http://www.maib.info

Mrs Gisela KALLENBACH
Member
Tel. +32 228-45339 (Brussels)
Fax +32 228-49339 (Brussels)
Tel. +33 3881-75339 (Strasbourg)
Fax +33 3881-79339 (Strasbourg)

Mr Sepp KUSSTATSCHER
Member
Tel. +32 228-45143 (Brussels)
Fax +32 228-49143 (Brussels)
Tel. +33 3881-75143 (Strasbourg)
Fax +33 3881-79143 (Strasbourg)
E-mail: sepp.kusstatscher@europarl.europa.eu
Website: http://www.kusstatscher.net

Mr Joost LAGENDIJK
Member
Tel. +32 228-45176 (Brussels)
Fax +32 228-49176 (Brussels)
Tel. +33 3881-75176 (Strasbourg)
Fax +33 3881-79176 (Strasbourg)
Website: http://www.groenlinks.nl

Mrs Jean LAMBERT
Member
Tel. +32 228-45507 (Brussels)
Fax +32 228-49507 (Brussels)
Tel. +33 3881-75507 (Strasbourg)
Fax +33 3881-79507 (Strasbourg)
E-mail: jean.lambert@europarl.europa.eu
Website: http://www.jeanlambertmep.org.uk

Mr Alain LIPIETZ
Member
Tel. +32 228-45207 (Brussels)
Fax +32 228-49207 (Brussels)
Tel. +33 3881-75207 (Strasbourg)
Fax +33 3881-79207 (Strasbourg)

Mrs Caroline LUCAS
Member
Tel. +32 228-45153 (Brussels)
Fax +32 228-49153 (Brussels)
Tel. +33 3881-75153 (Strasbourg)
Fax +33 3881-79153 (Strasbourg)
E-mail: caroline.lucas@europarl.europa.eu
Website: http://www.carolinelucasmep.org.uk

Mr Cem ÖZDEMIR
Member
Tel. +32 228-45446 (Brussels)
Fax +32 228-49446 (Brussels)
Tel. +33 3881-75446 (Strasbourg)
Fax +33 3881-79446 (Strasbourg)

Mr Gérard ONESTA
Member
Tel. +32 228-45505 (Brussels)
Fax +32 228-49505 (Brussels)
Tel. +33 3881-75505 (Strasbourg)
Fax +33 3881-79505 (Strasbourg)

Mr Raül ROMEVA i RUEDA
Member
Tel. +32 228-45645 (Brussels)
Fax +32 228-49645 (Brussels)
Tel. +33 3881-75645 (Strasbourg)
Fax +33 3881-79645 (Strasbourg)
Website: http://www.raulromeva.cat

Mrs Heide RÜHLE
Member
Tel. +32 228-45609 (Brussels)
Fax +32 228-49609 (Brussels)
Tel. +33 3881-75609 (Strasbourg)
Fax +33 3881-79609 (Strasbourg)
E-mail: heide.ruehle@europarl.europa.eu
Website: http://www.heide-ruehle.de

Mr Carl SCHLYTER
Member
Tel. +32 228-45273 (Brussels)
Fax +32 228-49273 (Brussels)
Tel. +33 3881-75273 (Strasbourg)
Fax +33 3881-79273 (Strasbourg)
Website: http://www.mp.se/carl

Mr Frithjof SCHMIDT
Member
Tel. +32 228-45215 (Brussels)
Fax +32 228-49215 (Brussels)
Tel. +33 3881-75215 (Strasbourg)
Fax +33 3881-79215 (Strasbourg)
E-mail: wichert@gruene-europa.de

Mrs Elisabeth SCHROEDTER
Member
Tel. +32 228-45234 (Brussels)
Fax +32 228-49234 (Brussels)
Tel. +33 3881-75234 (Strasbourg)
Fax +33 3881-79234 (Strasbourg)
Website: http://www.elisabeth-schroedter.de

Mr Alyn SMITH
Member
Tel. +32 228-45187 (Brussels)
Fax +32 228-49187 (Brussels)
Tel. +33 3881-75187 (Strasbourg)
Fax +33 3881-79187 (Strasbourg)

Mr Bart STAES
Member
Tel. +32 228-45642 (Brussels)
Fax +32 228-49642 (Brussels)
Tel. +33 3881-75642 (Strasbourg)
Fax +33 3881-79642 (Strasbourg)
E-mail: bart.staes@europarl.europa.eu
Website: http://www.bartstaes.be

Mr László TŐKÉS
Member
Tel. +32 228-45801 (Brussels)
Fax +32 228-49801 (Brussels)
Tel. +33 3881-75801 (Strasbourg)
Fax +33 3881-79801 (Strasbourg)

Mrs Helga TRÜPEL
Member
Tel. +32 228-45140 (Brussels)
Fax +32 228-49140 (Brussels)
Tel. +33 3881-75140 (Strasbourg)
Fax +33 3881-79140 (Strasbourg)
E-mail: helga.truepel@europarl.europa.eu
Website: http://www.helga-truepel.de

Mr Johannes VOGGENHUBER
Member
Tel. +32 228-45272 (Brussels)
Fax +32 228-49272 (Brussels)
Tel. +33 3881-75272 (Strasbourg)
Fax +33 3881-79272 (Strasbourg)

Mrs Tatjana ŽDANOKA
Member
Tel. +32 228-45912 (Brussels)
Fax +32 228-49912 (Brussels)
Tel. +33 3881-75912 (Strasbourg)
Fax +33 3881-79912 (Strasbourg)
E-mail: tatjana.zdanoka@europarl.europa.eu
Website: http://www.pctvl.lv

CONFEDERAL GROUP OF THE EUROPEAN UNITED LEFT/NORDIC GREEN LEFT

Mr Francis WURTZ
Chairman
Tel. +32 228-45106 (Brussels)
Fax +32 228-49106 (Brussels)
Tel. +33 3881-75106 (Strasbourg)
Fax +33 3881-79106 (Strasbourg)
E-mail: francis.wurtz@europarl.europa.eu
Website: http://www.francis-wurtz.eu

Mrs Ilda FIGUEIREDO
Vice-Chairwoman
Tel. +32 228-45465 (Brussels)
Fax +32 228-49465 (Brussels)
Tel. +33 3881-75465 (Strasbourg)
Fax +33 3881-79465 (Strasbourg)
E-mail: ilda.figueiredo@europarl.europa.eu

Mrs Kartika Tamara LIOTARD
Vice-Chairwoman
Tel. +32 228-45778 (Brussels)
Fax +32 228-45778 (Brussels)
Tel. +33 3881-75778 (Strasbourg)
Fax +33 3881-79778 (Strasbourg)

Mr Miloslav RANSDORF
Vice-Chairman
Tel. +32 228-45907 (Brussels)
Fax +32 228-49907 (Brussels)
Tel. +33 3881-75907 (Strasbourg)
Fax +33 3881-79907 (Strasbourg)
Website: http://www.ransdorf.com

Mrs Eva-Britt SVENSSON
Vice-Chairwoman
Tel. +32 228-45105 (Brussels)
Fax +32 228-49105 (Brussels)
Tel. +33 3881-75105 (Strasbourg)
Fax +33 3881-79105 (Strasbourg)

Mrs Mary Lou McDONALD
Member of the Bureau
Tel. +32 228-45945 (Brussels)
Fax +32 228-49945 (Brussels)
Tel. +33 3881-75945 (Strasbourg)
Fax +33 3881-79945 (Strasbourg)

Mr Willy MEYER PLEITE
Member of the Bureau
Tel. +32 228-45557 (Brussels)
Fax +32 228-49557 (Brussels)
Tel. +33 3881-75557 (Strasbourg)
Fax +33 3881-79557 (Strasbourg)
E-mail: willy.meyerpleite@europarl.europa.eu
Website: http://www.willymeyer.blogspot.com

Mr Roberto MUSACCHIO
Member of the Bureau
Tel. +32 228-45664 (Brussels)
Fax +32 228-49664 (Brussels)
Tel. +33 3881-75664 (Strasbourg)
Fax +33 3881-79664 (Strasbourg)
Website: http://www.robertomusacchio.eu

Mr Dimitrios PAPADIMOULIS
Member of the Bureau
Tel. +32 228-45719 (Brussels)
Fax +32 228-49719 (Brussels)
Tel. +33 3881-75719 (Strasbourg)
Fax +33 3881-79719 (Strasbourg)
E-mail: dimitrios.papadimoulis@europarl.europa.eu
Website: http://www.papadimoulis.gr

Mr Marco RIZZO
Member of the Bureau
Tel. +32 228-45252 (Brussels)
Fax +32 228-49252 (Brussels)
Tel. +33 3881-75252 (Strasbourg)
Fax +33 3881-79252 (Strasbourg)

Esko SEPPÄNEN
Member of the Bureau
Tel. +32 228-45271 (Brussels)
Fax +32 228-49271 (Brussels)
Tel. +33 3881-75271 (Strasbourg)
Fax +33 3881-79271 (Strasbourg)
E-mail: esko.seppanen@europarl.europa.eu
Website: http://www.eskoseppanen.net

Mr Kyriacos TRIANTAPHYLLIDES
Member of the Bureau
Tel. +32 228-45958 (Brussels)
Fax +32 228-49958 (Brussels)
Tel. +33 3881-75958 (Strasbourg)
Fax +33 3881-79958 (Strasbourg)
Website: http://www.triantaphyllides.org

Mr Helmuth MARKOV
Treasurer
Tel. +32 228-45980 (Brussels)
Fax +32 228-49980 (Brussels)
Tel. +33 3881-75980 (Strasbourg)
Fax +33 3881-79980 (Strasbourg)
E-mail: helmuth.markov@europarl.europa.eu
Website: http://www.pds-europa.de

Mr Jiří MAŠTÁLKA
Deputy-Treasurer
Tel. +32 228-45905 (Brussels)
Fax +32 228-49905 (Brussels)
Tel. +33 3881-75905 (Strasbourg)
Fax +33 3881-79905 (Strasbourg)

Mr Adamos ADAMOU
Member
Tel. +32 228-45964 (Brussels)
Fax +32 228-49964 (Brussels)
Tel. +33 3881-75964 (Strasbourg)
Fax +33 3881-79964 (Strasbourg)
E-mail: adamos.adamou@europarl.europa.eu

Mr Vittorio AGNOLETTO
Member
Tel. +32 228-45444 (Brussels)
Fax +32 228-49444 (Brussels)
Tel. +33 3881-75444 (Strasbourg)
Fax +33 3881-79444 (Strasbourg)

Mr Vincenzo AITA
Member
Tel. +32 228-45119 (Brussels)
Fax +32 228-49119 (Brussels)
Tel. +33 3881-75119 (Strasbourg)
Fax +33 3881-79119 (Strasbourg)
E-mail: vincenzo.aita@europarl.europa.eu

Mr André BRIE
Member
Tel. +32 228-45403 (Brussels)
Fax +32 228-49403 (Brussels)
Tel. +33 3881-75403 (Strasbourg)
Fax +33 3881-79403 (Strasbourg)
E-mail: andre.brie@europarl.europa.eu
Website: http://www.andrebrie.de

Mr Giusto CATANIA
Member
Tel. +32 228-45874 (Brussels)
Fax +32 228-49874 (Brussels)
Tel. +33 3881-75874 (Strasbourg)
Fax +33 3881-79874 (Strasbourg)
Website: http://www.giustocatania.eu

Mrs Bairbre de BRÚN
Member
Tel. +32 228-45222 (Brussels)
Fax +32 228-49222 (Brussels)
Tel. +33 3881-75222 (Strasbourg)
Fax +33 3881-79222 (Strasbourg)

Mr Konstantinos DROUTSAS
Member
Tel. +32 228-45163 (Brussels)
Fax +32 228-49163 (Brussels)
Tel. +33 3881-75163 (Strasbourg)
Fax +33 3881-79163 (Strasbourg)
E-mail: konstantinos.droutsas@europarl.europa.eu

Mrs Věra FLASAROVÁ
Member
Tel. +32 228-45913 (Brussels)
Fax +32 228-49913 (Brussels)
Tel. +33 3881-75913 (Strasbourg)
Fax +33 3881-79913 (Strasbourg)
Website: http://www.flasarova.cz

Mr Pedro GUERREIRO
Member
Tel. +32 228-45963 (Brussels)
Fax +32 228-49963 (Brussels)
Tel. +33 3881-75963 (Strasbourg)
Fax +33 3881-79963 (Strasbourg)

Mr Umberto GUIDONI
Member
Tel. +32 228-45722 (Brussels)
Fax +32 228-49722 (Brussels)
Tel. +33 3881-75722 (Strasbourg)
Fax +33 3881-79722 (Strasbourg)
E-mail: umberto.guidoni@europarl.europa.eu

Mr Jacky HÉNIN
Member
Tel. +32 228-45180 (Brussels)
Fax +32 228-49180 (Brussels)
Tel. +33 3881-75180 (Strasbourg)
Fax +33 3881-79180 (Strasbourg)
Website: http://www.europe-deputes-pcf.com/sites/jhenineurope/site/jackyhenin.php3

Mr Jens HOLM
Member
Tel. +32 228-45563 (Brussels)
Fax +32 228-49563 (Brussels)
Tel. +33 3881-75563 (Strasbourg)
Fax +33 3881-79563 (Strasbourg)
E-mail: jens.holm@europarl.europa.eu
Website: http://www.jensholm.se

Mrs Madeleine JOUYE DE GRANDMAISON
Member
Tel. +32 228-45124 (Brussels)
Fax +32 228-49124 (Brussels)
Tel. +33 3881-75124 (Strasbourg)
Fax +33 3881-79124 (Strasbourg)

Mrs Sylvia-Yvonne KAUFMANN
Member
Tel. +32 228-45756 (Brussels)
Fax +32 228-49756 (Brussels)
Tel. +33 3881-75756 (Strasbourg)
Fax +33 3881-79756 (Strasbourg)
Website: http://www.sylvia-yvonnekaufmann.de

Mr Jaromír KOHLÍČEK
Member
Tel. +32 228-45497 (Brussels)
Fax +32 228-49497 (Brussels)
Tel. +33 3881-75497 (Strasbourg)
Fax +33 3881-79497 (Strasbourg)

Mr Erik MEIJER
Member
Tel. +32 228-45492 (Brussels)
Fax +32 228-49492 (Brussels)
Tel. +33 3881-75492 (Strasbourg)
Fax +33 3881-79492 (Strasbourg)
E-mail: emeijer@sp.nl
Website: http://europa.sp.nl

Mrs Luisa MORGANTINI
Member
Tel. +32 228-45151 (Brussels)
Fax +32 228-49151 (Brussels)
Tel. +33 3881-75151 (Strasbourg)
Fax +33 3881-79151 (Strasbourg)
E-mail: luisa.morgantini@europarl.europa.eu
Website: http://www.luisamorgantini.net

Mr Athanasios PAFILIS
Member
Tel. +32 228-45911 (Brussels)
Fax +32 228-49911 (Brussels)
Tel. +33 3881-75911 (Strasbourg)
Fax +33 3881-79911 (Strasbourg)

Mr Tobias PFLÜGER
Member
Tel. +32 228-45555 (Brussels)
Fax +32 228-49555 (Brussels)
Tel. +33 3881-75555 (Strasbourg)
Fax +33 3881-79555 (Strasbourg)
E-mail: tobias.pflueger@europarl.europa.eu
Website: http://www.tobias-pflueger.de

Mr Miguel PORTAS
Member
Tel. +32 228-45123 (Brussels)
Fax +32 228-49123 (Brussels)
Tel. +33 3881-75123 (Strasbourg)
Fax +33 3881-79123 (Strasbourg)
Website: http://www.miguelportas.net

Mr Vladimír REMEK
Member
Tel. +32 228-45131 (Brussels)
Fax +32 228-49131 (Brussels)
Tel. +33 3881-75131 (Strasbourg)
Fax +33 3881-79131 (Strasbourg)
Website: http://www.vladimirremek.cz

Mr Søren Bo SØNDERGAARD
Member
Tel. +32 228-45152 (Brussels)
Fax +32 228-49152 (Brussels)
Tel. +33 3881-75152 (Strasbourg)
Fax +33 3881-79152 (Strasbourg)
E-mail: soren@politik.dk

Mr Daniel STROŽ
Member
Tel. +32 228-45456 (Brussels)
Fax +32 228-49456 (Brussels)
Tel. +33 3881-75456 (Strasbourg)
Fax +33 3881-79456 (Strasbourg)

Mr Georgios TOUSSAS
Member
Tel. +32 228-45278 (Brussels)
Fax +32 228-49278 (Brussels)
Tel. +33 3881-75278 (Strasbourg)
Fax +33 3881-79278 (Strasbourg)
E-mail: georgios.toussas@europarl.europa.eu

Mrs Feleknas UCA
Member
Tel. +32 228-45419 (Brussels)
Fax +32 228-49419 (Brussels)
Tel. +33 3881-75419 (Strasbourg)
Fax +33 3881-79419 (Strasbourg)
E-mail: feleknas.uca@europarl.europa.eu
Website: http://www.feleknasuca.de

Mrs Sahra WAGENKNECHT
Member
Tel. +32 228-45619 (Brussels)
Fax +32 228-49619 (Brussels)
Tel. +33 3881-75619 (Strasbourg)
Fax +33 3881-79619 (Strasbourg)
E-mail: sahra.wagenknecht@europarl.europa.eu
Website: http://www.sahrawagenknecht.de

Mrs Gabriele ZIMMER
Member
Tel. +32 228-45101 (Brussels)
Fax +32 228-49101 (Brussels)
Tel. +33 3881-75101 (Strasbourg)
Fax +33 3881-79101 (Strasbourg)
E-mail: zimmer.zimmer@t-online.de
Website: http://www.gabi-zimmer.de

UNION FOR EUROPE OF THE NATIONS GROUP

Mr Brian CROWLEY
Co-president
Tel. +32 228-45751 (Brussels)
Fax +32 228-49751 (Brussels)
Tel. +33 3881-75751 (Strasbourg)
Fax +33 3881-79751 (Strasbourg)
E-mail: briancrowleymep@eircom.net
Website: http://www.briancrowleymep.ie

Mrs Cristiana MUSCARDINI
Co-president
Tel. +32 228-45277 (Brussels)
Fax +32 228-49277 (Brussels)
Tel. +33 3881-75277 (Strasbourg)
Fax +33 3881-79277 (Strasbourg)
Website: http://www.muscardini-cristiana.com

Mr Adam BIELAN
Vice-Chairman
Tel. +32 228-45925 (Brussels)
Fax +32 228-49925 (Brussels)
Tel. +33 3881-75925 (Strasbourg)
Fax +33 3881-79925 (Strasbourg)
Website: http://www.bielan.pl

Mr Mogens CAMRE
Vice-Chairman
Tel. +32 228-45205 (Brussels)
Fax +32 228-49205 (Brussels)
Tel. +33 3881-75205 (Strasbourg)
Fax +33 3881-79205 (Strasbourg)
Website: http://www.mogenscamre.dk

Mr Gintaras DIDŽIOKAS
Vice-Chairman
Tel. +32 228-45546 (Brussels)
Fax +32 228-49546 (Brussels)
Tel. +33 3881-75546 (Strasbourg)
Fax +33 3881-79546 (Strasbourg)
E-mail: gintaras.didziokas@europarl.europa.eu
Website: http://www.gintaras.info

Mr Roberts ZĪLE
Vice-Chairman
Tel. +32 228-45224 (Brussels)
Fax +32 228-49224 (Brussels)
Tel. +33 3881-75224 (Strasbourg)
Fax +33 3881-79224 (Strasbourg)
Website: http://www.ep-uen.lv

Mr Ryszard CZARNECKI
Treasurer
Tel. +32 228-45441 (Brussels)
Fax +32 228-49441 (Brussels)
Tel. +33 3881-75441 (Strasbourg)
Fax +33 3881-79441 (Strasbourg)
E-mail: ryszard.czarnecki@europarl.europa.eu
Website: http://www.RyszardCzarnecki.pl

Mr Alessandro FOGLIETTA
Treasurer
Tel. +32 228-45181 (Brussels)
Fax +32 228-49181 (Brussels)
Tel. +33 3881-75181 (Strasbourg)
Fax +33 3881-79181 (Strasbourg)
E-mail: alessandro.foglietta@europarl.europa.eu

Mrs Roberta ANGELILLI
Member
Tel. +32 228-45902 (Brussels)
Fax +32 228-49902 (Brussels)
Tel. +33 3881-75902 (Strasbourg)
Fax +33 3881-79902 (Strasbourg)
E-mail: roberta.angelilli@europarl.europa.eu

Mr Liam AYLWARD
Member
Tel. +32 228-45782 (Brussels)
Fax +32 228-49782 (Brussels)
Tel. +33 3881-75782 (Strasbourg)
Fax +33 3881-79782 (Strasbourg)
E-mail: liam.aylward@europarl.europa.eu

Mr Domenico Antonio BASILE
Member
Tel. +32 228-45707 (Brussels)
Fax +32 228-49707 (Brussels)
Tel. +33 3881-75707 (Strasbourg)
Fax +33 3881-79707 (Strasbourg)
E-mail: dom.ant.basile@gmail.com

Mr Sergio BERLATO
Member
Tel. +32 228-45213 (Brussels)
Fax +32 228-49213 (Brussels)
Tel. +33 3881-75213 (Strasbourg)
Fax +33 3881-79213 (Strasbourg)
E-mail: info@sergioberlato.it
Website: http://www.sergioberlato.it

Mr Mario BORGHEZIO
Member
Tel. +32 228-45704 (Brussels)
Fax +32 228-49704 (Brussels)
Tel. +33 3881-75704 (Strasbourg)
Fax +33 3881-79704 (Strasbourg)
E-mail: mario.borghezio@europarl.europa.eu
Website: http://www.marioborghezio.org

Mr Erminio Enzo BOSO
Member
Tel. +32 228-45121 (Brussels)
Fax +32 228-49121 (Brussels)
Tel. +33 3881-75121 (Strasbourg)
Fax +33 3881-79121 (Strasbourg)
E-mail: bosoe@consiglio.provincia.tn.it

Mr Sylwester CHRUSZCZ
Member
Tel. +32 228-45571 (Brussels)
Fax +32 228-49571 (Brussels)
Tel. +33 3881-75571 (Strasbourg)
Fax +33 3881-79571 (Strasbourg)
Website: http://www.chruszcz.pl

Mrs Hanna FOLTYN-KUBICKA
Member
Tel. +32 228-45533 (Brussels)
Fax +32 228-49533 (Brussels)
Tel. +33 3881-75533 (Strasbourg)
Fax +33 3881-79533 (Strasbourg)
Website: http://www.foltynkubicka.pl

Mr Dariusz Maciej GRABOWSKI
Member
Tel. +32 228-45580 (Brussels)
Fax +32 228-49580 (Brussels)
Tel. +33 3881-75580 (Strasbourg)
Fax +33 3881-79580 (Strasbourg)
Website: http://www.grabowski.pl

Mr Mieczysław Edmund JANOWSKI
Member
Tel. +32 228-45263 (Brussels)
Fax +32 228-49263 (Brussels)
Tel. +33 3881-75263 (Strasbourg)
Fax +33 3881-79263 (Strasbourg)
E-mail: senator@janowski.rzeszow.pl
Website: http://www.janowski.rzeszow.pl

Mr Guntars KRASTS
Member
Tel. +32 228-45909 (Brussels)
Fax +32 228-49909 (Brussels)
Tel. +33 3881-75909 (Strasbourg)
Fax +33 3881-79909 (Strasbourg)
Website: http://www.ep-uen.lv

Mr Ģirts Valdis KRISTOVSKIS
Member
Tel. +32 228-45744 (Brussels)
Fax +32 228-49744 (Brussels)
Tel. +33 3881-75744 (Strasbourg)
Fax +33 3881-79744 (Strasbourg)
Website: http://www.ep-uen.lv

Mr Wiesław Stefan KUC
Member
Tel. +32 228-45198 (Brussels)
Fax +32 228-49198 (Brussels)
Tel. +33 3881-75198 (Strasbourg)
Fax +33 3881-79198 (Strasbourg)

Mr Zbigniew Krzysztof KUŹMIUK
Member
Tel. +32 228-45254 (Brussels)
Fax +32 228-49254 (Brussels)
Tel. +33 3881-75254 (Strasbourg)
Fax +33 3881-79254 (Strasbourg)
E-mail: zbigniewkrzysztof.kuzmiuk@europarl.europa.eu
Website: http://www.kuzmiuk.com.pl

Mr Marcin LIBICKI
Member
Tel. +32 228-45934 (Brussels)
Fax +32 228-49934 (Brussels)
Tel. +33 3881-75934 (Strasbourg)
Fax +33 3881-79934 (Strasbourg)
E-mail: marcin.libicki@europarl.europa.eu
Website: http://www.libicki.pl

Mr Eugenijus MALDEIKIS
Member
Tel. +32 228-45575 (Brussels)
Fax +32 228-49575 (Brussels)
Tel. +33 3881-75575 (Strasbourg)
Fax +33 3881-79575 (Strasbourg)
Website: http://www.maldeikis.lt

Mr Jan Tadeusz MASIEL
Member
Tel. +32 228-45211 (Brussels)
Fax +32 228-49211 (Brussels)
Tel. +33 3881-75211 (Strasbourg)
Fax +33 3881-79211 (Strasbourg)

Mr Antonio MUSSA
Member
Tel. +32 228-45914 (Brussels)
Fax +32 228-49914 (Brussels)
Tel. +33 3881-75914 (Strasbourg)
Fax +33 3881-79914 (Strasbourg)
E-mail: antonio.mussa@libero.it

Mr Sebastiano (Nello) MUSUMECI
Member
Tel. +32 228-45765 (Brussels)
Fax +32 228-49765 (Brussels)
Tel. +33 3881-75765 (Strasbourg)
Fax +33 3881-79765 (Strasbourg)
Website: http://www.nellomusumeci.it

Mr Seán Ó NEACHTAIN
Member
Tel. +32 228-45611 (Brussels)
Fax +32 228-49611 (Brussels)
Tel. +33 3881-75611 (Strasbourg)
Fax +33 3881-79611 (Strasbourg)
Website: http://www.oneachtain.com

Mr Bogdan PĚK
Member
Tel. +32 228-45584 (Brussels)
Fax +32 228-49584 (Brussels)
Tel. +33 3881-75584 (Strasbourg)
Fax +33 3881-79584 (Strasbourg)

Mr Mirosław Mariusz PIOTROWSKI
Member
Tel. +32 228-45588 (Brussels)
Fax +32 228-49588 (Brussels)
Tel. +33 3881-75588 (Strasbourg)
Fax +33 3881-79588 (Strasbourg)

Mr Umberto PIRILLI
Member
Tel. +32 228-45979 (Brussels)
Fax +32 228-49979 (Brussels)
Tel. +33 3881-75979 (Strasbourg)
Fax +33 3881-79979 (Strasbourg)
E-mail: umberto.pirilli@europarl.europa.eu

Mr Zdzisław Zbigniew PODKAŃSKI
Member
Tel. +32 228-45248 (Brussels)
Fax +32 228-49248 (Brussels)
Tel. +33 3881-75248 (Strasbourg)
Fax +33 3881-79248 (Strasbourg)

Mr Giovanni ROBUSTI
Member
Tel. +32 228-45735 (Brussels)
Fax +32 228-49735 (Brussels)

Mr Bogusław ROGALSKI
Member
Tel. +32 228-45616 (Brussels)
Fax +32 228-49616 (Brussels)
Tel. +33 3881-75616 (Strasbourg)
Fax +33 3881-79616 (Strasbourg)
Website: http://www.brogalski.pl

Mr Wojciech ROSZKOWSKI
Member
Tel. +32 228-45573 (Brussels)
Fax +32 228-49573 (Brussels)
Tel. +33 3881-75573 (Strasbourg)
Fax +33 3881-79573 (Strasbourg)
E-mail: wojciech@roszkowski.pl
Website: http://www.roszkowski.pl

Mr Leopold Józef RUTOWICZ
Member
Tel. +32 228-45217 (Brussels)
Fax +32 228-49217 (Brussels)
Tel. +33 3881-75217 (Strasbourg)
Fax +33 3881-79217 (Strasbourg)
E-mail: leopoldjozef.rutowicz@europarl.europa.eu
Website: http://www.leopoldrutowicz.pl

Mr Eoin RYAN
Member
Tel. +32 228-45612 (Brussels)
Fax +32 228-49612 (Brussels)
Tel. +33 3881-75612 (Strasbourg)
Fax +33 3881-79612 (Strasbourg)
E-mail: eoin.ryan@europarl.europa.eu

Mr Francesco Enrico SPERONI
Member
Tel. +32 228-45705 (Brussels)
Fax +32 228-49705 (Brussels)
Tel. +33 3881-75705 (Strasbourg)
Fax +33 3881-79705 (Strasbourg)
E-mail: francescoenrico.speroni@europarl.europa.eu

Mr Konrad SZYMAŃSKI
Member
Tel. +32 228-45136 (Brussels)
Fax +32 228-49136 (Brussels)
Tel. +33 3881-75136 (Strasbourg)
Fax +33 3881-79136 (Strasbourg)
Website: http://www.konradszymanski.pl

Mr Salvatore TATARELLA
Member
Tel. +32 228-45276 (Brussels)
Fax +32 228-49276 (Brussels)
Tel. +33 3881-75276 (Strasbourg)
Fax +33 3881-79276 (Strasbourg)
E-mail: salvatore.tatarella@europarl.europa.eu

Ewa TOMASZEWSKA
Member
Tel. +32 228-45927 (Brussels)
Fax +32 228-49927 (Brussels)
Tel. +33 3881-75927 (Strasbourg)
Fax +33 3881-79927 (Strasbourg)
E-mail: ewa.tomaszewska@europarl.europa.eu
Website: http://www.tomaszewska.pl

Mrs Inese VAIDERE
Member
Tel. +32 228-45639 (Brussels)
Fax +32 228-49639 (Brussels)
Tel. +33 3881-75639 (Strasbourg)
Fax +33 3881-79639 (Strasbourg)
Website: http://www.ep-uen.lv

Mr Janusz WOJCIECHOWSKI
Member
Tel. +32 228-45802 (Brussels)
Fax +32 228-49802 (Brussels)
Tel. +33 3881-75802 (Strasbourg)
Fax +33 3881-79802 (Strasbourg)
E-mail: janusz.wojciechowski@europarl.europa.eu

Mr Andrzej Tomasz ZAPAŁOWSKI
Member
Tel. +32 228-45926 (Brussels)
Fax +32 228-49926 (Brussels)
Tel. +33 3881-75926 (Strasbourg)
Fax +33 3881-79926 (Strasbourg)
E-mail: andrzejtomasz.zapalowski@europarl.europa.eu
Website: http://www.zapalowski.eu

INDEPENDENCE/DEMOCRACY GROUP

Mrs Hanne DAHL
Co-president
Tel. +32 228-45167 (Brussels)
Fax +32 228-49167 (Brussels)
Tel. +33 3881-75167 (Strasbourg)
Fax +33 3881-79167 (Strasbourg)
E-mail: hanne.dahl@europarl.europa.eu
Website: http://www.hannedahl.eu

Mr Nigel FARAGE
Co-president
Tel. +32 228-45855 (Brussels)
Fax +32 228-49855 (Brussels)
Tel. +33 3881-75855 (Strasbourg)
Fax +33 3881-79855 (Strasbourg)

Mr Johannes BLOKLAND
Chairman of the Bureau
Tel. +32 228-45820 (Brussels)
Fax +32 228-49820 (Brussels)
Tel. +33 3881-75820 (Strasbourg)
Fax +33 3881-79820 (Strasbourg)
E-mail: johannes.blokland@europarl.europa.eu
Website: http://www.eurofractie.nl

Mr Paul Marie COÛTEAUX
Member of the Bureau
Tel. +32 228-45206 (Brussels)
Fax +32 228-49206 (Brussels)
Tel. +33 3881-75206 (Strasbourg)
Fax +33 3881-79206 (Strasbourg)
E-mail: paulmarie.couteaux@europarl.europa.eu

Mr Georgios GEORGIOU
Member of the Bureau
Tel. +32 228-45724 (Brussels)
Fax +32 228-49724 (Brussels)
Tel. +33 3881-75724 (Strasbourg)
Fax +33 3881-79724 (Strasbourg)
E-mail: georgios.georgiou@europarl.europa.eu

Mrs Hélène GOUDIN
Member of the Bureau
Tel. +32 228-45674 (Brussels)
Fax +32 228-49674 (Brussels)
Tel. +33 3881-75674 (Strasbourg)
Fax +33 3881-79674 (Strasbourg)
E-mail: helene.goudin@europarl.europa.eu

Mrs Urszula KRUPA
Member of the Bureau
Tel. +32 228-45583 (Brussels)
Fax +32 228-49583 (Brussels)
Tel. +33 3881-75583 (Strasbourg)
Fax +33 3881-79583 (Strasbourg)
E-mail: biuro@urszulakrupa.pl
Website: http://www.urszulakrupa.pl

Mrs Kathy SINNOTT
Member of the Bureau
Tel. +32 228-45692 (Brussels)
Fax +32 228-49692 (Brussels)
Tel. +33 3881-75692 (Strasbourg)
Fax +33 3881-79692 (Strasbourg)
E-mail: kathy.sinnott@europarl.europa.eu
Website: http://www.kathysinnott.ie

Mr Bernard WOJCIECHOWSKI
Member of the Bureau
Tel. +32 228-45659 (Brussels)
Fax +32 228-49659 (Brussels)
Tel. +33 3881-75659 (Strasbourg)
Fax +33 3881-79659 (Strasbourg)
E-mail: bernard.wojciechowski@europarl.europa.eu
Website: http://www.bernardwojciechowski.pl

Mr Vladimír ŽELEZNÝ
Member of the Bureau
Tel. +32 228-45295 (Brussels)
Fax +32 228-49295 (Brussels)
Tel. +33 3881-75295 (Strasbourg)
Fax +33 3881-79295 (Strasbourg)

Mr Gerard BATTEN
Member
Tel. +32 228-45920 (Brussels)
Fax +32 228-49920 (Brussels)
Tel. +33 3881-75920 (Strasbourg)
Fax +33 3881-79920 (Strasbourg)

Mr Bastiaan BELDER
Member
Tel. +32 228-45270 (Brussels)
Fax +32 228-49270 (Brussels)
Tel. +33 3881-75270 (Strasbourg)
Fax +33 3881-79270 (Strasbourg)
E-mail: bastiaan.belder@europarl.europa.eu
Website: http://www.eurofractie.nl

Mr Godfrey BLOOM
Member
Tel. +32 228-45469 (Brussels)
Fax +32 228-49469 (Brussels)
Tel. +33 3881-75469 (Strasbourg)
Fax +33 3881-79469 (Strasbourg)

Mr Derek Roland CLARK
Member
Tel. +32 228-45552 (Brussels)
Fax +32 228-49552 (Brussels)
Tel. +33 3881-75552 (Strasbourg)
Fax +33 3881-79552 (Strasbourg)

Mr Trevor COLMAN
Member

Mr Patrick LOUIS
Member
Tel. +32 228-45961 (Brussels)
Fax +32 228-49961 (Brussels)
Tel. +33 3881-75961 (Strasbourg)
Fax +33 3881-79961 (Strasbourg)
E-mail: patrick.louis@europarl.europa.eu
Website: http://www.autre-europe.org

Mr Nils LUNDGREN
Member
Tel. +32 228-45725 (Brussels)
Fax +32 228-49725 (Brussels)
Tel. +33 3881-75725 (Strasbourg)
Fax +33 3881-79725 (Strasbourg)

Mr Michael Henry NATTRASS
Member
Tel. +32 228-45133 (Brussels)
Fax +32 228-49133 (Brussels)
Tel. +33 3881-75133 (Strasbourg)
Fax +33 3881-79133 (Strasbourg)

Mr Jeffrey TITFORD
Member
Tel. +32 228-45758 (Brussels)
Fax +32 228-49758 (Brussels)
Tel. +33 3881-75758 (Strasbourg)
Fax +33 3881-79758 (Strasbourg)
Website: http://www.jeffreytitfordmep.co.uk

Mr Witold TOMCZAK
Member
Tel. +32 228-45241 (Brussels)
Fax +32 228-49241 (Brussels)
Tel. +33 3881-75241 (Strasbourg)
Fax +33 3881-79241 (Strasbourg)

Mr Philippe de VILLIERS
Member
Tel. +32 228-45895 (Brussels)
Fax +32 228-49895 (Brussels)
Tel. +33 3881-75895 (Strasbourg)
Fax +33 3881-79895 (Strasbourg)

Mr John WHITTAKER
Member
Tel. +32 228-45169 (Brussels)
Fax +32 228-49169 (Brussels)
Tel. +33 3881-75169 (Strasbourg)
Fax +33 3881-79169 (Strasbourg)

NON-ATTACHED MEMBERS

Mr Jim ALLISTER
Member
Tel. +32 228-45275 (Brussels)
Fax +32 228-49275 (Brussels)
Tel. +33 3881-75275 (Strasbourg)
Fax +33 3881-79275 (Strasbourg)
Website: http://www.jimallister.org

Mr Peter BACO
Member
Tel. +32 228-45247 (Brussels)
Fax +32 228-49247 (Brussels)
Tel. +33 3881-75247 (Strasbourg)
Fax +33 3881-79247 (Strasbourg)
Website: http://www.peterbaco.eu

Mrs Irena BELOHORSKÁ
Member
Tel. +32 228-45251 (Brussels)
Fax +32 228-49251 (Brussels)
Tel. +33 3881-75251 (Strasbourg)
Fax +33 3881-79251 (Strasbourg)
Website: http://www.irenabelohorska.sk

Mr Slavi BINEV
Member
Tel. +32 228-45311 (Brussels)
Fax +32 228-49311 (Brussels)
Tel. +33 3881-75311 (Strasbourg)
Fax +33 3881-79311 (Strasbourg)
E-mail: slavi.binev@europarl.europa.eu
Website: http://www.slavibinev.com

Mrs Jana BOBOŠÍKOVÁ
Member
Tel. +32 228-45284 (Brussels)
Fax +32 228-49284 (Brussels)
Tel. +33 3881-75284 (Strasbourg)
Fax +33 3881-79284 (Strasbourg)
E-mail: tvosecka@euparlament.com
Website: http://www.bobosikova.cz

Mr Desislav CHUKOLOV
Member
Tel. +32 228-45379 (Brussels)
Fax +32 228-49379 (Brussels)
Tel. +33 3881-75379 (Strasbourg)
Fax +33 3881-79379 (Strasbourg)
E-mail: desislav.chukolov@europarl.europa.eu
Website: http://www.desislav.com

Mr Philip CLAEYS
Member
Tel. +32 228-45281 (Brussels)
Fax +32 228-49281 (Brussels)
Tel. +33 3881-75281 (Strasbourg)
Fax +33 3881-79281 (Strasbourg)
E-mail: philip.claeys@europarl.europa.eu
Website: http://www.philipclaeys.be

Mr Koenraad DILLEN
Member
Tel. +32 228-45282 (Brussels)
Fax +32 228-49282 (Brussels)
Tel. +33 3881-75282 (Strasbourg)
Fax +33 3881-79282 (Strasbourg)
E-mail: koen.dillen@skynet.be

Mr Roberto FIORE
Member
Tel. +32 228-45517 (Brussels)
Fax +32 228-49517 (Brussels)
Tel. +33 3881-75517 (Strasbourg)
Fax +33 3881-79517 (Strasbourg)
E-mail: roberto.fiore@europarl.europa.eu
Website: http://www.robertofiore.org

Mr Maciej Marian GIERTYCH
Member
Tel. +32 228-45237 (Brussels)
Fax +32 228-49237 (Brussels)
Tel. +33 3881-75237 (Strasbourg)
Fax +33 3881-79237 (Strasbourg)
E-mail: maciejmarian.giertych@europarl.europa.eu
Website: http://www.giertych.pl

Mr Bruno GOLLNISCH
Member
Tel. +32 228-45265 (Brussels)
Fax +32 228-49265 (Brussels)
Tel. +33 3881-75265 (Strasbourg)
Fax +33 3881-79265 (Strasbourg)
Website: http://www.gollnisch.com

Mr Daniel HANNAN
Member
Tel. +32 228-45137 (Brussels)
Fax +32 228-49137 (Brussels)
Tel. +33 3881-75137 (Strasbourg)
Fax +33 3881-79137 (Strasbourg)
E-mail: daniel.hannan@europarl.europa.eu
Website: http://www.hannan.co.uk

Mr Roger HELMER
Member
Tel. +32 228-45764 (Brussels)
Fax +32 228-49764 (Brussels)
Tel. +33 3881-75764 (Strasbourg)
Fax +33 3881-79764 (Strasbourg)
E-mail: roger.helmer@europarl.europa.eu
Website: http://www.rogerhelmer.com

Mr Robert KILROY-SILK
Member
Tel. +32 228-45195 (Brussels)
Fax +32 228-49195 (Brussels)
Tel. +33 3881-75195 (Strasbourg)
Fax +33 3881-79195 (Strasbourg)

Mr Roger KNAPMAN
Member
Tel. +32 228-45559 (Brussels)
Fax +32 228-49559 (Brussels)
Tel. +33 3881-75559 (Strasbourg)
Fax +33 3881-79559 (Strasbourg)
E-mail: roger.knapman@europarl.europa.eu

Mr Sergej KOZLÍK
Member
Tel. +32 228-45257 (Brussels)
Fax +32 228-49257 (Brussels)
Tel. +33 3881-75257 (Strasbourg)
Fax +33 3881-79257 (Strasbourg)
Website: http://www.sergejkozlik.sk

Mr Carl LANG
Member
Tel. +32 228-45261 (Brussels)
Fax +32 228-49261 (Brussels)
Tel. +33 3881-75261 (Strasbourg)
Fax +33 3881-79261 (Strasbourg)
Website: http://www.carl-lang.com

Mr Jean-Marie LE PEN
Member
Tel. +32 228-45720 (Brussels)
Fax +32 228-49720 (Brussels)
Tel. +33 3881-75720 (Strasbourg)
Fax +33 3881-79720 (Strasbourg)

Mrs Marine LE PEN
Member
Tel. +32 228-45709 (Brussels)
Fax +32 228-49709 (Brussels)
Tel. +33 3881-75709 (Strasbourg)
Fax +33 3881-79709 (Strasbourg)

Mr Fernand LE RACHINEL
Member
Tel. +32 228-45183 (Brussels)
Fax +32 228-49183 (Brussels)
Tel. +33 3881-75183 (Strasbourg)
Fax +33 3881-79183 (Strasbourg)

Mr Hans-Peter MARTIN
Member
Tel. +32 228-45157 (Brussels)
Fax +32 228-49157 (Brussels)
Tel. +33 3881-75157 (Strasbourg)
Fax +33 3881-79157 (Strasbourg)
Website: http://www.hpmartin.net

Mr Jean-Claude MARTINEZ
Member
Tel. +32 228-45968 (Brussels)
Fax +32 228-49968 (Brussels)
Tel. +33 3881-75968 (Strasbourg)
Fax +33 3881-79968 (Strasbourg)

Mr Andreas MÖLZER
Member
Tel. +32 228-45141 (Brussels)
Fax +32 228-49141 (Brussels)
Tel. +33 3881-75141 (Strasbourg)
Fax +33 3881-79141 (Strasbourg)
E-mail: a.moelzer@aon.at
Website: http://www.andreas-moelzer.at

Mr Ashley MOTE
Member
Tel. +32 228-45747 (Brussels)
Fax +32 228-49747 (Brussels)
Tel. +33 3881-75747 (Strasbourg)
Fax +33 3881-79747 (Strasbourg)
E-mail: ashley.mote@europarl.europa.eu
Website: http://www.ashleymote.co.uk

Mr Giovanni RIVERA
Member
Tel. +32 228-45524 (Brussels)
Fax +32 228-49524 (Brussels)
Tel. +33 3881-75524 (Strasbourg)
Fax +33 3881-79524 (Strasbourg)

Mr Luca ROMAGNOLI
Member
Tel. +32 228-45530 (Brussels)
Fax +32 228-49530 (Brussels)
Tel. +33 3881-75530 (Strasbourg)
Fax +33 3881-79530 (Strasbourg)

Mrs Lydia SCHENARDI
Member
Tel. +32 228-45256 (Brussels)
Fax +32 228-49256 (Brussels)
Tel. +33 3881-75256 (Strasbourg)
Fax +33 3881-79256 (Strasbourg)

Mr Dimitar STOYANOV
Member
Tel. +32 228-45654 (Brussels)
Fax +32 228-49654 (Brussels)
Tel. +33 3881-75654 (Strasbourg)
Fax +33 3881-79654 (Strasbourg)
E-mail: dimitar.stoyanov@europarl.europa.eu
Website: http://www.ataka.bg

Mr Frank VANHECKE
Member
Tel. +32 228-45108 (Brussels)
Fax +32 228-49108 (Brussels)
Tel. +33 3881-75108 (Strasbourg)
Fax +33 3881-79108 (Strasbourg)

Mr Thomas WISE
Member
Tel. +32 228-45598 (Brussels)
Fax +32 228 49598 (Brussels)
Tel. +33 3881-75598 (Strasbourg)
Fax +33 3881-79598 (Strasbourg)
E-mail: thomas.wise@europarl.europa.eu
Website: http://www.tomwisemep.co.uk

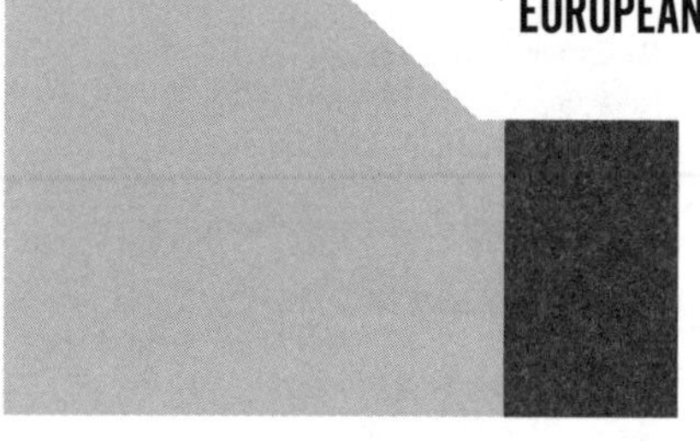

Parliamentary committees

COMMITTEE ON FOREIGN AFFAIRS

Mr Jacek SARYUSZ-WOLSKI
Chairman

Mr Michael GAHLER
Vice-Chairman

Mr Janusz ONYSZKIEWICZ
Vice-Chairman

Mr Ioan Mircea PAŞCU
Vice-Chairman

Mr Libor ROUČEK
Vice-Chairman

Mr Vittorio AGNOLETTO
Member

Sir Robert ATKINS
Member

Mr Christopher BEAZLEY
Member

Mrs Angelika BEER
Member

Mr Bastiaan BELDER
Member

Mrs Monika BEŇOVÁ
Member

Mr Adam BIELAN
Member

Mr Vito BONSIGNORE
Member

Mr André BRIE
Member

Mr Elmar BROK
Member

Mr Colm BURKE
Member

Mr Marco CAPPATO
Member

Mr Philip CLAEYS
Member

Mr Paul Marie COÛTEAUX
Member

Mrs Véronique DE KEYSER
Member

Mr Giorgos DIMITRAKOPOULOS
Member

Mrs Hélène FLAUTRE
Member

Mrs Hanna FOLTYN-KUBICKA
Member

Mr Jas GAWRONSKI
Member

Mr Georgios GEORGIOU
Member

Mr Maciej Marian GIERTYCH
Member

Mrs Ana Maria GOMES
Member

Mr Alfred GOMOLKA
Member

Mr Klaus HÄNSCH
Member

Mr Richard HOWITT
Member

Mrs Jana HYBÁŠKOVÁ
Member

Mrs Anna IBRISAGIC
Member

Mr Jelko KACIN
Member

Mr Ioannis KASOULIDES
Member

Mr Metin KAZAK
Member

Mrs Maria Eleni KOPPA
Member

Mr Helmut KUHNE
Member

Mr Joost LAGENDIJK
Member

Mr Vytautas LANDSBERGIS
Member

Mr Johannes LEBECH
Member

Mr Emilio MENÉNDEZ del VALLE
Member

Mr Willy MEYER PLEITE
Member

Mr Francisco José MILLÁN MON
Member

Mr Philippe MORILLON
Member

Mrs Pasqualina NAPOLETANO
Member

Mrs Annemie NEYTS-UYTTEBROECK
Member

Baroness NICHOLSON OF WINTERBOURNE
Member

Mr Raimon OBIOLS i GERMÀ
Member

Mr Vural ÖGER
Member

Mr Cem ÖZDEMIR
Member

Mrs Ria OOMEN-RUIJTEN
Member

Mr Justas Vincas PALECKIS
Member

Mrs Béatrice PATRIE
Member

Mr Alojz PETERLE
Member

Mr Tobias PFLÜGER
Member

Mr João de Deus PINHEIRO
Member

Mr Mirosław Mariusz PIOTROWSKI
Member

Mr Hubert PIRKER
Member

Mr Samuli POHJAMO
Member

Mrs Lydie POLFER
Member

Mr Miguel PORTAS
Member

Mr Bernd POSSELT
Member

Mr Poul Nyrup RASMUSSEN
Member

Mr Michel ROCARD
Member

Mr Raül ROMEVA i RUEDA
Member

Mr Christian ROVSING
Member

Mr Flaviu Călin RUS
Member

Mrs Katrin SAKS
Member

Mr José Ignacio SALAFRANCA SÁNCHEZ-NEYRA
Member

Mr György SCHÖPFLIN
Member

Mr Marek SIWIEC
Member

Mr Hannes SWOBODA
Member

Mr István SZENT-IVÁNYI
Member

Mr Konrad SZYMAŃSKI
Member

Dr Charles TANNOCK
Member

Mrs Inese VAIDERE
Member

Mr Geoffrey VAN ORDEN
Member

Ari VATANEN
Member

Mr Marcello VERNOLA
Member

Mr Kristian VIGENIN
Member

Andrzej WIELOWIEYSKI
Member

Mr Jan Marinus WIERSMA
Member

Mr Luis YAÑEZ-BARNUEVO GARCÍA
Member

Mr Zbigniew ZALESKI
Member

Mr Josef ZIELENIEC
Member

Mrs Laima Liucija ANDRIKIENĖ
Substitute

Mrs Roberta ANGELILLI
Substitute

Mr Francisco ASSIS
Substitute

Mrs Maria BADIA i CUTCHET
Substitute

Mrs Mariela Velichkova BAEVA
Substitute

Mr Gerard BATTEN
Substitute

Mrs Irena BELOHORSKÁ
Substitute

Mr Cristian Silviu BUŞOI
Substitute

Mrs Marie-Arlette CARLOTTI
Substitute

Mr David CASA
Substitute

Mr Giulietto CHIESA
Substitute

Mr Ryszard CZARNECKI
Substitute

Mr Dragoş Florin DAVID
Substitute

Mr Jean-Luc DEHAENE
Substitute

Mr Gianni DE MICHELIS
Substitute

Mrs Marielle DE SARNEZ
Substitute

Mr Nirj DEVA
Substitute

Mrs Alexandra DOBOLYI
Substitute

Mr Andrew DUFF
Substitute

Árpád DUKA-ZÓLYOMI
Substitute

Mr Saïd EL KHADRAOUI
Substitute

Mr James ELLES
Substitute

Mr Jonathan EVANS
Substitute

Mr Carlo FATUZZO
Substitute

Mr Glyn FORD
Substitute

Mrs Kinga GÁL
Substitute

Mr Patrick GAUBERT
Substitute

Mr Martí GRAU i SEGÚ
Substitute

Mr David HAMMERSTEIN
Substitute

Mr Milan HORÁČEK
Substitute

Mrs Marie Anne ISLER BÉGUIN
Substitute

Anneli JÄÄTTEENMÄKI
Substitute

Mr Georg JARZEMBOWSKI
Substitute

Mr Pierre JONCKHEER
Substitute

Mr Aurelio JURI
Substitute

Mrs Gisela KALLENBACH
Substitute

Mr Tunne KELAM
Substitute

Mr Evgeni KIRILOV
Substitute

Mr Jaromír KOHLÍČEK
Substitute

Mr Christoph KONRAD
Substitute

Mr Miloš KOTEREC
Substitute

Mr Ģirts Valdis KRISTOVSKIS
Substitute

Alexander Graf LAMBSDORFF
Substitute

Mr Kurt Joachim LAUK
Substitute

Mr Jo LEINEN
Substitute

Mr Jean-Marie LE PEN
Substitute

Mr Peter LIESE
Substitute

Mr Antonio LÓPEZ-ISTÚRIZ WHITE
Substitute

Baroness Sarah LUDFORD
Substitute

Mr Jules MAATEN
Substitute

Mr Edward McMILLAN-SCOTT
Substitute

Mr Marios MATSAKIS
Substitute

Mr Yiannakis MATSIS
Substitute

Mr Mario MAURO
Substitute

Mr Jaime MAYOR OREJA
Substitute

Mr Erik MEIJER
Substitute

Mr Íñigo MÉNDEZ DE VIGO
Substitute

Mr Nickolay MLADENOV
Substitute

Mr Miroslav OUZKÝ
Substitute

Mrs Doris PACK
Substitute

Mr Athanasios PAFILIS
Substitute

Mrs Maria Grazia PAGANO
Substitute

Mr Rihards PĪKS
Substitute

Mr Józef PINIOR
Substitute

Mr Luís QUEIRÓ
Substitute

Mrs Godelieve QUISTHOUDT-ROWOHL
Substitute

Mrs Frédérique RIES
Substitute

Mr Marco RIZZO
Substitute

Mr Bogusław ROGALSKI
Substitute

Mr Dariusz ROSATI
Substitute

Mr Wojciech ROSZKOWSKI
Substitute

Mrs Mechtild ROTHE
Substitute

Mr Aloyzas SAKALAS
Substitute

Mr Antolín SÁNCHEZ PRESEDO
Substitute

Mr Sebastiano SANZARELLO
Substitute

Mr Pierre SCHAPIRA
Substitute

Mrs Inger SEGELSTRÖM
Substitute

Mr Adrian SEVERIN
Substitute

Mrs Kathy SINNOTT
Substitute

Mr Jean SPAUTZ
Substitute

Mr Csaba Sándor TABAJDI
Substitute

Mr Johan VAN HECKE
Substitute

Mr Karl von WOGAU
Substitute

Mr Bernard WOJCIECHOWSKI
Substitute

Mr Francis WURTZ
Substitute

COMMITTEE ON DEVELOPMENT

Mr Josep BORRELL FONTELLES
Chairman

Mr Thijs BERMAN
Vice-Chairman

Mrs Danutė BUDREIKAITĖ
Vice-Chairwoman

Mrs Romana JORDAN CIZELJ
Vice-Chairwoman

Mr Frithjof SCHMIDT
Vice-Chairman

Mrs Margrete AUKEN
Member

Mr Alessandro BATTILOCCHIO
Member

Mrs Marie-Arlette CARLOTTI
Member

Mr Thierry CORNILLET
Member

Mrs Corina CREȚU
Member

Mr Ryszard CZARNECKI
Member

Mr Nirj DEVA
Member

Mr Koenraad DILLEN
Member

Mrs Alexandra DOBOLYI
Member

Mr Beniamino DONNICI
Member

Mr Fernando FERNÁNDEZ MARTÍN
Member

Mr Juan FRAILE CANTÓN
Member

Mrs Hélène GOUDIN
Member

Mr Alain HUTCHINSON
Member

Mrs Madeleine JOUYE DE GRANDMAISON
Member

Mr Filip KACZMAREK
Member

Mrs Glenys KINNOCK
Member

Mrs Maria MARTENS
Member

Mr Gay MITCHELL
Member

Mrs Luisa MORGANTINI
Member

Mr José Javier POMÉS RUIZ
Member

Mr Horst POSDORF
Member

Mr José RIBEIRO E CASTRO
Member

Mr Toomas SAVI
Member

Mr Pierre SCHAPIRA
Member

Mr Jürgen SCHRÖDER
Member

Mrs Feleknas UCA
Member

Mr Johan VAN HECKE
Member

Mrs Anna ZÁBORSKÁ
Member

Mr Jan ZAHRADIL
Member

Mr Mauro ZANI
Member

Mrs Marie-Hélène AUBERT
Substitute

Mrs Maria BERGER
Substitute

Mr John BOWIS
Substitute

Mr Carlo CASINI
Substitute

Mrs Françoise CASTEX
Substitute

Mr Călin Cătălin CHIRIȚĂ
Substitute

Mr Paul Marie COÛTEAUX
Substitute

Mr Roberto FIORE
Substitute

Mrs Ana Maria GOMES
Substitute

Mrs Fiona HALL
Substitute

Mr Mikel IRUJO AMEZAGA
Substitute

Mr Jan Jerzy KUŁAKOWSKI
Substitute

Mr Raymond LANGENDRIES
Substitute

Mr Bernard LEHIDEUX
Substitute

Mrs Elizabeth LYNNE
Substitute

Mrs Linda McAVAN
Substitute

Mr Miguel Angel MARTÍNEZ MARTÍNEZ
Substitute

Mr Manolis MAVROMMATIS
Substitute

Mr Willy MEYER PLEITE
Substitute

Mr Francisco José MILLÁN MON
Substitute

Mrs Pasqualina NAPOLETANO
Substitute

Mr Csaba ŐRY
Substitute

Mr Atanas PAPARIZOV
Substitute

Mr Tobias PFLÜGER
Substitute

Mr Józef PINIOR
Substitute

Mr Eoin RYAN
Substitute

Mrs Tokia SAÏFI
Substitute

Mr Horst SCHNELLHARDT
Substitute

Mrs Anne VAN LANCKER
Substitute

Mr Ralf WALTER
Substitute

Mrs Renate WEBER
Substitute

Mrs Åsa WESTLUND
Substitute

Mr Anders WIJKMAN
Substitute

Mrs Iva ZANICCHI
Substitute

Mrs Gabriele ZIMMER
Substitute

COMMITTEE ON INTERNATIONAL TRADE

Mr Helmuth MARKOV
Chairman

Mr Ignasi GUARDANS CAMBÓ
Vice-Chairman

Mrs Cristiana MUSCARDINI
Vice-Chairwoman

Mrs Godelieve QUISTHOUDT-ROWOHL
Vice-Chairwoman

Mrs Corien WORTMANN-KOOL
Vice-Chairwoman

Mr Kader ARIF
Member

Mr Francisco ASSIS
Member

Mr Carlos CARNERO GONZÁLEZ
Member

Mr Daniel CASPARY
Member

Mrs Françoise CASTEX
Member

Mr Nigel FARAGE
Member

Mr Christofer FJELLNER
Member

Mr Glyn FORD
Member

Mr Béla GLATTFELDER
Member

Mr Jacky HÉNIN
Member

Mr Krzysztof HOŁOWCZYC
Member

Mr Syed KAMALL
Member

Mr Ģirts Valdis KRISTOVSKIS
Member

Mr Jean-Marie LE PEN
Member

Mr Alain LIPIETZ
Member

Mrs Caroline LUCAS
Member

Mrs Marusya Ivanova LYUBCHEVA
Member

Mrs Erika MANN
Member

Mr David MARTIN
Member

Mr Vural ÖGER
Member

Mr Georgios PAPASTAMKOS
Member

Mrs Tokia SAÏFI
Member

Mr Peter ŠŤASTNÝ
Member

Mr Robert STURDY
Member

Mr David SUMBERG
Member

Mr Gianluca SUSTA
Member

Mr Daniel VARELA SUANZES-CARPEGNA
Member

Mr Iuliu WINKLER
Member

Mr Vittorio AGNOLETTO
Substitute

Mr Stavros ARNAOUTAKIS
Substitute

Mr Jean-Pierre AUDY
Substitute

Mr Bastiaan BELDER
Substitute

Mr Sebastian Valentin BODU
Substitute

Mr Reimer BÖGE
Substitute

Mrs Danutė BUDREIKAITĖ
Substitute

Mr Giorgio CAROLLO
Substitute

Mr Ole CHRISTENSEN
Substitute

Mr Joseph DAUL
Substitute

Mr Harlem DÉSIR
Substitute

Mr Albert DESS
Substitute

Mrs Elisa FERREIRA
Substitute

Mr Vasco GRAÇA MOURA
Substitute

Mr Jens HOLM
Substitute

Mr Sajjad KARIM
Substitute

Mrs Glenys KINNOCK
Substitute

Mrs Pia Elda LOCATELLI
Substitute

Mr Eugenijus MALDEIKIS
Substitute

Mr Jan Tadeusz MASIEL
Substitute

Mr Javier MORENO SÁNCHEZ
Substitute

Sirpa PIETIKÄINEN
Substitute

Mrs Rovana PLUMB
Substitute

Mr Bernd POSSELT
Substitute

Mrs Zuzana ROITHOVÁ
Substitute

Mr Salvador Domingo SANZ PALACIO
Substitute

Mr Carl SCHLYTER
Substitute

Mr Frithjof SCHMIDT
Substitute

Mr Ivo STREJČEK
Substitute

Hannu TAKKULA
Substitute

Mr Jan Marinus WIERSMA
Substitute

Mr Zbigniew ZALESKI
Substitute

COMMITTEE ON BUDGETS

Mr Reimer BÖGE
Chairman

Mr Janusz LEWANDOWSKI
Vice-Chairman

Mr Umberto PIRILLI
Vice-Chairman

Kyösti VIRRANKOSKI
Vice-Chairman

Mr Ralf WALTER
Vice-Chairman

Mrs Laima Liucija ANDRIKIENĖ
Member

Mr Richard James ASHWORTH
Member

Mr Glenn BEDINGFIELD
Member

Mr Herbert BÖSCH
Member

Mr Costas BOTOPOULOS
Member

Mr Simon BUSUTTIL
Member

Mr Paulo CASACA
Member

Mr Daniel DĂIANU
Member

Mr Gérard DEPREZ
Member

Mr Valdis DOMBROVSKIS
Member

Mrs Brigitte DOUAY
Member

Mr James ELLES
Member

Mr Göran FÄRM
Member

Mr Hynek FAJMON
Member

Mr Szabolcs FAZAKAS
Member

Mr Markus FERBER
Member

Mr Vicente Miguel GARCÉS RAMÓN
Member

Mr Salvador GARRIGA POLLEDO
Member

Mrs Ingeborg GRÄSSLE
Member

Mrs Nathalie GRIESBECK
Member

Mrs Catherine GUY-QUINT
Member

Mrs Jutta HAUG
Member

Ville ITÄLÄ
Member

Mrs Anne E. JENSEN
Member

Mrs Silvana KOCH-MEHRIN
Member

Mr Sergej KOZLÍK
Member

Mr Wiesław Stefan KUC
Member

Mr Zbigniew Krzysztof KUŹMIUK
Member

Mr Alain LAMASSOURE
Member

Mrs Eleonora LO CURTO
Member

Mr Nils LUNDGREN
Member

Mr Vladimír MAŇKA
Member

Mr Mario MAURO
Member

Mr Jan MULDER
Member

Mr Gérard ONESTA
Member

Mr Gianni PITTELLA
Member

Mr Margaritis SCHINAS
Member

Esko SEPPÄNEN
Member

Mrs Nina ŠKOTTOVÁ
Member

Mr Theodor Dumitru STOLOJAN
Member

Mr László SURJÁN
Member

Mr Gary TITLEY
Member

Mrs Helga TRÜPEL
Member

Mr Thijs BERMAN
Substitute

Mr Fabio CIANI
Substitute

Mr Daniel COHN-BENDIT
Substitute

Mr Richard CORBETT
Substitute

Mrs Bárbara DÜHRKOP DÜHRKOP
Substitute

Mr Michael GAHLER
Substitute

Mr Georgios GEORGIOU
Substitute

Mr Alfred GOMOLKA
Substitute

Mr Friedrich-Wilhelm GRAEFE zu BARINGDORF
Substitute

Mrs Lissy GRÖNER
Substitute

Mrs Jana HYBÁŠKOVÁ
Substitute

Mrs Romana JORDAN CIZELJ
Substitute

Mrs Ewa KLAMT
Substitute

Mr Holger KRAHMER
Substitute

Mrs Constanze Angela KREHL
Substitute

Mrs Esther de LANGE
Substitute

Mr Bogusław LIBERADZKI
Substitute

Mrs Marusya Ivanova LYUBCHEVA
Substitute

Mrs Mairead McGUINNESS
Substitute

Mr Hans-Peter MARTIN
Substitute

Mr Jean-Claude MARTINEZ
Substitute

Mr Emilio MENÉNDEZ del VALLE
Substitute

Mr Juan Andrés NARANJO ESCOBAR
Substitute

Baroness NICHOLSON OF WINTERBOURNE
Substitute

Mr Péter OLAJOS
Substitute

Mr Seán Ó NEACHTAIN
Substitute

Mr Rihards PĪKS
Substitute

Mr José Javier POMÉS RUIZ
Substitute

Mr Giovanni ROBUSTI
Substitute

Mrs Ulrike RODUST
Substitute

Mr Libor ROUČEK
Substitute

Mrs Martine ROURE
Substitute

Mr Paul RÜBIG
Substitute

Mr Jacek SARYUSZ-WOLSKI
Substitute

Mr José Albino SILVA PENEDA
Substitute

Mrs Margarita STARKEVIČIŪTĖ
Substitute

Mr Peter ŠŤASTNÝ
Substitute

Mr Gianluca SUSTA
Substitute

Mr Andrzej Jan SZEJNA
Substitute

Mr István SZENT-IVÁNYI
Substitute

Mr Michel TEYCHENNÉ
Substitute

Mr Alejo VIDAL-QUADRAS
Substitute

Mr Lars WOHLIN
Substitute

Mr Janusz WOJCIECHOWSKI
Substitute

Mr Francis WURTZ
Substitute

Mr Tomáš ZATLOUKAL
Substitute

COMMITTEE ON BUDGETARY CONTROL

Mr Herbert BÖSCH
Chairman

Mr Petr DUCHOŇ
Vice-Chairman

Mr Bogusław LIBERADZKI
Vice-Chairman

Mr Nils LUNDGREN
Vice-Chairman

Mr Bill NEWTON DUNN
Vice-Chairman

Mr Jean-Pierre AUDY
Member

Mrs Inés AYALA SENDER
Member

Mr Costas BOTOPOULOS
Member

Mr Paul van BUITENEN
Member

Mrs Ieke van den BURG
Member

Mr Mogens CAMRE
Member

Mr Paulo CASACA
Member

Mr Jorgo CHATZIMARKAKIS
Member

Mr Antonio DE BLASIO
Member

Mr James ELLES
Member

Mr Szabolcs FAZAKAS
Member

Mr Markus FERBER
Member

Mr Christofer FJELLNER
Member

Mr Lutz GOEPEL
Member

Mrs Ingeborg GRÄSSLE
Member

Mr Umberto GUIDONI
Member

Ville ITÄLÄ
Member

Mr Dan JØRGENSEN
Member

Mr Aurelio JURI
Member

Mrs Rodi KRATSA-TSAGAROPOULOU
Member

Mrs Esther de LANGE
Member

Mrs Eleonora LO CURTO
Member

Mrs Marusya Ivanova LYUBCHEVA
Member

Mr Hans-Peter MARTIN
Member

Mrs Eluned MORGAN
Member

Mr Ashley MOTE
Member

Mr Jan MULDER
Member

Mr Marco PANNELLA
Member

Mr Aldo PATRICIELLO
Member

Mr José Javier POMÉS RUIZ
Member

Mr Søren Bo SØNDERGAARD
Member

Mr Bart STAES
Member

Mr Jeffrey TITFORD
Member

Kyösti VIRRANKOSKI
Member

Mr Janusz WOJCIECHOWSKI
Member

Mr Milan CABRNOCH
Substitute

Mr Richard CORBETT
Substitute

Mrs Hanne DAHL
Substitute

Mr Chris DAVIES
Substitute

Mr Valdis DOMBROVSKIS
Substitute

Mrs Bárbara DÜHRKOP DÜHRKOP
Substitute

Mr Salvador GARRIGA POLLEDO
Substitute

Mr Robert GOEBBELS
Substitute

Mr Dariusz Maciej GRABOWSKI
Substitute

Mrs Cristina GUTIÉRREZ-CORTINES
Substitute

Mr Christopher HEATON-HARRIS
Substitute

Mrs Edit HERCZOG
Substitute

Mr Jens HOLM
Substitute

Mrs Silvana KOCH-MEHRIN
Substitute

Eija-Riitta KORHOLA
Substitute

Mrs Erika MANN
Substitute

Mrs Véronique MATHIEU
Substitute

Mr Juan Andrés NARANJO ESCOBAR
Substitute

Mr Jan OLBRYCHT
Substitute

Mr Pierre PRIBETICH
Substitute

Mr Wojciech ROSZKOWSKI
Substitute

Mr Paul RÜBIG
Substitute

Mr Carl SCHLYTER
Substitute

Esko SEPPÄNEN
Substitute

Mrs Margarita STARKEVIČIŪTĖ
Substitute

Mrs Gabriele STAUNER
Substitute

Mrs Petya STAVREVA
Substitute

Mr Andrzej Jan SZEJNA
Substitute

Mrs Helga TRÜPEL
Substitute

Mr Ralf WALTER
Substitute

COMMITTEE ON ECONOMIC AND MONETARY AFFAIRS

Mrs Pervenche BERÈS
Chairwoman

Mr José Manuel GARCÍA-MARGALLO Y MARFIL
Vice-Chairman

Mr Louis GRECH
Vice-Chairman

Mr Guntars KRASTS
Vice-Chairman

Mr John PURVIS
Vice-Chairman

Mr Rapisardo ANTINUCCI
Member

Mrs Mariela Velichkova BAEVA
Member

Mr Paolo BARTOLOZZI
Member

Mr Zsolt László BECSEY
Member

Mr Slavi BINEV
Member

Mr Sebastian Valentin BODU
Member

Mrs Sharon BOWLES
Member

Mr Udo BULLMANN
Member

Mrs Ieke van den BURG
Member

Mr David CASA
Member

Mr Christian EHLER
Member

Mr Jonathan EVANS
Member

Mrs Elisa FERREIRA
Member

Mr Jean-Paul GAUZÈS
Member

Mr Robert GOEBBELS
Member

Mr Bruno GOLLNISCH
Member

Mrs Donata GOTTARDI
Member

Mr Dariusz Maciej GRABOWSKI
Member

Mr Benoît HAMON
Member

Mr Gunnar HÖKMARK
Member

Mr Karsten Friedrich HOPPENSTEDT
Member

Mrs Sophia in 't VELD
Member

Mr Othmar KARAS
Member

Mr Wolf KLINZ
Member

Mr Christoph KONRAD
Member

Mr Kurt Joachim LAUK
Member

Mr Andrea LOSCO
Member

Mrs Astrid LULLING
Member

Mr Hans-Peter MARTIN
Member

Mr Gay MITCHELL
Member

Sirpa PIETIKÄINEN
Member

Mr Bernhard RAPKAY
Member

Mr Dariusz ROSATI
Member

Mrs Heide RÜHLE
Member

Mr Eoin RYAN
Member

Mr Antolín SÁNCHEZ PRESEDO
Member

Mr Manuel António dos SANTOS
Member

Mr Salvador Domingo SANZ PALACIO
Member

Mr Olle SCHMIDT
Member

Mr Peter SKINNER
Member

Mrs Margarita STARKEVIČIŪTĖ
Member

Mr Ivo STREJČEK
Member

Mr Cornelis VISSER
Member

Mrs Sahra WAGENKNECHT
Member

Mr John WHITTAKER
Member

Mr Jan ANDERSSON
Substitute

Mr Enrique BARÓN CRESPO
Substitute

Mrs Katerina BATZELI
Substitute

Mrs Jana BOBOŠÍKOVÁ
Substitute

Mr Daniel CASPARY
Substitute

Mrs Pilar del CASTILLO VERA
Substitute

Mr Jorgo CHATZIMARKAKIS
Substitute

Mr Daniel DĂIANU
Substitute

Mr Dragoş Florin DAVID
Substitute

Mrs Mia DE VITS
Substitute

Mr Valdis DOMBROVSKIS
Substitute

Mr Konstantinos DROUTSAS
Substitute

Mr Petr DUCHOŇ
Substitute

Mr Harald ETTL
Substitute

Mr Robert EVANS
Substitute

Mr Salvador GARRIGA POLLEDO
Substitute

Mrs Catherine GUY-QUINT
Substitute

Mr Ján HUDACKÝ
Substitute

Mr Syed KAMALL
Substitute

Mr Zbigniew Krzysztof KUŹMIUK
Substitute

Mr Werner LANGEN
Substitute

Mr Klaus-Heiner LEHNE
Substitute

Mr Janusz LEWANDOWSKI
Substitute

Mr Alain LIPIETZ
Substitute

Mr Patrick LOUIS
Substitute

Baroness Sarah LUDFORD
Substitute

Mr Vladimír MAŇKA
Substitute

Mr Thomas MANN
Substitute

Mr Sérgio MARQUES
Substitute

Mr Ashley MOTE
Substitute

Mr Janusz ONYSZKIEWICZ
Substitute

Mr Josu ORTUONDO LARREA
Substitute

Mr Umberto PIRILLI
Substitute

Mr Gianni PITTELLA
Substitute

Mrs Bilyana Ilieva RAEVA
Substitute

Mr Poul Nyrup RASMUSSEN
Substitute

Mrs Karin RIIS-JØRGENSEN
Substitute

Mr Gilles SAVARY
Substitute

Mr Margaritis SCHINAS
Substitute

Mr Andreas SCHWAB
Substitute

Mr Theodor Dumitru STOLOJAN
Substitute

Mr Kristian VIGENIN
Substitute

Mr Henri WEBER
Substitute

Mr Karl von WOGAU
Substitute

Mr Lars WOHLIN
Substitute

Mrs Corien WORTMANN-KOOL
Substitute

Mr Andrzej Tomasz ZAPAŁOWSKI
Substitute

Mr Josef ZIELENIEC
Substitute

COMMITTEE ON EMPLOYMENT AND SOCIAL AFFAIRS

Mr Jan ANDERSSON
Chairman

Mr Jean Louis COTTIGNY
Vice-Chairman

Mrs Ilda FIGUEIREDO
Vice-Chairwoman

Mrs Elizabeth LYNNE
Vice-Chairwoman

Mr Thomas MANN
Vice-Chairman

Edit BAUER
Member

Mr Jean-Luc BENNAHMIAS
Member

Mr Iles BRAGHETTO
Member

Mr Philip BUSHILL-MATTHEWS
Member

Mr Milan CABRNOCH
Member

Mr Alejandro CERCAS
Member

Mr Ole CHRISTENSEN
Member

Mr Derek Roland CLARK
Member

Mr Luigi COCILOVO
Member

Mr Jan CREMERS
Member

Mr Proinsias DE ROSSA
Member

Mr Harlem DÉSIR
Member

Mr Harald ETTL
Member

Mr Richard FALBR
Member

Mr Carlo FATUZZO
Member

Mr Joel HASSE FERREIRA
Member

Mr Roger HELMER
Member

Mr Stephen HUGHES
Member

Mrs Karin JÖNS
Member

Mrs Ona JUKNEVIČIENĖ
Member

Mr Sajjad KARIM
Member

Mr Jan Jerzy KUŁAKOWSKI
Member

Mrs Jean LAMBERT
Member

Mr Carl LANG
Member

Mr Raymond LANGENDRIES
Member

Mr Bernard LEHIDEUX
Member

Mrs Mary Lou McDONALD
Member

Mr Jan Tadeusz MASIEL
Member

Mr Jiří MAŠTÁLKA
Member

Mrs Maria MATSOUKA
Member

Mrs Elisabeth MORIN
Member

Mr Juan Andrés NARANJO ESCOBAR
Member

Mr Csaba ŐRY
Member

Mrs Siiri OVIIR
Member

Mrs Marie PANAYOTOPOULOS-CASSIOTOU
Member

Mr Pier Antonio PANZERI
Member

Mrs Rovana PLUMB
Member

Mr Jacek PROTASIEWICZ
Member

Mrs Bilyana Ilieva RAEVA
Member

Mrs Elisabeth SCHROEDTER
Member

Mr José Albino SILVA PENEDA
Member

Mrs Kathy SINNOTT
Member

Mr Jean SPAUTZ
Member

Mrs Gabriele STAUNER
Member

Ewa TOMASZEWSKA
Member

Mrs Anne VAN LANCKER
Member

Mrs Gabriele ZIMMER
Member

Mrs Elspeth ATTWOOLL
Substitute

Mr Jean Marie BEAUPUY
Substitute

Mr Erminio Enzo BOSO
Substitute

Mr Mihael BREJC
Substitute

Mr Udo BULLMANN
Substitute

Mr Martin CALLANAN
Substitute

Mrs Françoise CASTEX
Substitute

Mrs Corina CREŢU
Substitute

Mrs Gabriela CREŢU
Substitute

Mrs Véronique DE KEYSER
Substitute

Mr Gintaras DIDŽIOKAS
Substitute

Mr Beniamino DONNICI
Substitute

Mrs Donata GOTTARDI
Substitute

Mrs Marian HARKIN
Substitute

Mrs Ruth HIERONYMI
Substitute

Mr Richard HOWITT
Substitute

Mrs Anna IBRISAGIC
Substitute

Mrs Rumiana JELEVA
Substitute

Mrs Anne E. JENSEN
Substitute

Mr Dieter-Lebrecht KOCH
Substitute

Mrs Magda KÓSÁNÉ KOVÁCS
Substitute

Mr Sepp KUSSTATSCHER
Substitute

Lasse LEHTINEN
Substitute

Mrs Jamila MADEIRA
Substitute

Mrs Viktória MOHÁCSI
Substitute

Mr Claude MORAES
Substitute

Mr Roberto MUSACCHIO
Substitute

Mrs Ria OOMEN-RUIJTEN
Substitute

Mr Dimitrios PAPADIMOULIS
Substitute

Mrs Agnes SCHIERHUBER
Substitute

Mr Csaba SÓGOR
Substitute

Mrs María SORNOSA MARTÍNEZ
Substitute

Mr Struan STEVENSON
Substitute

Mrs Patrizia TOIA
Substitute

Mr Georgios TOUSSAS
Substitute

Mr Kyriacos TRIANTAPHYLLIDES
Substitute

Mr Claude TURMES
Substitute

Mrs Evangelia TZAMPAZI
Substitute

Mr Thomas ULMER
Substitute

Mr Frank VANHECKE
Substitute

Mr Geoffrey VAN ORDEN
Substitute

Mr Yannick VAUGRENARD
Substitute

Mrs Barbara WEILER
Substitute

Mrs Anja WEISGERBER
Substitute

Mrs Glenis WILLMOTT
Substitute

Mrs Iva ZANICCHI
Substitute

Mrs Tatjana ŽDANOKA
Substitute

COMMITTEE ON THE ENVIRONMENT, PUBLIC HEALTH AND FOOD SAFETY

Mr Miroslav OUZKÝ
Chairman

Mr Johannes BLOKLAND
Vice-Chairman

Mr Magor Imre CSIBI
Vice-Chairman

Satu HASSI
Vice-Chairwoman

Mr Dan JØRGENSEN
Vice-Chairman

Mr Adamos ADAMOU
Member

Mr Georgs ANDREJEVS
Member

Mrs Margrete AUKEN
Member

Mr Liam AYLWARD
Member

Mrs Pilar AYUSO
Member

Mrs Irena BELOHORSKÁ
Member

Mrs Maria BERGER
Member

Mr John BOWIS
Member

Mrs Frieda BREPOELS
Member

Mrs Hiltrud BREYER
Member

Mr Martin CALLANAN
Member

Mrs Dorette CORBEY
Member

Mr Chris DAVIES
Member

Mrs Avril DOYLE
Member

Mrs Mojca DRČAR MURKO
Member

Mrs Edite ESTRELA
Member

Mrs Jill EVANS
Member

Mrs Anne FERREIRA
Member

Mr Karl-Heinz FLORENZ
Member

Mr Alessandro FOGLIETTA
Member

Mrs Elisabetta GARDINI
Member

Mr Matthias GROOTE
Member

Mrs Françoise GROSSETÊTE
Member

Mrs Cristina GUTIÉRREZ-CORTINES
Member

Mr Gyula HEGYI
Member

Mr Jens HOLM
Member

Mrs Marie Anne ISLER BÉGUIN
Member

Mrs Caroline JACKSON
Member

Mrs Christa KLASS
Member

Eija-Riitta KORHOLA
Member

Mr Holger KRAHMER
Member

Mrs Urszula KRUPA
Member

Mr Aldis KUŠĶIS
Member

Mrs Marie-Noëlle LIENEMANN
Member

Mr Peter LIESE
Member

Mr Jules MAATEN
Member

Mrs Linda McAVAN
Member

Mr Marios MATSAKIS
Member

Mr Roberto MUSACCHIO
Member

Riitta MYLLER
Member

Mr Péter OLAJOS
Member

Mr Vladko Todorov PANAYOTOV
Member

Mr Dimitrios PAPADIMOULIS
Member

Mr Vittorio PRODI
Member

Mrs Frédérique RIES
Member

Mrs Dagmar ROTH-BEHRENDT
Member

Mr Guido SACCONI
Member

Mrs Daciana Octavia SÂRBU
Member

Mrs Amalia SARTORI
Member

Mr Carl SCHLYTER
Member

Mr Horst SCHNELLHARDT
Member

Mr Richard SEEBER
Member

Mrs Kathy SINNOTT
Member

Mr Bogusław SONIK
Member

Mrs María SORNOSA MARTÍNEZ
Member

Mr Salvatore TATARELLA
Member

Mr Antonios TRAKATELLIS
Member

Mrs Evangelia TZAMPAZI
Member

Mr Thomas ULMER
Member

Mrs Anja WEISGERBER
Member

Mrs Åsa WESTLUND
Member

Mr Anders WIJKMAN
Member

Mrs Glenis WILLMOTT
Member

Mr Kader ARIF
Substitute

Mrs Inés AYALA SENDER
Substitute

Mr Sergio BERLATO
Substitute

Mr Giovanni BERLINGUER
Substitute

Mr Iles BRAGHETTO
Substitute

Mrs Kathalijne Maria BUITENWEG
Substitute

Mr Nicodim BULZESC
Substitute

Mr Philip BUSHILL-MATTHEWS
Substitute

Mr Niels BUSK
Substitute

Mr Philippe BUSQUIN
Substitute

Mr Jerzy BUZEK
Substitute

Mr Luis Manuel CAPOULAS SANTOS
Substitute

Mr Marco CAPPATO
Substitute

Mr David CASA
Substitute

Mrs Hanne DAHL
Substitute

Mr Antonio DE BLASIO
Substitute

Mrs Bairbre de BRÚN
Substitute

Mrs Jolanta DIČKUTĖ
Substitute

Mr Antoine DUQUESNE
Substitute

Mrs Lena EK
Substitute

Mr Christofer FJELLNER
Substitute

Mrs Monica FRASSONI
Substitute

Mr Duarte FREITAS
Substitute

Mr Milan GAĽA
Substitute

Mr Adam GIEREK
Substitute

Mr Maciej Marian GIERTYCH
Substitute

Mr Ioannis GKLAVAKIS
Substitute

Mrs Hélène GOUDIN
Substitute

Mrs Genowefa GRABOWSKA
Substitute

Mr Ambroise GUELLEC
Substitute

Mr Umberto GUIDONI
Substitute

Mrs Rebecca HARMS
Substitute

Mrs Jutta HAUG
Substitute

Mrs Erna HENNICOT-SCHOEPGES
Substitute

Mrs Esther HERRANZ GARCÍA
Substitute

Mr Karsten Friedrich HOPPENSTEDT
Substitute

Mrs Karin JÖNS
Substitute

Mr Miloš KOTEREC
Substitute

Mr Stavros LAMBRINIDIS
Substitute

Mr Vytautas LANDSBERGIS
Substitute

Mr Raymond LANGENDRIES
Substitute

Mrs Anne LAPERROUZE
Substitute

Henrik LAX
Substitute

Mr Johannes LEBECH
Substitute

Mr Stéphane LE FOLL
Substitute

Mrs Kartika Tamara LIOTARD
Substitute

Mrs Caroline LUCAS
Substitute

Mr David MARTIN
Substitute

Mr Jiří MAŠTÁLKA
Substitute

Mr Miroslav MIKOLÁŠIK
Substitute

Mrs Eluned MORGAN
Substitute

Mrs Cristiana MUSCARDINI
Substitute

Mr Hartmut NASSAUER
Substitute

Mr Lambert van NISTELROOIJ
Substitute

Mr Justas Vincas PALECKIS
Substitute

Mr Alojz PETERLE
Substitute

Mrs Renate SOMMER
Substitute

Mr Bart STAES
Substitute

Mr Ulrich STOCKMANN
Substitute

Mr Robert STURDY
Substitute

Mr Andres TARAND
Substitute

Mrs Marianne THYSSEN
Substitute

Mr Claude TURMES
Substitute

Mrs Inese VAIDERE
Substitute

Mr Donato Tommaso VERALDI
Substitute

Mr Marcello VERNOLA
Substitute

Mr Philippe de VILLIERS
Substitute

COMMITTEE ON INDUSTRY, RESEARCH AND ENERGY

Mrs Angelika NIEBLER
Chairwoman

Mrs Anne LAPERROUZE
Vice-Chairwoman

Mr Aldo PATRICIELLO
Vice-Chairman

Mr Miloslav RANSDORF
Vice-Chairman

Mrs Catherine TRAUTMANN
Vice-Chairwoman

Mr John ATTARD-MONTALTO
Member

Mr Šarūnas BIRUTIS
Member

Mr Jan BŘEZINA
Member

Mr Philippe BUSQUIN
Member

Mr Jerzy BUZEK
Member

Mrs Pilar del CASTILLO VERA
Member

Mr Jorgo CHATZIMARKAKIS
Member

Mr Giles CHICHESTER
Member

Mr Dragoş Florin DAVID
Member

Mr Gianni DE MICHELIS
Member

Mr Den DOVER
Member

Mrs Lena EK
Member

Mrs Nicole FONTAINE
Member

Mr Adam GIEREK
Member

Mr Norbert GLANTE
Member

Mr Umberto GUIDONI
Member

Mr András GYÜRK
Member

Mrs Fiona HALL
Member

Mr David HAMMERSTEIN
Member

Mrs Rebecca HARMS
Member

Mrs Erna HENNICOT-SCHOEPGES
Member

Mrs Mary HONEYBALL
Member

Mr Ján HUDACKÝ
Member

Mrs Romana JORDAN CIZELJ
Member

Mr Werner LANGEN
Member

Mrs Pia Elda LOCATELLI
Member

Mr Patrick LOUIS
Member

Mr Eugenijus MALDEIKIS
Member

Mrs Eluned MORGAN
Member

Mr Antonio MUSSA
Member

Reino PAASILINNA
Member

Mr Atanas PAPARIZOV
Member

Mrs Francisca PLEGUEZUELOS AGUILAR
Member

Mrs Anni PODIMATA
Member

Mr Vladimír REMEK
Member

Mr Herbert REUL
Member

Mrs Teresa RIERA MADURELL
Member

Mrs Mechtild ROTHE
Member

Mr Paul RÜBIG
Member

Mrs Amalia SARTORI
Member

Mrs Lydia SCHENARDI
Member

Mr Andres TARAND
Member

Mrs Britta THOMSEN
Member

Mrs Patrizia TOIA
Member

Mr Claude TURMES
Member

Mr Nikolaos VAKALIS
Member

Mrs Adina-Ioana VĂLEAN
Member

Mr Alejo VIDAL-QUADRAS
Member

Mrs Dominique VLASTO
Member

Mr Gabriele ALBERTINI
Substitute

Mr Alexander ALVARO
Substitute

Mr Jean-Pierre AUDY
Substitute

Mrs Pilar AYUSO
Substitute

Mrs Etelka BARSI-PATAKY
Substitute

Mr Ivo BELET
Substitute

Mr Josep BORRELL FONTELLES
Substitute

Mrs Danutė BUDREIKAITĖ
Substitute

Mr Daniel CASPARY
Substitute

Mr Zdzisław Kazimierz CHMIELEWSKI
Substitute

Mrs Dorette CORBEY
Substitute

Mr Thierry CORNILLET
Substitute

Mrs Avril DOYLE
Substitute

Mr Christian EHLER
Substitute

Mr Göran FÄRM
Substitute

Mrs Hélène FLAUTRE
Substitute

Mr Juan FRAILE CANTÓN
Substitute

Mrs Neena GILL
Substitute

Mr Robert GOEBBELS
Substitute

Mr Matthias GROOTE
Substitute

Mrs Françoise GROSSETÊTE
Substitute

Mrs Cristina GUTIÉRREZ-CORTINES
Substitute

Mr Malcolm HARBOUR
Substitute

Satu HASSI
Substitute

Mr Jacky HÉNIN
Substitute

Mrs Edit HERCZOG
Substitute

Mr Gunnar HÖKMARK
Substitute

Mr Mieczysław Edmund JANOWSKI
Substitute

Eija-Riitta KORHOLA
Substitute

Mr Vincenzo LAVARRA
Substitute

Mr Fernand LE RACHINEL
Substitute

Mrs Marie-Noëlle LIENEMANN
Substitute

Mr Florencio LUQUE AGUILAR
Substitute

Mr Toine MANDERS
Substitute

Mrs Erika MANN
Substitute

Mr Lambert van NISTELROOIJ
Substitute

Mr João de Deus PINHEIRO
Substitute

Mr Paweł Bartłomiej PISKORSKI
Substitute

Mr Pierre PRIBETICH
Substitute

Mr Vittorio PRODI
Substitute

Mr John PURVIS
Substitute

Mr Bernhard RAPKAY
Substitute

Mr Manuel António dos SANTOS
Substitute

Esko SEPPÄNEN
Substitute

Mr Peter SKINNER
Substitute

Mr Alyn SMITH
Substitute

Mr Dirk STERCKX
Substitute

Mr Hannes SWOBODA
Substitute

Mrs Silvia-Adriana ŢICĂU
Substitute

Mr Antonios TRAKATELLIS
Substitute

Mr Vladimir URUTCHEV
Substitute

Mrs Sahra WAGENKNECHT
Substitute

Mr Roberts ZĪLE
Substitute

COMMITTEE ON THE INTERNAL MARKET AND CONSUMER PROTECTION

Mrs Arlene McCARTHY
Chairwoman

Eija-Riitta KORHOLA
Vice-Chairwoman

Alexander Graf LAMBSDORFF
Vice-Chairman

Mr Marco RIZZO
Vice-Chairman

Mrs Zuzana ROITHOVÁ
Vice-Chairwoman

Mr Cristian Silviu BUŞOI
Member

Mr Mogens CAMRE
Member

Mrs Charlotte CEDERSCHIÖLD
Member

Mr Desislav CHUKOLOV
Member

Mrs Gabriela CREŢU
Member

Mrs Mia DE VITS
Member

Mrs Janelly FOURTOU
Member

Mrs Evelyne GEBHARDT
Member

Mrs Hélène GOUDIN
Member

Mr Martí GRAU i SEGÚ
Member

Mrs Małgorzata HANDZLIK
Member

Mr Malcolm HARBOUR
Member

Mr Christopher HEATON-HARRIS
Member

Mrs Anna HEDH
Member

Mrs Edit HERCZOG
Member

Mrs Iliana Malinova IOTOVA
Member

Mr Pierre JONCKHEER
Member

Mr Kurt LECHNER
Member

Lasse LEHTINEN
Member

Mr Toine MANDERS
Member

Mrs Catiuscia MARINI
Member

Mr Nickolay MLADENOV
Member

Mrs Catherine NERIS
Member

Mr Bill NEWTON DUNN
Member

Mrs Zita PLEŠTINSKÁ
Member

Mr Guido PODESTÀ
Member

Mrs Karin RIIS-JØRGENSEN
Member

Mr Giovanni RIVERA
Member

Mrs Heide RÜHLE
Member

Mr Leopold Józef RUTOWICZ
Member

Mr Salvador Domingo SANZ PALACIO
Member

Mrs Christel SCHALDEMOSE
Member

Mr Andreas SCHWAB
Member

Mrs Eva-Britt SVENSSON
Member

Mrs Marianne THYSSEN
Member

Mr Jacques TOUBON
Member

Mrs Bernadette VERGNAUD
Member

Mrs Barbara WEILER
Member

Mr Marian ZLOTEA
Member

Mr Emmanouil ANGELAKAS
Substitute

Mr Šarūnas BIRUTIS
Substitute

Mr André BRIE
Substitute

Mr Wolfgang BULFON
Substitute

Mr Colm BURKE
Substitute

Mr Giles CHICHESTER
Substitute

Mrs Giovanna CORDA
Substitute

Mr Jan CREMERS
Substitute

Mr Magor Imre CSIBI
Substitute

Mrs Hanne DAHL
Substitute

Mr Bert DOORN
Substitute

Mrs Brigitte FOURÉ
Substitute

Mr Louis GRECH
Substitute

Mr András GYÜRK
Substitute

Mr Benoît HAMON
Substitute

Mr Joel HASSE FERREIRA
Substitute

Mr Ian HUDGHTON
Substitute

Mr Stephen HUGHES
Substitute

Mr Filip KACZMAREK
Substitute

Mrs Gisela KALLENBACH
Substitute

Mr Syed KAMALL
Substitute

Mr Othmar KARAS
Substitute

Mr Wolf KLINZ
Substitute

Mr Sergej KOZLÍK
Substitute

Mr Guntars KRASTS
Substitute

Mrs Marine LE PEN
Substitute

Mr Andrea LOSCO
Substitute

Mrs Maria MATSOUKA
Substitute

Mr Manuel MEDINA ORTEGA
Substitute

Mrs Angelika NIEBLER
Substitute

Mr Pier Antonio PANZERI
Substitute

Mrs Béatrice PATRIE
Substitute

Mr José Javier POMÉS RUIZ
Substitute

Mr Horst POSDORF
Substitute

Mr José RIBEIRO E CASTRO
Substitute

Mrs Dagmar ROTH-BEHRENDT
Substitute

Mrs Katrin SAKS
Substitute

Mr Olle SCHMIDT
Substitute

Mr Søren Bo SØNDERGAARD
Substitute

Mr Francesco Enrico SPERONI
Substitute

Mr Gary TITLEY
Substitute

Mrs Diana WALLIS
Substitute

Mrs Anja WEISGERBER
Substitute

Mr Stefano ZAPPALA'
Substitute

COMMITTEE ON TRANSPORT AND TOURISM

Mr Paolo COSTA
Chairman

Mr Gabriele ALBERTINI
Vice-Chairman

Mr Luís QUEIRÓ
Vice-Chairman

Mr Gilles SAVARY
Vice-Chairman

Mrs Silvia-Adriana ŢICĂU
Vice-Chairwoman

Mr Robert ATKINS
Member

Mrs Inés AYALA SENDER
Member

Mrs Etelka BARSI-PATAKY
Member

Mr Erminio Enzo BOSO
Member

Mr Sylwester CHRUSZCZ
Member

Mr Michael CRAMER
Member

Mr Arūnas DEGUTIS
Member

Mrs Christine DE VEYRAC
Member

Mr Petr DUCHOŇ
Member

Mr Saïd EL KHADRAOUI
Member

Mr Robert EVANS
Member

Mr Emanuel Jardim FERNANDES
Member

Mr Francesco FERRARI
Member

Mrs Brigitte FOURÉ
Member

Mr Luis de GRANDES PASCUAL
Member

Mr Mathieu GROSCH
Member

Mr Stanisław JAŁOWIECKI
Member

Mr Georg JARZEMBOWSKI
Member

Mr Timothy KIRKHOPE
Member

Mr Dieter-Lebrecht KOCH
Member

Mr Jaromír KOHLÍČEK
Member

Mrs Rodi KRATSA-TSAGAROPOULOU
Member

Mr Sepp KUSSTATSCHER
Member

Mr Jörg LEICHTFRIED
Member

Mr Fernand LE RACHINEL
Member

Mr Bogusław LIBERADZKI
Member

Mrs Eva LICHTENBERGER
Member

Mr Marian-Jean MARINESCU
Member

Mr Erik MEIJER
Member

Mr Michael Henry NATTRASS
Member

Mr Seán Ó NEACHTAIN
Member

Mr Josu ORTUONDO LARREA
Member

Mr Paweł Bartłomiej PISKORSKI
Member

Mr Reinhard RACK
Member

Mrs Ulrike RODUST
Member

Mr Luca ROMAGNOLI
Member

Mr Brian SIMPSON
Member

Mrs Renate SOMMER
Member

Mr Dirk STERCKX
Member

Mr Ulrich STOCKMANN
Member

Mr Michel TEYCHENNÉ
Member

Mr Georgios TOUSSAS
Member

Mr Yannick VAUGRENARD
Member

Mr Armando VENETO
Member

Mr Lars WOHLIN
Member

Mr Roberts ZĪLE
Member

Mr John ATTARD-MONTALTO
Substitute

Mrs Margrete AUKEN
Substitute

Mr Zsolt László BECSEY
Substitute

Mr Adam BIELAN
Substitute

Mr Johannes BLOKLAND
Substitute

Mr Guy BONO
Substitute

Mr Philip BRADBOURN
Substitute

Mr Philip CLAEYS
Substitute

Mr Luigi COCILOVO
Substitute

Mr Jean Louis COTTIGNY
Substitute

Mr Markus FERBER
Substitute

Mr Armando FRANÇA
Substitute

Mr Jas GAWRONSKI
Substitute

Mr Roland GEWALT
Substitute

Mr Bruno GOLLNISCH
Substitute

Mrs Nathalie GRIESBECK
Substitute

Mr Pedro GUERREIRO
Substitute

Mrs Zita GURMAI
Substitute

Mrs Jeanine HENNIS-PLASSCHAERT
Substitute

Mr Jim HIGGINS
Substitute

Mr Krzysztof HOŁOWCZYC
Substitute

Mr Ian HUDGHTON
Substitute

Mrs Caroline JACKSON
Substitute

Mrs Lily JACOBS
Substitute

Mrs Elisabeth JEGGLE
Substitute

Mrs Anne E. JENSEN
Substitute

Mr Dan JØRGENSEN
Substitute

Mr Jelko KACIN
Substitute

Mr Ioannis KASOULIDES
Substitute

Mrs Maria Eleni KOPPA
Substitute

Mr Aldis KUŠĶIS
Substitute

Mr Joost LAGENDIJK
Substitute

Mrs Eleonora LO CURTO
Substitute

Mr Antonio LÓPEZ-ISTÚRIZ WHITE
Substitute

Mr Helmuth MARKOV
Substitute

Mrs Rosa MIGUÉLEZ RAMOS
Substitute

Mr Vural ÖGER
Substitute

Mrs Marie PANAYOTOPOULOS-CASSIOTOU
Substitute

Mr Ioan Mircea PAŞCU
Substitute

Mr Aldo PATRICIELLO
Substitute

Mr Vladimír REMEK
Substitute

Mr Leopold Józef RUTOWICZ
Substitute

Mr Willem SCHUTH
Substitute

Mrs Catherine STIHLER
Substitute

Mr Salvatore TATARELLA
Substitute

Ari VATANEN
Substitute

Mr Oldřich VLASÁK
Substitute

Mrs Dominique VLASTO
Substitute

Mrs Corien WORTMANN-KOOL
Substitute

COMMITTEE ON REGIONAL DEVELOPMENT

Mr Gerardo GALEOTE
Chairman

Mr Rolf BEREND
Vice-Chairman

Mrs Filiz Hakaeva HYUSMENOVA
Vice-Chairwoman

Mr Evgeni KIRILOV
Vice-Chairman

Mr Jan OLBRYCHT
Vice-Chairman

Mr Emmanouil ANGELAKAS
Member

Mr Stavros ARNAOUTAKIS
Member

Mrs Elspeth ATTWOOLL
Member

Mr Jean Marie BEAUPUY
Member

Mrs Jana BOBOŠÍKOVÁ
Member

Mr Victor BOŞTINARU
Member

Mr Wolfgang BULFON
Member

Mr Giorgio CAROLLO
Member

Mr Antonio DE BLASIO
Member

Mrs Bairbre de BRÚN
Member

Mrs Iratxe GARCÍA PÉREZ
Member

Mr Eugenijus GENTVILAS
Member

Mrs Monica GIUNTINI
Member

Mr Ambroise GUELLEC
Member

Mr Pedro GUERREIRO
Member

Mrs Zita GURMAI
Member

Mr Gábor HARANGOZÓ
Member

Mrs Marian HARKIN
Member

Mr Jim HIGGINS
Member

Mr Mieczysław Edmund JANOWSKI
Member

Mrs Rumiana JELEVA
Member

Mrs Gisela KALLENBACH
Member

Mr Tunne KELAM
Member

Mr Miloš KOTEREC
Member

Mrs Constanze Angela KREHL
Member

Mr Florencio LUQUE AGUILAR
Member

Mrs Jamila MADEIRA
Member

Mr Sérgio MARQUES
Member

Mr Miguel Angel MARTÍNEZ MARTÍNEZ
Member

Mr Yiannakis MATSIS
Member

Mr Miroslav MIKOLÁŠIK
Member

Mr Sebastiano (Nello) MUSUMECI
Member

Mr James NICHOLSON
Member

Mr Lambert van NISTELROOIJ
Member

Mrs Maria PETRE
Member

Mr Markus PIEPER
Member

Mr Józef PINIOR
Member

Mr Bernard POIGNANT
Member

Mr Pierre PRIBETICH
Member

Mr Giovanni ROBUSTI
Member

Mr Wojciech ROSZKOWSKI
Member

Mrs Elisabeth SCHROEDTER
Member

Mrs Grażyna STANISZEWSKA
Member

Mrs Catherine STIHLER
Member

Mr Dimitar STOYANOV
Member

Mrs Margie SUDRE
Member

Mr Andrzej Jan SZEJNA
Member

Mr Kyriacos TRIANTAPHYLLIDES
Member

Mr Philippe de VILLIERS
Member

Mr Oldřich VLASÁK
Member

Mr Vladimír ŽELEZNÝ
Member

Mr Vincenzo AITA
Substitute

Mr Rapisardo ANTINUCCI
Substitute

Mr Alfredo ANTONIOZZI
Substitute

Mr Peter BACO
Substitute

Mr Domenico Antonio BASILE
Substitute

Mr Glenn BEDINGFIELD
Substitute

Mr Bastiaan BELDER
Substitute

Mr Jan BŘEZINA
Substitute

Mr Michael CASHMAN
Substitute

Mr Ole CHRISTENSEN
Substitute

Mr Jean-Paul DENANOT
Substitute

Mrs Brigitte DOUAY
Substitute

Mr Den DOVER
Substitute

Mrs Mojca DRČAR MURKO
Substitute

Mrs Jill EVANS
Substitute

Mr Göran FÄRM
Substitute

Mr Richard FALBR
Substitute

Mr Claudio FAVA
Substitute

Mr Emanuel Jardim FERNANDES
Substitute

Mr Fernando FERNÁNDEZ MARTÍN
Substitute

Mr Francesco FERRARI
Substitute

Mr Karl-Heinz FLORENZ
Substitute

Mrs Lidia Joanna GERINGER de OEDENBERG
Substitute

Mr Norbert GLANTE
Substitute

Mr Dariusz Maciej GRABOWSKI
Substitute

Mr Mathieu GROSCH
Substitute

Mr Stanisław JAŁOWIECKI
Substitute

Mrs Madeleine JOUYE DE GRANDMAISON
Substitute

Mr André LAIGNEL
Substitute

Mr Marcin LIBICKI
Substitute

Mrs Eleonora LO CURTO
Substitute

Mrs Ramona Nicole MĂNESCU
Substitute

Riitta MYLLER
Substitute

Mrs Ljudmila NOVAK
Substitute

Mr Vladko Todorov PANAYOTOV
Substitute

Mr Mirosław Mariusz PIOTROWSKI
Substitute

Mrs Francisca PLEGUEZUELOS AGUILAR
Substitute

Mrs Zita PLEŠTINSKÁ
Substitute

Mr Samuli POHJAMO
Substitute

Mrs Christa PRETS
Substitute

Mr Miloslav RANSDORF
Substitute

Mr Flaviu Călin RUS
Substitute

Mr Toomas SAVI
Substitute

Mr Jürgen SCHRÖDER
Substitute

Mr Richard SEEBER
Substitute

Mr Czesław Adam SIEKIERSKI
Substitute

Mr Bart STAES
Substitute

Mr László SURJÁN
Substitute

Mr Nikolaos VAKALIS
Substitute

Mr Daniel VARELA SUANZES-CARPEGNA
Substitute

Mr Riccardo VENTRE
Substitute

Mr Manfred WEBER
Substitute

Mr Iuliu WINKLER
Substitute

COMMITTEE ON AGRICULTURE AND RURAL DEVELOPMENT

Mr Neil PARISH
Chairman

Mr Sergio BERLATO
Vice-Chairman

Mr Friedrich-Wilhelm GRAEFE zu BARINGDORF
Vice-Chairman

Mr Stéphane LE FOLL
Vice-Chairman

Mr Janusz WOJCIECHOWSKI
Vice-Chairman

Mr Vincenzo AITA
Member

Mr Peter BACO
Member

Mr Niels BUSK
Member

Mr Luis Manuel CAPOULAS SANTOS
Member

Mrs Giovanna CORDA
Member

Mr Joseph DAUL
Member

Mr Jean-Paul DENANOT
Member

Mr Albert DESS
Member

Mr Gintaras DIDŽIOKAS
Member

Mr Konstantinos DROUTSAS
Member

Mr Constantin DUMITRIU
Member

Mr Michl EBNER
Member

Mrs Carmen FRAGA ESTÉVEZ
Member

Mr Duarte FREITAS
Member

Mr Ioannis GKLAVAKIS
Member

Mr Lutz GOEPEL
Member

Mr Bogdan GOLIK
Member

Mrs Esther HERRANZ GARCÍA
Member

Mrs Lily JACOBS
Member

Mrs Elisabeth JEGGLE
Member

Mr Heinz KINDERMANN
Member

Mr Vincenzo LAVARRA
Member

Mrs Mairead McGUINNESS
Member

Mr Jean-Claude MARTINEZ
Member

Mrs Véronique MATHIEU
Member

Mrs Rosa MIGUÉLEZ RAMOS
Member

Mr James NICHOLSON
Member

Mr Vincent PEILLON
Member

Mrs María Isabel SALINAS GARCÍA
Member

Mr Sebastiano SANZARELLO
Member

Mrs Agnes SCHIERHUBER
Member

Mr Willem SCHUTH
Member

Mr Czesław Adam SIEKIERSKI
Member

Mr Alyn SMITH
Member

Mrs Petya STAVREVA
Member

Mr Dimitar STOYANOV
Member

Mr Csaba Sándor TABAJDI
Member

Mr Jeffrey TITFORD
Member

Mr László TŐKÉS
Member

Mr Witold TOMCZAK
Member

Mr Donato Tommaso VERALDI
Member

Mr Andrzej Tomasz ZAPAŁOWSKI
Member

Mr Jim ALLISTER
Substitute

Mrs Marie-Hélène AUBERT
Substitute

Mr Liam AYLWARD
Substitute

Mrs Pilar AYUSO
Substitute

Mr Alessandro BATTILOCCHIO
Substitute

Mrs Katerina BATZELI
Substitute

Mr Herbert BÖSCH
Substitute

Mr Giorgio CAROLLO
Substitute

Mr Alejandro CERCAS
Substitute

Mr Jorgo CHATZIMARKAKIS
Substitute

Mr Hynek FAJMON
Substitute

Mrs Ilda FIGUEIREDO
Substitute

Mr Gerardo GALEOTE
Substitute

Mr José Manuel GARCÍA-MARGALLO Y MARFIL
Substitute

Mr Béla GLATTFELDER
Substitute

Mr Gábor HARANGOZÓ
Substitute

Mr Milan HORÁČEK
Substitute

Mrs Christa KLASS
Substitute

Mr Wolfgang KREISSL-DÖRFLER
Substitute

Mr Wiesław Stefan KUC
Substitute

Mrs Esther de LANGE
Substitute

Mrs Anne LAPERROUZE
Substitute

Mrs Roselyne LEFRANÇOIS
Substitute

Mrs Kartika Tamara LIOTARD
Substitute

Mrs Astrid LULLING
Substitute

Mr Hans-Peter MAYER
Substitute

Mr Jan MULDER
Substitute

Mr Sebastiano (Nello) MUSUMECI
Substitute

Mrs Catherine NERIS
Substitute

Mrs Maria PETRE
Substitute

Mr Markus PIEPER
Substitute

Mr Guido PODESTÀ
Substitute

Mr Zdzisław Zbigniew PODKAŃSKI
Substitute

Mrs Karin RESETARITS
Substitute

Mrs Teresa RIERA MADURELL
Substitute

Mr Guido SACCONI
Substitute

Mrs Lydia SCHENARDI
Substitute

Mr Brian SIMPSON
Substitute

Mr Struan STEVENSON
Substitute

Mr Robert STURDY
Substitute

Mr Armando VENETO
Substitute

Mrs Bernadette VERGNAUD
Substitute

Mr Philippe de VILLIERS
Substitute

Kyösti VIRRANKOSKI
Substitute

Mr Vladimír ŽELEZNÝ
Substitute

COMMITTEE ON FISHERIES

Mr Philippe MORILLON
Chairman

Mrs Elspeth ATTWOOLL
Vice-Chairwoman

Mrs Avril DOYLE
Vice-Chairwoman

Mr Pedro GUERREIRO
Vice-Chairman

Mrs Rosa MIGUÉLEZ RAMOS
Vice-Chairwoman

Mr Jim ALLISTER
Member

Mr Stavros ARNAOUTAKIS
Member

Mrs Marie-Hélène AUBERT
Member

Mr Iles BRAGHETTO
Member

Mr Niels BUSK
Member

Mr Luis Manuel CAPOULAS SANTOS
Member

Mr David CASA
Member

Mr Paulo CASACA
Member

Mr Zdzisław Kazimierz CHMIELEWSKI
Member

Mr Emanuel Jardim FERNANDES
Member

Mrs Carmen FRAGA ESTÉVEZ
Member

Mr Duarte FREITAS
Member

Mr Ioannis GKLAVAKIS
Member

Mr Alfred GOMOLKA
Member

Mrs Hélène GOUDIN
Member

Mr Daniel HANNAN
Member

Mr Ian HUDGHTON
Member

Mr Georg JARZEMBOWSKI
Member

Mr Heinz KINDERMANN
Member

Mr Willy MEYER PLEITE
Member

Mrs Marianne MIKKO
Member

Mr Sebastiano (Nello) MUSUMECI
Member

Mr Seán Ó NEACHTAIN
Member

Mrs Maria Grazia PAGANO
Member

Mrs Ulrike RODUST
Member

Mr Luca ROMAGNOLI
Member

Mr Struan STEVENSON
Member

Mrs Catherine STIHLER
Member

Mrs Margie SUDRE
Member

Mr Daniel VARELA SUANZES-CARPEGNA
Member

Mr Philippe de VILLIERS
Member

Mr Cornelis VISSER
Member

Mr Vincenzo AITA
Substitute

Mr Liam AYLWARD
Substitute

Mr Reimer BÖGE
Substitute

Mr Colm BURKE
Substitute

Mr Giorgio CAROLLO
Substitute

Mr Ole CHRISTENSEN
Substitute

Mrs Dorette CORBEY
Substitute

Mr Paolo COSTA
Substitute

Mr Brian CROWLEY
Substitute

Mr Chris DAVIES
Substitute

Mr Constantin DUMITRIU
Substitute

Mr Claudio FAVA
Substitute

Mr Béla GLATTFELDER
Substitute

Mrs Ewa KLAMT
Substitute

Mr Carl LANG
Substitute

Mrs Eleonora LO CURTO
Substitute

Mr Antonio MASIP HIDALGO
Substitute

Mr Jan MULDER
Substitute

Mr Josu ORTUONDO LARREA
Substitute

Mr Neil PARISH
Substitute

Mrs Teresa RIERA MADURELL
Substitute

Mr Raül ROMEVA i RUEDA
Substitute

Mrs María Isabel SALINAS GARCÍA
Substitute

Mr Carl SCHLYTER
Substitute

Mr Czesław Adam SIEKIERSKI
Substitute

Mrs Kathy SINNOTT
Substitute

Mr Riccardo VENTRE
Substitute

Mr Thomas WISE
Substitute

COMMITTEE ON CULTURE AND EDUCATION

Mrs Katerina BATZELI
Chairwoman

Mr Manolis MAVROMMATIS
Vice-Chairman

Mr Pál SCHMITT
Vice-Chairman

Hannu TAKKULA
Vice-Chairman

Mrs Helga TRÜPEL
Vice-Chairwoman

Mrs Maria BADIA i CUTCHET
Member

Mr Domenico Antonio BASILE
Member

Mr Ivo BELET
Member

Mr Giovanni BERLINGUER
Member

Mr Guy BONO
Member

Mr Nicodim BULZESC
Member

Mrs Marielle DE SARNEZ
Member

Mrs Marie-Hélène DESCAMPS
Member

Mrs Jolanta DIČKUTĖ
Member

Mrs Věra FLASAROVÁ
Member

Mr Milan GAĽA
Member

Mrs Claire GIBAULT
Member

Mr Vasco GRAÇA MOURA
Member

Mrs Lissy GRÖNER
Member

Mr Christopher HEATON-HARRIS
Member

Mr Luis HERRERO-TEJEDOR
Member

Mrs Ruth HIERONYMI
Member

Mr Mikel IRUJO AMEZAGA
Member

Mr Robert KILROY-SILK
Member

Mr André LAIGNEL
Member

Mrs Ramona Nicole MĂNESCU
Member

Mrs Marianne MIKKO
Member

Mrs Ljudmila NOVAK
Member

Mrs Doris PACK
Member

Mr Zdzisław Zbigniew PODKAŃSKI
Member

Mrs Christa PRETS
Member

Mrs Karin RESETARITS
Member

Mr Henri WEBER
Member

Mr Thomas WISE
Member

Mr Tomáš ZATLOUKAL
Member

Mr Jean-Luc BENNAHMIAS
Substitute

Mr Rolf BEREND
Substitute

Mr Slavi BINEV
Substitute

Mr Victor BOŞTINARU
Substitute

Mrs Emine BOZKURT
Substitute

Mr Giusto CATANIA
Substitute

Mr Jean-Marie CAVADA
Substitute

Mr Giorgos DIMITRAKOPOULOS
Substitute

Mr Den DOVER
Substitute

Mr Michl EBNER
Substitute

Mr Alessandro FOGLIETTA
Substitute

Mr Gerardo GALEOTE
Substitute

Mr Ignasi GUARDANS CAMBÓ
Substitute

Mrs Marian HARKIN
Substitute

Mr Gyula HEGYI
Substitute

Mrs Erna HENNICOT-SCHOEPGES
Substitute

Mrs Mary HONEYBALL
Substitute

Mrs Lívia JÁRÓKA
Substitute

Mr Mario MAURO
Substitute

Mr Andreas MÖLZER
Substitute

Mrs Viktória MOHÁCSI
Substitute

Mrs Elisabeth MORIN
Substitute

Mr Raimon OBIOLS i GERMÀ
Substitute

Reino PAASILINNA
Substitute

Mrs Maria ROBSAHM
Substitute

Mrs Amalia SARTORI
Substitute

Mrs Christel SCHALDEMOSE
Substitute

Mrs Nina ŠKOTTOVÁ
Substitute

Mr Sérgio SOUSA PINTO
Substitute

Mrs Grażyna STANISZEWSKA
Substitute

Mr Daniel STROŽ
Substitute

Mr László TŐKÉS
Substitute

Ewa TOMASZEWSKA
Substitute

Mrs Catherine TRAUTMANN
Substitute

Mr Cornelis VISSER
Substitute

Mr Jaroslav ZVĚŘINA
Substitute

Mr Tadeusz ZWIEFKA
Substitute

COMMITTEE ON LEGAL AFFAIRS

Mr Giuseppe GARGANI
Chairman

Mrs Lidia Joanna GERINGER de OEDENBERG
Vice-Chairwoman

Mr Francesco Enrico SPERONI
Vice-Chairman

Mr Rainer WIELAND
Vice-Chairman

Mr Carlo CASINI
Member

Mr Giulietto CHIESA
Member

Mr Marek Aleksander CZARNECKI
Member

Mr Bert DOORN
Member

Mrs Monica FRASSONI
Member

Mrs Neena GILL
Member

Mr Othmar KARAS
Member

Mr Klaus-Heiner LEHNE
Member

Mrs Katalin LÉVAI
Member

Mr Marcin LIBICKI
Member

Mr Alain LIPIETZ
Member

Mr Antonio LÓPEZ-ISTÚRIZ WHITE
Member

Mr Antonio MASIP HIDALGO
Member

Mr Hans-Peter MAYER
Member

Mr Manuel MEDINA ORTEGA
Member

Mr Hartmut NASSAUER
Member

Mr Marco PANNELLA
Member

Mr Aloyzas SAKALAS
Member

Mr Daniel STROŽ
Member

Mrs Diana WALLIS
Member

Mr Jaroslav ZVĚŘINA
Member

Mr Tadeusz ZWIEFKA
Member

Mrs Pervenche BERÈS
Substitute

Mr Costas BOTOPOULOS
Substitute

Mrs Sharon BOWLES
Substitute

Mrs Hiltrud BREYER
Substitute

Mrs Ieke van den BURG
Substitute

Mr Mogens CAMRE
Substitute

Mrs Charlotte CEDERSCHIÖLD
Substitute

Mr Brian CROWLEY
Substitute

Mr Jonathan EVANS
Substitute

Mrs Nicole FONTAINE
Substitute

Mrs Janelly FOURTOU
Substitute

Mr Vicente Miguel GARCÉS RAMÓN
Substitute

Mr Jean-Paul GAUZÈS
Substitute

Mr Luis de GRANDES PASCUAL
Substitute

Mr Sajjad KARIM
Substitute

Mr Kurt LECHNER
Substitute

Mrs Eva LICHTENBERGER
Substitute

Mrs Arlene McCARTHY
Substitute

Mr Rareş-Lucian NICULESCU
Substitute

Mr Georgios PAPASTAMKOS
Substitute

Mr Michel ROCARD
Substitute

Mrs Dagmar ROTH-BEHRENDT
Substitute

Mrs Gabriele STAUNER
Substitute

Mr József SZÁJER
Substitute

Mr Jacques TOUBON
Substitute

Mrs Renate WEBER
Substitute

COMMITTEE ON CIVIL LIBERTIES, JUSTICE AND HOME AFFAIRS

Mr Gérard DEPREZ
Chairman

Mr Philip BRADBOURN
Vice-Chairman

Mr Giusto CATANIA
Vice-Chairman

Mrs Kinga GÁL
Vice-Chairwoman

Mr Stavros LAMBRINIDIS
Vice-Chairman

Mr Alexander ALVARO
Member

Mrs Roberta ANGELILLI
Member

Mr Alfredo ANTONIOZZI
Member

Mr Mario BORGHEZIO
Member

Mrs Catherine BOURSIER
Member

Mrs Emine BOZKURT
Member

Mr Mihael BREJC
Member

Mrs Kathalijne Maria BUITENWEG
Member

Mrs Maddalena CALIA
Member

Mr Michael CASHMAN
Member

Mr Jean-Marie CAVADA
Member

Mr Fabio CIANI
Member

Mr Carlos COELHO
Member

Mr Panayiotis DEMETRIOU
Member

Mr Agustín DÍAZ DE MERA GARCÍA CONSUEGRA
Member

Mrs Bárbara DÜHRKOP DÜHRKOP
Member

Mr Claudio FAVA
Member

Mr Roberto FIORE
Member

Mr Armando FRANÇA
Member

Mrs Urszula GACEK
Member

Mr Patrick GAUBERT
Member

Mr Roland GEWALT
Member

Mrs Elly de GROEN-KOUWENHOVEN
Member

Mrs Jeanine HENNIS-PLASSCHAERT
Member

Mrs Lívia JÁRÓKA
Member

Mrs Ewa KLAMT
Member

Mr Roger KNAPMAN
Member

Mrs Magda KÓSÁNÉ KOVÁCS
Member

Mr Wolfgang KREISSL-DÖRFLER
Member

Mrs Esther de LANGE
Member

Henrik LAX
Member

Mrs Roselyne LEFRANÇOIS
Member

Mrs Marine LE PEN
Member

Mrs Kartika Tamara LIOTARD
Member

Baroness Sarah LUDFORD
Member

Mr Jaime MAYOR OREJA
Member

Mrs Viktória MOHÁCSI
Member

Mr Claude MORAES
Member

Mr Javier MORENO SÁNCHEZ
Member

Mr Rareş-Lucian NICULESCU
Member

Mr Athanasios PAFILIS
Member

Mrs Maria Grazia PAGANO
Member

Mr Bogdan PĚK
Member

Mrs Maria ROBSAHM
Member

Mr Bogusław ROGALSKI
Member

Mrs Martine ROURE
Member

Mr Sebastiano SANZARELLO
Member

Mrs Inger SEGELSTRÖM
Member

Mr Csaba SÓGOR
Member

Mr Søren Bo SØNDERGAARD
Member

Mr Vladimir URUTCHEV
Member

Mr Ioannis VARVITSIOTIS
Member

Mr Manfred WEBER
Member

Mrs Renate WEBER
Member

Mrs Tatjana ŽDANOKA
Member

Mr Adamos ADAMOU
Substitute

Edit BAUER
Substitute

Mrs Monika BEŇOVÁ
Substitute

Mrs Frieda BREPOELS
Substitute

Mr Simon BUSUTTIL
Substitute

Mr Marco CAPPATO
Substitute

Mr Carlo CASINI
Substitute

Mrs Charlotte CEDERSCHIÖLD
Substitute

Mrs Christine DE VEYRAC
Substitute

Mr Koenraad DILLEN
Substitute

Mr Giorgos DIMITRAKOPOULOS
Substitute

Mrs Maria da Assunção ESTEVES
Substitute

Mrs Anne FERREIRA
Substitute

Mrs Hanna FOLTYN-KUBICKA
Substitute

Mrs Iratxe GARCÍA PÉREZ
Substitute

Mrs Elisabetta GARDINI
Substitute

Mrs Evelyne GEBHARDT
Substitute

Mrs Monica GIUNTINI
Substitute

Mrs Genowefa GRABOWSKA
Substitute

Mr Ignasi GUARDANS CAMBÓ
Substitute

Mr Luis HERRERO-TEJEDOR
Substitute

Mrs Sophia in 't VELD
Substitute

Mrs Iliana Malinova IOTOVA
Substitute

Ville ITÄLÄ
Substitute

Mr Carlos José ITURGAIZ ANGULO
Substitute

Mrs Ona JUKNEVIČIENĖ
Substitute

Mrs Sylvia-Yvonne KAUFMANN
Substitute

Mr Metin KAZAK
Substitute

Mrs Jean LAMBERT
Substitute

Mr Jörg LEICHTFRIED
Substitute

Mrs Katalin LÉVAI
Substitute

Mrs Mary Lou McDONALD
Substitute

Mr Marian-Jean MARINESCU
Substitute

Mr Antonio MASIP HIDALGO
Substitute

Mrs Marianne MIKKO
Substitute

Mr Bill NEWTON DUNN
Substitute

Mr Cem ÖZDEMIR
Substitute

Mrs Siiri OVIIR
Substitute

Mr Marco PANNELLA
Substitute

Mr Vincent PEILLON
Substitute

Mr Hubert PIRKER
Substitute

Mr Nicolae Vlad POPA
Substitute

Mr Herbert REUL
Substitute

Mr Luca ROMAGNOLI
Substitute

Mrs María Isabel SALINAS GARCÍA
Substitute

Mrs Daciana Octavia SÂRBU
Substitute

Mrs Eva-Britt SVENSSON
Substitute

Mr Konrad SZYMAŃSKI
Substitute

Dr Charles TANNOCK
Substitute

Mrs Adina-Ioana VĂLEAN
Substitute

Mr Johannes VOGGENHUBER
Substitute

Mr Rainer WIELAND
Substitute

Mr Jan ZAHRADIL
Substitute

Mr Stefano ZAPPALA'
Substitute

COMMITTEE ON CONSTITUTIONAL AFFAIRS

Mr Jo LEINEN
Chairman

Anneli JÄÄTTEENMÄKI
Vice-Chairwoman

Mr Timothy KIRKHOPE
Vice-Chairman

Mr Johannes VOGGENHUBER
Vice-Chairman

Mrs Dushana ZDRAVKOVA
Vice-Chairwoman

Mr Jim ALLISTER
Member

Mr Enrique BARÓN CRESPO
Member

Mr Bastiaan BELDER
Member

Mr Daniel COHN-BENDIT
Member

Mr Richard CORBETT
Member

Mr Brian CROWLEY
Member

Mrs Hanne DAHL
Member

Mr Jean-Luc DEHAENE
Member

Mr Andrew DUFF
Member

Mrs Maria da Assunção ESTEVES
Member

Mr Ingo FRIEDRICH
Member

Mrs Genowefa GRABOWSKA
Member

Mr Aurelio JURI
Member

Mrs Sylvia-Yvonne KAUFMANN
Member

Mr Íñigo MÉNDEZ DE VIGO
Member

Mr Andreas MÖLZER
Member

Mr Ashley MOTE
Member

Mr Rihards PĪKS
Member

Mr Adrian SEVERIN
Member

Mr Sérgio SOUSA PINTO
Member

Mr József SZÁJER
Member

Mr Riccardo VENTRE
Member

Andrzej WIELOWIEYSKI
Member

Mr Bernard WOJCIECHOWSKI
Member

Mr Costas BOTOPOULOS
Substitute

Mrs Catherine BOURSIER
Substitute

Mr Elmar BROK
Substitute

Mr Carlos CARNERO GONZÁLEZ
Substitute

Mr Desislav CHUKOLOV
Substitute

Mr Trevor COLMAN
Substitute

Mr Panayiotis DEMETRIOU
Substitute

Mrs Monica FRASSONI
Substitute

Mr Klaus HÄNSCH
Substitute

Mr Daniel HANNAN
Substitute

Mr Roger HELMER
Substitute

Mrs Urszula KRUPA
Substitute

Mr Alain LAMASSOURE
Substitute

Mrs Luisa MORGANTINI
Substitute

Mr Gérard ONESTA
Substitute

Mr Georgios PAPASTAMKOS
Substitute

Mr Bogdan PĔK
Substitute

Sirpa PIETIKÄINEN
Substitute

Mr Bernard POIGNANT
Substitute

Mr Jacek PROTASIEWICZ
Substitute

Mr Reinhard RACK
Substitute

Mr György SCHÖPFLIN
Substitute

Mrs Kathy SINNOTT
Substitute

Mr Luis YAÑEZ-BARNUEVO GARCÍA
Substitute

Mr Mauro ZANI
Substitute

COMMITTEE ON WOMEN'S RIGHTS AND GENDER EQUALITY

Mrs Anna ZÁBORSKÁ
Chairwoman

Mrs Edite ESTRELA
Vice-Chairwoman

Mrs Zita GURMAI
Vice-Chairwoman

Mr Raül ROMEVA i RUEDA
Vice-Chairman

Mrs Eva-Britt SVENSSON
Vice-Chairwoman

Mrs Roberta ANGELILLI
Member

Edit BAUER
Member

Mrs Emine BOZKURT
Member

Mrs Hiltrud BREYER
Member

Mrs Ilda FIGUEIREDO
Member

Mrs Věra FLASAROVÁ
Member

Mrs Nicole FONTAINE
Member

Mrs Claire GIBAULT
Member

Mrs Lissy GRÖNER
Member

Mrs Esther HERRANZ GARCÍA
Member

Anneli JÄÄTTEENMÄKI
Member

Mrs Lívia JÁRÓKA
Member

Mrs Rodi KRATSA-TSAGAROPOULOU
Member

Mrs Urszula KRUPA
Member

Mrs Roselyne LEFRANÇOIS
Member

Mrs Pia Elda LOCATELLI
Member

Mrs Astrid LULLING
Member

Mrs Angelika NIEBLER
Member

Mrs Siiri OVIIR
Member

Mrs Doris PACK
Member

Mrs Marie PANAYOTOPOULOS-CASSIOTOU
Member

Mrs Zita PLEŠTINSKÁ
Member

Mrs Anni PODIMATA
Member

Mrs Christa PRETS
Member

Mrs Karin RESETARITS
Member

Mrs Teresa RIERA MADURELL
Member

Mr Giovanni RIVERA
Member

Mrs Maria ROBSAHM
Member

Mrs Lydia SCHENARDI
Member

Mr Konrad SZYMAŃSKI
Member

Mrs Britta THOMSEN
Member

Mrs Anne VAN LANCKER
Member

Mrs Corien WORTMANN-KOOL
Member

Mrs Iva ZANICCHI
Member

Mr Godfrey BLOOM
Substitute

Mrs Gabriela CREȚU
Substitute

Mrs Véronique DE KEYSER
Substitute

Mrs Lena EK
Substitute

Mrs Jill EVANS
Substitute

Mrs Iratxe GARCÍA PÉREZ
Substitute

Mr Eugenijus GENTVILAS
Substitute

Mrs Lidia Joanna GERINGER de OEDENBERG
Substitute

Mrs Ana Maria GOMES
Substitute

Mrs Donata GOTTARDI
Substitute

Mrs Anna HEDH
Substitute

Mrs Mary HONEYBALL
Substitute

Mrs Filiz Hakaeva HYUSMENOVA
Substitute

Mrs Sophia in 't VELD
Substitute

Mrs Elisabeth JEGGLE
Substitute

Mrs Karin JÖNS
Substitute

Mrs Christa KLASS
Substitute

Mrs Esther de LANGE
Substitute

Mrs Kartika Tamara LIOTARD
Substitute

Mrs Marusya Ivanova LYUBCHEVA
Substitute

Mrs Luisa MORGANTINI
Substitute

Mrs Cristiana MUSCARDINI
Substitute

Mrs Ria OOMEN-RUIJTEN
Substitute

Mrs Maria PETRE
Substitute

Mrs Zuzana ROITHOVÁ
Substitute

Mrs Heide RÜHLE
Substitute

Mrs Petya STAVREVA
Substitute

Mrs Feleknas UCA
Substitute

Mrs Bernadette VERGNAUD
Substitute

Mr Andrzej Tomasz ZAPAŁOWSKI
Substitute

COMMITTEE ON PETITIONS

Mr Marcin LIBICKI
Chairman

Mr Michael CASHMAN
Vice-Chairman

Mr Carlos José ITURGAIZ ANGULO
Vice-Chairman

Mrs Maria MATSOUKA
Vice-Chairwoman

Mrs Kathy SINNOTT
Vice-Chairwoman

Sir Robert ATKINS
Member

Mrs Margrete AUKEN
Member

Mrs Inés AYALA SENDER
Member

Mr Alessandro BATTILOCCHIO
Member

Mr Mario BORGHEZIO
Member

Mr Victor BOŞTINARU
Member

Mr Simon BUSUTTIL
Member

Mr Daniel CASPARY
Member

Mr Paolo COSTA
Member

Mr Proinsias DE ROSSA
Member

Mrs Alexandra DOBOLYI
Member

Mr Glyn FORD
Member

Mrs Janelly FOURTOU
Member

Mrs Lidia Joanna GERINGER de OEDENBERG
Member

Mrs Cristina GUTIÉRREZ-CORTINES
Member

Mr David HAMMERSTEIN
Member

Mrs Marian HARKIN
Member

Lasse LEHTINEN
Member

Mrs Mairead McGUINNESS
Member

Mr David MARTIN
Member

Mr Miguel Angel MARTÍNEZ MARTÍNEZ
Member

Mr Manolis MAVROMMATIS
Member

Mr Willy MEYER PLEITE
Member

Mr Gay MITCHELL
Member

Mrs Marie PANAYOTOPOULOS-CASSIOTOU
Member

Mr José Javier POMÉS RUIZ
Member

Mr Nicolae Vlad POPA
Member

Mr Eoin RYAN
Member

Mr Andreas SCHWAB
Member

Mr Richard SEEBER
Member

Mr Frank VANHECKE
Member

Mrs Diana WALLIS
Member

Mr Rainer WIELAND
Member

Mr Alexander ALVARO
Substitute

Mr Ivo BELET
Substitute

Mr Jean-Luc BENNAHMIAS
Substitute

Mr Thijs BERMAN
Substitute

Mr André BRIE
Substitute

Mr Carlos CARNERO GONZÁLEZ
Substitute

Mr Brian CROWLEY
Substitute

Mrs Marie-Hélène DESCAMPS
Substitute

Mr Georgios GEORGIOU
Substitute

Mr András GYÜRK
Substitute

Mr Roger HELMER
Substitute

Mr Mieczysław Edmund JANOWSKI
Substitute

Henrik LAX
Substitute

Mr Yiannakis MATSIS
Substitute

Mrs Cristiana MUSCARDINI
Substitute

Mr Juan Andrés NARANJO ESCOBAR
Substitute

Mrs María SORNOSA MARTÍNEZ
Substitute

Mrs Grażyna STANISZEWSKA
Substitute

Mrs Margie SUDRE
Substitute

Mr Andrzej Jan SZEJNA
Substitute

Mrs Tatjana ŽDANOKA
Substitute

Mrs Dushana ZDRAVKOVA
Substitute

Temporary committees

TEMPORARY COMMITTEE ON CLIMATE CHANGE

Mr Guido SACCONI
Chairman

Mr Liam AYLWARD
Vice-Chairman

Mrs Rebecca HARMS
Vice-Chairwoman

Mr Roberto MUSACCHIO
Vice-Chairman

Mr Vittorio PRODI
Vice-Chairman

Mrs Etelka BARSI-PATAKY
Member

Mrs Katerina BATZELI
Member

Mr Ivo BELET
Member

Mrs Maria BERGER
Member

Mr Johannes BLOKLAND
Member

Mr John BOWIS
Member

Mr Philippe BUSQUIN
Member

Mr Jerzy BUZEK
Member

Mrs Pilar del CASTILLO VERA
Member

Mr Giles CHICHESTER
Member

Mrs Dorette CORBEY
Member

Mr Chris DAVIES
Member

Mrs Avril DOYLE
Member

Mrs Lena EK
Member

Mrs Edite ESTRELA
Member

Mr Karl-Heinz FLORENZ
Member

Mr Alessandro FOGLIETTA
Member

Mr Duarte FREITAS
Member

Mr Adam GIEREK
Member

Mr Robert GOEBBELS
Member

Mr Matthias GROOTE
Member

Mrs Françoise GROSSETÊTE
Member

Satu HASSI
Member

Mr Roger HELMER
Member

Mrs Jeanine HENNIS-PLASSCHAERT
Member

Mr Jens HOLM
Member

Mr Dan JØRGENSEN
Member

Mrs Romana JORDAN CIZELJ
Member

Mr Dieter-Lebrecht KOCH
Member

Eija-Riitta KORHOLA
Member

Mr Holger KRAHMER
Member

Mrs Anne LAPERROUZE
Member

Henrik LAX
Member

Mrs Marie-Noëlle LIENEMANN
Member

Mrs Linda McAVAN
Member

Mr Marian-Jean MARINESCU
Member

Riitta MYLLER
Member

Mr Lambert van NISTELROOIJ
Member

Mr Dimitrios PAPADIMOULIS
Member

Mr Markus PIEPER
Member

Mr Herbert REUL
Member

Mr Luca ROMAGNOLI
Member

Mrs Amalia SARTORI
Member

Mrs María SORNOSA MARTÍNEZ
Member

Mr Csaba Sándor TABAJDI
Member

Mr Andres TARAND
Member

Mrs Silvia-Adriana ŢICĂU
Member

Mr Antonios TRAKATELLIS
Member

Mr Claude TURMES
Member

Mrs Adina-Ioana VĂLEAN
Member

Mr Alejo VIDAL-QUADRAS
Member

Mrs Åsa WESTLUND
Member

Mr Anders WIJKMAN
Member

Mrs Iva ZANICCHI
Member

Mr Adamos ADAMOU
Substitute

Mr Georgs ANDREJEVS
Substitute

Mrs Laima Liucija ANDRIKIENĖ
Substitute

Mr Richard James ASHWORTH
Substitute

Mrs Inés AYALA SENDER
Substitute

Mrs Pilar AYUSO
Substitute

Mrs Jana BOBOŠÍKOVÁ
Substitute

Mr Luis Manuel CAPOULAS SANTOS
Substitute

Mr David CASA
Substitute

Mr Giulietto CHIESA
Substitute

Mr Paolo COSTA
Substitute

Mr Michael CRAMER
Substitute

Mrs Bairbre de BRÚN
Substitute

Mr Michl EBNER
Substitute

Mr Robert EVANS
Substitute

Mrs Anne FERREIRA
Substitute

Mrs Elisa FERREIRA
Substitute

Mr Umberto GUIDONI
Substitute

Mrs Cristina GUTIÉRREZ-CORTINES
Substitute

Mrs Catherine GUY-QUINT
Substitute

Mrs Fiona HALL
Substitute

Mrs Erna HENNICOT-SCHOEPGES
Substitute

Mr Gunnar HÖKMARK
Substitute

Mrs Lily JACOBS
Substitute

Anneli JÄÄTTEENMÄKI
Substitute

Mr Timothy KIRKHOPE
Substitute

Mr Aldis KUŠĶIS
Substitute

Mr Zbigniew Krzysztof KUŹMIUK
Substitute

Mr Werner LANGEN
Substitute

Mr Vincenzo LAVARRA
Substitute

Mr Johannes LEBECH
Substitute

Mr Peter LIESE
Substitute

Mrs Caroline LUCAS
Substitute

Mr Jules MAATEN
Substitute

Mr David MARTIN
Substitute

Mrs Rosa MIGUÉLEZ RAMOS
Substitute

Mrs Eluned MORGAN
Substitute

Mr Ashley MOTE
Substitute

Mrs Cristiana MUSCARDINI
Substitute

Mr Bill NEWTON DUNN
Substitute

Mrs Angelika NIEBLER
Substitute

Mr Péter OLAJOS
Substitute

Mr Miroslav OUZKÝ
Substitute

Mr Justas Vincas PALECKIS
Substitute

Mrs Zita PLEŠTINSKÁ
Substitute

Mrs Dagmar ROTH-BEHRENDT
Substitute

Mrs Mechtild ROTHE
Substitute

Mr Paul RÜBIG
Substitute

Mrs Agnes SCHIERHUBER
Substitute

Mrs Kathy SINNOTT
Substitute

Mr Bogusław SONIK
Substitute

Mr Bart STAES
Substitute

Mr Dirk STERCKX
Substitute

Mr Ulrich STOCKMANN
Substitute

Mr Jacques TOUBON
Substitute

Mrs Evangelia TZAMPAZI
Substitute

Mr Thomas ULMER
Substitute

Mrs Inese VAIDERE
Substitute

Mr Nikolaos VAKALIS
Substitute

Interparliamentary delegations

DELEGATION FOR RELATIONS WITH SWITZERLAND, ICELAND AND NORWAY AND TO THE EUROPEAN ECONOMIC AREA (EEA) JOINT PARLIAMENTARY COMMITTEE

Mrs Bilyana Ilieva RAEVA
Chairwoman

Mrs Hanne DAHL
Vice-Chairwoman

Mr Aloyzas SAKALAS
Vice-Chairman

Mrs Etelka BARSI-PATAKY
Member

Mr Lutz GOEPEL
Member

Mr Mieczysław Edmund JANOWSKI
Member

Mrs Katalin LÉVAI
Member

Mrs Mary Lou McDONALD
Member

Mrs Marie PANAYOTOPOULOS-CASSIOTOU
Member

Mrs Dagmar ROTH-BEHRENDT
Member

Mr Paul RÜBIG
Member

Mr Willem SCHUTH
Member

Mrs Nina ŠKOTTOVÁ
Member

Mr Alyn SMITH
Member

Mrs Catherine STIHLER
Member

Mr Frank VANHECKE
Member

Mrs Diana WALLIS
Member

Mrs Roberta ANGELILLI
Substitute

Mrs Danutė BUDREIKAITĖ
Substitute

Mrs Jolanta DIČKUTĖ
Substitute

Mrs Bárbara DÜHRKOP DÜHRKOP
Substitute

Mrs Edit HERCZOG
Substitute

Mr Jens HOLM
Substitute

Mr Ján HUDACKÝ
Substitute

Mr Syed KAMALL
Substitute

Mr Timothy KIRKHOPE
Substitute

Mr Wolf KLINZ
Substitute

Mr Carl LANG
Substitute

Mrs Heide RÜHLE
Substitute

Mr Andreas SCHWAB
Substitute

Mr Peter SKINNER
Substitute

Mr Thomas ULMER
Substitute

DELEGATION FOR RELATIONS WITH THE COUNTRIES OF SOUTH-EAST EUROPE

Mrs Doris PACK
Chairwoman

Mr Hannes SWOBODA
Vice-Chairman

Mr Salvatore TATARELLA
Vice-Chairman

Mr Zsolt László BECSEY
Member

Mr Victor BOŞTINARU
Member

Mr Jan BŘEZINA
Member

Mr Ryszard CZARNECKI
Member

Mr Göran FÄRM
Member

Mr Jean-Paul GAUZÈS
Member

Mr Ioannis GKLAVAKIS
Member

Mrs Elly de GROEN-KOUWENHOVEN
Member

Mr Ignasi GUARDANS CAMBÓ
Member

Mrs Jeanine HENNIS-PLASSCHAERT
Member

Mrs Gisela KALLENBACH
Member

Mr Marian-Jean MARINESCU
Member

Mr Roberto MUSACCHIO
Member

Mrs Anni PODIMATA
Member

Mr Jacek PROTASIEWICZ
Member

Mr László TŐKÉS
Member

Mr Antonios TRAKATELLIS
Member

Mrs Adina-Ioana VĂLEAN
Member

Mr Marcello VERNOLA
Member

Mr Jan Marinus WIERSMA
Member

Mrs Glenis WILLMOTT
Member

Mr Domenico Antonio BASILE
Substitute

Mr Simon BUSUTTIL
Substitute

Mr Jorgo CHATZIMARKAKIS
Substitute

Mr Panayiotis DEMETRIOU
Substitute

Mr Jonathan EVANS
Substitute

Mr Jas GAWRONSKI
Substitute

Mr Gyula HEGYI
Substitute

Mr Jelko KACIN
Substitute

Mr Heinz KINDERMANN
Substitute

Mr Dieter-Lebrecht KOCH
Substitute

Mr Sepp KUSSTATSCHER
Substitute

Mr Joost LAGENDIJK
Substitute

Mr Antonio LÓPEZ-ISTÚRIZ WHITE
Substitute

Mr Erik MEIJER
Substitute

Mr Atanas PAPARIZOV
Substitute

Mr Bernd POSSELT
Substitute

Mr Guido SACCONI
Substitute

Mr Adrian SEVERIN
Substitute

Mr Geoffrey VAN ORDEN
Substitute

Mr Janusz WOJCIECHOWSKI
Substitute

DELEGATION TO THE EU-RUSSIA PARLIAMENTARY COOPERATION COMMITTEE

Mrs Ria OOMEN-RUIJTEN
Chairwoman

Reino PAASILINNA
Vice-Chairman

Esko SEPPÄNEN
Vice-Chairman

Mr Emmanouil ANGELAKAS
Member

Mr Milan CABRNOCH
Member

Mr Jean-Marie CAVADA
Member

Mrs Charlotte CEDERSCHIÖLD
Member

Mr Giulietto CHIESA
Member

Mrs Maria da Assunção ESTEVES
Member

Mrs Hanna FOLTYN-KUBICKA
Member

Mrs Anne E. JENSEN
Member

Mr Tunne KELAM
Member

Mrs Constanze Angela KREHL
Member

Mr Zbigniew Krzysztof KUŹMIUK
Member

Henrik LAX
Member

Mr Klaus-Heiner LEHNE
Member

Mr Jean-Marie LE PEN
Member

Mr Bogusław LIBERADZKI
Member

Mrs Eluned MORGAN
Member

Mr Justas Vincas PALECKIS
Member

Mr Georgios PAPASTAMKOS
Member

Mr Vladimír REMEK
Member

Mr Guido SACCONI
Member

Mr Jacek SARYUSZ-WOLSKI
Member

Mr Richard SEEBER
Member

Mr Bart STAES
Member

Mrs Margie SUDRE
Member

Mr Csaba Sándor TABAJDI
Member

Andrzej WIELOWIEYSKI
Member

Mrs Tatjana ŽDANOKA
Member

Mr Vladimír ŽELEZNÝ
Member

Mrs Laima Liucija ANDRIKIENĖ
Substitute

Mr Bastiaan BELDER
Substitute

Mr Antonio DE BLASIO
Substitute

Mr Arūnas DEGUTIS
Substitute

Mr Milan GAĽA
Substitute

Mrs Elisabetta GARDINI
Substitute

Mr Bogdan GOLIK
Substitute

Mrs Rebecca HARMS
Substitute

Mr Joel HASSE FERREIRA
Substitute

Satu HASSI
Substitute

Mrs Jeanine HENNIS-PLASSCHAERT
Substitute

Mr Richard HOWITT
Substitute

Ville ITÄLÄ
Substitute

Mrs Maria Eleni KOPPA
Substitute

Mr Holger KRAHMER
Substitute

Mrs Kartika Tamara LIOTARD
Substitute

Mr Alojz PETERLE
Substitute

Mr Rihards PĪKS
Substitute

Mr Zdzisław Zbigniew PODKAŃSKI
Substitute

Mr Samuli POHJAMO
Substitute

Mr Bernard POIGNANT
Substitute

Mr Libor ROUČEK
Substitute

Mrs Katrin SAKS
Substitute

Mrs Inger SEGELSTRÖM
Substitute

Mrs Gabriele STAUNER
Substitute

Dr Charles TANNOCK
Substitute

Mrs Inese VAIDERE
Substitute

Ari VATANEN
Substitute

Mr Manfred WEBER
Substitute

Mrs Gabriele ZIMMER
Substitute

DELEGATION TO THE EU-UKRAINE PARLIAMENTARY COOPERATION COMMITTEE

Mr Adrian SEVERIN
Chairman

Dr Charles TANNOCK
Vice-Chairman

Mr Andrzej Tomasz ZAPAŁOWSKI
Vice-Chairman

Mr Šarūnas BIRUTIS
Member

Mrs Jana BOBOŠÍKOVÁ
Member

Mr Jerzy BUZEK
Member

Mr Antonio DE BLASIO
Member

Mr Gábor HARANGOZÓ
Member

Mrs Rebecca HARMS
Member

Mrs Lily JACOBS
Member

Mr Guntars KRASTS
Member

Mr Helmuth MARKOV
Member

Mrs Zita PLEŠTINSKÁ
Member

Mr Marek SIWIEC
Member

Mrs Grażyna STANISZEWSKA
Member

Mrs Marianne THYSSEN
Member

Mr Stavros ARNAOUTAKIS
Substitute

Mr Christopher BEAZLEY
Substitute

Mr Herbert BÖSCH
Substitute

Mr Martin CALLANAN
Substitute

Mr Arūnas DEGUTIS
Substitute

Mr Alfred GOMOLKA
Substitute

Mr Milan HORÁČEK
Substitute

Mr Mieczysław Edmund JANOWSKI
Substitute

Mrs Constanze Angela KREHL
Substitute

Mr Aldis KUŠĶIS
Substitute

Mr Zbigniew Krzysztof KUŹMIUK
Substitute

Mrs Marusya Ivanova LYUBCHEVA
Substitute

Mrs Maria ROBSAHM
Substitute

Mrs Gabriele STAUNER
Substitute

Mrs Eva-Britt SVENSSON
Substitute

DELEGATION TO THE EU-MOLDOVA PARLIAMENTARY COOPERATION COMMITTEE

Mrs Marianne MIKKO
Chairwoman

Mr Jelko KACIN
Vice-Chairman

Mr Zdzisław Zbigniew PODKAŃSKI
Vice-Chairman

Mrs Laima Liucija ANDRIKIENĖ
Member

Mr Alfred GOMOLKA
Member

Mr Jiří MAŠTÁLKA
Member

Mrs Maria PETRE
Member

Mr Gianni PITTELLA
Member

Mrs Maria ROBSAHM
Member

Mrs Elisabeth SCHROEDTER
Member

Mr Theodor Dumitru STOLOJAN
Member

Mr Jan Marinus WIERSMA
Member

Mrs Corina CREŢU
Substitute

Mr Robert EVANS
Substitute

Mrs Urszula GACEK
Substitute

Mrs Anna IBRISAGIC
Substitute

Henrik LAX
Substitute

Mr Helmuth MARKOV
Substitute

Mrs Grażyna STANISZEWSKA
Substitute

Ewa TOMASZEWSKA
Substitute

Mr Rainer WIELAND
Substitute

Mr Tadeusz ZWIEFKA
Substitute

DELEGATION FOR RELATIONS WITH BELARUS

Mr Jacek PROTASIEWICZ
Chairman

Mr Aldis KUŠĶIS
Vice-Chairman

Mr Roberto FIORE
Member

Mr Christofer FJELLNER
Member

Mrs Věra FLASAROVÁ
Member

Mr Eugenijus GENTVILAS
Member

Mrs Claire GIBAULT
Member

Mr Alfred GOMOLKA
Member

Mr Krzysztof HOŁOWCZYC
Member

Mr Janusz ONYSZKIEWICZ
Member

Mr Justas Vincas PALECKIS
Member

Mrs Elisabeth SCHROEDTER
Member

Mr Konrad SZYMAŃSKI
Member

Mr Andres TARAND
Member

Mr Vladimir URUTCHEV
Member

Mr Bernard WOJCIECHOWSKI
Member

Mrs Laima Liucija ANDRIKIENĖ
Substitute

Mr Rolf BEREND
Substitute

Mrs Gabriela CREŢU
Substitute

Mr Magor Imre CSIBI
Substitute

Árpád DUKA-ZÓLYOMI
Substitute

Mrs Hanna FOLTYN-KUBICKA
Substitute

Mr Jacky HÉNIN
Substitute

Mr Milan HORÁČEK
Substitute

Mrs Anne E. JENSEN
Substitute

Mr Aloyzas SAKALAS
Substitute

Mr Bogusław SONIK
Substitute

Mr Tadeusz ZWIEFKA
Substitute

DELEGATION TO THE EU-KAZAKHSTAN, EU-KYRGYZSTAN AND EU-UZBEKISTAN PARLIAMENTARY COOPERATION COMMITTEES, AND FOR RELATIONS WITH TAJIKISTAN, TURKMENISTAN AND MONGOLIA

Mrs Ona JUKNEVIČIENĖ
Chairwoman

Mr Jas GAWRONSKI
Vice-Chairman

Mr Johannes BLOKLAND
Member

Mr Luigi COCILOVO
Member

Mr Jean-Paul DENANOT
Member

Mr Adam GIEREK
Member

Satu HASSI
Member

Mrs Elisabeth JEGGLE
Member

Mrs Marusya Ivanova LYUBCHEVA
Member

Mrs Véronique MATHIEU
Member

Mrs Viktória MOHÁCSI
Member

Mrs Cristiana MUSCARDINI
Member

Mr Péter OLAJOS
Member

Mr Markus PIEPER
Member

Mr Miloslav RANSDORF
Member

Mrs Katrin SAKS
Member

Mr Janusz WOJCIECHOWSKI
Member

Mr Tomáš ZATLOUKAL
Member

Mrs Maria BERGER
Substitute

Mr Slavi BINEV
Substitute

Mr Martin CALLANAN
Substitute

Mr Daniel CASPARY
Substitute

Mr Gintaras DIDŽIOKAS
Substitute

Mr Valdis DOMBROVSKIS
Substitute

Mrs Anne FERREIRA
Substitute

Mrs Genowefa GRABOWSKA
Substitute

Mr Metin KAZAK
Substitute

Mr Yiannakis MATSIS
Substitute

Mr Vural ÖGER
Substitute

Mr Horst SCHNELLHARDT
Substitute

Esko SEPPÄNEN
Substitute

Mr Bart STAES
Substitute

Mr Dirk STERCKX
Substitute

Mr Alejo VIDAL-QUADRAS
Substitute

DELEGATION TO THE EU-ARMENIA, EU-AZERBAIJAN AND EU-GEORGIA PARLIAMENTARY COOPERATION COMMITTEES

Mrs Marie Anne ISLER BÉGUIN
Chairwoman

Árpád DUKA-ZÓLYOMI
Vice-Chairman

Mr Vytautas LANDSBERGIS
Vice-Chairman

Mr Georgs ANDREJEVS
Member

Mr Alessandro BATTILOCCHIO
Member

Mr Johannes BLOKLAND
Member

Mr Panayiotis DEMETRIOU
Member

Mr Agustín DÍAZ DE MERA GARCÍA CONSUEGRA
Member

Mr Konstantinos DROUTSAS
Member

Mr Saïd EL KHADRAOUI
Member

Mr Evgeni KIRILOV
Member

Mr Marian-Jean MARINESCU
Member

Mrs Maria MATSOUKA
Member

Mrs Siiri OVIIR
Member

Mr Jean SPAUTZ
Member

Mrs Gabriele STAUNER
Member

Mr Hannes SWOBODA
Member

Mr Tadeusz ZWIEFKA
Member

Mr Jan BŘEZINA
Substitute

Mr Philip BUSHILL-MATTHEWS
Substitute

Mr Robert EVANS
Substitute

Mrs Urszula GACEK
Substitute

Mr Martí GRAU i SEGÚ
Substitute

Mrs Elisabeth JEGGLE
Substitute

Mrs Karin JÖNS
Substitute

Mr Holger KRAHMER
Substitute

Mrs Mary Lou McDONALD
Substitute

Mr Janusz ONYSZKIEWICZ
Substitute

Mrs Rovana PLUMB
Substitute

Mr Vladimir URUTCHEV
Substitute

Mrs Corien WORTMANN-KOOL
Substitute

Mrs Tatjana ŽDANOKA
Substitute

DELEGATION FOR RELATIONS WITH ISRAEL

Mrs Jana HYBÁŠKOVÁ
Chairwoman

Mr Bastiaan BELDER
Vice-Chairman

Mrs Monika BEŇOVÁ
Vice-Chairwoman

Mr Gabriele ALBERTINI
Member

Mr Giorgio CAROLLO
Member

Mr Alejandro CERCAS
Member

Mr Jan CREMERS
Member

Mr Marek Aleksander CZARNECKI
Member

Mr Markus FERBER
Member

Mr Patrick GAUBERT
Member

Mrs Cristina GUTIÉRREZ-CORTINES
Member

Mr David HAMMERSTEIN
Member

Mrs Marine LE PEN
Member

Mr Nickolay MLADENOV
Member

Mr Marco PANNELLA
Member

Mrs Frédérique RIES
Member

Mr Pierre SCHAPIRA
Member

Mr Peter ŠŤASTNÝ
Member

Mr Ulrich STOCKMANN
Member

Mrs Eva-Britt SVENSSON
Member

Mr Andrzej Jan SZEJNA
Member

Mr Johannes VOGGENHUBER
Member

Mr Zbigniew ZALESKI
Member

Mrs Margrete AUKEN
Substitute

Mr André BRIE
Substitute

Mr Paul van BUITENEN
Substitute

Mr Fabio CIANI
Substitute

Mrs Christine DE VEYRAC
Substitute

Mr Benoît HAMON
Substitute

Mr Gunnar HÖKMARK
Substitute

Mr Stanisław JAŁOWIECKI
Substitute

Mrs Katalin LÉVAI
Substitute

Mr Miroslav MIKOLÁŠIK
Substitute

Mr Herbert REUL
Substitute

Mrs Daciana Octavia SÂRBU
Substitute

Mrs Amalia SARTORI
Substitute

Mr Marek SIWIEC
Substitute

Hannu TAKKULA
Substitute

Dr Charles TANNOCK
Substitute

Mr Cornelis VISSER
Substitute

Mr Vladimír ŽELEZNÝ
Substitute

Mr Marian ZLOTEA
Substitute

DELEGATION FOR RELATIONS WITH THE PALESTINIAN LEGISLATIVE COUNCIL

Mr Kyriacos TRIANTAPHYLLIDES
Chairman

Mr Proinsias DE ROSSA
Vice-Chairman

Mr Ioannis KASOULIDES
Vice-Chairman

Mr Alexander ALVARO
Member

Mrs Margrete AUKEN
Member

Mr Mario BORGHEZIO
Member

Mr John BOWIS
Member

Mrs Frieda BREPOELS
Member

Mr Daniel CASPARY
Member

Mrs Françoise CASTEX
Member

Mr Chris DAVIES
Member

Mrs Christine DE VEYRAC
Member

Mrs Jill EVANS
Member

Mr Francesco FERRARI
Member

Mrs Anna HEDH
Member

Mr Stéphane LE FOLL
Member

Mrs Caroline LUCAS
Member

Mr Antonio MASIP HIDALGO
Member

Mrs Luisa MORGANTINI
Member

Mr Giovanni RIVERA
Member

Mr Hannes SWOBODA
Member

Mr Stefano ZAPPALA'
Member

Mr David HAMMERSTEIN
Substitute

Mrs Ruth HIERONYMI
Substitute

Mrs Jana HYBÁŠKOVÁ
Substitute

Mr Jelko KACIN
Substitute

Mr André LAIGNEL
Substitute

Mr Stavros LAMBRINIDIS
Substitute

Mrs Jamila MADEIRA
Substitute

Mr David MARTIN
Substitute

Mr Miguel PORTAS
Substitute

Mr Vittorio PRODI
Substitute

Mr Giovanni ROBUSTI
Substitute

Mr Georgios TOUSSAS
Substitute

Mr Johannes VOGGENHUBER
Substitute

Mr Mauro ZANI
Substitute

DELEGATION FOR RELATIONS WITH THE MAGHREB COUNTRIES AND THE ARAB MAGHREB UNION (INCLUDING LIBYA)

Mr Carlos José ITURGAIZ ANGULO
Chairman

Mr Simon BUSUTTIL
Vice-Chairman

Mr Alain HUTCHINSON
Vice-Chairman

Mr Jean-Pierre AUDY
Member

Mrs Inés AYALA SENDER
Member

Mrs Maddalena CALIA
Member

Mr Paul Marie COÛTEAUX
Member

Mr Gianni DE MICHELIS
Member

Mrs Carmen FRAGA ESTÉVEZ
Member

Mrs Iratxe GARCÍA PÉREZ
Member

Mrs Donata GOTTARDI
Member

Mrs Filiz Hakaeva HYUSMENOVA
Member

Mr Ģirts Valdis KRISTOVSKIS
Member

Mr André LAIGNEL
Member

Mrs Kartika Tamara LIOTARD
Member

Mrs Catiuscia MARINI
Member

Mrs Pasqualina NAPOLETANO
Member

Mr Rareş-Lucian NICULESCU
Member

Mr Manuel António dos SANTOS
Member

Mr Sebastiano SANZARELLO
Member

Mrs Lydia SCHENARDI
Member

Mr José Albino SILVA PENEDA
Member

Mr Bogusław SONIK
Member

Mr Ioannis VARVITSIOTIS
Member

Mr Costas BOTOPOULOS
Substitute

Mrs Catherine BOURSIER
Substitute

Mrs Marie-Arlette CARLOTTI
Substitute

Mrs Pilar del CASTILLO VERA
Substitute

Mr Giusto CATANIA
Substitute

Mr Brian CROWLEY
Substitute

Mr Giuseppe GARGANI
Substitute

Mr Jan Jerzy KUŁAKOWSKI
Substitute

Mr Edward McMILLAN-SCOTT
Substitute

Mr Hans-Peter MAYER
Substitute

Mr Raimon OBIOLS i GERMÀ
Substitute

Mr Aldo PATRICIELLO
Substitute

Mrs Lydie POLFER
Substitute

Mr Luca ROMAGNOLI
Substitute

Mrs Renate SOMMER
Substitute

Mr Armando VENETO
Substitute

Mrs Anna ZÁBORSKÁ
Substitute

Mr Stefano ZAPPALA'
Substitute

DELEGATION FOR RELATIONS WITH THE MASHREQ COUNTRIES

Mrs Béatrice PATRIE
Chairwoman

Mr Marco CAPPATO
Vice-Chairman

Mrs Catherine BOURSIER
Member

Mr Carlos CARNERO GONZÁLEZ
Member

Mr Carlo CASINI
Member

Mrs Véronique DE KEYSER
Member

Mrs Jolanta DIČKUTĖ
Member

Mr Giorgos DIMITRAKOPOULOS
Member

Mrs Hélène FLAUTRE
Member

Mr Giuseppe GARGANI
Member

Mrs Sophia in 't VELD
Member

Mrs Rumiana JELEVA
Member

Mrs Magda KÓSÁNÉ KOVÁCS
Member

Mr Kurt LECHNER
Member

Mr Patrick LOUIS
Member

Mrs Jamila MADEIRA
Member

Mr Sebastiano (Nello) MUSUMECI
Member

Mr Miguel PORTAS
Member

Mr John PURVIS
Member

Mr Dimitar STOYANOV
Member

Mr Riccardo VENTRE
Member

Mr Daniel CASPARY
Substitute

Mr Constantin DUMITRIU
Substitute

Mr Juan FRAILE CANTÓN
Substitute

Mrs Silvana KOCH-MEHRIN
Substitute

Mr Fernand LE RACHINEL
Substitute

Mrs Elisabeth MORIN
Substitute

Mr Roberto MUSACCHIO
Substitute

Mrs Pasqualina NAPOLETANO
Substitute

Baroness NICHOLSON OF WINTERBOURNE
Substitute

Mr Cem ÖZDEMIR
Substitute

Mrs Christa PRETS
Substitute

Mr Bogusław SONIK
Substitute

Mr Salvatore TATARELLA
Substitute

Mrs Bernadette VERGNAUD
Substitute

Mr Tadeusz ZWIEFKA
Substitute

DELEGATION FOR RELATIONS WITH THE GULF STATES, INCLUDING YEMEN

Mrs Avril DOYLE
Vice-Chairwoman

Mr Tobias PFLÜGER
Vice-Chairman

Mrs Roberta ANGELILLI
Member

Mr Luis Manuel CAPOULAS SANTOS
Member

Mr Gianni DE MICHELIS
Member

Mr Albert DESS
Member

Mrs Brigitte FOURÉ
Member

Mr Milan GAĽA
Member

Mr Sajjad KARIM
Member

Mr Patrick LOUIS
Member

Mrs Ramona Nicole MĂNESCU
Member

Riitta MYLLER
Member

Mrs Angelika NIEBLER
Member

Mr Horst POSDORF
Member

Mr Christian ROVSING
Member

Mrs Tokia SAÏFI
Member

Mrs Małgorzata HANDZLIK
Substitute

Mr Filip KACZMAREK
Substitute

Mr Claude MORAES
Substitute

Mr Rareş-Lucian NICULESCU
Substitute

Mr Neil PARISH
Substitute

Mrs Lydie POLFER
Substitute

Mr John PURVIS
Substitute

Mr Marco RIZZO
Substitute

Mrs María Isabel SALINAS GARCÍA
Substitute

Mrs Corien WORTMANN-KOOL
Substitute

Mrs Dushana ZDRAVKOVA
Substitute

DELEGATION FOR RELATIONS WITH IRAN

Mrs Angelika BEER
Chairwoman

Mr Antonio MUSSA
Vice-President

Mrs Christa PRETS
Vice-Chairwoman

Mr Iles BRAGHETTO
Member

Mr Philip BUSHILL-MATTHEWS
Member

Mr Paulo CASACA
Member

Mr Desislav CHUKOLOV
Member

Mr Agustín DÍAZ DE MERA GARCÍA CONSUEGRA
Member

Mr Ingo FRIEDRICH
Member

Mr Michael GAHLER
Member

Mr Jean-Paul GAUZÈS
Member

Mr Georgios GEORGIOU
Member

Mr Carl LANG
Member

Mr Johannes LEBECH
Member

Mrs Pia Elda LOCATELLI
Member

Baroness NICHOLSON OF WINTERBOURNE
Member

Sirpa PIETIKÄINEN
Member

Mr John PURVIS
Member

Mr Libor ROUČEK
Member

Mr Gilles SAVARY
Member

Mr John ATTARD-MONTALTO
Substitute

Mr Colm BURKE
Substitute

Mr Jorgo CHATZIMARKAKIS
Substitute

Mr Christofer FJELLNER
Substitute

Mrs Monica FRASSONI
Substitute

Mr Vicente Miguel GARCÉS RAMÓN
Substitute

Mrs Jana HYBÁŠKOVÁ
Substitute

Mrs Rumiana JELEVA
Substitute

Mr Kurt Joachim LAUK
Substitute

Mr Marcin LIBICKI
Substitute

Mr Tobias PFLÜGER
Substitute

Mr Sérgio SOUSA PINTO
Substitute

Mrs Margarita STARKEVIČIŪTĖ
Substitute

Mr Robert STURDY
Substitute

Mr Frank VANHECKE
Substitute

Mr Marcello VERNOLA
Substitute

DELEGATION FOR RELATIONS WITH THE UNITED STATES

Mr Jonathan EVANS
Chairman

Mr Vito BONSIGNORE
Vice-Chairman

Mr Benoît HAMON
Vice-Chairman

Mr Enrique BARÓN CRESPO
Member

Mr Domenico Antonio BASILE
Member

Mr Philip BRADBOURN
Member

Mr Elmar BROK
Member

Mrs Kathalijne Maria BUITENWEG
Member

Mr Nicodim BULZESC
Member

Mr Colm BURKE
Member

Mrs Corina CREŢU
Member

Mr Brian CROWLEY
Member

Mr Daniel DĂIANU
Member

Mrs Bairbre de BRÚN
Member

Mrs Marie-Hélène DESCAMPS
Member

Mr Petr DUCHOŇ
Member

Mr Carlo FATUZZO
Member

Mr Maciej Marian GIERTYCH
Member

Mr Vasco GRAÇA MOURA
Member

Mr Umberto GUIDONI
Member

Anneli JÄÄTTEENMÄKI
Member

Mr Pierre JONCKHEER
Member

Mrs Romana JORDAN CIZELJ
Member

Mr Christoph KONRAD
Member

Mr Helmut KUHNE
Member

Mr Stavros LAMBRINIDIS
Member

Alexander Graf LAMBSDORFF
Member

Mr Kurt Joachim LAUK
Member

Mrs Roselyne LEFRANÇOIS
Member

Baroness Sarah LUDFORD
Member

Mrs Arlene McCARTHY
Member

Mrs Erika MANN
Member

Mr Francisco José MILLÁN MON
Member

Mrs Annemie NEYTS-UYTTEBROECK
Member

Mr Pier Antonio PANZERI
Member

Mr Atanas PAPARIZOV
Member

Mr Józef PINIOR
Member

Mrs Karin RIIS-JØRGENSEN
Member

Mrs Kathy SINNOTT
Member

Mr Peter SKINNER
Member

Mr David SUMBERG
Member

Mrs Dushana ZDRAVKOVA
Member

Mr Vittorio AGNOLETTO
Substitute

Mr Gabriele ALBERTINI
Substitute

Mrs Mariela Velichkova BAEVA
Substitute

Mr Bastiaan BELDER
Substitute

Mr Cristian Silviu BUŞOI
Substitute

Mrs Charlotte CEDERSCHIÖLD
Substitute

Mr Alejandro CERCAS
Substitute

Mr Giles CHICHESTER
Substitute

Mr Christian EHLER
Substitute

Mr Saïd EL KHADRAOUI
Substitute

Mr James ELLES
Substitute

Mrs Urszula GACEK
Substitute

Mrs Ana Maria GOMES
Substitute

Mr Ignasi GUARDANS CAMBÓ
Substitute

Mr Gábor HARANGOZÓ
Substitute

Mrs Marian HARKIN
Substitute

Mrs Edit HERCZOG
Substitute

Mr Guntars KRASTS
Substitute

Mr Bogusław LIBERADZKI
Substitute

Mrs Caroline LUCAS
Substitute

Mr James NICHOLSON
Substitute

Mrs Ria OOMEN-RUIJTEN
Substitute

Mr Ioan Mircea PAŞCU
Substitute

Mr Mirosław Mariusz PIOTROWSKI
Substitute

Mrs Godelieve QUISTHOUDT-ROWOHL
Substitute

Mr Michel ROCARD
Substitute

Mr Dariusz ROSATI
Substitute

Mr Antolín SÁNCHEZ PRESEDO
Substitute

Mrs Christel SCHALDEMOSE
Substitute

Mr Peter ŠŤASTNÝ
Substitute

Mr József SZÁJER
Substitute

Mr Claude TURMES
Substitute

Ari VATANEN
Substitute

Andrzej WIELOWIEYSKI
Substitute

Mr Anders WIJKMAN
Substitute

Mr Francis WURTZ
Substitute

Mrs Iva ZANICCHI
Substitute

DELEGATION FOR RELATIONS WITH CANADA

Mr Seán Ó NEACHTAIN
Chairman

Lasse LEHTINEN
Vice-Chairman

Mr Toomas SAVI
Vice-Chairman

Mrs Elspeth ATTWOOLL
Member

Mr Sebastian Valentin BODU
Member

Mr Sylwester CHRUSZCZ
Member

Mr Den DOVER
Member

Mrs Bárbara DÜHRKOP DÜHRKOP
Member

Mr Duarte FREITAS
Member

Mrs Marian HARKIN
Member

Mrs Edit HERCZOG
Member

Mrs Ruth HIERONYMI
Member

Mr Jim HIGGINS
Member

Mr Ian HUDGHTON
Member

Mrs Iliana Malinova IOTOVA
Member

Mrs Urszula KRUPA
Member

Mr Nicolae Vlad POPA
Member

Mrs Christel SCHALDEMOSE
Member

Mrs Agnes SCHIERHUBER
Member

Mrs Catherine TRAUTMANN
Member

Mr Manfred WEBER
Member

Mr Jean-Luc BENNAHMIAS
Substitute

Mr Reimer BÖGE
Substitute

Mr Philip BRADBOURN
Substitute

Mr Wolfgang BULFON
Substitute

Mr Gérard DEPREZ
Substitute

Mrs Jolanta DIČKUTĖ
Substitute

Mr Alessandro FOGLIETTA
Substitute

Mr Martí GRAU i SEGÚ
Substitute

Mrs Romana JORDAN CIZELJ
Substitute

Mrs Ona JUKNEVIČIENĖ
Substitute

Mr Jean-Marie LE PEN
Substitute

Mr Mario MAURO
Substitute

Mr Manuel MEDINA ORTEGA
Substitute

Mr Miroslav MIKOLÁŠIK
Substitute

Mr Lambert van NISTELROOIJ
Substitute

Mr Neil PARISH
Substitute

Mrs Dagmar ROTH-BEHRENDT
Substitute

Mr Sebastiano SANZARELLO
Substitute

Mr Gary TITLEY
Substitute

DELEGATION FOR RELATIONS WITH THE COUNTRIES OF CENTRAL AMERICA

Mr Raimon OBIOLS i GERMÀ
Chairman

Mr José Manuel GARCÍA-MARGALLO Y MARFIL
Vice-Chairman

Mr Marco RIZZO
Vice-Chairman

Mr Raül ROMEVA i RUEDA
Vice-Chairman

Mr Paolo BARTOLOZZI
Member

Mrs Irena BELOHORSKÁ
Member

Mr David CASA
Member

Mr Jean Louis COTTIGNY
Member

Mrs Edite ESTRELA
Member

Mr Richard FALBR
Member

Mr Giuseppe GARGANI
Member

Mr Christopher HEATON-HARRIS
Member

Mr Luis HERRERO-TEJEDOR
Member

Mr Stephen HUGHES
Member

Mr Holger KRAHMER
Member

Mr Wiesław Stefan KUC
Member

Mr Jan Jerzy KUŁAKOWSKI
Member

Mrs Marie-Noëlle LIENEMANN
Member

Mr Peter LIESE
Member

Mr Eugenijus MALDEIKIS
Member

Mr Willy MEYER PLEITE
Member

Mr Josu ORTUONDO LARREA
Member

Mr Luís QUEIRÓ
Member

Mr Bogusław SONIK
Member

Mrs María SORNOSA MARTÍNEZ
Member

Mr Gianluca SUSTA
Member

Mr Francisco ASSIS
Substitute

Mrs Maria BADIA i CUTCHET
Substitute

Mr Guy BONO
Substitute

Mr Udo BULLMANN
Substitute

Mrs Bairbre de BRÚN
Substitute

Mrs Janelly FOURTOU
Substitute

Mr Dariusz Maciej GRABOWSKI
Substitute

Mr Friedrich-Wilhelm GRAEFE zu BARINGDORF
Substitute

Mr Luis de GRANDES PASCUAL
Substitute

Mr Filip KACZMAREK
Substitute

Mrs Esther de LANGE
Substitute

Mrs Anne LAPERROUZE
Substitute

Mr Johannes LEBECH
Substitute

Mr Jörg LEICHTFRIED
Substitute

Mrs Astrid LULLING
Substitute

Mr Miguel Angel MARTÍNEZ MARTÍNEZ
Substitute

Mrs Elisabeth MORIN
Substitute

Reino PAASILINNA
Substitute

Mr Nicolae Vlad POPA
Substitute

Mr José Ignacio SALAFRANCA SÁNCHEZ-NEYRA
Substitute

Mr Jürgen SCHRÖDER
Substitute

Mr José Albino SILVA PENEDA
Substitute

Mr Konrad SZYMAŃSKI
Substitute

DELEGATION FOR RELATIONS WITH THE COUNTRIES OF THE ANDEAN COMMUNITY

Mr Alain LIPIETZ
Chairman

Mrs Gabriela CREŢU
Vice-Chairwoman

Mr Fernando FERNÁNDEZ MARTÍN
Vice-Chairman

Mrs Danutė BUDREIKAITĖ
Member

Mr Arūnas DEGUTIS
Member

Mr Claudio FAVA
Member

Mr Karl-Heinz FLORENZ
Member

Mr Armando FRANÇA
Member

Mrs Ingeborg GRÄSSLE
Member

Mrs Esther HERRANZ GARCÍA
Member

Mr Jörg LEICHTFRIED
Member

Mr Jean-Claude MARTINEZ
Member

Mr Manuel MEDINA ORTEGA
Member

Mr Emilio MENÉNDEZ del VALLE
Member

Mr Lambert van NISTELROOIJ
Member

Mr Bogusław ROGALSKI
Member

Mr Marcello VERNOLA
Member

Mr Oldřich VLASÁK
Member

Mrs Sahra WAGENKNECHT
Member

Mrs Renate WEBER
Member

Mr Jean Marie BEAUPUY
Substitute

Mr Richard CORBETT
Substitute

Mr Dragoş Florin DAVID
Substitute

Mr Robert EVANS
Substitute

Mr José Manuel GARCÍA-MARGALLO Y MARFIL
Substitute

Mrs Małgorzata HANDZLIK
Substitute

Mr Karsten Friedrich HOPPENSTEDT
Substitute

Mr Wolfgang KREISSL-DÖRFLER
Substitute

Mr Sérgio MARQUES
Substitute

Mr Antonio MASIP HIDALGO
Substitute

Mr Marios MATSAKIS
Substitute

Mr Gérard ONESTA
Substitute

Mr Athanasios PAFILIS
Substitute

Mr Bogdan PĚK
Substitute

Mrs Frédérique RIES
Substitute

Mr José Ignacio SALAFRANCA SÁNCHEZ-NEYRA
Substitute

Mr David SUMBERG
Substitute

Mr Luis YAÑEZ-BARNUEVO GARCÍA
Substitute

DELEGATION FOR RELATIONS WITH MERCOSUR

Mr Sérgio SOUSA PINTO
Chairman

Mr Gérard DEPREZ
Vice-Chairman

Mr José Ignacio SALAFRANCA SÁNCHEZ-NEYRA
Vice-Chairman

Mr Richard James ASHWORTH
Member

Mrs Pilar AYUSO
Member

Mrs Ilda FIGUEIREDO
Member

Mrs Monica FRASSONI
Member

Mr Georgios GEORGIOU
Member

Mr Béla GLATTFELDER
Member

Mrs Nathalie GRIESBECK
Member

Mrs Małgorzata HANDZLIK
Member

Mrs Erna HENNICOT-SCHOEPGES
Member

Mr Ján HUDACKÝ
Member

Mr Wolfgang KREISSL-DÖRFLER
Member

Mr Andrea LOSCO
Member

Mr Javier MORENO SÁNCHEZ
Member

Mr Gérard ONESTA
Member

Mr João de Deus PINHEIRO
Member

Mrs Rovana PLUMB
Member

Mr Poul Nyrup RASMUSSEN
Member

Mr Luca ROMAGNOLI
Member

Mr Leopold Józef RUTOWICZ
Member

Mrs María Isabel SALINAS GARCÍA
Member

Mr Søren Bo SØNDERGAARD
Member

Mr Michel TEYCHENNÉ
Member

Ewa TOMASZEWSKA
Member

Mr Donato Tommaso VERALDI
Member

Mr Luis YAÑEZ-BARNUEVO GARCÍA
Member

Mr Vincenzo AITA
Substitute

Mr Adam BIELAN
Substitute

Mr Paolo COSTA
Substitute

Mr Beniamino DONNICI
Substitute

Mr Richard FALBR
Substitute

Mr Karl-Heinz FLORENZ
Substitute

Mr Armando FRANÇA
Substitute

Mr Duarte FREITAS
Substitute

Mr Gerardo GALEOTE
Substitute

Mr Norbert GLANTE
Substitute

Mr Vasco GRAÇA MOURA
Substitute

Mr Ambroise GUELLEC
Substitute

Mr Alain LIPIETZ
Substitute

Mrs Caroline LUCAS
Substitute

Mr Eugenijus MALDEIKIS
Substitute

Mrs Maria MATSOUKA
Substitute

Mr Emilio MENÉNDEZ del VALLE
Substitute

Mrs Ljudmila NOVAK
Substitute

Mr Josu ORTUONDO LARREA
Substitute

Mr Luís QUEIRÓ
Substitute

Mrs Frédérique RIES
Substitute

Mrs Amalia SARTORI
Substitute

Mrs Britta THOMSEN
Substitute

Mrs Silvia-Adriana ŢICĂU
Substitute

Mrs Bernadette VERGNAUD
Substitute

Mrs Sahra WAGENKNECHT
Substitute

DELEGATION FOR RELATIONS WITH JAPAN

Mr Georg JARZEMBOWSKI
Chairman

Mrs Karin RESETARITS
Vice-Chairwoman

Mr Jaroslav ZVĚŘINA
Vice-Chairman

Mr Jan ANDERSSON
Member

Mrs Hiltrud BREYER
Member

Mr Richard CORBETT
Member

Mrs Brigitte DOUAY
Member

Mr Bruno GOLLNISCH
Member

Mr Martí GRAU i SEGÚ
Member

Mr Matthias GROOTE
Member

Mr Malcolm HARBOUR
Member

Ville ITÄLÄ
Member

Mr Othmar KARAS
Member

Mrs Sylvia-Yvonne KAUFMANN
Member

Mr Dieter-Lebrecht KOCH
Member

Mr Janusz LEWANDOWSKI
Member

Mr Florencio LUQUE AGUILAR
Member

Mr Bill NEWTON DUNN
Member

Mr Ioan Mircea PAŞCU
Member

Mr Umberto PIRILLI
Member

Mr Wojciech ROSZKOWSKI
Member

Mr Antolín SÁNCHEZ PRESEDO
Member

Mrs Margarita STARKEVIČIŪTĖ
Member

Mr József SZÁJER
Member

Kyösti VIRRANKOSKI
Member

Mr Ralf WALTER
Member

Mrs Corien WORTMANN-KOOL
Member

Edit BAUER
Substitute

Mr Zdzisław Kazimierz CHMIELEWSKI
Substitute

Mr Constantin DUMITRIU
Substitute

Mr Jonathan EVANS
Substitute

Mr Carlo FATUZZO
Substitute

Mr Glyn FORD
Substitute

Mrs Claire GIBAULT
Substitute

Mr Mathieu GROSCH
Substitute

Mr Umberto GUIDONI
Substitute

Mrs Zita GURMAI
Substitute

Mr Jim HIGGINS
Substitute

Mr Dan JØRGENSEN
Substitute

Mr Ģirts Valdis KRISTOVSKIS
Substitute

Mrs Jean LAMBERT
Substitute

Alexander Graf LAMBSDORFF
Substitute

Mr Klaus-Heiner LEHNE
Substitute

Mr Javier MORENO SÁNCHEZ
Substitute

Mrs Siiri OVIIR
Substitute

Mr Vladko Todorov PANAYOTOV
Substitute

Mr Pier Antonio PANZERI
Substitute

Mr Reinhard RACK
Substitute

Mr Pál SCHMITT
Substitute

Mr Francesco Enrico SPERONI
Substitute

Mrs Catherine TRAUTMANN
Substitute

Mr Henri WEBER
Substitute

Mrs Barbara WEILER
Substitute

DELEGATION FOR RELATIONS WITH THE PEOPLE'S REPUBLIC OF CHINA

Mr Dirk STERCKX
Chairman

Mr Jean-Luc DEHAENE
Vice-Chairman

Mr Henri WEBER
Vice-Chairman

Mr Stavros ARNAOUTAKIS
Member

Sir Robert ATKINS
Member

Mrs Maria BADIA i CUTCHET
Member

Mrs Katerina BATZELI
Member

Mr Vito BONSIGNORE
Member

Mr Cristian Silviu BUŞOI
Member

Mr Philippe BUSQUIN
Member

Mrs Pilar del CASTILLO VERA
Member

Mr Jorgo CHATZIMARKAKIS
Member

Mrs Dorette CORBEY
Member

Mr Hynek FAJMON
Member

Mrs Evelyne GEBHARDT
Member

Mr Jacky HÉNIN
Member

Mr Karsten Friedrich HOPPENSTEDT
Member

Mr Dan JØRGENSEN
Member

Mrs Anne LAPERROUZE
Member

Mr Marcin LIBICKI
Member

Mr Toine MANDERS
Member

Mr Hans-Peter MARTIN
Member

Mr Manolis MAVROMMATIS
Member

Mr Jan OLBRYCHT
Member

Mr Vladko Todorov PANAYOTOV
Member

Mr Dimitrios PAPADIMOULIS
Member

Mr Neil PARISH
Member

Mr Bogdan PĚK
Member

Mr Rihards PĪKS
Member

Mr Herbert REUL
Member

Mr Libor ROUČEK
Member

Mrs Martine ROURE
Member

Mrs Daciana Octavia SÂRBU
Member

Mrs Helga TRÜPEL
Member

Mr Claude TURMES
Member

Mr Cornelis VISSER
Member

Mr Marian ZLOTEA
Member

Mrs Inés AYALA SENDER
Substitute

Mrs Pervenche BERÈS
Substitute

Mr Sergio BERLATO
Substitute

Mr Josep BORRELL FONTELLES
Substitute

Mrs Kathalijne Maria BUITENWEG
Substitute

Mr Philip BUSHILL-MATTHEWS
Substitute

Mrs Maddalena CALIA
Substitute

Mr Agustín DÍAZ DE MERA GARCÍA CONSUEGRA
Substitute

Mrs Avril DOYLE
Substitute

Mrs Edite ESTRELA
Substitute

Mr Bogdan GOLIK
Substitute

Mrs Cristina GUTIÉRREZ-CORTINES
Substitute

Mr Klaus HÄNSCH
Substitute

Mr Stephen HUGHES
Substitute

Mrs Sophia in 't VELD
Substitute

Mrs Caroline JACKSON
Substitute

Mr Othmar KARAS
Substitute

Mr Wiesław Stefan KUC
Substitute

Mr Werner LANGEN
Substitute

Mr Raymond LANGENDRIES
Substitute

Mr Vincenzo LAVARRA
Substitute

Mr Johannes LEBECH
Substitute

Mrs Eva LICHTENBERGER
Substitute

Mrs Pia Elda LOCATELLI
Substitute

Mr Jiří MAŠTÁLKA
Substitute

Mr Gay MITCHELL
Substitute

Mr Samuli POHJAMO
Substitute

Mr Flaviu Călin RUS
Substitute

Mr Czesław Adam SIEKIERSKI
Substitute

Mrs Petya STAVREVA
Substitute

Mr Struan STEVENSON
Substitute

Mr Csaba Sándor TABAJDI
Substitute

Mr Graham WATSON
Substitute

DELEGATION FOR RELATIONS WITH THE COUNTRIES OF SOUTH ASIA

Mr Robert EVANS
Chairman

Mr Nirj DEVA
Vice-Chairman

Mr Jaromír KOHLÍČEK
Vice-Chairman

Mrs Mariela Velichkova BAEVA
Member

Edit BAUER
Member

Mr Ivo BELET
Member

Mr Wolfgang BULFON
Member

Mr Philip BUSHILL-MATTHEWS
Member

Mrs Lidia Joanna GERINGER de OEDENBERG
Member

Mr Robert GOEBBELS
Member

Mr Bogdan GOLIK
Member

Mrs Lívia JÁRÓKA
Member

Mrs Jean LAMBERT
Member

Mr Jo LEINEN
Member

Mrs Elizabeth LYNNE
Member

Mr Thomas MANN
Member

Mr Jan Tadeusz MASIEL
Member

Mr Jan MULDER
Member

Mr James NICHOLSON
Member

Mr Mirosław Mariusz PIOTROWSKI
Member

Mr Enrique BARÓN CRESPO
Substitute

Mr Mario BORGHEZIO
Substitute

Mr John BOWIS
Substitute

Mr Philip BRADBOURN
Substitute

Mrs Maria da Assunção ESTEVES
Substitute

Mr Eugenijus GENTVILAS
Substitute

Mrs Lissy GRÖNER
Substitute

Mr Carlos José ITURGAIZ ANGULO
Substitute

Mrs Ewa KLAMT
Substitute

Lasse LEHTINEN
Substitute

Mrs Arlene McCARTHY
Substitute

Mr Edward McMILLAN-SCOTT
Substitute

Mrs Ramona Nicole MĂNESCU
Substitute

Mrs Marianne MIKKO
Substitute

Mr Hartmut NASSAUER
Substitute

Mr Miloslav RANSDORF
Substitute

Mrs Teresa RIERA MADURELL
Substitute

Mr Raül ROMEVA i RUEDA
Substitute

DELEGATION FOR RELATIONS WITH INDIA

Mrs Neena GILL
Chairwoman

Mr Magor Imre CSIBI
Vice-Chairman

Mr Athanasios PAFILIS
Vice-Chairman

Mr Alexander ALVARO
Member

Mr Bastiaan BELDER
Member

Mr Philip BUSHILL-MATTHEWS
Member

Mr Ole CHRISTENSEN
Member

Mr Paolo COSTA
Member

Mr Panayiotis DEMETRIOU
Member

Mrs Mia DE VITS
Member

Mr Christian EHLER
Member

Mr Harald ETTL
Member

Mr Alain LAMASSOURE
Member

Mrs Jean LAMBERT
Member

Mrs Mairead McGUINNESS
Member

Mr Ashley MOTE
Member

Mr Eoin RYAN
Member

Dr Charles TANNOCK
Member

Mrs Silvia-Adriana ŢICĂU
Member

Mr Nikolaos VAKALIS
Member

Mr Yannick VAUGRENARD
Member

Mr Jan ZAHRADIL
Member

Edit BAUER
Substitute

Mr Jean Marie BEAUPUY
Substitute

Mr Šarūnas BIRUTIS
Substitute

Mr Mihael BREJC
Substitute

Mr Paulo CASACA
Substitute

Mr Nirj DEVA
Substitute

Mrs Alexandra DOBOLYI
Substitute

Mrs Urszula GACEK
Substitute

Mr Robert GOEBBELS
Substitute

Mrs Gisela KALLENBACH
Substitute

Mr Jaromír KOHLÍČEK
Substitute

Mr Jo LEINEN
Substitute

Mr Emilio MENÉNDEZ del VALLE
Substitute

Mr James NICHOLSON
Substitute

Mr Józef PINIOR
Substitute

Mr Wojciech ROSZKOWSKI
Substitute

Mrs Lydia SCHENARDI
Substitute

Mr Horst SCHNELLHARDT
Substitute

Mr István SZENT-IVÁNYI
Substitute

Mr Geoffrey VAN ORDEN
Substitute

Mr Daniel VARELA SUANZES-CARPEGNA
Substitute

DELEGATION FOR RELATIONS WITH AFGHANISTAN

Mr Guido PODESTÀ
Chairman

Mrs Nicole FONTAINE
Vice-Chairwoman

Mr Philippe MORILLON
Vice-Chairman

Mrs Roberta ANGELILLI
Member

Mr John ATTARD-MONTALTO
Member

Mrs Angelika BEER
Member

Mr André BRIE
Member

Mr Giulietto CHIESA
Member

Mr Robert EVANS
Member

Mrs Urszula GACEK
Member

Mr Daniel HANNAN
Member

Mr Gunnar HÖKMARK
Member

Mrs Ona JUKNEVIČIENĖ
Member

Mrs Eleonora LO CURTO
Member

Mr Emilio MENÉNDEZ del VALLE
Member

Mr Vittorio AGNOLETTO
Substitute

Mr Alessandro BATTILOCCHIO
Substitute

Mrs Esther de LANGE
Substitute

Mr Nickolay MLADENOV
Substitute

Mrs Annemie NEYTS-UYTTEBROECK
Substitute

Mr Paweł Bartłomiej PISKORSKI
Substitute

Mr José Ignacio SALAFRANCA SÁNCHEZ-NEYRA
Substitute

Mr Jürgen SCHRÖDER
Substitute

Mr Geoffrey VAN ORDEN
Substitute

DELEGATION FOR RELATIONS WITH THE COUNTRIES OF SOUTH-EAST ASIA AND THE ASSOCIATION OF SOUTH-EAST ASIAN NATIONS (ASEAN)

Mr Hartmut NASSAUER
Chairman

Mrs Giovanna CORDA
Vice-Chairwoman

Mrs Véronique MATHIEU
Vice-Chairwoman

Mrs Sharon BOWLES
Member

Mr Gintaras DIDŽIOKAS
Member

Mr Bert DOORN
Member

Mr Jas GAWRONSKI
Member

Mr Dariusz Maciej GRABOWSKI
Member

Mr Vincenzo LAVARRA
Member

Mr Jules MAATEN
Member

Mr Csaba ŐRY
Member

Mr Alojz PETERLE
Member

Mr José Javier POMÉS RUIZ
Member

Mr Pierre PRIBETICH
Member

Mrs Teresa RIERA MADURELL
Member

Mr Frithjof SCHMIDT
Member

Mr Csaba SÓGOR
Member

Mr Kristian VIGENIN
Member

Mrs Barbara WEILER
Member

Mr Lars WOHLIN
Member

Mr Jean-Pierre AUDY
Substitute

Mr Liam AYLWARD
Substitute

Mr Ivo BELET
Substitute

Mr Jerzy BUZEK
Substitute

Mr Nirj DEVA
Substitute

Mrs Elisa FERREIRA
Substitute

Mr Juan FRAILE CANTÓN
Substitute

Mr Robert GOEBBELS
Substitute

Mrs Nathalie GRIESBECK
Substitute

Mr Filip KACZMAREK
Substitute

Mr Vladimír MAŇKA
Substitute

Mr Marco PANNELLA
Substitute

Mr Horst POSDORF
Substitute

Mr Bernhard RAPKAY
Substitute

Mr Bogusław ROGALSKI
Substitute

Mr Carl SCHLYTER
Substitute

Mrs Margie SUDRE
Substitute

Mr Karl von WOGAU
Substitute

DELEGATION FOR RELATIONS WITH THE KOREAN PENINSULA

Mr Hubert PIRKER
Chairman

Mr Louis GRECH
Vice-Chairman

Mr István SZENT-IVÁNYI
Vice-Chairman

Mr Vincenzo AITA
Member

Mr John ATTARD-MONTALTO
Member

Mr Philip CLAEYS
Member

Mrs Alexandra DOBOLYI
Member

Mr Glyn FORD
Member

Mr Roger HELMER
Member

Mr Georg JARZEMBOWSKI
Member

Mrs Astrid LULLING
Member

Mrs Godelieve QUISTHOUDT-ROWOHL
Member

Mr Giovanni ROBUSTI
Member

Mrs Petya STAVREVA
Member

Mr Thomas ULMER
Member

Mr Graham WATSON
Member

Mr Erminio Enzo BOSO
Substitute

Mr Nicodim BULZESC
Substitute

Mr Arūnas DEGUTIS
Substitute

Mr Bert DOORN
Substitute

Mr Jas GAWRONSKI
Substitute

Mrs Evelyne GEBHARDT
Substitute

Mr Bruno GOLLNISCH
Substitute

Mr Jelko KACIN
Substitute

Mrs Sylvia-Yvonne KAUFMANN
Substitute

Mr James NICHOLSON
Substitute

Mr Vural ÖGER
Substitute

Mr Csaba SÓGOR
Substitute

Mr Andrzej Jan SZEJNA
Substitute

DELEGATION FOR RELATIONS WITH AUSTRALIA AND NEW ZEALAND

Mr Giles CHICHESTER
Chairman

Mr Miloš KOTEREC
Vice-Chairman

Mr Mirosław Mariusz PIOTROWSKI
Vice-Chairman

Mr Adamos ADAMOU
Member

Mr Jean Marie BEAUPUY
Member

Mr Sergio BERLATO
Member

Mr Reimer BÖGE
Member

Mrs Ieke van den BURG
Member

Mr Michael CRAMER
Member

Mr Louis GRECH
Member

Mrs Françoise GROSSETÊTE
Member

Mr Klaus HÄNSCH
Member

Mr Timothy KIRKHOPE
Member

Mrs Ewa KLAMT
Member

Mr Fernand LE RACHINEL
Member

Mr David MARTIN
Member

Mr James NICHOLSON
Member

Mr Samuli POHJAMO
Member

Mr Reinhard RACK
Member

Mr Brian SIMPSON
Member

Hannu TAKKULA
Member

Mrs Evangelia TZAMPAZI
Member

Mr Daniel VARELA SUANZES-CARPEGNA
Member

Mr Alessandro BATTILOCCHIO
Substitute

Mr Paulo CASACA
Substitute

Mr Michael CASHMAN
Substitute

Mr Chris DAVIES
Substitute

Mr Den DOVER
Substitute

Mr András GYÜRK
Substitute

Mr Ian HUDGHTON
Substitute

Mrs Iliana Malinova IOTOVA
Substitute

Mr Wolf KLINZ
Substitute

Mrs Marine LE PEN
Substitute

Mrs Mairead McGUINNESS
Substitute

Mr Jan Tadeusz MASIEL
Substitute

Mr Jan OLBRYCHT
Substitute

Mr Markus PIEPER
Substitute

Mr Józef PINIOR
Substitute

Mrs Zita PLEŠTINSKÁ
Substitute

Mr Paul RÜBIG
Substitute

Mrs Margarita STARKEVIČIŪTĖ
Substitute

Mr Robert STURDY
Substitute

Mr Andres TARAND
Substitute

Mr Kyriacos TRIANTAPHYLLIDES
Substitute

Mr Roberts ZĪLE
Substitute

DELEGATION FOR RELATIONS WITH SOUTH AFRICA

Mr Vittorio PRODI
Chairman

Mr Sérgio MARQUES
Vice-Chairman

Mrs Britta THOMSEN
Vice-Chairwoman

Mrs Etelka BARSI-PATAKY
Member

Mr Jean-Luc BENNAHMIAS
Member

Mr Philip BRADBOURN
Member

Mr Mihael BREJC
Member

Mrs Anne FERREIRA
Member

Mr Roland GEWALT
Member

Mr Adam GIEREK
Member

Mrs Catherine GUY-QUINT
Member

Mrs Urszula KRUPA
Member

Mr Claude MORAES
Member

Mr Georgios TOUSSAS
Member

Mrs Inese VAIDERE
Member

Sir Robert ATKINS
Substitute

Mrs Maria BADIA i CUTCHET
Substitute

Mrs Frieda BREPOELS
Substitute

Mr Udo BULLMANN
Substitute

Mr Ole CHRISTENSEN
Substitute

Mr Daniel COHN-BENDIT
Substitute

Mr Michael GAHLER
Substitute

Mr Jan MULDER
Substitute

Mrs Angelika NIEBLER
Substitute

Mr Seán Ó NEACHTAIN
Substitute

Mr Miroslav OUZKÝ
Substitute

Mr Vladimír REMEK
Substitute

Mr Brian SIMPSON
Substitute

Mr David SUMBERG
Substitute

Mrs Glenis WILLMOTT
Substitute

DELEGATION FOR RELATIONS WITH THE NATO PARLIAMENTARY ASSEMBLY

Mrs Pia Elda LOCATELLI
Chairwoman

Mr Paweł Bartłomiej PISKORSKI
Vice-Chairman

Mrs Amalia SARTORI
Vice-Chairwoman

Mrs Angelika BEER
Member

Mr Beniamino DONNICI
Member

Mr Miloš KOTEREC
Member

Mr Holger KRAHMER
Member

Mr Tobias PFLÜGER
Member

Mr Geoffrey VAN ORDEN
Member

Mr Karl von WOGAU
Member

Mr Daniel COHN-BENDIT
Substitute

Mrs Ana Maria GOMES
Substitute

Mr Vasco GRAÇA MOURA
Substitute

Mr Christoph KONRAD
Substitute

Mr Willy MEYER PLEITE
Substitute

Mrs Teresa RIERA MADURELL
Substitute

Mr José Ignacio SALAFRANCA SÁNCHEZ-NEYRA
Substitute

Mr Willem SCHUTH
Substitute

Mr Josef ZIELENIEC
Substitute

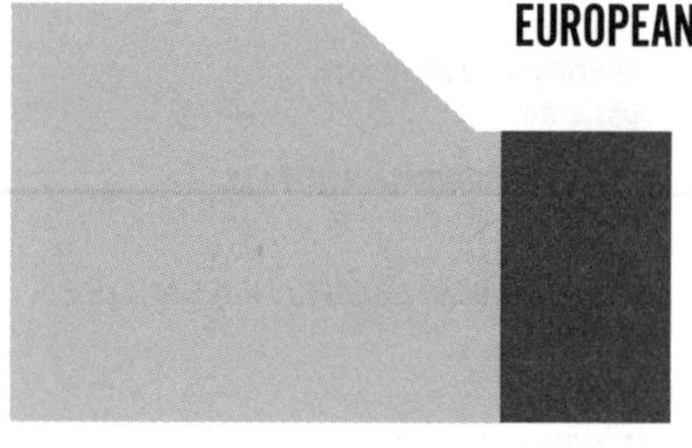

Delegations to the EU joint parliamentary committees

DELEGATION TO THE EU-CROATIA JOINT PARLIAMENTARY COMMITTEE

Mr Pál SCHMITT
Chairman

Mrs Lena EK
Vice-Chairwoman

Mr Peter BACO
Member

Mr Michl EBNER
Member

Mr Szabolcs FAZAKAS
Member

Mr Milan HORÁČEK
Member

Mr Aurelio JURI
Member

Mr Heinz KINDERMANN
Member

Mr Erik MEIJER
Member

Mrs Viktória MOHÁCSI
Member

Mr Bernd POSSELT
Member

Mr Czesław Adam SIEKIERSKI
Member

Mr Ivo STREJČEK
Member

Mr Gary TITLEY
Member

Mr Witold TOMCZAK
Member

Mr Georgs ANDREJEVS
Substitute

Mrs Katerina BATZELI
Substitute

Mr Zsolt László BECSEY
Substitute

Mrs Mojca DRČAR MURKO
Substitute

Mrs Elisabetta GARDINI
Substitute

Mrs Lidia Joanna GERINGER de OEDENBERG
Substitute

Mr Louis GRECH
Substitute

Mr Roger HELMER
Substitute

Mrs Anna IBRISAGIC
Substitute

Mrs Doris PACK
Substitute

Mrs Heide RÜHLE
Substitute

Mr Kristian VIGENIN
Substitute

Mr Oldřich VLASÁK
Substitute

DELEGATION TO THE EU-FORMER YUGOSLAV REPUBLIC OF MACEDONIA JOINT PARLIAMENTARY COMMITTEE

Mr Antonios TRAKATELLIS
Chairman

Mr Georgios GEORGIOU
Vice-Chairman

Mr Gyula HEGYI
Vice-Chairman

Mr Dragoş Florin DAVID
Member

Mrs Mojca DRČAR MURKO
Member

Mrs Kinga GÁL
Member

Mrs Iratxe GARCÍA PÉREZ
Member

Mrs Mary HONEYBALL
Member

Mr Sepp KUSSTATSCHER
Member

Mr Csaba ŐRY
Member

Mrs Anni PODIMATA
Member

Mrs Ulrike RODUST
Member

Mr Daniel STROŽ
Member

Mrs Angelika BEER
Substitute

Mr Victor BOŞTINARU
Substitute

Mr Konstantinos DROUTSAS
Substitute

Mr Lutz GOEPEL
Substitute

Mrs Jutta HAUG
Substitute

Mr Jelko KACIN
Substitute

Mr Evgeni KIRILOV
Substitute

Mr Hans-Peter MAYER
Substitute

Mrs Mechtild ROTHE
Substitute

Mr Riccardo VENTRE
Substitute

Mr Marcello VERNOLA
Substitute

DELEGATION TO THE EU-TURKEY JOINT PARLIAMENTARY COMMITTEE

Mr Joost LAGENDIJK
Chairman

Mr Andrew DUFF
Vice-Chairman

Mrs Maria Eleni KOPPA
Vice-Chairwoman

Mrs Renate SOMMER
Vice-Chairwoman

Mr Jacques TOUBON
Vice-Chairman

Mr Kader ARIF
Member

Mrs Emine BOZKURT
Member

Mr Mogens CAMRE
Member

Mr Luis de GRANDES PASCUAL
Member

Mr Joel HASSE FERREIRA
Member

Mr Gunnar HÖKMARK
Member

Mr Richard HOWITT
Member

Mr Stanisław JAŁOWIECKI
Member

Mr Metin KAZAK
Member

Mr Werner LANGEN
Member

Mr Nils LUNDGREN
Member

Mr Marios MATSAKIS
Member

Mr Yiannakis MATSIS
Member

Mr Andreas MÖLZER
Member

Mr Vural ÖGER
Member

Mr Cem ÖZDEMIR
Member

Mr Margaritis SCHINAS
Member

Mr György SCHÖPFLIN
Member

Mrs Feleknas UCA
Member

Mr Geoffrey VAN ORDEN
Member

Mr Adamos ADAMOU
Substitute

Mrs Marie-Hélène AUBERT
Substitute

Edit BAUER
Substitute

Mr Sebastian Valentin BODU
Substitute

Mr Marco CAPPATO
Substitute

Mr Carlos CARNERO GONZÁLEZ
Substitute

Mr David CASA
Substitute

Mr Philip CLAEYS
Substitute

Mr Daniel COHN-BENDIT
Substitute

Mr Szabolcs FAZAKAS
Substitute

Mr Jas GAWRONSKI
Substitute

Mrs Cristina GUTIÉRREZ-CORTINES
Substitute

Mrs Jeanine HENNIS-PLASSCHAERT
Substitute

Mrs Mary HONEYBALL
Substitute

Mr Sebastiano (Nello) MUSUMECI
Substitute

Sirpa PIETIKÄINEN
Substitute

Mrs Mechtild ROTHE
Substitute

Mr Willem SCHUTH
Substitute

Mrs Marianne THYSSEN
Substitute

Mr Manfred WEBER
Substitute

Mrs Åsa WESTLUND
Substitute

Mr Jan ZAHRADIL
Substitute

DELEGATION TO THE EU-MEXICO JOINT PARLIAMENTARY COMMITTEE

Mrs Erika MANN
Chairwoman

Mr András GYÜRK
Vice-Chairman

Mr Jürgen SCHRÖDER
Vice-Chairman

Mr Richard James ASHWORTH
Member

Mr Giovanni BERLINGUER
Member

Mr Guy BONO
Member

Mr Erminio Enzo BOSO
Member

Mr Vicente Miguel GARCÉS RAMÓN
Member

Mr Mathieu GROSCH
Member

Mr Ambroise GUELLEC
Member

Mr Pedro GUERREIRO
Member

Mr Wolf KLINZ
Member

Mrs Eva LICHTENBERGER
Member

Mr Juan Andrés NARANJO ESCOBAR
Member

Mr Alfredo ANTONIOZZI
Substitute

Mr Luis Manuel CAPOULAS SANTOS
Substitute

Mrs Brigitte DOUAY
Substitute

Mrs Věra FLASAROVÁ
Substitute

Mr Salvador GARRIGA POLLEDO
Substitute

Mr Luis HERRERO-TEJEDOR
Substitute

Mrs Magda KÓSÁNÉ KOVÁCS
Substitute

Mr Peter LIESE
Substitute

Mrs Rosa MIGUÉLEZ RAMOS
Substitute

Mr Raül ROMEVA i RUEDA
Substitute

Mr Leopold Józef RUTOWICZ
Substitute

Mr José Ignacio SALAFRANCA SÁNCHEZ-NEYRA
Substitute

Mrs Patrizia TOIA
Substitute

DELEGATION TO THE EU-CHILE JOINT PARLIAMENTARY COMMITTEE

Mr Giusto CATANIA
Chairman

Mrs Christa KLASS
Vice-Chairwoman

Mr László SURJÁN
Vice-Chairman

Mr Francisco ASSIS
Member

Mr Herbert BÖSCH
Member

Mr Giorgio CAROLLO
Member

Mr Alessandro FOGLIETTA
Member

Mrs Janelly FOURTOU
Member

Mr Norbert GLANTE
Member

Mr Friedrich-Wilhelm GRAEFE zu BARINGDORF
Member

Mr Luis de GRANDES PASCUAL
Member

Mrs Rosa MIGUÉLEZ RAMOS
Member

Mr Nicolae Vlad POPA
Member

Mr Struan STEVENSON
Member

Mrs Patrizia TOIA
Member

Mr Adamos ADAMOU
Substitute

Mr Mogens CAMRE
Substitute

Mr Zdzisław Kazimierz CHMIELEWSKI
Substitute

Mrs Marielle DE SARNEZ
Substitute

Mr Emanuel Jardim FERNANDES
Substitute

Mrs Esther HERRANZ GARCÍA
Substitute

Mr Mikel IRUJO AMEZAGA
Substitute

Mr Bernard LEHIDEUX
Substitute

Mr Lambert van NISTELROOIJ
Substitute

Mrs Francisca PLEGUEZUELOS AGUILAR
Substitute

Mr José Javier POMÉS RUIZ
Substitute

Mrs Catherine STIHLER
Substitute

Mr Ulrich STOCKMANN
Substitute

Mrs Anja WEISGERBER
Substitute

Subcommittees

SUBCOMMITTEE ON HUMAN RIGHTS

Mrs Hélène FLAUTRE
Chairwoman

Mr Patrick GAUBERT
Vice-Chairman

Mr Richard HOWITT
Vice-Chairman

Baroness Sarah LUDFORD
Vice-Chairwoman

Mr Józef PINIOR
Vice-Chairman

Mr Vittorio AGNOLETTO
Member

Mrs Laima Liucija ANDRIKIENĖ
Member

Mrs Irena BELOHORSKÁ
Member

Mr Marco CAPPATO
Member

Mrs Véronique DE KEYSER
Member

Mr Giorgos DIMITRAKOPOULOS
Member

Árpád DUKA-ZÓLYOMI
Member

Mrs Maria da Assunção ESTEVES
Member

Mr Juan FRAILE CANTÓN
Member

Mr Michael GAHLER
Member

Mrs Kinga GÁL
Member

Mr Milan HORÁČEK
Member

Mrs Madeleine JOUYE DE GRANDMAISON
Member

Mr Sajjad KARIM
Member

Mr Edward McMILLAN-SCOTT
Member

Mrs Luisa MORGANTINI
Member

Mrs Pasqualina NAPOLETANO
Member

Baroness NICHOLSON OF WINTERBOURNE
Member

Mr Raimon OBIOLS i GERMÀ
Member

Mr Alojz PETERLE
Member

Sirpa PIETIKÄINEN
Member

Mr José RIBEIRO E CASTRO
Member

Mrs Frédérique RIES
Member

Mr Raül ROMEVA i RUEDA
Member

Mrs Katrin SAKS
Member

Mr Francesco Enrico SPERONI
Member

Mr Csaba Sándor TABAJDI
Member

Mrs Inese VAIDERE
Member

Mr Riccardo VENTRE
Member

Mr Bernard WOJCIECHOWSKI
Member

Mrs Roberta ANGELILLI
Substitute

Mr Francisco ASSIS
Substitute

Mr John ATTARD-MONTALTO
Substitute

Mr Thijs BERMAN
Substitute

Mr Colm BURKE
Substitute

Mr Philip BUSHILL-MATTHEWS
Substitute

Mrs Maddalena CALIA
Substitute

Mr Michael CASHMAN
Substitute

Mr Carlo CASINI
Substitute

Mr Thierry CORNILLET
Substitute

Mr Robert EVANS
Substitute

Mr Claudio FAVA
Substitute

Mrs Hanna FOLTYN-KUBICKA
Substitute

Mr Jas GAWRONSKI
Substitute

Mr Maciej Marian GIERTYCH
Substitute

Mrs Genowefa GRABOWSKA
Substitute

Mr Alain HUTCHINSON
Substitute

Mr Pierre JONCKHEER
Substitute

Mrs Maria Eleni KOPPA
Substitute

Mrs Jean LAMBERT
Substitute

Mrs Esther de LANGE
Substitute

Mrs Elizabeth LYNNE
Substitute

Mrs Véronique MATHIEU
Substitute

Mr Marios MATSAKIS
Substitute

Mr Erik MEIJER
Substitute

Mr Dimitrios PAPADIMOULIS
Substitute

Mr Bernd POSSELT
Substitute

Mrs Kathy SINNOTT
Substitute

Mr Bogusław SONIK
Substitute

Hannu TAKKULA
Substitute

Dr Charles TANNOCK
Substitute

Mrs Feleknas UCA
Substitute

Mr Johan VAN HECKE
Substitute

Mrs Tatjana ŽDANOKA
Substitute

Mr Marian ZLOTEA
Substitute

SUBCOMMITTEE ON SECURITY AND DEFENCE

Mr Karl von WOGAU
Chairman

Mrs Ana Maria GOMES
Vice-Chairwoman

Mr Ģirts Valdis KRISTOVSKIS
Vice-Chairman

Mr Justas Vincas PALECKIS
Vice-Chairman

Mr Marian ZLOTEA
Vice-Chairman

Mr Gerard BATTEN
Member

Mrs Angelika BEER
Member

Mr Mihael BREJC
Member

Mr Cristian Silviu BUŞOI
Member

Mr Philip CLAEYS
Member

Mr Gianni DE MICHELIS
Member

Mr Giorgos DIMITRAKOPOULOS
Member

Mr Beniamino DONNICI
Member

Mr Glyn FORD
Member

Mrs Anna IBRISAGIC
Member

Mr Tunne KELAM
Member

Mr Evgeni KIRILOV
Member

Mrs Maria Eleni KOPPA
Member

Mr Helmut KUHNE
Member

Mr Joost LAGENDIJK
Member

Alexander Graf LAMBSDORFF
Member

Mr Vytautas LANDSBERGIS
Member

Mr Philippe MORILLON
Member

Mrs Annemie NEYTS-UYTTEBROECK
Member

Mr Janusz ONYSZKIEWICZ
Member

Mr Athanasios PAFILIS
Member

Mr Tobias PFLÜGER
Member

Mr Hubert PIRKER
Member

Mr Luís QUEIRÓ
Member

Mr Michel ROCARD
Member

Mr Geoffrey VAN ORDEN
Member

Mr Marcello VERNOLA
Member

Mr Jan Marinus WIERSMA
Member

Mr Luis YAÑEZ-BARNUEVO GARCÍA
Member

Mr Stefano ZAPPALA'
Member

Mr Richard James ASHWORTH
Substitute

Mr Mogens CAMRE
Substitute

Mr Giulietto CHIESA
Substitute

Mr Daniel COHN-BENDIT
Substitute

Mr Paul Marie COÛTEAUX
Substitute

Mr Jean-Luc DEHAENE
Substitute

Mr Proinsias DE ROSSA
Substitute

Mrs Alexandra DOBOLYI
Substitute

Mr Andrew DUFF
Substitute

Mr Christian EHLER
Substitute

Mrs Urszula GACEK
Substitute

Mr Bogdan GOLIK
Substitute

Mr Richard HOWITT
Substitute

Mrs Jana HYBÁŠKOVÁ
Substitute

Anneli JÄÄTTEENMÄKI
Substitute

Mr Christoph KONRAD
Substitute

Mrs Maria MARTENS
Substitute

Mr Willy MEYER PLEITE
Substitute

Mr Nickolay MLADENOV
Substitute

Mr Atanas PAPARIZOV
Substitute

Mr Ioan Mircea PAŞCU
Substitute

Mr Marco RIZZO
Substitute

Mr Raül ROMEVA i RUEDA
Substitute

Mrs Katrin SAKS
Substitute

Mr José Ignacio SALAFRANCA SÁNCHEZ-NEYRA
Substitute

Mr Toomas SAVI
Substitute

Mr György SCHÖPFLIN
Substitute

Mr Marek SIWIEC
Substitute

Mr Hannes SWOBODA
Substitute

Ari VATANEN
Substitute

EUROPEAN PARLIAMENT

Secretariat

Plateau du Kirchberg
L-2929 Luxembourg
Tel. +352 4300 + ext.

Rue Wiertz
B-1047 Brussels
Tel. +32 228-42111
Tel. +32 28 + ext.

Avenue du Président Robert Schuman 1
CS 91024
F-67070 Strasbourg Cedex
Tel. +33 3881-74001
Tel. +33 3881 + ext.

SECRETARY-GENERAL

Harald RØMER
Secretary-General
E-mail: harald.romer@europarl.europa.eu
Tel. +32 228-43028
Tel. +33 3881-74884
Tel. +352 4300-22553

President's Office

Klaus WELLE
Head of Cabinet
E-mail: klaus.welle@europarl.europa.eu
Tel. +32 228-46242
Tel. +33 3881-74831

Ciril STOKELJ
Deputy Head of Cabinet
E-mail: ciril.stokelj@europarl.europa.eu
Tel. +32 228-42979
Tel. +33 3881-72758

Gérard BOKANOWSKI
Special Adviser
E-mail: gerard.bokanowski@europarl.europa.eu
Tel. +32 228-42350
Tel. +33 3881-74731

Strategy and political bodies

Anthony TEASDALE
Team Leader
E-mail: anthony.teasdale@europarl.europa.eu
Tel. +32 228-41678
Tel. +33 3881-72769

Thomas SUBELACK
Adviser
E-mail: thomas.subelack@europarl.europa.eu
Tel. +32 228-41308
Tel. +33 3881-74894

Astrid WORUM
Speechwriter
E-mail: astrid.worum@europarl.europa.eu
Tel. +32 228-41333

Internal policies

Eschel ALPERMANN
Team Leader
E-mail: eschel.alpermann@europarl.europa.eu
Tel. +32 228-34324
Tel. +33 3881-74324

Karen FREDSGAARD
Adviser
E-mail: karen.fredsgaard@europarl.europa.eu
Tel. +32 228-32503
Tel. +33 3881-72291

Chiara MALASOMMA
Adviser
E-mail: chiara.malasomma@europarl.europa.eu
Tel. +32 228-43292
Tel. +33 3881-72733

Renate FEILER
Adviser
E-mail: renate.feiler@europarl.europa.eu
Tel. +32 228-40762
Tel. +33 3881-72654

External policies

Ciril STOKELJ
Deputy Head of Cabinet
E-mail: ciril.stokelj@europarl.europa.eu
Tel. +32 228-42979
Tel. +33 3881-72758

Ana FERNANDEZ PERLES
Adviser
E-mail: ana.fernandez@europarl.europa.eu
Tel. +32 228-32084
Tel. +33 3881-64094

Alexandre STUTZMANN
Adviser
E-mail: alexandre.stutzmann@europarl.europa.eu
Tel. +32 228-43439
Tel. +33 3881-74769

Press Service

Katrin RUHRMANN
Spokesperson
E-mail: katrin.ruhrmann@europarl.europa.eu
Tel. +32 228-42573
Tel. +33 3881-74830

Fearghas O'BEARA
Adviser
E-mail: fearghas.obeara@europarl.europa.eu
Tel. +32 228-41048
Tel. +33 3881-73031

Robert GOLANSKI
Adviser
E-mail: robert.golanski@europarl.europa.eu
Tel. +32 228-41601
Tel. +33 3881-73436

Jesús GÓMEZ
Adviser
E-mail: jesus.gomez@europarl.europa.eu
Tel. +32 228-32157
Tel. +33 3881-76771

Jörg-Dietrich NACKMAYR
E-mail: joerg.nackmayr@europarl.europa.eu
Tel. +32 228-32152
Tel. +33 3881-73281

Cabinet

Marie-Jeanne SMEETS
Team Leader
E-mail: marie-jeanne.smeets@europarl.europa.eu
Tel. +32 228-42778
Tel. +33 3881-78778

Internal organisation

Annamaria FORGACS
E-mail: annamaria.forgacs@europarl.europa.eu
Tel. +32 228-43448
Tel. +33 3881-72796

Secretary-General's Office

Fernando SUAREZ MELLA
Head of Cabinet
E-mail: fernando.suarez@europarl.europa.eu
Tel. +32 228-42439
Tel. +352 4300-25762
Tel. +33 3881-77014

Inge Gerd MORMINO
Adviser
E-mail: inge.mormino@europarl.europa.eu
Tel. +32 228-44521
Tel. +33 3881-74165
Tel. +352 4300-23036

Tessa RYAN
Adviser
E-mail: tessa.ryan@europarl.europa.eu
Tel. +32 228-40740
Tel. +33 3881-73350

Leena LINNUS
Adviser
E-mail: leena.linnus@europarl.europa.eu
Tel. +32 228-42825
Tel. +33 3881-76775

Alessandro CHIOCCHETTI
Adviser
E-mail: alessandro.chiocchetti@europarl.europa.eu
Tel. +32 228-40754
Tel. +33 3881-73461

Monika MIGO
Adviser
E-mail: monika.migo@europarl.europa.eu
Tel. +32 228-43035
Tel. +33 3881-74412

Directorate for Relations with the Political Group Secretariats

Olivia RATTI
Director
E-mail: olivia.ratti@europarl.europa.eu
Tel. +32 228-43377
Tel. +33 3881-75839

LEGAL SERVICE

Christian PENNERA
Jurisconsult
E-mail: jurisconsultus@europarl.europa.eu
Tel. +32 228-42724
Tel. +352 4300-22626
Tel. +33 388-1-74626

Olivier CAISOU-ROUSSEAU
E-mail: olivier.caisou-rousseau@europarl.europa.eu
Tel. +352 4300-20103
Tel. +33 388-1-74550
Tel. +32 228-32868

Directorate for Institutional and Parliamentary Affairs

Johann SCHOO
Director
E-mail: johann.schoo@europarl.europa.eu
Tel. +32 228-43943
Tel. +352 4300-22439
Tel. +33 388-1-77007

Unit for Institutional and Budgetary Law and External Relations

Ricardo PASSOS
Head of Unit
E-mail: ricardo.passos@europarl.europa.eu
Tel. +352 4300-22720
Tel. +33 388-1-74164
Tel. +32 228-41757

Auke BAAS
E-mail: auke.baas@europarl.europa.eu
Tel. +32 228-42369
Tel. +33 388-1-72418

Lisbeth Grodum KNUDSEN
E-mail: lisbeth.knudsen@europarl.europa.eu
Tel. +32 228-32311
Tel. +33 388-1-73305

Gabriele MAZZINI
E-mail: gabriele.mazzini@europarl.europa.eu
Tel. +32 228-44557
Tel. +33 3881-72418

Daniela GAUCI
E-mail: daniela.gauci@europarl.europa.eu
Tel. +32 228-31404
Tel. +33 3881-73611

Angelina GROS TCHORBADJIYSKA
E-mail: angelina.gros-tchorbadjiyska@europarl.europa.eu
Tel. +32 228-32878
Tel. +33 388-1-72418

Mihkel ALLIK
E-mail: mihkel.allik@europarl.europa.eu
Tel. +32 228-43954
Tel. +33 388-1-72418

Unit for Parliamentary Issues and Members' Rights

Hans KRÜCK
Head of Unit
E-mail: hans.krueck@europarl.europa.eu
Tel. +352 4300-24294
Tel. +33 388-1-73657
Tel. +32 228-42414

Christos KARAMARCOS
E-mail: christos.karamarcos@europarl.europa.eu
Tel. +352 4300-22051
Tel. +33 388-1-73650

Norbert LORENZ
E-mail: norbert.lorenz@europarl.europa.eu
Tel. +352 4300-20364
Tel. +33 388-1-73650

Evelyn WALDHERR
E-mail: evelyn.waldherr@europarl.europa.eu
Tel. +32 228-42345
Tel. +33 388-1-73611

Dominique MOORE
E-mail: dominique.moore@europarl.europa.eu
Tel. +32 228-40625
Tel. +33 388-1-73650

Anna POSPISILOVA PADOWSKA
E-mail: anna.padowska@europarl.europa.eu
Tel. +352 4300-25173
Tel. +33 388-1-73650

Marta WINDISCH
E-mail: marta.windisch@europarl.europa.eu
Tel. +352 4300-22438
Tel. +33 388-1-73650

Laetitia CHRÉTIEN
E-mail: laetitia.chretien@europarl.europa.eu
Tel. +352 4300-22054
Tel. +33 388-1-73650

Directorate for Legislative Affairs

Ezio PERILLO
Director
E-mail: ezio.perillo@europarl.europa.eu
Tel. +32 228-46336
Tel. +352 4300-21336
Tel. +33 388-1-74387

Legislation Unit

María GÓMEZ-LEAL
Head of Unit
E-mail: maria.gomez@europarl.europa.eu
Tel. +32 228-43209
Tel. +33 3881-73385

Guido RICCI
E-mail: guido.ricci@europarl.europa.eu
Tel. +32 228-46231
Tel. +33 388-1-73306

Anders NEERGAARD
E-mail: anders.neergaard@europarl.europa.eu
Tel. +32 228-43970
Tel. +33 388-1-73306

João RODRIGUES
E-mail: joao.rodrigues@europarl.europa.eu
Tel. +32 228-40780
Tel. +33 388-1-73306

Luca VISAGGIO
E-mail: luca.visaggio@europarl.europa.eu
Tel. +32 228-32589
Tel. +33 388-1-73306

Athanassios TROUPIOTIS
E-mail: athanassios.troupiotis@europarl.europa.eu
Tel. +32 228-43254
Tel. +33 388-1-73306

Ioanna ANAGNOSTOPOULOU
E-mail: ioanna.anagnostopoulou@europarl.europa.eu
Tel. +32 228-32037
Tel. +33 388-1-73306

Rasma KASKINA
E-mail: rasma.kaskina@europarl.europa.eu
Tel. +32 228-32174
Tel. +33 388-1-73307

Justice and Civil Liberties Unit

Kieran BRADLEY
Head of Unit
E-mail: kieran.bradley@europarl.europa.eu
Tel. +32 228-43280
Tel. +352 4300-24677
Tel. +33 388-1-73687

Antonio CAIOLA
E-mail: antonio.caiola@europarl.europa.eu
Tel. +352 4300-24818
Tel. +33 3881-72906

Ulrich RÖSSLEIN
E-mail: ulrich.rosslein@europarl.europa.eu
Tel. +32 228-42618
Tel. +33 388-1-73307

Andrej AUERSPERGER MATIC
E-mail: andrej.matic@europarl.europa.eu
Tel. +32 228-31463
Tel. +33 388-1-72906

Codification Team — Recasting

Fernando HERVÁS DEMPSTER
Team Leader
E-mail: fernando.hervas@europarl.europa.eu
Tel. +32 228-46207

Lutgart DENEYS
E-mail: lutgart.deneys@europarl.europa.eu
Tel. +32 228-46213

Peder BISTRÖM
E-mail: peder.bistrom@europarl.europa.eu
Tel. +32 228-40641

Directorate for Administrative and Financial Affairs

Hannu VON HERTZEN
Director
E-mail: hannu.vonhertzen@europarl.europa.eu
Tel. +352 4300-22330
Tel. +33 388-1-77039
Tel. +32 228-43974

Unit for Civil Service Law

Jan Frans DE WACHTER
Head of Unit
E-mail: janfrans.dewachter@europarl.europa.eu
Tel. +352 4300-23909
Tel. +33 388-1-73305

Cristina BURGOS ALCAIDE
E-mail: cristina.burgos@europarl.europa.eu
Tel. +352 4300-23701
Tel. +33 388-1-73305

Asta LUKOSIUTE
E-mail: asta.lukosiute@europarl.europa.eu
Tel. +352 4300-25318
Tel. +33 388-1-73305

Kamila ZEJDOVA
E-mail: kamila.zejdova@europarl.europa.eu
Tel. +32 228-42912
Tel. +33 3881-73305

Raluca IGNATESCU
E-mail: raluca.ignatescu@europarl.europa.eu
Tel. +352 4300-25794
Tel. +33 388-1-73305

Sibylle SEYR
E-mail: sibylle.seyr@europarl.europa.eu
Tel. +352 4300-24305
Tel. +33 388-1-73305

Unit for Contract and Financial Law

Didier PETERSHEIM
Head of Unit
E-mail: didier.petersheim@europarl.europa.eu
Tel. +352 4300-23608
Tel. +32 228-46302
Tel. +33 388-1-73608

François POILVACHE
E-mail: francois.poilvache@europarl.europa.eu
Tel. +32 228-46230
Tel. +33 388-1-74948

Paloma LOPEZ-CARCELLER
E-mail: paloma.lopez-carceller@europarl.europa.eu
Tel. +352 4300-22801
Tel. +33 388-1-74948

Monique ECKER
E-mail: monique.ecker@europarl.europa.eu
Tel. +352 4300-24348
Tel. +33 388-1-74948

András TAMÁS
E-mail: andras.tamas@europarl.europa.eu
Tel. +32 228-31406
Tel. +33 388-1-74948

DIRECTORATE-GENERAL FOR THE PRESIDENCY

David HARLEY
Deputy Secretary-General
Director-General
E-mail: david.harley@europarl.europa.eu
Tel. +352 4300-24909
Tel. +32 228-43909
Tel. +33 3881-74507

Patricia JIMENEZ LOZANO
E-mail: patricia.jimenez@europarl.europa.eu
Tel. +32 228-44174
Tel. +33 3881-76671

Monika STRASSER
E-mail: monika.strasser@europarl.europa.eu
Tel. +32 228-40623
Tel. +33 3881-64103

General Coordination Unit

Antoine CAHEN
Head of Unit
E-mail: antoine.cahen@europarl.europa.eu
Tel. +32 228-40660
Tel. +352 4300-22499
Tel. +33 3881-74420

Budget and Finance Unit

Nicolas FOSCOLOS
Head of Unit
E-mail: nicolas.foscolos@europarl.europa.eu
Tel. +32 228-42661
Tel. +33 3881-72117

Directorate for Presidency Services

Christine VERGER
Director
E-mail: christine.verger@europarl.europa.eu
Tel. +32 228-44461
Tel. +352 4300-24662
Tel. +33 3881-74323

Secretariat of the Bureau, the Conference of Presidents and the Quaestors

Freddy DREXLER
Head of Unit
E-mail: freddy.drexler@europarl.europa.eu
Tel. +32 228-43620
Tel. +33 3881-74056/78171

Éric PEGAZZANO
E-mail: eric.pegazzano@europarl.europa.eu
Tel. +32 228-40736
Tel. +33 3881-73713

Neophytos CALINOGLOU
E-mail: neophytos.calinoglou@europarl.europa.eu
Tel. +32 228-43637
Tel. +33 3881-77004

Sarah SHEIL
E-mail: sarah.sheil@europarl.europa.eu
Tel. +32 228-34046
Tel. +33 3881-78171

Michal CZAPLICKI
E-mail: michal.czaplicki@europarl.europa.eu
Tel. +32 228-44886
Tel. +33 3881-76674

Christian MANGOLD
E-mail: christian.mangold@europarl.europa.eu
Tel. +32 228-40770
Tel. +33 3881-72811

Rupert WILKINSON
E-mail: rupert.wilkinson@europarl.europa.eu
Tel. +32 228-44039
Tel. +33 3881-73996

Public Register and Access to Documents Unit

Brigitte NOUAILLE-DEGORCE
Head of Unit
Director ad personam
E-mail: brigitte.nouaille@europarl.europa.eu
Tel. +32 228-43097
Tel. +33 3881-74543

María Jesús CAUS GÁLVEZ
E-mail: maria.caus@europarl.europa.eu
Tel. +32 228-44548/43164
Tel. +33 3881-73496

Official Mail Unit

...
Head of Unit

Archive and Documentation Centre (CARDOC)

Donato ANTONA
Head of Unit
E-mail: donato.antona@europarl.europa.eu
Tel. +352 4300-22703
Tel. +33 3881-74624

Franco PIODI
E-mail: franco.piodi@europarl.europa.eu
Tel. +352 4300-24457

Margret SCHELLING
E-mail: margret.schelling@europarl.europa.eu
Tel. +352 4300-24104

Protocol Unit

François BRUNAGEL
Head of Unit
Director ad personam
E-mail: francois.brunagel@europarl.europa.eu
Tel. +32 228-44643/43016
Tel. +33 3881-74643/74166

Luis MARTINEZ GUILLEN
E-mail: luis.martinezguillen@europarl.europa.eu
Tel. +32 228-43403
Tel. +33 3881-72380

Julia GLINSKI
E-mail: julia.glinski@europarl.europa.eu
Tel. +32 228-34137
Tel. +33 3881-78172

Security Unit

Mathieu THOMANN
Head of Unit
E-mail: mathieu.thomann@europarl.europa.eu
Tel. +32 228-44927
Tel. +352 4300-24927
Tel. +33 3881-74927

Pascal HEYMANS
E-mail: pascal.heymans@europarl.europa.eu
Tel. +32 228-41060
Tel. +33 3881-75144

Jean-Pascal RIHOUX
E-mail: jean-pascal.rihoux@europarl.europa.eu
Tel. +32 228-43729
Tel. +33 3881-78213

Patrice BAGUET
E-mail: patrice.baguet@europarl.europa.eu
Tel. +32 228-34095
Tel. +33 3881-72273

Peter IDE-KOSTIC
E-mail: peter.ide-kostic@europarl.europa.eu
Tel. +32 228-44175
Tel. +33 3881-72910

Directorate for the Plenary

Birgitte STENSBALLE
Director
E-mail: birgitte.stensballe@europarl.europa.eu
Tel. +352 4300-22847
Tel. +32 228-44065
Tel. +33 3881-74505

Plenary Records Unit

Mr ...
Head of Unit

Andrea ANTONELLO
E-mail: andrea.antonello@europarl.europa.eu
Tel. +352 4300-23234
Tel. +33 3881-74703
Tel. +32 228-32127

Olivier DANJOUX
E-mail: olivier.danjoux@europarl.europa.eu
Tel. +352 4300-24934
Tel. +33 3881-73824
Tel. +32 228-44319

Julie GIESE
E-mail: julie.giese@europarl.europa.eu
Tel. +352 4300-23453
Tel. +33 3881-72517
Tel. +32 228-32127

Christina NYMAN
E-mail: christina.nyman@europarl.europa.eu
Tel. +352 4300-27796
Tel. +33 3881-72516
Tel. +32 228-44032

Ioannis Panayot TSIRIMOKOS
E-mail: ioannis.tsirimokos@europarl.europa.eu
Tel. +352 4300-24476
Tel. +33 3881-74434
Tel. +32 228-32127

Maite WEBER AMOREAU
E-mail: maite.weber@europarl.europa.eu
Tel. +352 4300-24261
Tel. +33 3881-73781
Tel. +32 228-32312

Members' Activities Unit

João CORREA
Head of Unit
E-mail: joao.correa@europarl.europa.eu
Tel. +352 4300-22289
Tel. +32 228-44027
Tel. +33 3881-74797

Fabio GALATIOTO
E-mail: fabio.galatioto@europarl.europa.eu
Tel. +32 228-41310
Tel. +352 4300-23423
Tel. +33 3881-72525

Plenary Programming Unit

Gabriel SÁNCHEZ RODRÍGUEZ
Head of Unit
E-mail: gabriel.sanchez@europarl.europa.eu
Tel. +32 228-43651
Tel. +33 3881-74777

Juan URBIETA GANDIAGA
E-mail: juan.urbieta@europarl.europa.eu
Tel. +32 228-42353
Tel. +33 3881-72054

Alfredo BROGGI
E-mail: alfredo.broggi@europarl.europa.eu
Tel. +32 228-44362
Tel. +33 3881-73594

Plenary Organisation and Follow-up Unit

Philip SCOTT
Head of Unit
E-mail: philip.scott@europarl.europa.eu
Tel. +352 4300-24363
Tel. +32 228-44064
Tel. +33 3881-74505

Francisco PEYRÓ LLOPIS
E-mail: fran.peyro@europarl.europa.eu
Tel. +352 4300-21137
Tel. +32 228-44063
Tel. +33 3881-74679

Erich EGGENHOFER
E-mail: erich.eggenhofer@europarl.europa.eu
Tel. +352 4300-24273
Tel. +33 3881-74517

Mihaela Adelina HUMINIC ORZU
E-mail: adelina.orzu@europarl.europa.eu
Tel. +32 228-44219
Tel. +33 3881-78159

Caroline INSON
E-mail: caroline.inson@europarl.europa.eu
Tel. +32 228-43603

Directorate for Legislative Acts

Eva DUDZINSKA
Director
E-mail: eva.dudzinska@europarl.europa.eu
Tel. +32 228-44020
Tel. +352 4300-23447
Tel. +33 3881-72529

Legislative Planning and Coordination Unit

Kristian KNUDSEN
Head of Unit
E-mail: kristian.knudsen@europarl.europa.eu
Tel. +32 228-31731
Tel. +352 4300-23197
Tel. +33 3881-74138

Ornella BUSON
E-mail: ornella.buson@europarl.europa.eu
Tel. +352 4300-24418
Tel. +33 3881-73823

Baldomero COELHO
E-mail: baldomero.coelho@europarl.europa.eu
Tel. +32 228-43778
Tel. +33 3881-64076

Lena HANSSON
E-mail: lena.hansson@europarl.europa.eu
Tel. +32 228-32484
Tel. +33 3881-64076

Kristina STEFANSSON
E-mail: kristina.stefansson@europarl.europa.eu
Tel. +352 4300-27005
Tel. +33 3881-64076

Tabling Desk Unit

Paul DUNSTAN
Head of Unit
E-mail: paul.dunstan@europarl.europa.eu
Tel. +32 228-44064
Tel. +33 3881-74919
Tel. +352 4300-22532

Aino SALMINEN
E-mail: aino.salminen@europarl.europa.eu
Tel. +352 4300-24361
Tel. +33 3881-72014
Tel. +32 228-331418

Steven WICKER
E-mail: steven.wicker@europarl.europa.eu
Tel. +32 228-42420
Tel. +33 3881-74121

Unit for Reception and Referral of Official Documents

Karl NATSCHERADETZ
Head of Unit
E-mail: karl.natscheradetz@europarl.europa.eu
Tel. +32 228-43488
Tel. +33 3881-72013

Legislative Quality Unit A (DE-ES-ET-FI-HU-IT-PT-SL Sections)

Ellen HEINEMANN
Head of Unit
E-mail: ellen.heinemann@europarl.europa.eu
Tel. +32 228-31716
Tel. +352 4300-24122
Tel. +33 3881-74746

Legislative Quality Unit B (BG-EL-EN-GA-MT Sections)

Ellen ROBSON
Head of Unit
E-mail: ellen.robson@europarl.europa.eu
Tel. +32 228-31408
Tel. +33 3881-74748

Legislative Quality Unit C (CS-DA-FR-LT-LV-NL-PL-RO-SK-SV Sections)

Kristian KNUDSEN
Head of Unit (acting)
E-mail: kristian.knudsen@europarl.europa.eu
Tel. +32 228-31731
Tel. +352 4300-23197
Tel. +33 3881-74138

BG — Bulgarian Section

Dessislava CHOUMELOVA
E-mail: dessislava.choumelova@europarl.europa.eu
Tel. +32 228-32293
Tel. +33 3881-73702

Hristo DORMISCHEV
E-mail: hristo.dormischev@europarl.europa.eu
Tel. +32 228-32756
Tel. +33 3881-73702

Kristina IVANOVA
E-mail: kristina.ivanova@europarl.europa.eu
Tel. +32 228-32290
Tel. +33 3881-72985

Radostina IVANOVA
E-mail: radostina.ivanova@europarl.europa.eu
Tel. +32 228-43216
Tel. +33 3881-72985

CS — Czech Section

Libor BOHAC
on secondment until 30.6.2009
E-mail: libor.bohac@europarl.europa.eu
Tel. +32 228-31736
Tel. +33 3881-72521

Hana BOSKOVA
E-mail: hana.boskova@europarl.europa.eu
Tel. +32 228-32434
Tel. +33 3881-72521

Vendula LANGOVA
E-mail: vendula.langova@europarl.europa.eu
Tel. +32 228-34120
Tel. +33 3881-74745

Radek PILAR
E-mail: radek.pilar@europarl.europa.eu
Tel. +32 228-31737
Tel. +33 3881-72514

DA — Danish Section

Peter KRISTENSEN
E-mail: peter.kristensen@europarl.europa.eu
Tel. +352 4300-23011
Tel. +33 3881-74310
Tel. +32 228-34035

Christine KYST
E-mail: christine.kyst@europarl.europa.eu
Tel. +32 228-31384
Tel. +33 3881-74310

Birthe Lise LANDSTED
E-mail: birthe.landsted@europarl.europa.eu
Tel. +32 228-32546
Tel. +33 3881-73698

Steffen RYOM
E-mail: steffen.ryom@europarl.europa.eu
Tel. +32 228-44024
Tel. +33 3881-73698

DE — German Section

Michael FUCHS
E-mail: michael.fuchs@europarl.europa.eu
Tel. +32 228-44051
Tel. +33 3881-74467

Susanne KNÖFEL
E-mail: susanne.knoefel@europarl.europa.eu
Tel. +32 228-31730
Tel. +33 3881-74467

Claudia LINDEMANN
E-mail: claudia.lindemann@europarl.europa.eu
Tel. +32 228-44179
Tel. +33 3881-73814

Philipp REIFENRATH
E-mail: philipp.reifenrath@europarl.europa.eu
Tel. +32 228-44013
Tel. +33 3881-74467

Thomas WEBER
E-mail: thomas.weber@europarl.europa.eu
Tel. +32 228-44035
Tel. +33 3881-73814

EL — Greek Section

Perikles CHRISTODOULOU
E-mail: perikles.christodoulou@europarl.europa.eu
Tel. +32 228-41420
Tel. +33 3881-74646

Vasilios MAGNIS
E-mail: vasilios.magnis@europarl.europa.eu
Tel. +32 228-46206
Tel. +33 3881-74910

Konstantina TSILONI
E-mail: konstantina.tsiloni@europarl.europa.eu
Tel. +32 228-40659
Tel. +33 3881-74646

Heleni VLASTARA
E-mail: heleni.vlastara@europarl.europa.eu
Tel. +32 228-44009
Tel. +33 3881-74910

EN — English Section

David ASHTON
E-mail: david.ashton@europarl.europa.eu
Tel. +32 228-32287
Tel. +33 3881-74330

Mark BEAMISH
E-mail: mark.beamish@europarl.europa.eu
Tel. +32 228-32892
Tel. +33 3881-74330

James Hamilton BENN
E-mail: james.benn@europarl.europa.eu
Tel. +32 228-44016
Tel. +33 3881-74330

Hugo DE CHASSIRON
E-mail: hugo.dechassiron@europarl.europa.eu
Tel. +32 228-44199
Tel. +33 3881-73806

Katherine DUMBLETON
E-mail: katherine.dumbleton@europarl.europa.eu
Tel. +32 228-31169
Tel. +33 3881-73806

Isobel FINDLAY
E-mail: isobel.findlay@europarl.europa.eu
Tel. +32 228-32890
Tel. +33 3881-73806

June O'KEEFFE
E-mail: june.okeeffe@europarl.europa.eu
Tel. +32 228-32550
Tel. +33 3881-73806

Stéphanie RIDLEY
E-mail: stephanie.ridley@europarl.europa.eu
Tel. +32 228-32573
Tel. +33 3881-74330

ES — Spanish Section

Monica FUENTES GARCIA
E-mail: monica.fuentes@europarl.europa.eu
Tel. +32 228-44650
Tel. +33 3881-73202

Mercedes RODRIGUEZ SARRO
E-mail: mercedes.rodriguez@europarl.europa.eu
Tel. +32 228-40766
Tel. +33 3881-73807

Amparo RUEDA BUESO
E-mail: amparo.ruedabueso@europarl.europa.eu
Tel. +32 228-44018
Tel. +33 3881-73202

Leticia ZULETA DE REALES ANSALDO
E-mail: leticia.zuleta@europarl.europa.eu
Tel. +32 228-44351
Tel. +33 3881-73807

ET — Estonian Section

Moonika ARRAS
E-mail: moonika.arras@europarl.europa.eu
Tel. +32 228-34042
Tel. +33 3881-73818

Kadri BRÜGEL
E-mail: kadri.brugel@europarl.europa.eu
Tel. +32 228-32653
Tel. +33 3881-72526

Kristiina MILT
E-mail: kristiina.milt@europarl.europa.eu
Tel. +32 228-31727
Tel. +33 3881-72377

Kadri PARIS
E-mail: kadri.paris@europarl.europa.eu
Tel. +32 228-31755
Tel. +33 3881-73818

FI — Finnish Section

Eeva ERIKSSON
E-mail: eeva.eriksson@europarl.europa.eu
Tel. +32 228-32033
Tel. +33 3881-72376

Tuomas HELINKO
E-mail: tuomas.helinko@europarl.europa.eu
Tel. +32 228-43714
Tel. +33 3881-72376

Sointu RAUTIAINEN-MURIAS
E-mail: sointu.rautiainen@europarl.europa.eu
Tel. +352 4300-22866
Tel. +33 3881-72378

FR — French Section

Bruno BILQUIN
E-mail: bruno.bilquin@europarl.europa.eu
Tel. +32 228-32314
Tel. +33 3881-74788

Xavier DEBROUX
E-mail: xavier.debroux@europarl.europa.eu
Tel. +32 228-40708
Tel. +33 3881-74788

Alix DELASNERIE
E-mail: alix.delasnerie@europarl.europa.eu
Tel. +32 228-40707
Tel. +33 3881-74788

Christine HUVELIN
E-mail: christine.huvelin@europarl.europa.eu
Tel. +32 228-34033
Tel. +33 3881-74788

Vincent MEUNIER
E-mail: vincent.meunier@europarl.europa.eu
Tel. +32 228-43726
Tel. +33 3881-74657

Marianne SALOU
E-mail: marianne.salou@europarl.europa.eu
Tel. +32 228-32477
Tel. +33 3881-74657

GA — Irish Section

Fionnuala CROKER
E-mail: fionnuala.croker@europarl.europa.eu
Tel. +32 228-32578
Tel. +33 3881-74330

HU — Hungarian Section

Dora BOYTHA
E-mail: dora.boytha@europarl.europa.eu
Tel. +32 228-43581
Tel. +33 3881-72919

Janos HARCSA
E-mail: janos.harcsa@europarl.europa.eu
Tel. +32 228-31798
Tel. +33 3881-72919

Tamás LUKÁCSI
E-mail: tamas.lukacsi@europarl.europa.eu
Tel. +32 228-31714
Tel. +33 3881-75731

Kinga WYNANDS-SZENTMARY
E-mail: kinga.wynands-szentmary@europarl.europa.eu
Tel. +32 228-31715
Tel. +33 3881-72919

IT — Italian Section

Luca DI PRESO
E-mail: luca.dipreso@europarl.europa.eu
Tel. +32 228-32570
Tel. +33 3881-75827

Maria GANDOLFO
E-mail: maria.gandolfo@europarl.europa.eu
Tel. +32 228-43064
Tel. +33 3881-75827

Barbara MARTINELLO
E-mail: barbara.martinello@europarl.europa.eu
Tel. +32 228-41423
Tel. +33 3881-75827

LT — Lithuanian Section

Vilija CEILITKAITE
E-mail: vilija.ceilitkaite@europarl.europa.eu
Tel. +32 228-31541
Tel. +33 3881-74738

Saulius MILIUS
E-mail: saulius.milius@europarl.europa.eu
Tel. +32 228-32795
Tel. +33 3881-74738

Julija VARNAITE
E-mail: julija.varnaite@europarl.europa.eu
Tel. +32 228-32828
Tel. +33 3881-73834

LV — Latvian Section

Linda RUPPEKA-RUPEIKA
E-mail: linda.ruppeka@europarl.europa.eu
Tel. +32 228-32658
Tel. +33 3881-73802

MT — Maltese Section

Lucienne ATTARD
E-mail: lucienne.attard@europarl.europa.eu
Tel. +32 228-40726
Tel. +33 3881-73804

Josanne BONNICI
E-mail: josanne.bonnici@europarl.europa.eu
Tel. +32 228-32562
Tel. +33 3881-73804

Hubert DALLI
E-mail: hubert.dalli@europarl.europa.eu
Tel. +32 228-31720
Tel. +33 3881-73203

Pamela VASSALLO
E-mail: pamela.vassallo@europarl.europa.eu
Tel. +32 228-32810
Tel. +33 3881-72519

NL — Dutch Section

Sven CORTHOUT
E-mail: sven.corthout@europarl.europa.eu
Tel. +32 228-44017
Tel. +33 3881-73693

Marc HULSBOSCH
E-mail: marc.hulsbosch@europarl.europa.eu
Tel. +32 228-40806
Tel. +33 3881-73693

Jan SIFFERT
E-mail: jan.siffert@europarl.europa.eu
Tel. +32 228-40752
Tel. +33 3881-73201

Patricia VAN DE PEER
E-mail: patricia.vandepeer@europarl.europa.eu
Tel. +32 228-44037
Tel. +33 3881-73201

PL — Polish Section

Grzegorz DEMBOWSKI
E-mail: grzegorz.dembowski@europarl.europa.eu
Tel. +32 228-31717
Tel. +33 3881-74181

Urszula MOJKOWSKA
E-mail: urszula.mojkowska@europarl.europa.eu
Tel. +32 228-34044
Tel. +33 3881-74711

Michal RUDZIECKI
E-mail: michal.rudziecki@europarl.europa.eu
Tel. +32 228-31718
Tel. +33 3881-74711

Jacek Marek SWIDRAK
E-mail: jacek.swidrak@europarl.europa.eu
Tel. +32 228-31719
Tel. +33 3881-74181

Dorota ZOLNIERCZYK
E-mail: dorota.zolnierczyk@europarl.europa.eu
Tel. +32 228-40665
Tel. +33 3881-74711

PT — Portuguese Section

Manuel ALEIXO
E-mail: manuel.aleixo@europarl.europa.eu
Tel. +32 228-34039
Tel. +33 3881-73692

Carla CARVALHO
E-mail: carla.carvalho@europarl.europa.eu
Tel. +32 228-44025
Tel. +33 3881-72513

Antonio GONCALVES
E-mail: antonio.goncalves@europarl.europa.eu
Tel. +352 4300-22315
Tel. +33 3881-73692

Henrique MENDES BRANCO
E-mail: henrique.mendes@europarl.europa.eu
Tel. +32 228-44026
Tel. +33 3881-72513

Ines MORGADO
E-mail: ines.morgado@europarl.europa.eu
Tel. +32 228-44043
Tel. +33 3881-73692

RO — Romanian Section

Angela Mariana BALAN
E-mail: angela.balan@europarl.europa.eu
Tel. +32 228-32291
Tel. +33 3881-73148

Alina Monica MEDELEANU
E-mail: monica.medeleanu@europarl.europa.eu
Tel. +32 228-32783
Tel. +33 3881-73832

Jean-Viorel MIRICESCU
E-mail: viorel.miricescu@europarl.europa.eu
Tel. +32 228-32556
Tel. +33 3881-73148

Andreea Elena POPESCU
E-mail: andreea.popescu@europarl.europa.eu
Tel. +32 228-32292
Tel. +33 3881-73148

SK — Slovak Section

Zuzana ALEXANDRE
E-mail: zuzana.alexandre@europarl.europa.eu
Tel. +32 228-31738
Tel. +33 3881-72515

Miriam KORTEWEG
E-mail: miriam.korteweg@europarl.europa.eu
Tel. +32 228-31725
Tel. +33 3881-72515

Tatiana MRAZIKOVA
E-mail: tatiana.mrazikova@europarl.europa.eu
Tel. +32 228-31739
Tel. +33 3881-73836

Radoslav SVITANA
E-mail: radoslav.svitana@europarl.europa.eu
Tel. +32 228-34045
Tel. +33 3881-73836

Peter VAVRIK
E-mail: peter.vavrik@europarl.europa.eu
Tel. +32 228-31726
Tel. +33 3881-73836

SL — Slovene Section

Sabina BALAZIC
E-mail: sabina.balazic@europarl.europa.eu
Tel. +32 228-31835
Tel. +33 3881-73816

Andreja BEGUS
E-mail: andreja.begus@europarl.europa.eu
Tel. +32 228-32374
Tel. +33 3881-73816

Anze ERBEZNIK
E-mail: anze.erbeznik@europarl.europa.eu
Tel. +32 228-32811
Tel. +33 3881-73816

Safet KALTAK
E-mail: safet.kaltak@europarl.europa.eu
Tel. +32 228-40637
Tel. +33 3881-73816

Vasja LUTAR
E-mail: vasja.lutar@europarl.europa.eu
Tel. +32 228-31723
Tel. +33 3881-73816

SV — Swedish Section

Kristina FÖH
E-mail: kristina.foeh@europarl.europa.eu
Tel. +32 228-44223
Tel. +33 3881-72375

Magnus HAGMAN
E-mail: magnus.hagman@europarl.europa.eu
Tel. +32 228-32419
Tel. +33 3881-72375

Magnus NORDANSKOG
E-mail: magnus.nordanskog@europarl.europa.eu
Tel. +32 228-31475
Tel. +33 3881-72458

Peter NORMAN
E-mail: peter.norman@europarl.europa.eu
Tel. +32 228-41366
Tel. +33 3881-72458

Directorate for Relations with National Parliaments

Piotr NOWINA-KONOPKA
Director
E-mail: piotr.nowinakonopka@europarl.europa.eu
Tel. +32 228-42172
Tel. +33 3881-74258

Josep María RIBOT IGUALADA
E-mail: josep.ribot@europarl.europa.eu
Tel. +32 228-32354
Tel. +33 3881-76742

Ulrich HUESCHEN
E-mail: ulrich.hueschen@europarl.europa.eu
Tel. +32 228-44870
Tel. +33 3881-72631

Multilateral Relations Unit

Krzysztof BERNACKI
Head of Unit
E-mail: krzysztof.bernacki@europarl.europa.eu
Tel. +32 228-32685
Tel. +33 3881-64061

Dionyz HOCHEL
E-mail: dionyz.hochel@europarl.europa.eu
Tel. +32 228-43133
Tel. +33 3881-72775

Paolo MEUCCI
E-mail: paolo.meucci@europarl.europa.eu
Tel. +32 228-43676
Tel. +33 3881-73265

Maximilian SCHRÖDER
E-mail: maximilian.schroeder@europarl.europa.eu
Tel. +32 228-32250
Tel. +33 3881-76741

Ausra RAKSTELYTE
E-mail: ausra.rakstelyte@europarl.europa.eu
Tel. +32 228-34161

Bilateral Relations Unit

Patricia PRODE
Head of Unit
E-mail: patricia.prode@europarl.europa.eu
Tel. +32 228-43510
Tel. +33 3881-73096

Francisco GOMEZ MARTOS
E-mail: francisco.gomezmartos@europarl.europa.eu
Tel. +32 228-42687
Tel. +33 3881-73009

Niall O'NEILL
E-mail: niall.oneill@europarl.europa.eu
Tel. +32 228-43944
Tel. +33 3881-74264

Eszter Sarolta ZSILINSZKY
E-mail: eszter.zsilinszky@europarl.europa.eu
Tel. +32 228-43300
Tel. +33 3881-73839

Directorate for the Library

Alfredo DE FEO
Director
E-mail: alfredo.defeo@europarl.europa.eu
Tel. +32 228-43632
Tel. +33 3881-77070

Allan TOMLINS
E-mail: allan.tomlins@europarl.europa.eu
Tel. +32 228-43688

Policy Services Unit

Sven BACKLUND
Head of Unit
E-mail: sven.backlund@europarl.europa.eu
Tel. +32 228-46205

Christopher NEEDHAM
E-mail: christopher.needham@europarl.europa.eu
Tel. +32 228-32850

Andras SCHWARCZ
E-mail: andras.schwarcz@europarl.europa.eu
Tel. +32 228-32651

Jacques LECARTE
E-mail: jacques.lecarte@europarl.europa.eu
Tel. +32 228-43445

Marta LATEK
E-mail: marta.latek@europarl.europa.eu
Tel. +32 228-32149

Graham STULL
E-mail: graham.stull@europarl.europa.eu
Tel. +32 228-32859

Jan REBRINA
E-mail: jan.rebrina@europarl.europa.eu
Tel. +32 228-40534

Szabolcs TAPASZTO
E-mail: szabolcs.tapaszto@europarl.europa.eu
Tel. +32 228-31721

Irmgard ANGLMAYER
E-mail: irmgard.anglmayer@europarl.europa.eu
Tel. +32 228-43177

Alexandru FOLESCU
E-mail: alexandru.folescu@europarl.europa.eu
Tel. +32 228-32586

Peter BAJTAY
E-mail: peter.bajtay@europarl.europa.eu
Tel. +32 228-46086

Client Services Unit

Iain WATT
Head of Unit
E-mail: iain.watt@europarl.europa.eu
Tel. +32 228-43113
Tel. +352 4300-23684

Teresa MARTO DE OLIVEIRA
E-mail: teresa.marto@europarl.europa.eu
Tel. +32 228-42277

Milvia PRIANO
E-mail: milvia.priano@europarl.europa.eu
Tel. +32 228-43760
Tel. +33 3881-74812

Peter BERNINGER
E-mail: peter.berninger@europarl.europa.eu
Tel. +32 228-43460

Gregor ERBACH
E-mail: gregor.erbach@europarl.europa.eu
Tel. +32 228-32259

Katerina VAVROVA
E-mail: katerina.vavrova@europarl.europa.eu
Tel. +32 228-31467

Polona CAR
E-mail: polona.car@europarl.europa.eu
Tel. +32 228-32027

Riccardo RIBERA D'ALCALA
Director-General
E-mail: riccardo.ribera@europarl.europa.eu
Tel. +32 228-43923
Tel. +33 3881-74432

Raquel DE VICENTE
Adviser
Tel. +32 228-41040
Tel. +33 3881-72426

General Coordination Unit

Christina RUPP
Head of Unit
E-mail: christina.rupp@europarl.europa.eu
Tel. +32 228-43794
Tel. +33 3881-64041

Informatics Service

Juho ESKELINEN
Head of Service
E-mail: juho.eskelinen@europarl.europa.eu
Tel. +32 228-42267
Tel. +33 3881-73901

Training and Assistance for Committees Service

Jutta SCHULZE-HOLLMEN
Head of Service
E-mail: jutta.schulze@europarl.europa.eu
Tel. +32 228-42615
Tel. +33 3881-64047

Budget Service

Niels FISCHER
Head of Service
E-mail: niels.fischer@europarl.europa.eu
Tel. +32 228-41012

Directorate for Economic and Scientific Policies

Thérèse LEPOUTRE-DUMOULIN
Director
E-mail: therese.lepoutre@europarl.europa.eu
Tel. +32 228-44374
Tel. +33 3881-72556

Secretariat of the Committee on Employment and Social Affairs

Panos KONSTANTOPOULOS
Head of Unit
E-mail: panos.konstantopoulos@europarl.europa.eu
Tel. +32 228-44550
Tel. +33 3881-75055

Bozica MATIC
E-mail: bozica.matic@europarl.europa.eu
Tel. +32 228-34084
Tel. +33 3881-72616

Juan Carlos PEREZ NAVAS
E-mail: juancarlos.pereznavas@europarl.europa.eu
Tel. +32 228-42815
Tel. +33 3881-72616

Aurel SAVA
E-mail: aurel.sava@europarl.europa.eu
Tel. +32 228-44346

Erika SCHULZE
E-mail: erika.schulze@europarl.europa.eu
Tel. +32 228-31245

Secretariat of the Committee on Economic and Monetary Affairs

Karl-Peter REPPLINGER
Head of Unit
E-mail: karl-peter.repplinger@europarl.europa.eu
Tel. +32 228-32235
Tel. +33 3881-72504

Adolfo BARBERA DEL ROSAL
E-mail: adolfo.barbera@europarl.europa.eu
Tel. +32 228-32160
Tel. +33 3881-72580

Kajus HAGELSTAM
E-mail: kajus.hagelstam@europarl.europa.eu
Tel. +32 228-32856
Tel. +33 3881-72580

Manica HAUPTMAN
E-mail: manica.hauptman@europarl.europa.eu
Tel. +32 228-31488
Tel. +33 3881-72722

Johannes LITZELMANN
E-mail: johannes.litzelmann@europarl.europa.eu
Tel. +32 228-32219
Tel. +33 3881-74017

Ivo VAN ES
E-mail: ivo.vanes@europarl.europa.eu
Tel. +32 228-42109
Tel. +33 3881-73331

Zuzana VAVROVA
E-mail: zuzana.vavrova@europarl.europa.eu
Tel. +32 228-42457
Tel. +33 3881-72722

Sonia WOLLNY
E-mail: sonia.wollny@europarl.europa.eu
Tel. +32 228-31065
Tel. +33 3881-74870

Secretariat of the Committee on the Internal Market and Consumer Protection

Joseph DUNNE
Head of Unit
E-mail: joseph.dunne@europarl.europa.eu
Tel. +32 228-42491
Tel. +33 3881-74192

Elke BALLON
E-mail: elke.ballon@europarl.europa.eu
Tel. +32 228-40649
Tel. +33 3881-64193

Irena HOMOLOVA
E-mail: irena.homolova@europarl.europa.eu
Tel. +32 228-43583
Tel. +33 3881-74319

Tarvo KUNGLA
E-mail: tarvo.kungla@europarl.europa.eu
Tel. +32 228-32175
Tel. +33 3881-74450

Andreas STRIEGNITZ
E-mail: andreas.striegnitz@europarl.europa.eu
Tel. +32 228-32665
Tel. +33 3881-64035

Peter TRAUNG
E-mail: peter.traung@europarl.europa.eu
Tel. +32 228-43105
Tel. +33 3881-64147

Constantinos YERARIS
E-mail: constantinos.yeraris@europarl.europa.eu
Tel. +32 228-32919
Tel. +33 3881-64035

Secretariat of the Committee on Industry, Research and Energy

Luis MARTÍN OAR
Head of Unit
E-mail: luis.martinoar@europarl.europa.eu
Tel. +32 228-43629
Tel. +33 3881-77069

Georges CARAVELIS
E-mail: georges.caravelis@europarl.europa.eu
Tel. +32 228-43502
Tel. +33 3881-74529

Walter GÖTZ
E-mail: walter.goetz@europarl.europa.eu
Tel. +32 228-32587
Tel. +33 3881-72283

Julio GUZMAN
E-mail: julio.guzman@europarl.europa.eu
Tel. +32 228-40761
Tel. +33 3881-74131

Nora KOVACHEVA
E-mail: nora.kovacheva@europarl.europa.eu
Tel. +32 228-42244
Tel. +33 3881-73282

Zsuzsanna LAKY
E-mail: zsuzsanna.laky@europarl.europa.eu
Tel. +32 228-32196
Tel. +33 3881-72395

Felix Alexander LUTZ
E-mail: felix.lutz@europarl.europa.eu
Tel. +32 228-31329
Tel. +33 3881-76670

Gai OREN
E-mail: gai.oren@europarl.europa.eu
Tel. +32 228-41026
Tel. +33 3881-74313

Secretariat of the Committee on the Environment, Public Health and Food Safety

Andreas HUBER
Head of Unit
E-mail: andreas.huber@europarl.europa.eu
Tel. +32 228-42418
Tel. +33 3881-74767

Georgios AMANATIDIS
E-mail: georgios.amanatidis@europarl.europa.eu
Tel. +32 228-34086
Tel. +33 3881-74143

Bérangère BASIN
E-mail: berangere.basin@europarl.europa.eu
Tel. +32 228-34052
Tel. +33 3881-72105

Siegfried BREIER
E-mail: siegried.breier@europarl.europa.eu
Tel. +32 228-31283
Tel. +33 3881-74057

Edwin KOEKKOEK
E-mail: edwin.koekkoek@europarl.europa.eu
Tel. +32 228-32746
Tel. +33 3881-74353

Virpi KÖYKKÄ
E-mail: virpi.koykka@europarl.europa.eu
Tel. +32 228-46222
Tel. +33 3881-72104

Tina OHLIGER
E-mail: tina.ohliger@europarl.europa.eu
Tel. +32 228-31477
Tel. +33 3881-72586

Cecilia SUNDBERG
E-mail: cecilia.sundberg@europarl.europa.eu
Tel. +32 228-40993
Tel. +33 3881-74057

Joseph VERVLOET
E-mail: jos.vervloet@europarl.europa.eu
Tel. +32 228-44732
Tel. +33 3881-74041

Policy Department for Economic, Scientific and Quality of Life Policies

Theodoros KARAPIPERIS
Head of Unit
E-mail: theodoros.karapiperis@europarl.europa.eu
Tel. +32 228-43812
Tel. +33 3881-72579

Moira ANDREANELLI
E-mail: moira.andreanelli@europarl.europa.eu
Tel. +32 228-34101
Tel. +33 3881-64196

Christine BAHR
E-mail: christine.bahr@europarl.europa.eu
Tel. +32 228-40722
Tel. +33 3881-72677

Camilla BURSI
E-mail: camilla.bursi@europarl.europa.eu
Tel. +32 228-32233

Jarka CHLOUPKOVA
E-mail: jarka.chloupkova@europarl.europa.eu
Tel. +32 228-40606
Tel. +33 3881-74712

Miklós László GYŐRFFI
E-mail: miklos.gyoerffi@europarl.europa.eu
Tel. +32 228-32505
Tel. +33 3881-72259

Karin HYLDELUND
E-mail: karin.hyldelund@europarl.europa.eu
Tel. +32 228-32234

Josina KAMERLING
E-mail: josina.kamerling@europarl.europa.eu
Tel. +32 228-31413
Tel. +33 3881-76744

Christa KAMMERHOFER-SCHLEGEL
E-mail: christa.kammerhofer@europarl.europa.eu
Tel. +32 228-31232
Tel. +33 3881-64120

Arttu MÄKIPÄÄ
E-mail: arttu.makipaa@europarl.europa.eu
Tel. +32 228-32620
Tel. +33 3881-76744

Balazs MELLAR
E-mail: balazs.mellar@europarl.europa.eu
Tel. +32 228-32202
Tel. +33 3881-73662

Gianpaolo MENEGHINI
E-mail: gianpaolo.meneghini@europarl.europa.eu
Tel. +32 228-32204
Tel. +33 3881-72920

Patricia SILVEIRA DA CUNHA
E-mail: patricia.silveira@europarl.europa.eu
Tel. +32 228-43069
Tel. +33 3881-73789

Marcelo SOSA IUDICISSA
E-mail: marcelo.sosa@europarl.europa.eu
Tel. +32 228-41776
Tel. +33 3881-72645

Directorate for Structural and Cohesion Policies

Ismael OLIVARES MARTÍNEZ
Director
E-mail: ismael.olivares@europarl.europa.eu
Tel. +32 228-43297
Tel. +33 3881-74316

Angel ANGELIDIS
Adviser
E-mail: angel.angelidis@europarl.europa.eu
Tel. +32 228-44858
Tel. +352 4300-24113
Tel. +33 3881-74902

Étienne BOUMANS
Adviser
E-mail: etienne.boumans@europarl.europa.eu
Tel. +32 228-42399
Tel. +33 3881-72644

Editorial Committee

Jari Pekka ERHOLM
Head of Service
E-mail: jari.erholm@europarl.europa.eu
Tel. +32 228-43238
Tel. +33 3881-72455

Secretariat of the Committee on Agriculture and Rural Development

Gerhard KALB
Head of Unit
E-mail: gerhard.kalb@europarl.europa.eu
Tel. +32 228-43655
Tel. +33 3881-76782

Patrick BARAGIOLA
E-mail: patrick.baragiola@europarl.europa.eu
Tel. +32 228-43251
Tel. +33 3881-72138

Oliver EMMES
E-mail: oliver.emmes@europarl.europa.eu
Tel. +32 228-42436
Tel. +33 3881-73738

Éduard REIJNDERS
E-mail: eduard.reijnders@europarl.europa.eu
Tel. +32 228-32531

Nicolae STEFANUTA
E-mail: nicolae.stefanuta@europarl.europa.eu
Tel. +32 228-44474

Secretariat of the Committee on Fisheries

Philippe MUSQUAR
Head of Unit
E-mail: philippe.musquar@europarl.europa.eu
Tel. +32 228-32078
Tel. +33 3881-74102

Marilia CRESPO
E-mail: marilia.crespo@europarl.europa.eu
Tel. +32 228-43702
Tel. +33 3881-64017

Jésus PARDO LOPEZ
E-mail: jesus.pardo@europarl.europa.eu
Tel. +32 228-43675
Tel. +33 3881-76760

Einars PUNKSTINS
E-mail: einars.punkstins@europarl.europa.eu
Tel. +32 228-43702
Tel. +33 3881-64017

Claudio QUARANTA
E-mail: claudio.quaranta@europarl.europa.eu
Tel. +32 228-32281
Tel. +33 3881-72488

Secretariat of the Committee on Regional Development

Miguel TELL CREMADES
Head of Unit
E-mail: miguel.tell@europarl.europa.eu
Tel. +32 228-42433
Tel. +33 3881-72620

Christian CHOPIN
E-mail: christian.chopin@europarl.europa.eu
Tel. +32 228-42920
Tel. +33 3881-74970

Elisa DAFARRA
E-mail: elisa.dafarra@europarl.europa.eu
Tel. +32 228-31387
Tel. +33 3881-74081

Diana HAASE
E-mail: diana.haase@europarl.europa.eu
Tel. +32 228-32254
Tel. +33 3881-73891

Agnieszka KUNAT
E-mail: agnieszka.kunat@europarl.europa.eu
Tel. +32 228-32644
Tel. +33 3881-64036

Secretariat of the Committee on Transport and Tourism

Ute KASSNITZ
Head of Unit
E-mail: ute.kassnitz@europarl.europa.eu
Tel. +32 228-44269
Tel. +33 3881-74355

Vanessa AULEHLA
E-mail: vanessa.aulehla@europarl.europa.eu
Tel. +32 228-40670
Tel. +33 3881-73492

Mario DAMEN
E-mail: mario.damen@europarl.europa.eu
Tel. +32 228-43617
Tel. +33 3881-72099

Christopher FORD
E-mail: christopher.ford@europarl.europa.eu
Tel. +32 228-40777
Tel. +33 3881-72588

Ioannis GEROCHRISTOS
E-mail: ioannis.gerochristos@europarl.europa.eu
Tel. +32 228-46009
Tel. +33 3881-72588

Hannes KUGI
E-mail: hannes.kugi@europarl.europa.eu
Tel. +32 228-42989
Tel. +33 3881-73492

Mónika MAKAY
E-mail: monika.makay@europarl.europa.eu
Tel. +32 228-32378
Tel. +33 3881-72099

Gérard MEEHAN
E-mail: gerard.meehan@europarl.europa.eu
Tel. +32 228-42546
Tel. +33 3881-74765

Secretariat of the Committee on Culture and Education

Stephen SALTER
Head of Unit
E-mail: stephen.salter@europarl.europa.eu
Tel. +32 228-42772
Tel. +33 3881-72421

Jürgen DITTHARD
E-mail: jurgen.ditthard@europarl.europa.eu
Tel. +32 228-32340
Tel. +33 3881-74480

Constanze ITZEL
E-mail: constanze.itzel@europarl.europa.eu
Tel. +32 228-32265
Tel. +33 3881-73328

Artemissia KEFALOPOULOU
E-mail: artemissia.kefalopoulou@europarl.europa.eu
Tel. +32 228-42776
Tel. +33 3881-74480

Policy Department for Structural and Cohesion Policies

Beatriz OLIVEIRA-GOUMAS
Head of Unit
E-mail: beatriz.oliveiragoumas@europarl.europa.eu
Tel. +32 228-42936
Tel. +33 3881-73062

Nils DANKLEFSEN
E-mail: nils.danklefsen@europarl.europa.eu
Tel. +32 228-32681
Tel. +33 3881-64053

Jesús IBORRA MARTÍN
E-mail: jesus.iborra@europarl.europa.eu
Tel. +32 228-44566
Tel. +33 3881-74142

Ivana KATSAROVA
E-mail: ivana.katsarova@europarl.europa.eu
Tel. +32 228-32528

Gonçalo MACEDO
E-mail: goncalo.macedo@europarl.europa.eu
Tel. +32 228-41361

Albert MASSOT MARTI
E-mail: albert.massot@europarl.europa.eu
Tel. +32 228-43616
Tel. +33 3881-74326

Piero SOAVE
E-mail: piero.soave@europarl.europa.eu
Tel. +32 228-43378
Tel. +33 3881-64053

Odile TROUVE-TEYCHENNE
E-mail: odile.trouveteychenne@europarl.europa.eu
Tel. +32 228-43489
Tel. +33 3881-72743

Directorate for Citizens' Rights and Constitutional Affairs

Gérard LAPRAT
Director
E-mail: gerard.laprat@europarl.europa.eu
Tel. +32 228-43757
Tel. +33 3881-75052

Secretariat of the Committee on Civil Liberties, Justice and Home Affairs

Emilio DE CAPITANI
Head of Unit
E-mail: emilio.decapitani@europarl.europa.eu
Tel. +32 228-43508
Tel. +33 3881-74022

Tomasz BANKA
E-mail: tomasz.banka@europarl.europa.eu
Tel. +32 228-31484
Tel. +33 3881-76669

Anje BULTENA
E-mail: anje.bultena@europarl.europa.eu
Tel. +32 228-42532
Tel. +33 3881-74038

Ollivier GIMENEZ ESPINOS
E-mail: ollivier.gimenez@europarl.europa.eu
Tel. +32 228-31186

Emanuela ILARIO
E-mail: emanuela.ilario@europarl.europa.eu
Tel. +32 228-31302
Tel. +33 3881-73135

Inke KALB
E-mail: inke.kalb@europarl.europa.eu
Tel. +32 228-43090
Tel. +33 3881-64149

François NEMOZ-HERVENS
E-mail: francois.nemozhervens@europarl.europa.eu
Tel. +32 228-40605
Tel. +33 3881-74932

Fabienne PONDEVILLE
E-mail: fabienne.pondeville@europarl.europa.eu
Tel. +32 228-44848
Tel. +33 3881-73341

Martina SUDOVA
E-mail: martina.sudova@europarl.europa.eu
Tel. +32 228-31476

Elena VASILIU
E-mail: elena.vasiliu@europarl.europa.eu
Tel. +32 228-32870
Tel. +33 3881-74038

Secretariat of the Committee on Legal Affairs

Maria José MARTINEZ IGLESIAS
Head of Unit
E-mail: mariajose.martinez@europarl.europa.eu
Tel. +32 228-43150
Tel. +33 3881-74054

Robert BRAY
E-mail: robert.bray@europarl.europa.eu
Tel. +32 228-46337
Tel. +33 3881-72978

Giorgio MUSSA
E-mail: giorgio.mussa@europarl.europa.eu
Tel. +32 228-32840
Tel. +33 3881-64121

Jan TYMOWSKI
E-mail: jan.tymowski@europarl.europa.eu
Tel. +32 228-32059
Tel. +33 3881-74586

Ewa WOJTOWICZ
E-mail: ewa.wojtowicz@europarl.europa.eu
Tel. +32 228-32920
Tel. +33 3881-74586

Secretariat of the Committee on Constitutional Affairs

Hans-Peter SCHIFFAUER
Head of Unit
E-mail: peter.schiffauer@europarl.europa.eu
Tel. +32 228-43192
Tel. +33 73881-3192

Guy DEREGNAUCOURT
E-mail: guy.deregnaucourt@europarl.europa.eu
Tel. +32 228-44603
Tel. +33 3881-74322

Wolfgang LEONHARDT
E-mail: wolfgang.leonhardt@europarl.europa.eu
Tel. +32 228-42478
Tel. +33 3881-74494

Michal MARTELA
E-mail: michal.martela@europarl.europa.eu
Tel. +32 228-43117
Tel. +33 3881-64119

Pauliina MURTO-LEHTINEN
E-mail: pauliina.murto@europarl.europa.eu
Tel. +32 228-42563
Tel. +33 3881-73532

Claire PERETIE
E-mail: claire.peretie@europarl.europa.eu
Tel. +32 228-34147
Tel. +33 3881-74322

Secretariat of the Committee on Women's Rights and Gender Equality

Elvy SVENNERSTÅL
Head of Unit
E-mail: elvy.svennerstal@europarl.europa.eu
Tel. +32 228-46223
Tel. +33 3881-74926

Elena MAINARDI
E-mail: elena.mainardi@europarl.europa.eu
Tel. +32 228-32711
Tel. +33 3881-72016

Malgorzata SZLENDAK
E-mail: malgorzata.slzendak@europarl.europa.eu
Tel. +32 228-42111
Tel. +33 3881-74556

Secretariat of the Committee on Petitions

David LOWE
Head of Unit
E-mail: david.lowe@europarl.europa.eu
Tel. +32 228-42396
Tel. +33 3881-74278

Karen CHIOTI
E-mail: karen.chioti@europarl.europa.eu
Tel. +32 228-40702
Tel. +33 3881-75053

Johannes HEEZEN
E-mail: johannes.heezen@europarl.europa.eu
Tel. +32 228-42598
Tel. +33 3881-75053

Carolina LECOCQ-PEREZ
E-mail: carolina.lecocq@europarl.europa.eu
Tel. +32 228-42407
Tel. +33 3881-74043

Alina VASILE
E-mail: alina.vasile@europarl.europa.eu
Tel. +32 228-31181
Tel. +33 3881-74043

Policy Department for Citizens' Rights and Constitutional Affairs

Danièle RECHARD
Head of Unit
E-mail: daniele.rechard@europarl.europa.eu
Tel. +32 228-43730
Tel. +33 3881-72991

Jean-Louis ANTOINE-GRÉGOIRE
E-mail: jean-louis.antoine@europarl.europa.eu
Tel. +32 228-42753
Tel. +33 3881-72662

Joanna APAP
E-mail: joanna.apap@europarl.europa.eu
Tel. +32 228-32105
Tel. +33 3881-72662

Hélène CALERS
E-mail: helene.calers@europarl.europa.eu
Tel. +32 228-40768

Alessandro DAVOLI
E-mail: alessandro.davoli@europarl.europa.eu
Tel. +32 228-32207
Tel. +33 3881-72662

Wilhelm LEHMANN
E-mail: wilhelm.lehmann@europarl.europa.eu
Tel. +32 228-42711
Tel. +33 3881-72653

Roberta PANIZZA
E-mail: roberta.panizza@europarl.europa.eu
Tel. +32 228-31433
Tel. +33 3881-72693

Directorate for Budgetary Affairs

Anne VITREY
Director
E-mail: anne.vitrey@europarl.europa.eu
Tel. +32 228-43632
Tel. +33 3881-77070

Secretariat of the Committee on Budgets

...
Head of Unit

Udo BUX
E-mail: udo.bux@europarl.europa.eu
Tel. +32 228-41468
Tel. +33 3881-76692

Rita CALATOZZOLO
E-mail: rita.calatozzolo@europarl.europa.eu
Tel. +32 228-44894
Tel. +33 3881-72268

Beata GRZEBIELUCH
E-mail: beata.grzebieluch@europarl.europa.eu
Tel. +32 228-31317
Tel. +33 3881-64068

Karl MINAIRE
E-mail: karl.minaire@europarl.europa.eu
Tel. +32 228-32188
Tel. +33 3881-76781

José Luís PACHECO
E-mail: joseluis.pacheco@europarl.europa.eu
Tel. +32 228-43454
Tel. +33 3881-72655

Richard WESTER
E-mail: richard.wester@europarl.europa.eu
Tel. +32 228-42432
Tel. +33 3881-72067

Secretariat of the Committee on Budgetary Control

José Luis RUFAS QUINTANA
Head of Unit
E-mail: joseluis.rufas@europarl.europa.eu
Tel. +32 228-43956
Tel. +33 3881-74916

Bent ADAMSEN
E-mail: bent.adamsen@europarl.europa.eu
Tel. +32 228-43707
Tel. +33 3881-74390

József BLASZAUER
E-mail: jozsef.blaszauer@europarl.europa.eu
Tel. +32 228-40609
Tel. +33 3881-64164

Roger BRAWN
E-mail: roger.brawn@europarl.europa.eu
Tel. +32 228-42096
Tel. +33 3881-74194

Carmen CASTILLO DEL CARPIO
E-mail: carmen.castillo@europarl.europa.eu
Tel. +32 228-40538
Tel. +33 3881-64066

Lotte TITTOR
E-mail: lotte.tittor@europarl.europa.eu
Tel. +32 228-40785
Tel. +33 3881-72411

Rudolf VERDINS
E-mail: rudolf.verdins@europarl.europa.eu
Tel. +32 228-31083
Tel. +33 3881-72763

Policy Department for Budgetary Affairs

Christian EHLERS
Head of Unit (acting)
E-mail: christian.ehlers@europarl.europa.eu
Tel. +32 228-43379
Tel. +33 3881-72257

Jean-Jacques GAY
E-mail: jean-jacques.gay@europarl.europa.eu
Tel. +32 228-42253
Tel. +33 3881-77080

Françoise JAVELLE
E-mail: françoise.javelle@europarl.europa.eu
Tel. +32 228-42282
Tel. +33 3881-77080

Fabia JONES
E-mail: fabia.jones@europarl.europa.eu
Tel. +32 228-31280
Tel. +33 3881-77080

Helmut WERNER
E-mail: helmut.werner@europarl.europa.eu
Tel. +32 228-43750
Tel. +33 3881-72668
Tel. +352 4300-22225

Directorate for Legislative Coordination and Conciliations

Els VANDENBOSCH
Director (acting)
E-mail: els.vandenbosch@europarl.europa.eu
Tel. +32 228-42736
Tel. +33 3881-73679

Conciliations and Co-decision Unit

Klaus BAIER
Head of Unit
E-mail: klaus.baier@europarl.europa.eu
Tel. +32 228-44873
Tel. +33 3881-74369

Sarah BLAU
E-mail: sarah.blau@europarl.europa.eu
Tel. +32 228-32504
Tel. +33 3881-74676

Katrin HUBER
E-mail: katrin.huber@europarl.europa.eu
Tel. +32 228-44692
Tel. +33 3881-73342

Christian MAURIN DE FARINA
E-mail: christian.maurin@europarl.europa.eu
Tel. +32 228-42787
Tel. +33 3881-73041

Nikolaos TZIORKAS
E-mail: nikolaos.tziorkas@europarl.europa.eu
Tel. +32 228-42341
Tel. +33 3881-74357

Unit for Legislative Coordination and Programming

Els VANDENBOSCH
Head of Unit
E-mail: els.vandenbosch@europarl.europa.eu
Tel. +32 228-42736
Tel. +33 3881-73679

Gonzalo DE MENDOZA ASENSI
E-mail: gonzalo.demendoza@europarl.europa.eu
Tel. +32 228-32380
Tel. +33 3881-64134

Sune HANSEN
E-mail: sune.hansen@europarl.europa.eu
Tel. +32 228-42642
Tel. +33 3881-64064

Hans-Joachim HAUCK
E-mail: hans-joachim.hauck@europarl.europa.eu
Tel. +32 228-42199
Tel. +33 3881-73288

Stephan HUBER
E-mail: stephan.huber@europarl.europa.eu
Tel. +32 228-41301
Tel. +33 3881-73236

Sophie KERR
E-mail: sophie.kerr@europarl.europa.eu
Tel. +32 228-42085
Tel. +33 3881-73438

Christine LEMPEREUR
E-mail: christine.lempereur@europarl.europa.eu
Tel. +32 228-43813
Tel. +33 3881-73418

Maria Angeles MARTINEZ VALLS
E-mail: mariaangeles.martinez@europarl.europa.eu
Tel. +32 228-42007
Tel. +33 3881-72560

Andrea SCRIMALI
E-mail: andrea.scrimali@europarl.europa.eu
Tel. +32 228-44366

Secretariat of the Temporary Committee on Climate Change (mandate expiring on 10.2.2009)

Sabina MAGNANO
Head of Service
E-mail: sabina.magnano@europarl.europa.eu
Tel. +32 228-43685
Tel. +33 3881-77058

Rinse Johannes VAN ARUM
E-mail: rinsejohannes.vanarum@europarl.europa.eu
Tel. +32 228-32351
Tel. +33 3881-73290

Maria Elena EFTHYMIOU
E-mail: mariaelena.efthymiou@europarl.europa.eu
Tel. +32 228-42268
Tel. +33 3881-73507

DIRECTORATE-GENERAL FOR EXTERNAL POLICIES OF THE UNION

Dietmar NICKEL
Director-General
E-mail: dietmar.nickel@europarl.europa.eu
Tel. +32 228-42759
Tel. +33 3881-74079
Tel. +352 4300-22911

Dick TOORNSTRA
E-mail: dick.toornstra@europarl.europa.eu
Tel. +32 228-42138
Tel. +33 3881-75685

Maria FIALHO
Head of Unit
E-mail: mariajose.fialho@europarl.europa.eu
Tel. +32 228-43524
Tel. +33 3881-77073

Judith ECKER
E-mail: judith.ecker@europarl.europa.eu
Tel. +32 228-42629
Tel. +33 3881-72466

General Coordination Unit

Bernard HELLOT
Head of Unit
E-mail: bernard.hellot@europarl.europa.eu
Tel. +32 228-43715
Tel. +33 3881-74047

Heikki SUORTTI
E-mail: heikki.suortti@europarl.europa.eu
Tel. +32 228-43709
Tel. +33 3881-74162

Directorate A — Committees and Multilateral Bodies

Secretariat of the Committee on Foreign Affairs

Christian HUBER
Head of Unit
E-mail: christian.huber@europarl.europa.eu
Tel. +32 228-41756
Tel. +33 3881-74059

Silvio GONZATO
E-mail: silvio.gonzato@europarl.europa.eu
Tel. +32 228-44556
Tel. +33 3881-74265

Rosemary OPACIC
E-mail: rosemary.opacic@europarl.europa.eu
Tel. +32 228-42498
Tel. +33 3881-72234

Eva MAHR
E-mail: eva.mahr@europarl.europa.eu
Tel. +32 228-32048
Tel. +33 3881-72656

Elina VIILUP
E-mail: elina.viilup@europarl.europa.eu
Tel. +32 228-31250
Tel. +33 3881-72643

Eva PALATOVA
E-mail: eva.palatova@europarl.europa.eu
Tel. +32 228-32402

Secretariat of the Subcommittee on Security and Defence

Armand FRANJULIEN
Head of Unit
E-mail: armand.franjulien@europarl.europa.eu
Tel. +32 228-42511
Tel. +33 3881-74359

Giovanna BONO
E-mail: giovanna.bono@europarl.europa.eu
Tel. +32 228-31002

Michal MALOVEC
E-mail: michal.malovec@europarl.europa.eu
Tel. +32 228-32241
Tel. +33 3881-75072

Luis BALSELLS TRAVER
E-mail: luis.balsells@europarl.europa.eu
Tel. +32 228-32386
Tel. +33 3881-76346

Secretariat of the Committee on International Trade

Alberto RODAS
Head of Unit
E-mail: alberto.rodas@europarl.europa.eu
Tel. +32 228-43514
Tel. +33 3881-74405

Donatella PRIBAZ
E-mail: donatella.pribaz@europarl.europa.eu
Tel. +32 228-40723
Tel. +33 3881-73905

Michael TOPPING
E-mail: michael.topping@europarl.europa.eu
Tel. +32 228-43960
Tel. +33 3881-77016

Roberto BENDINI
E-mail: roberto.bendini@europarl.europa.eu
Tel. +32 228-32574

Secretariat of the Committee on Development

Michael WOOD
Head of Unit
E-mail: michael.wood@europarl.europa.eu
Tel. +32 228-46060
Tel. +33 3881-76060

Marika LERCH
E-mail: marika.lerch@europarl.europa.eu
Tel. +32 228-32765

Guido VAN HECKEN
E-mail: guido.vanhecken@europarl.europa.eu
Tel. +32 228-43740
Tel. +33 3881-72578

Wolfgang HERZIG
E-mail: wolfgang.herzig@europarl.europa.eu
Tel. +33 3881-74680
Tel. +32 228-43548

Anne MCLAUCHLAN
E-mail: anne.mclauchlan@europarl.europa.eu
Tel. +32 228-41327
Tel. +33 3881-74105

Francis COLE
E-mail: francis.cole@europarl.europa.eu
Tel. +32 228-42788
Tel. +33 3881-64169

Tom MORGAN
E-mail: tom.morgan@europarl.europa.eu
Tel. +32 228-31028

Observation of Elections

Pietro DUCCI
Head of Unit
E-mail: pietro.ducci@europarl.europa.eu
Tel. +33 3881-72491
Tel. +32 228-46656

Alina GEORGESCU
E-mail: alina.georgescu@europarl.europa.eu
Tel. +32 228-32427
Tel. +33 3881-74425

Emilia GALLEGO PERONA
E-mail: emilia.gallego@europarl.europa.eu
Tel. +32 228-44061
Tel. +33 3881-74468

Secretariat of the Subcommittee on Human Rights / Human Rights Unit

Geoffrey HARRIS
Head of Unit
E-mail: geoffrey.harris@europarl.europa.eu
Tel. +32 228-43608
Tel. +33 3881-72020

Helena HALLDORF
E-mail: helena.halldorf@europarl.europa.eu
Tel. +32 228-32214

Michael RUPP
E-mail: michael.rupp@europarl.europa.eu
Tel. +32 228-42078
Tel. +33 3881-77003

Zsuzsanna KISS
E-mail: zsuzsanna.kiss@europarl.europa.eu
Tel. +32 228-40615
Tel. +33 3881-74354

Maria Conceição GONÇALVES
E-mail: conceicao.goncalves@europarl.europa.eu
Tel. +32 228-43706
Tel. +33 3881-74317

Euromed Unit

Michael REINPRECHT
Head of Unit
E-mail: michael.reinprecht@europarl.europa.eu
Tel. +32 228-43667
Tel. +33 3881-74946

Morag DONALDSON
E-mail: morag.donaldson@europarl.europa.eu
Tel. +32 228-43667
Tel. +33 3881-74946

Camelia OAIDA
E-mail: camelia.oaida@europarl.europa.eu
Tel. +32 228-43939
Tel. +33 3881-72031

Isabelle MONTOYA
E-mail: isabelle.montoya@europarl.europa.eu
Tel. +32 228-44149
Tel. +33 3881-72031

Eurolat Unit

José Javier FERNANDEZ FERNANDEZ
Head of Unit
E-mail: josejavier.fernandez@europarl.europa.eu
Tel. +32 228-42381
Tel. +33 3881-74408

Pedro VALENTE DA SILVA
E-mail: pedro.valentedasilva@europarl.europa.eu
Tel. +32 228-44344

Directorate B — Interparliamentary Delegations and Policy Support

Secretariat of the Interparliamentary Delegations — European Countries

Thomas GRUNERT
Head of Unit
E-mail: thomas.grunert@europarl.europa.eu
Tel. +32 228-43743
Tel. +33 3881-73743

Stefan PFITZNER
E-mail: stefan.pfitzner@europarl.europa.eu
Tel. +32 228-42604
Tel. +33 3881-72575

Henrik OLSEN
E-mail: henrik.olsen@europarl.europa.eu
Tel. +32 228-42779
Tel. +33 3881-74477

Sabina MAZZI-ZISSIS
E-mail: sabina.mazzi@europarl.europa.eu
Tel. +32 228-42643
Tel. +33 3881-72352

Aneta POPESCU-BLACK
E-mail: aneta.popescu@europarl.europa.eu
Tel. +32 228-42291
Tel. +33 3881-72456

Arnoldas PRANCKEVICIUS
E-mail: arnoldas.pranckevicius@europarl.europa.eu
Tel. +32 228-32569
Tel. +33 3881-72710

Secretariat of the Interparliamentary Delegations — Non-European Countries

Jean-Louis BERTON
Head of Unit
E-mail: jeanlouis.berton@europarl.europa.eu
Tel. +32 228-42442
Tel. +33 3881-72442

Hans-Hermann KRAUS
E-mail: hans-hermann.kraus@europarl.europa.eu
Tel. +32 228-43721
Tel. +33 3881-74471

Carlo CHICCO
E-mail: carlo.chicco@europarl.europa.eu
Tel. +32 228-42708
Tel. +33 3881-77061

Thierry JACOB
E-mail: thierry.jacob@europarl.europa.eu
Tel. +32 228-42277
Tel. +33 3881-72532

Timothy BODEN
E-mail: timothy.boden@europarl.europa.eu
Tel. +32 228-43459
Tel. +33 3881-72459

Philippe KAMARIS
E-mail: philippe.kamaris@europarl.europa.eu
Tel. +32 228-46670
Tel. +33 3881-73777

Policy Department — External Relations

Étienne BASSOT
Head of Unit
E-mail: etienne.bassot@europarl.europa.eu
Tel. +32 228-44741
Tel. +33 3881-74201

Georgios GHIATIS
E-mail: georgios.ghiatis@europarl.europa.eu
Tel. +32 228-42216
Tel. +33 3881-64043

Anna CAPRILE
E-mail: anna.caprile@europarl.europa.eu
Tel. +32 228-42550
Tel. +33 3881-74180

Dag SOURANDER
E-mail: dag.sourander@europarl.europa.eu
Tel. +32 228-46592
Fax +32 228-31401

Stefan SCHULZ
E-mail: stefan.schulz@europarl.europa.eu
Tel. +32 228-42640
Tel. +33 3881-75066

Maria Elena EFTHYMIOU
E-mail: mariaelena.efthymiou@europarl.europa.eu
Tel. +32 228-42268
Tel. +33 3881-73507

Pedro NEVES
E-mail: pedro.neves@europarl.europa.eu
Tel. +32 228-43752
Tel. +33 3881-75063

Stefan KRAUSS
E-mail: stefan.krauss@europarl.europa.eu
Tel. +32 228-32256
Tel. +33 3881-75032

Karsten MECKLENBURG
E-mail: karsten.mecklenburg@europarl.europa.eu
Tel. +32 228-31471
Tel. +33 3881-75046

Armelle DOUAUD
E-mail: armelle.douaud@europarl.europa.eu
Tel. +32 228-43806
Tel. +33 3881-75041

Levente CSASZI
E-mail: levente.csaszi@europarl.europa.eu
Tel. +32 228-31464
Tel. +33 3881-75014

Xavier NUTTIN
E-mail: xavier.nuttin@europarl.europa.eu
Tel. +32 228-32257
Tel. +33 3881-75015

Gerrard QUILLE
E-mail: gerrard.quille@europarl.europa.eu
Tel. +32 228-32260
Tel. +33 3881-73170

Francesca RATTI
Director-General
E-mail: francesca.ratti@europarl.europa.eu
Tel. +352 4300-22188
Tel. +33 3881-73913
Tel. +32 228-43921

Pekka HAKALA
Adviser
E-mail: pekka.hakala@europarl.europa.eu
Tel. +32 228-46273
Tel. +33 3881-72085

Alexander KLEINIG
Project Manager Visitors' Centre
E-mail: alexander.kleinig@europarl.europa.eu
Tel. +32 228-44397
Tel. +33 3881-74018

General Coordination Unit

Nikolas LANE
Head of Unit
E-mail: nikolas.lane@europarl.europa.eu
Tel. +32 228-42486
Tel. +33 3881-77020

LSA Service

Carmelo ATTARDO
E-mail: carmelo.attardo@europarl.europa.eu
Tel. +32 228-42942
Tel. +33 3881-73354

Pierre MAIGRET
E-mail: pierre.maigret@europarl.europa.eu
Tel. +32 228-42934
Tel. +33 3881-76745

Planning, Media Analysis and Interinstitutional Coordination Unit

Susanne OBERHAUSER
Head of Unit
E-mail: susanne.oberhauser@europarl.europa.eu
Tel. +32 228-43048
Tel. +33 3881-73871

Remi PIEROT
E-mail: remi.pierot@europarl.europa.eu
Tel. +32 228-41091
Tel. +33 3881-73646

Resources Unit

Elio CAROZZA
Head of Unit
E-mail: elio.carozza@europarl.europa.eu
Tel. +32 228-40936
Tel. +33 3881-72230

Human Resources Service

Luigi RAVACCHIOLI
E-mail: luigi.ravacchioli@europarl.europa.eu
Tel. +32 228-44752
Tel. +352 4300-23703
Tel. +33 3881-75188

Budget Service

Roger BRETNACHER
E-mail: roger.bretnacher@europarl.europa.eu
Tel. +32 228-41875
Tel. +33 3881-72888

Deborah HOAR-DEVESSE
E-mail: deborah.hoar@europarl.europa.eu
Tel. +32 228-40648
Tel. +33 3881-73352

Directorate for Media

Jaume DUCH GUILLOT
Director
E-mail: jaume.duch@europarl.europa.eu
Tel. +32 228-43000
Tel. +33 3881-74705

Zaneta VEGNERE
Adviser
E-mail: zaneta.vegnere@europarl.europa.eu
Tel. +32 228-32255
Tel. +33 3881-74874

Press Room Unit

Marjory VAN DEN BROEKE
Head of Unit
E-mail: marjory.vandenbroeke@europarl.europa.eu
Tel. +32 228-44304
Tel. +33 3881-74336

Press team

Jack BLACKWELL
E-mail: jack.blackwell@europarl.europa.eu
Tel. +32 228-42929
Tel. +33 3881-77015

Maria ANDRES MARIN
E-mail: maria.andres@europarl.europa.eu
Tel. +32 228-44299
Tel. +33 3881-73603

Ralph PINE
E-mail: ralph.pine@europarl.europa.eu
Tel. +32 228-42941
Tel. +33 3881-74751

Piotr ZALEWSKI
E-mail: piotr.zalewski@europarl.europa.eu
Tel. +32 228-32232
Tel. +33 3881-74151

Yves HANON
E-mail: yves.hanon@europarl.europa.eu
Tel. +32 228-42456

Constanze BECKERHOFF
E-mail: constanze.beckerhoff@europarl.europa.eu
Tel. +32 228-44302
Tel. +33 3881-73780

Andrew BOREHAM
E-mail: andrew.boreham@europarl.europa.eu
Tel. +32 228-42319

Hélène CUISINIER
E-mail: helene.cuisinier@europarl.europa.eu
Tel. +32 228-32692

Federico DE GIROLAMO
E-mail: federico.degirolamo@europarl.europa.eu
Tel. +32 228-31389
Tel. +33 3881-72850

Thomas DUDRAP
E-mail: thomas.dudrap@europarl.europa.eu
Tel. +32 228-44524
Tel. +33 3881-77015

Cezary LEWANOWICZ
E-mail: cezary.lewanowicz@europarl.europa.eu
Tel. +32 228-44659
Tel. +33 3881-74903

Europarl Webmaster Unit

Ennio PINTON
Head of Unit
E-mail: ennio.pinton@europarl.europa.eu
Tel. +32 228-42001
Tel. +33 3881-74288

Pascal JOST
E-mail: pascal.jost@europarl.europa.eu
Tel. +32 228-31222

Noëlle-Anne O'SULLIVAN
E-mail: noelle-anne.osullivan@europarl.europa.eu
Tel. +32 228-43286

Drafting and Dissemination Unit

Ioannis DARMIS
Head of Unit
E-mail: ioannis.darmis@europarl.europa.eu
Tel. +32 228-43816
Tel. +33 3881-74692

Paula FERNANDEZ HERVAS
Coordinator
E-mail: paula.fernandez-hervas@europarl.europa.eu
Tel. +32 228-42535
Tel. +33 3881-74768

Bertrand PELTIER
E-mail: bertrand.peltier@europarl.europa.eu
Tel. +32 228-42471
Tel. +33 3881-73074

Andrzej SANDERSKI
E-mail: andrzej.sanderski@europarl.europa.eu
Tel. +32 228-31051
Tel. +33 3881-73479

Richard FREEDMAN
E-mail: richard.freedman@europarl.europa.eu
Tel. +32 228-41448
Tel. +33 3881-73785

Michel PLUMLEY
E-mail: michel.plumley@europarl.europa.eu
Tel. +32 228-41056
Tel. +33 3881-74909

Isabel NADKARNI
E-mail: isabel.nadkarni@europarl.europa.eu
Tel. +32 228-32198
Tel. +33 3881-75825

Nikos SALLIARELIS
E-mail: nikos.salliarelis@europarl.europa.eu
Tel. +32 228-32017
Tel. +33 3881-74076

Jana JALVI
E-mail: jana.jalvi@europarl.europa.eu
Tel. +32 228-32192
Tel. +33 3881-74794

Fabienne GUTMANN-VORMUS
E-mail: fabienne.gutmann@europarl.europa.eu
Tel. +32 228-40650
Tel. +33 3881-74779

Corinne CORDINA
E-mail: corinne.cordina@europarl.europa.eu
Tel. +32 228-31082
Tel. +33 3881-74588

Marika ARMANOVICA
E-mail: marika.armanovica@europarl.europa.eu
Tel. +32 228-31032
Tel. +33 3881-74651

Federico ROSSETTO
E-mail: federico.rossetto@europarl.europa.eu
Tel. +32 228-40955
Tel. +33 3881-74133

Robertas POGORELIS
E-mail: robertas.pogorelis@europarl.europa.eu
Tel. +32 228-32006
Tel. +33 3881-74642

István PERGER
E-mail: istvan.perger@europarl.europa.eu
Tel. +32 228-40924
Tel. +33 3881-74845

Janez VOUK
E-mail: janez.vouk@europarl.europa.eu
Tel. +32 228-31053
Tel. +33 3881-74897

Andreas KLEINER
E-mail: andreas.kleiner@europarl.europa.eu
Tel. +32 228-32266
Tel. +33 3881-72336

Malène CHAUCHEPRAT
E-mail: malene.chaucheprat@europarl.europa.eu
Tel. +32 228-42530
Tel. +33 3881-64123

Teodor STOYCHIEV
E-mail: teodor.stoychiev@europarl.europa.eu
Tel. +32 228-40764
Tel. +33 3881-74601

Radka HEJTMANKOVA
E-mail: radka.hejtmankova@europarl.europa.eu
Tel. +32 228-31056
Tel. +33 3881-73477

Natalia DASILVA
E-mail: natalia.dasilva@europarl.europa.eu
Tel. +32 228-44301
Tel. +33 3881-73661

Sanne DE RYCK
E-mail: sanne.deryck@europarl.europa.eu
Tel. +32 228-42531
Tel. +33 3881-73605

Ioana BOBES
E-mail: ioana.bobes@europarl.europa.eu
Tel. +32 228-32460
Tel. +33 3881-76725

Press attachés

Leonidas ANTONAKOPOULOS
E-mail: leonidas.antonakopoulos@europarl.europa.eu
Tel. +33 3881-74536
Tel. +30 2103278900

Jens POTTHARST
E-mail: jens.pottharst@europarl.europa.eu
Tel. +33 3881-64025
Tel. +49 3022801000

Ivana JANIKOVA-STAVROVSKA
E-mail: ivana.janikova@europarl.europa.eu
Tel. +421 259203296
Tel. +33 3881-74880

Madalina MIHALACHE
E-mail: madalina.mihalache@europarl.europa.eu
Tel. +33 3881-64044
Tel. +40 213057986

Andrea LÖVEI
E-mail: andrea.lovei@europarl.europa.eu
Tel. +33 3881-64093
Tel. +361 4113540

Jens JENSEN
E-mail: jens.jensen@europarl.europa.eu
Tel. +33 3881-74713
Tel. +45 33143377

Eimear NI BHROIN
E-mail: eimear.nibhroin@europarl.europa.eu
Tel. +353 16057900
Tel. +33 3881-64122

Minna OLLIKAINEN
E-mail: minna.ollikainen@europarl.europa.eu
Tel. +33 3881-74906
Tel. +358 96220450

Léon PEIJNENBURG
E-mail: leon.peijnenburg@europarl.europa.eu
Tel. +31 703135400
Tel. +33 3881-72546

Massimo FARRUGIA
E-mail: massimo.farrugia@europarl.europa.eu
Tel. +356 21235075

Teresa COUTINHO
E-mail: teresa.coutinho@europarl.europa.eu
Tel. +351 213504900
Tel. +33 3881-72673

Ana MOURA
E-mail: ana.moura@europarl.europa.eu
Tel. +351 213504900
Tel. +33 3881-72673

Maja KEZUNOVIC KRASEK
E-mail: maja.kezunovic@europarl.europa.eu
Tel. +386 12528830
Tel. +33 3881-76724

Caroline BOYLE
E-mail: caroline.boyle@europarl.europa.eu
Tel. +44 2072274300
Tel. +33 3881-74822

Damian CASTANO MARTIN
E-mail: damian.castano@europarl.europa.eu
Tel. +33 3881-72147
Tel. +34 914238000

Alexandra ATTALIDES
E-mail: alexandra.attalides@europarl.europa.eu
Tel. +357 22870500

Dominique ROBERT BESSE
E-mail: dominique.robert@europarl.europa.eu
Tel. +33 140634000
Tel. +33 3881-73609

Jan PATEK
E-mail: jan.patek@europarl.europa.eu
Tel. +420 255708208
Tel. +33 3881-74240

Iveta KELPE
E-mail: iveta.kelpe@europarl.europa.eu
Tel. +371 7085460
Tel. +33 3881-74695

Manuela CONTE
E-mail: manuela.conte@europarl.europa.eu
Tel. +39 06699501
Tel. +33 3881-74156

Michayl CHRISTOV
E-mail: michayl.christov@europarl.europa.eu
Tel. +359 29853545

Marina LÄHTEENMAA
E-mail: marina.lahteenmaa@europarl.europa.eu
Tel. +46 856244455

Mare HAAB
E-mail: mare.haab@europarl.europa.eu
Tel. +33 3881-64057
Tel. +372 6306969

Piotr WOLSKI
E-mail: piotr.wolski@europarl.europa.eu
Tel. +48 225952470

Georg PFEIFER
E-mail: georg.pfeifer@europarl.europa.eu
Tel. +43 1516170
Tel. +33 3881-74848

Rolandas PYRAGIS
E-mail: rolandas.pyragis@europarl.europa.eu
Tel. +370 52120766

Audiovisual Unit

Anne-Margrete WACHTMEISTER
Head of Unit
E-mail: anne-margrete.wachtmeister@europarl.europa.eu
Tel. +32 228-40713
Tel. +33 3881-74582

Fernando CARBAJO
E-mail: fernando.carbajo@europarl.europa.eu
Tel. +32 228-44816
Tel. +33 3881-74737

Ronald EVERS
E-mail: ronald.evers@europarl.europa.eu
Tel. +32 228-32624
Tel. +33 3881-74484

Elena ESPEJO VERDÚ-EBS
E-mail: elena.espejo@europarl.europa.eu
Tel. +32 228-42921
Tel. +33 3881-72023

Johanna DEN HERTOG
E-mail: johanna.denhertog@europarl.europa.eu
Tel. +32 228-43418
Tel. +33 3881-72079

Philippe MASSON
E-mail: philippe.masson@europarl.europa.eu
Tel. +32 228-44813
Tel. +33 3881-73991

Denis LUXEN
E-mail: denis.luxen@europarl.europa.eu
Tel. +32 228-43417
Tel. +33 3881-73335

Michael MANZ
E-mail: michael.manz@europarl.europa.eu
Tel. +32 228-43710
Tel. +33 3881-74184

Robert SERMEK
E-mail: robert.sermek@europarl.europa.eu
Tel. +32 228-42824

Web Communications Unit

Stephen CLARK
Head of Unit
E-mail: stephen.clark@europarl.europa.eu
Tel. +32 228-43281
Tel. +33 3881-74399

Thibault LESENECAL
E-mail: thibault.lesenecal@europarl.europa.eu
Tel. +32 228-40709
Tel. +33 3881-73050

Jozef DUCH
E-mail: jozef.duch@europarl.europa.eu
Tel. +32 228-32455

Hanneke WESTERBAAN
E-mail: hanneke.westerbaan@europarl.europa.eu
Tel. +32 228-31069

Anete BANDONE
E-mail: anete.bandone@europarl.europa.eu
Tel. +32 228-40773

Hannariikka NIEMINEN
E-mail: hannariikka.nieminen@europarl.europa.eu
Tel. +32 228-43076

Christian MESETH
E-mail: christian.meseth@europarl.europa.eu
Tel. +32 228-43208

Mindaugas KOJELIS
E-mail: mindaugas.kojelis@europarl.europa.eu
Tel. +32 228-32727

Pavel CERNOCH
E-mail: pavel.cernoch@europarl.europa.eu
Tel. +32 228-43217

Peter LANG
E-mail: peter.lang@europarl.europa.eu
Tel. +32 228-43223

Svetla TANOVA-ENCKE
E-mail: svetla.tanova@europarl.europa.eu
Tel. +32 228-30192

Europarl TV Unit

Michael SHACKLETON
Head of Unit
E-mail: michael.shackleton@europarl.europa.eu
Tel. +32 228-42732
Tel. +33 3881-72404

Jean-Yves LOOG
E-mail: jeanyves.loog@europarl.europa.eu
Tel. +32 228-44652
Tel. +33 3881-72624

Directorate for Information Offices

Information Offices Coordination Unit

Alain CRESPINET
Head of Unit
E-mail: alain.crespinet@europarl.europa.eu
Tel. +32 228-42861
Tel. +33 3881-73312

Daniela CARVALHO
E-mail: daniela.carvalho@europarl.europa.eu
Tel. +32 228-43234
Tel. +33 3881-75250

Pierfrancesco SABBATUCCI
E-mail: pierfrancesco.sabbatucci@europarl.europa.eu
Tel. +32 228-40653
Tel. +33 3881-72310

Enrico D'AMBROGIO
E-mail: enrico.dambrogio@europarl.europa.eu
Tel. +32 228-42591
Tel. +33 3881-72795

European Parliament Information Office in Belgium

Rue de Trèves 3
B-1047 Brussels
E-mail: epbrussels@europarl.europa.eu
Website: http://www.europarl.europa.eu/brussels
Tel. +32 228-42005
Fax +32 22307555

André DE MUNTER
E-mail: andre.demunter@europarl.europa.eu
Tel. +32 228-42802
Tel. +33 3881-74115

European Parliament Information Office in Bulgaria

9, Moskovska St.
BG-1000 Sofia
E-mail: epsofia@europarl.europa.eu
Website: http://www.europarl.bg
Tel. +359 29853545

Antonius Jozef STREPPEL
Head of Unit
E-mail: toon.streppel@europarl.europa.eu
Tel. +33 3881-75096

European Parliament Information Office in the Czech Republic

Jungmannova 24
CZ-110 00 Prague 1
Czech republic
E-mail: eppraha@europarl.europa.eu
Website: http://www.evropsky-parlament.cz
Tel. +420 255708208
Fax +420 255708200

Jiri KUBICEK
Head of Unit
E-mail: jiri.kubicek@europarl.europa.eu
Tel. +33 3881-74479

Jindrich PIETRAS
E-mail: jindrich.pietras@europarl.europa.eu

European Parliament Information Office in Denmark

Gothersgade 115
DK-1123 Copenhagen K
E-mail: epkobenhavn@europarl.europa.eu
Website: http://www.europarl.dk
Tel. +45 33143377
Fax +45 33150805

Søren SØNDERGAARD
Head of Unit
E-mail: soren.sondergaard@europarl.europa.eu
Tel. +33 3881-75767

Henrik Gerner HANSEN
E-mail: henrik.hansen@europarl.europa.eu
Tel. +33 3881-75656

European Parliament Information Office in Germany

Unter den Linden 78
D-10117 Berlin
E-mail: epberlin@europarl.europa.eu
Website: http://www.europarl.de
Tel. +49 302280-1000
Fax +49 302280-1111

Klaus LOEFFLER
Head of Unit
E-mail: klaus.loeffler@europarl.europa.eu
Tel. +33 3881-74605

Bernd KUNZMANN
E-mail: bernd.kunzmann@europarl.europa.eu
Tel. +33 3881-74479

Anja FUCHS-KOENIG
E-mail: anja.fuchs@europarl.europa.eu
Tel. +33 3881-74108

Munich Regional Office

Erhardtstraße 27
D-80331 Munich
Tel. +49 89202087970

Paul-Joachim KUBOSCH
E-mail: paul-joachim.kubosch@europarl.europa.eu
Tel. +33 3881-74108

European Parliament Information Office in Estonia

Rävala, 4
EE-10143 Tallinn
E-mail: eptallinn@europarl.europa.eu
Website: http://www.europarl.ee
Tel. +372 6306969
Fax +372 6306968

Kadi HERKUEL
Head of Unit
E-mail: kadi.herkuel@europarl.europa.eu
Tel. +33 3881-73491

European Parliament Information Office in Ireland

European Union House
43 Molesworth Street
Dublin 2
Ireland
E-mail: epdublin@europarl.europa.eu
Website: http://www.europarl.ie
Tel. +353 16057900
Fax +353 16057999

Francis JACOBS
Head of Unit
E-mail: francis.jacobs@europarl.europa.eu
Tel. +33 3881-74102

European Parliament Information Office in Greece

Λεωφ. Αμαλίας/Leof. Amalias 8
GR-10557 Αθήνα/Athens
E-mail: epathinai@europarl.europa.eu
Website: http://www.europarl.gr
Tel. +30 2103278900
Fax +30 2103311540

George KASIMATIS
Head of Unit
E-mail: george.kasimatis@europarl.europa.eu
Tel. +33 3881-72068

Ioannis COCCALAS
E-mail: ioannis.coccalas@europarl.europa.eu
Tel. +33 3881-72068

European Parliament Information Office in Spain

Paseo de la Castellana, 46
E-28046 Madrid
E-mail: epmadrid@europarl.europa.eu
Website: http://www.europarl.es
Tel. +34 914238000
Fax +34 915783171

Ignacio SAMPER
Head of Unit
E-mail: ignacio.samper@europarl.europa.eu
Tel. +33 3881-72427

Maria Isabel MATEO
E-mail: mariaisabel.mateo@europarl.europa.eu
Tel. +33 3881-74098

Mercedes ROS AGUDO
E-mail: mercedes.ros@europarl.europa.eu

Barcelona Regional Office

Passeig de García, 90, 1°
E-08008 Barcelona
Tel. +34 932722044
Fax +34 932722045

Maria Teresa CALVO MAYALS
E-mail: maria-teresa.calvo@europarl.europa.eu
Tel. +33 3881-74436

European Parliament Information Office in France

288, boulevard Saint-Germain
F-75341 Paris Cedex 07
E-mail: epparis@europarl.europa.eu
Website: http://www.europarl.europa.eu/paris
Tel. +33 140634000
Fax +33 145515253

Alain BARRAU
Head of Unit
E-mail: alain.barrau@europarl.europa.eu
Tel. +33 3881-72452

Marie-Christine DE SAINT ARAILLE
E-mail: marie-christine.de-saintaraille@europarl.europa.eu
Tel. +33 3881-74112

Marseilles Regional Office

2, rue Henri Barbusse
F-13241 Marseille Cedex 01
E-mail: epmarseille@europarl.europa.eu
Website: http://www.europarl.europa.eu/marseille
Tel. +33 496115290
Fax +33 491909503

Isabelle COUSTET
E-mail: isabelle.coustet@europarl.europa.eu
Tel. +33 3881-74112

European Parliament Information Office in Strasbourg

Allée du Printemps
Bâtiment Louise Weiss
B.P.1024/F
F-67070 Strasbourg Cedex
E-mail: epstrasbourg@europarl.europa.eu
Tel. +33 3881-74001
Fax +33 3881-75184

Jean-Jacques FRITZ
Head of Unit
E-mail: jean-jacques.fritz@europarl.europa.eu
Tel. +33 3881-74499

Otmar PHILIPP
E-mail: otmar.philipp@europarl.europa.eu
Tel. +33 3881-74574

European Parliament Information Office in Italy

Via IV Novembre, 149
I-00187 Rome
E-mail: eproma@europarl.europa.eu
Website: http://www.europarl.it
Tel. +39 06699501
Fax +39 0669950200

Clara ALBANI
Head of Unit
E-mail: clara.albani@europarl.europa.eu
Tel. +33 3881-72997

Massimo PALUMBO
E-mail: massimo.palumbo@europarl.europa.eu
Tel. +33 3881-74481

Milan Regional Office

Corso Magenta, 59
I-20123 Milan
Tel. +39 024344171
Fax +39 02434417500

Maria Grazia CAVENAGHI-SMITH
E-mail: mariagrazia.cavenaghi@europarl.europa.eu
Tel. +33 3881-72255

European Parliament Information Office in Cyprus

EU House
30 Vyronos Avenue
CY-1683 Nicosia
E-mail: epnicosia@europarl.europa.eu
Website: http://www.europarl.europa.eu/nicosia
Tel. +357 22870500
Fax +357 22767733

Tasos GEORGIOU
Head of Unit
E-mail: tasos.georgiou@europarl.europa.eu
Tel. +33 3881-74569

European Parliament Information Office in Latvia

Aspazijas Boulevard, 28
LV-1050 Riga
E-mail: epriga@europarl.europa.eu
Website: http://www.europarl.lv
Tel. +371 7085460
Fax +371 7085470

Maris Indulis GRAUDINS
Head of Unit
E-mail: maris.graudins@europarl.europa.eu
Tel. +33 3881-74514

European Parliament Information Office in Lithuania

Naugarduko st.10
LT-01141 Vilnius
E-mail: epvilnius@europarl.europa.eu
Website: http://www.europarl.lt
Tel. +370 52120766
Fax +370 52619828

Daiva JAKAITE
Head of Unit
E-mail: daiva.jakaite@europarl.europa.eu
Tel. +33 3881-74512

European Parliament Information Office in Luxembourg

Maison de l'Europe
7, rue du Marché-aux-Herbes
L-1728 Luxembourg
E-mail: epluxembourg@europarl.europa.eu
Tel. +352 4300-22596
Fax +352 4300-22457

Marie-Thérèse KLOPP
E-mail: marie-therese.klopp@europarl.europa.eu
Tel. +352 4300-22597
Tel. +33 3881-72597

European Parliament Information Office in Hungary

Deák Ferenc u. 15
H-1052 Budapest
E-mail: epbudapest@europarl.europa.eu
Website: http://www.europarl.hu
Tel. +36 14113540
Fax +36 14113560

Zoltan SZALAI
Head of Unit
E-mail: zoltan.szalai@europarl.europa.eu
Tel. +33 3881-74461

Annamaria CZUGLER
E-mail: annamaria.czugler@europarl.europa.eu

European Parliament Information Office in Malta

280, Republic Street — 4th Floor
Valletta VLT1112
Malta
E-mail: epvalletta@europarl.europa.eu
Website: http://www.europarl.europa.eu/valletta
Tel. +356 21235075
Fax +356 21230661

Julian VASSALLO
Head of Unit
E-mail: julian.vassallo@europarl.europa.eu
Tel. +33 3881-74568

European Parliament Information Office in the Netherlands

Korte Vijverberg 6
2513 AB The Hague
Netherlands
E-mail: epdenhaag@europarl.europa.eu
Website: http://www.europarl.europa.eu/denhaag
Tel. +31 703135400
Fax +31 703647001

Sjerp VAN DER VAART
Head of Unit
E-mail: sjerp.vandervaart@europarl.europa.eu
Tel. +33 3881-75696

Danny DE PAEPE
E-mail: danny.depaepe@europarl.europa.eu
Tel. +33 3881-74103

European Parliament Information Office in Austria

Kärntnerring 5-7
A-1010 Vienna
E-mail: epwien@europarl.europa.eu
Website: http://www.europarl.europa.at
Tel. +43 1516170
Fax +43 15132515

Wolfgang HILLER
Head of Unit
E-mail: wolfgang.hiller@europarl.europa.eu
Tel. +33 3881-74946

European Parliament Information Office in Poland

Buro Informacyjne Parlamentu Europejskiego
w Polsce ul. Jasna 14/16 a
PL-00-041 Warsaw
E-mail: epwarszawa@europarl.europa.eu
Website: http://www.europarl.europa.eu/warszawa
Tel. +48 225952470
Fax +48 225952480

Jacek SAFUTA
Head of Unit
E-mail: jacek.safuta@europarl.europa.eu
Tel. +33 3881-74496

Lukasz P. KEMPARA
E-mail: lukasz.kempara@europarl.europa.eu
Tel. +33 3881-73122

European Parliament Information Office in Portugal

Centro Europeu Jean Monnet
Largo Jean Monnet, 1-6.°
P-1250 Lisbon
E-mail: eplisboa@europarl.europa.eu
Website: http://www.parleurop.pt
Tel. +351 213504900
Fax +351 213540004

Paulo SANDE
Head of Unit
E-mail: paulo.sande@europarl.europa.eu
Tel. +33 3881-74251

Antonio José SOBRINHO
E-mail: antonio-jose.sobrinho@europarl.europa.eu
Tel. +33 3881-74251

European Parliament Information Office in Romania

Strada Boteanu, 1 — Sector1
RO-010027 Bucharest
E-mail: epbucarest@europarl.europa.eu
Website: http://www.europarl.ro
Tel. +40 21053057986
Fax +40 213157929

Hélène LANVERT
Head of Unit
E-mail: helene.lanvert@europarl.europa.eu
Tel. +33 3881-74520
Tel. +32 228-42239

European Parliament Information Office in Slovenia

Breg 14
SLO-1000 Ljubljana
E-mail: epljubljana@europarl.europa.eu
Website: http://www.europarl.si
Tel. +386 12528830
Fax +386 12528840

Natasa GORSEK MENCIN
Head of Unit
E-mail: natasa.gorsek@europarl.europa.eu
Tel. +33 3881-74466

European Parliament Information Office in Slovakia

Palisady 29
SK-81106 Bratislava
E-mail: epbratislava@europarl.europa.eu
Website: http://www.europskyparlament.sk
Tel. +421 259203296
Fax +421 254648013

Robert HAJSEL
Head of Unit
E-mail: robert.hajsel@europarl.europa.eu
Tel. +33 3881-74489

European Parliament Information Office in Finland

Pohjoisesplanadi 31/
Norra esplanaden 31
PL/PB 26
FI-0131 Helsinki/Helsingfors
E-mail: ephelsinki@europarl.europa.eu
Website: http://www.europarl.fi
Tel. +358 96220450
Fax +358 96222610

Pekka NURMINEN
Head of Unit
E-mail: pekka.nurminen@europarl.europa.eu
Tel. +33 3881-72349

Pia SIITONEN
E-mail: pia.siitonen@europarl.europa.eu
Tel. +33 3881-73610

European Parliament Information Office in Sweden

Regeringsgatan 65, 6 tr.
S-11156 Stockholm
E-mail: epstockholm@europarl.europa.eu
Website: http://www.europarl.se
Tel. +46 856244455
Fax +46 856244499

Björn KJELLSTRÖM
Head of Unit
E-mail: bjorn.kjellstrom@europarl.europa.eu
Tel. +33 3881-72390

Markus BONEKAMP
E-mail: markus.bonekamp@europarl.europa.eu
Tel. +33 3881-73615

European Parliament Information Office in the United Kingdom

2 Queen Anne's Gate
London SW1H 9AA
United Kingdom
E-mail: eplondon@europarl.europa.eu
Website: http://www.europarl.org.uk
Tel. +44 2072274300
Fax +44 2072274302

Dermot SCOTT
Head of Unit
E-mail: dermot.scott@europarl.europa.eu
Tel. +33 3881-74256

Simon DUFFIN
E-mail: simon.duffin@europarl.europa.eu
Tel. +33 3881-74256

Daniel RACTLIFFE
E-mail: daniel.ractliffe@europarl.europa.eu
Tel. +33 3881-74256

Edinburgh Regional Office

4 Jackson's Entry
Holyrood Road
Edinburgh EH8 8PJ
United Kingdom
E-mail: epedinburgh@europarl.europa.eu
Tel. +44 1315577866
Fax +44 1315574977

John EDWARD
E-mail: john.edward@europarl.europa.eu
Tel. +33 3881-74436

Directorate for Relations with Citizens

European Union Visitors Programme Service (EUVP)

Eduardus VAN KOOLWIJK
E-mail: eduardus.vankoolwijk@europarl.europa.eu
Tel. +33 3881-72086
Tel. +32 22950326

Events Unit

Francis GUTMANN
Head of Unit
E-mail: francis.gutmann@europarl.europa.eu
Tel. +32 228-32328
Tel. +33 3881-74036

Leone RIZZO
E-mail: leone.rizzo@europarl.europa.eu
Tel. +32 228-31473
Tel. +33 3881-76677

Mar CORROCHANO
E-mail: mar.corrochano@europarl.europa.eu
Tel. +32 228-43593

Magdalena STAROSTIN
E-mail: magdalena.starostin@europarl.europa.eu
Tel. +32 228-32279
Tel. +33 3881-74535

Marta GONZALEZ
E-mail: marta.gonzalez@europarl.europa.eu
Tel. +32 228-43277

Pernilla JOURDE
E-mail: pernilla.jourde@europarl.europa.eu
Tel. +32 228-43411

Correspondence with Citizens Unit

Jean-Louis COUGNON
Head of Unit
E-mail: jean-louis.cougnon@europarl.europa.eu
Tel. +352 4300-23940
Tel. +33 3881-74816

Gérard MOTEL
E-mail: gerard.motel@europarl.europa.eu
Tel. +32 228-42676

Graham Robert CHAMBERS
E-mail: graham.chambers@europarl.europa.eu
Tel. +352 4300-22511

Peter PALINKAS
E-mail: peter.palinkas@europarl.europa.eu
Tel. +352 4300-22920

Roderich WEISSENFELS
E-mail: roderich.weissenfels@europarl.europa.eu
Tel. +352 4300-23902

John VINCENT
E-mail: john.vincent@europarl.europa.eu
Tel. +352 4300-22236

Gianmarco ADDIMANDO
E-mail: gianmarco.addimando@europarl.europa.eu
Tel. +352 4300-23850

Daria NAVARRO
E-mail: daria.navarro@europarl.europa.eu
Tel. +32 228-40676

Dorina BODEA
E-mail: dorina.bodea@europarl.europa.eu
Tel. +352 4300-25356

Visits and Seminars Unit

Frank PIPLAT
Head of Unit
E-mail: frank.piplat@europarl.europa.eu
Tel. +32 228-42103
Tel. +33 3881-74439

John FORDHAM
E-mail: john.fordham@europarl.europa.eu
Tel. +32 228-43841
Tel. +33 3881-74006

Jean-Claude THOMAS
E-mail: jean-claude.thomas@europarl.europa.eu
Tel. +32 228-42718
Tel. +33 3881-74084

Jean-Louis BURBAN
E-mail: jean.burban@europarl.europa.eu
Tel. +32 228-42632
Tel. +33 3881-74578

Juan RODRÍGUEZ
E-mail: juan.rodriguez@europarl.europa.eu
Tel. +32 228-40932
Tel. +33 3881-74248

Joachim BEHMER
E-mail: joachim.behmer@europarl.europa.eu
Tel. +32 228-44697
Tel. +33 3881-74607

Olaf SCHNEIDER
E-mail: olaf.schneider@europarl.europa.eu
Tel. +32 228-40938
Tel. +33 3881-73861

Dagmara STÖRRING
E-mail: dagmara.stoerring@europarl.europa.eu
Tel. +33 3881-74448
Tel. +32 228-46676

Marco MARINAI
E-mail: marco.marinai@europarl.europa.eu
Tel. +32 228-34175
Tel. +33 3881-74081

Alexandros KARIDES
E-mail: alexandros.karides@europarl.europa.eu
Tel. +32 228-31140

Rok KOZELJ
E-mail: rok.kozelj@europarl.europa.eu
Tel. +32 228-32690
Tel. +33 3881-73311

Radka CISCATOVA
E-mail: radka.ciscatova@europarl.europa.eu
Tel. +32 228-43611
Tel. +33 3881-74451

Gergely POLNER
E-mail: gergely.polner@europarl.europa.eu
Tel. +32 228-32220
Tel. +33 3881-74447

Petra DE MARNEFFE
E-mail: petra.demarneffe@europarl.europa.eu
Tel. +32 228-32213
Tel. +33 3881-73308

Evelin RIKKAS
E-mail: evelin.rikkas@europarl.europa.eu
Tel. +32 228-31212

Margita BRAZE
E-mail: margita.braze@europarl.europa.eu
Tel. +32 228-32453
Tel. +33 3881-72878

Olaf PRIES
E-mail: olaf.pries@europarl.europa.eu
Tel. +32 228-44835
Tel. +33 3881-73860

Antonios KAILIS
E-mail: antonios.kailis@europarl.europa.eu
Tel. +32 228-44290
Tel. +33 3881-72263

Antonio OROBITG I ROSELLÓ
E-mail: antonio.orobitg@europarl.europa.eu
Tel. +32 228-43975
Tel. +33 3881-74248

Mariana COSAC
E-mail: mariana.cosac@europarl.europa.eu
Tel. +32 228-31210
Tel. +33 3881-73858

Wilhelm SCHÖLLMANN
E-mail: wilhelm.schoellmann@europarl.europa.eu
Tel. +32 228-31245
Tel. +33 3881-73859

Georgi TOMOV
E-mail: georgi.tomov@europarl.europa.eu
Tel. +32 228-44007

Anne Marie GENSØ
E-mail: annemarie.genso@europarl.europa.eu
Tel. +32 228-42196
Tel. +33 3881-72237

Elina KAARTINEN
E-mail: elina.kaartinen@europarl.europa.eu
Tel. +32 228-44311
Tel. +33 3881-74077

Alexandra PIZZUTO
E-mail: alexandra.pizzuto@europarl.europa.eu
Tel. +32 228-48564
Tel. +33 3881-73049

Ana ANTUNES VIEIRA
E-mail: ana.antunes@europarl.europa.eu
Tel. +32 228-32519
Tel. +33 3881-73921

Public Opinion Monitoring Unit

Jacques NANCY
Head of Unit
E-mail: jacques.nancy@europarl.europa.eu
Tel. +32 228-42485
Tel. +33 3881-74082

Steffen SCHNEIDER
E-mail: steffen.schneider@europarl.europa.eu
Tel. +32 228-32852

DIRECTORATE-GENERAL FOR PERSONNEL

Barry WILSON
Director-General
E-mail: barry.wilson@europarl.europa.eu
Tel. +352 4300-22068
Tel. +33 3881-74307
Tel. +32 228-42068

Personal Data Protection Service

Jonathan STEELE
E-mail: jonathan.steele@europarl.europa.eu
Tel. +352 4300-24864

Budget Coordination Unit

Michael GORDON
Head of Unit
E-mail: michael.gordon@europarl.europa.eu
Tel. +352 4300-23285
Tel. +33 3881-73139

Petr POSPISIL
E-mail: petr.pospisil@europarl.europa.eu
Tel. +352 4300-23806

Information Technology Unit

Pierre POULLET
Head of Unit
E-mail: pierre.poullet@europarl.europa.eu
Tel. +352 4300-24839
Tel. +33 3881-74152
Tel. +32 228-42467

Medical Office Luxembourg

Sandro COLANTONIO
Head of Unit, Doctor
E-mail: sandro.colantonio@europarl.europa.eu
Tel. +352 4300-22592
Tel. +33 3881-74282

Séverine SCHEEFER
Doctor
E-mail: severine.scheefer@europarl.europa.eu
Tel. +352 4300-22592

Medical Office Brussels

Giampiero DI PAOLANTONIO
Head of Unit, Doctor
E-mail: giampiero.dipaolantonio@europarl.europa.eu
Tel. +32 228-42123
Tel. +33 3881-74282

Harry DE WILDE
Doctor
E-mail: harry.dewilde@europarl.europa.eu
Tel. +32 228-43396
Tel. +33 3881-74282

Luc VANDENITTE
Doctor
E-mail: luc.vandenitte@europarl.europa.eu
Tel. +32 228-41534
Tel. +33 3881-74282

Régine ESCH-HAMACHER
Doctor
E-mail: regine.esch-hamacher@europarl.europa.eu
Tel. +32 228-41535

Legal Affairs Unit

Poul RUNGE NIELSEN
Head of Unit
E-mail: poul.rungenielsen@europarl.europa.eu
Tel. +352 4300-24414

Directorate A — Human Resources Strategy

Yves QUITIN
Director
E-mail: yves.quitin@europarl.europa.eu
Tel. +352 4300-20116
Tel. +32 228-43512
Tel. +33 3881-72287

Isabelle DE FRAIPONT
E-mail: isabelle.defraipont@europarl.europa.eu
Tel. +32 228-32156
Tel. +33 3881-74152

Internal Communication Department

Jacques HINCKXT
Head of Unit
E-mail: jacques.hinckxt@europarl.europa.eu
Tel. +32 228-31028
Tel. +352 4300-24101

Internal Organisation and Human Resources Planning Unit

Gianluca BRUNETTI
Head of Unit
E-mail: gianluca.brunetti@europarl.europa.eu
Tel. +32 228-442846
Tel. +33 3881-72846

María Grazia TANESE
E-mail: mariagrazia.tanese@europarl.europa.eu
Tel. +32 228-42716

Competitions and Selection Procedures Unit

Glória PERES
Head of Unit
E-mail: gloria.peres@europarl.europa.eu
Tel. +352 4300-23804

Professional Training Unit

Erika LANDI-GIETEMA
Head of Unit
E-mail: erika.landi@europarl.europa.eu
Tel. +352 4300-23435
Tel. +33 3881-73138

Darryl WHITELEY
E-mail: darryl.whiteley@europarl.europa.eu
Tel. +352 4300-24420

IT Department

Alun HOTCHKISS
E-mail: alun.hotchkiss@europarl.europa.eu
Tel. +352 4300-23517

Language Department

Hannah Suzy IVERSEN
E-mail: suzy.iversen@europarl.europa.eu
Tel. +352 4300-22405

Human Resources Department

Karin KAUFFELD
E-mail: karin.kauffeld@europarl.europa.eu
Tel. +352 4300-23263

Budget Coordination Department

Hilde GRAFFIEDI
E-mail: hilde.graffiedi@europarl.europa.eu
Tel. +352 4300-22803

Professional Training (Brussels) Department

Pierre DEBATY
E-mail: pierre.debaty@europarl.europa.eu
Tel. +32 228-32677

Relations with staff in Brussels

Cécilia MORO
Head of Unit
E-mail: cecilia.moro@europarl.europa.eu
Tel. +32 228-472484
Tel. +33 3881-43285

Equal Opportunities and Diversity Unit

Rosa María BRIGNONE
Head of Unit
E-mail: rosa.brignone@europarl.europa.eu
Tel. +352 4300-23822

Directorate B — Administrative Staff Management

Janet PITT
Director
E-mail: janet.pitt@europarl.europa.eu
Tel. +32 228-32332
Tel. +352 4300-23196
Tel. +33 3881-73556

María FLAVIAN
E-mail: maria.flavian@europarl.europa.eu
Tel. +352 4300-24389

Recruitment and Transfers Unit

Suzanne KOENIG
Head of Unit
E-mail: suzanne.koenig@europarl.europa.eu
Tel. +352 4300-27034
Tel. +33 3881-72629

Stéphane VIVARD
E-mail: stephane.vivard@europarl.europa.eu
Tel. +352 4300-27789

Staff Management and Careers Unit

Alberto ROSSETTI
Head of Unit
E-mail: alberto.rossetti@europarl.europa.eu
Tel. +352 4300-22032
Tel. +33 3881-72632

María KOUTSAKOU
E-mail: maria.koutsakou@europarl.europa.eu
Tel. +352 4300-23747

Marco REDOLFI TEZZAT
E-mail: marco.redolfitezzat@europarl.europa.eu
Tel. +352 4300-22973

Individual rights

Vassilios KALENTZIS
Head of Unit
E-mail: vassilios.kalentzis@europarl.europa.eu
Tel. +352 4300-24045

Pay and Allowances Unit

Wolfdieter HELL
Head of Unit
E-mail: wolfdieter.hell@europarl.europa.eu
Tel. +352 4300-22570

Hervé DI LUCIA
E-mail: herve.dilucia@europarl.europa.eu
Tel. +352 4300-22842

Missions Unit

Pierre-Antoine BARTHELEMY
Head of Unit
E-mail: pierre-antoine.barthelemy@europarl.europa.eu
Tel. +352 4300-23029

Pensions and Social Insurance Unit

Jésus MORENO DIAZ
E-mail: jesus.morenodiaz@europarl.europa.eu
Tel. +352 4300-24848

Luxembourg Crèches and Social Services Unit

Pietro ALBA
E-mail: pietro.alba@europarl.europa.eu
Tel. +352 4300-22546

Prevention and Well-being at Work Unit

Lambert KRAEWINKELS
Head of Unit
E-mail: lambert.kraewinkels@europarl.europa.eu
Tel. +32 228-43490
Tel. +352 4300-22429
Tel. +33 3881-75637

Paul STORMS
E-mail: paul.storms@europarl.europa.eu
Tel. +352 4300-23479

André LOMMEL
E-mail: andre.lommel@europarl.europa.eu
Tel. +33 3881-24521

DIRECTORATE-GENERAL FOR INFRASTRUCTURE AND LOGISTICS

Constantin STRATIGAKIS
Director-General
E-mail: constantin.stratigakis@europarl.europa.eu
Tel. +352 4300-22874
Tel. +32 228-43928
Tel. +33 3881-74551

General Coordination Unit

Tom SKINNER
Head of Unit
E-mail: tom.skinner@europarl.europa.eu
Tel. +32 228-43933
Tel. +352 4300-23345
Tel. +33 3881-64195

Alain DONADONI
E-mail: alain.donadoni@europarl.europa.eu
Tel. +32 228-40913
Tel. +352 4300-22496
Tel. +33 3881-72825

Dimitrios KARAMAVROS
E-mail: dimitrios.karamavros@europarl.europa.eu
Tel. +32 228-44194
Tel. +352 4300-27044
Tel. +33 3881-74707

Directorate for Infrastructure

Stavros GAVRIIL
Director
Tel. +352 4300-22278
E-mail: stavros.gavriil@europarl.europa.eu
Tel. +32 228-43905
Tel. +33 3881-75689

Catherine SCHAAL
E-mail: catherine.schaal@europarl.europa.eu
Tel. +32 228-41370
Tel. +33 3881-72106

Unit for Property Management of the Three Workplaces

Diogo QUINTELA
Head of Unit
E-mail: diogo.quintela@europarl.europa.eu
Tel. +32 228-31179
Tel. +352 4300-23180
Tel. +33 3881-73180

Karin COLLIN
E-mail: karin.collin@europarl.europa.eu
Tel. +352 4300-20321

Lotar CANDIDI
E-mail: lotar.candidi@europarl.europa.eu
Tel. +32 228-43132

Mihaita Sorinel SORESCU
E-mail: mihaita.sorescu@europarl.europa.eu
Tel. +32 228-44194
Tel. +352 4300-24267
Tel. +33 3881-64050

Eva NEDVES
E-mail: eva.nedves@europarl.europa.eu
Tel. +33 3881-73252

Luxembourg Property Management Service

Olivier PESESSE
Head of the KAD extension
E-mail: olivier.pesesse@europarl.europa.eu
Tel. +352 4300-24527
Tel. +33 3881-73412

Stéphane HOOGEWIJS
E-mail: stephane.hoogewijs@europarl.europa.eu
Tel. +352 4300-20039

Bernd LIPPERT
Head of the Luxembourg site
E-mail: bernd.lippert@europarl.europa.eu
Tel. +352 4300-25154
Tel. +33 3881-72289

Brussels Property Management Service

Pascal DE BACKER
Head of the Brussels site
E-mail: pascal.debacker@europarl.europa.eu
Tel. +32 228-44653
Tel. +33 3881-73411

Védat EKER
E-mail: vedat.eker@europarl.europa.eu
Tel. +32 228-42401
Tel. +33 3881-72849

Marco CONSORTI
E-mail: marco.consorti@europarl.europa.eu
Tel. +32 228-43622
Tel. +33 3881-72289

Xavier LACROIX
E-mail: xavier.lacroix@europarl.europa.eu
Tel. +32 228-41352
Tel. +33 3881-72849

Patrick DE SCHRIJVER
E-mail: patrick.deschrijver@europarl.europa.eu
Tel. +32 228-31139

Marianthi MINIATI
E-mail: marianthi.miniati@europarl.europa.eu
Tel. +32 228-32643

Strasbourg Property Management Service

Dimitrios TENEZAKIS
Head of the Strasbourg site
E-mail: dimitrios.tenezakis@europarl.europa.eu
Tel. +33 3881-74426

Patrick VANDER ELST
E-mail: patrick.vanderelst@europarl.europa.eu
Tel. +33 3881-72889

Unit for Property Management of the Information Offices

Xavier LACROIX
Head of Unit (acting)
E-mail: xavier.lacroix@europarl.europa.eu
Tel. +32 228-41352
Tel. +33 3881-73251

Jacques REYNEN
E-mail: jacques.reynen@europarl.europa.eu
Tel. +32 228-42349
Tel. +352 4300-20231
Tel. +33 3881-75988

Directorate for Logistics

Gonzalo ALABART
Director (acting)
E-mail: gonzalo.alabart@europarl.europa.eu
Tel. +32 228-42395
Tel. +352 4300-24074
Tel. +33 3881-72674

Planning and Financial Management Unit

Lothar BAUER
Head of Unit
E-mail: lothar.bauer@europarl.europa.eu
Tel. +32 228-44520
Tel. +352 4300-22575
Tel. +33 3881-76660

Contract Management and Budgetary Posts Service

Ioan COERMAN
E-mail: ioan.coerman@europarl.europa.eu
Tel. +352 4300-23136

Budgetary Coordination and Planning Service

Florence BARBIN
E-mail: florence.barbin@europarl.europa.eu
Tel. +352 4300-22834

Joseph BEETS
E-mail: jozef.beets@europarl.europa.eu
Tel. +32 228-42197
Tel. +33 3881-75147

Transport and Removals Unit

Dieter WILS
Head of Unit
E-mail: dieter.wils@europarl.europa.eu
Tel. +32 228-43941
Tel. +352 4300-22814
Tel. +33 3881-74684

Ushers Unit

Robert PEDERSEN
Head of Unit
E-mail: robert.pedersen@europarl.europa.eu
Tel. +32 228-44615
Tel. +352 4300-24964
Tel. +33 3881-74011

Movable Property Unit

Jean-Pascal LANGE
Head of Unit
E-mail: jean-pascal.lange@europarl.europa.eu
Tel. +352 4300-22949
Tel. +32 228-43425
Tel. +33 3881-72599

Catering and Staff Shop Unit

Gonzalo ALABART
Head of Unit
E-mail: gonzalo.alabart@europarl.europa.eu
Tel. +352 4300-24074
Tel. +32 228-42395
Tel. +33 3881-72674

DIRECTORATE-GENERAL FOR TRANSLATION

Juana LAHOUSSE-JUÁREZ
Director-General
E-mail: juana.lahousse@europarl.europa.eu
Tel. +352 4300-22893
Tel. +33 3881-77050
Tel. +32 228-43479

Markus WARASIN
Adviser
E-mail: markus.warasin@europarl.europa.eu
Tel. +352 4300-24781
Tel. +32 228-31074
Tel. +33 3881-64225

Multilingualism and External Relations Service

Rebecca WEST
Head of Service
E-mail: rebecca.west@europarl.europa.eu
Tel. +32 228-40539
Tel. +352 4300-22942

General Coordination Unit

Johannes VAN HOOF
Head of Unit
E-mail: johannes.vanhoof@europarl.europa.eu
Tel. +352 4300-24699
Tel. +32 228-43372
Tel. +33 3881-73210

Chantal WIAZMITINOFF
Principal Administrator
Tel. +352 4300-23513
Tel. +33 3881-74838

Planning and Translation Demand Management Unit

Alessandro PETTINI
E-mail: alessandro.pettini@europarl.europa.eu
Tel. +352 4300-23379
Tel. +32 228-44077
Tel. +33 3881-75087

Directorate for Support and Technological Services for Translation

...
Director

Training and Traineeships Unit

Ángela LLAMAS ÁLVAREZ
Head of Unit
E-mail: angela.llamas@europarl.europa.eu
Tel. +352 4300-24248

External Translation Unit

Maria HÄRDIN HOWAT
Head of Unit
E-mail: maria.haerdin@europarl.europa.eu
Tel. +352 4300-22176

José COIMBRA DE MATOS
E-mail: jose.coimbradematos@europarl.europa.eu
Tel. +352 4300-24811

Sylva SALACOVA
E-mail: sylva.salacova@europarl.europa.eu
Tel. +352 4300-25776

Information Technology Support Unit

Peter HJORTSØ
Head of Unit
E-mail: peter.hjortso@europarl.europa.eu
Tel. +352 4300-23313

Filiep SPYCKERELLE
E-mail: filiep.spyckerelle@europarl.europa.eu
Tel. +352 4300-23882

Carlos COLLADO MARCOS
E-mail: carlos.collado@europarl.europa.eu
Tel. +352 4300-25543

Pre-Translation/Euramis Unit

Gonzalo GIL CATALINA
Head of Unit
E-mail: gonzalo.gilcatalina@europarl.europa.eu
Tel. +352 4300-24337

Carmen BARTOLOME CORROCHANO
E-mail: carmen.bartolome@europarl.europa.eu
Tel. +352 4300-24822

Directorate for Translation and Terminology

Helmut SPINDLER
Director
E-mail: helmut.spindler@europarl.europa.eu
Tel. +352 4300-23145
Tel. +33 3881-74286

Ramón GARCÍA FERNÁNDEZ
Adviser
E-mail: ramon.garcia@europarl.europa.eu
Tel. +352 4300-23586

Terminology Service

Rodolfos MASLIAS
Head of Service
E-mail: rodolfos.maslias@europarl.europa.eu
Tel. +352 4300-23872

Bulgarian Translation Unit

Vitor BASTOS
Head of Unit (acting)
E-mail: vitor.bastos@europarl.europa.eu
Tel. +352 4300-23798

Czech Translation Unit

Karel HRUSKA
Head of Unit
E-mail: karel.hruska@europarl.europa.eu
Tel. +352 4300-23388

Danish Translation Unit

Hans DRANGSFELDT
Head of Unit
E-mail: hans.drangsfeldt@europarl.europa.eu
Tel. +352 4300-23165

German Translation Unit

Reinhard KLOSE
Head of Unit (acting)
Tel. +352 4300-23274

Greek Translation Unit

Maria IKONOMOPOULOU
Head of Unit
E-mail: maria.ikonomopoulou@europarl.europa.eu
Tel. +352 4300-23581

English Translation Unit

Philip COLE
Head of Unit
E-mail: philip.cole@europarl.europa.eu
Tel. +352 4300-23240

Spanish Translation Unit

Inigo VALVERDE MORDT
Head of Unit
E-mail: inigo.valverde@europarl.europa.eu
Tel. +352 4300-24386

Estonian Translation Unit

Helena RAUTALA
Head of Unit (acting)
E-mail: helena.rautala@europarl.europa.eu
Tel. +352 4300-24805

Finnish Translation Unit

Kaija KOPONEN
Head of Unit
E-mail: kaija.koponen@europarl.europa.eu
Tel. +352 4300-27786

French Translation Unit

Daniel DELMÉE
Head of Unit
E-mail: daniel.delmee@europarl.europa.eu
Tel. +352 4300-23147

Hungarian Translation Unit

Bernadette LIGETI
Head of Unit
E-mail: bernadette.ligeti@europarl.europa.eu
Tel. +352 4300-22333

Italian Translation Unit

Luisa FORSINGDAL
Head of Unit
E-mail: luisa.forsingdal@europarl.europa.eu
Tel. +352 4300-23422

Lithuanian Translation Unit

Maria BALI
Head of Unit (acting)
E-mail: maria.bali@europarl.europa.eu
Tel. +352 4300-23294

Latvian Translation Unit

Uldis KRASTINS
Head of Unit
E-mail: uldis.krastins@europarl.europa.eu
Tel. +352 4300-22038

Maltese Translation Unit

Carmel AZZOPARDI
Head of Unit (acting)
E-mail: carmel.azzopardi@europarl.europa.eu
Tel. +352 4300-27779

Dutch Translation Unit

Frans DE GROOT
Head of Unit
E-mail: frans.degroot@europarl.europa.eu
Tel. +352 4300-23462

Polish Translation Unit

Dariusz CHMIEL
Head of Unit
E-mail: dariusz.chmiel@europarl.europa.eu
Tel. +352 4300-22180

Portuguese Translation Unit

Vitor BASTOS
Head of Unit
E-mail: vitor.bastos@europarl.europa.eu
Tel. +352 4300-23798

Romanian Translation Unit

Philip COLE
Head of Unit (acting)
E-mail: philip.cole@europarl.europa.eu
Tel. +352 4300-23240

Slovak Translation Unit

Pavol TVAROZEK
Head of Unit
E-mail: pavol.tvarozek@europarl.europa.eu
Tel. +352 4300-25321

Slovene Translation Unit

Valter MAVRIC
Head of Unit
E-mail: valter.mavric@europarl.europa.eu
Tel. +352 4300-25158

Swedish Translation Unit

Ann-Christine BRANDT
Head of Unit
E-mail: ann-christine.brandt@europarl.europa.eu
Tel. +352 4300-22173

DIRECTORATE-GENERAL FOR INTERPRETATION AND CONFERENCES

Olga COSMIDOU
Director-General
Tel. +352 4300-22892
Tel. +32 228-43433
Tel. +33 3881-73433

General Coordination Unit

...
Head of Unit

Financial Management Unit

Lambert MICHA
Head of Unit
E-mail: lambert.micha@europarl.europa.eu
Tel. +32 228-44618
Tel. +33 3881-72043
Tel. +352 4300-22892

Support to Multilingualism Unit (Prospecting and Traineeships)

Martin WOODING
Head of Unit
E-mail: martin.wooding@europarl.europa.eu
Tel. +32 228-44636
Tel. +33 3881-74673

Directorate for Interpretation

Sjef (Josephus) COOLEGEM
Director
E-mail: sjef.coolegem@europarl.europa.eu
Tel. +32 228-42848
Tel. +33 3881-77001

Danish Interpretation Unit

Torben Bagge HANSEN
Head of Unit
E-mail: torbenbagge.hansen@europarl.europa.eu
Tel. +32 228-42444
Tel. +33 3881-72444

German Interpretation Unit

Susanne ALTENBERG
Head of Unit
E-mail: susanne.altenberg@europarl.europa.eu
Tel. +32 228-34172
Tel. +33 3881-78302

Greek Interpretation Unit

Konstantinos MASTOROS
Head of Unit
E-mail: konstantinos.mastoros@europarl.europa.eu
Tel. +32 228-43482
Tel. +33 3881-72293

English Interpretation Unit

Miguel GOMES
Head of Unit
E-mail: miguel.gomes@europarl.europa.eu
Tel. +32 228-43301
Tel. +33 3881-72948

Spanish Interpretation Unit

Francisco Javier ALVAREZ WIESE
Head of Unit
E-mail: francisco.alvarez@europarl.europa.eu
Tel. +32 228-44842
Tel. +33 3881-72701

Finnish Interpretation Unit

Jouko NIKKINEN
Head of Unit
E-mail: jouko.nikkinen@europarl.europa.eu
Tel. +32 228-42719
Tel. +33 3881-72246

French Interpretation Unit

Anne-Marie WIDLUND-FANTINI
Head of Unit
E-mail: anne-marie.widlund@europarl.europa.eu
Tel. +32 228-43404
Tel. +33 3881-72723

Italian Interpretation Unit

Marie-Claire TROIAN
Head of Unit
E-mail: marie-claire.troian@europarl.europa.eu
Tel. +32 228-44622
Tel. +33 3881-72721

Dutch Interpretation Unit

Nick GHEYSEN
Head of Unit (acting)
E-mail: nick.gheysen@europarl.europa.eu
Tel. +32 228-32061
Tel. +33 3881-76675

Portuguese Interpretation Unit

Francisco FALCAO
Head of Unit
E-mail: francisco.falcao@europarl.europa.eu
Tel. +32 228-34444
Tel. +33 3881-72701

Swedish Interpretation Unit

Cecilia ÅBERG
Head of Unit
E-mail: cecilia.aberg@europarl.europa.eu
Tel. +32 228-43435
Tel. +33 3881-72281

Polish Interpretation Unit

Anna GRZYBOWSKA
Head of Unit
E-mail: anna.grzybowska@europarl.europa.eu
Tel. +32 228-42112
Tel. +33 3881-72045

Czech Interpretation Unit

Gertrud DIETZE
Head of Unit (acting)
E-mail: gertrud.dietze@europarl.europa.eu
Tel. +32 228-32604
Tel. +33 3881-73226

Hungarian Interpretation Unit

Fiona DOW
Head of Unit
E-mail: fiona.dow@europarl.europa.eu
Tel. +32 228-34199
Tel. +33 3881-78340

Slovak Interpretation Unit

Gertrud DIETZE
Head of Unit (acting)
E-mail: gertrud.dietze@europarl.europa.eu
Tel. +32 228-32604
Tel. +33 3881-73226

Slovene Interpretation Unit

Anne-Marie WIDLUND-FANTINI
Head of Unit (acting)
E-mail: anne-marie.widlund@europarl.europa.eu
Tel. +32 228-43404
Tel. +33 3881-72723

Estonian Interpretation Unit

Mari-Liis AROELLA
Head of Unit
E-mail: mari-liis.aroella@europarl.europa.eu
Tel. +32 228-44529
Tel. +33 3881-73230

Lithuanian Interpretation Unit

Jouko NIKKINEN
Head of Unit (acting)
E-mail: jouko.nikkinen@europarl.europa.eu
Tel. +32 228-42719
Tel. +33 3881-72246

Latvian Interpretation Unit

Dina SILE
Head of Unit
E-mail: dina.sile@europarl.europa.eu
Tel. +32 228-31494
Tel. +33 3881-76869

Maltese Interpretation Unit

Anne-Marie WIDLUND-FANTINI
Head of Unit (acting)
E-mail: anne-marie.widlund@europarl.europa.eu
Tel. +32 228-43404
Tel. +33 3881-72723

Bulgarian Interpretation Unit

Anne-Marie WIDLUND-FANTINI
Head of Unit (acting)
E-mail: anne-marie.widlund@europarl.europa.eu
Tel. +32 228-43404
Tel. +33 3881-72723

Romanian Interpretation Unit

Anne-Marie WIDLUND-FANTINI
Head of Unit (acting)
E-mail: anne-marie.widlund@europarl.europa.eu
Tel. +32 228-43404
Tel. +33 3881-72723

Interpreters for Non-European Union Languages

Anne-Marie WIDLUND-FANTINI
Head of Unit
E-mail: anne-marie.widlund@europarl.europa.eu
Tel. +32 228-43404
Tel. +33 3881-72723

Directorate for Organisation and Planning

Joaquina Rita SILVA
Director
E-mail: rita.silva@europarl.europa.eu
Tel. +32 228-43542
Tel. +33 3881-72046

Unit for the Recruitment of Auxiliary Conference Interpreters

Juan-Carlos JIMENEZ MARIN
Head of Unit
E-mail: juan-carlos.jimenezmarin@europarl.europa.eu
Tel. +32 228-46427

Stéphane GROSJEAN
E-mail: stephane.grosjean@europarl.europa.eu
Tel. +32 228-32862
Tel. +33 3881-64206

Susanna MATTILA
E-mail: susanna.mattila@europarl.europa.eu
Tel. +32 228-43560
Tel. +33 3881-72701

Jyrki TUONONEN
E-mail: jyrki.tuononen@europarl.europa.eu
Tel. +32 228-42192
Tel. +33 3881-72554

Programming Unit

...
Head of Unit

Ronald CHAINEY
E-mail: ronald.chainey@europarl.europa.eu
Tel. +32 228-40686
Tel. +33 3881-72993

Maria CHOULI
E-mail: maria.chouli@europarl.europa.eu
Tel. +32 228-43560
Tel. +33 3881-72701

Gerard HENDRICKX
E-mail: gerard.hendrickx@europarl.europa.eu
Tel. +32 228-43450
Tel. +33 3881-72701

Tapani LEHTOVIRTA
E-mail: tapani.lehtovirta@europarl.europa.eu
Tel. +32 228-43409

Carine SMETS
E-mail: carine.smets@europarl.europa.eu
Tel. +32 228-42519
Tel. +33 3881-72701

Marc THEODOSSIADIS
E-mail: marc.theodossiadis@europarl.europa.eu
Tel. +32 228-43560
Tel. +33 3881-72701

Susana CARRILES
E-mail: susana.carriles@europarl.europa.eu
Tel. +32 228-42488

Meetings and Conferences Unit

Nick GHEYSEN
Head of Unit
E-mail: nick.gheysen@europarl.europa.eu
Tel. +32 228-32061
Tel. +33 3881-76675

DIRECTORATE-GENERAL FOR FINANCE

Roger VANHAEREN
Director-General
E-mail: roger.vanhaeren@europarl.europa.eu
Tel. +352 4300-25100
Tel. +33 3881-75100
Tel. +32 228-45100

General Coordination Unit

Elise KERGLONOU
Head of Unit
E-mail: elise.kerglonou@europarl.europa.eu
Tel. +32 228-32310
Tel. +352 4300-23149
Tel. +33 3881-77011

Budget and Verification Service

Konstantinos GIANNOPOULOS
Head of Service
E-mail: konstantinos.giannopoulos@europarl.europa.eu
Tel. +352 4300-23684

Matthias SANDER
E-mail: matthias.sander@europarl.europa.eu
Tel. +352 4300-22689

Internal Audit Unit

Robert GALVIN
Head of Unit
E-mail: robert.galvin@europarl.europa.eu
Tel. +352 4300-22875
Tel. +33 3881-74971
Tel. +32 228-42331

Andrea ARMELLIN
E-mail: andrea.armellin@europarl.europa.eu
Tel. +352 4300-24281

Gabriele BABILON-HARRISON
E-mail: gabriele.babilon@europarl.europa.eu
Tel. +352 4300-22448

Catrine BOOGH-DAHLBERG
E-mail: catrine.boogh@europarl.europa.eu
Tel. +352 4300-22870

Etienne HENTGEN
E-mail: etienne.hentgen@europarl.europa.eu
Tel. +352 4300-22831

Michiel JANSSENS
E-mail: michiel.janssens@europarl.europa.eu
Tel. +352 4300-25902

Carlos Manuel de JESUS MARQUES
E-mail: carlos.jesus@europarl.europa.eu
Tel. +352 4300-23256

Corinne NICOLAI
E-mail: corinne.nicolai@europarl.europa.eu
Tel. +352 4300-22865

Ridge RAJAONAH
E-mail: ridge.rajaonah@europarl.europa.eu
Tel. +352 4300-21133

Robert WILMS
E-mail: robert.wilms@europarl.europa.eu
Tel. +352 4300-22836

Directorate for Budget and Financial Services

Clare WELLS-SHADDAD
Director
E-mail: clare.wells@europarl.europa.eu
Tel. +32 228-42606
Tel. +352 4300-22606
Tel. +33 3881-72606

Budget Unit

Didier KLETHI
Head of Unit
E-mail: didier.klethi@europarl.europa.eu
Tel. +32 228-44862
Tel. +352 4300-22791
Tel. +33 3881-72308

Olga GAJDA LUPKE
E-mail: olga.gajdalupke@europarl.europa.eu
Tel. +352 4300-23199

Accounting and Treasury Unit

Pascal DE POORTERE
Head of Unit
E-mail: pascal.depoortere@europarl.europa.eu
Tel. +352 4300-22498
Tel. +33 3881-74245

Ville-Veikko TIMBERG
E-mail: ville.timberg@europarl.europa.eu
Tel. +352 4300-25130

Central Financial Unit

Emile CEUPPENS
Head of Unit
E-mail: emile.ceuppens@europarl.europa.eu
Tel. +32 228-41076
Tel. +352 4300-22749

Miguel GOMEZ GOMEZ
E-mail: miguel.gomez@europarl.europa.eu
Tel. +352 4300-22120

Carlo FOSSATI
E-mail: carlo.fossati@europarl.europa.eu
Tel. +352 4300-20232

Lucien PETERS
E-mail: lucien.peters@europarl.europa.eu
Tel. +352 4300-22699

Directorate for Members' Financial and Social Entitlements

Angel GUILLEN ZANON
Director
E-mail: angel.guillenzanon@europarl.europa.eu
Tel. +32 228-44080
Tel. +352 4300-22486
Tel. +33 3881-74497

Members' Salaries and Social Entitlements Unit

Lorenzo MANNELLI
Head of Unit
E-mail: lorenzo.mannelli@europarl.europa.eu
Tel. +32 228-42435
Tel. +352 4300-25526
Tel. +33 3881-74013

Jose Luis ACEDO CASTRO
E-mail: jose.acedo@europarl.europa.eu
Tel. +352 4300-24318

Parliamentary Assistance and Members' General Expenditure Unit

Paulo CAMPILHO
Head of Unit
E-mail: paulo.campilho@europarl.europa.eu
Tel. +32 228-31105
Tel. +33 3881-73323

Haris KOUNTOUROS
E-mail: haris.kountouros@europarl.europa.eu
Tel. +32 228-32709
Tel. +33 3881-73422

Xavier THOUVENIN
E-mail: xavier.thouvenin@europarl.europa.eu
Tel. +32 228-32548

Members' Travel and Subsistence Expenses Unit

Francisco José ESTELA BURRIEL
Head of Unit
E-mail: francisco.estela@europarl.europa.eu
Tel. +32 228-43078
Tel. +352 4300-22790
Tel. +33 3881-72840

Directorate for Political Structures Financing and Other Services

Karl COLLING
Director
E-mail: karl.colling@europarl.europa.eu
Tel. +352 4300-22762
Tel. +33 3881-74762
Tel. +32 228-43584

Travel Agency and Members' Professional Training Unit

Koenraad SNIJDERS
Head of Unit
E-mail: koenraad.snijders@europarl.europa.eu
Tel. +32 228-42193
Tel. +33 3881-74629

Members' Professional Training

Angelo ANGIONI
E-mail: angelo.angioni@europarl.europa.eu
Tel. +32 228-32684
Tel. +352 4300-24632
Tel. +33 3881-74186

Political Structures Financing and Inventory Unit

Helmut BETZ
Head of Unit
E-mail: helmut.betz@europarl.europa.eu
Tel. +32 228-43183
Tel. +352 4300-22055
Tel. +33 3881-72075

Gabor MOTIKA
E-mail: gabor.motika@europarl.europa.eu
Tel. +352 4300-24088

Jean-Marc LAFOREST
Director-General
E-mail: jean-marc.laforest@europarl.europa.eu
Tel. +32 228-43116
Tel. +352 4300-22515
Tel. +33 3881-74270

Marie-Cécile BERNARD
Adviser
E-mail: marie-cecile.bernard@europarl.europa.eu
Tel. +32 228-42075
Tel. +33 3881-73357

General Coordination Unit

Carlos NETO
Head of Unit
E-mail: carlos.neto@europarl.europa.eu
Tel. +352 4300-25781
Tel. +33 3881-74120

Central Finances Unit

Michel KOHNER
Head of Unit
E-mail: michel.kohner@europarl.europa.eu
Tel. +352 4300-22020
Tel. +33 3881-74576

Hansjörg BEIRER
E-mail: hansjoerg.beirer@europarl.europa.eu
Tel. +352 4300-25530

Philippe VAN AVERMAET
E-mail: philippe.vanavermaet@europarl.europa.eu
Tel. +352 4300-24330

Directorate for Information Technologies

Pierre JEGU
Director a.i.
E-mail: pierre.jegu@europarl.europa.eu
Tel. +352 4300-22285, 22325
Tel. +32 228-42285
Tel. +33 3881-72285, 74205

Unit for Information Technologies Infrastructure Management

Gilbert SCHILT
Head of Unit (acting)
E-mail: gilbert.schilt@europarl.europa.eu
Tel. +352 4300-27070
Tel. +33 3881-74771
Tel. +32 228-43475

Computer Centre Operation and Engineering Service

Éric BENOÎT
Head of Service
E-mail: eric.benoit@europarl.europa.eu
Tel. +352 4300-24910
Tel. +32 228-41460
Tel. +33 3881-72011

Rafael RUIZ DE LA TORRE
Deputy Head of Service
E-mail: rafael.ruiz@europarl.europa.eu
Tel. +32 228-44525

Management of Telecommunication Infrastructures

Wim DELBARE
Head of Service (acting)
E-mail: wim.delbare@europarl.europa.eu
Tel. +352 4300-24108
Tel. +32 228-32019
Tel. +33 3881-64111

Michel DAUTREMONT
E-mail: michel.dautremont@europarl.europa.eu
Tel. +352 4300-24551
Tel. +33 3881-74572
Tel. +32 228-44707

Claude VERHEYDEN
E-mail: claude.verheyden@europarl.europa.eu
Tel. +352 4300-24049, 24826
Tel. +32 228-44049
Tel. +33 3881-74049

Antonella PUCCIO
E-mail: antonella.puccio@europarl.europa.eu
Tel. +32 228-42360
Tel. +33 3881-74360

Information Technologies User Support Unit

Wouter OFFEREINS
Head of Unit
E-mail: wouter.offereins@europarl.europa.eu
Tel. +32 228-42523
Tel. +33 3881-73680
Tel. +352 4300-22523

LSU Members Service

François NAEGEL
Head of Service
E-mail: francois.naegel@europarl.europa.eu
Tel. +32 228-42449
Tel. +33 3881-72548

LSA Support and Coordination Service

Jean-Marc MARIOTTI
Head of Service
E-mail: jean-marc.mariotti@europarl.europa.eu
Tel. +352 4300-22017
Tel. +32 228-43569
Tel. +33 3881-73121

Applications Service Desk (ASD)

Ana JUSTE GILABERT
E-mail: ana.juste@europarl.europa.eu
Tel. +32 228-44053
Tel. +33 3881-73140
Tel. +352 4300-23609

Multi DG Support Team

Erik DE BECKER
Head of Service
E-mail: erik.debecker@ europarl.europa.eu
Tel. +32 228-43146
Tel. +33 3881-72396
Tel. +352 4300-24271

Administrative Information Systems Unit

Iain URQUHART
Head of Unit
E-mail: iain.urquhart@europarl.europa.eu
Tel. +352 4300-21126
Tel. +33 3881-64099

Alexandra SARIDAKI
E-mail: alexandra.saridaki@europarl.europa.eu
Tel. +352 4300-22702

Joachim SPRENGER
E-mail: joachim.sprenger@europarl.europa.eu
Tel. +352 4300-27038

Marco AMABILINO
E-mail: marco.amabilino@europarl.europa.eu
Tel. +352 4300-23614

Parliamentary Information Systems Unit

Roland THORPE
Head of Unit
E-mail: roland.thorpe@europarl.europa.eu
Tel. +352 4300-22851
Tel. +32 228-31190
Tel. +33 3881-74261

Olivier JADOT
E-mail: olivier.jadot@europarl.europa.eu
Tel. +352 4300-23612

Systems for the Committees and the Groups Service

Flemming SORENSEN
Head of Service
E-mail: flemming.sorensen@europarl.europa.eu
Tel. +32 228-41429
Tel. +33 3881-79077
Tel. +352 4300-25775

Gerrit POTOMS
E-mail: gerrit.potoms@europarl.europa.eu
Tel. +32 228-40969
Tel. +33 3881-64140

Systems for the Presidency and Translation Service

Ludovic DELEPINE
Head of Service
E-mail: ludovic.delepine@europarl.europa.eu
Tel. +352 4300-22091
Tel. +33 3881-72640
Tel. +32 228-43080

Olivier LEBOEUF
E-mail: olivier.leboeuf@europarl.europa.eu
Tel. +352 4300-21143

Jesus RUBIO DOMINGUEZ
E-mail: jesus.rubio-dominguez@europarl.europa.eu
Tel. +352 4300-25082

Information Dissemination Systems Service

Marc ROSSI
E-mail: marc.rossi@europarl.europa.eu
Tel. +32 228-42447
Tel. +33 3881-72637
Tel. +352 4300-22839

Engineering and Project Support Unit

Pascal PARIDANS
Head of Unit
E-mail: pascal.paridans@europarl.europa.eu
Tel. +32 228-43080
Tel. +33 3881-73080
Tel. +352 4300-23080

Engineering and New Solutions Service

Luca RETTORE
Head of Service
E-mail: luca.rettore@europarl.europa.eu
Tel. +32 228-42058
Tel. +33 3881-64161
Tel. +352 4300-27037

Stavros LINGRIS
E-mail: stavros.lingris@europarl.europa.eu
Tel. +32 228-42828

Mario SCILLIA
E-mail: mario.scillia@europarl.europa.eu
Tel. +32 228-44745

Project Support Service

Claude WEISSLINGER
Head of Service
E-mail: claude.weisslinger@europarl.europa.eu
Tel. +352 4300-20226
Tel. +33 3881-73588

Directorate for Publishing and Distribution

Carlos NETO
Director (acting)
E-mail: carlos.neto@europarl.europa.eu
Tel. +352 4300-25781
Tel. +33 3881-74120

Distribution Unit

Franky DEPUYDT
Head of Unit
E-mail: franky.depuydt@europarl.europa.eu
Tel. +352 4300-24044
Tel. +33 3881-74070
Tel. +32 228-43523

Luxembourg Distribution Service

Peter MILES
Head of Workshop
E-mail: peter.miles@europarl.europa.eu
Tel. +32 228-44440
Tel. +352 4300-22235
Tel. +33 3881-74200

Brussels Distribution Service

Geert KEYAERTS
Head of Workshop
E-mail: geert.keyaerts@europarl.europa.eu
Tel. +32 228-46617
Tel. +33 3881-72049

Intranet Services Unit

Christian AUGUSTIN
Head of Unit
E-mail: christian.augustin@europarl.europa.eu
Tel. +32 228-40671
Tel. +352 4300-22440
Tel. +33 3881-72290

Luxembourg Intranet Service

Fernando SIMOES
E-mail: fernando.simoes@europarl.europa.eu
Tel. +352 4300-27110

Brussels Intranet Service

Jean-Bernard BAUDRY
E-mail: jean-bernard.baudry@europarl.europa.eu
Tel. +32 228-42956

Karoline KOWALD
E-mail: karoline.kowald@europarl.europa.eu
Tel. +32 228-43093

Nastja KLEMENCIC-SCHMIDT
E-mail: nastja.klemencic@europarl.europa.eu
Tel. +32 228-44642

Maria Elena MURRU
E-mail: elena.murru@europarl.europa.eu
Tel. +32 228-31489

Official Journal Unit

Michel BROGARD
Head of Unit
E-mail: michel.brogard@europarl.europa.eu
Tel. +352 4300-22480
Tel. +33 3881-73069

Official Journal Service

Joseph KOPPERS
Head of Workshop
E-mail: joseph.koppers@europarl.europa.eu
Tel. +352 4300-22318

Printing Unit

Roger-Marie DUBOIS
Head of Unit
E-mail: roger-marie.dubois@europarl.europa.eu
Tel. +32 228-43356
Tel. +33 3881-74660
Tel. +352 4300-23356

Brussels Printshop Service

Francis BERTH
Head of Workshop
E-mail: francis.berth@europarl.europa.eu
Tel. +32 228-42317
Tel. +33 3881-74957

Luxembourg Printshop Service

Jean-Claude FELTEN
Head of Workshop
E-mail: jean-claude.felten@europarl.europa.eu
Tel. +352 4300-22714
Tel. +33 3881-73443

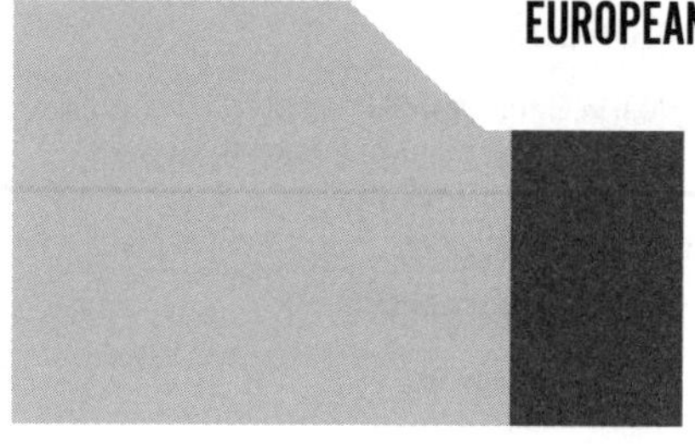

Political group secretariats

EPP-ED: Group of the European People's Party (Christian Democrats) and European Democrats

Brussels
Belgium
Tel. +32 228-42111
Parliamentary work: +32 228-44620, 42572
Press: +32 228-42228, 42290
Fax Parliamentary work: +32 228-49042, 41740
Fax press: +30 228-41718

Strasbourg
France
Tel. +33 3881-74001
Parliamentary work: +33 3881-74862, 72232
Press: +33 3881-74144/74956
Fax Parliamentary work: +33 3881-76954
Fax press: +33 3881-76926

Chairman

Joseph DAUL
Tel. +32 228-45525/47525
Tel. +33 3881-75525, 77525

Secretary-General

Martin KAMP
Secretary-General
E-mail: martin.kamp@europarl.europa.eu
Tel. +32 228-43265
Tel. +33 3881-74419

John BIESMANS
Deputy Secretary-General
E-mail: john.biesmans@europarl.europa.eu
Tel. +32 228-43026
Tel. +33 3881-74852

Paolo LICANDRO
Deputy Secretary-General
E-mail: paolo.licandro@europarl.europa.eu
Tel. +32 228-42596
Tel. +33 3881-74501

Miguel PAPI BOUCHER
Deputy Secretary-General
E-mail: miguel.papi@europarl.europa.eu
Tel. +32 228-44620
Tel. +33 3881-74862

Antoine RIPOLL
Deputy Secretary-General
E-mail: antoine.ripoll@europarl.europa.eu
Tel. +32 228-42688
Tel. +33 3881-73513

Pascal FONTAINE
Special Adviser
E-mail: pascal.fontaine@europarl.europa.eu
Tel. +32 228-42445, 2843294
Tel. +33 3881-74857

Press

Robert FITZHENRY
Group Spokesperson
E-mail: robert.fitzhenry@europarl.europa.eu
Tel. +32 228-42228
Tel. +33 3881-74144

Relations with national parliaments

Béatrice SCARASCIA MUGNOZZA
E-mail: beatrice.scarascia-mugnozza@europarl.europa.eu
Tel. +32 228-42599
Tel. +33 3881-74150

International relations — Delegations

Arthur HILDEBRANDT
E-mail: arthur.hildebrandt@europarl.europa.eu
Tel. +32 228-42607/44717
Tel. +33 3881-72744

Chairman's Office

Antoine RIPOLL
Deputy Secretary-General
Spokesperson for the President
E-mail: antoine.ripoll@europarl.europa.eu
Tel. +32 228-42688
Tel. +33 3881-73513

Marek EVISON
E-mail: marek.evison@europarl.europa.eu
Tel. +32 228-40662
Tel. +33 3881-73906

Daniela SENK
E-mail: daniela.senk@europarl.europa.eu
Tel. +32 228-41033
Tel. +33 3881-73124

Jorge SOUTULLO-SÁNCHEZ
E-mail: jorge.soutullo@europarl.europa.eu
Tel. +32 228-42385
Tel. +33 3881-74404

Alwyn STRANGE
E-mail: alwyn.strange@europarl.europa.eu
Tel. +32 228-43029
Tel. +33 3881-72098

Office of the Secretary-General

Johan RYNGAERT
E-mail: johan.ryngaert@europarl.europa.eu
Tel. +32 228-42398
Tel. +33 3881-73897

Internal Auditor

Martin HARE
E-mail: martin.hare@europarl.europa.eu
Tel. +32 228-43920
Tel. +33 3881-72813

Legal Advisor

Oliver DREUTE
Legal Adviser
E-mail: oliver.dreute@europarl.europa.eu
Tel. +32 228-41313
Tel. +33 3881-72720

Parliamentary work

Miguel PAPI BOUCHER
Deputy Secretary-General
E-mail: miguel.papi@europarl.europa.eu
Tel. +32 228-44620
Tel. +33 3881-74862

Working Group A

Arthur HILDEBRANDT
Official responsible
E-mail: arthur.hildebrandt@europarl.europa.eu
Tel. +32 228-42607
Tel. +33 3881-72744

Coordination on Urgent Issues

Charislaos PALASSOF
E-mail: charislaos.palassof@europarl.europa.eu
Tel. +32 228-43260
Tel. +33 3881-74146

Jan-Willem VLASMAN
E-mail: janwillem.vlasman@europarl.europa.eu
Tel. +32 228-46407
Tel. +33 3881-73439

Committee on Foreign Affairs

Juan SALAFRANCA
E-mail: juan.salafranca@europarl.europa.eu
Tel. +32 228-46355
Tel. +33 3881-74663

Andreas-Renatus HARTMANN
E-mail: andreas.hartmann@europarl.europa.eu
Tel. +32 228-42571
Tel. +33 3881-74887

Edyta TARCZYNSKA
E-mail: edyta.tarczynska@europarl.europa.eu
Tel. +32 228-44252
Tel. +33 3881-73486

Luigi MAZZA
E-mail: luigi.mazza@europarl.europa.eu
Tel. +32 228-42336
Tel. +33 3881-72834

Committee on Development

Charislaos PALASSOF
E-mail: charislaos.palassof@europarl.europa.eu
Tel. +32 228-43260
Tel. +33 3881-74146

Jesper HAGLUND
E-mail: jesper.haglund@europarl.europa.eu
Tel. +32 228-43738
Tel. +33 3881-73505

Committee on International Trade

Adriaan BASTIAANSEN
E-mail: adriaan.bastiaansen@europarl.europa.eu
Tel. +32 228-41342
Tel. +33 3881-72824

Botond TÖRÖK-ILLYÉS
E-mail: botond.torok-illyes@europarl.europa.eu
Tel. +32 228-32552
Tel. +33 3881-77054

Working Group B

Mario SCHWETZ
Official responsible
E-mail: mario.schwetz@europarl.europa.eu
Tel. +32 228-43992
Tel. +33 3881-72097

Committee on Industry, Research and Energy

Joao SOUSA DE JESUS
E-mail: alfredo.sousa@europarl.europa.eu
Tel. +32 228-32781
Tel. +33 3881-73219

Edina TÓTH
E-mail: edina.toth@europarl.europa.eu
Tel. +32 228-40758
Tel. +33 3881-74472

Committee on Employment and Social Affairs

Klaus KELLERSMANN
E-mail: klaus.kellersmann@europarl.europa.eu
Tel. +32 228-42777
Tel. +33 3881-74179

Alena CARNA
E-mail: alena.carna@europarl.europa.eu
Tel. +32 228-41548
Tel. +33 3881-72681

Committee on Culture and Education

Véronique DONCK
E-mail: veronique.donck@europarl.europa.eu
Tel. +32 228-42888
Tel. +33 3881-74402

Andrea CEPOVA-FOURTOY
E-mail: andrea.cepova@europarl.europa.eu
Tel. +32 228-31293
Tel. +33 3881-74411

Committee on Women's Rights and Gender Equality

Anne VAHL
E-mail: anne.vahl@europarl.europa.eu
Tel. +32 228-42219
Tel. +33 3881-74547

Working Group C

Werner KRÖGEL
Official responsible
E-mail: werner.kroegel@europarl.europa.eu
Tel. +32 228-42565
Tel. +33 3881-74064

Committee on Budgets

Marianna PARI
E-mail: marianna.pari@europarl.europa.eu
Tel. +32 228-40921
Tel. +33 3881-74125

Nicole WIRTZ
E-mail: nicole.wirtz@europarl.europa.eu
Tel. +32 228-32796
Tel. +33 3881-74917

Committee on Budgetary Control

Balazs SZECHY
E-mail: balazs.szechy@europarl.europa.eu
Tel. +32 228-31399
Tel. +33 3881-72430

Stephen WOODARD
E-mail: stephen.woodard@europarl.europa.eu
Tel. +32 228-43184
Tel. +33 3881-74510

Committee on Agriculture and Rural Development

Jorge SOUTULLO-SÁNCHEZ
E-mail: jorge.soutullo@europarl.europa.eu
Tel. +32 228-42385
Tel. +33 3881-74404

Alwyn STRANGE
E-mail: alwyn.strange@europarl.europa.eu
Tel. +32 228-43029
Tel. +33 3881-72098

Andreas SCHNEIDER
E-mail: andreas.schneider@europarl.europa.eu
Tel. +32 228-42306
Tel. +33 3881-64145

Committee on Fisheries

Mauro BELARDINELLI
E-mail: mauro.benardinelli@europarl.europa.eu
Tel. +32 228-44826
Tel. +33 3881-72741

Committee on Regional Development

Fani ZARIFOPOULOU
E-mail: fani.zarifopoulou@europarl.europa.eu
Tel. +32 228-31360
Tel. +33 3881-64027

Madalina STOIAN
E-mail: madalina.stoian@europarl.europa.eu
Tel. +32 228-42528
Tel. +33 3881-78114

Working Group D

Adam ISAACS
Official responsible
E-mail: adam.isaacs@europarl.europa.eu
Tel. +32 228-42603
Tel. +33 3881-72826

Committee on Legal Affairs

Andrea LASKAVA
E-mail: andrea.laskava@europarl.europa.eu
Tel. +32 228-32129
Tel. +33 3881-72928

Boglárka BÓLYA
E-mail: boglarka.bolya@europarl.europa.eu
Tel. +32 228-42116
Tel. +33 3881-72492

Marie-Christine AMIOT
E-mail: mariechristine.amiot@europarl.europa.eu
Tel. +32 228-42845
Tel. +33 3881-73585

Committee on Civil Liberties, Justice and Home Affairs

Mercedes ALVARGONZALEZ
E-mail: mercedes.alvargonzalez@europarl.europa.eu
Tel. +32 228-44333
Tel. +33 3881-73584

Michael Alexander SPEISER
E-mail: michael.speiser@europarl.europa.eu
Tel. +32 228-32475
Tel. +33 3881-73908

Committee on Constitutional Affairs

Béatrice SCARASCIA MUGNOZZA
E-mail: beatrice.scarascia@europarl.europa.eu
Tel. +32 228-42599
Tel. +33 3881-74150

Rupert KRIETEMEYER
E-mail: rupert.krietemeyer@europarl.europa.eu
Tel. +33 3881-73126
Tel. +32 228-40661

Committee on Petitions

Leo COX
E-mail: leo.cox@europarl.europa.eu
Tel. +32 228-43446
Tel. +33 3881-72719

Working Group E

Catarina CALDEIRA DA SILVA
Official responsible
E-mail: catarina.caldeira@europarl.europa.eu
Tel. +32 228-43171
Tel. +33 3881-72713

Committee on the Environment, Public Health and Food Safety

Amarylli GERSONY
E-mail: amarylli.gersony@europarl.europa.eu
Tel. +32 228-42689
Tel. +33 3881-72865

Harald KANDOLF
E-mail: harald.kandolf@europarl.europa.eu
Tel. +32 228-43246
Tel. +33 3881-74833

Géraldine PHILIBERT
E-mail: geraldine.philibert@europarl.europa.eu
Tel. +32 228-41523
Tel. +33 3881-72090

Committee on Transport and Tourism

Romain STRASSER
E-mail: romain.strasser@europarl.europa.eu
Tel. +32 228-43264
Tel. +33 3881-74421

Stefano GUCCIONE
E-mail: stefano.guccione@europarl.europa.eu
Tel. +32 228-43189
Tel. +33 3881-72833

Committee on Economic and Monetary Affairs

José BOTELLA
E-mail: jose.botella@europarl.europa.eu
Tel. +32 228-44824
Tel. +33 3881-72734

Christian SCHEINERT
E-mail: christian.scheinert@europarl.europa.eu
Tel. +32 228-46358
Tel. +33 3881-72740

David BATT
E-mail: david.batt@europarl.europa.eu
Tel. +32 228-43375
Tel. +33 3881-72767

Committee on the Internal Market and Consumer Protection

Oliver DREUTE
E-mail: oliver.dreute@europarl.europa.eu
Tel. +32 228-41313
Tel. +33 3881-72720

Mina DERMENDJIEVA
E-mail: mina.dermendjieva@europarl.europa.eu
Tel. +32 228-43844
Tel. +33 3881-72812

Tereza PINTO DE REZENDE
E-mail: tereza.pintoderezende@europarl.europa.eu
Tel. +32 228-41767
Tel. +33 3881-72434

Plenary Sittings and Legislative Coordination

Natacha SCRIBAN-CUVELIER
Official responsible
E-mail: natacha.scriban@europarl.europa.eu
Tel. +32 228-42254
Tel. +33 3881-74236

Timothy BEYER-HELM
E-mail: timothy.beyer@europarl.europa.eu
Tel. +32 228-43024
Tel. +33 3881-64079

Géraldine PHILIBERT
E-mail: geraldine.philibert@europarl.europa.eu
Tel. +32 228-41523
Tel. +33 3881-72090

Botond TÖRÖK-ILLYÉS
E-mail: botond.torok-illyes@europarl.europa.eu
Tel. +32 228-32552
Tel. +33 3881-77054

Kai WYNANDS
E-mail: kai.wynands@europarl.europa.eu
Tel. +32 228-32039
Tel. +33 3881-73006

Political Strategy

Christine DETOURBET
E-mail: christine.detourbet@europarl.europa.eu
Tel. +32 228-42287
Tel. +33 3881-74095

Guillermo MARTINEZ-CASAÑ
E-mail: guillermo.martinezcasan@europarl.europa.eu
Tel. +32 228-31456
Tel. +33 3881-76663

Peter ADLER
E-mail: peter.adler@europarl.europa.eu
Tel. +32 228-43986
Tel. +33 3881-74904

Marek EVISON
E-mail: marek.evison@europarl.europa.eu
Tel. +32 228-40662
Tel. +33 3881-73906

Philipp SCHULMEISTER
E-mail: philipp.schulmeister@europarl.europa.eu
Tel. +32 228-41381
Tel. +33 3881-73515

Stephen WOODARD
E-mail: stephen.woodard@europarl.europa.eu
Tel. +32 228-43184
Tel. +33 3881-74510

International relations

Arthur HILDEBRANDT
E-mail: arthur.hildebrandt@europarl.europa.eu
Tel. +32 228-42607
Tel. +33 3881-72744

Interparliamentary Delegations

Joanna JARECKA-GOMEZ
E-mail: joanna.jarecka@europarl.europa.eu
Tel. +32 228-43393
Tel. +33 3881-76764

Relations with National Parliaments

Béatrice SCARASCIA MUGNOZZA
E-mail: beatrice.scarascia-mugnozza@europarl.europa.eu
Tel. +32 228-42599
Tel. +33 3881-74150

Adriaan BASTIAANSEN
E-mail: adriaan.bastiaansen@europarl.europa.eu
Tel. +32 228-41342
Tel. +33 3881-72824

Greet GYSEN
E-mail: greet.gysen@europarl.europa.eu
Tel. +32 228-32247
Tel. +33 3881-73654

Miriam LEXMANN
E-mail: miriam.lexmann@europarl.europa.eu
Tel. +32 228-32467
Tel. +33 3881-72679

Daniela SENK
E-mail: daniela.senk@europarl.europa.eu
Tel. +32 228-41033
Tel. +33 3881-73124

Press and Communication

Robert FITZHENRY
Group spokesperson
E-mail: robert.fitzhenry@europarl.europa.eu
Tel. +32 228-42228
Tel. +33 3881-74144

Press — Germany and Luxembourg

Knut GÖLZ
E-mail: knut.goelz@europarl.europa.eu
Tel. +32 228-41341
Tel. +33 3881-72797

Thomas BICKL
E-mail: thomas.bickl@europarl.europa.eu
Tel. +32 228-32002
Tel. +33 3881-73406

Lasse BOEHM
E-mail: lasse.boehm@europarl.europa.eu
Tel. +32 228-40774
Tel. +33 3881-72766

Press — Austria

Philipp SCHULMEISTER
E-mail: philipp.schulmeister@europarl.europa.eu
Tel. +32 228-41381
Tel. +33 3881-73515

Press — Belgium

Greet GYSEN
E-mail: greet.gysen@europarl.europa.eu
Tel. +32 228-32227
Tel. +33 3881-73654

Press — Bulgaria

Mina DERMENDJIEVA
E-mail: mina.dermendjieva@europarl.europa.eu
Tel. +32 228-43844
Tel. +33 3881-72812

Press — Cyprus

Eva MITSOPOULOU
E-mail: eva.mitsopoulou@europarl.europa.eu
Tel. +32 228-41662
Tel. +33 3881-73510

Press — Denmark

Peter ADLER
E-mail: peter.adler@europarl.europa.eu
Tel. +32 228-43986
Tel. +33 3881-74904

Press — Spain

Pedro LÓPEZ DE PABLO
E-mail: pedro.lopez@europarl.europa.eu
Tel. +32 228-42786
Tel. +33 3881-74871

Press — Estonia

Kaja SORG
E-mail: kaja.sorg@europarl.europa.eu
Tel. +32 228-41483
Tel. +33 3881-74825

Press — Finland

Antti TIMONEN
E-mail: antti.timonen@europarl.europa.eu
Tel. +32 228-32714
Tel. +33 3881-64124

Press — France and Luxembourg

Marion JEANNE
E-mail: marion.jeanne@europarl.europa.eu
Tel. +32 228-43635
Tel. +33 3881-73233

Anne VAHL
E-mail: anne.vahl@europarl.europa.eu
Tel. +32 228-42219
Tel. +33 3881-74547

Press — Greece

Theodoros GEORGITSOPOULOS
E-mail: theodoros.georgitsopoulos@europarl.europa.eu
Tel. +32 228-32001
Tel. +33 3881-76664

Press — Hungary

György HÖLVÉNYI
E-mail: gyorgy.holvenyi@europarl.europa.eu
Tel. +32 228-42393
Tel. +33 3881-73718

Press — Ireland

Majella O'DOHERTY
E-mail: majella.odoherty@europarl.europa.eu
Tel. +33 3881-72996
Tel. +32 228-31482

Press — Italy

Mariangela FONTANINI
E-mail: mariangela.fontanini@europarl.europa.eu
Tel. +32 228-43129
Tel. +33 3881-72812

Press — Latvia

Girts SALMGRIEZIS
E-mail: girts.salmgriezis@europarl.europa.eu
Tel. +32 228-32073
Tel. +33 3881-73007

Press — Lithuania

Zivile DIDZGALVIENE ANDRENAITE
E-mail: zivile.didzgalviene@europarl.europa.eu
Tel. +32 228-41660
Tel. +33 3881-74878

Press — Netherlands

Eduardus SLOOTWEG
E-mail: edouardus.slootweg@europarl.europa.eu
Tel. +32 228-42230
Tel. +33 3881-72096

Press — Poland

Marzena ROGALSKA
E-mail: marzena.rogalska@europarl.europa.eu
Tel. +32 228-43845
Tel. +33 3881-72877

Press — Portugal

Miguel SEABRA
E-mail: miguel.seabra@europarl.europa.eu
Tel. +32 228-42856
Tel. +33 3881-72819

Press — Czech Republic

Marek HANNIBAL
E-mail: marek.hannibal@europarl.europa.eu
Tel. +32 228-41659
Tel. +33 3881-74877

Press — Romania

Delia VLASE
E-mail: delia.vlase@europarl.europa.eu
Tel. +32 228-32551
Tel. +33 3881-77090

Press — Slovakia

Attila AGARDI
E-mail: atilla.agardi@europarl.europa.eu
Tel. +32 228-41609
Tel. +33 3881-74876

Press — Slovenia

Klemen ZUMER
E-mail: klemen.zumer@europarl.europa.eu
Tel. +33 3881-74875
Tel. +32 228-41661

Press — Sweden

Per HEISTER
E-mail: per.heister@europarl.europa.eu
Tel. +32 228-42697
Tel. +33 3881-74483

Press — Croatia

Lada JURICA
E-mail: lada.jurica@europarl.europa.eu
Tel. +32 228-32493
Tel. +33 3881-73485

Communication Strategy

Robert FITZHENRY
E-mail: robert.fitzhenry@europarl.europa.eu
Tel. +32 228-42228
Tel. +33 3881-74144

Peter ADLER
E-mail: peter.adler@europarl.europa.eu
Tel. +32 228-43986
Tel. +33 3881-74904

Knut GÖLZ
E-mail: knut.goelz@europarl.europa.eu
Tel. +32 228-41341
Tel. +33 3881-72797

Pedro LÓPEZ DE PABLO
E-mail: pedro.lopez@europarl.europa.eu
Tel. +32 228-42786
Tel. +33 3881-74871

Antoine RIPOLL
E-mail: antoine.ripoll@europarl.europa.eu
Tel. +32 228-42688
Tel. +33 3881-73513

Christine DETOURBET
E-mail: christine.detourbet@europarl.europa.eu
Tel. +32 228-42287
Tel. +33 3881-74095

Per HEISTER
E-mail: per.heister@europarl.europa.eu
Tel. +32 228-42697
Tel. +33 3881-74483

Walter PETRUCCI
E-mail: walter.petrucci@europarl.europa.eu
Tel. +32 228-43537
Tel. +33 3881-73537

Miguel SEABRA
E-mail: miguel.seabra@europarl.europa.eu
Tel. +32 228-42856
Tel. +33 3881-72819

Philipp SCHULMEISTER
E-mail: philipp.schulmeister@europarl.europa.eu
Tel. +32 228-41381
Tel. +33 3881-73515

Eduardus SLOOTWEG
E-mail: eduardus.slootweg@europarl.europa.eu
Tel. +32 228-42230
Tel. +33 3881-72096

Internet Cell

Miguel SEABRA
Official responsible
E-mail: miguel.seabra@europarl.europa.eu
Tel. +32 228-42856
Tel. +33 3881-72819

Per HEISTER
E-mail: per.heister@europarl.europa.eu
Tel. +32 228-42697
Tel. +33 3881-74483

Walter PETRUCCI
E-mail: walter.petrucci@europarl.europa.eu
Tel. +32 228-43537
Tel. +33 3881-73537

Ioannis ZOGRAFOS
E-mail: ioannis.zografos@europarl.europa.eu
Tel. +32 228-42227
Tel. +33 3881-72095

Internal organisation

John BIESMANS
Deputy Secretary-General
E-mail: john.biesmans@europarl.europa.eu
Tel. +32 228-43026
Tel. +33 3881-74852

Finance

Andreas FOLZ
Head of Unit
E-mail: andreas.folz@europarl.europa.eu
Tel. +32 228-40954
Tel. +33 3881-74544

Human Resources

Delia CARRO
Head of Unit
E-mail: delia.carro@europarl.europa.eu
Tel. +32 228-43237

Information Technology

Walter PETRUCCI
Head of Unit
E-mail: walter.petrucci@europarl.europa.eu
Tel. +32 228-43537
Tel. +33 3881-73537

Neighbourhood and Intercultural Activities Policy

Paolo LICANDRO
Deputy Secretary-General
E-mail: paolo.licandro@europarl.europa.eu
Tel. +32 228-42596
Tel. +33 3881-74501

Edyta TARCZYNSKA
E-mail: edyta.tarczynska@europarl.europa.eu
Tel. +32 228-44252
Tel. +33 3881-73486

Relations with Parties, the Council of Europe, the Committee of the Regions, European Neighbourhood Policy Countries and Mediterranean Countries, and Intercultural and Religious Dialogue

Guy KORTHOUDT
Official responsible
E-mail: guy.korthoudt@europarl.europa.eu
Tel. +32 228-31209
Tel. +33 3881-74890

György HÖLVÉNYI
E-mail: gyorgy.holvenyi@europarl.europa.eu
Tel. +32 228-42393
Tel. +33 3881-73718

Jorge SOUTULLO-SÁNCHEZ
E-mail: jorge.soutullo@europarl.europa.eu
Tel. +32 228-42385
Tel. +33 3881-74404

Eduardus SLOOTWEG
E-mail: edouardus.slootweg@europarl.europa.eu
Tel. +32 228-42230
Tel. +33 3881-72096

Mauro BELARDINELLI
E-mail: mauro.belardinelli@europarl.europa.eu
Tel. +32 228-44826
Tel. +33 3881-72741

Edyta TARCZYNSKA
E-mail: edyta.tarczynska@europarl.europa.eu
Tel. +32 228-44252
Tel. +33 3881-73486

Fani ZARIFOPOULOU
E-mail: fani.zarifopoulou@europarl.europa.eu
Tel. +32 228-31360
Tel. +33 3881-64027

Presidency

Antoine RIPOLL
Deputy Secretary-General
E-mail: antoine.ripoll@europarl.europa.eu
Tel. +32 228-42688
Tel. +33 3881-73513

Preparation of Meetings of EP Bodies and Group Meetings

Johan RYNGAERT
E-mail: johan.ryngaert@europarl.europa.eu
Tel. +32 228-42398
Tel. +33 3881-73897

Michael HAHN
E-mail: michael.hahn@europarl.europa.eu
Tel. +32 228-41725
Tel. +33 3881-72002

External Offices

Germany (Berlin)

Markus ARENS
E-mail: markus.arens@europarl.europa.eu
Tel. +32 228-4-2233
Fax +32 228-4-9361
Tel. +33 3881-73034
Tel. +49 30227-75775
Fax +49 30227-76958

Spain (Madrid)

Maria Nieves AGUIRRE
Tel. +32 228-40642
Tel. +33 3881-72126
Tel. +34 915577331, 577330

Great Britain (London)

James TEMPLE-SMITHSON
E-mail: james.temple@europarl.europa.eu
Tel. +44 2072221994
Fax +44 2072222501
Tel. +33 3881-74826

Italy (Rome)

Orazio PARISOTTO
E-mail: orazio.parisotto@europarl.europa.eu
Tel. +39 066990095
Tel. +33 3881-72303

France (Paris)

Marie-Claude DELAHAYE
E-mail: marieclaude.delahaye@europarl.europa.eu
Tel. +33 145559868
Tel. +32 228-42650
Tel. +33 3881-74230

Poland (Warsaw)

Marcin TROJANOWSKI
E-mail: marcin.trojanowski@europarl.europa.eu
Tel. +48 228929305
Tel. +33 3881-72877

Romania (Bucharest)

Radu NEGREA
E-mail: radu.negrea@europarl.europa.eu
Tel. +33 3881-72025

Documentation — Publications — Research

Pascal FONTAINE
Special Adviser
E-mail: pascal.fontaine@europarl.europa.eu
Tel. +32 228-42445
Tel. +33 3881-74857

Sandrine DAUCHELLE
E-mail: sandrine.dauchelle@europarl.europa.eu
Tel. +32 228-31412
Tel. +33 3881-76285

European People's Party (EPP)

Rue du Commerce 10
B-1000 Brussels
Website: http://www.epp.eu
Tel. +32 228-54140
Fax +32 228-54141

Wilfried MARTENS
President
Member-President
E-mail: president@epp.eu
Tel. +32 228-54189
Fax +32 228-54155

Antonio Lopez ISTURIZ
Secretary-General
E-mail: alopez@epp.eu
Tel. +32 228-54246

Christian KREMER
Deputy Secretary-General
E-mail: ckremer@epp.eu
Tel. +32 228-54248

Luc VANDEPUTTE
Deputy Secretary-General
E-mail: lvandeputte@epp.eu
Tel. +32 228-54251

Kostas SASMATZOGLOU
Secretary for External Relations
E-mail: relex@epp.eu
Tel. +32 228-54247

Nicolas BRIEC
Political Adviser
E-mail: nbriec@epp.eu
Tel. +32 23008008

Juan MAGAZ
Political Adviser
E-mail: jmagaz@epp.eu
Tel. +32 228-54153

Javier JIMENEZ
Press Advisor
E-mail: jjimenez@epp.eu
Tel. +32 228-54156

Emanuela FARRIS
Political Adviser
Tel. +32 228-54143

Galina FOMENCHENKO
Political Adviser
E-mail: gfomenchenko@epp.eu
Tel. +32 228-54162

Gemma SLAYMAKER
Political Adviser (press and communications)
E-mail: gslaymaker@epp.eu
Tel. +32 228-54142

PES: Socialist Group in the European Parliament

Brussels
Belgium
Tel. +32 228-42309

Strasbourg
France
Tel. +33 3881-73091

Secretariat-General

Anna COLOMBO
Secretary-General
E-mail: anna.colombo@europarl.europa.eu
Tel. +32 228-42270
Tel. +33 3881-74386

Jean-Louis VERHEYDEN
E-mail: jeanlouis.verheyden@europarl.europa.eu
Tel. +32 228-46576
Tel. +33 3881-74291

Robert VAN DE WATER
E-mail: robert.vandewater@europarl.europa.eu
Tel. +32 228-43138
Tel. +33 3881-74374

President's Office

Markus WINKLER
E-mail: markus.winkler@europarl.europa.eu
Tel. +32 228-40737
Tel. +33 3881-74938

Armin MACHMER
E-mail: armin.machmer@europarl.europa.eu
Tel. +32 228-44151
Tel. +33 3881-74134

Internal Coordination Unit

Antony BEUMER
Head of Unit
E-mail: antony.beumer@europarl.europa.eu
Tel. +32 228-42973
Tel. +33 3881-74335

Teresa PEREIRA
E-mail: teresa.pereira@europarl.europa.eu
Tel. +32 228-43197

Eloise TODD
E-mail: eloise.todd@europarl.europa.eu
Tel. +32 228-43452
Tel. +33 3881-73772

Peter BURU
E-mail: peter.buru@europarl.europa.eu
Tel. +32 228-31155
Tel. +33 3881-73320

External Institutional Coordination Unit

Fabian VALLI
Head of Unit
E-mail: fabien.valli@europarl.europa.eu
Tel. +32 228-40530
Tel. +33 3881-74947

Cristina BAPTISTA
E-mail: cristina.baptista@europarl.europa.eu
Tel. +32 228-44846
Tel. +33 3881-72890

Nicolas MACIAS
E-mail: nicolas.macias@europarl.europa.eu
Tel. +32 228-40946
Tel. +33 3881-72847

Press and Communications Unit

Tony ROBINSON
Head of Unit
E-mail: tony.robinson@europarl.europa.eu
Tel. +32 228-43061
Tel. +33 3881-72998

Solange HELIN-VILLES
E-mail: solange.helin@europarl.europa.eu
Tel. +32 228-32147
Tel. +33 3881-74779

Dimitris KOMODROMOS
E-mail: dimitris.komodromos@europarl.europa.eu
Tel. +32 228-31459
Tel. +33 3881-74698

Gabriela LANGADA
E-mail: gabriela.langada@ europarl.europa.eu
Tel. +32 228-44082
Tel. +33 3881-64146

Isuka PALAU
E-mail: isuka.palau@europarl.europa.eu
Tel. +32 228-32716
Tel. +33 3881-73214

Silvia PELZ
E-mail: silvia.pelz@europarl.europa.eu
Tel. +32 228-48712
Tel. +33 3881-78164

Sergio SERGI
E-mail: sergio.sergi@europarl.europa.eu
Tel. +32 228-43001
Tel. +33 3881-78158

David POYSER
E-mail: david.poyser@europarl.europa.eu
Tel. +32 228-32414
Tel. +33 3881-64146

Maggie COULTHARD
E-mail: maggie.coulthard@europarl.europa.eu
Tel. +32 228-41877
Tel. +33 3881-74376

Parliamentary Matters Department

Herwig KAISER
Deputy Secretary-General
E-mail: herwig.kaiser@europarl.europa.eu
Tel. +32 228-43826
Tel. +33 3881-74380

Foreign Affairs Unit

Ruth DE CESARE-MUELLER
Head of Unit
E-mail: ruth.decesaremueller@europarl.europa.eu
Tel. +32 228-43071
Tel. +33 3881-74246

Anita TUSAR
E-mail: anita.tusar@europarl.europa.eu
Tel. +32 228-31156
Tel. +33 3881-72109

Jean-François VALLIN
E-mail: jeanfrancois.vallin@europarl.europa.eu
Tel. +32 228-43104
Tel. +33 3881-72983

Armelle WEILL
E-mail: armelle.weill@europarl.europa.eu
Tel. +32 228-32537
Tel. +33 3881-72973

Chris WILLIAMS
E-mail: christopher.williams@europarl.europa.eu
Tel. +32 228-41016
Tel. +33 3881-73267

José Antonio GIL DE MURO
E-mail: joseantonio.gildemuro@europarl.europa.eu
Tel. +32 228-42977
Tel. +33 3881-72874

Eldar MAMEDOV
E-mail: eldar.mamedov@europarl.europa.eu
Tel. +32 228-48313
Tel. +33 3881-64154

Joana TRIANA
E-mail: joana.triana@europarl.europa.eu
Tel. +32 228-31628

Maria Teresa MOLERES
E-mail: mariateresa.moleres@europarl.europa.eu
Tel. +32 228-43211
Tel. +33 3881-74260

Budget and Cohesion Policy Unit

José Carlos MARIN
Head of Unit
E-mail: josecarlos.marin@europarl.europa.eu
Tel. +32 228-43118
Tel. +33 3881-72856

Xavier DUTRENIT
E-mail: xavier.dutrenit@europarl.europa.eu
Tel. +32 228-73750
Tel. +352 4300-32452

Annalisa GLIUBIZZI
E-mail: annalisa.gliubizzi@europarl.europa.eu
Tel. +32 228-31367
Tel. +33 3881-64098

Kirsten LÜDDECKE
E-mail: kirsten.luddecke@europarl.europa.eu
Tel. +32 228-41384
Tel. +33 3881-72848

Petros KOUPEGKOS
E-mail: petros.koupegkos@europarl.europa.eu
Tel. +32 228-43257
Tel. +33 3881-75723

Brigitte BATAILLE
E-mail: brigitte.bataille@europarl.europa.eu
Tel. +32 228-43112
Tel. +33 3881-72887

Sonja STEENHAUT
E-mail: sonja.steenhaut@europarl.europa.eu
Tel. +32 228-42590
Tel. +33 3881-72879

Elke ESDERS
E-mail: elke.esders@europarl.europa.eu
Tel. +32 228-43070
Tel. +33 3881-73760

Economic and Social Model Policy Unit

Derek REED
Head of Unit
E-mail: derek.reed@europarl.europa.eu
Tel. +32 228-43086
Tel. +33 3881-73766

Peter RUSZ
E-mail: peter.rusz@europarl.europa.eu
Tel. +32 228-32322
Tel. +33 3881-74750

Nicolas MACIAS
E-mail: nicolas.macias@europarl.europa.eu
Tel. +32 228-40946
Tel. +33 3881-72847

Ute MULLER
E-mail: ute.muller@europarl.europa.eu
Tel. +32 228-43750
Tel. +33 3881-72884

Annabel GARNIER
E-mail: annabel.garnier@europarl.europa.eu
Tel. +32 228-41604
Tel. +33 3881-72882

Emmanuelle LE TEXIER
E-mail: emmanuelle.letexier@europarl.europa.eu
Tel. +32 228-32710
Tel. +33 3881-72590

Rasa RUDZKYTE
E-mail: rasa.rudzkyte@europarl.europa.eu
Tel. +32 228-31106
Tel. +33 3881-76716

Jean-Marie TRIACCA
E-mail: jeanmarie.triacca@europarl.europa.eu
Tel. +32 228-43081
Tel. +33 3881-72321

Stine Laerke LARSEN
E-mail: stine.larsen@europarl.europa.eu
Tel. +32 228-43467
Tel. +33 3881-64131

Sustainable Development and Competitiveness Unit

Marcel MERSCH
Head of Unit
E-mail: marcel.mersch@europarl.europa.eu
Tel. +32 228-42785
Tel. +33 3881-74372

Francisco GUERRA
E-mail: francisco.guerra@europarl.europa.eu
Tel. +32 228-31381
Tel. +33 3881-64097

Giovanna PARESCHI
E-mail: giovanna.pareschi@europarl.europa.eu
Tel. +32 228-42464
Tel. +33 3881-73867

Ulrike SCHONER
E-mail: ulrike.schoner@europarl.europa.eu
Tel. +32 228-32488
Tel. +33 3881-72451

Cristina TRAVAGLIATI
E-mail: cristina.travagliati@europarl.europa.eu
Tel. +32 228-34048

Vincent BOCQUILLON
E-mail: vincent.bocquillon@europarl.europa.eu
Tel. +32 228-31453
Tel. +33 3881-72875

Silvestro LATELLA
E-mail: silvestro.latella@europarl.europa.eu
Tel. +32 228-43050
Tel. +33 3881-74959

René TAMMIST
E-mail: rene.tammist@europarl.europa.eu
Tel. +32 228-32191
Tel. +33 3881-74469

Valborg LINDEN JONSTEN
E-mail: valborg.lindenjonsten@europarl.europa.eu
Tel. +32 228-42266
Tel. +33 3881-75906

Igor HORNAK
E-mail: igor.hornak@europarl.europa.eu
Tel. +32 228-31160
Tel. +33 3881-73462

Teresa MERGULHAO
E-mail: teresa.mergulhao@europarl.europa.eu
Tel. +32 228-43167
Tel. +33 3881-72869

Bartosz LERCEL
E-mail: bartosz.lercel@europarl.europa.eu
Tel. +32 228-32787
Tel. +33 3881-73299

Jakub SEMRAU
E-mail: jakub.semrau@europarl.europa.eu
Tel. +32 228-32807
Tel. +33 3881-73399

Josephine WOOD
E-mail: josephine.wood@europarl.europa.eu
Tel. +32 228-43723

Citizens' Europe Unit

Frazer CLARKE
Head of Unit
E-mail: frazer.clarke@europarl.europa.eu
Tel. +32 228-43175
Tel. +33 3881-73759

Annie LEMARCHAL
E-mail: annie.lemarchal@europarl.europa.eu
Tel. +32 228-43057
Tel. +33 3881-72267

Daniela VON BETHLENFALVY
E-mail: daniela.vonbethlenfalvy@europarl.europa.eu
Tel. +32 228-73440
Tel. +33 3881-73440

Maria Soledad GUIRAO GALDON
E-mail: mariasoledad.guiraogaldon@europarl.europa.eu
Tel. +32 228-44850
Tel. +33 3881-73812

Fabrizia PANZETTI
E-mail: fabrizia.panzetti@europarl.europa.eu
Tel. +32 228-31417
Tel. +33 3881-73089

Matilda SISATTO
E-mail: matilda.sisatto@europarl.europa.eu
Tel. +32 228-32133

External Action Department

Michael HOPPE
Deputy Secretary-General
E-mail: michael.hoppe@europarl.europa.eu
Tel. +32 228-44845
Tel. +33 3881-73866

Odilia HENRIQUES
E-mail: mariaodilia.henriques@europarl.europa.eu
Tel. +32 228-43381
Tel. +33 3881-73892

Javier RAMOS DIAZ
E-mail: javier.ramos@europarl.europa.eu
Tel. +32 228-41028

Enlargement and Transatlantic Relations Unit

Bogna SUDA
Head of Unit
E-mail: bogna.suda@europarl.europa.eu
Tel. +32 228-41107
Tel. +33 3881-72980

Keith AZZOPARDI
E-mail: keith.azzopardi@europarl.europa.eu
Tel. +32 228-31460
Tel. +33 3881-72984

Ciprian MATEI
E-mail: ciprian.matei@europarl.europa.eu
Tel. +32 228-31263
Tel. +33 3881-64021

Maria MUNIZ DE URQUIZA
E-mail: maria.muniz@europarl.europa.eu
Tel. +32 228-31452
Tel. +33 3881-72573

Corina Daniela POPA
E-mail: corina.popa@europarl.europa.eu
Tel. +32 228-32888

Mediterranean and Middle East Unit

Bruno MARASA
Head of Unit
E-mail: bruno.marasa@europarl.europa.eu
Tel. +32 228-42195
Tel. +33 3881-72861

Evangelos LEPOURAS
E-mail: evangelos.lepouras@europarl.europa.eu
Tel. +32 228-43087
Tel. +33 3881-74869

Radostina MUTAFCHIEVA
E-mail: radostina.mutafchieva@europarl.europa.eu
Tel. +32 228-32396
Tel. +33 3881-73212

Vasilios MYLONAS
E-mail: vasilios.mylonas@europarl.europa.eu
Tel. +32 228-43202
Tel. +33 3881-74770

Ambroise PERRIN
E-mail: ambroise.perrin@europarl.europa.eu
Tel. +32 228-43062
Tel. +33 3881-73889

Peter REICHERT
E-mail: peter.reichert@europarl.europa.eu
Tel. +32 228-43059
Tel. +33 3881-73887

Zoltán SIMON
E-mail: zoltan.simon@europarl.europa.eu
Tel. +32 228-32352
Tel. +33 3881-72974

Organisational Matters Department

Jesper SCHUNCK
Deputy Secretary-General
E-mail: jesper.schunck@europarl.europa.eu
Tel. +32 228-43084
Tel. +33 3881-74373

Ex-Ante Control Unit

Doriano DRAGONI
Head of Unit
E-mail: doriano.dragoni@europarl.europa.eu
Tel. +32 228-43518
Tel. +33 3881-73763

Accounts Unit

Freddy NAEGELS
Head of Unit
E-mail: freddy.naegels@europarl.europa.eu
Tel. +32 228-43119
Tel. +33 3881-74346

Human Resources Unit

Giancarlo VILELLA
Head of Unit
E-mail: giancarlo.vilella@europarl.europa.eu
Tel. +32 228-41348
Tel. +33 3881-74378

Gerd KRAMER
E-mail: gerd.kramer@europarl.europa.eu
Tel. +32 228-43085
Tel. +33 3881-74372

Information Technology Unit

Georges KOTTOS
Head of Unit
E-mail: georges.kottos@europarl.europa.eu
Tel. +32 228-42852
Tel. +33 3881-74384

ALDE: Alliance of Liberals and Democrats for Europe

Rue Wiertz (PHS)
B-1047 Brussels
Tel. +32 228-42111
Fax +32 22302485, 22309674, 22309534, 22846613

LOW et WIC
F-67070 Strasbourg
Tel. +33 3881-74001
Fax +33 3881-79044, 3881-76929, 3881-76941, 3882-56471

Leader's Office

Philip DRAUZ
Head of Leader's Office
E-mail: philip.drauz@europarl.europa.eu
Tel. +32 228-32187
Tel. +33 3881-76783

Tsveti NACHEVA
E-mail: tsvetelina.nacheva@europarl.europa.eu
Tel. +32 228-32598
Tel. +33 3881-73134

Euan Neil RODDIN
E-mail: euan.roddin@europarl.europa.eu
Tel. +32 228-44157
Tel. +33 3881-72431

Federica TERZI
E-mail: federica.terzi@europarl.europa.eu
Tel. +32 228-32324
Tel. +33 3881-73553

Secretary-General's Office

Alexander BEELS
E-mail: alexander.beels@europarl.europa.eu
Tel. +32 228-42561
Tel. +33 3881-74216

Deputy Secretary-General's Office

Niccolò RINALDI
E-mail: niccolo.rinaldi@europarl.europa.eu
Tel. +32 228-42073
Tel. +33 3881-74170

François PAULI
E-mail: francois.pauli@europarl.europa.eu
Tel. +32 228-41415
Tel. +33 3881-76650

Parliamentary Work

Marieta COLERA
Head of Unit
Coordinator of Working Groups A, B and C
E-mail: marieta.colera@europarl.europa.eu
Tel. +32 228-42089
Tel. +33 3881-74163

Working Group A

Ursa PONDELEK
Political Adviser
E-mail: ursa.pondelek@europarl.europa.eu
Tel. +32 228-43308
Tel. +33 3881-74907

Legal Affairs

Ursa PONDELEK
E-mail: ursa.pondelek@europarl.europa.eu
Tel. +32 228-43308
Tel. +33 3881-74907

Internal Market and Consumer Protection

Karin SAUERTEIG
E-mail: karin.sauerteig@europarl.europa.eu
Tel. +32 228-32189
Tel. +33 3881-76768

Ophélie SPANNEUT
E-mail: ophelie.spanneut@europarl.europa.eu
Tel. +32 228-43592
Tel. +33 3881-64105

Economic and Monetary Affairs

Delphine DESCAMPS-RICCI
E-mail: delphine.descampsricci@europarl.europa.eu
Tel. +32 228-31137
Tel. +33 3881-64085

Culture and Education

Rosario GALOFRE
E-mail: rosario.galofre@europarl.europa.eu
Tel. +32 228-42198
Tel. +33 3881-74519

Petitions

Thierry MASSON
E-mail: thierry.masson@europarl.europa.eu
Tel. +32 228-32367
Tel. +33 3881-64216

Women's Rights and Gender Equality

Milena DIMITROVA
E-mail: milena.dimitrova@europarl.europa.eu
Tel. +32 228-32499
Tel. +33 3881-64107

Employment and Social Affairs

Valérie GLATIGNY
E-mail: valerie.glatigny@europarl.europa.eu
Tel. +32 228-32370
Tel. +33 3881-64185

Working Group B

Nicola MAZZARO
Political Adviser
E-mail: nicola.mazzaro@europarl.europa.eu
Tel. +32 228-42784
Tel. +33 3881-72381

Industry, Research and Energy

Nicola MAZZARO
E-mail: nicola.mazzaro@europarl.europa.eu
Tel. +32 228-42784
Tel. +33 3881-72381

Giedre SVETIKAITE
E-mail: giedre.svetikaite@europarl.europa.eu
Tel. +32 228-43764
Tel. +33 3881-73229

Titus POENARU
E-mail: titus.poenaru@europarl.europa.eu
Tel. +32 228-34114
Tel. +33 3881-73065

Environment, Public Health and Food Safety

Tue FOSDAL
E-mail: tue.fosdal@europarl.europa.eu
Tel. +32 228-32747
Tel. +33 3881-74172

Thierry MASSON
E-mail: thierry.masson@europarl.europa.eu
Tel. +32 228-32367
Tel. +33 3881-64216

Regional Development

Anu AHOPELTO
E-mail: anu.ahopelto@europarl.europa.eu
Tel. +32 228-32181
Tel. +33 3881-74206

Ophélie SPANNEUT
E-mail: ophelie.spanneut@europarl.europa.eu
Tel. +32 228-43592
Tel. +33 3881-64105

Agriculture and Rural Development

Wilhelm BARGUM
E-mail: wilhelm.bargum@europarl.europa.eu
Tel. +32 228-32087
Tel. +33 3881-64159

Fisheries

Michele BARNESCHI
E-mail: michele.barneschi@europarl.europa.eu
Tel. +32 228-40705
Tel. +33 3881-64106

Transport and Tourism

Anne-Christine DESNUELLE
E-mail: anne-christine.desnuelle@europarl.europa.eu
Tel. +32 228-34102
Tel. +33 3881-64101

Michele BARNESCHI
E-mail: michele.barneschi@europarl.europa.eu
Tel. +32 228-40705
Tel. +33 3881-64106

Working Group C

Rune GLASBERG
Political Adviser
E-mail: rune.glasberg@europarl.europa.eu
Tel. +32 228-42910
Tel. +33 3881-72788

Foreign Affairs

Rune GLASBERG
E-mail: rune.glasberg@europarl.europa.eu
Tel. +32 228-42910
Tel. +33 3881-72788

Renaldas VAISBRODAS
E-mail: renaldas.vaisbrodas@europarl.europa.eu
Tel. +32 228-32745
Tel. +33 3881-74204

Isabella MARZULLO
E-mail: isabella.marzullo@europarl.europa.eu
Tel. +32 228-43181
Tel. +33 3881-73455

Development

Jean-Pierre TRAUFFLER
E-mail: jeanpierre.trauffler@europarl.europa.eu
Tel. +32 228-42869
Tel. +33 3881-74209

Katia STASINOPOULOU
E-mail: katia.stasinopoulou@europarl.europa.eu
Tel. +32 228-32091
Tel. +33 3881-64101

International Trade

Barbara MELIS
E-mail: barbara.melis@europarl.europa.eu
Tel. +32 228-41546
Tel. +33 3881-72872

Isabella MARZULLO
E-mail: isabella.marzullo@europarl.europa.eu
Tel. +32 228-43181
Tel. +33 3881-73455

Human Rights — Security and Defence (Subcommittees)

Isabella MARZULLO
Human Rights
E-mail: isabella.marzullo@europarl.europa.eu
Tel. +32 228-43181
Tel. +33 3881-73455

Renaldas VAISBRODAS
Security and Defence
E-mail: renaldas.vaisbrodas@europarl.europa.eu
Tel. +32 228-32745
Tel. +33 3881-74204

Civil Liberties, Justice and Home Affairs

Anders RASMUSSEN
E-mail: anders.rasmussen@europarl.europa.eu
Tel. +32 228-41493
Tel. +33 3881-72765

Ottavio MARZOCCHI
E-mail: ottavio.marzocchi@europarl.europa.eu
Tel. +32 228-43995
Tel. +33 3881-74231

Joëlle FISS
E-mail: joelle.fiss@europarl.europa.eu
Tel. +32 228-31088
Tel. +33 3881-73656

Constitutional Affairs

Guillaume Mc LAUGHLIN
E-mail: guillaume.mclaughlin@europarl.europa.eu
Tel. +32 228-32036
Tel. +33 3881-64086

Budgets

Paulina KUZNIAK
E-mail: paulina.kuzniak@europarl.europa.eu
Tel. +32 228-32155
Tel. +33 3881-76767

Carole PERRIN
E-mail: carole.perrin@europarl.europa.eu
Tel. +32 228-31328
Tel. +33 3881-64084

Budgetary Control

Dominykas MORDAS
E-mail: dominykas.mordas@europarl.europa.eu
Tel. +32 228-31123
Tel. +33 3881-72777

Services

Finance

Arjen BOUTER
Head of Unit
E-mail: arjen.bouter@europarl.europa.eu
Tel. +32 228-43990
Tel. +33 3881-72781

Communication

Sylwia REMISZEWSKA
Head of Unit
E-mail: sylwia.remiszewska@europarl.europa.eu
Tel. +32 228-31070
Tel. +33 3881-74908

Airis MEIER
E-mail: airis.meier@europarl.europa.eu
Tel. +32 228-31132
Tel. +33 3881-73063

Lucian GOLEANU
E-mail: lucian.goleanu@europarl.europa.eu
Tel. +32 228-34020
Tel. +33 3881-74219

Human Resources

Roger CHADWICK
Head of Unit
E-mail: roger.chadwick@europarl.europa.eu
Tel. +32 228-42084
Tel. +33 3881-75887

Interinstitutional Relations

Willem VANDEN BROUCKE
Head of Unit
E-mail: willem.vandenbroucke@europarl.europa.eu
Tel. +32 228-44380
Tel. +33 3881-72784

Renaldas VAISBRODAS
E-mail: renaldas.vaisbrodas@europarl.europa.eu
Tel. +32 228-32745
Tel. +33 3881-74204

Itziar MUNOA
E-mail: itziar.munoa@europarl.europa.eu
Tel. +32 228-43328
Tel. +33 3881-73551

Press

Neil CORLETT
Head of Unit
E-mail: neil.corlett@europarl.europa.eu
Tel. +32 228-42077
Tel. +33 3881-74167

Yannick LAUDE
E-mail: yannick.laude@europarl.europa.eu
Tel. +32 228-43169
Tel. +33 3881-72776

Paolo ALBERTI
E-mail: paolo.alberti@europarl.europa.eu
Tel. +32 228-31130
Tel. +33 3881-73528

Neringa GAIDYTE
E-mail: neringa.gaidyte@europarl.europa.eu
Tel. +32 228-32599
Tel. +33 3881-64083

Axel HEYER
E-mail: axel.heyer@europarl.europa.eu
Tel. +32 228-44703
Tel. +33 3881-72327

Dave McCULLOUGH
E-mail: dave.mccullough@europarl.europa.eu
Tel. +32 228-43128
Tel. +33 3881-73134

Jeroen REIJNEN
E-mail: jeroen.reijnen@europarl.europa.eu
Tel. +32 228-32518
Tel. +33 3881-74275

Greens/EFA: The Greens/European Free Alliance

Brussels
Belgium
Tel. +32 228-43045, 43327, 42274, 41693
Fax +32 22307837, 22284915

Strasbourg
France
Tel. +33 3881-75880, 74153, 74321
Fax +33 3882-41196

Strasbourg
France
Fax +33 3883-52777

Secretariat-General

Vula TSETSI
Secretary-General
E-mail: vula.tsetsi@europarl.europa.eu
Tel. +32 228-42117
Tel. +33 3881-75879

Joachim DENKINGER
Deputy Secretary-General
E-mail: joachim.denkinger@europarl.europa.eu
Tel. +32 228-43095
Tel. +33 3881-74865

José Luis LINAZASORO
Deputy Secretary-General
E-mail: joseluis.linazasoro@europarl.europa.eu
Tel. +32 228-43040
Tel. +33 3881-74033

Daniela RECINELLA
Assistant to the Secretary-General
E-mail: daniela.recinella@europarl.europa.eu
Tel. +32 228-43327
Tel. +33 3881-74153

Heike LEBERLE
Assistant to the Deputy Secretary-General
E-mail: heike.leberle@europarl.europarl.eu
Tel. +32 228-32140
Tel. +33 3881-76787

Central Secretariat and Administration

Claire KWAN
Assistant in the Central Secretariat
E-mail: claire.kwan@europarl.europa.eu
Tel. +32 228-31033
Tel. +33 3881-73133

Laurent DEVELAY
E-mail: laurent.develay@europarl.europa.eu
Tel. +32 228-41693
Tel. +33 3881-75880

Barbara WERNER
E-mail: barbara.werner@europarl.europa.eu
Tel. +32 228-42274
Tel. +33 3881-74321

Press and Communication

Helmut WEIXLER
Press Attaché
E-mail: helmut.weixler@europarl.europa.eu
Tel. +32 228-44683
Tel. +33 3881-74760

Isabelle ZERROUK
Deputy Press Attaché
E-mail: isabelle.zerrouk@europarl.europa.eu
Tel. +32 228-44683
Tel. +33 3881-74760

Chris COAKLEY
Assistant (press and communications)
E-mail: chris.coakley@europarl.europa.eu
Tel. +32 228-41667
Tel. +33 3881-74375

Steven CORNELIUS
Press Attaché — EFA
E-mail: steven.cornelius@europarl.europa.eu
Tel. +32 228-41665
Tel. +33 3881-72936

Human Resources

Laurence DUGNIOLLE
E-mail: laurence.dugniolle@europarl.europa.eu
Tel. +32 228-41699
Tel. +33 3881-73758

Nelly BALTIDE
E-mail: nelly.baltide@europarl.europa.eu
Tel. +32 228-41699

Accounting

Gérard DI FILIPPO
E-mail: gerard.difilippo@europarl.europa.eu
Tel. +32 228-44341

Ex-Ante control

Jean-Pierre DULLAERT
E-mail: jean-pierre.dullaert@europarl.europa.eu
Tel. +32 228-46072
Tel. +33 3881-73744

Webmaster and Communication

Jean-Marie KUTTEN
E-mail: jean-marie.kutten@europarl.europa.eu
Tel. +32 228-41664
Tel. +33 3881-72927

Multimedia and Communication

Sonja MEYRL
E-mail: sonja.meyrl@europarl.europa.eu
Tel. +32 228-41667
Tel. +33 3881-74428

Inga KEILMANN
E-mail: inga.keilmann@europarl.europa.eu
Tel. +32 228-32902
Tel. +33 3881-74428

Information Technology

Willy DRIEUX
E-mail: willy.drieux@europarl.europa.eu
Tel. +32 228-42134
Tel. +33 3881-74027

Thomas STAQUET
E-mail: thomas.staquet@europarl.europa.eu
Tel. +32 228-43840
Tel. +33 3881-74027

Parliamentary Committees and Political Priorities

Foreign Affairs

Paolo BERGAMASCHI
E-mail: paolo.bergamaschi@europarl.europa.eu
Tel. +32 228-42019
Tel. +33 3881-73544

Sabine MEYER
E-mail: sabine.meyer@europarl.europa.eu
Tel. +32 228-43353
Tel. +33 3881-74872

Subcommittee on Human Rights

Mychelle RIEU
E-mail: mychelle.rieu@europarl.europa.eu
Tel. +32 228-41668
Tel. +33 3881-72947

Subcommittee on Security and Defence

Ernst GÜLCHER
E-mail: ernst.guelcher@europarl.europa.eu
Tel. +32 228-43613
Tel. +33 3881-73545

Dvelopment

Tsiguereda WALELIGN
E-mail: tsiguereda.walelign@europarl.europa.eu
Tel. +32 228-43354
Tel. +33 3881-73736

Civil Liberties, Justice and Home Affairs

Jean-Luc ROBERT
E-mail: jean-luc.robert@europarl.europa.eu
Tel. +32 228-42052
Tel. +33 3881-74169

Christine SIDENIUS
E-mail: christine.sidenius@europarl.europa.eu
Tel. +32 228-46526
Tel. +33 3881-74533

Aleksejs DIMITROVS
EFA
E-mail: aleksejs.dimitrovs@europarl.europa.eu
Tel. +32 228-47912
Tel. +33 3881-77912

Women's Rights and Gender Equality

Elisabeth HORSTKÖTTER
E-mail: elisabeth.horstkoetter@europarl.europa.eu
Tel. +32 228-43925
Tel. +33 3881-73543

Employment and Social Affairs

Philine SCHOLZE
E-mail: philine.scholze@europarl.europa.eu
Tel. +32 228-32153
Tel. +33 3881-76720

Constitutional Affairs

Petra PROSSLINER
E-mail: petra.prossliner@europarl.europa.eu
Tel. +32 228-43360
Tel. +33 3881-74854

Frank INGELAERE
EFA
(also deals with the Committee on Regional Development)
E-mail: frank.ingelaere@europarl.europa.eu
Tel. +32 228-41690
Tel. +33 3881-72921

Regional Development

Simone REINHART
E-mail: simone.reinhart@europarl.europa.eu
Tel. +32 228-42202
Tel. +33 3881-74796

Legal Affairs

Francesca BELTRAME
E-mail: francesca.beltrame@europarl.europa.eu
Tel. +32 228-32146
Tel. +33 3881-76718

Petitions

Kjell SEVON
E-mail: kjell.sevon@europarl.europa.eu
Tel. +32 228-42169
Tel. +33 3881-73740

International Trade

Martin KÖHLER
E-mail: martin.koehler@europarl.europa.eu
Tel. +32 228-42188
Tel. +33 3881-74969

Gabriele KÜPPERS
E-mail: gabriele.kueppers@europarl.europa.eu
Tel. +32 228-43392
Tel. +33 3881-74068

Industry, Research and Energy

Michel RAQUET
E-mail: michel.raquet@europarl.europa.eu
Tel. +32 228-42358
Tel. +33 3881-73746

Laurence VAN DE WALLE
E-mail: laurence.vandewalle@europarl.europa.eu
Tel. +32 228-41695
Tel. +33 3881-73723

Economic and Monetary Affairs

Inès TREPANT
E-mail: ines.trepant@europarl.europa.eu
Tel. +32 228-31454
Tel. +33 3881-76860

Transport and Tourism

Paul BEECKMANS
E-mail: paul.beeckmans@europarl.europa.eu
Tel. +32 228-43114
Tel. +33 3881-75840

Internal Market and Consumer Protection

Stanislas GRUDZIELSKI
E-mail: stanislas.grudzielski@europarl.europa.eu
Tel. +32 228-31455
Tel. +33 3881-73741

Lachlan MUIR
EFA
(also deals with the Committee on Fisheries)
E-mail: lachlan.muir@europarl.europa.eu
Tel. +32 228-44595
Tel. +33 3881-75091

Fisheries

Michael EARLE
E-mail: michael.earle@europarl.europa.eu
Tel. +32 228-42849
Tel. +33 3881-74188

Environment, Public Health and Food Safety

Terhi LEHTONEN
E-mail: terhi.lehtonen@europarl.europa.eu
Tel. +32 228-43052
Tel. +33 3881-75878

Axel SINGHOFEN
E-mail: axel.singhofen@europarl.europa.eu
Tel. +32 228-42836
Tel. +33 3881-73550

Corinna ZERGER
E-mail: corinna.zerger@europarl.europa.eu
Tel. +32 228-44484
Tel. +33 3881-64150

Agriculture and Rural Development

Hans Martin LORENZEN
E-mail: hansmartin.lorenzen@europarl.europa.eu
Tel. +32 228-43362
Tel. +33 3881-73546

Daniel WYLIE
EFA (also deals with the Committee on Transport and Tourism and the Committee on Industry, Research and Energy)
E-mail: daniel.wylie@europarl.europa.eu
Tel. +32 228-42250
Tel. +33 3881-75024

Culture

Karen BEN TOLILA
E-mail: karen.bentolila@europarl.europa.eu
Tel. +32 228-42218
Tel. +33 3881-73739

Zsuzsa FERENCZY
EFA
E-mail: zsuzsa.ferenczy@europarl.europa.eu
Tel. +32 228-43324

Budgets

Annemieke BEUGELINK
E-mail: annemieke.beugelink@europarl.europa.eu
Tel. +32 228-42025
Tel. +33 3881-74533

Budgetary Control

Henk PRUMMEL
E-mail: hendrik.prummel@europarl.europa.eu
Tel. +32 228-43820
Tel. +33 3881-74190

Turkish Delegation

Ali YURTTAGÜL
E-mail: ali.yurttagul@europarl.europa.eu
Tel. +32 228-43047
Tel. +33 3881-74850

Climate Change Campaign

Richard MORE O'FERRALL
E-mail: richard.moreoferrall@europarl.europa.eu
Tel. +32 228-41669
Tel. +33 3881-74042

Kristian AUTH
E-mail: kristian.auth@europarl.europa.eu
Tel. +32 228-42280
Tel. +33 3881-64190

Liaison between the Green Parties of Central and Eastern Europe

Bartosz LECH
E-mail: bartosz.lech@europarl.europa.eu
Tel. +32 228-43038
Tel. +33 3881-78108

Campaign for Human Rights in China

Jean-Bernard PIERINI
E-mail: jean-bernard.pierini@europarl.europa.eu
Tel. +32 228-32865

GUE/NGL: Confederal Group of the European United Left/Nordic Green Left

Brussels
Belgium
Tel. +32 228-42683, 42682, 42686
Fax +32 228-41780, 41774 (Secretariat-general of the group)

Strasbourg
France
Tel. +33 3881-74397, 74462, 74396
Fax +33 3881-74244, 72018

Maria D'ALIMONTE
Secretary-General
E-mail: maria.dalimonte@europarl.europa.eu
Tel. +32 228-42682
Tel. +33 3881-74396

Thomas RAECK
E-mail: thomas.raeck@europarl.europa.eu
Tel. +32 228-46282
Tel. +33 3881-72940

Roberto GALTIERI
E-mail: roberto.galtieri@europarl.europa.eu
Tel. +32 228-43716
Tel. +33 3881-74990

Gabriela POZZOBON
E-mail: gabriella.pozzobon@europarl.europa.eu
Tel. +32 228-42269
Tel. +33 3881-74398

Kallikatridas KYRIAZIS
E-mail: kallikatridas.kyriazis@europarl.europa.eu
Tel. +32 228-42272

Pedro CARVALHO
E-mail: pedro.carvalho@europarl.europa.eu
Tel. +32 228-42585
Tel. +33 3881-73536

Carolina FALK
E-mail: carolina.falk@europarl.europa.eu
Tel. +32 228-44572
Tel. +33 3881-72941

Patrick ALEXANIAN
Tel. +32 228-46524
Tel. +33 3881-73535

Karin SCHUTTPELZ
E-mail: karin.schuttpelz@europarl.europa.eu
Tel. +32 228-73538
Tel. +352 4300-43337

Andreas WEHR
E-mail: andreas.wehr@europarl.europa.eu
Tel. +32 228-46280
Tel. +33 3881-72963

Mette TONSBERG
E-mail: mette.tonsberg@europarl.europa.eu
Tel. +32 228-43195
Tel. +33 3881-72941

Declan O'FARRELL
E-mail: declan.ofarrell@europarl.europa.eu
Tel. +32 228-41388

René ROOVERS
E-mail: rene.roovers@europarl.europa.eu
Tel. +32 228-42070

Stefano SQUARCINA
E-mail: stefano.squarcina@europarl.europa.eu
Tel. +32 228-46667
Tel. +33 3881-73541

Dionisio FERNÁNDEZ DÍAZ
E-mail: SMTP:dionisio.fernandez@europarl.europa.eu
Tel. +32 228-42684
Tel. +33 3881-73710

Soultana PANTAZIDOU
E-mail: soultana.pantazidou@europarl.europa.eu
Tel. +32 228-43316
Tel. +33 3881-74393

James O'DONNELL
E-mail: james.odonnell@europarl.europa.eu
Tel. +32 228-42069

IND/DEM: Independence/Democracy Group

Brussels
Belgium
Tel. +32 228-42111
Fax +32 228-49144

Strasbourg
France
Tel. +33 3881-74091
Fax +33 3881-79041

Group Secretariat

Emmanuel BORDEZ
Secretary-General
Tel. +32 228-46385
Tel. +33 3881-75010

Central Secretariat of the Group

Administration and Central Secretariat

Fouad MELLOUL
E-mail: fouad.melloul@europarl.europa.eu
Tel. +32 228-42276
Tel. +33 3881-72261

Anne Michelle DEMATHELIN
E-mail: anne.demathelin@europarl.europa.eu
Tel. +32 228-43140

Daniel VAN MOER
E-mail: daniel.vanmoer@europarl.europa.eu
Tel. +32 228-43700

Accounting

Nele DE SMEDT
E-mail: nele.desmedt@europarl.europa.eu
Tel. +32 228-42774

Human Resources

Carole HECTOR
E-mail: carole.hector@europarl.europa.eu
Tel. +32 228-32393

Informatics and Internet Site

Oumar DOUMBOUYA
E-mail: oumar.doumbouya@europarl.europa.eu
Tel. +32 228-44588
Tel. +33 3881-72467

Press Attaché

Gawain TOWLER
E-mail: gawain.towler@europarl.europa.eu
Tel. +32 228-46384
Tel. +33 3881-73549

Communication

Kevin ELLUL BONICI
E-mail: kevin.bonici@europarl.europa.eu
Tel. +32 228-41738

Plenary Sessions

Pierre VAUGIER
E-mail: pierre.vaugier@europarl.europa.eu
Tel. +32 228-44574
Tel. +33 3881-74315

Parliamentary Committees

Foreign Affairs

Melinda GIJSBERTSE
Tel. +32 228-47270
Tel. +33 3881-73564

Glykeria BYSMPA
Tel. +32 228-47724
Tel. +33 3881-77724

Development

Philip LE RULF
Tel. +32 228-44576
Tel. +33 3881-73564

Melinda GIJSBERTSE
Tel. +32 228-47270
Tel. +33 3881-73564

External Trade

Dick Jan DIEPENBROECK
Tel. +32 228-47270
Tel. +33 3881-73564

Budget

Klaus HEEGER
Tel. +32 228-43215
Tel. +33 3881-78303

Frank VAN DER MAAS
Tel. +32 228-47270
Tel. +33 3881-77270

Economic and Monetary Affairs

Jan-Harm BOITEN
Tel. +32 228-47820
Tel. +33 3881-77820

Employment and Social Affairs

Ralph ATKINSON
Tel. +32 228-47552
Tel. +33 3881-76265

Environment

Walter VANLUIK
Tel. +32 228-47270
Tel. +33 3881-77270

Industry, Research and Energy

Frank VAN DER MAAS
Tel. +32 228-47270
Tel. +33 3881-77270

Internal Market

Andrew REED
E-mail: andrew.reed@europarl.europa.eu
Tel. +32 228-47855
Tel. +33 3881-77855

Line MUNK OLSEN
Tel. +32 228-31241
Tel. +33 3881-75167

Markus NYMAN
E-mail: markus.nyman@europarl.europa.eu
Tel. +32 228-46567
Tel. +33 3881-72082

Benjamin BELDMAN
Tel. +32 228-41018
Tel. +33 3881-73564

Transport and Tourism

Benjamin BELDMAN
Tel. +32 228-41018
Tel. +33 3881-73564

Andrew REED
Tel. +32 228-47855
Tel. +33 3881-77855

Regional Development

Martina ROZSIVALOVA
Tel. +32 228-47295
Tel. +33 3881-77295

Peter DE GROOT
Tel. +32 228-41018
Tel. +33 3881-73564

Agriculture

Roman IZDEBSKI
E-mail: roman.izdebski@europarl.europa.eu
Tel. +32 228-32491
Tel. +33 3881-64092

Aurélie LALOUX
E-mail: aurelie.laloux@europarl.europa.eu
Tel. +32 228-47758
Tel. +33 3881-77758

Peter DE GROOT
Tel. +32 228-41018
Tel. +33 3881-73564

Culture, Youth, Sport, Education, Media

Ralph ATKINSON
Tel. +32 228-47552
Tel. +33 3881-76265

Melinda GIJSBERTSE
Tel. +32 228-47270
Tel. +33 3881-73564

Legal Affairs

Iman BAYAZI
Tel. +32 228-47725
Tel. +33 3881-77725

Benjamin BELDMAN
Tel. +32 228-41018
Tel. +33 3881-73564

Civil Liberties, Justice

Jan-Harm BOITEN
Tel. +32 228-47820
Tel. +33 3881-77820

Constitutional Affairs

Christophe BEAUDOUIN
E-mail: christophe.beaudouin@europarl.europa.eu
Tel. +32 228-43777
Tel. +33 3881-78304

Dick Jan DIEPENBROECK
Tel. +32 228-47270
Tel. +33 3881-73564

Marek SZYMCZAK
Tel. +32 228-44127
Tel. +33 3881-77659

Budgetary Control

Aurélie LALOUX
E-mail: aurelie.laloux@europarl.europa.eu
Tel. +32 228-47758
Tel. +33 3881-77758

Iman BAYAZI
Tel. +32 228-47725
Tel. +33 3881-77725

Frank VAN DER MAAS
Tel. +32 228-47270
Tel. +33 3881-77270

Fisheries

Aurélie LALOUX
Tel. +32 228-47758
Tel. +33 3881-77758

Peter DE GROOT
Tel. +32 228-41018
Tel. +33 3881-73564

Petitions

Hannah LANE
Tel. +32 228-47692

Glykeria BYSMPA
Tel. +32 228-47724
Tel. +33 3881-77724

Benjamin BELDMAN
Tel. +32 228-41018
Tel. +33 3881-73564

Women's Rights

Melinda GIJSBERTSE
Tel. +32 228-47270
Tel. +33 3881-73564

Defence and Security

Melinda GIJSBERTSE
Tel. +32 228-47270
Tel. +33 3881-73564

Human Rights

Richard KING
E-mail: richard.king@europarl.europa.eug
Tel. +32 228-32210
Tel. +33 3881-77692

Ewa PYKALO
Tel. +32 228-47241

Melinda GIJSBERTSE
Tel. +32 228-47270
Tel. +33 3881-73564

UEN: Union for Europe of the Nations Group

Brussels
Belgium
Tel. +32 228-42111
Fax +32 228-46972

Strasbourg
France
Tel. +33 3881-74001, 79084

Frank BARRETT
Secretary-General
E-mail: frank.barrett@europarl.europa.eu
Tel. +32 228-42971
Tel. +33 3881-74224

Eugenio PRETA
Deputy Secretary-General
E-mail: eugenio.preta@europarl.europa.eu
Tel. +32 228-44359
Tel. +33 3881-74659
Tel. +352 4300-22800/24941

Gabriel BESZLEJ
Deputy Secretary-General
E-mail: gabriel.beszlej@europarl.europa.eu
Tel. +32 228-44348
Tel. +33 3881-73737

Secretariat-General

Head of Press Office and Internet Site Editor

Italian Press

Pasquale CIUFFREDA
E-mail: pasquale.ciuffreda@europarl.europa.eu
Tel. +32 228-41418
Tel. +33 3881-73516

Latvian Press

Aija DULEVSKA
E-mail: aija.dulevska@europarl.europa.eu
Tel. +32 228-32510
Tel. +33 3881-76656

UK and Irish Press

David HARMON
E-mail: david.harmon@europarl.europa.eu
Tel. +32 228-42960
Tel. +33 3881-72557

Lithuanian Press

Egle KROPAITE
E-mail: egle.kropaite@europarl.europa.eu
Tel. +32 228-32295
Tel. +33 3881-76658

Polish Press

Tomasz POREBA
E-mail: tomasz.poreba@europarl.europa.eu
Tel. +32 228-40781
Tel. +33 3881-72445

Danish Press

Anna ROSBACH
E-mail: anna.rosbach@europarl.europa.eu
Tel. +32 228-43449
Tel. +33 3881-74636

Committees

Rino TROMBETTA
E-mail: rino.trombetta@europarl.europa.eu
Tel. +32 228-31437
Tel. +33 3881-74234

Foreign Affairs, Human Rights, Security

Tomasz POREBA
E-mail: tomasz.poreba@europarl.europa.eu
Tel. +32 228-40781
Tel. +33 3881-72445

Joanna REJDYCH
E-mail: joanna.rejdych@europarl.europa.eu
Tel. +32 228-46144
Tel. +33 3881-72292

Andrzej NERMER
E-mail: andrzej.nermer@europarl.europa.eu
Tel. +32 228-31182
Tel. +33 3881-76234

Rino TROMBETTA
E-mail: rino.trombetta@europarl.europa.eu
Tel. +32 228-31437
Tel. +33 3881-74234

Security and Defence

Eriks VEITS
E-mail: eriks.veits@europarl.europa.eu
Tel. +32 228-42539
Tel. +33 3881-76657

Human Rights

Aija DULEVSKA
E-mail: aija.dulevska@europarl.europa.eu
Tel. +32 228-32510

Development

Joanna REJDYCH
E-mail: joanna.rejdych@europarl.europa.eu
Tel. +32 228-46144
Tel. +33 3881-72292

Claire DONLON
E-mail: claire.donlon@europarl.europa.eu
Tel. +32 228-42251
Tel. +33 3881-74226

Alina PIECH
E-mail: alina.piech@europarl.europa.eu
Tel. +32 228-44309
Tel. +33 3881-77441

International Trade

Piero RIZZA
E-mail: piero.rizza@europarl.europa.eu
Tel. +32 228-44681
Tel. +33 3881-72531

Eriks VEITS
E-mail: eriks.veits@europarl.europa.eu
Tel. +32 228-42539
Tel. +33 3881-76657

Vilma RADVILAITE
E-mail: vilma.radvilaite@europarl.europa.eu
Tel. +32 228-44568
Tel. +33 3881-76654

Budgets

Aleksander GRABCZEWSKI
E-mail: aleksander.grabczewski@europarl.europa.eu
Tel. +32 228-44734
Tel. +33 3881-77580

Piero RIZZA
E-mail: piero.rizza@europarl.europa.eu
Tel. +32 228-44681
Tel. +33 3881-72531

Budgetary Control

Anna ROSBACH
E-mail: anna.rosbach@europarl.europa.eu
Tel. +32 228-43449
Tel. +33 3881-74636

Aleksander GRABCZEWSKI
E-mail: aleksander.grabczewski@europarl.europa.eu
Tel. +32 228-44734
Tel. +33 3881-77580

Edyta NEDZIAK
E-mail: edyta.nedziak@europarl.europa.eu
Tel. +32 228-44343
Tel. +33 3881-77254

Employment and Social Affairs

Marcin EMILEWICZ
E-mail: marcin.emilewicz@europarl.europa.eu
Tel. +32 228-44411

Agnieszka SZCZESNIAK
E-mail: agnieszka.szczesniak@europarl.europa.eu
Tel. +32 228-44310
Tel. +33 3881-64132

Magdalena MAJERCZYK
E-mail: magdalena.majerczyk@europarl.europa.eu
Tel. +32 228-43408
Tel. +33 3881-64020

Economic

Aivars BERNERS
E-mail: aivars.berners@europarl.europa.eu
Tel. +32 228-32297
Tel. +33 3881-74229

Mide NI SHUILLEABAHAIN
E-mail: mide.nishuilleabahain@europarl.europa.eu
Tel. +32 228-31248
Tel. +33 3881-73177

Regional

Tania LAIKAUF
E-mail: tania.laikauf@europarl.europa.eu
Tel. +32 228-42074
Tel. +33 3881-72801

Agnieszka SZCZESNIAK
E-mail: agnieszka.szczesniak@europarl.europa.eu
Tel. +32 228-44310
Tel. +33 3881-64132

Industry

Ance GULBE
E-mail: ance.gulbe@europarl.europa.eu
Tel. +32 228-42714
Tel. +33 3881-73709

Maria Michela LAERA
E-mail: michela.laera@europarl.europa.eu
Tel. +32 228-44338
Tel. +33 3881-73717

Elisabetta MONTANO
E-mail: elisabetta.montano@europarl.europa.eu
Tel. +32 228-42135
Tel. +33 3881-74847

Internal Market

Sylwia WOJCIECHOWSKA
E-mail: sylwia.wojciechowska@europarl.europa.eu
Tel. +32 228-40925

Aivars BERNERS
E-mail: aivars.berners@europarl.europa.eu
Tel. +32 228-32297
Tel. +33 3881-74229

Civil Liberties

Silvia LOCATI
E-mail: silvia.locati@europarl.europa.eu
Tel. +32 228-44339
Tel. +33 3881-72306

Barbara MAZZOTTI
E-mail: barbara.mazzotti@europarl.europa.eu
Tel. +32 228-46409
Tel. +33 3881-77704

Alina PIECH
E-mail: alina.piech@europarl.europa.eu
Tel. +32 228-44309
Tel. +33 3881-77441

Legal Affairs

Valeria GHILARDI
E-mail: valeria.ghilardi@europarl.europa.eu
Tel. +32 228-46471
Tel. +33 3881-72803

Witold ZIOBRO
E-mail: witold.ziobro@europarl.europa.eu
Tel. +32 228-42588
Tel. +33 3881-73174

David HARMON
E-mail: david.harmon@europarl.europa.eu
Tel. +32 228-42960
Tel. +33 3881-72557

Environment and Climate Change

Valeria FIORE
E-mail: valeria.fiore@europarl.europa.eu
Tel. +32 228-32296
Tel. +33 3881-73717

Regina O'CONNOR
E-mail: regina.oconnor@europarl.europa.eu
Tel. +32 228-47751
Tel. +33 3881-77751

Constitutional Affairs

Regina O'CONNOR
E-mail: regina.oconnor@europarl.europa.eu
Tel. +32 228-47751
Tel. +33 3881-77751

Roberto GIANNELLA
E-mail: roberto.giannella@europarl.europa.eu
Tel. +32 228-46436
Tel. +33 3881-77277

Culture and Education

Roberto GIANNELLA
E-mail: roberto.giannella@europarl.europa.eu
Tel. +32 228-46436
Tel. +33 3881-77277

Ewa PASZKO
E-mail: ewa.paszko@europarl.europa.eu
Tel. +32 228-46675
Tel. +33 3881-77616

Kamila SLUSARCZYK
E-mail: kamila.slusarczyk@europarl.europa.eu
Tel. +32 228-41896
Tel. +33 3881-64180

Agriculture

Magdalena MAJERCZYK
E-mail: magdalena.majerczyk@europarl.europa.eu
Tel. +32 228-43408
Tel. +33 3881-74020

Claire DONLON
E-mail: claire.donlon@europarl.europa.eu
Tel. +32 228-42251
Tel. +33 3881-74226

Anita SERWATKO
E-mail: anita.serwatko@europarl.europa.eu
Tel. +32 228-44802
Tel. +33 3881-77926

Pasquale CIUFFREDA
E-mail: pasquale.ciuffreda@europarl.europa.eu
Tel. +32 228-41418
Tel. +33 3881-73516

Maria Paola DE ANGELIS
E-mail: mariapaola.deangelis@europarl.europa.eu
Tel. +32 228-43161
Tel. +33 3881-74431

Fisheries

Claire DONLON
E-mail: claire.donlon@europarl.europa.eu
Tel. +32 228-42251
Tel. +33 3881-74226

Rino TROMBETTA
E-mail: rino.trombetta@europarl.europa.eu
Tel. +32 228-31437
Tel. +33 3881-74234

Transport and Tourism

Mide NI SHUILLEABAHAIN
E-mail: mide.nishuilleabahain@europarl.europa.eu
Tel. +32 228-31248
Tel. +33 3881-73177

Ance GULBE
E-mail: ance.gulbe@europarl.europa.eu
Tel. +32 228-42714
Tel. +33 3881-73709

Women

Michela LAERA
E-mail: michela.laera@europarl.europa.eu
Tel. +32 228-44338
Tel. +33 3881-73717

Elisabetta MONTANO
E-mail: elisabetta.montano@europarl.europa.eu
Tel. +32 228-42135
Tel. +33 3881-74847

Petitions

Witold ZIOBRO
E-mail: witold.ziobro@europarl.europa.eu
Tel. +32 228-42588
Tel. +33 3881-73174

Barbara MAZZOTTI
E-mail: barbara.mazzotti@europarl.europa.eu
Tel. +32 228-46409
Tel. +33 3881-77704

Finance, personnel and internal organisation

Internal Organisation

Egle KROPAITE
E-mail: egle.kropaite@europarl.europa.eu
Tel. +32 228-32295
Tel. +33 3881-76658

Accounts

Jean-Jacques GUEZ
E-mail: jeanjacques.guez@europarl.europa.eu
Tel. +32 228-44268
Tel. +33 3881-73175

Ex-Ante Controller

Piergiorgio DI BONITO
E-mail: piergiorgio.dibonito@europarl.europa.eu
Tel. +32 228-44575
Tel. +33 3881-74221

Information Technology — LSA

Benoît PHILIPPART
E-mail: benoit.philippart@europarl.europa.eu
Tel. +32 228-4-2850
Tel. +33 3881-73520

Human Resources

Alessia PICCAROLO
E-mail: alessia.piccarolo@europarl.europa.eu
Tel. +32 228-44581
Tel. +33 3881-74232

External Meetings — GBI, Offices

Iliana ZONNEDDA
E-mail: iliana.zonnedda@europarl.europa.eu
Tel. +32 228-43959
Tel. +33 3881-73519

Group Meetings — Room Reservations

Maria Paola DE ANGELIS
E-mail: mariapaola.deangelis@europarl.europa.eu
Tel. +32 228-43161
Tel. +33 3881-74431

Monika KORDULA
E-mail: monika.kordula@europarl.europa.eu
Tel. +32 228-44532
Tel. +33 3881-76786

Bureaux Co-Presidents

Roberto GIANNELLA
E-mail: roberto.giannella@europarl.europa.eu
Tel. +32 228-47277
Tel. +33 3881-77277

Regina O'CONNOR
E-mail: regina.oconnor@europarl.europa.eu
Tel. +32 228-47751
Tel. +33 3881-77751

Research

Arek ROSZAK
E-mail: arek.roszak@europarl.europa.eu
Tel. +32 228-31420
Tel. +33 3881-74528

NA: Group of non-attached Members

Coordinator

Eduardo BUGALHO
E-mail: eduardo.bugalho@europarl.europa.eu
Tel. +32 228-42466/42579
Tel. +33 3881-72297

Secretariats

Paola CASADEI
E-mail: paola.casadei@europarl.europa.eu
Tel. +32 228-42579/43173
Tel. +33 3881-73567

Paolo ATZORI
E-mail: paolo.atzori@europarl.europa.eu
Tel. +32 228-43306
Tel. +33 3881-73724

TUV Secretariat

Susan KERR
E-mail: susan.kerr@europarl.europa.eu
Tel. +32 228-47275
Tel. +33 3881-77275

UK Independence Party Secretariat

Alberto PAOLETTI
E-mail: alberto.paoletti@europarl.europa.eu
Tel. +32 228-47747/43571
Tel. +33 3881-64183

L'S-HZDS Secretariat

Ivana KAPRALIKOVA
E-mail: ivana.kapralikova@europarl.europa.eu
Tel. +32 228-46411
Tel. +33 3881-76870

Norbert HAL'KO
E-mail: norbert.halko@europarl.europa.eu
Tel. +32 228-42602
Tel. +33 3881-76651

Liga polskich rodzin Secretariat

Marcin FRYDRYCH
E-mail: marcin.frydrych@europarl.europa.eu
Tel. +32 228-44876
Tel. +33 3881-73559

Lucasz DOMINIKOWSKI
E-mail: lucasz.dominikowski@europarl.europa.eu
Tel. +32 228-44867
Tel. +33 3881-73731

Nezávislí Secretariat

Aneta TRAKALOVÁ
E-mail: aneta.trakalova@europarl.europa.eu
Tel. +32 228-43543
Tel. +33 3881-76899

Movimento civico federativo popolare Secretariat

Mathilde KLIFMAN
E-mail: mathilde.klifman@europarl.europa.eu
Tel. +32 228-47524
Fax +33 3881-77524

FPÖ Secretariat

Georg MAYER
E-mail: georg.mayer@europarl.europa.eu
Tel. +32 228-46412
Tel. +33 3881-72804

Bernhard GLASER
E-mail: bernhard.glaser@europarl.europa.eu
Tel. +32 228-44349
Tel. +33 3881-72805

Front National Secretariat

Olivier DESTOUCHES
E-mail: olivier.destouches@europarl.europa.eu
Tel. +32 228-42587
Tel. +33 3881-72789

Catherine SALAGNAC
E-mail: catherine.salagnac@europarl.europa.eu
Tel. +32 228-43349
Tel. +33 3881-72295

Michel HUBAULT
E-mail: michel.hubault@europarl.europa.eu
Tel. +32 228-43347
Tel. +33 3881-72296

Isabelle BARDY
E-mail: isabelle.bardy@europarl.europa.eu
Tel. +32 228-42492
Tel. +33 3881-72298

Sylvie GODDYN
E-mail: sylvie.goddyn@europarl.europa.eu
Tel. +32 228-42503
Fax +32 228-32060
Tel. +33 3881-72294
Fax +33 3881-79042

Vlaams Belang Secretariat

Dirk CROLS
E-mail: dirk.crols@europarl.europa.eu
Tel. +32 228-47108
Fax +32 228-49108
Tel. +33 3881-73529
Fax +33 3881-79108

Robrecht VERREYCKEN
E-mail: robrecht.verreycken@europarl.europa.eu
Tel. +32 228-43599
Fax +32 228-49282
Tel. +33 3881-64213
Fax +33 3881-79108

Fiamma Tricolore Secretariat

Manlio MASSEI
E-mail: manlio.massei@europarl.europa.eu
Tel. +32 228-41491
Fax +32 228-49530
Tel. +33 3881-76652
Fax +33 3881-79530

Alternativa Sociale Secretariat

...
Tel. +32 228-
Fax +33 3881-

Ataka Secretariat

Milena STOIMENOVA
E-mail: milena.stoimenova@europarl.europa.eu
Tel. +32 228-47654
Fax +32 228-49654
Tel. +33 3881-77654
Fax +33 3881-79654

Uniti Nell'Ulivo Secretariat

Mathilde KLIFMAN
Tel. +32 228-47524
Fax +33 3881-77524

LSA

Marc CARLOT
E-mail: marc.carlot@europarl.europa.eu
Tel. +32 228-42170/43947
Tel. +33 3881-72547/73517

COUNCIL OF THE EUROPEAN UNION

Representatives of the Governments of the Member States who regularly take part in Council meetings

BELGIUM

Federal Government

Yves LETERME
Prime Minister

Didier REYNDERS
Deputy Prime Minister and Minister for Finance and Institutional Reforms

Laurette ONKELINX
Deputy Minister and Minister for Social Affairs and Public Health

Patrick DEWAEL
Deputy Prime Minister and Minister for the Interior

Jo VANDEURZEN
Deputy Prime Minister and Minister for Justice and Institutional Reforms

Joëlle MILQUET
Deputy Prime Minister and Minister for Employment and Equal Opportunities

Karel DE GUCHT
Minister for Foreign Affairs

Sabine LARUELLE
Minister for SMEs, the Self-Employed, Agriculture and Science Policy

Marie ARENA
Minister for Social Integration, Pensions and the Cities

Pieter DE CREM
Minister for Defence

Paul MAGNETTE
Minister for Climate and Energy

Charles MICHEL
Minister for Development Cooperation

Inge VERVOTTE
Minister for the Civil Service and Public Undertakings

Vincent VAN QUICKENBORNE
Minister for Enterprise and Simplification

Annemie TURTELBOOM
Minister for Policy on Migration and Asylum

Etienne SCHOUPPE
State Secretary for Mobility, attached to the Prime Minister

Carl DEVLIES
State Secretary for Coordination of Fraud Prevention, attached to the Prime Minister, and State Secretary, attached to the Minister for Justice

Bernard CLERFAYT
State Secretary, attached to the Minister for Finance

Olivier CHASTEL
State Secretary for Foreign Affairs with responsibility for preparing for the EU Presidency, attached to the Minister for Foreign Affairs

Jean-Marc DELIZÉE
State Secretary for Poverty Prevention, attached to the Minister for Social Integration, Pensions and the Cities

Julie FERNANDEZ-FERNANDEZ
State Secretary for the Disabled, attached to the Minister for Social Affairs and Public Health

Melchior WATHELET
State Secretary for the Budget, attached to the Prime Minister, and State Secretary for Family Policy, attached to the Minister for Employment and, for matters relating to law of persons and family law, attached to the Minister for Justice

Flemish Government

Kris PEETERS
Minister President of the Flemish Government and Flemish Minister for Institutional Reform, Ports, Agriculture, Sea Fisheries and Rural Policy

Dirk VAN MECHELEN
Vice-Minister President of the Flemish Government and Flemish Minister for Finance and the Budget and Town and Country Planning

Frank VANDENBROUCKE
Vice-Minister President of the Flemish Government and Flemish Minister for Work, Education and Training

Bert ANCIAUX
Flemish Minister for Culture, Youth, Sport and Brussels

Geert BOURGEOIS
Flemish Minister for Administrative Affairs, Foreign Policy, the Media and Tourism

Hilde CREVITS
Flemish Minister for Public Works, Energy, the Environment and Nature

Marino KEULEN
Flemish Minister for Home Affairs, Urban Policy, Housing and Civic Integration

Kathleen VAN BREMPT
Flemish Minister for Mobility, the Social Economy and Equal Opportunities

Patricia CEYSENS
Flemish Minister for Economic Affairs, Enterprise, Science, Innovation and Foreign Trade

Steven VANACKERE
Flemish Minister for Welfare, Public Health and the Family

Walloon Government

Rudy DEMOTTE
Minister President of the Walloon Government

André ANTOINE
Vice-President and Minister for Housing, Transport and Territorial Development (Walloon Region)

Michel DAERDEN
Vice-President and Minister for the Budget, Finance and Infrastructure (Walloon Region)

Marc TARABELLA
Minister for Training (Walloon Region)

Philippe COURARD
Minister for Internal Affairs and the Civil Service (Walloon Region)

Marie-Dominique SIMONET
Minister for Research, New Technologies and External Relations (Walloon Region)

Jean-Claude MARCOURT
Minister for Economic Affairs, Employment, Foreign Trade and Heritage (Walloon Region)

Didier DONFUT
Minister for Health, Social Action and Equal Opportunities (Walloon Region)

Benoît LUTGEN
Minister for Agriculture, Rural Affairs, the Environment and Tourism (Walloon Region)

Government of the German-speaking Community

Karl-Heinz LAMBERTZ
Minister President, Minister for Local Authorities (German-speaking Community)

Bernd GENTGES
Vice-Minister President, Minister for Training and Employment, Social Affairs and Tourism (German-speaking Community)

Olivier PAASCH
Minister for Education and Scientific Research (German-speaking Community)

Isabelle WEYKMANS
Minister for Culture and the Media, the Protection of Monuments, Youth and Sport (German-speaking Community)

Government of the French-speaking Community

Marie ARENA
Minister President, Minister for Compulsory Education (French Community)

Marie-Dominique SIMONET
Vice-Minister President and Minister for Higher Education, Scientific Research and International Relations (French Community)

Michel DAERDEN
Vice-Minister President, Minister for the Budget, Finance, the Civil Service and Sport (French Community)

Fadila LAANAN
Minister for Culture and the Audiovisual Sector (French Community)

Marc TARABELLA
Minister for Youth and Further Education (French Community)

Catherine FONCK
Minister for Children, Youth Welfare and Health (French Community)

Brussels Capital Regional Government

Charles PICQUÉ
Minister President of the Brussels Capital Regional Government, with responsibility for local authorities, regional planning, monuments and sites, urban regeneration, housing, public hygiene and development cooperation

Guy VANHENGEL
Minister of the Brussels Capital Regional Government, with responsibility for finance, the budget, the civil service and external relations

Benoît CEREXHE
Minister of the Brussels Capital Regional Government, with responsibility for employment, economic affairs, scientific research, fire prevention and emergency medical aid

Evelyne HUYTEBROECK
Minister of the Brussels Capital Regional Government, with responsibility for the environment, energy and water policy

Pascal SMET
Minister of the Brussels Capital Regional Government, with responsibility for mobility and public works

Françoise DUPUIS
State Secretary of the Brussels Capital Regional Government, with responsibility for housing and town planning

Emir KIR
State Secretary of the Brussels Capital Regional Government, with responsibility for public hygiene and monuments and sites

Brigitte GROUWELS
State Secretary of the Brussels Capital Regional Government, with responsibility for the civil service, equal opportunities and the Port of Brussels

BULGARIA

Sergei STANISHEV
Prime Minister of the Republic of Bulgaria

Ivailo Georgiev KALFIN
Deputy Prime Minister and Minister for Foreign Affairs

Meglena PLUGCHIEVA
Deputy Prime Minister for EU Funds Management

Daniel Vassilev VALTCHEV
Deputy Prime Minister and Minister for Education and Science

Emel ETEM
Deputy Prime Minister and Minister for Emergency Situations

Plamen Vassilev ORESHARSKI
Minister for Finance

Mihail Raykov MIKOV
Minister for the Interior

Nickolay Georgiev TSONEV
Minister for Defence

Miglena Ianakieva TACHEVA
Minister for Justice

Nikolay Vassilev VASSILEV
Minister for Public Administration and Administrative Reform

Petar Vladimirov DIMITROV
Minister for Economic Affairs and Energy

Petar Vassilev MUTAFCHIEV
Minister for Transport

Assen Dimitrov GAGAUZOV
Minister for Regional Development and Public Works

Dzhevdet CHAKAROV
Minister for the Environment and Water

Valeri Mitkov TSVETANOV
Minister for Agriculture and Food

Emilia Radkova MASLAROVA
Minister for Labour and Social Affairs

Evgenii Zhelev ZHELEV
Minister for Health

Stefan Lambov DANAILOV
Minister for Culture

Gergana Hristova GRANCHAROVA
Minister for European Affairs

Lyubomir KYUCHUKOV
Deputy Minister for Foreign Affairs

Radion POPOV
Deputy Minister for Foreign Affairs

Todor Ivanov CHUROV
Deputy Minister for Foreign Affairs

Milen Georgiev KEREMEDCHIEV
Deputy Minister for Foreign Affairs

Kircho ATANASSOV
Deputy Minister for Education and Science

Mukaddes NALBANT
Deputy Minister for Education and Science

Vanya DOBREVA
Deputy Minister for Education and Science

Delian Slavchev PEEVSKI
Deputy Minister for Emergency Situations

Alexander FILIPOV
Deputy Minister for Emergency Situations

Angel Marinov CHAKUROV
Deputy Minister for Emergency Situations

Kiril ANANIEV
Deputy Minister for Finance

Lyubomir DATZOV
Deputy Minister for Finance

Nahit ZIYA
Deputy Minister for Finance

Dimitar IVANOVSKI
Deputy Minister for Finance

Kiril ZHELEV
Deputy Minister for Finance

Goran YONOV
Deputy Minister for the Interior

Sonya Atanasova YANKULOVA
Deputy Minister for the Interior

Raif Shaban MUSTAFA
Deputy Minister for the Interior

Roumen Genov ANDREEV
Deputy Minister for the Interior

Ivan Gavrilov IVANOV
Deputy Minister for Defence

Spas PANCHEV
Deputy Minister for Defence

Kameliya Stoyanova NEYKOVA
Deputy Minister for Defence

Ilonka Nikolova IVANCHEVA-RAYCHINOVA
Deputy Minister for Justice

Sabrie Tayfi SAPUNDZHIEVA
Deputy Minister for Justice

Boyko Iliev RASHKOV
Deputy Minister for Justice

Stefan Petrov FIKOV
Deputy Minister for Justice

Angel IVANOV
Deputy Minister for State Administration and Administrative Reform

Buzhka LUKICH
Deputy Minister for State Administration and Administrative Reform

Gyuner RAMIS
Deputy Minister for State Administration and Administrative Reform

Maria DIVIZIEVA
Deputy Minister for State Administration and Administrative Reform

Valentin IVANOV
Deputy Minister for the Economy and Energy

Nina RADEVA
Deputy Minister for the Economy and Energy

Yavor KUIUMDJIEV
Deputy Minister for the Economy and Energy

Galina TOSHEVA
Deputy Minister for the Economy and Energy

Anna YANEVA
Deputy Minister for the Economy and Energy

Youdjel Naim ATILLA
Deputy Minister for Transport

Krasimira Radkova MARTINOVA
Deputy Minister for Transport

Vessela Borissova GOSPODINOVA
Deputy Minister for Transport

Daniela Vladimirova NIKIFOROVA
Deputy Minister for Transport

Dimcho MIHALEVSKI
Deputy Minister for Regional Development and Public Works

Savin KOVACHEV
Deputy Minister for Regional Development and Public Works

Iskra MIHAYLOVA
Deputy Minister for Regional Development and Public Works

Kalin ROGACHEV
Deputy Minister for Regional Development and Public Works

Atanas KOSTADINOV
Deputy Minister for the Environment and Water

Lubka KATCHAKOVA
Deputy Minister for the Environment and Water

Chavdar GEORGIEV
Deputy Minister for the Environment and Water

Byurhan ABAZOV
Deputy Minister for Agriculture and Food Supply

Dimitar PEYTCHEV
Deputy Minister for Agriculture and Food Supply

Svetla BATCHVAROVA
Deputy Minister for Agriculture and Food Supply

Yasen YANEV
Deputy Minister for Labour and Social Policy

Lazar LAZAROV
Deputy Minister for Labour and Social Policy

Dimitar DIMITROV
Deputy Minister for Labour and Social Policy

Vasil VOYNOV
Deputy Minister for Labour and Social Policy

Emil RAYNOV
Deputy Minister for Health

Valery TZEKOV
Deputy Minister for Health

Matey MATEEV
Deputy Minister for Health

Ivan Danev TOKADJIEV
Deputy Minister for Culture

Yavor Todorov MILUSHEV
Deputy Minister for Culture

Nadejda ZAHARIEVA-DAMIANOVA
Deputy Minister for Culture

CZECH REPUBLIC

Mirek TOPOLÁNEK
Prime Minister

Jiří ČUNEK
First Deputy Prime Minister and Minister for Regional Development

Martin BURSÍK
Deputy Prime Minister and Minister for the Environment

Petr NEČAS
Deputy Prime Minister and Minister for Labour and Social Affairs

Alexandr VONDRA
Vice-Premier ministre, chargé des affaires européennes

Ivan LANGER
Minister for the Interior

Karel SCHWARZENBERG
Minister for Foreign Affairs

Vlasta PARKANOVÁ
Minister for Defence

Miroslav KALOUSEK
Minister for Finance

Jiří POSPÍŠIL
Minister for Justice

Aleš ŘEBÍČEK
Minister for Transport

Martin ŘÍMAN
Minister for Industry and Trade

Václav JEHLIČKA
Minister for Culture

Ondřej LIŠKA
Minister for Education, Youth and Sport

Tomáš JULÍNEK
Minister for Health

Petr GANDALOVIČ
Minister for Agriculture

Cyril SVOBODA
Minister without Portfolio and Chairman of the Legislative Council of the Government

Džamila STEHLÍKOVÁ
Minister without Portfolio with responsibility for human rights and national minorities

Ivan FUKSA
First Deputy Minister for Finance, State Property Management Section

Jiří VOLF
Deputy Minister for Finance, Office of the Ministry

Peter CHRENKO
Deputy Minister for Finance, Tax and Customs Section

Eduard JANOTA
Deputy Minister for Finance, Public Budgets Section

Jan MÁLEK
Deputy Minister for Finance, Financial Analysis Section and Contracts Unit

Milan ŠIMÁČEK
Deputy Minister for Finance, Financial Market Section

Tomáš ZÍDEK
Deputy Minister for Finance, International Relations and Financial Policy Section

Petr ŠIMERKA
State Secretary, Deputy Minister for Labour and Social Affairs, Legislation, Labour Law, Salaries and Safety at Work Department

Marián HOŠEK
Deputy Minister for Labour and Social Affairs, Social Policy, Social Services and Family Policy Department

Miroslav JENÍK
Deputy Minister for Labour and Social Affairs, Economic Affairs Department

Vladimír KRÁL
First Deputy Minister for Justice, Judicial Affairs Section

František STEINER
Deputy Minister for Justice, Economic Affairs Section

Martin MOULIS
Deputy Minister for Justice, International Relations Section

František KORBEL
Deputy Minister for Justice, Legislation and Legal Affairs Section

Pavel STANĚK
Deputy Minister for Justice, Minister's Office Section

Rudolf VYČICHLA
First Deputy Minister for Transport, Administrative Affairs Section

Vojtěch KOCOUREK
Deputy Minister for Transport, Rail Transport Section

Ivo VYKYDAL
Deputy Minister for Transport, Road and Air Transport Section

Jiří HODAČ
Deputy Minister for Transport, Infrastructure and EU Funds Section

Daniela KOVALČÍKOVÁ
Deputy Minister for Transport, Legislation Section

Emanuel ŠÍP
Deputy Minister for Transport, Transport Policy Section

Petr ŠLEGR
Deputy Minister for Transport, Public Transport and Environment Section

Tomáš POJAR
First Deputy Minister for Foreign Affairs

Martin ČERMÁK
Deputy Minister for Foreign Affairs with responsibility for transformation and management

Helena BAMBASOVÁ
Deputy Minister for Foreign Affairs

Martin BARTÁK
First Deputy Minister for Defence

Radek ŠMERDA
Deputy Minister for Defence — Director of the Office of the Ministry of Defence

František PADĚLEK
Deputy Minister for Defence

Jaroslav KOPŘIVA
Deputy Minister for Defence with responsibility for defence procurement

Vlastimil PICEK
Chief of the General Staff of the Armed Forces of the Czech Republic

Jaroslav SALIVAR
First Deputy Minister for the Interior with responsibility for internal security

Zdeněk ZAJÍČEK
Deputy Minister for the Interior with responsibility for public administration, information technology, legislation and archives

Blanka VYSLOUŽILOVÁ
Deputy Minister for the Interior with responsibility for economic affairs and operational matters

Lenka PTÁČKOVÁ MELICHAROVÁ
Deputy Minister for the Interior with responsibility for European affairs

Milan HOVORKA
Deputy Minister for Industry and Trade, Trade Section

Martin TLAPA
Deputy Minister for Industry and Trade, European Union Section

Tomáš HÜNER
Deputy Minister for Industry and Trade, Energy Section

Jiří KOLIBA
Deputy Minister for Industry and Trade, Interministerial Affairs Section

Luboš VANĚK
Deputy Minister for Industry and Trade, Restructuring of Subordinate Organisations Section

Ivo HLAVÁČ
First Deputy Minister for Agriculture

Ivo VRZAL
Deputy Minister for Agriculture, Economics and Administrative Affairs Section

Karel TRŮBL
Deputy Minister for Agriculture, Forestry and Water Management Section

Stanislav KOZÁK
Deputy Minister for Agriculture, Commodities Section

Karel TUREČEK
Deputy Minister for Agriculture with responsibility for science and research

Marek ŠNAJDR
First Deputy Minister for Health with responsibility for administrative, economic and legal affairs

Pavel HROBOŇ
Deputy Minister for Health with responsibility for health insurance

Markéta HELLEROVÁ
Deputy Minister for Health with responsibility for health care

Michael VÍT
Deputy Minister for Health with responsibility for the protection and promotion of public health, Chief Public Health Officer of the Czech Republic

Eva BARTOŇOVÁ
Deputy Minister for Education, Youth and Sport with responsibility for finance, legal affairs and the Ministry Administration Section

Jindřich KITZBERGER
Deputy Minister for Education, Youth and Sport with responsibility for the General, Vocational and Further Education Section

Jan KOCOUREK
Deputy Minister for Education, Youth and Sport with responsibility for the Sport, Youth and Information Technology Section

Rut BÍZKOVÁ
Deputy Minister for the Environment, Economic Affairs and Environmental Policy Section

František PELC
Deputy Minister for the Environment, Nature and Landscape Protection Section

Karel BLÁHA
Deputy Minister for the Environment, Technical Protection of the Environment Section

Jan DUSÍK
First Deputy Minister for the Environment, International Affairs, Legislation and Public Administration Section

Aleš KUTÁK
Deputy Minister for the Environment, Climate and Atmospheric Protection Section

František MIKEŠ
First Deputy Minister for Culture

Jaromír TALÍŘ
Deputy Minister for Culture

Antonín TESAŘÍK
Deputy Minister for Culture

Milan PŮČEK
Deputy Minister for Regional Development, Ministry Administration and Financial Flows Section

Jiří VAČKÁŘ
First Deputy Minister for Regional Development, Regional Policy and Tourism Section

Petr PÁVEK
Deputy Minister for Regional Development, Housing Policy, Town-Planning and Building Regulations Section

Miroslav KALOUS
Deputy Minister for Regional Development, Legislation Section

Daniel TOUŠEK
Deputy Minister for Regional Development, European Affairs Section

DENMARK

Anders Fogh RASMUSSEN
Prime Minister

Lene ESPERSEN
Minister for Economic Affairs, Trade and Industry

Per Stig MØLLER
Minister for Foreign Affairs

Lars Løkke RASMUSSEN
Minister for Finance

Claus Hjort FREDERIKSEN
Minister for Employment

Brian MIKKELSEN
Minister for Justice

Kristian JENSEN
Minister for Taxation

Connie HEDEGAARD
Minister for Climate and Energy

Bertel HAARDER
Minister for Education and Minister for Nordic Cooperation

Karen JESPERSEN
Minister for Welfare and Minister for Equal Opportunities

Helge SANDER
Minister for Science, Technology and Development

Ulla TØRNÆS
Minister for Development Assistance

Søren Gade JENSEN
Minister for Defence

Eva Kjer HANSEN
Minister for Food

Lars BARFOED
Minister for Transport

Carina CHRISTENSEN
Minister for Culture

Jakob Axel NIELSEN
Minister for Health and Prevention

Birthe Rønn HORNBECH
Minister for Refugees, Immigration and Integration, and Minister for Church Affairs

Troels Lund POULSEN
Minister for the Environment

...
State Secretary

GERMANY

Angela MERKEL
Federal Chancellor

Frank-Walter STEINMEIER
Deputy Federal Chancellor and Federal Minister for Foreign Affairs

Wolfgang SCHÄUBLE
Federal Minister for the Interior

Brigitte ZYPRIES
Federal Minister for Justice

Peer STEINBRÜCK
Federal Minister for Finance

Michael GLOS
Federal Minister for Economic Affairs and Technology

Olaf SCHOLZ
Federal Minister for Labour and Social Affairs

Ilse AIGNER
Federal Minister for Food, Agriculture and Consumer Protection

Josef Franz JUNG
Federal Minister for Defence

Ursula VON DER LEYEN
Federal Minister for Family Affairs, Senior Citizens, Women and Youth

Ulla SCHMIDT
Federal Minister for Health

Wolfgang TIEFENSEE
Federal Minister for Transport, Building and Urban Development

Sigmar GABRIEL
Federal Minister for the Environment, Nature Conservation and Reactor Safety

Annette SCHAVAN
Federal Minister for Education and Research

Heidemarie WIECZOREK-ZEUL
Federal Minister for Economic Cooperation and Development

Thomas DE MAIZIÈRE
Federal Minister for Special Tasks and Head of the Federal Chancellery

Gert HALLER
State Secretary, Head of the Federal President's Office

Bernd NEUMANN
Minister of State in the Federal Chancellery, Federal Government Representative for Culture and Media

Hermann GRÖHE
Minister of State in the Federal Chancellery for Coordination between the Federal Government and the Länder

Maria BÖHMER
Minister of State in the Federal Chancellery and Federal Government Representative for Migration, Refugees and Integration

Ulrich WILHELM
Spokesman for the Federal Government and Head of the Press and Information Office of the Federal Government, State Secretary

Gernot ERLER
Minister of State, Foreign Affairs

Günter GLOSER
Minister of State, Foreign Affairs

Georg BOOMGARDEN
State Secretary, Ministry of Foreign Affairs

Reinhard SILBERBERG
Permanent Secretary, Ministry of Foreign Affairs

Heinrich TIEMANN
State Secretary, Ministry of Foreign Affairs

Peter ALTMAIER
Parliamentary State Secretary to the Federal Minister for the Interior

Christoph BERGNER
Parliamentary State Secretary to the Federal Minister for the Interior

Hans Bernhard BEUS
State Secretary, Federal Ministry of the Interior

August HANNING
State Secretary, Federal Ministry of the Interior

Hans-Peter KEMPER
Federal Government Representative for Matters concerning Ethnic German Immigrants and National Minorities

Alfred HARTENBACH
Parliamentary State Secretary to the Federal Minister for Justice

Lutz DIWELL
State Secretary, Federal Ministry of Justice

Karl DILLER
Parliamentary State Secretary to the Federal Minister for Finance

Nicolette KRESSL
Parliamentary State Secretary to the Federal Minister for Finance

Werner GATZER
State Secretary, Federal Ministry of Finance

Thomas MIROW
State Secretary, Federal Ministry of Finance

Axel NAWRATH
State Secretary, Federal Ministry of Finance

Peter HINZE
Parliamentary State Secretary to the Federal Minister for Economic Affairs and Technology

Hartmut SCHAUERTE
Parliamentary State Secretary to the Federal Minister for Economic Affairs and Technology

Dagmar WÖHRL
Parliamentary State Secretary to the Federal Minister for Economic Affairs and Technology

Jochen HOMANN
State Secretary, Federal Ministry of Economic Affairs and Technology

Walther OTEMBRA
State Secretary, Federal Ministry of Economic Affairs and Technology

Bernd PFAFFENBACH
State Secretary, Federal Ministry of Economic Affairs and Technology

Klaus BRANDNER
Parliamentary State Secretary to the Federal Minister for Labour and Social Affairs

Franz THÖNNES
Parliamentary State Secretary to the Federal Minister for Labour and Social Affairs

Franz-Josef LERSCH-MENSE
State Secretary, Federal Ministry of Labour and Social Affairs

Detlef SCHEELE
State Secretary, Federal Ministry of Labour and Social Affairs

Karl-Josef WASSERHÖVEL
State Secretary, Federal Ministry of Labour and Social Affairs

Ursula HEINEN
Parliamentary State Secretary to the Federal Minister for Food, Agriculture and Consumer Protection

Gerd MÜLLER
Parliamentary State Secretary to the Federal Minister for Food, Agriculture and Consumer Protection

Gert LINDEMANN
State Secretary, Federal Ministry of Food, Agriculture and Consumer Protection

Thomas KOSSENDEY
Parliamentary State Secretary to the Federal Minister for Defence

Christian SCHMIDT
Parliamentary State Secretary to the Federal Minister for Defence

Peter WICHERT
State Secretary, Federal Ministry of Defence

Rüdiger WOLF
State Secretary, Federal Ministry of Defence

Hermann KUES
Parliamentary State Secretary to the Federal Minister for Family Affairs, Senior Citizens, Women and Youth

Gerd HOOFE
State Secretary, Federal Ministry of Family Affairs, Senior Citizens, Women and Youth

Marion CASPERS-MERK
Parliamentary State Secretary to the Federal Minister for Health

Rolf SCHWANITZ
Parliamentary State Secretary to the Federal Minister for Health

Klaus Theo SCHRÖDER
State Secretary, Federal Ministry of Health

Achim GROSSMANN
Parliamentary State Secretary to the Federal Minister for Transport, Building and Urban Development

Ulrich KASPARICK
Parliamentary State Secretary to the Federal Minister for Transport, Building and Urban Development

Karin ROTH
Parliamentary State Secretary to the Federal Minister for Transport, Building and Urban Development

Engelbert LÜTKE DALDRUP
State Secretary, Federal Ministry of Transport, Building and Urban Development

Matthias VON RANDOW
State Secretary, Federal Ministry of Transport, Building and Urban Development

Astrid KLUG
Parliamentary State Secretary to the Federal Minister for the Environment, Nature Conservation and Reactor Safety

Michael MÜLLER
Parliamentary State Secretary to the Federal Minister for the Environment, Nature Conservation and Reactor Safety

Matthias MACHNIG
State Secretary, Federal Ministry of the Environment, Nature Conservation and Reactor Safety

Thomas RACHEL
Parliamentary State Secretary to the Federal Minister for Education and Research

Andreas STORM
Parliamentary State Secretary to the Federal Minister for Education and Research

Frieder MEYER-KRAHMER
State Secretary, Federal Ministry of Education and Research

Michael THIELEN
State Secretary, Federal Ministry of Education and Research

Karin KORTMANN
Parliamentary State Secretary to the Federal Minister for Economic Cooperation and Development

Erich STATHER
State Secretary, Federal Ministry of Economic Cooperation and Development

Ministers of the Länder delegated by the Bundesrat

Ute ERDSIEK-RAVE
Minister for Education and Women, Schleswig-Holstein

Thomas GOPPEL
Minister for Science, Research and the Arts, Bavaria

Kurt BECK
Prime Minister, Rhineland-Palatinate

Eberhard SINNER
Minister and Head of State Chancellery, Bavaria

Peter Harry CARSTENSEN
Prime Minister, Schleswig-Holstein

Peter FRANKENBERG
Minister for Science, Research and the Arts, Baden-Württemberg

Erhart KÖRTING
Senator for the Interior and Sport, Berlin

Jörg SCHÖNBOHM
Minister for the Interior, Brandenburg

ESTONIA

Andrus ANSIP
Prime Minister

Heiki LOOT
State Secretary

Tõnis LUKAS
Minister for Education and Science

Rein LANG
Minister for Justice

Jaak AAVIKSOO
Minister for Defence

Jaanus TAMKIVI
Minister for the Environment

Laine JÄNES
Minister for Culture

Juhan PARTS
Minister for Economic Affairs and Communications

Helir-Valdor SEEDER
Minister for Agriculture

Ivari PADAR
Minister for Finance

Jüri PIHL
Minister for the Interior

Maret MARIPUU
Minister for Social Affairs

Urmas PAET
Minister for Foreign Affairs

Siim-Valmar KIISLER
Minister for Regional Affairs

Urve PALO
Minister for Population

IRELAND

Brian COWEN
Taoiseach (Prime Minister)

Mary COUGHLAN
Tánaiste (Deputy Prime Minister) and Minister for Enterprise, Trade and Employment

Brian LENIHAN
Minister for Finance

Mary HARNEY
Minister for Health and Children

Noel DEMPSEY
Minister for Transport

Dermot AHERN
Minister for Justice, Equality and Law Reform

Micheál MARTIN
Minister for Foreign Affairs

Martin CULLEN
Minister for Arts, Sport and Tourism

Éamon Ó CUÍV
Minister for Community, Rural and Gaeltacht Affairs

Mary HANAFIN
Minister for Social and Family Affairs

Willie O'DEA
Minister for Defence

John GORMLEY
Minister for the Environment, Heritage and Local Government

Eamon RYAN
Minister for Communications, Energy and Natural Resources

Brendan SMITH
Minister for Agriculture, Fisheries and Food

Batt O'KEEFFE
Minister for Education and Science

Pat CAREY
Government Chief Whip and Minister of State at the Department of the Taoiseach (with special responsibility for the active citizenship agenda) and at the Department of Defence

Barry ANDREWS
Minister of State at the Department of Health and Children (with special responsibility for children and youth affairs)

Trevor SARGENT
Minister of State at the Department of Agriculture, Fisheries and Food (with special responsibility for food and horticulture)

Dick ROCHE
Minister of State at the Department of Foreign Affairs (with special responsibility for European Affairs)

Noel AHERN
Minister of State at the Department of Transport (with special responsibility for road safety)

Seán POWER
Minister of State at the Department of Communications, Energy and Natural Resources (with special responsibility for the information society and natural resources)

Tony KILLEEN
Minister of State at the Department of Agriculture, Fisheries and Food (with special responsibility for fisheries and forestry)

Conor LENIHAN
Minister of State at the Department of Community, Rural and Gaeltacht Affairs, at the Department of Education and Science, and at the Department of Justice, Equality and Law Reform (with special responsibility for integration policy)

Mary WALLACE
Minister of State at the Department of Health and Children (with special responsibility for health promotion and food safety)

Seán HAUGHEY
Minister of State at the Department of Education and Science and at the Department of Enterprise, Trade and Employment (with special responsibility for lifelong learning and school transport)

Micheal KITT
Minister of State at the Department of the Environment, Heritage and Local Government (with special responsibility for local services)

Billy KELLEHER
Minister of State at the Department of Enterprise, Trade and Employment (with special responsibility for labour affairs)

John MCGUINNESS
Minister of State at the Department of Enterprise, Trade and Employment (with special responsibility for trade and commerce)

Jimmy DEVINS
Minister of State at the Department of Enterprise, Trade and Employment and at the Department of Education and Science (with special responsibility for science, technology and innovation)

Máire HOCTOR
Minister of State at the Department of Health and Children, at the Department of Social and Family Affairs and at the Department of the Environment, Heritage and Local Government (with cross-cutting special responsibility for older people)

Jhon MOLONEY
Minister of State at the Department of Health and Children, at the Department of Education and Science, at the Department of Enterprise, Trade and Employment and at the Department of Justice, Equality and Law Reform (with special responsibility for equality, disability issues and mental health)

Michael FINNERAN
Minister of State at the Department of the Environment, Heritage and Local Government (with special responsibility for housing, urban renewal and developing areas)

John CURRAN
Minister of State at the Department of Community, Rural and Gaeltacht Affairs (with special responsibility for drugs strategy and community affairs)

Peter POWER
Minister of State at the Department of Foreign Affairs (with special responsibility for overseas development)

Martin MANSERGH
Minister of State at the Department of Foreign Affairs (with special responsibility for overseas development)

Paul GALLAGHER
Attorney-General

GREECE

Konstantinos KARAMANLIS
Prime Minister

Prokopios PAVLOPOULOS
Minister for the Interior

Georgios ALOGOSKOUFIS
Minister for Economic Affairs and Finance

Dora BAKOYANNI
Minister for Foreign Affairs

Evangelos-Vassilios MEIMARAKIS
Minister for Defence

Christos FOLIAS
Minister for Development

Georgios SOUFLIAS
Minister for the Environment, Regional Planning and Public Works

Evripidis STYLIANIDIS
Minister for Education and Religious Affairs

Fani PALLI-PETRALIA
Minister for Employment and Social Protection

Dimitrios AVRAMOPOULOS
Minister for Health and Social Solidarity

Alexandros CONTOS
Minister for Rural Development and Food

Sotirios HADJIGAKIS
Minister for Justice

Mihail-Georgios LIAPIS
Minister for Culture

Aristovoulos SPILIOTOPOULOS
Minister for Tourism Development

Konstantinos HADJIDAKIS
Minister for Transport and Communications

Anastasios PAPALIGOURAS
Minister for the Mercantile Marine, the Aegean and Island Policy

Margaritis TZIMAS
Minister for Macedonia and Thrace

Athanasios NAKOS
State Secretary for the Interior

Christos ZOIS
State Secretary for the Interior

Panagiotis CHINOFOTIS
State Secretary for the Interior

Antonios BEZAS
State Secretary for Economic Affairs and Finance

Ioannis PAPATHANASSIOU
State Secretary for Economic Affairs and Finance

Nikolaos LEGAS
State Secretary for Economic Affairs and Finance

Ioannis VALINAKIS
State Secretary for Foreign Affairs

Theodoros KASSIMIS
State Secretary for Foreign Affairs

Petros DOUKAS
State Secretary for Foreign Affairs

Konstantinos TASSOULAS
State Secretary for Defence

Ioannis PLAKIOTAKIS
State Secretary for Defence

Georgios VLACHOS
State Secretary for Development

Stavros KALAFATIS
State Secretary for Development

Stavros KALOGIANNIS
State Secretary for the Environment, Regional Planning and Public Works

Themistoklis XANTHOPOULOS
State Secretary for the Environment, Regional Planning and Public Works

Spyridon TALIADOUROS
State Secretary for Education and Religious Affairs

Andreas LYKOURENTZOS
State Secretary for Education and Religious Affairs

Sofia KALANTZAKOU
State Secrtary for Employment and Social Protection

Georgios PAPAGEORGIOU
State Secretary for Health and Social Solidarity

Georgios KONSTANTOPOULOS
State Secretary for Health and Social Solidarity

Konstantinos KILTIDIS
State Secretary for Rural Development and Food

Ioannis IOANNIDIS
State Secretary for Culture

Panagiotis KAMMENOS
State Secretary for Mercantile Marine, the Aegean and Island Policy

SPAIN

José Luis RODRÍGUEZ ZAPATERO
Prime Minister

María Teresa FERNÁNDEZ DE LA VEGA SANZ
First Deputy Prime Minister, Minister for the Office of the Prime Minister and Government Spokeswoman

Pedro SOLBES MIRA
Second Deputy Prime Minister and Minister for Economic Affairs and Finance

Miguel Ángel MORATINOS CUYAUBÉ
Minister for Foreign Affairs and Cooperation

Mariano FERNÁNDEZ BERMEJO
Minister for Justice

Carme CHACÓN PIQUERAS
Minister for Defence

Mr Alfredo PÉREZ RUBALCABA
Minister for the Interior

Magdalena ÁLVAREZ ARZA
Minister for Infrastructure and Transport

Mercedes CABRERA CALVO-SOTELO
Minister for Education, Social Policy and Sport

Celestino CORBACHO CHAVES
Minister for Labour and Immigration

Miguel SEBASTIÁN GASCÓN
Minister for Industry, Tourism and Trade

Elena ESPINOSA MANGANA
Minister for Minister for the Environment and the Rural and Marine Environment

Elena SALGADO MÉNDEZ
Minister for Public Administration

César Antonio MOLINA SÁNCHEZ
Minister for Culture

Bernat SORIA ESCOMS
Minister for Health and Consumer Affairs

Beatriz CORREDOR SIERRA
Minister for Housing

Cristina GARMENDIA MENDIZÁBAL
Minister for Science and Innovation

Bibiana AÍDO ALMAGRO
Minister for Equality

Ángel LOSSADA TORRES-QUEVEDO
State Secretary for Foreign Affairs

Diego LÓPEZ GARRIDO
State Secretary for the European Union

Leire PAJÍN IRAOLA
State Secretary for International Cooperation

Trinidad JIMÉNEZ GARCÍA-HERRERA
State Secretary for Latin America

Julio PÉREZ HERNÁNDEZ
State Secretary for Justice

Constantino MÉNDEZ MARTÍNEZ
State Secretary for Defence

Alberto SAIZ CORTÉS
State Secretary, Director of the National Intelligence Centre

Carlos OCAÑA Y PÉREZ DE TUDELA
State Secretary for Finance and the Budget

David VEGARA FIGUERAS
State Secretary for Economic Affairs

Antonio CAMACHO VIZCAÍNO
State Secretary for Security

Víctor MORLÁN GRACIA
State Secretary for Planning and Institutional Relations

Josefina CRUZ VILLALÓN
State Secretary for Infrastructure

Eva ALMUNIA BADÍA
State Secretary for Education and Training

Amparo VALCARCE GARCÍA
State Secretary for Social Policy, the Family, Long-Term Care and Care of the Disabled

Octavio José GRANADO MARTÍNEZ
State Secretary for Social Security

María Consuelo RUMÍ IBÁÑEZ
State Secretary for Immigration and Emigration

Joan MESQUIDA FERRANDO
State Secretary for Tourism

Silvia IRANZO GUTIÉRREZ
State Secretary for Trade

Francisco ROS PERÁN
State Secretary for Telecommunications and the Information Society

Teresa RIBERA RODRÍGUEZ
State Secretary for Climate Change

Josep PUXEU ROCAMORA
State Secretary for the Rural Environment and Water

Francisco CAAMAÑO DOMÍNGUEZ
State Secretary for Constitutional and Parliamentary Affairs

Nieves GOICOECHEA GONZÁLEZ
State Secretary for Communications

Mercedes Elvira DEL PALACIO TASCÓN
State Secretary for Public Administration

Fernando PUIG DE LA BELLACASA AGUIRRE
State Secretary for Regional Cooperation

Marius RUBIRALTA I ALCAÑIZ
State Secretary for Universities

Carlos MARTÍNEZ ALONSO
State Secretary for Research

FRANCE

François FILLON
Prime Minister

Jean-Louis BORLOO
Minister of State, for Ecology, Energy, Sustainable Development and Town and Country Planning

Michèle ALLIOT-MARIE
Minister for the Interior, Overseas Territories and Local and Regional Authorities

Bernard KOUCHNER
Minister for Foreign and European Affairs

Christine LAGARDE
Minister for Economic Affairs, Industry and Employment

Brice HORTEFEUX
Minister for Immigration, Integration, National Identity and Development Solidarity

Rachida DATI
Keeper of the Seals, Minister for Justice

Michel BARNIER
Minister for Agriculture and Fisheries

Xavier BERTRAND
Minister for Labour, Labour Relations, the Family and Solidarity

Xavier DARCOS
Minister for National Education

Valérie PÉCRESSE
Minister for Higher Education and Research

Hervé MORIN
Minister for Defence

Roselyne BACHELOT-NARQUIN
Minister for Health, Youth, Sport and the Voluntary Sector

Christine BOUTIN
Minister for Housing and Urban Affairs

Christine ALBANEL
Minister for Culture and Communication

Éric WOERTH
Minister for the Budget, Public Accounts and the Civil Service

Roger KAROUTCHI
Minister of State with responsibility for relations with Parliament

Jean-Pierre JOUYET
Minister of State with responsibility for European affairs

Laurent WAUQUIEZ
Minister of State with responsibility for Employment

Luc CHATEL
Minister of State with responsibility for industry and consumer affairs, Government Spokesperson

Éric BESSON
Minister of State with responsibility for forward planning, assessment of public policies and the development of the digital economy

Valérie LÉTARD
Minister of State with responsibility for solidarity

Dominique BUSSEREAU
Minister of State with responsibility for transport

Nathalie KOSCIUSKO-MORIZET
Minister of State with responsibility for ecology

André SANTINI
Minister of State with responsibility for the civil service

Jean-Marie BOCKEL
Minister of State with responsibility for defence and ex-servicemen

Hervé NOVELLI
Minister of State with responsibility for trade, craft trades, small and medium-sized undertakings, tourism and services

Fadela AMARA
Minister of State with responsibility for urban policy

Alain MARLEIX
Minister of State with responsibility for the interior and local and regional authorities

Rama YADE
Minister of State with responsibility for foreign affairs and human rights

Bernard LAPORTE
Minister of State with responsibility for sports, youth and the voluntary sector

Christian BLANC
Minister of State with responsibility for development of the Capital Region

Hubert FALCO
Minister of State with responsibility for town and country planning

Anne-Marie IDRAC
Minister of State with responsibility for foreign trade

Yves JÉGO
Minister of State with responsibility for overseas territories

Alain JOYANDET
Minister of State with responsibility for cooperation and the French-speaking World

Nadine MORANO
Minister of State with responsibility for the family

Martin HIRSCH
High Commissioner for active solidarity against poverty

ITALY

Silvio BERLUSCONI
Prime Minister

Franco FRATTINI
Minister for Foreign Affairs

Roberto MARONI
Minister for the Interior

Angelino ALFANO
Minister for Justice

Ignazio LA RUSSA
Minister for Defence

Giulio TREMONTI
Minister for Economic Affairs and Finance

Claudio SCAJOLA
Minister for Economic Development

Mariastella GELMINI
Minister for Education, Universities and Research

Maurizio SACCONI
Minister for Labour, Health and Social Policy

Luca ZAIA
Minister for Agriculture and Forestry

Stefania PRESTIGIACOMO
Minister for the Environment and the Protection of Natural Resources and the Sea

Altero MATTEOLI
Minister for Infrastructure and Transport

Sandro BONDI
Minister for Cultural Assets and Activities

Raffaele FITTO
Minister without portfolio, Minister for Relations with the Regions

Gianfranco ROTONDI
Minister without Portfolio, Minister for Implementation of the Programme

Renato BRUNETTA
Minister without portfolio, Minister for Public Administration and Innovation

Mara CARFAGNA
Minister without portfolio, Minister for Equal Opportunities

Andrea RONCHI
Minister without portfolio, Minister for Community Policies

Elio VITO
Minister without portfolio, Minister for Relations with Parliament

Umberto BOSSI
Minister without portfolio, Minister for Federal Reforms

Giorgia MELONI
Minister without portfolio, Minister for Youth Policy

Roberto CALDEROLI
Minister without portfolio, Minister for Regulatory Simplification

Gianni LETTA
State Secretary, Prime Minister's Office

Paolo BONAIUTI
State Secretary, Prime Minister's Office, responsible for Publishing

Gianfranco MICCICHÈ
State Secretary, Prime Minister's Office, responsible for the Interministerial Economic Planning Committee

Carlo GIOVANARDI
State Secretary, Prime Minister's Office, responsible for the Family, Drug Policy and Civilian Service

Michela Vittoria BRAMBILLA
State Secretary, Prime Minister's Office, responsible for Tourism

Aldo BRANCHER
State Secretary, Prime Minister's Office, responsible for Federal Reforms

Rocco CRIMI
State Secretary, Prime Minister's Office, responsible for Sport

Maurizio BALOCCHI
State Secretary, Prime Minister's Office, responsible for Regulatory Simplification

Guido BERTOLASO
State Secretary, Prime Minister's Office, responsible for solving the refuse emergency in the Campania Region

Stefania Gabriella Anastasia CRAXI
State Secretary for Foreign Affairs

Alfredo MANTICA
State Secretary for Foreign Affairs

Enzo SCOTTI
State Secretary for Foreign Affairs

Michelino DAVICO
State Secretary for the Interior

Alfredo MANTOVANO
State Secretary for the Interior

Nitto Francesco PALMA
State Secretary for the Interior

Maria Elisabetta ALBERTI CASELLATI
State Secretary for Justice

Giacomo CALIENDO
State Secretary for Justice

Giuseppe COSSIGA
State Secretary for Defence

Guido CROSETTO
State Secretary for Defence

Alberto GIORGETTI
State Secretary for Economic Affairs and Finance

Daniele MOLGORA
State Secretary for Economic Affairs and Finance

Nicola COSENTINO
State Secretary for Economic Affairs and Finance

Luigi CASERO
State Secretary for Economic Affairs and Finance

Giuseppe VEGAS
State Secretary for Economic Affairs and Finance

Ugo MARTINAT
State Secretary for Economic Development

Paolo ROMANI
State Secretary for Economic Development

Adolfo URSO
State Secretary for Economic Development

Roberto CASTELLI
State Secretary for Infrastructure and Transport

Bartolomeo GIACHINO
State Secretary for Infrastructure and Transport

Mario MANTOVANI
State Secretary for Infrastructure and Transport

Giuseppa Maria REINA
State Secretary for Infrastructure and Transport

Antonio BONFIGLIO
State Secretary for Agricultural and Forestry Policy

Pasquale VIESPOLI
State Secretary for Labour, Health and Social Policy

Ferruccio FAZIO
State Secretary for Labour, Health and Social Policy

Francesca MARTINI
State Secretary for Labour, Health and Social Policy

Eugenia Maria ROCCELLA
State Secretary for Labour, Health and Social Policy

Giuseppe PIZZA
State Secretary for Education, Universities and Research

Francesco Maria GIRO
State Secretary for Cultural Assets and Activities

Roberto MENIA
State Secretary for the Environment and the Protection of Natural Resources and the Sea

CYPRUS

Demetris CHRISTOFIAS
President of the Republic of Cyprus

Stefanos STEFANOU
Government Spokesman

Titos CHRISTOFIDIS
Deputy Minister to the President

Marcos KYPRIANOU
Minister for Foreign Affairs

Alexandros ZENON
State Secretary, Ministry of Foreign Affairs

Charilaos STAVRAKIS
Minister for Finance

Christos PATSALIDES
State Secretary at the Ministry of Finance

Neoklis SYLIKIOTIS
Minister for the Interior

Lazaros SAVVIDES
State Secretary, Ministry of the Interior

Sotiroulla CHARALAMBOUS
Minister for Labour and Social Insurance

Elpiniki KOUTOUROUSHI
Permanent Secretary, Ministry of Labour and Social Insurance

Costas PAPACOSTAS
Minister for Defence

Petros KAREKLAS
Permanent Secretary, Ministry of Defence

Kypros CHRISOSTOMIDES
Minister for Justice and Public Order

Andis TRYFONIDES
Permanent Secretary, Ministry of Justice and Public Order

Andreas DEMETRIOU
Minister for Education and Culture

Olympia STYLIANOU
Permanent Secretary, Ministry of Education and Culture

Antonis PASCHALIDES
Minister for Commerce, Industry and Tourism

Efstathios HAMBOULLAS
Permanent Secretary, Ministry of Commerce, Industry and Tourism

Christos PATSALIDES
Minister for Health

Sotiris SOTIRIOU
Permanent Secretary, Ministry of Health

Nicos NICOLAIDES
Minister for Communications and Works

Makis CONSTANDINIDES
Permanent Secretary, Ministry of Communications and Works

Michalis POLYNIKI CHARALAMBIDES
Minister for Agriculture, Natural Resources and Environment

Panicos POUROS
Permanent Secretary, Ministry of Agriculture, Natural Resources and Environment

LATVIA

Ivars GODMANIS
Prime Minister

Vinets VELDRE
Minister for Defence

Edgars RINKĒVIČS
Permanent Secretary, Ministry of Defence

Māris RIEKSTIŅŠ
Minister for Foreign Affairs

Normans PENKE
Permanent Secretary, Ministry of Foreign Affairs

Ainars BAŠTIKS
Minister for Children and the Family

Iveta ZALPĒTERE
State Secretary, Ministry of Children and the Family

Kaspars GERHARDS
Minister for the Economy

Anrijs MATĪSS
State Secretary at the Ministry of the Economy

Atis SLAKTERIS
Minister for Finance

Irēna KRŪMANE
State Secretary at the Ministry of Finance

Mareks SEGLIŅŠ
Minister for the Interior

Aivars STRAUME
State Secretary, Ministry of the Interior

Tatjana KOĶE
Minister for Education and Science

Mareks GRUŠKEVICS
State Secretary, Ministry of Education and Science

Helēna DEMAKOVA
Minister for Culture

Solvita ZVIDRIŅA
State Secretary, Ministry of Culture

Iveta PURNE
Minister for Welfare

Baiba PAŠEVICA
State Secretary, Ministry of Welfare

Edgars ZALĀNS
Minister for Regional Development and Local Government

Laimdota STRAUJUMA
State Secretary, Ministry of Regional Development and Local Government

Ainārs ŠLESERS
Minister for Transport and Communications

Jānis MARŠĀNS
State Secretary, Ministry of Transport and Communications

Gaidis BĒRZIŅŠ
Minister for Justice

Mārtiņš BIČEVSKIS
State Secretary at the Ministry of Justice

Ivars EGLĪTIS
Minister for Health

Armands PLORIŅŠ
State Secretary, Ministry of Health

Raimonds VĒJONIS
Minister for the Environment

Guntis PUĶĪTIS
State Secretary, Ministry of the Environment

Mārtiņš ROZE
Minister for Agriculture

Dace LUCAUA
State Secretary, Ministry of Agriculture

Ina GUDELE
Minister with special responsibility for e-administration

Oskars KASTĒNS
Minister with special responsibility for societal integration

Normunds BROKS
Minister with special responsibility for the administration of European Union funds

LITHUANIA

Gediminas KIRKILAS
Prime Minister

Valdemaras SARAPINAS
Chancellor

Olegas ROMANČIKAS
Deputy Chancellor

Darius ŽERUOLIS
Deputy Chancellor with responsibility for European affairs

Algirdas BUTKEVIČIUS
Minister for Transport and Communications

Česlovas ŠIKŠNELIS
Deputy Minister for Transport and Communications

Alminas MAČIULIS
State Secretary at the Ministry of Transport and Communications

Vilija BLINKEVIČIŪTĖ
Minister for Social Security and Labour

Povilas Vytautas ŽIŪKAS
Deputy Minister for Social Security and Labour

Rimantas KAIRELIS
State Secretary at the Ministry of Social Security and Labour

Raimondas ŠUKYS
Minister for the Interior

Regimantas ČIUPAILA
Deputy Minister for the Interior

Evaldas GUSTAS
State Secretary at the Ministry of the Interior

Vytas NAVICKAS
Minister for the Economy

Vytautas NAUDUŽAS
Deputy Minister for the Economy

Gediminas MIŠKINIS
State Secretary at the Ministry for the Economy

Rimantas ŠADŽIUS
Minister for Finance

Valentinas MILTIENIS
Deputy Minister for Finance

Giedrius RIMŠA
State Secretary at the Ministry of Finance

Kazimira Danutė PRUNSKIENĖ
Minister for Agriculture

Virginija ŽOŠTAUTIENĖ
Deputy Minister for Agriculture

Vidmantas KANOPA
State Secretary at the Ministry of Agriculture

Artūras PAULAUSKAS
Minister for the Environment

Raimundas PALIUKAS
Deputy Minister for the Environment

Arvydas DRAGŪNAS
State Secretary at the Ministry of the Environment

Juozas OLEKAS
Minister for Defence

Antanas VALYS
Deputy Minister for Defence

Valdemaras SARAPINAS
State Secretary at the Ministry of Defence

Petras BAGUŠKA
Minister for Justice

Eglė RADUŠYTĖ
Deputy Minister for Justice

Paulius KOVEROVAS
State Secretary at the Ministry of Justice

Algirdas MONKEVIČIUS
Minister for Education and Science

...
Deputy Minister for Education and Science

Dainius NUMGAUDIS
State Secretary at the Ministry of Education and Science

Rimvydas TURČINSKAS
Minister for Health

Janina KUMPIENĖ
Deputy Minister for Health

Mindaugas PLIESKIS
State Secretary at the Ministry of Health

Petras VAITIEKŪNAS
Minister for Foreign Affairs

Jaroslav NEVEROVIČ
Deputy Minister for Foreign Affairs

Algimantas RIMKŪNAS
State Secretary at the Ministry of Foreign Affairs

Albinas JANUŠKA
Under-Secretary at the Ministry of Foreign Affairs with responsibility for EU affairs

Oskaras JUSYS
Under-Secretary at the Ministry of Foreign Affairs

Jonas JUČAS
Minister for Culture

Gintaras SODEIKA
Deputy Minister for Culture

Diana PAKNYTĖ
State Secretary at the Ministry of Culture

LUXEMBOURG

Jean-Claude JUNCKER
Prime Minister, Minister of State, Minister for Finance

Jean ASSELBORN
Deputy Prime Minister, Minister for Foreign Affairs and Immigration

Fernand BODEN
Minister for Agriculture, Viticulture and Rural Development, Minister for Small and Medium-sized Businesses, the Liberal Professions and the Self-Employed, Tourism and Housing

Marie-Josée JACOBS
Minister for the Family and Integration, Minister for Equal Opportunities

Mady DELVAUX-STEHRES
Minister for Education and Vocational Training

Luc FRIEDEN
Minister for Justice, Minister for the Treasury and the Budget

François BILTGEN
Minister for Labour and Employment, Minister for Culture, Higher Education and Research, Minister for Religious Affairs

Jeannot KRECKÉ
Minister for Economic Affairs and Foreign Trade, Minister for Sport

Mars DI BARTOLOMEO
Minister for Health and Social Security

Lucien LUX
Minister for the Environment, Minister for Transport

Jean-Marie HALSDORF
Minister for the Interior and Regional Planning

Claude WISELER
Minister for the Civil Service and Administrative Reform, Minister for Public Works

Jean-Louis SCHILTZ
Minister for Cooperation and Humanitarian Action, Minister for Communications, Minister for Defence

Nicolas SCHMIT
Minister with responsibility for foreign affairs and immigration

Octavie MODERT
State Secretary for Relations with Parliament, State Secretary for Agriculture, Viticulture and Rural Development, State Secretary for Culture, Higher Education and Research

HUNGARY

Ferenc GYURCSÁNY
Prime Minister

Tibor DRASKOVICS
Minister for Justice and Law Enforcement

Péter KISS
Minister responsible for the Prime Minister's Office

Tamás SZÉKELY
Minister for Health

Pál SZABÓ
Minister for Transport, Telecommunications and Energy

Imre SZEKERES
Minister for Defence

György SZILVÁSY
Minister without Portfolio

Imre SZABÓ
Minister for the Environment and Water Management

Kinga GÖNCZ
Minister for Foreign Affairs

Erika SZŰCS
Minister for Social Affairs and Labour

János VERES
Minister for Finance

István HILLER
Minister for Education and Culture

József GRÁF
Minister for Agriculture and Rural Development

Gordon BAJNAI
Minister for National Development and Economic Affairs

Károly MOLNÁR
Minister without portfolio, responsible for science policy and research and development

István GYENESEI
Minister for Local Government

Ádám FICSOR
State Secretary, Prime Minister's Office

Ferenc BAJA
State Secretary, Prime Minister's Office

István KOLBER
State Secretary, Prime Minister's Office

Imre IVÁNCSIK
State Secretary, Prime Minister's Office

Csaba TORDAI
State Secretary, Prime Minister's Office

Gábor CSIZMÁR
State Secretary, Prime Minister's Office

Péter MAKSZIN
Deputy State Secretary, Prime Minister's Office

Ferenc GÉMESI
Deputy State Secretary, Prime Minister's Office

Zsuzsanna KOVÁCSNÉ, SZILÁGYI-FARKAS
Deputy State Secretary, Prime Minister's Office

Gábor SIMON
State Secretary, Ministry of Social Affairs and Labour

Lajos KORÓZS
State Secretary, Ministry of Social Affairs and Labour

László HERCZOG
State Secretary (with special responsibility), Ministry of Social Affairs and Labour

Judit SZÉKELY
State Secretary (with special responsibility), Ministry of Social Affairs and Labour

Mária VOJNIK
Permanent Secretary, Ministry of Health

Mariann BARACZKA
Deputy State Secretary, Ministry of Health

Ilona GÁL
Deputy State Secretary, Ministry of Health

Márta HORVÁTHNÉ FEKSZI
State Secretary, Ministry of Foreign Affairs

Gábor IVÁN
Deputy State Secretary, Ministry of Foreign Affairs

László VÁRKONYI
Deputy State Secretary, Ministry of Foreign Affairs

György GILYÁN
Deputy State Secretary, Ministry of Foreign Affairs

Gábor SZENTIVÁNYI
Deputy State Secretary, Ministry of Foreign Affairs

Jenő FALLER
Deputy State Secretary, Ministry of Foreign Affairs

Gergely ARATÓ
State Secretary, Ministry of Education and Culture

Ferenc CSÁK
State Secretary, Ministry of Education and Culture

Katalin BOGYAY
State Secretary (with special responsibility), Ministry of Education and Culture

Károly MANHERZ
State Secretary (with special responsibility), Ministry of Education and Culture

Márta SCHNEIDER
State Secretary (with special responsibility), Ministry of Education and Culture

János SZÜDI
State Secretary (with special responsibility), Ministry of Education and Culture

Ferenc ZÁVECZ
State Secretary (with special responsibility), Ministry of Education and Culture

László KELLER
State Secretary, Ministry of Finance

Bernadett CSÁKY
Deputy State Secretary, Ministry of Finance

Imréné KARÁCSONY
Deputy State Secretary, Ministry of Finance

Álmos KOVÁCS
Deputy State Secretary, Ministry of Finance

Andrea MARKÓ
Deputy State Secretary, Ministry of Finance

István VÁRFALVI
Deputy State Secretary, Ministry of Finance

Ágnes VADAI
Permanent Secretary, Ministry of Defence

József BALI
Deputy State Secretary, Ministry of Defence

Károly FÜREDI
Deputy State Secretary, Ministry of Defence

Péter JÓZSEF
Deputy State Secretary, Ministry of Defence

András HAVRIL
Chief of Staff, Ministry of Defence

János MIKITA
Deputy Chief of Staff, Ministry of Defence

Gábor JUHÁSZ
State Secretary, Ministry of Justice and Law Enforcement

Dezső AVARKESZI
State Secretary, Ministry of Justice and Law Enforcement

Judit FAZEKAS
State Secretary (with special responsibility), Ministry of Justice and Law Enforcement

Gábor GADÓ
State Secretary (with special responsibility), Ministry of Justice and Law Enforcement

Imre PAPP
State Secretary (with special responsibility), Ministry of Justice and Law Enforcement

Lajos OLÁH
State Secretary, Ministry of the Environment and Water Management

György ERDEY
State Secretary (with special responsibility), Ministry of the Environment and Water Management

László HARASZTHY
State Secretary (with special responsibility), Ministry of the Environment and Water Management

László KÓTHAY
State Secretary (with special responsibility), Ministry of the Environment and Water Management

László DIÓSSY
State Secretary (with special responsibility), Ministry of the Environment and Water Management

László PUCH
State Secretary, Ministry of Transport, Telecommunications and Energy

Ákos BÓNA
State Secretary (with special responsibility), Ministry of Transport, Telecommunications and Energy

Zoltán GŐGÖS
State Secretary, Ministry of Agriculture and Rural Development

Barnabás FORGÁCS
Deputy State Secretary, Ministry of Agriculture and Rural Development

Miklós SÜTH
Deputy State Secretary, Ministry of Agriculture and Rural Development

András MÁHR
Deputy State Secretary, Ministry of Agriculture and Rural Development

Ferenc SIRMAN
Deputy State Secretary, Ministry of Agriculture and Rural Development

István JAUERNIK
State Secretary, Ministry of Local Government

Sándor BUJDOSÓ
State Secretary (with special responsibility), Ministry of Local Government

Gábor ELBERT
State Secretary (with special responsibility), Ministry of Local Government

Miklós KOVÁCS
State Secretary (with special responsibility), Ministry of Local Government

Péter SZALÓ
State Secretary (with special responsibility), Ministry of Local Government

Rudolf VIRÁG
State Secretary (with special responsibility), Ministry of Local Government

Sándor BURÁNY
State Secretary, Ministry of National Development and Economic Affairs

Géza EGYED
State Secretary (with special responsibility), Ministry of National Development and Economic Affairs

Ábel GARAMHEGYI
State Secretary (with special responsibility), Ministry of National Development and Economic Affairs

Gabriella MÉSZÁROSNÉ PEREDY
State Secretary (with special responsibility), Ministry of National Development and Economic Affairs

MALTA

Lawrence GONZI
Prime Minister

Tonio BORG
Deputy Prime Minister and Minister for Foreign Affairs

Giovanna DEBONO
Minister for Gozo

Austin GATT
Minister for Infrastructure, Transport and Communications

George PULLICINO
Minister for Resources and Rural Affairs

Dolores CRISTINA
Minister of Education, Culture, Youth and Sport

John DALLI
Minister for Social Policy

Tonio FENECH
Minister of Finance, Economy and Investment

Carmelo MIFSUD BONNICI
Minister for Justice and Home Affairs

Mario DE MARCO
Parliamentary Secretary for Tourism in the Office of the Prime Minister

Chris SAID
Parliamentary Secretary for Public Dialogue and Information in the Office of the Prime Minister

Clyde PULI
Parliamentary Secretary for Youth and Sport in the Ministry of Education and Culture

Mario GALEA
Parliamentary Secretary for the Elderly and Community Care in the Ministry for Social Policy

Joe CASSAR
Parliamentary Secretary for Health in the Ministry for Social Policy

Jason AZZOPARDI
Parliamentary Secretary for Revenues and Land in the Ministry of Finance, the Economy and Investment

THE NETHERLANDS

Jan Peter BALKENENDE
Prime Minister, Minister for General Affairs

Wouter BOS
Minister for Finance, Deputy Prime Minister

André ROUVOET
Minister for Youth and the Family, Deputy Prime Minister

Maxime VERHAGEN
Minister for Foreign Affairs

Ernst HIRSCH BALLIN
Minister for Justice

Guusje ter HORST
Minister for the Interior and Kingdom Relations

Ronald PLASTERK
Minister for Education, Cultural Affairs and Science

Eimert van MIDDELKOOP
Minister for Defence

Jacqueline CRAMER
Minister for Housing, Spatial Planning and the Environment

Camiel EURLINGS
Minister for Transport, Public Works and Water Management

Maria van der HOEVEN
Minister for the Economy

Gerda VERBURG
Minister for Agriculture, Nature and Food Quality

Piet Hein DONNER
Minister for Social Affairs and Employment

Ab KLINK
Minister for Health, Welfare and Sport

Bert KOENDERS
Minister for Development Cooperation

Eberhard Edzard van der LAAN
Minister for Housing, Communities and Integration

Frans TIMMERMANS
State Secretary for Foreign Affairs (in international context: Minister for European Affairs)

Nebahat ALBAYRAK
State Secretary for Justice

Ank BIJLEVELD-SCHOUTEN
State Secretary for the Interior and Kingdom Relations

Marja van BIJSTERVELDT-VLIEGENTHART
State Secretary for Education, Cultural Affairs and Science

Sharon DIJKSMA
State Secretary for Education, Cultural Affairs and Science

Jan Kees de JAGER
State Secretary for Finance

Jack de VRIES
State Secretary for Defence

Tineke HUIZINGA-HERINGA
State Secretary for Transport, Public Works and Water Management

Frank HEEMSKERK
State Secretary for Economic Affairs (in international context: Minister for Foreign Trade)

Jetta KLIJNSMA
State Secretary for Social Affairs and Employment

Jet BUSSEMAKER
State Secretary for Health, Welfare and Sport

AUSTRIA

Alfred GUSENBAUER
Federal Chancellor

Wilhelm MOLTERER
Vice Chancellor and Federal Minister for Finance

Heidrun SILHAVY
Federal Minister for Women, Media and Regional Policy

Ursula PLASSNIK
Federal Minister for European and International Affairs

Andrea KDOLSKY
Federal Minister for Health, the Family and Youth

Maria FEKTER
Federal Minister for the Interior

Maria BERGER
Federal Minister for Justice

Norbert DARABOS
Federal Minister for Defence

Josef PRÖLL
Federal Minister for Agriculture, Forestry, the Environment and Water Management

Erwin BUCHINGER
Federal Minister for Social Affairs and Consumer Protection

Claudia SCHMIED
Federal Minister for Education, the Arts and Culture

Werner FAYMANN
Federal Minister for Transport, Innovation and Technology

Martin BARTENSTEIN
Federal Minister for Economic Affairs and Labour

Johannes HAHN
Federal Minister for Science and Research

Reinhold LOPATKA
State Secretary, Federal Chancellery

Andreas SCHIEDER
State Secretary, Federal Chancellery

Hans WINKLER
State Secretary, Federal Ministry of European and International Affairs

Christoph MATZNETTER
State Secretary, Federal Ministry of Finance

Christa KRANZL
State Secretary, Federal Ministry of Transport, Innovation and Technology

Christine MAREK
State Secretary, Federal Ministry of Economic Affairs and Labour

POLAND

Donald TUSK
Prime Minister

Tomasz ARABSKI
Head of the Prime Minister's Office

Władysław BARTOSZEWSKI
State Secretary, Prime Minister's Office

Rafał Szymon GRUPIŃSKI
State Secretary, Prime Minister's Office

Sławomir NOWAK
State Secretary, Prime Minister's Office

Julia PITERA
State Secretary, Prime Minister's Office

Michał BONI
State Secretary, Prime Minister's Office

Jacek CICHOCKI
State Secretary, Prime Minister's Office

Eugeniusz GRZESZCZAK
State Secretary, Prime Minister's Office

Agnieszka LISZKA
Deputy State Secretary, Prime Minister's Office

Adam LESZKIEWICZ
Deputy State Secretary, Prime Minister's Office

Igor OSTACHOWICZ
Deputy State Secretary, Prime Minister's Office

Zbigniew DERDZIUK
Minister, Member of the Council of Ministers

Grzegorz SCHETYNA
Deputy Prime Minister, Minister for the Interior and Administration

Tomasz SIEMONIAK
State Secretary, Ministry of the Interior and Administration

Witolod DROŻDŻ
Deputy State Secretary, Ministry of the Interior and Administration

Adam RAPACKI
Deputy State Secretary, Ministry of the Interior and Administration

Piotr STACHAŃCZYK
Deputy State Secretary, Ministry of the Interior and Administration

Antoni PODOLSKI
Deputy State Secretary, Ministry of the Interior and Administration

Zbigniew SOSNOWSKI
Deputy State Secretary, Ministry of the Interior and Administration

Jolanta FEDAK
Minister for Labour and Social Policy

Jarosław DUDA
State Secretary, Ministry of Labour and Social Policy

Czesława OSTROWSKA
Deputy State Secretary, Ministry of Labour and Social Policy

Agnieszka CHŁOŃ-DOMIŃCZAK
Deputy State Secretary, Ministry of Labour and Social Policy

Radosław MLECZKO
Deputy State Secretary, Ministry of Labour and Social Policy

Marek BUCIOR
Deputy State Secretary, Ministry of Labour and Social Policy

Cezary GRABARCZYK
Minister for Infrastructure

Tadeusz JARMUZIEWICZ
State Secretary, Ministry of Infrastructure

Olgierd DZIEKOŃSKI
Deputy State Secretary, Ministry of Infrastructure

Juliusz ENGELHARDT
Deputy State Secretary, Ministry of Infrastructure

Maciej JANKOWSKI
Deputy State Secretary, Ministry of Infrastructure

Andrzej PANASIUK
Deputy State Secretary, Ministry of Infrastructure

Anna WYPYCH-NAMIOTKO
Deputy State Secretary, Ministry of Infrastructure

Piotr STYCZEŃ
Deputy State Secretary, Ministry of Infrastructure

Zbigniew RAPCIAK
Deputy State Secretary, Ministry of Infrastructure

Patrycja WOLIŃSKA
Deputy State Secretary, Ministry of Infrastructure

Radosław SIKORSKI
Minister for Foreign Affairs

Jan BORKOWSKI
State Secretary, Ministry of Foreign Affairs

Ryszard SCHNEPF
Deputy State Secretary, Ministry of Foreign Affairs

Grażyna BERNATOWICZ
Deputy State Secretary, Ministry of Foreign Affairs

Przemysław GRUDZIŃSKI
Deputy State Secretary, Ministry of Foreign Affairs

Andrzej KREMER
Deputy State Secretary, Ministry of Foreign Affairs

Aleksander GRAD
Minister for the Treasury

Jan BURY
State Secretary, Ministry of the Treasury

Michał Jan CHYCZEWSKI
Deputy State Secretary, Ministry of the Treasury

Zdzisław GAWLIK
Deputy State Secretary, Ministry of the Treasury

Krzysztof Hubert ŁASZKIEWICZ
Deputy State Secretary, Ministry of the Treasury

Krzysztof Jan ŻUK
Deputy State Secretary, Ministry of the Treasury

Joanna SCHMIT
Deputy State Secretary, Ministry of the Treasury

Bogdan ZDROJEWSKI
Minister for Culture and National Heritage

Piotr ŻUCHOWSKI
State Secretary, Ministry of Culture and National Heritage

Tomasz MERTA
Deputy State Secretary, Ministry of Culture and National Heritage

Monika Alicja SMOLEŃ
Deputy State Secretary, Ministry of Culture and National Heritage

Mikołaj DOWGIELEWICZ
State Secretary, Office of the Committee for European Integration

Sidonia Elżbieta JĘDRZEJEWSKA
Deputy State Secretary, Office of the Committee for European Integration

Piotr SERAFIN
Deputy State Secretary, Office of the Committee for European Integration

Elżbieta BIEŃKOWSKA
Minister for Regional Development

Hanna JAHNS
State Secretary, Ministry of Regional Development

Janusz MIKUŁA
Deputy State Secretary, Ministry of Regional Development

Krzysztof HETMAN
Deputy State Secretary, Ministry of Regional Development

Jarosław PAWŁOWSKI
Deputy State Secretary, Ministry of Regional Development

Augustyn KUBIK
Deputy State Secretary, Ministry of Regional Development

Barbara KUDRYCKA
Minister for Science and Higher Education

Maria Elżbieta ORŁOWSKA
State Secretary, Ministry of Science and Higher Education

Maria PRAWELSKA-SKRZYPEK
Deputy State Secretary, Ministry of Science and Higher Education

Jerzy DUSZYŃSKI
Deputy State Secretary, Ministry of Science and Higher Education

Zbigniew ĆWIĄKALSKI
Minister for Justice

Marian CICHOSZ
Parliamentary Under Secretary of State, Ministry of Justice

Jacek CZAJA
Deputy State Secretary, Ministry of Justice

Łukasz Antoni RĘDZINIAK
Deputy State Secretary, Ministry of Justice

Marek STASZAK
Deputy State Secretary, Ministry of Justice

Zbigniew WRONA
Deputy State Secretary, Ministry of Justice

Mirosław DRZEWIECKI
Minister for Sport and Tourism

Zbigniew PACELT
State Secretary, Ministry of Sport and Tourism

Tomasz PÓŁGRABSKI
Deputy State Secretary, Ministry of Sport and Tourism

Katarzyna Danuta SOBIERAJSKA
Deputy State Secretary, Ministry of Sport and Tourism

Jan VINCENT-ROSTOWSKI
Minister for Finance

Elżbieta SUCHOCKA-ROGUSKA
State Secretary, Ministry of Finance

Elżbieta CHOJNA-DUCH
Deputy State Secretary, Ministry of Finance

Jacek DOMINIK
Deputy State Secretary, Ministry of Finance

Katarzyna ZAJDEL-KUROWSKA
Deputy State Secretary, Ministry of Finance

Andrzej Tadeusz PARAFIANOWICZ
Deputy State Secretary, Ministry of Finance

Dariusz DANILUK
Deputy State Secretary, Ministry of Finance

Jacek KAPICA
Deputy State Secretary, Ministry of Finance

Ludwik KOTECKI
Deputy State Secretary, Ministry of Finance

Ewa KOPACZ
Minister for Health

Jakub SZULC
Permanent Secretary, Ministry of Health

Mariola DWORNIKOWSKA
Deputy State Secretary, Ministry of Health

Adam FRONCZAK
Deputy State Secretary, Ministry of Health

Marek TWARDOWSKI
Deputy State Secretary, Ministry of Health

Marek HABER
Deputy State Secretary, Ministry of Health

Bogdan KLICH
Minister for Defence

Czesław PIĄTAS
Permanent Secretary, Ministry of Defence

Stanisław KOMOROWSKI
Deputy State Secretary, Ministry of Defence

Zenon KOSINIAK-KAMYSZ
Deputy State Secretary, Ministry of Defence

Maciej NOWICKI
Minister for the Environment

Stanisław GAWŁOWSKI
State Secretary, Ministry of the Environment

Henryk Jacek JEZIERSKI
Deputy State Secretary, Ministry of the Environment

Maciej TRZECIAK
Deputy State Secretary, Ministry of the Environment

Janusz ZALESKI
Deputy State Secretary, Ministry of the Environment

Bernard BŁASZCZYK
Deputy State Secretary, Ministry of the Environment

Marek SAWICKI
Minister for Agriculture and Rural Development

Kazimierz Florian PLOCKE
State Secretary, Ministry of Agriculture and Rural Development

Andrzej DYCHA
Deputy State Secretary, Ministry of Agriculture and Rural Development

Artur ŁAWNICZAK
Deputy State Secretary, Ministry of Agriculture and Rural Development

Marian ZALEWSKI
Deputy State Secretary, Ministry of Agriculture and Rural Development

Waldemar PAWLAK
Deputy Prime Minister, Minister for Economic Affairs

Adam SZEJNFELD
State Secretary at the Ministry of the Economy

Rafał BANIAK
Deputy State Secretary, Ministry of Economic Affairs

Dariusz BOGDAN
Deputy State Secretary, Ministry of Economic Affairs

Marcin KOROLEC
Deputy State Secretary, Ministry of Economic Affairs

Joanna STRZELEC-ŁOBODZIŃSKA
Deputy State Secretary, Ministry of Economic Affairs

Grażyna HENCLEWSKA
Deputy State Secretary, Ministry of Economic Affairs

Katarzyna HALL
Minister for National Education

Krystyna SZUMILAS
State Secretary, Ministry of National Education

Krzysztof Piotr STANOWSKI
Deputy State Secretary, Ministry of National Education

Zbigniew MARCINIAK
Deputy State Secretary, Ministry of National Education

Zbigniew WŁODKOWSKI
Deputy State Secretary, Ministry of National Education

PORTUGAL

José SÓCRATES
Prime Minister

Rui PEREIRA
Minister for the Interior

Luís AMADO
Ministro de Estado, Minister for Foreign Affairs

Fernando TEIXEIRA DOS SANTOS
Ministro de Estado, Minister for Finance

Pedro SILVA PEREIRA
Minister for the Prime Minister's Office

Nuno SEVERIANO TEIXEIRA
Minister for Defence

Alberto COSTA
Minister for Justice

Francisco NUNES CORREIA
Minister for the Environment, Regional Planning and Regional Development

Manuel PINHO
Minister for Economic Affairs and Innovation

Jaime SILVA
Minister for Agriculture, Rural Development and Fisheries

Mário LINO
Minister for Public Works, Transport and Communications

José VIEIRA DA SILVA
Minister for Labour and Social Solidarity

Ana JORGE
Minister for Health

Maria de Lurdes RODRIGUES
Minister for Education

José MARIANO GAGO
Minister for Science, Technology and Higher Education

José António PINTO RIBEIRO
Minister for Culture

Augusto SANTOS SILVA
Minister for Parliamentary Affairs

Filipe BAPTISTA
State Secretary attached to the Prime Minister

Eduardo CABRITA
State Secretary for Local Government, attached to the Minister for the Interior

José MAGALHÃES
State Secretary for the Interior, attached to the Minister for the Interior

Ascenso SIMÕES
State Secretary for the Interior

Fernando ROCHA ANDRADE
Deputy State Secretary for the Interior

João GOMES CRAVINHO
State Secretary for Foreign Affairs and Cooperation

Teresa RIBEIRO
Minister of State with responsibility for European affairs

António BRAGA
State Secretary for the Portuguese Communities Abroad

Emanuel AUGUSTO SANTOS
State Secretary for the Budget, attached to the Minister for Finance

Carlos COSTA PINA
State Secretary for the Treasury and Financial Affairs

João AMARAL TOMAZ
State Secretary for Tax Affairs

João FIGUEIREDO
State Secretary for Public Administration

Jorge LACÃO
State Secretary, Prime Minister's Office

Laurentino DIAS
State Secretary for Young People and Sport

João MIRA GOMES
State Secretary for Defence and Maritime Affairs

José Manuel CONDE RODRIGUES
State Secretary for Justice, attached to the Minister for Justice

João Tiago SILVEIRA
State Secretary for Justice

Humberto ROSA
State Secretary for the Environment

João FERRÃO
State Secretary for Regional Planning and Urban Areas

Rui BALEIRAS
State Secretary for Regional Development

António CASTRO GUERRA
Deputy Permanent Secretary for Industry and Innovation

Fernando SERRASQUEIRO
State Secretary for Trade, Services and Consumer Protection

Bernando TRINDADE
State Secretary for Tourism

Luís VIEIRA
State Secretary for Agriculture and Fisheries, attached to the Minister for Agriculture, Rural Development and Fisheries

Rui NOBRE GONÇALVES
State Secretary for Rural Development and Forestry

Paulo CAMPOS
State Secretary for Public Works and Communications, attached to the Minister for Public Works, Transport and Communications

Ana Paula VITORINO
Parliamentary Under Secretary of State for Transport

Pedro MARQUES
State Secretary for Social Security

Fernando MEDINA
State Secretary for Employment and Vocational Training

Idália MONIZ
State Secretary for Rehabilitation, attached to the Minister for Labour and Social Solidarity

Francisco RAMOS
State Secretary for Health, attached to the Minister for Health

Manuel PIZARRO
State Secretary for Health

Jorge PEDREIRA
State Secretary for Education, attached to the Minister for Education

Valter LEMOS
State Secretary for Education

Manuel HEITOR
State Secretary for Science, Technology and Higher Education

Paula FERNANDES DOS SANTOS
State Secretary for Culture

ROMANIA

Călin Constantin Anton POPESCU TĂRICEANU
Prime Minister

Lazăr COMĂNESCU
Minister for Foreign Affairs

Teodor MELEŞCANU
Minister for Defence

Varujan VOSGANIAN
Minister for Economic Affairs and Finance

Ludovic ORBAN
Minister for Transport

Karoly BORBELY
Minister for Communications and Information Technology

Cătălin Marian PREDOIU
Minister for Justice

Cristian DAVID
Minister for Internal Affairs and Administrative Reform

Paul PĂCURARU
Minister for Labour, the Family and Equal Opportunities

Eugen NICOLĂESCU
Minister for Public Health

Adrian IORGULESCU
Minister for Culture and Religious Affairs

Cristian ADOMNIŢEI
Minister for Education, Research and Youth

Attila KORODI
Minister for the Environment and Sustainable Development

Dacian CIOLOŞ
Minister for Agriculture and Rural Development

Ovidiu SILAGHI
Minister for Small and Medium-Sized Companies, Trade, Tourism and Liberal Professions

Laszlo BORBELY
Minister for Development, Public Works and Housing

Mihai VOICU
Minister with responsibility for relations with Parliament

Anton NICULESCU
State Secretary for International Affairs and Interinstitutional Relations, Ministry of Foreign Affairs

Răduţa Dana MATACHE
State Secretary for European Affairs

Iulian BUGA
State Secretary for Political Affairs

Mihai GHEORGHIU
Head of the Department for relations with Romanians worldwide, State Secretary

Alexandru Victor MICULA
State Secretary for the organisation of the 2008 NATO summit

Corneliu DOBRIŢOIU
State Secretary and Head of Defence and Planning Policy Department, Ministry of Defence

Georgeta Elisabeta IONESCU
State Secretary and Head of the Department for Relations with Parliament and Public Information

Gheorghe MARIN
Head of the General Staff

Darius MESCA
State Secretary for Energy Policies, Ministry of the Economy and Finance

Viorel PALAŞCĂ
State Secretary for Industrial Policy

Eugen TEODOROVICI
State Secretary for the Treasury and External Public Finances

Doina Elena DASCĂLU
State Secretary for the Budget and Other Monies Levied

Alice BÎTU
State Secretary for the Pre-Accession Fund, Legislative Harmonisation and European Integration

Călin DOICĂ
State Secretary for Relations with Parliament and the Unions

Septimiu BUZASU
State Secretary, Ministry of Transport

Barna TÁNCZOS
State Secretary, Ministry of Transport

Antonel TĂNASE
State Secretary, Ministry of Transport

Zoltan SOMODI
State Secretary, Ministry of Communications and Information Technology

Constantin TEODORESCU
State Secretary, Ministry of Communications and Information Technology

Katalin Barbara KIBEDI
State Secretary, Ministry of Justice

Gheorghe MOCUŢA
State Secretary, Ministry of Justice

Zsuzsanna PETER
State Secretary, Ministry of Justice

Liviu RADU
State Secretary for Public Admininstration Reform

Paul Victor DOBRE
State Secretary for Relations with the Prefectures, Ministry of Internal Affairs and Administrative Reform

Marian PETRACHE
State Secretary for Local Communities

Marin PĂTULEANU
State Secretary for Relations with the Parliament and European Affairs, Ministry of Internal Affairs and Administrative Reform

Vasile-Gabriel NIŢĂ
Chief Police Commissioner, State Secretary, Head of the Schengen Department

Anghel ANDREESCU
Commissioner-General of Police (Chestor general), State Secretary, Head of the Department of Public Order and Safety, Ministry of Administration and Interior

Anghel ANDREESCU
State Secretary, Head of the Public Order and Safety Department, Ministry of Internal Affairs and Administrative Reform

Akos DERZSI
State Secretary with responsibility for the Department for Workforce Strategy and Employment, Ministry of Labour, the Family and Equal Opportunities

Denisa-Oana PĂTRAŞCU
State Secretary with responsibility for the Department for Social Dialogue, Labour Law and Relations with the Parliament, Ministry of Labour, the Family and Equal Opportunities

Valer BINDEA
State Secretary with responsibility for the Department for European Affairs and External Relations, Ministry of Labour, the Family and Equal Opportunities

Theodora BERTZI
State Secretary with responsibility for the Department for Social Affairs and Equal Opportunities, Ministry of Labour, the Family and Equal Opportunities

Ervin Zoltan SZEKELY
State Secretary for Relations with the Parliament, Ministry of Public Health

Vlad ILIESCU
State Secretary for European Integration, Ministry of Public Health

Mircea MĂNUC
State Secretary, Ministry of Public Health

Gigel Sorinel ŞTIRBU
State Secretary, Ministry of Culture and Religious Affairs

Andras Demeter ISTVAN
State Secretary, Ministry of Culture and Religious Affairs

Zvetlana PREOTEASA
State Secretary for Pre-University Education, Ministry of Education, Research and Youth

Remus PRICOPIE
State Secretary for Higher Education, Ministry of Education, Research and Youth

Gabriella PÁZSTOR
State Secretary for Education in Languages of National Minorities and Relations with the Parliament, Ministry of Education, Research and Youth

Lucia VARGA
State Secretary for Water, Ministry of the Environment and Sustainable Development

Silviu STOICA
State Secretary, Ministry of the Environment and Sustainable Development

Gheorghe ALBU
State Secretary for Agriculture, Ministry of Agriculture and Rural Development

István TŐKE
State Secretary for Forestry, Ministry of Agriculture and Rural Development

Cornelia HARABAGIU
State Secretary for SAPARD, Rural Development, Fisheries and Aquaculture, Ministry of Agriculture and Rural Development

Stefan IMRE
State Secretary, Ministry for Small and Medium-Sized Companies, Trade, Tourism and Liberal Professions

Lucia MORARIU
State Secretary, Ministry for Small and Medium-Sized Companies, Trade, Tourism and Liberal Professions

Anna HORVÁTH
State Secretary, Ministry of Development, Public Works and Housing

Horia IRIMIA
State Secretary, Ministry of Development, Public Works and Housing

SLOVENIA

Janez JANŠA
Prime Minister

Andrej BAJUK
Minister for Finance

Andrej VIZJAK
Minister for the Economy

Mojca KUCLER DOLINAR
Minister for Higher Education, Science and Technology

Zofija MAZEJ KUKOVIČ
Minister for Health

Dragutin MATE
Minister for the Interior

Dimitrij RUPEL
Minister for Foreign Affairs

Lovro ŠTURM
Minister for Justice

Gregor VIRANT
Minister for Public Administration

Marjeta COTMAN
Minister for Labour, the Family and Social Affairs

Radovan ŽERJAV
Minister for Transport

Iztok JARC
Minister for Agriculture, Forestry and Food

Janez PODOBNIK
Minister for the Environment and Town and Country Planning

Vasko SIMONITI
Minister for Culture

Milan ZVER
Minister for Education and Sport

Karl Viktor ERJAVEC
Minister for Defence

Ivan ŽAGAR
Minister without portfolio, responsible for local government and regional policy

Žiga TURK
Minister without portfolio responsible for growth

Vinko GORENAK
State Secretary at the Office of the Prime Minister

Anton ROUS
State Secretary at the Office of the Prime Minister

Matjaž ŠINKOVEC
State Secretary at the Office of the Prime Minister

Andrej ŠIRCELJ
State Secretary at the Office of the Prime Minister

Aleksander ZORN
State Secretary at the Office of the Prime Minister

Zorko PELIKAN
State Secretary at the Office of the Prime Minister, Director of the Government Office for Slovenes Abroad

Žiga LAVRIČ
State Secretary at the Ministry of Finance

Tomaž JERŠIČ
State Secretary at the Ministry of the Economy

Dušan LESJAK
State Secretary at the Ministry of Higher Education, Science and Technology

Darko ŽIBERNA
State Secretary at the Ministry of Health

Zvonko ZINRAJH
State Secretary at the Ministry of the Interior

Andrej ŠTER
State Secretary, Ministry of Foreign Affairs

Robert MAROLT
State Secretary at the Ministry of Justice

Roman REP
State Secretary at the Ministry of Public Administration

Marko ŠTROVS
State Secretary at the Ministry of Labour, the Family and Social Affairs

Peter VERLIČ
State Secretary at the Ministry of Transport

Branka TOME
State Secretary at the Ministry of Agriculture, Forestry and Food

Mitja BRICELJ
State Secretary at the Ministry of the Environment and Town and Country Planning

Jelka PIRKOVIČ
State Secretary, Ministry of Culture

Magdalena ŠVERC
State Secretary at the Ministry of Education and Sport

Franci ŽNIDARŠIČ
State Secretary at the Ministry of Defence

Marko STARMAN
State Secretary at the Government Office for Local Government and Regional Policy

Katja LAUTAR
State Secretary at the Government Office for Growth

Barbra BOROTA
State Secretary at the Government Office for European Affairs

SLOVAKIA

Robert FICO
Prime Minister

Dušan ČAPLOVIČ
Deputy Prime Minister for the Knowledge-Based Society, European Affairs, Human Rights and Minorities

Robert KALIŇÁK
Deputy Prime Minister and Minister for the Interior

Ján MIKOLAJ
Deputy Prime Minister and Minister for Education

Štefan HARABIN
Deputy Prime Minister and Minister for Justice

Ľubomír JAHNÁTEK
Minister for the Economy

Ján POČIATEK
Minister for Finance

Ján KUBIŠ
Minister for Foreign Affairs

Jaroslav BAŠKA
Minister for Defence

Marek MAĎARIČ
Minister for Culture

Richard RAŠI
Minister for Health

Zdenka KRAMPLOVÁ
Minister for Agriculture

Ľubomír VÁŽNY
Minister for Transport, Post and Telecommunications

Marián JANUŠEK
Minister for Building and Regional Development

Viera TOMANOVÁ
Minister for Labour, Social Affairs and the Family

Jaroslav IZÁK
Minister for the Environment

František PALKO
State Secretary at the Ministry of Finance

Peter KAŽIMÍR
State Secretary at the Ministry of Finance

Peter ŽIGA
State Secretary at the Ministry for the Economy

Ivan RYBÁRIK
State Secretary at the Ministry of the Economy

Anna VITTEKOVÁ
Parliamentary Under Secretary of State, Ministry of Justice

Daniel HUDÁK
Parliamentary Under Secretary of State, Ministry of Justice

Diana ŠTROFOVÁ
State Secretary at the Ministry of Foreign Affairs

Oľga ALGAYEROVÁ
State Secretary at the Ministry of Foreign Affairs

Ivan SEČÍK
State Secretary at the Ministry of Culture

Augustín Jozef LANG
State Secretary at the Ministry of Culture

Bibiana OBRIMČÁKOVÁ
State Secretary at the Ministry of Education

Jozef HABÁNIK
State Secretary at the Ministry of Education

Vladimír PALŠA
State Secretary at the Ministry of Agriculture

Viliam TURSKÝ
State Secretary at the Ministry of Agriculture

Milan MOJŠ
State Secretary at the Ministry of Transport, Post and Telecommunications

Dušan ŠVANTNER
State Secretary at the Ministry of Transport, Post and Telecommunications

Jaroslav JADUŠ
State Secretary at the Ministry of the Environment

Dušan MUŇKO
State Secretary at the Ministry of the Environment

FINLAND

Matti VANHANEN
Prime Minister

Jyrki KATAINEN
Deputy Prime Minister and Minister for Finance

Alexander STUBB
Minister for Foreign Affairs

Paavo VÄYRYNEN
Minister for Foreign Trade and Development

Tuija BRAX
Minister for Justice

Anne HOLMLUND
Minister for the Interior

Astrid THORS
Minister for Migration and European Affairs

Jyri HÄKÄMIES
Minister for Defence

Mari KIVINIEMI
Minister for Public Administration and Local Government

Henna VIRKKUNEN
Minister for Education

Stefan WALLIN
Minister for Culture and Sport

Sirkka-Liisa ANTTILA
Minister for Agriculture and Forestry

Anu VEHVILÄINEN
Minister for Transport

Suvi LINDÉN
Minister for Communications

Mauri PEKKARINEN
Minister for the Economy

Liisa HYSSÄLÄ
Minister for Social Affairs and Health

Paula RISIKKO
Minister of Health and Social Services

Tarja CRONBERG
Minister for Labour

Paula LEHTOMÄKI
Minister for the Environment

Jan VAPAAVUORI
Minister for Housing

SWEDEN

Fredrik REINFELDT
Prime Minister

Maud OLOFSSON
Deputy Prime Minister and Minister for Enterprise and Energy

Mats ODELL
Minister for Local Government and Financial Markets

Carl BILDT
Minister for Foreign Affairs

Beatrice ASK
Minister for Justice

Cristina HUSMARK PEHRSSON
Minister for Social Security

Lars LEIJONBORG
Minister for Higher Education and Research

Maria LARSSON
Minister for the Elderly and Public Health

Eskil ERLANDSSON
Minister for Agriculture

Åsa TORSTENSSON
Minister for Infrastructure

Andreas CARLGREN
Minister for the Environment

Göran HÄGGLUND
Minister for Welfare

Jan BJÖRKLUND
Minister for Education

Gunilla CARLSSON
Minister for Development Aid

Sven Otto LITTORIN
Minister for Employment

Anders BORG
Minister for Finance

Cecilia MALMSTRÖM
Minister for European Affairs

Nyamko SABUNI
Minister for Integration and Equal Opportunities

Tobias BILLSTRÖM
Minister for Migration

Lena ADELSOHN LILJEROTH
Minister for Culture

Sten TOLGFORS
Minister for Defence

Ewa BJÖRLING
Minister for Trade

Nicola CLASE
State Secretary to the Prime Minister

Hans Gustaf WESSBERG
State Secretary to the Prime Minister

Anna-Karin ALTERÅ
State Secretary, Prime Minister's Office

Helena DYRSSEN
State Secretary, Prime Minister's Office

Jakob FORSSMED
State Secretary, Prime Minister's Office

Mikael SANDSTRÖM
State Secretary, Prime Minister's Office

Håkan JONSSON
State Secretary to the Minister for European Affairs

Christer HALLERBY
State Secretary to the Minister for Integration and Equal Opportunities

Frank BELFRAGE
State Secretary, Ministry of Foreign Affairs

Joakim STYMNE
State Secretary to the Minister for Development Aid

Håkan JEVRELL
State Secretary to the Minister for Defence

Karin JOHANSSON
State Secretary to the Minister for Social Affairs

Bettina KASHEFI
State Secretary to the Minister for Social Security

Johan TIEDEMANN
State Secretary to the Minister for Social Security

Ragnwi MARCELIND
State Secretary to the Minister for Care of the Elderly and Public Health

Per JANSSON
State Secretary to the Minister for Finance

Hans LINDBLAD
State Secretary to the Minister for Finance

Ingemar HANSSON
State Secretary to the Minister for Finance

Peter HONETH
State Secretary to the Minister for Higher Education and Research

Bertil ÖSTBERG
State Secretary to the Minister for Education

Ingrid EIKEN
State Secretary to the Minister for Culture

Rolf ERIKSSON
State Secretary to the Minister for Agriculture

Elisabet FALEMO
State Secretary to the Minister for the Environment

Åsa-Britt KARLSSON
State Secretary to the Minister for the Environment

Ola ALTERÅ
State Secretary to the Minister for Enterprise and Energy

Jöran HÄGGLUND
State Secretary to the Minister for Enterprise and Energy

Leif ZETTERBERG
State Secretary to the Minister for Infrastructure

Eva UDDÉN SONNEGÅRD
State Secretary to the Minister for Employment

Magnus GRANER
State Secretary to the Minister for Justice

Gustaf LIND
State Secretary to the Minister for Migration

Dan ERICSSON
State Secretary to the Minister for Local Government and Financial Markets

UNITED KINGDOM

Gordon BROWN
Prime Minister, First Lord of the Treasury and Minister for the Civil Service

Jack STRAW
Secretary of State for Justice and Lord Chancellor

Alistair DARLING
Chancellor of the Exchequer

Jacqui SMITH
Minister for the Interior

David MILIBAND
Secretary of State for Foreign and Commonwealth Affairs

John HUTTON
Secretary of State for Business, Enterprise and Regulatory Reform

Harriet HARMAN
Leader of the House of Commons (and Lord Privy Seal), Minister for Women and Equality

Ed BALLS
Secretary of State for Children, Schools and Families

Yvette COOPER
Chief Secretary to the Treasury

James PURNELL
Secretary of State for Work and Pensions

Shaun WOODWARD
Secretary of State for Northern Ireland

Paul MURPHY
Secretary of State for Wales

Andy BURNHAM
Secretary of State for Culture, Media and Sport

John DENHAM
Secretary of State for Innovation, Universities and Skills

Des BROWNE
Secretary of State for Defence and Secretary of State for Scotland

Alan JOHNSON
Minister for Health

Ruth KELLY
Minister for Transport

Baroness ROYALL of BLAISDON
Lords Chief Whip and Captain of the Honourable Corps of Gentlemen at Arms

Baroness ASHTON of UPHOLLAND
Leader of the House of Lords and Lord President of the Council

Hilary BENN
Secretary of State for the Environment, Food and Rural Affairs

Ed MILIBAND
Minister for the Cabinet Office (and Chancellor of the Duchy of Lancaster)

Hazel BLEARS
Minister of Communities and Local Government

Douglas ALEXANDER
Secretary of State for International Development

Geoff HOON
Parliamentary Secretary to the Treasury and Chief Whip

Lord ROOKER
Minister of State for Sustainable Food and Farming and Animal Health

Phil WOOLAS
Minister of State for the Environment

Bob AINSWORTH
Minister of State for the Armed Forces

Baroness TAYLOR
Minister of State for Defence Equipment and Support

Jim KNIGHT
Minister of State for Schools and Learners

Beverley HUGHES
Minister of State for Children, Young People and Families and Minister for the North West

Bill RAMMELL
Minister of State for Lifelong Learning, Further and Higher Education

Ian PEARSON
Minister of State for Science and Innovation

Rosie WINTERTON
Minister of State for Transport and Minister for Yorkshire and the Humber

Caroline FLINT
Minister of State for Housing

John HEALEY
Minister of State for Local Government

Stephen TIMMS
Minister of State for Employment and Welfare Reform

Lord JONES
Minister of State for Trade and Investment

Pat McFADDEN
Minister of State for Employment Relations and Postal Affairs

Malcolm WICKS
Minister of State for Energy

Jim MURPHY
Minister of State for Europe

Mark MALLOCH-BROWN
Minister of State for Africa, Asia and the UN

Kim HOWELLS
Minister of State with responsibility for the Middle East

Dawn PRIMAROLO
Minister of State for Public Health

Ben BRADSHAW
Minister of State for Health Services and Minister for the South West

Liam BYRNE
Minister of State for Borders and Immigration and Minister for the West Midlands

Tony McNULTY
Minister of State for Security, Counter-Terrorism, Crime and Policing

Baroness SCOTLAND of ASTHAL
Attorney General

Vera BAIRD
Solicitor General

Paul GOGGINS
Minister of State, Northern Ireland Office

Mike O'BRIEN
Minister of State for Pensions Reform

David HANSON
Minister of State for Justice

Michael WILLS
Minister of State for Justice

Jane KENNEDY
Financial Secretary to the Treasury

Kitty USSHER
Economic Secretary to the Treasury

Margaret HODGE
Minister of State for Culture, Creative Industries and Tourism

David CAIRNS
Minister of State, Scotland Office

Tessa JOWELL
Minister of State for the Olympics and London

Phil HOPE
Parliamentary Secretary, Cabinet Office, and Minister for the East Midlands

Gillian MERRON
Parliamentary Under-Secretary of State, Department of International Development

Shahid MALIK
Parliamentary Under-Secretary of State, Department of International Development

Gareth THOMAS
Parliamentary Under-Secretary of State, Department of International Development

Joan RUDDOCK
Parliamentary Under Secretary of State for Climate Change, Biodiversity and Waste

Jonathan SHAW
Parliamentary Under Secretary of State for Marine, Landscape and Rural Affairs, and Minister for the South East

Derek TWIGG
Parliamentary Under-Secretary of State for Defence and Minister for Veterans

Kevin BRENNAN
Parliamentary Under-Secretary of State for Children, Young People and Families

Lord Andrew ADONIS
Parliamentary Under-Secretary of State for Schools and Learners

David LAMMY
Parliamentary Under-Secretary of State for Skills

Baroness MORGAN
Parliamentary Under-Secretary of State for Intellectual Property and Quality

Tom HARRIS
Parliamentary Under Secretary of State for Transport

Jim FITZPATRICK
Parliamentary Under-Secretary of State, Department of Transport

Baroness ANDREWS
Parliamentary Under-Secretary of State, Department for Communities and Local Government

Iain WRIGHT
Parliamentary Under-Secretary of State, Department for Communities and Local Government

Parmjit DHANDA
Parliamentary Under-Secretary of State, Department for Communities and Local Government

Gareth THOMAS
Parliamentary Under Secretary of State for Trade and Consumer Affairs

Meg MUNN
Parliamentary Under-Secretary of State, Foreign and Commonwealth Office

Lord DARZI
Parliamentary Under-Secretary of State with responsibility for NHS review

Ann KEEN
Parliamentary Under-Secretary of State for Health Services

Ivan LEWIS
Parliamentary Under-Secretary of State for Care Services

Vernon COAKER
Parliamentary Under-Secretary of State for Crime Reduction

ADMIRAL BARON WEST of SPITHEAD, GCB DSC
Parliamentary Under-Secretary of State for Security and Counter-Terrorism

Meg HILLIER
Parliamentary Under-Secretary of State for Identity

Anne McGUIRE
Parliamentary Under-Secretary of State for Disabled People

Lord McKENZIE of LUTON
Parliamentary Under-Secretary of State, Department for Work and Pensions

James PLASKITT
Parliamentary Under-Secretary of State, Department for Work and Pensions

Barbara FOLLETT
Parliamentary Under Secretary of State, Government Equalities Office, and Minister for the East of England

Bridget PRENTICE
Parliamentary Under Secretary of State, Ministry of Justice

Lord HUNT of KINGS HEATH
Parliamentary Under Secretary of State, Ministry of Justice

Maria EAGLE
Parliamentary Under Secretary of State, Ministry of Justice

Gerry SUTCLIFFE
Parliamentary Under-Secretary of State for Sport

Helen GOODMAN
Deputy Leader of the House of Commons

Huw IRRANCA-DAVIES
Parliamentary Under Secretary of State, Wales Office

Baroness VADERA
Parliamentary Under Secretary of State for Business and Competitiveness

Permanent Representatives Committee

The Council is assisted by a committee consisting of Permanent Representatives of the Member States. The Permanent Representatives Committee's task is to prepare the Council's work and to carry out any instructions given to it by the Council.

In order to deal with all the tasks entrusted to it, the Permanent Representatives Committee meets in two parts: Part 1 (Deputy Permanent Representatives) and Part 2 (Ambassadors). Items for examination are divided between the agendas for each part of the Committee.

PART 2 (COREPER II)

HE Mr Jean DE RUYT
Ambassador Extraordinary and Plenipotentiary
Permanent Representative of Belgium
Rue de la Loi 61-63
B-1040 Brussels
E-mail: dispatch.belgoeurop@diplobel.fed.be
Tel. +32 22332111
Fax +32 22311075, 22332165

HE Mr Boyko KOTZEV
Ambassador Extraordinary and Plenipotentiary
Permanent Representative of Bulgaria
Square Marie Louise, 49
B-1000 Brussels
E-mail: Boyko.Kotzev@bg-permrep.eu
Tel. +32 22358300
Fax +32 23749188

HE Mrs Milena VICENOVÁ
Ambassador Extraordinary and Plenipotentiary
Permanent Representative of the Czech Republic
Chairperson of the Permanent Representatives Committee
Rue Caroly 15
B-1050 Brussels
E-mail: eu.brussels@embassy.mzv.cz
Tel. +32 22139111
Fax +32 22139186

HE Mr Claus GRUBE
Ambassador Extraordinary and Plenipotentiary
Permanent Representative of Denmark
Rue d'Arlon 73
B-1040 Brussels
E-mail: brurep@um.dk
Tel. +32 22330811
Fax +32 22309384

HE Mr Edmund DUCKWITZ
Ambassador Extraordinary and Plenipotentiary
Permanent Representative of Germany
Rue Jacques de Lalaing 8-14
B-1040 Brussels
E-mail: info@eu-vertretung.de
Tel. +32 27871000
Fax +32 27872000

HE Mr Raul MÄLK
Ambassador Extraordinary and Plenipotentiary
Permanent Representative of Estonia
Rue Guimard 11/13
B-1040 Brussels
E-mail: permrep.eu@mfa.ee
Tel. +32 22273910
Fax +32 22273925

HE Mr Bobby McDONAGH
Ambassador Extraordinary and Plenipotentiary
Permanent Representative of Ireland
Rue Froissart 89-93
B-1040 Brussels
E-mail: permanentrepresentativesoffice@dfa.ie
Tel. +32 22308580
Fax +32 22303203

HE Mr Vassilis KASKARELIS
Ambassador Extraordinary and Plenipotentiary
Permanent Representative of Greece
Rue Jacques de Lalaing 19-21
B-1040 Brussels
E-mail: mea.bruxelles@rp-grece.be
Tel. +32 25515611
Fax +32 25515651

HE Mr Carlos BASTARRECHE SAGÜES
Ambassador Extraordinary and Plenipotentiary
Permanent Representative of Spain
Boulevard du Régent 52-54
B-1000 Brussels
E-mail: reper.reper@mae.es
Tel. +32 25098611
Fax +32 25111023, 25111940, 25112630

HE Mr Pierre SELLAL
Ambassador Extraordinary and Plenipotentiary
Permanent Representative of France
Place de Louvain 14
B-1000 Brussels
E-mail: courrier.bruxelles-dfra@diplomatie.gouv.fr
Tel. +32 22298211
Fax +32 22298282

HE Mr Ferdinando NELLI FEROCI
Ambassador Extraordinary and Plenipotentiary
Permanent Representative of Italy
Rue du Marteau 7-15
B-1000 Brussels
E-mail: rpue@rpue.esteri.it
Tel. +32 22200411
Fax +32 22193449, 22200426

HE Mr Andreas MAVROYIANNIS
Ambassador Extraordinary and Plenipotentiary
Permanent Representative of Cyprus
Avenue de Cortenbergh 61
B-1000 Brussels
E-mail: cy.perm.rep@mfa.gov.cy
Tel. +32 27395111
Fax +32 27354552

HE Mr Normunds POPENS
Ambassador Extraordinary and Plenipotentiary
Permanent Representative of Latvia
Avenue des Arts 23
B-1000 Brussels
E-mail: permrep.eu@mfa.gov.lv
Tel. +32 22383100
Fax +32 22383250

HE Mr Rytis MARTIKONIS
Ambassador Extraordinary and Plenipotentiary
Permanent Representative of Lithuania
Rue Belliard 41-43
B-1040 Brussels
E-mail: office@eurep.mfa.lt
Tel. +32 27710140
Fax +32 27714597

HE Mr Christian BRAUN
Ambassador Extraordinary and Plenipotentiary
Permanent Representative of Luxembourg
Avenue de Cortenbergh 75
B-1000 Brussels
E-mail: secretariat@rpue.etat.lu
Tel. +32 27352060, 27375600
Fax +32 27361429, 27375610

Tibor KISS
Ambassador Extraordinary and Plenipotentiary
Permanent Representative of Hungary
Rue de Trèves 92-98
B-1040 Brussels
E-mail: sec.beu@kum.hu
Tel. +32 22341200
Fax +32 22340784

HE Mr Richard CACHIA CARUANA
Ambassador Extraordinary and Plenipotentiary
Permanent Representative of Malta
Rue Archimède 25
B-1000 Brussels
E-mail: maltarep@gov.mt
Tel. +32 23430195
Fax +32 23430106

HE Mr T.J.A.M. DE BRUIJN
Ambassador Extraordinary and Plenipotentiary
Permanent Representative of the Netherlands
Avenue Hermann Debroux 48
B-1160 Brussels
E-mail: bre@minbuza.nl
Tel. +32 26791511
Fax +32 26791795

HE Mr Hans Dietmar SCHWEISGUT
Ambassador Extraordinary and Plenipotentiary
Permanent Representative of Austria
Avenue de Cortenbergh 30
B-1040 Brussels
E-mail: bruessel-ov@bmeia.gv.at
Tel. +32 22345100
Fax +32 22345300

HE Mr Jan TOMBIŃSKI
Ambassador Extraordinary and Plenipotentiary
Permanent Representative of Poland
Avenue de Tervuren 282-284
B-1150 Brussels
E-mail: mail@plrep.eu
Tel. +32 27777220ou7777224
Fax +32 27777297ou7777298

HE Mr Manuel LOBO ANTUNES
Ambassador Extraordinary and Plenipotentiary
Permanent Representative of Portugal
Avenue de Cortenbergh 12
B-1040 Brussels
E-mail: reper@reper-portugal.be
Tel. +32 22864211
Fax +32 22310026

HE Mr Mihnea MOTOC
Ambassador Extraordinary and Plenipotentiary
Permanent Representative of Romania
Rue Montoyer 12
B-1000 Brussels
E-mail: bru@rpro.eu
Tel. +32 27000640
Fax +32 27000641

HE Mr Igor SENČAR
Ambassador Extraordinary and Plenipotentiary
Permanent Representative of Slovenia
Rue du Commerce 44
B-1000 Brussels
E-mail: spbr@gov.si
Tel. +32 22136300
Fax +32 22136301

HE Mr Maroš ŠEFČOVIČ
Ambassador Extraordinary and Plenipotentiary
Permanent Representative of Slovakia
Avenue de Cortenbergh 79
B-1000 Brussels
E-mail: slovakmission@pmsreu.be
Tel. +32 27436811
Fax +32 27436888

HE Mr Jan STORE
Ambassador Extraordinary and Plenipotentiary
Permanent Representative of Finland
Rue de Trèves 100
B-1040 Brussels
E-mail: firstname.lastname@formin.fi
Tel. +32 22878411
Fax +32 22878400

HE Mr Christian DANIELSSON
Ambassador Extraordinary and Plenipotentiary
Permanent Representative of Sweden
Square de Meeûs 30
B-1000 Brussels
E-mail: christian.danielsson@foreign.ministry.se
Tel. +32 22895611
Fax +32 22895600

HE Mr Kim DARROCH
Ambassador Extraordinary and Plenipotentiary
Permanent Representative of the United Kingdom
Avenue d'Auderghem 10
B-1040 Brussels
E-mail: ukrep@fco.gov.uk
Tel. +32 22878211
Fax +32 22878398

PART 1 (COREPER I)

HE Mr Didier SEEUWS
Deputy Permanent Representative of Belgium
Rue de la Loi 61-63
B-1040 Brussels
Belgique
E-mail: dispatch.belgoeurop@diplobel.fed.be
Tel. +32 22332111
Fax +32 22311075
Fax +32 22332165

HE Mr Mario MILOUCHEV
Ambassador
Deputy Permanent Representative of Bulgaria
Square Marie Louise 49
B-1000 Brussels
E-mail: Mario.Milouchev@bg-permrep.eu
Tel. +32 22358300
Fax +32 23749188

HE Mrs Jana REINIŠOVÁ
Minister Counsellor
Deputy Permanent Representative of the Czech Republic
Chairman of the Permanent Representatives Committee Part 1
Rue Caroly 15
B-1050 Brussels
E-mail: eu.brussels@embassy.mzv.cz
Tel. +32 22139111
Fax +32 22139186

HE Mr Jens KISLING
Ambassador
Deputy Permanent Representative of Denmark
Rue d'Arlon 73
B-1040 Brussels
E-mail: brurep@um.dk
Tel. +32 22330811
Fax +32 22309384

HE Mr Guido PERUZZO
Ambassador
Deputy Permanent Representative of Germany
Rue Jacques de Lalaing 8-14
B-1040 Brussels
E-mail: info@eu-vertretung.de
Tel. +32 27871000
Fax +32 27872000

HE Mr Gert ANTSU
Deputy Permanent Representative of Estonia
Rue Guimard 11/13
B-1040 Brussels
E-mail: permrep.eu@mfa.ee
Tel. +32 22273910
Fax +32 22273925

HE Mrs Geraldine BYRNE NASON
Ambassador
Deputy Permanent Representative of Ireland
Rue Froissart 89-93
B-1040 Brussels
E-mail: irlprb@dfa.ie
Tel. +32 22308580
Fax +32 22303203

HE Mr Leonidas C. ROKANAS
Minister Plenipotentiary
Deputy Permanent Representative of Greece
Rue Jacques de Lalaing 19-21
B-1040 Brussels
E-mail: mea.bruxelles@rp-grece.be
Tel. +32 25515611
Fax +32 25515651

HE Mr Cristóbal GONZÁLEZ-ALLER JURADO
Ambassador
Deputy Permanent Representative of Spain
Boulevard du Régent 52-54
B-1000 Brussels
E-mail: reper.reper@mae.es
Tel. +32 25098611
Fax +32 25111023, 25111940, 25112630

HE Mr Philippe LEGLISE-COSTA
Deputy Permanent Representative of France
Place de Louvain 14
B-1000 Brussels
E-mail: courrier.bruxelles-dfra@diplomatie.gouv.fr
Tel. +32 22298211
Fax +32 22298282

HE Mr Vincenzo GRASSI
Minister Plenipotentiary
Deputy Permanent Representative of Italy
Rue du Marteau 7-15
B-1000 Brussels
E-mail: rpue@rpue.esteri.it
Tel. +32 22200411
Fax +32 22193449, 22200426

HE Mr George CHACALLI
Minister Plenipotentiary
Deputy Permanent Representative of Cyprus
Avenue de Cortenbergh 61
B-1000 Brussels
E-mail: cy.perm.rep@mfa.gov.cy
Tel. +32 27395102
Fax +32 27354552

HE Mrs Lelde LICE-LICITE
Ambassador
Deputy Permanent Representative of Latvia
Avenue des Arts 23
B-1000 Brussels
E-mail: permrep.eu@mfa.gov.lv
Tel. +32 22383100
Fax +32 22383250

HE Mr Raimundas KAROBLIS
Ambassador-at-large
Deputy Permanent Representative of Lithuania
Rue Belliard 41-43
B-1040 Brussels
E-mail: office@eurep.mfa.lt
Tel. +32 27710140
Fax +32 27714597

HE Mrs Michèle EISENBARTH
Deputy Permanent Representative of Luxembourg
Avenue de Cortenbergh 75
B-1000 Brussels
E-mail: secretariat@rpue.etat.lu
Tel. +32 27352060, 27375600
Fax +32 27361429, 27375610

HE Mrs Ágnes VARGHA
Ambassador
Deputy Permanent Representative of Hungary
Rue de Trèves 92-98
B-1040 Brussels
E-mail: deputy.beu@kum.hu
Tel. +32 22341200
Fax +32 22340784

HE Mrs Theresa CUTAJAR
Deputy Permanent Representative of Malta
Rue Archimède 25
B-1000 Brussels
E-mail: maltarep@gov.mt
Tel. +32 23430195
Fax +32 23430106

HE Mr Peter W. KOK
Minister Plenipotentiary
Deputy Permanent Representative of the Netherlands
Avenue Hermann Debroux 48
B-1160 Brussels
E-mail: bre@minbuza.nl
Tel. +32 26791511
Fax +32 26791774

HE Mr Walter GRAHAMMER
Minister
Deputy Permanent Representative of Austria
Avenue de Cortenbergh 30
B-1040 Brussels
E-mail: bruessel-ov@bmeia.gv.at
Tel. +32 22345122
Fax +32 22356122

HE Mrs Karolina OSTRZYNIEWSKA
Minister Counsellor
Deputy Permanent Representative of Poland
Avenue de Tervueren 282-284
B-1150 Brussels
E-mail: mail@plrep.eu
Tel. +32 27777266, 7777200
Fax +32 27777297, 7777298

HE Mrs Ana Paula ZACARIAS
Deputy Permanent Representative of Portugal
Avenue de Cortenbergh 12
B-1040 Brussels
E-mail: reper@reper-portugal.be
Tel. +32 22864211
Fax +32 22310026

HE Mr Marius HIRTE
Minister Counsellor
Deputy Permanent Representative of Romania
Rue Montoyer 12
B-1000 Brussels
E-mail: bru@rpro.eu
Tel. +32 27000640
Fax +32 27000641

HE Mrs Mary Veronika TOVŠAK PLETERSKI
Minister Plenipotentiary
Deputy Permanent Representative of Slovenia
Rue du Commerce 44
B-1000 Brussels
E-mail: spbr@gov.si
Tel. +32 22136300
Fax +32 22136301

HE Mr Peter JAVORČIK
Counsellor
Deputy Permanent Representative of Slovakia
Avenue de Cortenbergh 79
B-1000 Brussels
E-mail: slovakmission@pmsreu.be
Tel. +32 27436811
Fax +32 27436888

HE Mrs Marja RISLAKKI
Minister
Deputy Permanent Representative of Finland
Rue de Trèves 100
B-1040 Brussels
E-mail: firstname.lastname@formin.fi
Tel. +32 22878411
Fax +32 22878400

HE Mrs Ulrika BARKLUND LARSSON
Minister Plenipotentiary
Deputy Permanent Representative of Sweden
Square de Meeûs 30
B-1000 Brussels
E-mail: ulrika.barklund-larsson@foreign.ministry.se
Tel. +32 22895611
Fax +32 22895600

HE Mr Andrew LEBRECHT
Deputy Permanent Representative of the United Kingdom
Avenue d'Auderghem 10
B-1040 Brussels
E-mail: ukrep@fco.gov.uk
Tel. +32 22878211
Fax +32 22878398

Permanent Representations

PERMANENT REPRESENTATION OF BELGIUM

Rue de la Loi 61-63
B-1040 Brussels
E-mail: dispatch.belgoeurop@diplobel.fed.be
Tel. +32 22332111
Fax +32 22311075, 22332165

HE Mr Jean DE RUYT
Ambassador Extraordinary and Plenipotentiary
Permanent Representative

Mrs Sheila ARORA

HE Mr Didier SEEUWS
Deputy Permanent Representative

Permanent Representation to the European Union, Belgian delegation to the PSC

HE Mr Dirk WOUTERS
Ambassador
Permanent Representative

Mrs WOUTERS

Mr Koen DASSEN
Minister Counsellor

Mrs RAUTER

Mr Alexis DE CROMBRUGGHE DE PICQUENDAELE
First Secretary

Mrs DE CROMBRUGGHE DE PICQUENDAELE

Mr Bert VERSMESSEN
Politico-Military Counsellor

Mrs Marie GEUKENS

Mr Peter VERBRUGGHE
Attaché

Mr Charles-Henri DELCOUR
Lieutenant General
Military Representative

Mrs DELCOUR

Mr Bertrand HAYEZ
Colonel
Deputy Military Representative

Mrs HAYEZ

Mr Karel VAN MULDERS
Colonel

Mrs VAN MULDERS

Mr Luc CAMELBEKE
Lieutenant Colonel, Aviation

Mr Philippe SURKIJN
Lieutenant Colonel

Mr Pierre TRUILLET
Major

Mrs TRUILLET

Mr Guido DEPOORTER
Senior Captain

Federal public service 'Foreign Affairs, External Trade and Development Cooperation'

Mr Ivo SCHALBROECK
Counsellor

Mrs Greet RAL

Mrs Véronique PETIT
First Secretary

Mr Jean Luc RONGE

Mrs Maria-Antoinetta SIMONS
First Secretary

Mr Alexander KLEINBART

Mr Frank ARNAUTS
First Secretary

Mrs Linda HOEBEN

Mr Peter VAN KEMSEKE
First Embassy Secretary (Coreper I– Mertens)

Mr Damien ANGELET
First Secretary

Mrs Yuri ANGELET-KASE

Mr Olivier QUINAUX
First Secretary

Mr Frank DUHAMEL
Secretary

Mrs Annelies WATTÉ

Mr Luc TRUYENS
Secretary

Mr Bernard QUINTIN
Secretary (Coreper II - Antici)

Mr Stijn MOLS
Secretary

Mrs RENAP MOLS

Mr Hubert ROISIN
Counsellor

Mr Michel VERSAILLES
Counsellor

Mrs Delphine COLARD
Attaché

Mr Michel VRYDAG

Mr Guy RAYEE
Attaché (cooperation and development)

Mrs Karima SAQUI
Attaché (cooperation and development)

Mr Philippe FABRY
ICT Coordinator

Mrs FABRY

Federal public service 'Economy, Small and Medium-Sized Businesses, the Liberal Professions, the Self-Employed and Energy'

Mr Eric VAN DEN ABEELE
Adviser

Mrs VAN DEN ABEELE

Mrs Françoise DE VLEESCHOUWER
Counsellor

Mr HELLINGS

Mr Patrick LAMOT
Counsellor

Mrs LAMOT

Federal public service 'Employment, Labour and Social Dialogue'

Mrs Annemie PERNOT
Counsellor

Mr RENARD

Miss Thérèse BOUTSEN
Adviser

Federal public service 'Social Security'

Mrs Muriel RABAU
Counsellor (social affairs)

Federal public service 'Public Health, Safety of the Food Chain and Environment'

Mrs Marleen STEENBRUGGHE
Counsellor

Mr VERSTRAETE

Mr Denis VAN EECKHOUT
Adviser

Federal Agency for the Safety of the Food Chain

Mr Herman CLAEYS
Veterinary Council

Federal public service 'finance'

Mr Marc VANDENBORRE
Director-General

Mr Pierre VERKAEREN
Inspector-General for Finance

Mrs VERKAEREN

Mr Steven COSTERS
Counsellor

Mr Jean-Marc WILLEMS
First Attaché

Mrs WILLEMS

National Bank of Belgium

Mr Aimery CLERBAUX

Mr Geert TEMMERMAN
Counsellor

Mrs Danielle TEMMERMAN HENDRICKX

Federal public service 'Mobility and Transport'

Mr Jean-Marie NEVENS
Counsellor

Mrs NEVENS

Mrs Nathalie GENDARME
Counsellor

Federal public service 'The Interior'

Mrs Isabelle RAES
Counsellor

Aliens Office

Mr Stijn DE DECKER
Counsellor (Aliens Office)

Federal police

Mr Jacques VAN BELLE
Counsellor (police cooperation and civil protection)

Mrs VAN BELLE

Federal public service 'Justice'

Mrs Irène LAMBRETH
Adviser

Mr Serge DE BIOLLEY
Counsellor

French-speaking Community of the Belgium/Walloon Region

Mr Thierry DELAVAL
General delegate of the Walloon Region and the French Community

Mrs Isabelle PAPY
Legal Adviser (multilingualism)

Mrs Fabienne THIRION
Counsellor

Mr WATTEYNE

Mr Eric POPPE
Attaché

Mr Luc HEYNEMAN
Attaché

Mrs Joëlle BASTIN
Attaché

Mrs Véronique PATTE
Attaché

Mr David ROYAUX
Attaché

Wallonia Business Bureau and Export Office

Mrs Chantal LEONARD

Mrs Milena GVOZDEN

Flemish Community/Region

Mr Axel BUYSE
Representative of the Flemish Government

Mrs Inge MOORS
Attaché

Mr Dries WILLEMS
Attaché

Mrs Marjan DECROOS
Attaché

Mr Christophe LECHAT
Attaché

Mr Jan DE MULDER
Attaché

Mr Kristof GEUTJENS
Attaché

Miss Jelle REYNAERT
Attaché

Mrs Nele HAEGEMANS
Attaché

Mr Frederic GEERS
Attaché

Mr Bart LAETHEM
Attaché

Mr Karel BOUTENS
Attaché

Mrs Jill EVERAERDT
Attaché

Mr Jan VANHEE
Attaché

German-speaking Community

Mr Xavier KALBUSCH
Delegate

Brussels Region

Mr Pascal GOERGEN
Representative

Mr Bernd SCHNEIDER
Economic Counsellor

Mr Henk VAN NOTEN
Attaché

PERMANENT REPRESENTATION OF BULGARIA

Square Marie-Louise 49
B-1000 Brussels
E-mail: info@bg-permrep.eu
Website: http://www.bg permrep.eu
Tel. +32 22358300
Fax +32 23749188

HE Mr Boyko KOTZEV
Ambassador Extraordinary and Plenipotentiary
Permanent Representative
E-mail: Boyko.Kotzev@bg-permrep.eu

Mrs Ganka KOTZEVA

HE Mr Mario MILOUCHEV
Ambassador
Deputy Permanent Representative
E-mail: Mario.Milouchev@bg-permrep.eu

Mrs Amélia MILOUCHEVA

HE Mr Vesselin VALKANOV
Ambassador representative to the EU political and security committee (PSC)
E-mail: Vesselin.Valkanov@bg-permrep.eu

Mrs Hermina VALKANOV

Coordination

Mr Rumen ALEXANDROV
First Secretary (Antici, general coordination — Coreper II, institutional affairs)
E-mail: Rumen.Alexandrov@bg-permrep.eu

Mr Boyan HADJIEV
Second Secretary (Mertens, general coordination — Coreper I)
E-mail: Boyan.Hadjiev@bg-permrep.eu

Mrs Roumiana EVTIMOVA

Mrs Adelina TOMOVA-LIHOVA
Technical assistant Coreper II
E-mail: Adelina.Tomova@bg-permrep.eu

Mr Teodor LIHOV

Mr Dorian TODOROV
Attaché (assistant COPS, Coreu)
E-mail: Dorian.Todorov@bg-permrep.eu

Mrs Galina SPASSOVA
Technical assistant Coreper I
E-mail: Galina.Spassova@bg-permrep.eu

Mrs Doroteya GEORGIEVA
Technical assistant Coreper I
E-mail: Dorotheya.Georgieva@bg-permrep.eu

Press and information

Mrs Betina JOTEVA
First Secretary (spokesperson, press and information, public relations)
E-mail: Betina.Joteva@bg-permrep.eu

Legal and institutional affairs

Mrs Albena PEEVA
Third Secretary (human rights, legal and institutional affairs, legislative codification, Court of Justice)
E-mail: albena.peeva@bg-permrep.eu

Administrative matters and protocol, accounts office

Mr Andrei VLAHOV
Second Secretary (adminstrative affairs and protocol, consular affairs)
E-mail: Andrei.Vlahov@bg-permrep.eu

Mrs Irena VLAHOVA

Mrs Bonka BOJILOVA
Accountant

Common foreign and security policy, development

Mr Emil KAZAKOV
Counsellor (RELEX)
E-mail: Emil.Kazakov@bg-permrep.eu

Mrs Daniela KAZAKOVA

Mr Traiko SPASOV
Counsellor (Western Balkans region, OSCE)
E-mail: Traiko.Spasov@bg-permrep.eu

Mrs Katri TEEDUMÄE

Mrs Diana DZHAMBAZOVA
Third Secretary (Middle East, Mashrak/Maghreb, Gulf)
E-mail: Diana.Dzhambazova@bg-permrep.eu

Mr Kiril DZHAMBAZOV

Mrs Nina SIMOVA
First Secretary (COEST, COLAT, Eastern Europe and Central Asia, Black Sea Economic Cooperation (BSEC)
E-mail: Nina.Simova@bg-permrep.eu

Miss ALEXANDRA POPOVA
Third Secretary (development, humanitary aid, ACT, CONUN)
E-mail: Alexandra.Popova@bg-permrep.eu

Mrs Vessela DIKOVA-KUMANOVA
First Secretary (Asia/Oceania, ASEAN, EU staff policy)
E-mail: Vessela.Dikova@bg-permrep.eu

Miss Ralitza YOTOVA
Third Secretary (enlargement, cooperation and verification mechanism, infringements correspondent)
E-mail: Ralitza.Yotova@bg-permrep.eu

European security and defence policy

Mrs Gergana KARADJOVA
First Secretary (Nicolaïdis Group, transatlantic relations)
E-mail: Gergana.Karadjova@bg-permrep.eu

Mr Ilian KARADJOV

Mrs Diana DZHAMBAZOVA
Third Secretary (disarmament, non-proliferation and arms control)
E-mail: Diana.Dzhambazova@bg-permrep.eu

Mr Kiril DZHAMBAZOV

Mrs Margarita NIKOLOVA-IVANOVA
Attaché (civilian crisis management, COAFR, PMG)
E-mail: Margarita.Nikolova@bg-permrep.eu

Mr Hristo IVANOV

Mr Anri GEORGIEV
Colonel
Politico-military Group
E-mail: Anri.Georgiev@bg-permrep.eu

Mrs Marieta GEORGIEVA

Mrs Teodora GENCHOVSKA
First Secretary (Politico-Military Group)
E-mail: Teodora.Genchovska@bg-permrep.eu

Mr Evgeni GENCHOVSKI

Mrs Nevjana NEKOVA
Technical Assistant
(Military Representation and Politico-Military Group)
E-mail: Nevjana.Nekova@bg-permrep.eu

Military Committee

Mr Atanas ZAPRIANOV
Lieutenant General
Military representative to the EU Military Committee.
E-mail: azaprianov@bg-nato.be

Mr Todor SERTOV
Colonel
Deputy Military Representative to the EU Military Committee
E-mail: Todor.Sertov@bg-permrep.eu

Mrs Nadezhda SERTOVA

Mr Petar TSOLOV
Lieutenant Colonel
Military Working Group (EUMC)
E-mail: Petar.Tsolov@bg-permrep.eu

Mrs Elena TSOLOVA

Mr Ivan VARBANOV
Lieutenant Colonel
Military Working Group (EUMC)
E-mail: Ivan.Varbanov@bg-permrep.eu

Mrs Radka VARBANOVA

Trade policy

Mr Boyan NATAN
Minister plenipotentiary
(Head of Unit, Article 133 Committee full/alternate members, experts/services, experts/steel, trade policy/anti-dumping, EFTA)
E-mail: Boyan.Natan@bg-permrep.eu

Mrs Margarita YOTSOVA
Adviser (ACP, GSP, export credits, commodities)
E-mail: Margarita.Yotsova@bg-permrep.eu

Miss Rossitza VASSILEVA
First Secretary (Article 133 Committee experts/textiles, trade policy)
E-mail: Rossitza.Vassileva@bg-permrep.eu

Mrs Maria MIRAZCHIYSKA
Second Secretary (Article 133 Committee experts/motor vehicles, mutual recognition)
E-mail: Maria.Mirazchiyska@bg-permrep.eu

Mr Ivaylo DOSEV

Mr Vassil ZHIVKOV
Third Secretary (taxation, customs matters)
E-mail: Vassil.Zhivkov@bg-permrep.eu

Financial, economic and monetary policies

Mrs Mariana VALEVA-HRISTCHEVA
Minister Plenipotentiary (Head of Unit, Ecofin, Economic and Financial Committee, economic and monetary questions)
E-mail: Mariana.Hristcheva@bg-permrep.eu

Mr Vassil HRISTCHEV

Mrs Daniela SHAPTCHEVA
Adviser (Structural Funds, Cohesion Fund)
E-mail: Daniela.Shaptcheva@bg-permrep.eu

Mr Ivo SHAPTCHEV

Mrs Iren ROUSINOVA-DIMITROVA
Counsellor (budget, financial control)
E-mail: Iren.Rusinova@bg-permrep.eu

Mr Emil DIMITROV

Mrs Denitza DESSIMIROVA
Second Secretary (financial services, insurance and services)
E-mail: Denitza.Dessimirova@bg-permrep.eu

Mrs Yordanka CHOBANOVA
Attaché (regional policy)
E-mail: Yordanka.Chobanova@bg-permrep.eu

Mr HVYRCHILKOV

Justice and home affairs

Mr Petar RASHKOV
Adviser (justice and judicial reform, judicial cooperation in criminal matters)
E-mail: Petar.Rashkov@bg-permrep.eu

Mrs Aneliya IVANCHEVA
Adviser (home affairs, terrorism, drugs, Schengen, police cooperation, fight against fraud and organised crime, OLAF, Europol)
E-mail: Aneliya.Ivancheva@bg-permrep.eu

Mr Aleksandar IVANCHEV

Mrs Valentina TASKOVA
Adviser (visas, consular affairs, Schengen, terrorism — international aspects)
E-mail: Valentina.Taskova@bg-permrep.eu

Mrs Aneliya STEFANOVA
First Secretary (asylum, migration, frontiers, civil protection, data protection, Security Committee (Infosec, GNSS, SAPs), Frontex Agency)
E-mail: Anelya.Stefanova@bg-permrep.eu

Mr Stefan STEFANOV

Mr Plamen ANGELOV
First Secretary (Schengen, migration, borders, asylum)

Mr Iovko TSARKOV
Minister Plenipotentiary (Security Committee/INFOSEC, GNSS, SAPs)
E-mail: Iovko.Tsarkov@bg-permrep.eu

Miss Arnel YAHOVA
Third Secretary (civil protection)
E-mail: Arnel.Yahova@bg-permrep.eu

Mr Dimiter TZVETANOV
First Secretary (judicial cooperation on civil matters, company law, intellectual property)
E-mail: Dimiter.Tzvetanov@bg-permrep.eu

Miss Milena PETKOVA
First Secretary (judicial cooperation on civil matters, company law, intellectual property)
E-mail: Milena.Petkova@bg-permrep.eu

Competitiveness (internal market, industry)

Mr Boyan NATAN
Minister plenipotentiary (Head of Unit)
E-mail: Boyan.Natan@bg-permrep.eu

Miss Rossitza VASSILEVA
First Secretary (competitiveness, consumer protection)
E-mail: Rossitza.Vassileva@bg-permrep.eu

Mrs Maria MIRAZCHIYSKA
Second Secretary (technical harmonisation, foodstuffs, chemicals)
E-mail: Maria.Mirazchiyska@bg-permrep.eu

Mr Ivaylo DOSEV

Mrs Lyubomira NESHEVA
Second Secretary (public procurement, competition, statistics, pharmaceuticals and medical devices, standardisation, sustainable development)
E-mail: Lyubomira.Nesheva@bg-permrep.eu

Agriculture and fisheries

Mrs Charlina VITCHEVA
Minister Plenipotentiary (Head of Unit, agriculture, fisheries and food security)
Representative to the Special Committee on Agriculture, CAP
E-mail: Charlina.Vitcheva@bg-permrep.eu

Mr Krassimir VITCHEV

Mrs Neli GEORGIEVA
Counsellor (agriculture, CAP)
E-mail: Neli.Georgieva@bg-permrep.eu

Mr Valentin MIHAYLOV

Mrs Teodora PETKOVA
Adviser (food security, veterinary and phytosanitary matters)
E-mail: Teodora.Petkova@bg-permrep.eu

Mrs Margarita MIHAYLOVA
Counsellor (fisheries, CAP — arable crops)
E-mail: Margarita.Mihaylova@bg-permrep.eu

Mr Mihail MIHAYLOV

Mrs Petia MONEVSKA
Second Secretary (Coreper I coordination — agriculture and food security)
E-mail: Petia.Monevska@bg-permrep.eu

Energy

Miss Diana IVANOVA
Adviser (conventional energy)
E-mail: Diana.Ivanova@bg-permrep.eu

Mrs Krasimira PISHTUHINA
Counsellor (nuclear questions)
E-mail: Krasimira.Pishtuhina@bg-permrep.eu

Mr Vasily PISHCHUKHIN

Transport and communications

Mrs Anna KARDZHIEVA
Counsellor (Head of Unit, sea transport, inland waterways)
E-mail: Anna.Kardzhieva@bg-permrep.eu

Mr Ivan TZOLOV

Mrs Lyudmila TRENKOVA
Counsellor (transport - intermodal questions and networks, rail transport, horizontal questions)
E-mail: Lyudmila.Trenkova@bg-permrep.eu

Mrs Elitza STOYANOVA-PODVARZACHOVA
First Secretary (rail transport, aviation, Eurocontrol, ICAO)
E-mail: Elitza.Stoyanova@bg-permrep.eu

Mr Zdravko PODVARZACHOV

Mr Myuren MUSTAFOV
Second Secretary (rail transport, TEN-T Programmes, operational programme 2007–13)
E-mail: Myuren.Mustafov@bg-permrep.eu

Mrs Yoanna BORISOVA-MUSTAFOVA

Telecommunications

Mrs Iskra BONEVA
Adviser (telecommunications, information society, postal services)
E-mail: Iskra.Boneva@bg-permrep.eu

Mr Lachezar TSONEV

Environment

Mrs Svetlana ZHEKOVA
First Secretary (environment)
E-mail: Svetlana.Zhekova@bg-permrep.eu

Mr Svetlozar ZHEKOV

Mrs Tzonka DRYANKOVA
Third Secretary (environment)
E-mail: Tzonka.Dryankova@bg-permrep.eu

Employment, social policy, health and consumer affairs

Mr Alexander EVTIMOV
Counsellor (social policy and employment, European Economic and Social Committee (EESC))
E-mail: Alexander.Evtimov@bg-permrep.eu

Mrs Elvira EVTIMOVA

Mr Trifon NESHKOV
Second Secretary (public health, pharmaceuticals and medical devices, drugs)
E-mail: Trifon.Neshkov@bg-permrep.eu

Mrs Violeta NESHKOVA

Mrs Rossitza VASSILEVA
First Secretary (consumer protection)
E-mail: Rossitza.Vassileva@bg-permrep.eu

Miss Rozalina PETROVA
Third Secretary (free movement of persons)
E-mail: Rozalina.Petrova@bg-permrep.eu

Education, research, youth and culture

Mrs Stefanka HRISTOSKOVA-GUENOVA
First Secretary (education)
E-mail: Stefanka.Hristoskova@bg-permrep.eu

Mr Latchezar GUENOV

Mrs Demetra DULEVA
First Secretary (research)
E-mail: Demetra.Duleva@bg-permrep.eu

Mr Tsanko DULEV

Mrs Iveta DIMOVA
First Secretary (culture, audiovisual matters, intellectual and industrial property rights)
E-mail: Iveta.Dimova@bg-permrep.eu

PERMANENT REPRESENTATION OF THE CZECH REPUBLIC

Rue Caroly 15
B-1050 Brussels
E-mail: eu.brussels@embassy.mzv.cz
Website: http://www.czechrep.be
Tel. +32 22139111
Fax +32 22139186

HE Mrs Milena VICENOVÁ
Ambassador Extraordinary and Plenipotentiary
Permanent Representative

HE Mrs Jana REINIŠOVÁ
Minister Counsellor
Deputy Permanent Representative

HE Mr Ivo ŠRÁMEK
Ambassador
Representative to the Political and Security Committee

Mr Zdeněk LAŠTOVKA
Minister Counsellor
Head of administration, EU personnel policy, SNEs

Coordination and information

Mrs Andrea HYNIOVÁ
Second Secretary (Antici, general coordination - Coreper II)

Mr Jiří ŠURMAN
Third Secretary (Antici deputy, general coordination, Coreper II)

Mrs Radka BORDES
Third Secretary
Coordinator, Czech Presidency

Mr Michal PONIK
Attaché
Coordinator, Czech Presidency

Mr Jiří KOLDA
Attaché
Coordinator, Czech Presidency

Press service

Mr Jan VYTOPIL
Adviser (spokesperson, press and information, transparency, public relations)

Mrs Alice MŽYKOVÁ
First Secretary (public relations)

Mr Jan SLÍVA
Third Secretary (spokesperson, Coreper II)

Mr Radek HONZÁK
Third Secretary (spokesperson, Coreper I)

Mr Jiří ŠEBEK
Third Secretary (communication with the media)

Private Office of the Deputy Permanent Representative

Mr Richard KADLČÁK
Head of Private Office
Second Secretary (Mertens, general coordination, Coreper I)

Mrs Radana KRULIŠOVÁ
Second Secretary (private secretary, Deputy Permanent Represerntive)

Mrs Alena TEZNEROVÁ
Third Secretary (Mertens deputy, general coordination, Coreper I)

Institutional and legal affairs, European Parliament, general affairs

Mr Václav KOLAJA
Second Secretary (Head of Unit, relations with the European Parliament, general affairs)

Mrs Olga HOŘICKÁ
Third Secretary (relations with the European Parliament, general affairs)

Mr Zdeněk PETZL
Third Secretary (relations with the European Parliament, general affairs)

Mr Michal JIRÁČEK
Third Secretary (relations with the European Parliament, general affairs)

Enlargement

Mrs Irena OBER LEICMANOVÁ
Second Secretary (Enlargement)

Mr Marek GAJDOŠ
Attaché
National delegate

Legal affairs

Mrs Jana KRESTÝNOVÁ
Third Secretary
Legal Counsel (EU external relations, public international law)

Mrs Markéta ŠTĚRBOVÁ
Third Secretary
Legal Counsel (Coreper II, Lisbon Treaty)

Mr David HADROUŠEK
Third Secretary
Legal Counsel (Coreper I, committee procedure, infringements)

Mrs Eva MARTINICOVÁ
Third Secretary
Legal Counsel (Coreper I, committee procedure)

Human rights

Mrs Karolína CVEKLOVÁ
Third Secretary

Protocol

Mrs Jana ŠIKULOVÁ
Third Secretary
(Diplomatic protocol)

Trade

Mrs Dita CHARANZOVÁ
Third Secretary (Head of trade policy section, Article 133 Committee members, alternates)

Mrs Renata BRANDSTÄTTEROVÁ
Third Secretary (Article 133 Committee services)

Mrs Lenka ŠUSTROVÁ
First Secretary (Article 133 Committee — steel, textiles; trade barriers regulation)

Mr Petr JEŽEK
Third Secretary (Coordination, Article 133 Committee — members, alternates, steel, textiles)

Mr Jiří PRECLÍK
Third Secretary (Coordination, Article 133 Committee — members, alternates, services)

Mrs Alice SOUKUPOVÁ
Third Secretary (EFTA, dual-use goods, export credits)

Mr Petr HALAXA
Troisième secrétaire (coopération au développement et politique humanitaire)

Mrs Dagmar ZÍKOVÁ
Second Secretary (ACP countries, EDF, commodities)

Mrs Isabelle WAHEDOVÁ
Third Secretary (national representative — ACP countries and CODEV Working Party)

Mr Libor MYNÁŘ
Third Secretary (customs union, customs policy, WCO)

Mr David CHOVANEC
Second Secretary (customs cooperation, generalised system of preferences)

Economic and financial policy Unit

Mrs Šárka DYBCZAKOVÁ
First Secretary (Head of Unit, ECOFIN Council follow-up, EU financial perspective)

Mr Eduard OPLATEK
First Secretary (Economic and Monetary Union, EIB, statistics, EU external representation in the economic and financial area, external financial instruments)

Mr Jakub MAZUR
Attaché (follow-up ECOFIN Council — EFC, EPC)

Mrs Romana POLENDOVÁ
Third Secretary (EU budget, including own resources, financial control, European Court of Auditors, European Anti-Fraud Office)

Mr Jan WEINERT
Third Secretary (EU budget, including own resources, financial control, European Court of Auditors, European Anti-Fraud Office)

Mrs Hana ŠTULAJTEROVÁ
Third Secretary (taxation - consumer taxes, direct taxation)

Mr Richard KNOBLOCH
Third Secretary (taxation — VAT)

Mr Tomáš TRNKA
Third Secretary (free movement of financial services and capital, money laundering)

Mrs Soňa MACHOVÁ
Attaché (free movement of financial services and capital, accounting, statutory audit of annual accounts)

Mr Tomáš NEJDL
Third Secretary (regional development, structural funds, future cohesion policy)

Mr Stanislav SCHNEIDR
Third Secretary (Cohesion Fund, Committee of the Regions, outermost regions)

Mrs Iva BASOVNÍKOVÁ
Attaché (coordination of relations with the European Parliament in the economic and budget area)

Home affairs and justice

Mr Petr SOLSKÝ
Second Secretary (Head of Unit, coordination of justice and home affairs, CATS coordination)

Mr Jakub PASTUSZEK
Third Secretary (judicial cooperation in criminal matters, CATS and MDG relating to justice and the European Judicial Network)

Mr Miroslav HRSTKA
Third Secretary (judicial cooperation in civil-law matters, civil law)

Mrs Denisa FIKAROVÁ
Third Secretary (substantive criminal law, CATS and MDG relating to justice)

Mrs Zuzana POLANSKÁ
Attaché (Legal Affairs Committee of the European Parliament, e-justice)

Mrs Daniela MŰNZBERGOVÁ
Third Secretary (asylum, migration, SCIFA)

Mr Martin ŠUSTR
Third Secretary (borders, Schengen, SIS, SCIFA)

Mr Karel BŘEZINA
Attaché (Committee on Civil Liberties, Justice and Home Affairs of the European Parliament, police cooperation, exchange of information)

Mrs Kateřina ŠIMOVÁ
Third Secretary (external relations in justice and home affairs)

Mr Bohdan KOVERDYNSKÝ
Third secretary (terrorism, drugs, organised crime, PNR)

Mr Michal KOUKAL
Attaché (visas, VIS, consular cooperation, CIREFI)

Mrs Olga ŠOLCOVÁ
Third Secretary (horizontal problems, implementation of the Lisbon Treaty)

Mr Jiří CHALUPA
Second Secretary (civil protection and crisis coordination)

External relations

Mrs Blanka FAJKUSOVÁ
First Secretary (Head of Unit, COTRA)

Mrs Lucie MAREŠOVÁ
Attaché (delegate, COTRA)

Mr Petr KOPŘIVA
Ambassador (COAFR)

Mrs Petra POSTLEROVÁ
Attaché (delegate, COAFR)

Mr Lubomir FREBORT
First Secretary (COASI)

Mrs Kateřina BECKOVÁ
Third Secretary (COLAT/AMLAT)

Mrs Radka PÁŤALOVÁ
Third Secretary (delegate, COLAT/AMLAT and COASI)

Mr Michal STROUHAL
Counsellor (COEST)

Mr Tomáš POSPÍŠIL
Attaché (delegate, COEST)

Mr Jiří KALAŠNIKOV
Minister Counsellor (COWEB)

Mrs Kamila Xenie VETIŠKOVÁ
Attaché (delegate, COWEB)

Mr Tomáš SMETÁNKA
Ambassador (coordinator, Middle East and North Africa, COMEP)

Mr Marek JANOVSKÝ
Third Secretary (Maghreb-Mashreq, Euromed)

Mrs Klára WEGEROVÁ
Attaché (delegate, Maghreb-Mashreq, MOG, COMEP, Euromed)

Agriculture and environment

Mr Jiří ŠÍR
First Secretary (Head of Unit, trade in agricultural products, phytosanitary matters)

Mr Zdeněk HÁJEK
First Secretary (food safety, veterinary matters)

Mr Václav DVOŘÁK
First Secretary (environment)

Mr Martin HLAVÁČEK
Third Secretary (agriculture)

Mr Roman DIATKA
Third Secretary (environment)

Mrs Marcela KROUTILOVÁ
Third Secretary (environment)

Mr Jiří JÍLEK
Third Secretary (fisheries, Sapard programme)

Mr Josef TABERY
Third Secretary (agricultural products)

Mr Jiří MUCHKA
Third Secretary (Health Check)

Mr Lukáš VÍŠEK
Third Secretary (rural development)

Mr Tomáš SLUNÉČKO
Third Secretary (food, Codex Alimentarius)

Mr Miloš PINKAS
Attaché (fisheries)

Mr Petr DOLEŽAL
Third Secretary (phyto)

Mrs Petra RATHOUSKÁ
Attaché (SCA, coordinator, CZ PRES)

Industry, energy, information society, internal market, transport

Mr Jaroslav ZAJÍČEK
First Secretary (Head of Unit, internal market horizontal issues, Lisbon process)

Mr Petr VOTOUPAL
First Secretary (free movement of goods, technical harmonisation)

Mr Viktor VODIČKA
First Secretary (support for entrepreneurs, external project assistance, technical harmonisation)

Mr Petr DOLEJŠÍ
Second Secretary (SMEs, competitiveness, industrial policy, tourism)

Mrs Věra KNOBLOCHOVÁ
Third Secretary (consumer protection)

Mr Aleš PECKA
Third Secretary (Better regulation)

Mr David SCHREIB
Third Secretary (free movement of goods, free movement of services)

Mrs Magdaléna KUBEČKOVÁ
Attaché (internal market, Better regulation, consumer protection)

Mr Ondřej DOSTAL
Third Secretary (competition, State aid, public contracts)

Mrs Lucie ČIHÁKOVÁ
Third Secretary (energy, nuclear safety)

Mrs Hana KYNCLOVÁ
Attaché (energy, nuclear safety)

Mrs Věra ZÁZVORKOVÁ
Third Secretary (air and rail transport)

Mr Jiři VESELÝ
Third Secretary (sea transport, inland waterway transport, intermodal and horizontal issues)

Mr Jan NĚMEC
Third Secretary (road transport)

Mr Martin PEČÁNKA
Attaché (air and sea transport, inland waterway transport, intermodal and horizontal issues)

Mrs Michaela GLOSÍKOVÁ
Attaché (road and rail transport)

Mr Filip ŠVÁB
Third Secretary (information society, telecommunications, postal services, data protection)

Mr Petr REIMER
Attaché (information society, telecommunications, postal services, data protection, Galileo)

Employment, social affairs, health, consumer affairs, education, research, culture, youth

Mr Miroslav FUCHS
Adviser (social policy and employment)

Mrs Hana VLČKOVÁ
Third Secretary (research and development, professional qualifications)

Mrs Marie KOLMANOVÁ
Attaché (research and development, professional qualifications)

Mr Josef JIRKAL
Third Secretary (social policy and employment)

Mrs Zuzana ZAJAROŠOVÁ
Third Secretary (social policy and employment)

Mrs Světlana KOPECKÁ
First Secretary (intellectual property, industrial property, TAIEX)

Mrs Martina NĚMCOVÁ
Attaché (company law)

Mrs Lenka RAMPULOVÁ
Attaché (intellectual property, company law, TAIEX)

Mrs Ivana SCHAFFEROVÁ
Attaché (education, youth, sport)

Mrs Klaudie FALTYSOVÁ
Third Secretary (public health)

Mrs Lenka TICHÁ
Third Secretary (pharmaceuticals and medical devices)

Mrs Lenka KOSTELECKÁ
Attaché (public health, pharmaceuticals and medical devices)

Mrs Blanka HAŠOVÁ
Attaché (culture, audiovisual and multilingualism)

Mr Artuš REJENT
Third Secretary (audiovisual and culture)

Political and Security Committee matters

Mr Jiří PAVLÍČEK
First Secretary (Head of Unit, external relations)

Mr Juraj FOGADA
First Secretary (national delegate/PSC)

Mr Zdenek BUČEK
First Secretary (CIVCOM)

Mr Jan LANGER
First Secretary (security issues)

Mrs Pavlína VAŠINOVÁ
Second Secretary (PMG, Nikolaidis group)

Mrs Eva KORDOVÁ
Second Secretary (CFSP,PMG)

Mrs Debora LANÍČKOVÁ
Defence Counsellor

Mr Ondřej VOSÁTKA
Defence Counsellor

Mr Vladimír ŠILHAN
Defence Counsellor (capability, EUSC)

Mr Jiří MATÉJOVIČ
Defence Counsellor

Mr Dušan ŠVARC
Defence Counsellor

Mr Martin VOBOŘIL
Attaché (CFSP, PMG)

Mr Josef VRCHOTA
Attaché (external relations)

Administration

Mr Ivan SOBOTKA
Attaché (Office Manager)

Mr Petr KOS
First Secretary (IT)

PERMANENT REPRESENTATION OF DENMARK

Rue d'Arlon 73
B-1040 Brussels
E-mail: brurep@um.dk
Tel. +32 22330811
Fax +32 22309384

HE Mr Claus GRUBE
Ambassador Extraordinary and Plenipotentiary
Permanent Representative
Tel. +32 22330865

Mrs Susanne FOURNAIS

HE Mr Jens KISLING
Ambassador
Deputy Permanent Representative
Tel. +32 22330866

Mrs Alice Kjaer KISLING

HE Mr Lars FAABORG-ANDERSEN
Ambassador
Representative of Denmark to the PSC
Permanent Representative of Denmark to the WEU
Tel. +32 22330970

Mrs Jean-Marie MURPHY

Ministry of Foreign Affairs

Mr Flemming NICHOLS
Minister Counsellor
Tel. +32 22330826

Mrs Marianne NICHOLS

Mrs Vibeke Paternak JØRGENSEN
Counsellor
Tel. +32 22330869

Mr Kasper Pasternak JØRGENSEN

Mr Søren HALSKOV
Counsellor
Tel. +32 22330860

Mrs Renate Kubicki HALSKOV

Mr Claus WINTOP
Counsellor
Tel. +32 22330978

Mrs Kanokkarn WINTOP

Mr Jes Brogaard NIELSEN
Counsellor
Tel. +32 22330968

Mrs Annette HOLEK

Mrs Thea Lund CHRISTIANSEN
Counsellor
Tel. +32 22330973

Mr Niels THYGESEN

Mr Peter GEBERT
Counsellor
Tel. +32 22330807

Mrs Elrica D'OYEN-GEBERT

Mr Carsten GRØNBECH-JENSEN
First Secretary
Tel. +32 22330868

Mrs Katrien BEULS

Mr Mads Thuesen LUNDE
Counsellor
Tel. +32 22330893

Mr Michael Bremerskov JENSEN
First Secretary
Tel. +32 22330979

Mrs Camilla CADELL

Mr Stefan ILCUS
First Secretary
Tel. +32 22330852

Mr Klaus Juel WERNER
Secretary
Tel. +32 22330946

Mrs Rie Odsbjerg WERNER

Mrs Seemab SHEIKH
Secretary
Tel. +32 22330977

Mr Wasim Ahmed ZAFAR

Mr Kenneth Lindharth MADSEN
Secretary
Tel. +32 22330854

Mrs Mette Møbjerg MADSEN

Mrs Lene MANDEL
Secretary
Tel. +32 22330945

Mr Troels VENSILD

Mrs Mette Sicard FILTENBORG
EU Commercial and External Assistance Attaché
Tel. +32 22330830

Mr Guido PRUD'HOMME

Ministry of Economic Affairs, Trade and Industry

Mrs Susanne Bo CHRISTENSEN
Counsellor (economic affairs and trade)
Tel. +32 22330902

Mr Brian Adrian WESSEL
Counsellor (economic affairs and trade)
Tel. +32 22330808

Mrs Marie WESSEL

Mr Jeppe Torp VESTENTOFT
Counsellor (economic affairs and trade)
Tel. +32 22330894

Mrs Mette VESTENTOFT

Ministry of Finance

Mr Jens Anton Kjærgaard LARSEN
Conseiller (financial issues)
Tel. +32 22330881

Mr Jacob Gunnar NIELSEN
Attaché (budget)
Tel. +32 22330905

Mrs Helle Carlsen NIELSEN

Ministry of Employment

Mrs Lone HENRIKSEN
Counsellor (employment)
Tel. +32 22330812

Ministry of Justice

Mrs Moya-Louise LINDSAY-POULSEN
Attaché (legal questions)
Tel. +32 22330898

Mrs Jessica AUKEN
Attaché (legal questions)
Tel. +32 22330805

Ministry of Culture and Ministry of Education

Mr Hans Kristian KRISTENSEN
Attaché (culture and education)
Tel. +32 22330929

Mrs Caroline Marott CLAUSEN

Ministry of Transport and Energy

Mr Jørn HOLDT
Minister Counsellor (transport)
Tel. +32 22330804

Mrs Merete HOLDT

Mr Andreas FÆRGEMANN
Attaché (transport)
Tel. +32 22330935

Mrs Jane Glinvad KRISTENSEN
Counsellor (energy questions)
Tel. +32 22330889

Ministry of Science, Technology and Innovation

Mrs Vibeke Hein OLSEN
Minister Counsellor (research)
Tel. +32 22330825

Mrs Susanne Bro LUNDGREN
Counsellor (telecommunications and information technology)
Tel. +32 22330858

Ministry of Food, Agriculture and Fisheries

Mr Mikkel STAGE
Attaché (food)
Tel. +32 22330862

Mr Lars STAGE

Mr Troels VENSILD
Attaché (food)
Tel. +32 22330863

Mrs Lene MANDEL

Mrs Tanja ANDERSEN
Attaché (consumers and food safety)
Tel. +32 22330833

Mr Søren ANDERSEN

Mr Uffe SVEISTRUP
Attaché (food)
Tel. +32 22330888

Ministry of the Interior and Health

Mr Kåre GEIL
Counsellor (health)
Tel. +32 22330815

Ministry of Defence

Mr Jeppe Søndergaard PEDERSEN
Deputy Adviser (defence)
Tel. +32 22330974

Mrs Trine Bielefeldt STJERNØ

Mrs Pernille BRUNSE
Deputy Counsellor (defence and civil protection)
Tel. +32 22330839

Mr Niels Henrik HEDEGAARD
Minister Counsellor (defence and civil protection)
Tel. +32 27076109

Mrs Kathryn HEDEGAARD

Ministry of Social Affairs and Equal Opportunities

Mr Jakob JENSEN
Minister Counsellor
Tel. +32 22330838

Mrs Signe Louise Tholstrup BERTELSEN

Ministry of the Environment

Mrs Sonja CANGER
Counsellor (environment)
Tel. +32 22330801

Mr Morten Damkjær NIELSEN

Mrs Ellen Hvidt THELLE
Attaché (environment)
Tel. +32 22330802

Mr Martin Hvidt THELLE

Mrs Rikke Reumert SCHALTZ
Attaché (climate)
Tel. +32 22330906

Ministry of Taxation

Mrs Mette WERDELIN AZZAM
Fiscal Attaché
Tel. +32 22330949

Mr Hassan AZZAM

Mr Allan Stagaard TOFT
Fiscal Attaché
Tel. +32 22330908

Mrs Li Dong TOFT

Ministry of refugees, immigrants and integration

Mr Anders Hess LARSEN
Attaché (refugees, immigrants and integration)
Tel. +32 22330853

Administration

Mrs Iben DUPONT
Counsellor
Tel. +32 22330944

Mrs Pia TESDORF

Mr Bjarne RASMUSSEN
Attaché (data processing)
Tel. +32 22330821

PERMANENT REPRESENTATION OF GERMANY

Rue Jacques de Lalaing 8-14
B-1040 Brussels
E-mail: info@eu-vertretung.de
Website: http://www.eu-vertretung.de
Tel. +32 27871000
Fax +32 27872000

HE Mr Edmund DUCKWITZ
Ambassador Extraordinary and Plenipotentiary
Permanent Representative

Mrs Joke DUCKWITZ

Mrs Dorette ALTENBERND
Attaché

HE Mr Guido PERUZZO
Ambassador
Deputy Permanent Representative

Mrs Martina BECK
Attaché

Political affairs

Mr Clemens VON GOETZE
Ambassador
Permanent Representative to the WEU
PSC Representative

Mrs Sonja VON GOETZE

Mr Andreas ZOBEL
Minister

Mrs Jutta HOFFMANN-ZOBEL

Mr Michael HILDEBRANDT
First Counsellor

Mrs Nelly Josefina HILDEBRANDT

Mr Manfred DEGEN
Counsellor

Mr Bertrand GOBBAERTS

Mr Wolfgang RUDISCHHAUSER
Counsellor

Mr Georg FELSHEIM
Counsellor

Mrs Isabelle FELSHEIM

Mrs Ursula POLZER
Counsellor (labour questions)

Mr Friedrich RÖHRS
Counsellor (cultural matters)

Mr Andreas KINDL
Counsellor

Mrs Ina Maria WEINTRAUTNER

Mrs Jutta HABETS
First Secretary

Mrs Angela GANNINGER
First Secretary

Mr Daniel KREBBER
First Secretary

Mrs Wiebke RÜCKERT

Mr Jochen MOELLER
First Secretary

Mrs Anne Mathilde JENNEN

Mr Günter SAUTTER
First Secretary

Mrs Xóchil Nicoletta GUILLÈN-SAUTTER

Mr Johannes SCHLICHT
First Secretary

Mr Christoph WOLFRUM
First Secretary

Mrs Olivia BENTE LOEWE

Mrs Lasia BLOß
Second Secretary

Mr Rainer BREUL
Second Secretary

Mr Boris GEHRKE
Second Secretary

Mrs Stefanie GEHRKE

Mr Olaf POESCHKE
Second Secretary

Mr Wolfgang STEUER
Second Secretary

Mrs Angela MARZOLINI

Mrs Renate BERTHOLD
Third Secretary

Mr Joachim KEMPA
Third Secretary

Mrs Maren SULZER
Third Secretary

Mr Rainer SULZER

Mrs Elvira KELLER
Attaché

Mr Claus Dieter KELLER

Mrs Cora KREUTZ
Attaché

Mrs Marina MEYER
Attaché

Mrs Heidemarie REUL
Attaché

Press Office

Mr Martin KOTTHAUS
Counsellor (press)

Mrs Mathilde Elisabeth MÜLLER

Mrs Valerie KARADENIZLI
Attaché

Mr Hasan KARADENIZLI

Mr Ricklef BEUTIN
First Secretary

Mr Jörg DANZ
Attaché

Military policy and arms questions

Mr Hilmar LINNENKAMP
Minister

Mrs Ariane LINNENKAMP

Armin STAIGIS
Minister Counsellor

Mrs Brunhilde STAIGIS

Mr Thomas LEHNEN
Counsellor

Mrs Martina LEHNEN

Mr Alfons MAIS
Counsellor

Mr Michael STOLZKE
Counsellor

Mrs Carmen STOLZKE

Mr Kai CORDRUWISCH
First Secretary

Mrs Heike CORDRUWISCH

Mr Matthias JOACHIM
Attaché

Mrs Annette JOACHIM

Mrs Kathrin MATHOW
Attaché

Internal affairs

Mrs Martina WEBER
First Counsellor

Mr Ulrich STRACK

Mr Rudolf ROY
First Counsellor

Mrs Christine Pascale FRANCOIS

Mr Horst Jörg HUPERZ
Counsellor

Mrs Claudia EMDE

Mr Holger SPERLICH
Counsellor

Mrs Martina WENSKE
Counsellor

Mr Manfred HÄHNEL
Second Secretary

Mrs Olga HÄHNEL

Mr Wolfgang HAMMER
Second Secretary

Mrs Silvia SPAETH
Third Secretary

Justice

Mr Dirk MIROW
Counsellor

Mrs Andrea Ingrid MIROW

Mr Jan MACLEAN
Counsellor

Mrs Jill MACLEAN

Mr Bertholdt GEDEON
Counsellor

Mrs Wenke GEDEON

Mrs Sigrid JACOBY
Counsellor

Mrs Bettina VON TEICHMAN UND LOGISCHEN
Counsellor

Family affairs, senior citizens, women and youth

Mr Félix BARCKHAUSEN
First Secretary

Mrs Yvonne BARCKHAUSEN

Mr David ROCKOFF
Third Secretary

Economic affairs and technology

Mrs Elfriede BIERBRAUER
Counsellor

Mr Frank GOEBBELS
Counsellor

Mrs Ariane GOEBBELS

Mr Thomas LAUT
Counsellor

Mrs Andrea LAUT

Mrs Cornelia RANK
Counsellor

Mr Christian STOROST
First Secretary

Mr Oliver BORNKAMM
First Secretary

Mr Michael KUXENKO
First Secretary

Mr Gunnar ZILLMANN
Counsellor

Mrs Edda ZILLMANN

Mrs Kirstin LOESER
Second Secretary

Mrs Ursula VOSSENKUHL
Second Secretary

Mr Kristian WELLIGE
Second Secretary

Mrs Kirsten MÜLLER-PONTOW

Mrs Andrea ROMEIS
Third Secretary

Mrs Antje WÄGENBAUR
Attaché

Mr Bertrand WÄGENBAUR

Environment

Mr Rainer STEFFENS
Minister Counsellor

Mrs Sandra SCHÖNEWOLF

Mrs Christine WISTUBA
Counsellor

Mr Walter DEFFAA

Mrs Ellen VON ZITZEWITZ
First Secretary

Mr Tobias TUNKEL

Mrs Verena KLINGER-DERING
Second Secretary

Mr Peter DERING

Economic cooperation

Mr Christoph RAUH
Counsellor

Mrs Maria Del Carmen CORRO DELGADO

Mr Michael SCHLOMS
Second Secretary

Mrs Katrin VIERHUSS-SCHLOMS

Mrs Anette BRAUN
Second Secretary

Finance

Mr Thomas WESTPHAL
Minister Counsellor

Mrs Ulrike WESTPHAL

Mrs Susanne AHRENS
Second Secretary

Mr Stefan VAN HEECK
Second Secretary

Mrs Renate KRAMER
Second Secretary

Mr Simon RACH
Second Secretary

Mrs Nicole ROSIN
Second Secretary

Mrs Vera WEYAND
Third Secretary

Mrs Heidemarie SCHARF
Attaché

Mr Andreas SCHARF

Financial services

Mrs Silvia BOSCH
Counsellor

Mr Jürgen BAUM
Counsellor

Mrs Ute JÜLLY

Mr Christoph VON BUSEKIST
First Secretary

Mrs Elke VON BUSEKIST

Mrs Katja GÖDEKE
Second Secretary

Federal Bank

Mr Marc HAUSMANN
Second Secretary

Mrs Marianne FLINT
Attaché

Mr Heiko Erich FLINT

Consumer protection, food and agriculture

Mr Alois BAUER
First Counsellor

Mrs Tanja MINDERMANN
First Counsellor

Mr Jürgen WEIS
First Secretary

Mrs Sabine WEIS

Mr Bernd MÜLLER
Second Secretary

Mrs Vera MÜLLER

Mrs Ulrike KASSNER
Second Secretary

Mrs Sybille SCHINDLER
Attaché

Education and research

Mr Wilfried KRAUS
First Counsellor

Mrs Eva Maria HERMES-KRAUS

Mrs Gisela SCHMITZ-DUMONT
Counsellor

Mr Hans-Joachim SCHMITZ-DUMONT

Mr Frank PETRIKOWSKI
First Secretary

Mrs Guieshuba GALLEGOS FERRER

Mrs Anke ARETZ
Second Secretary

Transport and public works

Mr Norbert SCHULDT
First Counsellor

Mrs Annette FRIEDRICHS

Mr Johannes BRETTSCHNEIDER
Counsellor

Mrs Sabine BRETTSCHNEIDER

Mr Ulrich BERNER
Second Secretary

Mrs Stefanie SCHRÖDER
Second Secretary

Mr Albert WEBER
Second Secretary

Mrs Meike HINRICHS

Labour and social affairs

Mrs Iris KRÖNING
Counsellor

Mr Thomas SCHMID-SCHÖNBEIN

Mr Ermano MEICHSNER
Counsellor

Mrs Ute RÖNSBERG
Second Secretary

Mr Stephan KLITSCHER
Second Secretary

Mrs Petra-Andrea KLITSCHER

Mrs Anne Katrin LUTZ
Second Secretary

Health

Mrs Irene WITTMANN-STAHL
Counsellor

Mr Gerhard STAHL

Mrs Elke SCHROER
Second Secretary

Mr Peter SCHROER

Administration

Mrs Sabine LAMMERS
Counsellor

Mrs Barbara DICK
Third Secretary

Mrs Andrea WEINIG
Third Secretary

Mr Axel RENK
Third Secretary

Mrs Stefanie RENK

Mr Jochen BASNER
Attaché

Mr Martin BÜCKING
Attaché

Mr Jörg-Emil GAUDIAN
Attaché

Mrs Claudia GAUDIAN

Mrs Angela HENKE
Attaché

Mr Karl-Heinz WIERSCHEM

Mr JAKOB HOFMANN
Attaché

Mr Andreas KOENIG
Attaché

Mr Wilfried MORENA
Attaché

Mrs Roswitha MORENA

Mr Wjatscheslaw PETROW
Attaché

Mrs Kerstin RAIFARTH
Attaché

Mr Olivier RAIFARTH

Mr Daniel REICHWALD
Attaché

Mrs Irmgard REICHWALD

Mrs Ellen RICHTER
Attaché

Mr Rainer SWOBODA
Attaché

Mr Stephan WASSONG
Attaché

Mrs Diana WASSONG

Mr Ralf WODRICH
Attaché

Mrs Astrid WODRICH

PERMANENT REPRESENTATION OF ESTONIA

Rue Guimard 11/13
1040 Brussels
E-mail: permrep.eu@mfa.ee
firstname.lastname@mfa.ee
Tel. +32 22273910
Fax +32 22273925

HE Mr Raul MÄLK
Ambassador Extraordinary and Plenipotentiary
Permanent Representative
Tel. +32 22274312

HE Mr Gert ANTSU
Deputy Permanent Representative
Tel. +32 22274303

Coreper coordination

Mr Klen JÄÄRATS
Counsellor (Antici, Coreper II)
Tel. +32 22274312

Mrs Sirje SEPP
First Secretary (Mertens, Coreper I)
Tel. +32 22274303

Press and information

Mrs Marika POST
Third Secretary (spokesperson)
E-mail: eupress@mfa.ee
Tel. +32 22273922

Mrs Riia SALSA
Third Secretary (press and information)
E-mail: eupress@mfa.ee
Tel. +32 22274319

European Parliament, institutional affairs

Mrs Margot ENDJÄRV
Second Secretary (Coreper I, ESC, SNEs)
Tel. +32 22274357

Mr Lauri KUUSING
Third Secretary (Coreper II, GAG, TAIEX, COR)
Tel. +32 22274357

Enlargement

Mrs Julika LUTS
Third Secretary
Tel. +32 22274312

Political and Security Committee

HE Mr Sander SOONE
Ambassador
Representative to the Political and Security Committee of the European Union
Permanent Representative to the WEU
Tel. +32 22274318

Mrs Inna SOONE

Mrs Luule RAND
Third Secretary (Nicolaïdis Group, COAFR)
Tel. +32 22274318

Mr Vello LOEMAA
Lieutenant General
Military Representative to the EUMC
Tel. +32 27079540

Mrs Ludmilla LOEMAA

Mr Rein VAABEL
Lieutenant Colonel
Deputy Representative to the EUMC
Tel. +32 22274352

Mr Margus PURLAU
Lieutenant Colonel
Assistant to the Military Representative to the EUMC
Tel. +32 22274352

Mr Hanno PARKSEPP
Counsellor (RELEX)
Tel. +32 22274318

Mrs Kätrin MÖLDER
First Secretary(ESDP)
Tel. +32 22273910

Mrs Maris LAUK
Third Secretary (COWEB, CONUN, COHOM)
Tel. +32 22274318

Mrs Erika ELLAMAA-OTS
Second Secretary (COEST, AMLAT, COSCE)
Tel. +32 22274318

Mrs Kaie KORK
Third Secretary (COEST, ENP, AMLAT)
Tel. +32 22274318

Mr Tanel SEPP
Second Secretary (CIVCOM, COTER, CONOP, CODUN, COARM)
Tel. +32 22274318

Mrs Kristel KEERMA
Third Secretary (COMAG, COMED, COMEP, COMEM)
Tel. +32 22274318

Mr Marek ÜHTEGI
Counsellor (ESDP, PMG)
Tel. +32 22274318

External trade

Mrs Kersti EESMAA
First Secretary (133 Committee, COTRA)
Tel. +32 22274357

Mrs Aune KOTLI
First Secretary (EFTA, GSP, COASI)
Tel. +32 22274357

Development cooperation

Mr Tanel TANG
Third Secretary (DEVGEN, ACP, ALIM)
Tel. +32 22274357

Legal issues

Mrs Marika LINNTAM
Third Secretary (Legal Adviser)
Tel. +32 22274303

Internal and judicial affairs

Mr Uku SÄREKANNO
Counsellor (visas, migration, Schengen)
Tel. +32 22274350

Mr Kristo PÕLLU
Counsellor (police cooperation, terrorism, Schengen)
Tel. +32 22274350

Mr Tõnu PIHELGAS
Counsellor (judicial cooperation, ICC)
Tel. +32 22274350

Mrs Kaisa PARKEL
Counsellor (judicial cooperation)
Tel. +32 22274350

Economic and financial affairs

Mrs Kadri UUSTAL
Adviser (EU resources, regional policy)
Tel. +32 22274335

Mrs Tiiu-Tatjana REINBUSCH
Counsellor (ECOFIN, EU budget, financial perspectives)
Tel. +32 22273935

Mr Valner LILLE
Counsellor (financial services, auditing)
Tel. +32 22274335

Mr Meelis MEIGAS
Counsellor (taxation)
Tel. +32 22274335

Mrs Pille JÕGISOO
Counsellor (customs)
Tel. +32 22274335

Mr Raoul LÄTTEMÄE
Counsellor (Representative of the Bank of Estonia)
Tel. +32 22274335

Industrial policy, energy, internal market, transport and communications

Mrs Reesi-Reena RUNNEL
Counsellor (energy matters)
Tel. +32 22274342

Mr Silver TAMMIK
Adviser (economic affairs, telecommunications)
Tel. +32 22274342

Mrs Kristi REITSAK
Adviser (competiveness, internal market, SMEs)
Tel. +32 22274342

Mrs Reet JAAGUS
Counsellor (transport)
Tel. +32 22274342

Mr Tarmo OTS
Counsellor (sea and air transport)
Tel. +32 22274342

Agriculture and fisheries

Mr Olavi PETRON
Adviser (SCA)
Tel. +32 22274340

Mrs Signe AASKIVI
Counsellor (fisheries, forestry)
Tel. +32 22274340

Mrs Pille TAMMEMÄGI
Counsellor (veterinary matters, food safety)
Tel. +32 22274340

Mrs Katrin PUHM
Counsellor (rural policy, trade in agricultural products)
Tel. +32 22274340

Environment

Mr Kerli KIILI
Attaché (nature protection)
Tel. +32 22274340

Mr Aare SIRENDI
Counsellor (climate change, industrial pollution, chemicals)
Tel. +32 22274340

Mr Mart UNDREST
Counsellor (fisheries)
Tel. +32 22274340

Employment, social affairs and health

Mrs Leili ZAGELMAYER
Counsellor (social policy)
Tel. +32 22274337

Mrs Elen OHOV
Counsellor (health)
Tel. +32 22274337

Mrs Carita RAMMUS
Counsellor (employment)
Tel. +32 22274337

Education and research

Mrs Ülle KURVITS
Counsellor (education)
Tel. +32 22274337

Mrs Reesi LEPA
Counsellor (research, FP7)
Tel. +32 22274337

Cultural affairs

Mrs Tamara LUUK
Counsellor (cultural relations, audiovisual policy)
Tel. +32 22274337

Administrative affairs

Mr Heiti MÄEMEES
Counsellor (head of administration)
Tel. +32 22273910

PERMANENT REPRESENTATION OF IRELAND

Rue Froissart 89-93
B-1040 Brussels
E-mail: irlprb@dfa.ie
Website: http://www.dfa.ie
Tel. +32 22308580
Fax +32 22303203

HE Mr Bobby McDONAGH
Ambassador Extraordinary and Plenipotentiary
Permanent Representative

Mrs McDONAGH

HE Mrs Geraldine BYRNE NASON
Ambassador
Deputy Permanent Representative

HE Mr Brian NASON

HE Mrs Marie CROSS
Ambassador
Representative of Ireland to the PSC

Mr John CROSS

Mr Liam Mac NAMEE
Brigadier General
Military representative to the EUMC

Mrs Mac NAMEE

Ministry of Foreign Affairs

Mrs Aingeal O'DONOGHUE
Counsellor

Mr BULLEN

Mr Keith MCBEAN
Adviser (Antici)

Mrs REID

Miss Deirdre FARRELL
First Secretary

Mrs Joana BETSON
First Secretary

Mr Padraig FRANCIS
First Secretary

Mrs TIFFIN

Mrs Fiona LUNNY
First Secretary

Mr Michael SANFEY
First Secretary

Mr David BRUCK
First Secretary

Mr Julian CLARE
First Secretary

Mrs TRACEY

Mr Nigel HUTSON
First Secretary

Miss Ciara O'FLOINN
Third Secretary

Mr Barry TUMELTY
Third secretary (Mertens)

Mr Andrew HARWOOD
First Secretary

Mrs HARWOOD

Mr Tom LUCAS
Attaché (administrative affairs)

Mrs LUCAS

Irish delegation to the PSC

HE Mrs Marie CROSS
Ambassador
Representative of Ireland to the PSC

Mr John CROSS

Mr Liam CONOLLY
Counsellor (defence)

Mrs CONOLLY

Mr Tim HARRINGTON
First Secretary

Mrs O'DOHERTY

Mr Kevin O'CONNELL
First Secretary (defence)

Mrs Ní CHONGHAILE

Mr Ciaran DESMOND
First Secretary

Mrs DESMOND

Mr Colum HATCHELL
Third Secretary

Mr Liam Mac NAMEE
Brigadier General
Military Representative

Mrs Mac NAMEE

Mr Brendan FARRELLY
Colonel
Deputy Military Representative

Mrs FARRELLY

Mr David GLAVIN
Lieutenant Colonel
Assistant Military Representative

Mrs GLAVIN

Mr Anthony CUDMORE
Major
Assistant Military Representative

Mrs CUDMORE

Minister for Agriculture, Fisheries and Food

Mr Jarlath COLEMAN
Counsellor

Mrs COLEMAN

Mrs Jane DEMPSEY
First Secretary

Mr Colm HAYES
First Secretary

Mrs HAYES

Ministry of Arts, Sport and Tourism

Mr Caoimhín O'CIARUÁIN
First Secretary

Mrs MULLIGAN

Office of the Attorney-General (including the Parliamentary Draftsman's Office)

Mr Denis KELLEHER
Counsellor

Mrs MURRAY

Minister for Communications, Energy and Natural Resources

Miss Una DIXON
First Secretary (energy)

Mr Des HACKETT
First Secretary (telecommunications)

Department of Education and Science

Mrs Joanne TOBIN
First Secretary

Department of Enterprise, Trade and Employment

Mr Maurice KENNEDY
Counsellor

Mrs KENNEDY

Mr Paraig HENNESSY
Counsellor

Mrs CORSCADDEN

Mr Philip LYNCH
First Secretary

Mrs LYNCH

Mr Robert MCLEAN
First Secretary

Mrs MCLEAN

Mrs Pauline MULLIGAN
First Secretary

Mr Ó CIARUÁIN

Department of the Environment and Local Government

Mr Donal ENRIGHT
Counsellor

Mrs ENRIGHT

Mr Patrick Terry SHERIDAN
First Secretary

Mrs O'BRIAN-SHERIDAN

Ministry of Finance

Mr Frederick COOPER
Counsellor (economic and financial affairs)

Mrs MULHALL

Mrs Mary LAWLESS
First Secretary

Mr Brendan COOGAN
First Secretary

Mrs KILKENNY

Mrs Clare McNAMARA
First Secretary

Department of Health and Children

Mr Greg CANNING
First Secretary

Mrs CANNING

Department of Justice, Equality and Law Reform

Mr Barry O'CONNOR
Counsellor

Mrs SCANLAN

Mr Padraig DEVINE
First Secretary

Mr Daniel KELLEHER
First Secretary

Mrs KIRWAN

Mrs Sile BENNETT
Third Secretary

Mr DORAN

Revenue Commissioners

Mr Norman O'GRADY
First Secretary

Mrs O'GRADY

Mr Denis SHEEHAN
Third Secretary

Mrs BANNON

Minister for Social and Family Affairs

Mrs Dympna BOYLE
First Secretary

Ministry of Transport

Mrs Doreen KEANEY
Counsellor (transport)

Mr KEANEY

Mrs Nicola HAYES
First Secretary

Mr HAYES

Representative of the National Parliament (Oireacthas)

Mr John HAMILTON
First Secretary

Mrs HAMILTON

PERMANENT REPRESENTATION OF GREECE

Rue Jacques de Lalaing 19-21
B-1040 Brussels
E-mail: mea.bruxelles@rp-grece.be
Tel. +32 25515611
Fax +32 25515651

HE Mr Vassilis KASKARELIS
Ambassador Extraordinary and Plenipotentiary
Permanent Representative
E-mail: rp@rp-grece.be
Tel. +32 25515637
Fax +32 25126950

Mrs KASKARELIS

HE Mr Leonidas C. ROKANAS
Minister Plenipotentiary
Deputy Permanent Representative
E-mail: rp-adj@rp-grece.be
Tel. +32 25515601
Fax +32 25515602

Mrs Eleni KYRIAKIDOU

Mrs Iphigenia KANARA
Second Secretary (Antici, general coordination — Coreper II)
E-mail: i.kanara@rp-grece.be
Tel. +32 25515703

Mr Gerassimos DONTAS
Second embassy secretary (coordination Coreper I — Mertens)
E-mail: gdontas@rp-grece.be
Tel. +32 25515681

Mrs DARLA

External Relations — Enlargement Unit

Mr Ioannis VRAILAS
First Counsellor
Head of Unit
E-mail: i.vrailas@rp-grece.be
Tel. +32 25515665

Mrs BOURLOYANNIS-VRAILAS

Mrs Maria SARANTI
First Counsellor (MASHREQ/MAGHREB, Middle East/Gulf, EUROMED, IRAN, IRAQ)
E-mail: m.saranti@rp-grece.be
Tel. +32 25515607

Mrs Vassiliki DICOPOULOU
First Counsellor (COHOM, COSCE, CONUN, human rights)
E-mail: v.dicopoulou@rp-grece.be
Tel. +32 25515780

Mr Dionyssis KALAMVREZOS
First Adviser (development)
E-mail: d.kalamvrezos@rp-grece.be
Tel. +32 25515636

Mrs DERMARI

Mrs Eleni LIANIDOU
First Counsellor (RELEX)
E-mail: elenilianidou@rp-grece.be
Tel. +32 25515604

Mr YIANNOYRAKOS

Mr Evangelos SEKERIS
First Counsellor (COWEB)
E-mail: e.sekeris@rp-grece.be
Tel. +32 25515713

Mrs Maria KAZANA

Mrs Ekaterini FOUNTOULAKI
First Counsellor (COTRA)
E-mail: a.fountoulaki@rp-grece.be
Tel. +32 25515697

Mr Alexis KONSTANTOPOULOS
Second Counsellor (Middle East)
E-mail: a.konstantopoulos@rp-grece.be
Tel. +32 25515649

Mrs AGIER

Mr Gaspar VLAHAKIS
First Secretary (COELA, Ad hoc Working Party on the follow-up to the Council conclusions on Cyprus, and Bulgaria/Romania)
E-mail: g.vlahakis@rp-grece.be
Tel. +32 25515669

Mrs GHINI

Mrs Christina VALASSOPOULOU
Second Secretary (ACP, COAFR, EDF management committee)
E-mail: c.valassopoulou@rp-grece.be
Tel. +32 25515736

Mrs Lydia PNEVMATICOU
Legal Counsel (COARM, CODUN, CONOP, COTER, dual use, Nuclear Security Cooperation Committee, COARM seminar with NGOs)
E-mail: lydia.pnevmaticou@rp-grece.be
Tel. +32 25515756

Mr Sofoklis KOUKKOULLIS
Expert Minister Counsellor (humanitarian and food aid)
E-mail: s.koukkoullis@rp-grece.be
Tel. +32 25515768

Mr Panayotis BENIADIS
Expert Minister Counsellor (COEST, ENP, Black Sea Synergy)
E-mail: beniadis@rp-grece.be
Tel. +32 25515606

Mrs Anastasia BACOPOULOU

Mr Ioannis BRACHOS
Expert Counsellor (COLAT, COASI)
E-mail: brachos@rp-grece.be
Tel. +32 25515635

Mrs Katerina THEOFANAKI

Mr Dimitrios ZOMAS
First Counsellor (economic and commercial affairs, EFTA, EEA)
E-mail: d.zomas@rp-grece.be
Tel. +32 25515696

Mrs ZOMA

Mr Panayotis PAPANASTASSIOU
First Counsellor (economic and commercial affairs, Africa Trust Fund, Neighbourhood Investment Fund, financial perspectives)
E-mail: p.papanastassiou@rp-grece.be
Tel. +32 25515634

Mrs E. MYLONI

Mrs Ageliki SKARAMANGA-SKAMI
Adviser (Article 133 Committee full members/deputies)
E-mail: a.skami@rp-grece.be
Tel. +32 25515645

Mr SKARAMANGAS

Mr Georgios MEZOPOULOS
Counsellor (Commercial affairs,commodities, Article 133 Committee steel, market access, anti-dumping, anti-subsidy, safeguards)
E-mail: mezopoulos@rp-grece.be
Tel. +32 25515782

Mrs CHRISTODOULOPOULOU

Mr Georgios MOUSSOURIS
Secretary (Article 133 Committee services and textiles, GSP, export credits, commodities)
E-mail: g.moussouris@rp-grece.be
Tel. +32 25515614

Economic and Financial Policy Unit

Mr Andreas GALANAKIS
Counsellor
Head of Unit
E-mail: a.galanakis@rp-grece.be
Tel. +32 25515695

Mrs Helene-Pulchérie PSARROS
Counsellor (internal market, State aids)
E-mail: e.psarros@rp-grece.be
Tel. +32 25515676

Mr KARTSONAS

Mr Odysefs PYLALIS
Counsellor (customs cooperation, customs union — excise duties)
E-mail: o.pylalis@rp-grece.be
Tel. +32 25515686

Mrs PYLALI

Mrs Garyfallia KOTTI
Counsellor (foodstuffs, chemical products)
E-mail: g.kotti@rp-grece.be
Tel. +32 25515783

Mr KOTTIS

Mrs Eleni-Styliani ROMAIDOU
Counsellor (budgetary affairs)
E-mail: e.romaidou@rp-grece.be
Tel. +32 25515664

Mrs Athina KALIVA
Counsellor (tax matters)
E-mail: kalyva@rp-grece.be
Tel. +32 25515633

Mr BERTHELOT

Mrs Sofia BALLA
Adviser (Statistics)
E-mail: s.balla@rp-grece.be
Tel. +32 25515704

Mrs Angeliki LIOKOU
Secretary (European economic issues)
E-mail: a.liokou@rp-grece.be
Tel. +32 25515765

Mrs Christina PAPAKONSTANTINOU
Secretary (financial services)
E-mail: papaconstantinou@rp-grece.be
Tel. +32 25515654

Mr NIKOLAIDIS

Mr Symeon TIKFESIS
Secretary (cohesion policy and Structural Funds)
E-mail: mtikfesis@rp-grece.be
Tel. +32 25515682

Justice and Home Affairs Unit

Mr Konstantinos KOUTRAS
First Secretary, Head of Unit
E-mail: jai@rp-grece.be
Tel. +32 25515603

Mrs PAVLI

Mr Efthymios CHARLAFTIS
Second Secretary (CATS, HLWG, fight against terrorism)
E-mail: e.charlaftis@rp-grece.be
Tel. +32 25515687

Mrs GIOUROUKOU

Mr Leonidas NIKOLOPOULOS
Expert Counsellor (VISA, SCIFA)
E-mail: l.nikolopoulos@rp-grece.be
Tel. +32 25515689

Mrs SOFRONI

Mr Michail KOSMIDIS
Secretary (legal migration and integration, fundamental rights)
E-mail: m.kosmidis@rp-grece.be
Tel. +32 25515700

Mr Odyssefs TSORBATZOGLOU
Counsellor (judicial cooperation (COPEN), CRIMORG)
E-mail: o.tsorbatzoglou@rp-grece.be
Tel. +32 25515760

Mrs ELLINA

Mrs Ageliki KABANARI
Secretary (judicial cooperation, JUSTICIV)
E-mail: a.kabanari@rp-grece.be
Tel. +32 25515733

Mr Alexandros THEOFANOPOULOS
Counsellor (FRONTEX)
E-mail: a.theofanopoulos@rp-grece.be
Tel. +32 25515639

Mr Konstantinos SOLDATOS
Counsellor (SCIFA, borders, illegal immigration, expulsion)
E-mail: k.soldatos@rp-grece.be
Tel. +32 25515701

Mrs BRAZIA

Mr Vassilios LALIOTIS
Counsellor (police cooperation, organised crime, drugs)
E-mail: v.laliotis@rp-grece.be
Tel. +32 25515769

Legal Service

Mrs Ioanna GALANIS-MARAGOUDAKIS
Minister Counsellor (head of legal service unit)
E-mail: maragoudakis@rp-grece.be
Tel. +32 25515662

Mr Panagiotis PANAYOTOPOULOS-TSIROS
Expert — Minister Counsellor
E-mail: panayotopoulos@rp-grece.be
Tel. +32 25515630

Mrs VARDAKA

Mrs Doxa SKEBOPOULOU
Attaché (administration)
E-mail: d.skebopoulou@rp-grece.be
Tel. +32 25515659

Agriculture Unit

Mrs Sofia KONDYLAKI
Counsellor, Head of Unit (SCA spokesperson)
E-mail: s.kondylaki@rp-grece.be
Tel. +32 25515767

Mrs Olga AGIOVLASSITI
Counsellor (fisheries, aquaculture, national aid)
E-mail: o.agiovlassiti@rp-grece.be
Tel. +32 25515723

Mr AGIOVLASSITIS

Mr Sotirios EVANGELOU
Counsellor (fruit and vegetables, olive oil, wine, rural development, promotion of agricultural products, agricultural statistics)
E-mail: s.evangelou@rp-grece.be
Tel. +32 25515772

Mrs STAVRIDI

Mr Antonios PERDIKARIS
Counsellor (GMOs, smaller Aegean Islands, cereals, tobacco, cotton, clearance of accounts)
E-mail: a.perdikaris@rp-grece.be
Tel. +32 25515747

Mrs BARMPAGALOU

Mr Charalambos MOULKIOTIS
Counsellor (CAP, plant health, WTO, organic farming, fisheries)
E-mail: c.moulkiotis@rp-grece.be
Tel. +32 25515730

Mrs TSOUNI

Mr Konstantinos ANAGNOSTOU
Counsellor (animal products, CAP, forests, crop protection, food security, clearance of accounts)
E-mail: k.anagnostou@rp-grece.be
Tel. +32 25515660

Mrs KONSTANTOPOULOU

Mrs Panayota PAPADAKI
Secretary (veterinary public health, TSEs, animal protection and nutrition, veterinary pharmaceutical products, fisheries)
E-mail: p.papadaki@rp-grece.be
Tel. +32 25515626

Mr GKIKAS

Mrs Anna LYMPEROPOULOU
Adviser (administration)
E-mail: a.lymperopoulou@rp-grece.be
Tel. +32 25515666

Mr ZOIS

Coreper I

Mr Alexandros KONSTAS
Third Secretary
Coordination, Coreper I (MERTENS deputy)
E-mail: a.konstas@rp-grece.be
Tel. +32 25515620

Mr Theodoros RALLIS
Attaché (administration)
E-mail: t.rallis@rp-grece.be
Tel. +32 25515624

Mrs DIMITRIOU

Employment, social affairs

Mr Konstantinos CHABIDIS
Counsellor
E-mail: k.chabidis@rp-grece.be
Tel. +32 25515605

Mrs WANNAN

Mrs Vassiliki KYRITSI
Counsellor
E-mail: v.kyritsi@rp-grece.be
Tel. +32 25515692

Mr XIROGIANNIS

Health

Mrs Dimitra ANASTASSOPOULOU
Counsellor
E-mail: d.anastassopoulou@rp-grce.be
Tel. +32 25515775

Mr Ilias SAMARAS
Counsellor
E-mail: i.samaras@rp-grece.be
Tel. +32 25515663

Mrs MORAITOU

Industry, energy, research, internal market, consumer affairs

Mr Theodoros CHRISTOPOULOS
Counsellor (energy questions)
E-mail: t.christopoulos@rp-grece.be
Tel. +32 25515688

Mrs LIAOUTSI

Mr Christos VASSILAKOS
Counsellor (research and technology)
E-mail: c.vassilakos@rp-grece.be
Tel. +32 25515685

Mrs KOZANOGLOU

Mrs Elli TZANETI-FRANGAKI
Counsellor (public procurement, consumers, tourism)
E-mail: e.frangaki@rp-grece.be
Tel. +32 25515705

Mr TZANETIS

Mr Georgios KAPANTAIDAKIS
Secretary (industry)
E-mail: g.kapantaidakis@rp-grece.be
Tel. +32 25515661

Mrs BOURA

Mr Christos GEROULANOS
Secretary (company law, insurance, competition, price of medicines)
E-mail: c.geroulanos@rp-grece.be
Tel. +32 25515640

Mr Petros MAMALIS
Secretary (technical harmonisation, internal market)
E-mail: p.mamalis@rp-grece.be
Tel. +32 25515789

Mrs TSISKAKI

Transport and telecommunications

Mr Sarantis POULIMENAKOS
Counsellor (Eurocontrol)
E-mail: s.poulimenakos@rp-grece.be
Tel. +32 25515790

Mr Nikolaos KOUVELIS
Secretary (telecommunications matters)
E-mail: n.kouvelis@rp-grece.be
Tel. +32 25515653

Mr Georgios PATRIS
Secretary (transport)
E-mail: g.patris@rp-grece.be
Tel. +32 25515762

Mrs AVRAMIDOU

Maritime transport

Mrs Venetia KALLIPOLITOU
Counsellor (maritime transport)
E-mail: v.kallipolitou@rp-grece.be
Tel. +32 25515623

Mr KREATSOULAS

Environment

Mr Kyriakos PSYCHAS
Counsellor (environment)
E-mail: k.psychas@rp-grece.be
Tel. +32 25515609

Mrs GLOVER

Mr Petros VARELIDIS
Secretary (environment)
E-mail: p.varelidis@rp-grece.be
Tel. +32 25515785

Mrs FOTAKI

Culture and education

Mr Panayotis LAMBIRIS
Expert — Minister Counsellor (cultural affairs)
E-mail: p.lambiris@rp-grece.be
Tel. +32 25515615

Mrs MUSTAKA

Mrs Despoina KARANTINOU
Counsellor (education, youth)
E-mail: d.karantinou@rp-grece.be
Tel. +32 25515641

Mrs Glykeria MITROPOULOU
Adviser (audiovisual affairs and the media)
E-mail: gl.mitropoulou@rp-grece.be
Tel. +32 25515786

Mr PAGKALOS

Mr Dimitrios KARAMATSKOS
Adviser (religious affairs)
Tel. +32 25515611

Mrs KARAMATSKOS

European Parliament Unit

Mr Iakovos IAKOVIDIS
Second Secretary (Head of European Parliament Unit, European Economic and Social Committee, GAG, Committee of the Regions)
E-mail: iakovidis@rp-grece.be
Tel. +32 25515644

Mrs SIDERI

Mr Vasileios KONIAKOS
Third Secretary (WPGA, Committee of the Regions, Economic and Social Committee)
E-mail: v.koniakos@rp-grece.be
Tel. +32 25515721

Administration and Planning Unit

Mrs Ekaterini FOUNTOULAKI
First Counsellor, Head of Unit
E-mail: a.fountoulaki@rp-grece.be
Tel. +32 25515697

Mrs Charoula-Iro TSAPARAS
Attaché (administration)
E-mail: c.tsapara@rp-grece.be
Tel. +32 25515612

Mr GEORGIADIS

Mr Konstantinos GAMOURAS
Attaché (administration)
E-mail: c.gamouras@rp-grece.be
Tel. +32 25515612

Mrs GAMOURA

Mr Panayotis TSOLAKOPOULOS
Attaché (administration)
E-mail: p.tsolakopoulos@rp-grece.be
Tel. +32 25515624

Mrs TSOLAKOPOULOU

Mrs Theano NIROU
Attaché (administration)
E-mail: th.nirou@rp-grece.be
Tel. +32 25515677

Mr ANTONIOU

Mr Efstathios LOUCOPOULOS
Attaché (administration)
E-mail: e.loucopoulos@rp-grece.be
Tel. +32 25515698

Mrs BARADAKI

Mrs Vasiliki SKALISTIRA
Attaché (administration)
E-mail: v.skalistira@rp-grece.be
Tel. +32 25515621

Mr PETROPOULOS

Mr Alcibiade BRIKIS
Attaché (administration)
E-mail: a.brikis@rp-grece.be
Tel. +32 25515655

Mrs BRIKIS

Mrs Patra ANDREDAKI
Attaché (Office of the Permanent Representation — Justus Lipsius)
E-mail: delegation.gr@consilium.europa.eu
Tel. +32 22816345

Mrs Constantina KALOUPIS
Attaché (administration)
E-mail: c.kaloupis@rp-grece.be
Tel. +32 25515752

Mr ECONOMOU

Mr Periklis PARAPONIARIS
Attaché (administration)
E-mail: paraponiaris@rp-grece.be
Tel. +32 25515643

Mrs VITALI

Mrs Maria KELLARI
Attaché (administration)
E-mail: m.kellari@rp-grece.be
Tel. +32 25515791

Mr MATSOPOULOS

Greek Parliament

Mr Georgios PAPACOSTAS
First Adviser
E-mail: gpapacostas@europarl.europa.eu
Tel. +32 22844564

Eurojust

Mr Lampros PATSAVELLAS
Secretary
E-mail: lpatsavellas@eurojust.europa.eu
Tel. +31 704125180

Mrs THOMOPOULOU

Political and Security Committee

Rue des Petits Carmes 10
B-1000 Brussels
E-mail: madee@skynet.be
Tel. +32 25455550
Fax +32 25455566

HE Mr Themistoklis DEMIRIS
Ambassador
Representative of Greece to the Political and Security Committee
E-mail: demiris@mfa.gr
Tel. +32 25455560

Mrs PAPANIKOLAOU

Mr Ioannis GHIKAS
Second Counsellor
Deputy Representative of Greece to the Political and Security Committee
Representative to the PMG
E-mail: ig@mfa.gr
Tel. +32 25455552

Mrs PAPAGIANNI

Mr Stavros KYRIMIS
First Embassy Secretary (civilian/military questions and PMG)
E-mail: skyrimis@mfa.gr
Tel. +32 25455557

Mrs LHUILLIER

Mr Nikolaos YOTOPOULOS
Second Secretary (CIVCOM)
E-mail: nikyot@mfa.gr
Tel. +32 25455554

Mrs Sophia-Maria GIOUROUKOU
Third Secretary (Nicolaïdis Group)
E-mail: sophia.giouroukou@mfa.gr
Tel. +32 25455558

Mr CHARLAFTIS

Mrs Evangelia KALAITZI
Third Secretary (Nicolaïdis Group, PMG)
E-mail: ekalaitzi@mfa.gr
Tel. +32 25455553

Mr PELEKANOS

Mr Platon ANTONIOU
Capitain (HENA) (EDA, POC, EU Nadrep, Polarm)
E-mail: platonantoniou@yahoo.gr
Tel. +32 25455539

Mrs SPILIOTOPOULOU

Military delegation

Mr Ioannis MENAGIAS
General (HEAF)
Representative of Greece to the Military Committee
E-mail: ellasmilrepeu@skynet.be
Tel. +32 25455530

Mrs MENAGIAS

Mr Konstantinos GKATZOGIANNIS
Colonel (HEAR)
Deputy representative of Greece to the Military Committee
Representative EUMC/WG
E-mail: ellasmilrepeu@skynet.be
Tel. +32 25455531

Mrs BIBALA

Mr Nikolaos BELLIAS
Commander (HEAR)
Deputy EUMC/WG
E-mail: ellasmilrepeu@skynet.be
Tel. +32 25455543

Mrs PAPASTAMOU

Mr Emmanouil MANOS
Colonel (HAF)
Deputy representative EUMC/WG
E-mail: ellasmilrepeu@skynet.be
Tel. +32 25455533

Mrs MANOS

Mr Thomas STAVROTHANASOPOULOS
Commander (HENA)
Deputy representative EUMC/WG
E-mail: ellasmilrepeu@skynet.be
Tel. +32 25455534

Mrs PSYCHOGIOU

Mr Fotios ADAMOPOULOS
Major (HEAR)
Deputy EUMC/WG
E-mail: ellasmilrepeu@skynet.be
Tel. +32 25455541

Mrs KIRIAKIDOU

Mr Dimitrios SIDERIDIS
Lieutenant Colonel (HEAF)
Deputy EUMC/WG
E-mail: ellasmilrepeu@skynet.be
Tel. +32 25455547

Mrs KONTOCHRISTOPOULOU

Press Office

Avenue des Arts 39
B-1040 Brussels
E-mail: greekpressoffice@gpo.be
Website: http://www.greekembassy-press.be
Tel. +32 22350370
Fax +32 22306651

Mr Konstantinos PAPPAS
Counsellor (Press Office)
E-mail: kpappas@gpo.be
Tel. +32 22350375

Mrs REGOS-PAPPAS

Mr Dimitrios BAKOULIS
Attaché (press and communications)
E-mail: Bakoulis@gpo.be
Tel. +32 22350373

Mrs WILLEMSEN

Mrs Eleftheria VOLIOTOU
Attaché (press and communications)
E-mail: volioti@gpo.be
Tel. +32 22350376

Mr KAIMAKIS

Mrs Magdalini VAROUCHA
Attaché (press and communications)
E-mail: varoucha@gpo.be
Tel. +32 22350377

Mr Christos BLATSIOTIS
Administration
E-mail: blatsiotis@gpo.be
Tel. +32 22350374

Mrs ORFANIDOU

Mrs Katerina KARANASIOU
Administration
E-mail: karanasiou@gpo.be
Tel. +32 22350381

PERMANENT REPRESENTATION OF SPAIN

Boulevard du Régent 52
B-1000 Brussels
Tel. +32 25098611
Fax +32 25111940/5112630

HE Mr Carlos BASTARRECHE SAGÜES
Ambassador Extraordinary and Plenipotentiary
Permanent Representative

Mrs Rosalia GÓMEZ-PINEDA

HE Mr Cristóbal GONZÁLEZ-ALLER JURADO
Deputy Permanent Representative Ambassador

Mrs Cristina Katia CASTILLO

Foreign affairs

Mr Antonio BULLÓN CAMARASA
Counsellor

Mrs Anne Marie CASSIS MUSSAVER

Mr Bernardo DE SICART ESCODA
Counsellor

Mr Antonio TORRES-DULCE RUIZ
Counsellor

Mrs Maria Lourdes GUTIERREZ VALLEJO

Mrs Beatriz LARROTCHA PALMA
Counsellor

Mr Bernardo DE SICART ESCODA

Mr Juan Antonio MARTIN BURGOS
Counsellor

Mrs María Belén GARTIEIZ-GOXEASCOA MINA

Mrs Cecilia YUSTE ROJAS
Counsellor

Mr José Ricardo GÓMEZ ACEBO

Mr Ignacio YBÁÑEZ RUBIO
Counsellor (Mertens)

Mrs Rosa María RABADÁN

Mr Juan ARISTEGUI LABORDE
Adviser (Antici)

Mrs María Teresa ORJALES VIDAL-ABASCAL

Mr Guillermo ARDIZONE GARCIA
Counsellor

Mrs Susana PECIÑA RODRIGUEZ

Mr Gabriel FERRAN CARRION
Counsellor

Mrs Ana Maria de la Victoria CIFUENTES CUENCAS

Mrs Miryam Isabel NAVIERAS TORRES-QUIROGA
Counsellor

Mr Raúl FUENTES MILANI
Counsellor

Mrs Maria Belén MARTÍNEZ CARBONELL

Mr Felix FERNÁNDEZ-SHAW
Counsellor

Mrs Christina DE LORENZO BROTONS

Mrs Cecilia YUSTE ROJAS
Counsellor

Mr Javier MELENDO GASPAR
Counsellor

Mrs Maria Angeles MONTOJO PAVIA

Mr Javier ROMERA PINTOR
Counsellor

Mr Emilio LORENZO SERRA
Counsellor

Mr Cándido CREIS ESTRADA
Counsellor

Mrs Carla CAVERO

Mr José Luís MARTÍN-YAGÜE
Counsellor

Political and Security Committee

Mr José Ricardo GÓMEZ-ACEBO
Counsellor ESPD

Mrs Cecilia YUSTE

Mr José Luis ANDRES MARTIN
T. Colonel
Defence Counsellor

Mrs María Belén VAQUERO

Mr Fernando JIMÉNEZ PÁEZ
T. Colonel
Counsellor

Mr Enrique ESQUIVEL LALINDE
Frigate Captain
Counsellor

Mrs Lucia DE COIG O'DONNELL MARQUINA

Mr Leonardo SANCHEZ PELAEZ
Counsellor

Mrs Purificación GARCÍA

Mr Victor Manuel PASTOR LLORD
T. Colonel
Defence Counsellor

Mrs Maria Jesús LOPEZ-PUIGCERVER PORTILLO

Interim Military Body

Mr Francisco Javier GARCIA ARNAIZ
Brigadier General
Deputy Military Representative

Mr José Ignacio CORDON SCHARFAUSEN
Frigate Captain
Military Counsellor

Mr Carlos CORDON SCHARFAUSEN
Military Counsellor

Mrs María Laura CASTOSA GACIO

Mr Alfonso BAREA MESTANZA
Military Counsellor

Mrs María Rosa LARA PELAEZ

Mr Juan Carlos MARTIN TORRIJOS
Counsellor

Mrs Ramira JORQUERA LUCERGA

Mr Victoriano GILABERT AGOTE
Frigate Captain
Military Counsellor

Mrs María Rosa GAMBOA HERRAIZ

Mr José Alfonso ROMAN BIENES
Counsellor

Justice

Mr Juan José MOLINOS COBO
Counsellor

Mrs María Isabel SANCHEZ BUSTOS

Mr Rafael GIL NIEVAS
Counsellor

Mrs Marta PRADANOS

Mr Luís AGUILERA RUIZ
Counsellor

Mrs Lourdes BUJ PRADILLA

Legal service

Mrs Eva CHAMIZO LLATAS
Counsellor

Mr Nicolas ROCH

Mr Miguel SAMPOL PUCURULL
Counsellor

Mrs Sonia RUIZ MORAN

Economic affairs

Mrs Isabel RIAÑO IBAÑEZ
Counsellor

Mr Fernando VALERO SAN PAULO
Counsellor

Mrs María Isabel COLINA SANCHEZ
Counsellor

Mr Eduardo BRYANT CEREZO
Counsellor

Mrs Maria José CANO ALEMÁN

Finance and customs

Mr Tomás ALBERDI ALONSO
Coordinator Counsellor

Mrs Isabel SAENZ-DIEZ GANDARO

Mr Antonio BLANCO DALMAU
Counsellor

Mrs Maria Eugenia MORENO LABORDA

Mr José Luis FERNANDEZ RANZ
Counsellor

Mrs Teresa GORROÑO ECHEBARRIA

Mrs Pilar SAENZ DE ORMIJANA
Counsellor

Mr Vicente RODRIGUEZ SAEZ
Counsellor

Mrs María LACASA DIAZ

Trade

Mr José Carlos GARCÍA DE QUEVEDO RUIZ
Counsellor, Chief-Coordinator

Mrs María ORTIZ AGUILAR

Mr Juan Ramón CALAF SOLE
Counsellor

Mrs Maria Dolores FERNANDEZ GOMEZ

Mrs María ORTIZ AGUILAR
Counsellor

Mr José Carlos GARCÍA DE QUEVEDO RUIZ

Mrs Cristina CALVO MAYAYO
Counsellor

Mr Pablo ASO MIRANDA

Mercedes MONEDERO HIGUERO
Counsellor

Mr José Lucas MARTIN DE LORENZO CACERES
Counsellor

Interior

Mr Francisco-Javier ALBALADEJO CAMPOS
Coordinator Counsellor

Mrs Paloma FERNANDEZ SANTOS

Mr Eugenio BURGOS NIETO
Coordinator Counsellor

Mrs Teresa CASTILLO GUTIERREZ-MATURANA
Counsellor

Mr José PEREZ NAVARETTE
Counsellor

Mrs Katia BELLIS LADEIRO

Mrs Yolanda RODRIGUEZ GOMEZ
Counsellor

Public works, transport and communications

Mr Jesús P. IZARZUGAZA URIARTE
Counsellor (transport)

Mrs Mauricette PERÓN DUNO

Mr Carlos ORTIZ BRU
Counsellor (telecommunications)

Mrs Amelia MUÑOZ CABEZÓN

Education and culture

Mrs Matilde VAZQUEZ FERNANDEZ
Counsellor

Culture

Mrs Guadalupe MELGOSA
Counsellor

Research and development

Mrs Milagros CANDELA CASTILLO
Counsellor

Mr Joaquín ALMUNIA

Labour and social security

Mr Carlos GARCIA DE CORTAZAR
Coordinator Counsellor

Mrs Carmen MILLAN

Mr Ignacio BERNARDO JIMENEZ
Counsellor

Mrs Florentina FERNANDEZ

Mr Valentín DUEÑAS JIMENEZ
Counsellor

Mrs Delmira Paz SEARA SOTO
Adviser

Industry and energy

Mr J. Ramón FERNÁNDEZ CIENFUEGOS
Coordinator counsellor

Mrs Monika ENGEN TORNQUIST

Mr Ignacio ATARROSAGASTI TELLERIA
Counsellor

Mrs Gema GARCÍA CAAMAÑO

Mrs Maria Jesús ONEGA COLADAS
Counsellor

Mr Antonio SANCHEZ LÓPEZ

Mr Carlos Luis GONZALEZ DIEGO
Counsellor

Mr Miguel-Francisco AZORIN ALBIÑANA-LOPEZ
Counsellor

Agriculture, fisheries and food

Mrs Maria ECHEVARRIA VIÑUELA
Coordinator Counsellor

Mr Valentín ALMANSA DE LARA
Counsellor

Mrs Ana FERNANDEZ Y MARTIN

Mr Alfonso PINO MAESO
Adviser

Mr Francisco Antonio BARDON ARTACHO
Counsellor

Press and information

Mrs Ana DE MIGUEL LANGA
Counsellor

Mrs Beatriz MONGE MORENO
Attaché

Public authorities

Mrs Justina BERMUDEZ MEDINA
Counsellor

Mr Johan VAN DER WERFF

Autonomous communities

Mr Estanislau VIDAL-FOLCH DE BALANZÓ
Counsellor

Health and consumer questions

Mr Carlos CRESPO SABARIS
Counsellor

Mrs Rosa VAZQUEZ CORTIJO

Mr Francisco SEVILLA PEREZ
Counsellor

Mr Enrique TEROL GARCÍA
Counsellor

Environment

Mr Miguel CASTROVIEJO BOLIBAR
Coordinator Counsellor

Mrs Esther FERNÁNDEZ BERJÓN

Mrs Pilar GARCIA DOÑORO
Counsellor

Mr Iñigo ASCASIBAR ZUBIZARRETA
Counsellor

Economic and administrative questions

Mr Domingo SORIANO GÓMEZ
Counsellor

Mrs María Francisca SÁNCHEZ ANDÚJAR

Mr Ramón CARNICERO SANCHIS
Head of Chancery — Administrative Attaché

Mrs Victoria COLLADO COBO

PERMANENT REPRESENTATION OF FRANCE

Place de Louvain 14
B-1000 Brussels
E-mail: courrier.bruxelles-dfra@diplomatie.gouv.fr
Website: http://www.rpfrance.eu
Tel. +32 22298211
Fax +32 22298282

HE Mr Pierre SELLAL
Ambassador Extraordinary and Plenipotentiary
Permanent Representative

HE Mr Philippe LEGLISE-COSTA
Deputy Permanent Representative

Mrs LEGLISE-COSTA

Mr Gautier MIGNOT
Counsellor (Coreper II, Antici)

Mrs MIGNOT

Mr Emmanuel PUISAIS-JAUVIN
Counsellor (Coreper I, Mertens)

Mrs PUISAIS-JAUVIN

Legal affairs

Mr Jean-Philippe MOCHON
Legal Adviser

Mrs MOCHON

Estelle AIRAULT
Assistant Legal Adviser

French presence in the European institutions

Mr Yves TEYSSIER D'ORFEUIL
Counsellor

Press and information

Mrs Marine de CARNE
Press Counsellor, Spokesperson

Mr Philippe RAY
Deputy Counsellor

Mrs RAY

Mrs Michele-Ann OKOLOTOWICZ
Deputy Counsellor

European Parliament

Mr Nicolas THIRIET
Counsellor

Mrs THIRIET

Mr Stéphane PAILLER
Adviser

External action

Mr Gautier MIGNOT
Counsellor

Mrs MIGNOT

Mrs Raja RABIA
Counsellor

Mr Frédérik ROGGE
Counsellor

Mr Christophe PARISOT
Counsellor

Mrs PARISOT

Mrs Claire RAULIN
Counsellor

Mrs Alix EVERARD
Counsellor

Mr Maxime LEFEBVRE
Counsellor

Mrs Natasha BUTLER
Counsellor

Mr Jean-Paul SEYTRE
Counsellor

Mr Xavier STICKER
Counsellor

Mr Frank PARIS
Counsellor

Mr Emmanuel VIVET
Economic Counsellor

Commercial policy

Mr Philippe O'QUIN
Minister Counsellor

Mrs O'QUIN

Mr François KRUGER
Economic Counsellor

Mrs KRUGER

Mr Emmanuel VIVET
Economic Counsellor

Mrs Suzanne VON COESTER
Economic Counsellor

Mr VON COESTER

Mrs Emmanuelle IVANOV-DURAND
Economic Attaché

Mr IVANOV

Mrs Valérie LIANG-CHAMPRENAULT
Economic Attaché

Mr CHAMPRENAULT

Mrs Chloé ALLIO
Economic Attaché

International financial and monetary relations

Mrs Valérie BROS
Minister Counsellor

Internal market

Mr Emmanuel PUISAIS-JAUVIN
Counsellor

Mr Guillaume DELVALLÉE
Counsellor

Mr Yves ULMANN
Counsellor (customs questions)

Mrs ULMANN

Mr Jean-Philippe MOCHON
Legal Adviser

Mrs Estelle AIRAULT
Assistant Legal Adviser

Justice, freedom and security

Mr Daniel LECRUBIER
Head of Department

Mrs Claudine JACOB
Adviser

Mr Ziad KHOURY
Counsellor

Mrs Claire ROCHETEAU
Counsellor

Mr Frédéric BAAB
Counsellor

Mrs Marie SALORD
Counsellor

Mr Yves GIMARD
Counsellor

Mr Damien HENDRICKX
Counsellor

Mrs HENDRICKX

Mr Pierre SIMUNEK
Counsellor

Mrs SIMUNEK

Mr Philippe RIO
Counsellor

Mrs RIO

Mr Jean-Louis DOMONT
Deputy Counsellor

Mr Yves ULMANN
Counsellor (customs questions)

Mrs ULMANN

Economic, financial and monetary affairs

Mrs Valérie BROS
Financial Counsellor

Mr Alexis ZAJDENWEBER
Deputy Financial Counsellor

Mr Ludovic HEHN
Deputy Financial Counsellor

Mrs HEHN

Mr Christophe POURREAU
Deputy Financial Counsellor

Mrs POURREAU

Mr Antoine SAINTOYANT
Deputy Financial Counsellor

Mrs SAINTOYANT

Mr Stéphane SAUREL
Deputy Financial Counsellor

Mrs Fanny LETIER
Deputy Financial Counsellor

Mr Ronan GUERLOT
Counsellor

Industry, information society

Mrs Lise DEGUEN
Counsellor

Mr Charles-Henri LEVAILLANT
Counsellor

Mrs Camille BONENFANT-JEANNENEY
Counsellor

Mr BONENFANT

Mr Alexandre ROESCH
Assistant Industry Counsellor

Ecology and sustainable development

Mr Marc STRAUSS
Counsellor

Transport

Mr Thierry BUTTIN
Adviser

Mrs BUTTIN

Mr Philippe DUMONT
Adviser

Mrs DUMONT

Mr Jean PREAT
Deputy Counsellor

Mr Michaël MASTIER
Deputy Counsellor

Environment

Mr François GAVE
Counsellor

Mr Michel COLIN
Deputy Counsellor

Mrs Anne-Marie MASKAY
Counsellor

Energy

Mrs Lise DEGUEN
Counsellor

Regional policy

Mr Jean-Sébastien LAMONTAGNE
Counsellor

Mr Sujiro SEAM
Counsellor

Mrs SEAM

Mr Guillaume HUET
Head of Mission

Nuclear questions

Guillaume GILLET
Counsellor

Agriculture and fisheries

Mr Yves MADRE
Delegate for agricultural affairs

Mrs MADRE

Mr Jean-Christophe LEGRIS
Deputy Delegate

Mr Bertrand GUILLOU
Deputy Delegate

Mrs GUILLOU

Mr Olivier PRUNAUX
Deputy Delegate

Mrs PRUNAUX

Mrs Caroline COGNAULT
Deputy Delegate

Mr Sujiro SEAM
Adviser

Mrs SEAM

Research — Education — Culture — Audiovisual questions — Youth and sport

Mr Florent STORA
Counsellor

Mr Eric-Olivier PALLU
Adviser

Mrs PALLU

Mrs Michèle BARON
Deputy Counsellor

Mrs Marie-Claire PETIT-PERRIN
Counsellor

Mr Mathieu WEISS
Counsellor

Mrs WEISS

Employment, social policy and health

Mr Cyril COSME
Counsellor

Mrs COSME

Mrs Nathalie NIKITENKO
Deputy Counsellor

Mr NIKITENKO

Mr Jean-Baptiste BRUNET
Counsellor (health)

Mrs Valérie SAINTOYANT
Deputy Counsellor

Mr SAINTOYANT

Mrs Evelyne FALIP
Deputy Counsellor

Mrs Morgane LESAGE
Deputy Counsellor

Political and Security Committee

HE Mrs Christine ROGER
Ambassador
Representative of France to the PSC

Mr Didier CHABERT
Deputy Representative

Mrs CHABERT

Mr Thomas BERTIN
Counsellor (politico-military affairs)

Mr Guillaume de LA BROSSE
Counsellor (politico-military affairs)

Mrs Céline PLACE
Counsellor (civilian crisis management)

Mr Alexandre MONEGER
Counsellor (civilian crisis management)

Mrs MONEGER

Mr Jean-René LE GOFF
Counsellor (armaments)

Mr Jean-Youri MARTY
Deputy Counsellor (armaments)

Mrs MARTY

Military Representation (Military Committee)

Mr Patrick de ROUSIERS
Air Marshal
Head of Mission

Mrs de ROUSIERS

Mr François LE JARIEL DES CHATELETS
Brigadier-General (land)
Counsellor

Mrs LE JARIEL DES CHATELETS

Mr Pascal ROUX
Colonel (air)
Counsellor

Mrs ROUX

Mr Cyrille CLAVER
Colonel (air)
Counsellor

Mrs CLAVER

Mr Yvan GOURIOU
Lieutenant Colonel (land)
Counsellor

Mrs GOURIOU

Mr Alain FAUGERAS
Colonel (Gendarmerie)
Counsellor

Mr Marc DE BECDELIÈVRE
Colonel (Ground Force)
Counsellor

Mrs DE BECDELIÈVRE

Mr Jean-Pierre MONTEGU
Colonel (air)
Counsellor

Mrs MONTEGU

Mr Denis BERTRAND
Captain
Counsellor

Mrs BERTRAND

Mr Pascal RUFFIN
Commander (air),
Support section

Mrs RUFFIN

Mr Fabrice COHELEACH
Commander
French Presidency relations

Mrs COHELEACH

Participation in external aid programmes — Enterprises

Mr Pierre Jean VERNHES
Economic Counsellor

Mrs VERNHES

Mr Lionel FRANCESCHINI
Economic Attaché

Mrs Valentine DELCOUSTAL
Economic Attaché

Mr Roger DEL RIO
Economic Attaché

Mrs DEL RIO

Administrative and institutional cooperation

Mr Jean-Paul SEYTRE
Counsellor

Mr Patrice BUDRY
Attaché

Mrs BUDRY

Mrs Marie-Christine JAUNET
Attaché

Mrs Marie-Claire PETIT-PERRIN
Counsellor

Administrative Department

Mrs Françoise MICHAULT
Second Secretary with responsibility for administrative matters

Coordination of French Presidency of the European Union

Mrs Jacqueline GUILLERMOZ
Second Secretary

PERMANENT REPRESENTATION OF ITALY

Chancellerie:
Rue du Marteau 7-15
B-1000 Brussels
E-mail: rpue@rpue.esteri.it
Website: http://www.italiaue.org
Tel. +32 22200411;
from 1 pm to 4 pm: +32 22200410
Fax +32 22193449, 22200426

HE Mr Ferdinando NELLI FEROCI
Ambassador Extraordinary and Plenipotentiary
Permanent Representative of Italy

Mrs Patrizia NELLI FEROCI

HE Mr Vincenzo GRASSI
Minister Plenipotentiary
Deputy Permanent Representative

Political and Security Committee

HE Mr Andrea MELONI
Ambassador (PSC-WEU)

Mrs Paola MELONI

Ministry of Defence

Mr Carmine DE PASCALE
Brigadier General
Counsellor

Mrs Rosa DE PASCALE

Ministry of Foreign Affairs

Mr Francesco CALOGERO
First Counsellor

Mrs Emanuela CALOGERO

Mr Mauro CONCIATORI
First Counsellor

Mr Marco PERONACI
First Counsellor

Mrs Pamela Audo PERONACI

Mr Stefano BALDI
First Counsellor

Mrs Antonella BALDI

Mr Vincenzo CELESTE
First Counsellor

Mrs Marzia CELESTE

Mr Gabriele ALTANA
First Counsellor

Mrs Alessandra ALTANA

Mr Armando BARUCCO
First Counsellor

Mrs Paola AMADEI
First Counsellor

Mrs Tosca BARUCCO
First Counsellor

Mr Fabrizio DI MICHELE
Counsellor

Mr Vincenzo DEL MONACO
Counsellor

Mr Ludovico SERRA
First Secretary

Mrs Valeria SERRA

Mr Marco CANAPARO
First Secretary

Mr Alessandro PRUNAS
First Secretary

Mr Giuseppe Sean COPPOLA
First Secretary

Mrs Luisa Isabella COPPOLA

Mrs Simona DE MARTINO
First Secretary

Mr Pierluigi D'ELIA
First Secretary

Mr Lorenzo ORTONA
First Secretary

Mrs Sheila Hanson ORTONA

Mr Alberto PETRANGELI
First Secretary

Mrs Arianna Maria PETRANGELI

Mrs Maria Liberatrice VICENTINI
Administrative Attaché

Mr Felice Antonio MAGGIA

Mr Annibale MARINELLI
Commercial Attaché

Mrs Maria Caterina MARINELLI

Mr Antonio CASARETTA
Attaché (data processing)

Mrs Elisabetta CASARETTA

Mrs Lucia ORLANDINI
Attaché (Social Affairs)

Mr Giuliano STELLA
Administrative Attaché

Mrs Stefania STELLA

Mrs Gigliola PAGLIARINI
Commercial Attaché

Mr Guiseppe CASCARDO

Mrs Lorena MASCHIETTO
Commercial Attaché

Mr Salvatore FAMÀ
Administrative Attaché

Mrs Sabrina FAMÀ

Mr Filippo ALESSI
Attaché

Bureau for Military Affairs

Mr Antonio PADULA
Colonel
Attaché and Nadrep

Mr Francesco SALVATI
Colonel
Assistant Adviser

Presidency of the Council of Ministers

Mr Antonio CENINI
Attaché

Mrs Giorgia CENINI

Ministry of the Interior

Mr Andrea PORTUESI
Attaché

Mrs Karolina PORTUESI

Ministry of Justice

Mr Biagio Roberto CIMINI
Attaché

Mr Benedetto ONORATO
Attaché

Mrs Olga MIGNOLO
Attaché

Ministry of Economic Affairs and Finance

Mr Giampaolo BOLOGNA
Attaché

Mrs Bettina BOLOGNA

Mrs Anna Maria TATARELLI
Attaché

Mr Marco IUVINALE
Attaché

Mrs Tiziana Laura FABBRIS
Attaché

Mr Maurizio PULCIANESE
Attaché

Mrs Nadia PULCIANESE

Mr Corrado CHECCHERINI
Attaché

Mrs Isabella CHECCHERINI

Mr Antonio CALABRESE
Attaché

Ministry of Economic Development

Mr Michele D'ERCOLE
Attaché

Mr Aldo DORIA
Attaché

Mrs Claudia DORIA

Mr Francesco PICCARRETA
Attaché

Mr Alessandro RIZZI
Attaché

Mrs Neelam RIZZI

Mrs Daniela FIORI
Attaché

Mr Stefano SANTACROCE
Attaché

Mrs Erika SANTACROCE

Mr Gaetano Andrea LO PRESTI
Attaché

Ministry for Agricultural and Forestry Policy

Mr Luigi POLIZZI
Attaché

Mrs Angela MILANO
Attaché

Mrs Francesca CIONCO
Attaché

Mr Riccardo RIGILLO
Attaché

Ministry for the Environment and Protection of Land and Sea

Mr Fabrizio FABBRI
Attaché

Ministry of Transport

Mr Gaetano DE SALVO
Attaché

Mr Angelo RICCI
Attaché

Ministry of Labour and Social Security

Mr Andrea DIONISI
Attaché

Mrs Carla ANTONUCCI
Attaché

Mr Pierdavide LECCHINI
Attaché

Mrs Tatiana ESPOSITO
Attaché

Ministry for Education, Universities and Research

Mr Marcello LIMINA
Attaché

Mr Roberto BARATTA
Attaché (legal questions)

Mrs Monica BARATTA

Mr Vittorio DE CRESCENZO
Attaché

Mrs Luciana DE CRESCENZO

Bank of Italy

Mr Francesco MAURO
Financial Attaché

Regions

Mrs Gabriella GUACCI
Attaché

Mr Felice BONANNO
Attaché

Mr Massimiliano BENELLI
Attaché

Mrs Paola POMPERMAIER
Attaché

Mr Giancarlo PRINA PERA
Attaché

Mrs Renata PRINA PERA

PERMANENT REPRESENTATION OF CYPRUS

Avenue de Cortenbergh 61
B-1000 Brussels
E-mail: cy.perm.rep@mfa.gov.cy
Tel. +32 27395111
Fax +32 27354552

HE Mr Andreas MAVROYIANNIS
Ambassador Extraordinary and Plenipotentiary
Permanent Representative
E-mail: amavroyiannis@mfa.gov.cy
Tel. +32 27395137

Mrs Calliopi MAVROYIANNIS

HE Mr George CHACALLI
Deputy Permanent Representative,
Minister Plenipotentiary
E-mail: gchacallis@mfa.gov.cy
Tel. +32 27395102

HE Mr Costas MILTIADES
Representative to the Political and Security Committee (PSC)
E-mail: cmiltiades@mfa.gov.cy
Tel. +32 27395159

Mrs Véronique MILTIADES

Foreign affairs

Mrs Elena RAFTI
First Secretary (RELEX)
E-mail: erafti@mfa.gov.cy
Tel. +32 27395133

Mr Stavros HATZIYIANNIS
First Secretary (Nicolaïdis Group, Civcom, Athena Special Committee)
E-mail: shatziyiannis@mfa.gov.cy
Tel. +32 27395151

Mr Haralambos KAFKARIDES
First Secretary (European Parliament)
E-mail: hkafkarides@mfa.gov.cy
Tel. +32 27395152

Mrs Maria HADJITHEODOSIOU
First Secretary (COEST)
E-mail: mhadjitheodosiou@mfa.gov.cy
Tel. +32 27395116

Mr Pavlos KOMBOS
Second Secretary (Antici, Coreper II coordination, institutional affairs)
E-mail: pkombos@mfa.gov.cy
Tel. +32 27395112

Mr Andreas PHOTIOU
Second Secretary (Enlargement)
E-mail: aphotiou@mfa.gov.cy
Tel. +32 27395109

Mr Andreas KETTIS
Second Secretary (Euromed, European Parliament)
E-mail: akettis@mfa.gov.cy
Tel. +32 27395123

Mr Petros MAVRIKIOS
Second Secretary (MOG, MAMA)
E-mail: pmavrikios@mfa.gov.cy
Tel. +32 27395138

Mrs Georgia APEYITOU
Second Secretary (Coreper I coordination, Mertens)
E-mail: gapeyitou@mfa.gov.cy
Tel. +32 27395140

Mr Andreas ELIADES
Attaché (PMG, COLAT)
E-mail: aeliades@mfa.gov.cy
Tel. +32 27395117

Mr Konstantinos POLYKARPOU
Attaché (COASI, COTRA)
E-mail: kpolykarpou@mfa.gov.cy
Tel. +32 27398209

Mrs Nektaria KAKOUTSI
Attaché (European Parliament)
E-mail: nkakoutsi@mfa.gov.cy
Tel. +32 27398206

Mrs Marina RAFTI
Attaché (Humanitarian and Food Aid, ACP, COAFR)
E-mail: mrafti@mfa.gov.cy
Tel. +32 27398208

Mrs Paraskevi NEOPHYTOU
Attaché (COWEB)
E-mail: pneophytou@mfa.gov.cy
Tel. +32 27398207

Mr Ioannis ADAMOU
Attaché (Development - European Parliament)
E-mail: iadamou@mfa.gov.cy
Tel. +32 27398205

Defence

Mr Antonis DEMETRIADES
Colonel
Military Representative
E-mail: cymilrep.eu@skynet.be
Tel. +32 27395136

Mr Spyros CHARALAMBIDES
Lieutenant Colonel
Representative of the National Armaments Director
E-mail: spcharalambides@mod.gov.cy
Tel. +32 27395157

Mr Theoklitos PACHOULIDES
Major
Deputy Military Representative
E-mail: cymilrep.eu@skynet.be
Tel. +32 27395135

Legal Service of the Republic

Mrs Nicoletta IOANNOU
Attaché (cooperation in civil matters, Court of Justice, fundamental rights)
E-mail: nioannou@eudep.law.gov.cy
Tel. +32 27395130

Mrs Eleni KOUZOUPI-ZALEWSKI
Attaché (cooperation in criminal matters, criminal law, offences)
E-mail: ekouzoupi@eudep.law.gov.cy
Tel. +32 27395129

Agriculture, natural resources and the environment

Mr Petros XYSTOURIS
Attaché (agriculture)
E-mail: pxystouris@da.moa.gov.cy
Tel. +32 27395114

Mr Costas HADJIPANAYIOTOU
Attaché (environment, climate change)
E-mail: chadjipanayiotou@environment.moa.gov.cy
Tel. +32 27395122

Mrs Vassilia THEOPHILOU
Attaché (environment, nature protection)
E-mail: vtheophilou@environment.moa.gov.cy
Tel. +32 27395195

Christodoulos PIPIS
Attaché (veterinary matters)
E-mail: hpipis@vs.moa.gov.cy
Tel. +32 27395115

Mr Charis MAVROKORDATOS
Attaché (fisheries)
E-mail: cmavrokordatos@dfmr.moa.gov.cy
Tel. +32 27398210

Mr Sokratis SOKRATOUS
Attaché (agriculture)
E-mail: ssokratous@da.moa.gov.cy
Tel. +32 27395113

Mrs Militsa CHRISTOFOROU
Attaché (agriculture)
E-mail: mchristoforou@da.moa.gov.cy
Tel. +32 27398212

Justice and Home Affairs

Mr Savvas STEPHANIDES
Attaché (police cooperation, MDG, Europol)
E-mail: sstephanides@police.gov.cy
Tel. +32 27395128

Mrs Mary EPIPHANIOU
Attaché (visas, Strategic Committee on Immigration, asylum)
E-mail: mepifaniou@crmd.moi.gov.cy
Tel. +32 27395127

Mrs Myria ANDREOU
Attaché (civil protection, Strategic Committee on Immigration, migration and deportation)
E-mail: mandreou@moi.gov.cy
Tel. +32 27395126

Mr Andreas ANDREOU
Attaché (terrorism, borders, Scheval, SIS-SIRENE)
E-mail: aandreou@police.gov.cy
Tel. +32 27395187

Commerce, industry and energy

Mr Constantinos KARAGEORGIS
Adviser (competition and growth)
E-mail: ckarageorgis@mcit.gov.cy
Tel. +32 27395186

Mrs Georgia PAVLOU
Attaché (intellectual property, company law)
E-mail: gpavlou@drcor.mcit.gov.cy
Tel. +32 27395107

Mrs Rona-Marie PANTELI
Attaché (Article 133 Committee, trade issues, GSP)
E-mail: rpanteli@mcit.gov.cy
Tel. +32 27395141

Mr Christos GOGAKIS
Attaché (energy)
E-mail: cgogakis@mcit.gov.cy
Tel. +32 27395104

Mrs Leoni THEODORIDOU
Attaché (energy)
E-mail: ltheodoridou@mcit.gov.cy
Tel. +32 27395183

Finance

Mrs Chryso KOLOKOTRONI-MARANDA
Adviser (financial questions, own resources)
E-mail: ckmaranda@papd.mof.gov.cy
Tel. +32 27395143

Mrs Florentia EVRIPIDOU HERACLEOUS
Counsellor (budget)
Website: fheracleous@mof.gov.cy
Tel. +32 27395106

Mrs Irene MANTI
Attaché (direct taxation)
E-mail: imanti@ird.mof.gov.cy
Tel. +32 27395156

Mr Antonis PELIDES
Attaché (customs and excise)
E-mail: apelides@customs.mof.gov.cy
Tel. +32 27395148

Mrs Elpida GEORGIADOU
Attaché (indirect taxation (VAT))
E-mail: egeorgiadou@vat.mof.gov.cy
Tel. +32 27395149

Mrs Maria BOTSARI
Attaché (customs and excise)
E-mail: mmbotsari@vat.mof.gov.cy
Tel. +32 27395121

Mr George SKLAVOS
Attaché (financial services)
E-mail: gsklavos@mof.gov.cy
Tel. +32 27395170

Communications and public works

Mr Nicolaos LYRAKIDES
Adviser (transport, telecommunications, aviation)
E-mail: nlyrakides@mfa.gov.cy
Tel. +32 27395105

Mr Vassilis DEMETRIADES
Conseiller (maritime transport)
E-mail: vdemetriades@dms.mcw.gov.cy
Tel. +32 27395103

Mrs Maria TSINGOU
Attaché (transport)
E-mail: mtsingou@rtd.mcw.gov.cy
Tel. +32 27395193

Labour and social security

Mrs Carola THEODOSIOU
Attaché (employment and social affairs)
E-mail: ctheodosiou@mlsi.gov.cy
Tel. +32 27395124

Mrs Chrysanthi SOFOKLEOUS
Attaché (labour inspection, atomic questions)
E-mail: csofokleous@dli.mlsi.gov.cy
Tel. +32 27395184

Education and culture

Dr Christina VALANIDOU
Attaché (education, culture, youth, audiovisual affairs)
E-mail: cvalanidou@mfa.gov.cy
Tel. +32 27395146

Health

Mrs Charitini FRENARITOU
Attaché (health)
E-mail: cfrenaritou@sgl.moh.gov.cy
Tel. +32 27395153

Mrs Chloe SPATHARI
Attaché (health, pharmaceuticals)
E-mail: cspathari@phs.moh.gov.cy
Tel. +32 27395125

Planning Bureau

Mrs Melina SAVVA
Attaché (Structural Funds)
E-mail: msavva@mfa.gov.cy
Tel. +32 27395155

Mr Telemachos TELEMACHOU
Attaché (research and information society)
E-mail: ttelemachou@planning.gov.cy
Tel. +32 27395131

Press

Mrs Maria PHANTI
Press Advisor
E-mail: mphanti@pio.moi.gov.cy
Tel. +32 27395139

Mrs Marianna KARAGEORGIS
Press Attaché
E-mail: mkarageorgis@pio.moi.gov.cy
Tel. +32 27395189

Administration

Mrs Chryso KOLOKOTRONI-MARANDA
Counsellor
E-mail: ckmaranda@papd.mof.gov.cy
Tel. +32 27395143

Mr Leontios LEONTIOU
Attaché
E-mail: lleontiou@papd.mof.gov.cy
Tel. +32 27395108

Mrs Irene PATSALOSAVVI LEONTIOU
Attaché
E-mail: ileontiou@mfa.gov.cy
Tel. +32 27395142

Mr Constantinos MISTRELLIDES
Attaché (electronic communication)
E-mail: cmistrellides@mfa.gov.cy
Tel. +32 27395160

Mrs Christiana STEPHANIDE
Attaché (security)
E-mail: cstefanides@police.gov.cy
Tel. +32 27395144

Mr Ioannis CONSTANTINOU
Attaché (accounting)
E-mail: iconstantinou@treasury.gov.cy
Tel. +32 27395118

Mrs Styliani CONSTANTINOU
Attaché
E-mail: sconstantinou@papd.mof.gov.cy
Tel. +32 27395191

PERMANENT REPRESENTATION OF LATVIA

Avenue des Arts 23
B-1000 Brussels
E-mail: permrep.eu@mfa.gov.lv
Website: http://www.mfa.gov.lv/brussels
Tel. +32 22383100
Fax +32 22383250

HE Mr Normunds POPENS
Ambassador Extraordinary and Plenipotentiary
Permanent Representative

Mrs Dina POPENA

HE Mrs Lelde LICE-LICITE
Ambassador
Deputy Permanent Representative

Coordination

Mrs Kristīne NAŠENIECE
First Secretary (Antici)
E-mail: kristine.naseniece@mfa.gov.lv
Tel. +32 22383217

Mrs Rita ROZITE
Third Secretary (Mertens)
E-mail: rita.rozite@mfa.gov.lv
Tel. +32 22383225

Mrs Aija INDRIĶE
Attaché (assistant to the Permanent Representative)
E-mail: aija.indrike@mfa.gov.lv
Tel. +32 22383201

Mrs Anna LAVRENTJEVA
Attaché (assistant to the Deputy Permanent Representative)
E-mail: anna.lavrentjeva@mfa.gov.lv
Tel. +32 22383203

Political and Security Committee (PSC)

HE Mrs Dace TREIJA-MASĪ
Ambassador
Representative of Latvia to the PSC

Mr Jānis SĪLIS
Counsellor (RELEX)
E-mail: janis.silis@mfa.gov.lv
Tel. +32 22383214

Mrs Irita KĪSE
First Secretary (Nicolaïdis)
E-mail: irita.kise@mfa.gov.lv
Tel. +32 22383212

Mrs Stella ANKRAVA
Second Secretary (Civcom)
E-mail: stella.ankrava@mfa.gov.lv
Tel. +32 22383227

Mrs Ilona EKMANE
Attaché (defence)
E-mail: ilona.ekmane@mfa.gov.lv
Tel. +32 22383110

External relations

Mrs Evelīna MELBĀRZDE
Counsellor (institutional affairs, European Parliament)
E-mail: evelina.melbarzde@mfa.gov.lv
Tel. +32 22383220

Mrs Dace DOBRĀJA
Counsellor (enlargement)
E-mail: dace.dobraja@mfa.gov.lv
Tel. +32 22383207

Una ĶEPĪTE
Second Secretary (commercial and transatlantic relations, EFTA, Latin America)
E-mail: una.kepite@mfa.gov.lv
Tel. +32 22383230

Mr Aldis KARALAUSKIS
Second Secretary (Eastern Europe and Central Asia)
E-mail: aldis.karalauskis@mfa.gov.lv
Tel. +32 22383216

Mrs Solvita APALA
Second Secretary (Western Balkans)
E-mail: solvita.apala@mfa.gov.lv
Tel. +32 22383226

Mrs Kristine STEPA-ABATNIECE
Second Secretary (development policy)
E-mail: kristine.stepa@mfa.gov.lv
Tel. +32 22383218

Mrs Inga PAVLINA
Third Secretary (Middle East, Asia)
E-mail: inga.pavlina@mfa.gov.lv
Tel. +32 22383233

EU Military Committee

Mr Intars JUNDZE
Lieutenant Colonel
Deputy Military Representative
E-mail: latmil@hq.nato.int
Tel. +32 22383146

Economic and financial affairs

Mrs Daina ISPODKINA
Counsellor (financial services, accounting)
E-mail: daina.ispodkina@mfa.gov.lv
Tel. +32 22383149

Mr Mihails KOZLOVS
Counsellor (ECOFIN, taxation, state aid)
E-mail: mihails.kozlovs@mfa.gov.lv
Tel. +32 22383121

Mr Imants TIESNIEKS
Counsellor (regional policy, Structural Funds, public procurement)
E-mail: imants.tiesnieks@mfa.gov.lv
Tel. +32 22383119

Mr Aldis AUSTERS
Counsellor (Exchange Rate Mechanism II, European Monetary Union)
E-mail: aldis.austers@mfa.gov.lv
Tel. +32 22383128

Mrs Edīte DZALBE
Attaché (budget, financial perspectives)
E-mail: edite.dzalbe@mfa.gov.lv
Tel. +32 22383118

Mr Larijs MARTINSONS
Attaché (customs questions)
E-mail: larijs.martinsons@mfa.gov.lv
Tel. +32 22383120

Justice and home affairs

Mrs Egita ŠĶIBELE
Counsellor (company law, Court of justice)
E-mail: egita.skibele@mfa.gov.lv
Tel. +32 22383135

Mr Ārijs JANSONS
Counsellor (borders, CIREFI)
E-mail: arijs.jansons@mfa.gov.lv
Tel. +32 22383122

Mrs Jeļena JANSONE

Mr Gatis ŠVIKA
Counsellor (home affairs, police cooperation, COTER, Article 36 Committee (CATS), Schengen
E-mail: gatis.svika@mfa.gov.lv
Tel. +32 22383124

Mrs Iveta MUCENIECE
Counsellor (immigration, asylum, visas)
E-mail: iveta.muceniece@mfa.gov.lv
Tel. +32 22383123

Mr Inguss KALNIŅŠ
Attaché (legal affairs, criminal matters, intellectual property)
E-mail: inguss.kalnins@mfa.gov.lv
Tel. +32 22383134

Economics, internal market, energy, trade

Mr Janis ZAKOVICS
Adviser (trade)
E-mail: janis.zakovics@mfa.gov.lv
Tel. +32 22383117

Mrs Inese BALODE
Counsellor (competitiveness, competition)
E-mail: inese.balode1@mfa.gov.lv
Tel. +32 22383116

Mrs Arta DENIŅA
Counsellor (energy, construction, tourism)
E-mail: arta.denina@mfa.gov.lv
Tel. +32 22383115

Mr Gints ZADRAKS
Counsellor (internal market, consumer protection)
E-mail: gints.zadraks@mfa.gov.lv
Tel. +32 22383114

Social policy

Mrs Rūta ZILVERE
Counsellor (employment, labour, anti-discrimination, equality of the sexes)
E-mail: ruta.zilvere@mfa.gov.lv
Tel. +32 22383130

Mrs Renata ORLOVA
Attaché (social policy)
E-mail: renata.orlova@mfa.gov.lv
Tel. +32 22383129

Health

Mrs Silvija JUŠČENKO
Attaché (public health, pharmaceuticals and medical appliances)
E-mail: silvija.juscenko@mfa.gov.lv
Tel. +32 22383138

Agriculture and fisheries

Mrs Gundega MIČULE
Counsellor (veterinary, nutritional, phytosanitairy issues)
E-mail: gundega.micule@mfa.gov.lv
Tel. +32 22383142

Mrs Olga ORLOVA
Counsellor (food safety, plant protection and biotechnology)
E-mail: olga.orlova@mfa.gov.lv
Tel. +32 22383145

Mrs Dace ARĀJA
Attaché (Special Committee on Agriculture, common agricultural policy)
E-mail: dace.araja@mfa.gov.lv
Tel. +32 22383140

Mr Māris BĒRZIŅŠ
Attaché (fisheries)
E-mail: maris.berzins@mfa.gov.lv
Tel. +32 22383144

Mrs Linda ČĪČE
Attaché (rural development, forestry)
E-mail: linda.cice@mfa.gov.lv
Tel. +32 22383143

Environment

Mrs Ieva SALENIECE
Counsellor (investment, sustainable environmental development)
E-mail: ieva.saleniece@mfa.gov.lv
Tel. +32 22383137

Mrs Anita DRONDINA
Counsellor (waste, air quality, nuclear safety, chemicals)
E-mail: anita.drondina@mfa.gov.lv
Tel. +32 22383136

Education, science, culture and youth

Mrs Signe MARTIŠŪNE
Attaché (science and research)
E-mail: signe.martisune@mfa.gov.lv
Tel. +32 22383126

Mrs Liene GRĪNVALDE
Attaché (education)
E-mail: liene.grinvalde@mfa.gov.lv
Tel. +32 22383125

Mrs Jolanta MIĶELSONE
Attaché (culture, audiovisual policy, copyright and related rights)
E-mail: jolanta.mikelsone@mfa.gov.lv
Tel. +32 22383127

Mrs Marians NĪLENDERS
Attaché (training, youth, sport and diplomas)
E-mail: marians.nilenders@mfa.gov.lv
Tel. +32 22383147

Transport and telecommunication

Mrs Elina VOLKSONE
Attaché (transport, telecommunications, information society)
E-mail: elina.volksone@mfa.gov.lv
Tel. +32 22383152

Mr Andris GAVARS
Attaché (maritime transport, inland waterways, aviation)
E-mail: andris.gavars@mfa.gov.lv
Tel. +32 22824430

Mr Ģirts BRAMANS
Attaché (land transport)
E-mail: girts.bramans@mfa.gov.lv
Tel. +32 22383133

Parliamentary cooperation

Mrs Inese KRIŠKĀNE
Attaché
E-mail: inese.kriskane@europarl.europa.eu
Tel. +32 22843312

Administration

Mrs Līga ROZENIECE
Adviser
E-mail: liga.rozeniece@mfa.gov.lv
Tel. +32 22383210

Mr Uģis SKUJA
Second Secretary
E-mail: ugis.skuja@mfa.gov.lv

Mrs Valda MANGALE
Head of Chancellery
E-mail: valda.mangale@mfa.gov.lv

PERMANENT REPRESENTATION OF LITHUANIA

Rue Belliard 41-43
B-1040 Brussels
E-mail: office@eurep.mfa.lt
Website: http://www.eurep.mfa.lt
Tel. +32 27710140
Fax +32 27714597

HE Mr Rytis MARTIKONIS
Ambassador
Permanent Representative, Representative to Coreper II
Tel. +32 27759083

HE Mr Raimundas KAROBLIS
Roving Ambassador, Representative to Coreper I, Deputy Permanent Representative
Tel. +32 27881871

HE Mr Darius Jonas SEMAŠKA
Deputy Permanent Representative, Itinerant Ambassador, Representative to PSC
Tel. +32 27881865

HE Mr Kęstutis JANKAUSKAS
Roving Ambassador
Tel. +32 27759091

Mr Erikas PETRIKAS
Minister Plenipotentiary, Deputy Permanent Representative, Head of Administration
Tel. +32 27759081

Mr Gintaras ČIURLIONIS
Minister Counsellor
Tel. +32 24013507

Mr Saulius DANIŪNAS
Minister Counsellor (Mertens)
Tel. +32 27759097

Mr Ramūnas STANIONIS
Adviser (Antici)
Tel. +32 27759080

Mrs Ona KOSTINAITĖ-GRINKEVIČIENĖ
Senior Officer
Assistant, Mertens and Antici
Tel. +32 27792065

Political and Security Committee

Mr Gintaras STONYS
Counsellor, Deputy Representative to the PSC (civilian aspects of the ESDP, arms of mass destruction, non-proliferation of weapons, export of conventional weapons, disarmament and arms control, human rights, United Nations and international conferences)
Tel. +32 27759096

Mr Gediminas KASPUTIS
Counsellor (EU external relations, sanctions, coordination of counter-terrorism)
Tel. +32 27881895

Mr Gediminas VILKAS
Third Secretary (Nicolaïdis) (political and military aspects of the ESDP, European arms policy, EU Satellite Centre, information security)
Tel. +32 27759093

Mr Vitalijus VAIKŠNORAS
Major-General, Military Representative to NATO and the EU
Tel. +32 27072845

Mr Jurijus GVOZDAS
Lieutenant Colonel, Deputy Military representative (EU affairs)
Tel. +32 27881884

Mr Marius ČESNULEVIČIUS
Major, Deputy Military Representative (EU affairs)
Tel. +32 27715911

Mrs Aušra RAIŠYTĖ-DAUKANTIENĖ
Deputy Defence Counsellor (EU affairs) (development of ESDP military capabilities)
Tel. +32 27881869

Mr Linas IDZELIS
Captain, Assistant to the Military Representative to NATO and the EU
Tel. +32 27072492, 27881884

Mrs Giedrė PETKEVIČIENĖ
Assistant to the Military Representative to NATO and the EU (administrative affairs)
Tel. +32 27881885

External relations

Mrs Agnė SKAISTYTĖ
Second Secretary (Asia and Oceania, Latin America, Africa, Middle East)
Tel. +32 27881883

Mr Robertas BRUŽILAS
Third Secretary (enlargement)
Tel. +32 27759086

Mr Mantas JAKIMAVIČIUS
Third Secretary (Maghreb-Mashreq, European Neighbourhood Policy, Visa Policy, Barcelona process)
Tel. +32 27759087

Mrs Edita RAZMĖNAITĖ
Third Secretary (development)
Tel. +32 27881881

Mrs Lina SUČILAITĖ
Third Secretary (Eastern Europe and Central Asia, OSCE, consular cooperation, Council of Europe)
Tel. +32 27881886

Mrs Lina RAMANAUSKAITĖ
First Secretary (external trade, transatlantic relations)
Tel. +32 27759085

Mr Antanas VENCKUS
Attaché (external trade, EFTA)
Tel. +32 27759089

Mrs Giedrė RAMANAUSKAITĖ
Attaché (economic affairs, external trade)
Tel. +32 24013504

Justice and home affairs

Mrs Agnė PUTELYTĖ
Attaché (home affairs)
Tel. +32 27630434

Mr Tomas ŽILINSKAS
Attaché (home affairs)
Tel. +32 25031878

Mrs Anna FIODOROVA
Attaché (police)
Tel. +32 24013505

Mr Darius MICKEVIČIUS
Attaché (justice)
Tel. +32 27881864

Finances and structural policy

Mrs Asta KUNIYOSHI
Financial Attaché
Tel. +32 27704149

Laura IEŠMANTAVIČIŪTĖ
Attaché (structural policy)
Tel. +32 27881875

Mr Vaidotas LINKEVIČIUS
Attaché (taxation)
Tel. +32 25025854

Mrs Diana DIRGĖLAITĖ
Attaché (financial services)
Tel. +32 24013506

Mrs Ramunė TARTILAITĖ
Attaché (customs)
Tel. +32 25020466

Mr Robertas TAMUŠAUSKAS
Attaché (monetary affairs and banking)
Tel. +32 24013514

Legal issues

Mr Andrius GRIKIENIS
First Secretary
Tel. +32 27881893

Cooperation with the European Parliament

Mr Tomas KUPRYS
Third Secretary
Tel. +32 27881877

Press and information

Mrs Jurgita APANAVIČIŪTĖ
First Secretary
Tel. +32 27759098

Protocol, recruitment in the European institutions

Mrs Žydra SENKUVIENĖ
Third Secretary
Tel. +32 27881866

Social security and health protection

Mr Vitalijus NOVIKOVAS
Attaché (social security and labour)
Tel. +32 27881898

Mr Robertas LUKAŠEVIČIUS
Attaché (social security and labour)
Tel. +32 25135484

Mr Mindaugas PLIESKIS
Attaché (health protection)
Tel. +32 27881863

Mr Kęstutis KUZMICKAS
Attaché (health protection)
Tel. +32 27881879

Industry, internal market and energy

Mrs Ilona PINTUKĖ
Attaché (energy)
Tel. +32 25130152

Mr Saulius KOLYTA
Attaché (internal market)
Tel. +32 27881894

Mrs Marija KAZLAUSKAITE
Deputy Attaché (tourism)
Tel. +32 24013521

Mr Žilvinas DANYS
Attaché (industrial property)
Tel. +32 27881876

Mr Algis BALEŽENTIS
Attaché (consumers, civil law)
Tel. +32 27759094

Transport and telecommunication, post

Mrs Vaiva OBELEVIČIENĖ
Attaché (ground transportation)
Tel. +32 27798272

Mr Vilius VEITAS
Attaché (transport navigation and aviation)
Tel. +32 27881892

Mr Paulius VAINA
Attaché (telecommunications and post)
Tel. +32 25137854

Agriculture and fisheries

Mr Rolandas TARAŠKEVIČIUS
Attaché (agriculture)
Tel. +32 27759088

Mrs Jūratė BRIEDIENĖ
Attaché (veterinary and phytosanitary issues, food safety)
Tel. +32 25031607

Mrs Adrija GASILIAUSKIENĖ
Attaché (fisheries)
Tel. +32 27881897

Environment

Mrs Lina ČAPLIKAITĖ
Attaché (environment)
Tel. +32 25028170

Mrs Indrė VENCKŪNAITĖ
Attaché (environment)
Tel. +32 24013503

Culture, education and research

Mrs Karina FIRKAVIČIŪTĖ
Attaché (research)
Tel. +32 27881874

Mrs Jolanta BALČIŪNIENĖ
Attaché (education)
Tel. +32 27881861

Mrs Vida GRAŽIENĖ
Attaché (culture)
Tel. +32 25132096

Sports questions

Mrs Karolina GARBALIAUSKAITĖ
Assistant to Permanent Representative
Tel. +32 24013530

PERMANENT REPRESENTATION OF LUXEMBOURG

Avenue de Cortenbergh 75
B-1000 Brussels
E-mail: prénom.nom@rpue.etat.lu
Tel. +32 27375600
Fax +32 27361429, 27375610

HE Mr Christian BRAUN
Ambassador Extraordinary and Plenipotentiary
Permanent Representative

HE Mrs Michèle EISENBARTH
Deputy Permanent Representative

HE Mrs Michèle PRANCHERE-TOMASSINI
Ambassador Extraordinary and Plenipotentiary
Permanent Representative to the WEU
PSC Representative

General coordination

Mr Léon DELVAUX
First Secretary of the Legation (Mertens — Coreper I preparation and coordination)

Mrs Antonia BATTAGLIA DELVAUX

Mr Jean-Claude MEYER
Legation Counsellor, first class (Nicolaïdis — PSC preparation and coordination)

Mr Henri SCHUHMACHER
First Legation Secretary (Antici — Coreper II preparation and coordination)

Mrs Unni KLØVSTAD

Relations with the European Parliament

Mr Raoul WIRTZ
Secretary of the Legation (general coordination, general affairs)

Legal affairs and institutional matters

Mr Léon DELVAUX
First Secretary of the Legation (legal adviser)

External relations

Mr Roland ENGELDINGER
Counsellor of the Legation (Central and Eastern Europe, Central Asia)

Mr Michel LEESCH
Secretary of the Legation (Counsellor RELEX)

Mr Tom KOLLER
First Legation Secretary (development cooperation, ACP)

Mr Orlando PINTO
Legation Attaché (Asia, Mashrek/Maghreb, Middle East/Gulf)

Mrs Patricia POMMERELL
Legation Secretary (enlargement, central and south-eastern Europe, Western Balkans, drafting of accession treaties, ad hoc Cyprus Group, ad hoc Bulgaria and Romania Group, EFTA)

Mr Raoul WIRTZ
Secretary of the Legation (transatlantic relations, Latin America)

Policy and Security Committee

HE Mrs Michèle PRANCHERE-TOMASSINI
Ambassador Extraordinary and Plenipotentiary Representative to PSC

Mr Jean-Claude MEYER
Legation Counsellor, first class, Deputy Representative to the PSC (PSC coordination, politico-military questions)

Mr Fabien RAUM
First Legation Secretary
Civilian crisis management

Military representation

Mr Jean-Louis NURENBERG
Lieutenant Colonel
Military Representative (EU Military Committee (EUMC))

Mr Alain SCHOEBEN
Lieutenant Colonel
Military Adviser

Commercial affairs

Mr Roland ENGELDINGER
Counsellor of the Legation (commercial questions, anti-dumping SPG)

Economic affairs, competitiveness and internal market

Mr Robert BEVER
Government Attaché (company law)

Mrs Anne VAN GOETHEM
Management Counsellor, first class (competitiveness, competition and consumers)

Energy, Lisbon process

Mr Guy LENTZ
Government Attaché (coordination)

Financial affairs and budgetary matters

Mr Antoine KASEL
Government Attaché (financial and budgetary affairs)

Justice and home affairs

Mrs Béatrice ABONDIO
Management Counsellor (terrorism coordination assistant)

Mrs Rachel BAYANI
Government Attaché (asylum and immigration, borders, visas)

Mr Robert BEVER
Government Attaché (judicial cooperation in civil matters)

Mr Pascal SCHUMACHER
Senior Divisional Commissioner
Police cooperation, terrorism coordinator, Schengen

Mr Raoul UEBERECKEN
Deputy Management Counsellor (horizontal issues, judicial cooperation in criminal matters, external relations, Frontex)

Agriculture, fisheries and food security

Mr Marc KREIS
Management Counsellor, first class (agricultural, veterinary and plant health policies)

Transport

Mr Sam WEISSEN
Government Attaché (air transport, land transport, networks and horizontal issues)

Employment, health and social policy

Mrs Anne CALTEUX
Government Attaché (health and social security)

Mr Luc WIES
First Grade Management Adviser (employment policy, labour market, social policies)

Environment

Mr Claude FRANCK
Management Counsellor, first class (general coordination)

Information technology, information

Mr Carlo MULLESCH
IT Attaché (IT issues, electronic networks, working party on information)

Mrs Karin MULLESCH

Accounting

Mr David VANDERHAEGHEN
Accounting, information technology

Archives

Mrs Sandrine GORGON
Archiving and documentation, GEDIS

PERMANENT REPRESENTATION OF HUNGARY

Rue de Trèves 92-98
B-1040 Brussels
E-mail: sec.beu@kum.hu
Website: http://www.hunrep.be
Tel. +32 22341200
Fax +32 23720784

HE Mr Tibor KISS
Ambassador Extraordinary and Plenipotentiary
Permanent Representative
E-mail: sec.beu@kum.hu
Tel. +32 22341205

HE Mrs Ágnes VARGHA
Ambassador
Deputy Permanent Representative
E-mail: deputy.beu@kum.hu
Tel. +32 22341339

HE Mr András KÓS
Ambassador Representative to PSC
E-mail: PSCHu.beu@kum.hu
Tel. +32 22341216

Antici

Mr Csaba ZALAI
Envoy Extraordinary and Minister Plenipotentiary
E-mail: csaba.zalai@kum.hu
Tel. +32 22341208

Enlargement

Mrs Zsuzsanna Zsófia MÁTRAI
Second Secretary
E-mail: zsuzsanna.matrai@kum.hu
Tel. +32 22341255

Mertens

Mr Tibor STELBACZKY
First Secretary
E-mail: tibor.stelbaczky@kum.hu
Tel. +32 22341202

Cabinet

Mrs Szilvia DÓRA
First Secretary (institutional questions, transatlantic relations)
E-mail: szilvia.dora@kum.hu
Tel. +32 22341275

Regional policy

Mrs Gabriella IGLÓI
Second Secretary (cohesion policy)
E-mail: gabriella.igloi@kum.hu
Tel. +32 22341226

Mrs Anita MAYER
Second Secretary (regional policy)
E-mail: anita.mayer@kum.hu
Tel. +32 22341273

Mrs Hajnalka SZABÓ
Second Secretary (local authorities, COR)
E-mail: hajnalka.szabo@kum.hu
Tel. +32 22341293

European Parliament

Mr Zsigmond HETYEI
Counsellor
E-mail: zsigmond.hetyei@kum.hu
Tel. +32 22341271

Press and Protocol

Mrs Júlia MÁNYIK
Counsellor (press, communication)
E-mail: julia.manyik@kum.hu
Tel. +32 22341410

Mr Gábor BIRÓ
Counsellor (protocol)
E-mail: gabor.biro@kum.hu
Tel. +32 22341280

Mrs Melinda KERESZTES
Third Secretary (protocol and EP relations)
E-mail: melinda.keresztes@kum.hu
Tel. +32 22341210

Mrs Zsófia ZALAI-ZEMPLÉNI
Attaché (staff regulations, culture)
E-mail: zsofia.zempleni@kum.hu
Tel. +32 22341234

Legal Service

Mrs Ágnes KERTÉSZ
Second Secretary
E-mail: agnes.kertesz@kum.hu
Tel. +32 22341272

Mrs Krisztina GOSZTONYI
Second Secretary
E-mail: krisztina.gosztonyi@kum.hu
Tel. +32 22341211

Economic and Financial Unit

Mrs Zsuzsanna BESZTERI
Second Secretary, Head of Unit
E-mail: zsuzsa.beszteri@kum.hu
Tel. +32 22341218

Mr Lajos RAJCZY
Counsellor (customs and OLAF Affairs)
E-mail: lajos.rajczy@kum.hu
Tel. +32 22341228

Mr Péter KERESZTES
Counsellor (financial perspectives)
E-mail: peter.keresztes@kum.hu
Tel. +32 22341274

Mrs Ágnes DOBÓ
Third Secretary (budget, financial control)
E-mail: agnes.dobo@kum.hu
Tel. +32 22341286

Mr Barnabás DEZSÉRI
Attaché (financial services)
E-mail: katalin.koos-hutas@kum.hu
Tel. +32 22341267

Mr Péter TÁRNOKI-ZÁCH
Attaché (taxation)
E-mail: peter.tarnoki@kum.hu
Tel. +32 22341288

Mr Csaba ZSARNÓCI
Attaché (state aid, combating fraud, accounting-auditing, fight against money laundering and terrorist financing)
E-mail: csaba.zsarnoci@kum.hu
Tel. +32 22341249

Mr Tamás JAKAB
Attaché (EMU, statistics)
E-mail: tamas.jakab@kum.hu
Tel. +32 22341250

Justice and Home Affairs Unit

Mr Mátyás HEGYALJAI
Counsellor (police cooperation, organised crime, EUROPOL, HDG)
E-mail: matyas.hegyaljai@kum.hu
Tel. +32 22341372

Mrs Vivien VADASI
Second Secretary (asylum and migration)
E-mail: vivien.vadasi@kum.hu
Tel. +32 22341229

Mr György RÉTHÁZI
Second Secretary, Head of Unit (JHA coordination, judicial cooperation in criminal matters)
E-mail: gyorgy.rethazi@kum.hu
Tel. +32 22341214

Mr Dániel CSÖRGŐ
Third Secretary (visas, external aspects of JHA)
E-mail: daniel.csorgo@kum.hu
Tel. +32 22341292

Mrs Timea ANDICS
Third Secretary (Schengen enlargement, SIS, border management, document security)
E-mail: timea.andics@kum.hu
Tel. +32 22341214

Mr Pál SZIRÁNYI
Third secretary (judicial cooperation in civil matters, E-Justice, EJN)
E-mail: pal.sziranyi@kum.hu
Tel. +32 22341400

Trade Policy Unit

Mr Gusztáv FALUSSY
Counsellor, Head of Unit (TDI, textile, steel, transatlantic trade relations, trade relations with the Asian and Pacific region)
E-mail: gusztav.falussy@kum.hu
Tel. +32 22341322

Mr Erik SZARVAS
Counsellor (133 suppléants, 133 titulaires, Groupe "Mashreq/Maghreb", autres questions concernant le commerce)
E-mail: erik.szarvas@kum.hu
Tel. +32 22341243

Mrs Gabriella PAPP
Second Secretary (EFTA, trade relations with Latin American, Eastern European and Central Asian countries)
E-mail: gabriella.papp@kum.hu
Tel. +32 22341269

Mr Levente GAZDAG
Third Secretary (commodities, GSP, trade in services, trade relations with Balkans, trade relations with ACP countries)
E-mail: levente.gazdag@kum.hu

Agricultural Unit

Mr András CZETI
Counsellor, Head of Unit (agricultural policy, rural development)
E-mail: andras.czeti@kum.hu
Tel. +32 22341285

Mrs Anikó KORMOS
Counsellor (CAP, CMO — plants, GMO, financial agricultural questions)
E-mail: aniko.kormos@kum.hu
Tel. +32 22341284

Mr Tamás TARPATAKI
Third Secretary (fisheries, forestry, organic farming)
E-mail: tamas.tarpataki@kum.hu
Tel. +32 22341254

Mrs Barbara BÓNÉ
Third Secretary (veterinary questions, food safety)
E-mail: barbara.bone@kum.hu
Tel. +32 22341266

Infrastructure and Environment Unit

Mr László POLGÁR
Counsellor, Head of Unit (transport)
E-mail: laszlo.polgar@kum.hu
Tel. +32 22341219

Mrs Katalin GARA NAGY
Counsellor (environment)
E-mail: katalin.gara@kum.hu
Tel. +32 22341268

Mr István ERÉNYI
Counsellor (information society, post and competitiveness)
E-mail: istvan.erenyi@kum.hu
Tel. +32 22341212

Mr Péter LENGYEL
First Secretary (telecommunication, information society, Lisbon strategy)
E-mail: peter.lengyel@kum.hu
Tel. +32 22341334

Mr Péter BARTHA
Second Secretary (environment)
E-mail: peter.bartha@kum.hu
Tel. +32 22341220

Mrs Réka MÁRTON
Third Secretary (transport)
E-mail: reka.marton@kum.hu
Tel. +32 22341332

Mr Attila NAGY
Third Secretary (energy)
E-mail: attila.nagy@kum.hu
Tel. +32 22341221

Mr László IGNÉCZI
Third Secretary (telecommunications)
E-mail: laszlo.igneczi@kum.hu
Tel. +32 22341246

Competitiveness and Human Resources Unit

Mr Endre SCHUCHTÁR
Counsellor, Head of Unit (competitiveness, SMEs, industrial affairs)
E-mail: endre.schuchtar@kum.hu
Tel. +32 22341281

Mrs Katalin NAGY
Counsellor (free movement of persons, employment policy, labour law, health and safety at work, social dialogue, public health)
E-mail: katalin.nagy@kum.hu
Tel. +32 22341245

Mrs Katalin ALFÖLDI
Second Secretary (science and technology)
E-mail: katalin.alfoldi@kum.hu
Tel. +32 22341233

Mrs Nóra KAJTÁR
Third Secretary (public health, medicinal products)
E-mail: nora.kajtar@kum.hu
Tel. +32 22341237

Mr Áron BALÁZS
Third Secretary (culture and education)
E-mail: aron.balazs@kum.hu
Tel. +32 22341253

Mr György KOZMA
Third Secretary (intellectual property rights, data protection, competition law)
E-mail: gyorgy.kozma@kum.hu
Tel. +32 22341294

Foreign Policy Unit

Mr Sándor MOLNÁR
Envoy Extraordinary and Minister Plenipotentiary (RELEX), Head of Unit
E-mail: sandor.molnar@kum.hu
Tel. +32 22341419

Mr Károly SÁRDI
Counsellor (COWEB)
E-mail: karoly.sardi@kum.hu
Tel. +32 22341415

Mr Attila NYITRAI
First Secretary (COASI)
E-mail: attila.nyitrai@kum.hu
Tel. +32 22341418

Mrs Enikő JACZÓ
First Secretary (COARM, CODUN, CONOP)
E-mail: eniko.jaczo@kum.hu
Tel. +32 22341333

Mrs Carmen CSERNELHÁZI
Second Secretary (Nicolaidïs, AMLAT)
E-mail: carmen.csernelhazi@kum.hu
Tel. +32 22341335

Mr Kálmán PUSZTAI
Second Secretary (COMAG, COMEM, COMED, COMEP)
E-mail: kalman.pusztai@kum.hu
Tel. +32 22341414

Mrs Andrea STEMLER
Third Secretary (COEST, COSCE)
E-mail: andrea.stemler@kum.hu
Tel. +32 22341407

Mrs Éva Réka VASAS
Third Secretary (COAFR, ACP)
E-mail: reka.vasas@kum.hu
Tel. +32 22341321

Mrs Bea BOKOR
Attaché (CODEV, ALIM)
E-mail: bea.bokor@kum.hu
Tel. +32 22341287

Security and Defence Policy Unit

Mr István SIPOS
Counsellor (CIVCOM, PROCIV, CONUN)
E-mail: istvan.sipos@kum.hu
Tel. +32 22341408

Mr Péter GYILA
First Secretary (PMG, ESDC SC)
E-mail: peter.gyila@kum.hu
Tel. +32 22341295

Mrs Katalin HORVÁTH
Second Secretary (PMG, capability development, EDA, EU-NATO Capability Group)
E-mail: katalin.horvath@kum.hu
Tel. +32 22341409

Mr László TÓTH
Colonel, Counsellor, Deputy Military Representative to EUMC, EUMCWG
E-mail: laszlo.toth@kum.hu
Tel. +32 22341411

Mr Attila GRINÁCZ
Lieutenant Colonel, First Secretary, Senior Liaison Officer (EUMCWG/HTF)
E-mail: attila.grinacz@kum.hu
Tel. +32 22341412

Mr Ferenc KERÉKGYÁRTÓ
Lieutenant Colonel, First Secretary, Senior Liaison Officer (operations, exercises, training, concepts)
E-mail: ferenc.kerekgyarto@kum.hu
Tel. +32 22341413

Administrative Section

Mr Péter HORVÁTH
First Secretary, Head of Unit (administrative affairs)
E-mail: peter.horvath@kum.hu
Tel. +32 22341290

Mr Ferenc INKOVICS
Head of ITC Section, Attaché (informatics, COTEL, Comelec)
E-mail: ferenc.inkovics@kum.hu
Tel. +32 22341215

Mr Imre MÉSZÁROS
First Secretary (security matters)
E-mail: imre.meszaros@kum.hu
Tel. +32 22341207

Mr Krisztian BERZE
Third Secretary (Head of building management)
E-mail: krisztian.berze@kum.hu
Tel. +32 22341251

Mr András VÁCZI
Attaché (security questions, INFOSEC)
E-mail: andras.vaczi@kum.hu
Tel. +32 22341289

Mr György VICZIAN
Attaché
Tel. +32 22341473

Mr Csaba SIPOS
Attaché

Mr Zoltan TOTH
Attaché
Tel. +32 22341374

Mr Béla GROF
Attaché
Tel. +32 22341472

Mr Andras HOLLIK
Attaché
Tel. +32 22341200

Mr Istvan NEMES
Attaché
Tel. +32 22341200

Mr Istvan VARGA
Attaché
Tel. +32 22341200

Mr Istvan SILLE
Attaché
Tel. +32 22341200

Mr Lajos SZABO
Attaché
Tel. +32 22341200

Mr Lajos FODOR
Attaché
Tel. +32 22341200

Mr Sandor PAVITS
Attaché
Tel. +32 22341200

Mr Laszlo SZILI
Attaché
Tel. +32 22341200

Mr György MULLER
Attaché
Tel. +32 22341200

PERMANENT REPRESENTATION OF MALTA

Rue Archimède 25
B-1000 Brussels
E-mail: maltarep@gov.mt
Tel. +32 23430195
Fax +32 23430106

HE Mr Richard CACHIA CARUANA
Ambassador Extraordinary and Plenipotentiary
Permanent Representative
Tel. +32 22382715
Fax +32 23430106

HE Mrs Theresa CUTAJAR
Deputy Permanent Representative
Tel. +32 22382781
Fax +32 23430106

HE Mr Tarcisio ZAMMIT
Ambassador
Representative to the Political and Security Committee (PSC)
Tel. +32 22382600
Fax +32 23430106

Mrs ZAMMIT

Mrs Emily TUFIGNO
Counsellor (Private Office)
E-mail: emily.tufigno@gov.mt
Tel. +32 22382720
Fax +32 23430106

Mr TUFIGNO

Mrs Sharon ZARB
First Secretary (Cabinet)
E-mail: sharon.zarb@gov.mt
Tel. +32 22382723
Fax +32 23430106

Mr Jean MICALLEF GRIMAUD
First Secretary (Cabinet)
E-mail: jean.micallef-grimaud@gov.mt
Tel. +32 22382724
Fax +32 23430106

Mrs MICALLEF GRIMAUD

Mr Cajetan SCHEMBRI
First Secretary (policy)
E-mail: cajetan.schembri@gov.mt
Tel. +32 22382763
Fax +32 23430106

Mrs SCHEMBRI WORLEY

Mrs Corinne CASHA
First Secretary (policy)
E-mail: corinne.casha@gov.mt
Tel. +32 22382762
Fax +32 23430106

Mr Ian CAUSON
First Secretary (policy)
E-mail: ian-andrew.causon@gov.mt
Tel. +32 22382761

Private Office of the Permanent Representative (Coreper and Interinstitutional Affairs)

Mrs Christine PACE LUPI
Head of Cabinet
E-mail: christine.pace-lupi@gov.mt
Tel. +32 22382718
Fax +32 23430106

Mrs Rebecca VELLA
First Secretary (Antici)
E-mail: antici@gov.mt
rebecca.a.vella@gov.mt
Tel. +32 22382720
Fax +32 23430106

Mr GALEA

Mrs Therese BRINCAT
First Secretary (Mertens)
E-mail: mertens@gov.mt
therese.brincat@gov.mt
Tel. +32 22382769
Fax +32 23430106

Political affairs

Mr Stephen BORG
Adviser (political affairs)
E-mail: stephen.d.borg@gov.mt
Tel. +32 22382766
Fax +32 23430106

Mr Martin CAUCHI INGLOTT
Lieutenant Colonel
CFSP/ESDP Attaché
E-mail: martin.cauchi-inglott@gov.mt
Tel. +32 22382765
Fax +32 23430106

Mrs CAUCHI INGLOTT

Mrs Joanne MERCIECA
Adviser (political affairs)
E-mail: joanne.mercieca@gov.mt
Tel. +32 22382764
Fax +32 23430106

Public and legal affairs

Mr Ian GALEA
Attaché (Press and Parliament)
E-mail: ian.p.galea@gov.mt
Tel. +32 22382680
Fax +32 23430106

Mrs VELLA

Mr Jean Pierre SCHEMBRI
Attaché (institutions)
E-mail: jean-pierre.schembri@gov.mt
Tel. +32 22382684

Mr Claude DEPASQUALE
Attaché (legal questions)
E-mail: claude.depasquale@gov.mt
Tel. +32 22382686

EU funds, programming and human resources

Mr David MUSCAT
First Secretary (EU funds)
E-mail: david.muscat@gov.mt
Tel. +32 22382694
Fax +32 23430106

Justice and home affairs

Mr Antoine CASHA
Attaché (police)
E-mail: antoine.casha@gov.mt
Tel. +32 22382743
Fax +32 23430106

Mrs CASHA

Mrs Elayne CUTAJAR
Attaché (Schengen and asylum)
E-mail: elaine.cutajar@gov.mt
Tel. +32 22382742
Fax +32 23430106

Mrs Roberta TEDESCO TRICCAS
Attaché (legal cooperation)
E-mail: roberta.tedesco-triccas@gov.mt
Tel. +32 22382741
Fax +32 23430106

METSOLA

Economic and financial affairs

Mrs Elaine MILLER
Attaché (finance, tax and budget)
E-mail: elaine.miller@gov.mt
Tel. +32 22382688
Fax +32 23430106

Mr BUFITHIS

Mr John BUSUTTIL
Attaché (trade)
E-mail: john-andrew.busuttil@gov.mt
Tel. +32 22382689
Fax +32 23430106

Mrs BUSUTTIL

Mr Matthew BUTTIGIEG
Fiscal Attaché
E-mail: matthew.buttigieg@gov.mt
Tel. +32 22382690
Fax +32 23430106

Mr Ryan BORG
Fiscal Attaché
E-mail: ryan.borg@gov.mt
Tel. +32 22382692
Fax +32 23430106

Competition

Mrs Charmaine HOGAN
Attaché (competition)
E-mail: charmaine.hogan@gov.mt
Tel. +32 22382652
Fax +32 23430106

Mr Andrew BIANCO
Attaché (competition)
E-mail: andrew.bianco@gov.mt
Tel. +32 22382653
Fax +32 23430106

Transport, telecommunications and energy

Mrs Nicolette CAMILLERI
Attaché (sea transport)
E-mail: nicolette.camilleri@gov.mt
Tel. +32 22382639
Fax +32 23430106

Mr CAMILLERI

Mr Gordon BUHAGIAR
Attaché (land transport and energy)
E-mail: gordon.buhagiar@gov.mt
Tel. +32 22382636
Fax +32 23430106

Mrs Dulcie TABONE
Attaché (air transport and telecommunications)
E-mail: dulcie.tabone@gov.mt
Tel. +32 22382638
Fax +32 23430106

Agriculture and fisheries

Mr Justin ZAHRA
Attaché (horizontal issues, agriculture)
E-mail: justin.zahra@gov.mt
Tel. +32 22382633
Fax +32 23430106

Mrs ZAHRA

Mr John BRINCAT
Attaché (fisheries)
E-mail: john.brincat@gov.mt
Tel. +32 22382630
Fax +32 23430106

Mrs Sarah BUGEJA
Attaché (agriculture, veterinary matters)
E-mail: sarah.bugeja@gov.mt
Tel. +32 22382631
Fax +32 23430106

Mr CAMILLERI

Mrs Paula CALAMATTA
Attaché (agriculture, plant health matters)
E-mail: paula.calamatta@gov.mt
Tel. +32 22382632
Fax +32 23430106

Environment

Mrs Nathalie CHETCUTI
Attaché (environment)
E-mail: nathalie.chetcuti@gov.mt
Tel. +32 22382651
Fax +32 23430106

Mr BUTTIGIEG

Mr Adrian MIFSUD
Attaché (environment)
E-mail: adrian.a.mifsud@gov.mt
Tel. +32 22382650
Fax +32 23430106

Employment, social policy, health and consumer affairs

Mr Stephen MIFSUD
Attaché (health and consumer protection)
E-mail: stephen.m.mifsud@gov.mt
Tel. +32 22382657
Fax +32 23430106

Mrs Claudia VELLA
Attaché (social affairs and employment)
E-mail: claudia.vella@gov.mt
Tel. +32 22382656
Fax +32 23430106

Education, youth and culture

Mr Karsten XUEREB
Attaché (culture and audiovisual matters)
E-mail: karsten.xuereb@gov.mt
Tel. +32 22382660
Fax +32 23430106

Mrs XUEREB

Mr Neil KERR
Attaché (education and research)
E-mail: neil.keer@gov.mt
Tel. +32 22382661
Fax +32 23430106

Mrs KERR

Administration

Mr Victor GRECH
Adviser (administration)
E-mail: victor.h.grech@gov.mt
Tel. +32 22382671

Mrs GRECH

PERMANENT REPRESENTATION OF THE NETHERLANDS

Avenue Herrmann Debroux 48
B-1160 Brussels
Website: http://www.eu-nederland.be
Tel. +32 26791511
Fax +32 26791715

HE Mr T. J. A. M. DE BRUIJN
Ambassador Extraordinary and Plenipotentiary
Permanent Representative
Tel. +32 26791502
Fax +32 26791795

HE Mr P. W. KOK
Minister Plenipotentiary
Deputy Permanent Representative
Tel. +32 26791508
Fax +32 26791774

Mrs W. KOK-VAN DE KEMP

HE Mr R. MILDERS
Representative to the Political and Security Committee
Permanent Representative of the Kingdom of the Netherlands to the WEU
Tel. +32 26791602
Fax +32 27263299

Mrs E. E. RUTGERS

Mrs L. A. O. D'HUY
First Secretary (Coreper II, Antici)
Tel. +32 26791501
Fax +32 26791795

Mr G. TIELMAN
First Secretary (Mertens, Coreper I)
Tel. +32 26791507
Fax +32 26791774

Mrs E. A. C. VAN GINNEKEN
First Secretary
Tel. +32 26791636
Fax +32 27263299

Press and Information Service

Mr J. W. H. M. BEAUJEAN
Spokesperson, Counsellor
Tel. +32 26791509
Fax +32 26791774

Political and Security Committee

Mr M. R. O. BENTINCK
Deputy representative to European Union Policy and Security Committee
Counsellor
Tel. +32 26791761
Fax +32 27263299

J. A. KLARENBEEK
Counsellor (RELEX, PSC and Coreper II)
Tel. +32 26791504
Fax +32 27263299

Mrs E. VERSCHUUR

Mr A. J. MOLENAAR
Defence Counsellor
Tel. +32 26791720
Fax +32 27263299

Mrs M. R. ORE BRICENO

Mrs E. A. C. VAN GINNEKEN
First Secretary
Tel. +32 26791636
Fax +32 27263299

Mrs E. S. A. BRANDS
Defence Counsellor
Tel. +32 26791746
Fax +32 27263299

Military Committee

Mr A. G. D. VAN OSCH
Lt. General of Army, Military Representative
Tel. +32 27076693
Fax +32 27264748

Mr J. W. BEEKMAN
Brigadier General, Deputy Military Representative
Tel. +32 26791758
Fax +32 27263299

Mr P. A. A. OPPERS
Colonel, Assistant Military Representative
Tel. +32 26791713
Fax +32 27263299

Mr A. P. N. STAM
Lieutenant Colonel
Assistant Military Representative
Tel. +32 26791681
Fax +32 27263299

Research and Atomic Questions Division

Mr K. A. NEDERLOF
Counsellor (research and atomic questions)
Tel. +32 26791527
Fax +32 26791591

Mrs M. TELEGENHOF
First Secretary (research) ansd science and technology Attaché
Tel. +32 26791665
Fax +32 26791591

Home Affairs

Mr W. VAN SLUIJS
Counsellor (justice and home affairs, Europol, police cooperation and terrorism)
Tel. +32 26791525
Fax +32 26791793

Mr R. BRUNSVELD
First Secretary (justice and home affairs, public administration, staff regulations, civil protection)
Tel. +32 26791526
Fax +32 26791793

Mr A. K. JAHIER
Counsellor
Tel. +32 26791643
Fax +32 27263299

Ministry of Economic Affairs

Mr L. GROENENDAL
Minister Plenipotentiary (competitiveness Council/Lisbon strategy, industrial policy, SMEs, better regulation)
Tel. +32 26791514, 26791512
Fax +32 26791792

Mr L. A. DUIJVENDIJK
Counsellor (better legislation)
Tel. +32 26791513
Fax +32 26791792

Mr M. A. HAIJER
First Secretary (internal market, consumer policy, competitiveness, state aid)
Tel. +32 26791516
Fax +32 26791792

Mr A. P. BADER
Counsellor
(energy, telecommunications and post)
Tel. +32 26791561
Fax +32 26791792

Mrs N. M. UNDERBERG

Mr M. JACOBS
Adviser (external economic relations, Eastern Europe, Central Asia, Russia, EFTA)
Tel. +32 26791730
Fax +32 26791792

Mrs W. SLOT
Counsellor
(telecommunications, information society, external energy policy, technical harmonisation, Structural Funds, public procurement, small business act)
Tel. +32 26791608
Fax +32 26791792

Ministry of Finance

Mr P. VAN BALLEKOM
Financial Counsellor
Tel. +32 26791555
Fax +32 26791790

Mrs K. VAN BALLEKOM

Mr O. J. H. SCHOUW
Financial Counsellor (fiscal and customs affairs)
Tel. +32 26791559
Fax +32 26791790

Mr L. DE BLIECK
Adviser (customs)
Tel. +32 26791563
Fax +32 26791790

Mr R. DEBETS
Financial Counsellor
Tel. +32 26791556
Fax +32 26791790

Mr H. HACK
Financial Counsellor
Tel. +32 26791567
Fax +32 26791790

Legal and Institutional Affairs

Mr M. E. C. VAN DER PLAS
Counsellor (legal and institutional affairs, justice and home affairs coordination, intellectual property, e-commerce)
Tel. +32 26791510
Fax +32 26791774

Mrs K. CORCORAN

Mrs M. DE JONG
First Secretary
(legal and institutional affairs, justice and home affairs coordination, intellectual property, e-commerce
Tel. +32 26791650
Fax +32 26791793

Ministry of Justice

Mr P. M. DIEZ
Counsellor (justice and home affairs, asylum and migration, free movement of persons)
Tel. +32 26791530
Fax +32 26791793

Mrs E. DE WILDE

Mr J. S. VAN DEN OOSTERKAMP
Counsellor (justice and home affairs, civil law questions, intellectual property, company law)
Tel. +32 26791620
Fax +32 26791793

Mr J. J. MESU
Counsellor (justice and home affairs, cooperation in criminal matters, substantive criminal law)
Tel. +32 26791639
Fax +32 26791793

Mr P. SPAAN
Counsellor (justice and home affairs, data protection, organised crime, drugs)
Tel. +32 26791647
Fax +32 26791793

Mrs J. SCHRIKS

Mr N. COLEMAN
First Secretary
(justice and home affairs, borders, visas, Cirefi, Schengen)
Tel. +32 26791625
Fax +32 26791793

Ministry for Agriculture, Nature and Food Quality

Mr G. P. G. KUNST
Head of Unit
Counsellor, Agriculture
Tel. +32 26791543
Fax +32 26791776

Mrs M. KNOBBE

Mr A. M. AKKERMAN
Counsellor (veterinary questions)
Tel. +32 26791549
Fax +32 26791776

Mrs L. NAGEL

Mr J. J. M. PAARDEKOOPER
Fisheries Attaché
Tel. +32 26791544
Fax +32 26791776

Mrs C. J. R. HERWEIJER

Mrs A. SMOLDERS
Attaché
Tel. +32 26791628
Fax +32 26791776

Mr H. J. BUNING
Attaché
Tel. +32 26791629
Fax +32 26791776

Mediterrannean and Middle East

Mrs B. G. TAHZIB-LIE
Adviser (Middle East/Gulf/Mashrek/Maghreb)
Tel. +32 26791523
Fax +32 26791783

Mr B. W. SCHOLTZ
Second Secretary (Middle East/Gulf/Mashrek/Maghreb)
Tel. +32 26791658
Fax +32 26791783

European Parliament Section

Mr S. VAN DER SLUIS
Counsellor (European Parliament)
Tel. +32 26791606
Fax +32 26791779

Mrs A. K. RYDBERG

Mr H. BOEREKAMP
Second Secretary (European Parliament)
Tel. +32 26791524
Fax +32 26791779

Environment and nature policy

Mr A. H. GIERVELD
Counsellor (environment)
Tel. +32 26791519
Fax +32 26791591

Mrs F. VAN ZOMEREN
First Secretary (environment)
Tel. +32 26791521
Fax +32 26791591

Mr R. M. BOUCKE
First Secretary (environment)
Tel. +32 26791541
Fax +32 26791591

Mr L. PELTZER
Second Secretary (environment)
Tel. +32 26791515
Fax +32 26791591

EU enlargement

Mr J. FLAMAND
Counsellor (enlargement of the European Union, accession negotiations)
Tel. +32 26791607
Fax +32 26791778

Mrs S. PANTELIC
Second Secretary (enlargement)
Tel. +32 26791538
Fax +32 26791795

Office for the Senior Public Service

Mr F. MOLLEN
Adviser (coordinator for the appointment of senior EU posts)
Tel. +32 26791611
Fax +32 26791777

Mrs M. CONWAY

Mr D-J. BROUWER
Counsellor (business assistance unit)
Tel. +32 26791536
Fax +32 26791777

Mrs A. THIADENS

Ministry of Education, Culture and Science

Mr J. W. RIENKS
Counsellor
Tel. +32 26791617
Fax +32 26791778

Mr L. J. BEKKENS

Mr R. VAN IERSEL
Counsellor
Tel. +32 26791617
Fax +32 26791778

Mrs I. WELBERGEN
Counsellor
Tel. +32 26791617
Fax +32 26791778

Development policy

Mr T. PETERS
Counsellor (development cooperation)
Tel. +32 26791503
Fax +32 26791778

Mrs A. LANDE

Mr R. VAN DIJK
Second Secretary
Tel. +32 26791533
Fax +32 26791778

Mr J. BOGAERTS
Second Secretary
Tel. +32 26791569
Fax +32 26791778

Ministry of Employment and Social Security

Mr F. SCHUMACHER
Adviser
Tel. +32 26791551
Fax +32 26791791

Mrs M. I. VAN HEUKELOM

Mrs K. G. SCHEEPERS
Social Attaché
Tel. +32 26791732
Fax +32 26791791

Mr P. L. ROOK
Social Attaché
Tel. +32 26791548
Fax +32 26791791

Mrs S. GREENE

Ministry of Transport, Public Works and Water Management

Mr J. M. VAN HEEST
Adviser
Tel. +32 26791539
Fax +32 26791778

Mrs J. A. SCHUT

Mr A. W. B. DE JONG
Attaché (transport)
Tel. +32 26791540
Fax +32 26791778

Mrs R. CADEE

...
Attaché (transport)
Tel. +32 26791724
Fax +32 26791778

Ministry of Health, Welfare and Sport

Mr J. G. H. DRAIJER
Diplomatic Head of Unit
Counsellor, External Relations (WHO, OECD, etc.) public health, public health strategy, sport, patients' rights and cross-border healthcare, 7th framework programme for research and development
E-Health, healthy ageing and family strategy
Tel. +32 26791528
Fax +32 26791791

Mr J. P. G. M. VOLLEMAN
Public health (alcohol, tobacco, obesity), products and cosmetics directive, animal experiments, youth policy, food safety and foodstuffs
Tel. +32 26791529
Fax +32 26791791

Mrs C. M. VAN LINGEN
Public health, infectious diseases, avian influenza, HIV/AIDS, health action programme, medicines and medical products, organ donation(s), drugs and the directive on blood, tissue and cells
Tel. +32 26791668
Fax +32 26791791

Head, Joint Management Office

Mrs M. BALTUS
First Secretary (administrative affairs)
Tel. +32 26791705
Fax +32 26791771

Mr A. VAN DER ROEST
Attaché (administrative affairs)
Tel. +32 26791705
Fax +32 26791771

PERMANENT REPRESENTATION OF AUSTRIA

Avenue de Cortenbergh 30
B-1040 Brussels
E-mail: bruessel-ov@bmeia.gv.at
Tel. +32 22345-extension (operator: 100)
Fax +32 22356300

HE Mr Hans Dietmar SCHWEISGUT
Ambassador Extraordinary and Plenipotentiary
Permanent Representative
Tel. +32 22345130
Fax +32 22345318

HE Mr Walter GRAHAMMER
Minister Plenipotentiary
Deputy Permanent Representative
(Coreper I)
E-mail: bruessel-ov@bmaa.gv.at
Tel. +32 22345122
Fax +32 22356122

Political affairs

Mrs Elisabeth BERTAGNOLI
Minister
Tel. +32 22345124
Fax +32 22356124

Mrs Jutta EDTHOFER
Second Secretary
Tel. +32 22345-158
Fax +32 22356-158

Mrs Lucia KRONSTEINER
First Secretary
Tel. +32 22345219
Fax +32 22356219

Mrs Simone KNAPP
First Secretary
Tel. +32 22345435
Fax +32 22356435

Mr Robert WEISS
First Secretary
Tel. +32 22345248
Fax +32 22356248

Mr Philippos AGATHONOS
First Secretary
Tel. +32 22345293
Fax +32 22356293

Mrs Larissa LASSMANN
First Secretary
Tel. +32 22345194
Fax +32 22356194

Mr Karl EHRLICH
Second Secretary
Tel. +32 22345337
Fax +32 22356337

Mr Johann-Raphael LASSMANN
Second Secretary
Tel. +32 22345346
Fax +32 22356346

Mr Katharina RAUSCHER
Second Secretary
Tel. +32 22345203
Fax +32 22356203

Mr Ralf HOSPODARSKY
Second Secretary
Tel. +32 22345204
Fax +32 22356204

Legal affairs

Mr Gregor SCHUSTERSCHITZ
Counsellor
Tel. +32 22345123
Fax +32 22356123

Visitors' service

Mrs Martina SCHUBERT
Counsellor
Tel. +32 22345145
Fax +32 22356145

Press and information

Mrs Sonja ROSENBERGER
Tel. +32 22345215
Fax +32 22356215

Mr Alexander PAIER
Tel. +32 22345344
Fax +32 22356344

Administration

Mrs Monika MÜLLER-FEMBECK
Counsellor
Tel. +32 22345262
Fax +32 22356262

Mr Thomas SCHMIDT
Second Secretary (administrative affairs)
Tel. +32 22345272
Fax +32 22356272

Mr Gerald RAUCH
Deputy Attaché (administrative issues)
Tel. +32 22345115
Fax +32 22356115

Office of the Federal Chancellor

Mrs Judith GEBETSROITHNER
Minister
Tel. +32 22345197
Fax +32 22356197

Mrs Regina KOTHMAYR
Counsellor
Tel. +32 22345227
Fax +32 22356227

Mrs Helga ZECHTL
Counsellor
Tel. +32 22345290
Fax +32 22356290

Mrs Heidi HAVRANEK
Attaché
Tel. +32 22345226
Fax +32 22356226

Federal Ministry of Finance

Mr Gerhard LERCHBAUMER
Minister
Tel. +32 22345157
Fax +32 22356157

Mrs Andrea BINDER
Counsellor
Tel. +32 22345166
Fax +32 22356166

Mrs Brigitte LEITGEB
Counsellor
Tel. +32 22345252
Fax +32 22356252

Mr Klaus FEDERMAIR
Attaché
Tel. +32 22345159
Fax +32 22356159

Mr Markus METSCHITZER
Attaché
Tel. +32 22345127
Fax +32 22356127

Federal Ministry of Health, Family Affairs and Youth

Mr Philipp TILLICH
Attaché
Tel. +32 22345209
Fax +32 22356209

Mr Robert PICHLER
Attaché
Tel. +32 22345221
Fax +32 22356221

Federal Ministry of the Interior

Mr Willy KEMPEL
Minister
Tel. +32 22345471
Fax +32 22356471

Mr Andreas FELLNER
Attaché
Tel. +32 22345472
Fax +32 22356472

Mrs Eva WIPLER
Attaché
Tel. +32 22345475
Fax +32 22356475

Mr Martin HUMER
Attaché
Tel. +32 22345480
Fax +32 22356480

Federal Ministry of Justice

Mrs Barbara MAKAL
Attaché
Tel. +32 22345222
Fax +32 22356222

Mr Nikolaus OBROVSKI
Attaché
Tel. +32 22345269
Fax +32 22356269

Federal Ministry of Agriculture and Forestry, the Environment and Water Management

Mrs Christa BAUER
Minister
Tel. +32 22345-168
Fax +32 22356-168

Mrs Cornelia JÄGER
Attaché
Tel. +32 22345264
Fax +32 22356264

Mrs Claudia KOREIMANN
Attaché
Tel. +32 22345164
Fax +32 22356164

Mr Johann DOPPELBAUER
Attaché
Tel. +32 22345228
Fax +32 22356228

Mrs Nora HAHNKAMPER-VANDENBULCKE
Attaché
Tel. +32 22345196
Fax +32 22356196

Federal Ministry of Social Affairs and Consumer Protection

Mr Clemens THALHAMMER
Attaché
Tel. +32 22345276
Fax +32 22345312

Mrs Stephanie MATTES
Attaché
Tel. +32 22345216
Fax +32 22345312

Federal Ministry of Education, the Arts and Culture

Mrs Mirjam RINDERER
Attaché
Tel. +32 22345207
Fax +32 22356207

Mrs Heidemarie MEISSNITZER
Counsellor
Tel. +32 22345251
Fax +32 22356251

Federal Ministry of Transport, Innovation and Technology

Mr Thomas EGERMAIER
Attaché
Tel. +32 22345258
Fax +32 22356258

Mrs Angelika BERGER
Attaché
Tel. +32 22345283
Fax +32 22356283

Mr Rudolf KASCHNITZ
Attaché
Tel. +32 22345442
Fax +32 22356442

Mrs Sabine PONTZEN
Tel. +32 22345225
Fax +32 22356225

Federal Ministry of Economic Affairs and Labour

Mr Othmar HORVATH
Minister
Tel. +32 22345150
Fax +32 22356150

Mrs Elisabeth WEISSENBÖCK
Attaché
Tel. +32 22345137
Fax +32 22356137

Mr Martin FAGERER
Attaché
Tel. +32 22345141
Fax +32 22356141

Mr Roland MEINECKE
Counsellor
Tel. +32 22345212
Fax +32 22356212

Mrs Ingrid ZEHETNER
Attaché
Tel. +32 22345241
Fax +32 22356241

Mr Jochen PENKER
Attaché
Tel. +32 22345249
Fax +32 22356249

Mrs Sylvia KNITTEL
Attaché
Tel. +32 22345349
Fax +32 22356349

Federal Ministry of Science and Research

Mr Martin SCHMID
Attaché
Tel. +32 22345184
Fax +32 22356184

Mrs Sabine NEYER
Attaché
Tel. +32 22345144
Fax +32 22356144

Office of the Federal Provinces (Länder)

Mr Klemens FISCHER
Minister
Tel. +32 22345234
Fax +32 22302544

Confederation of Austrian Towns

Mrs Simone WOHLESER
Attaché
Tel. +32 22345288
Fax +32 22820682

Confederation of Austrian Local Authorities

Mrs Daniela FRAISS
Attaché
Tel. +32 22345254
Fax +32 22820688

National Bank of Austria

Mrs Marlies STUBITS
Attaché
Tel. +32 22345170
Fax +32 22854848

Mr Paul SCHMIDT
Tel. +32 22345173
Fax +32 22854848

Austrian Federal Economic Chamber

Mrs Barbara SCHENNACH
Counsellor
Tel. +32 22345180
Fax +32 22865899

Mrs Verena MARTELANZ
Attaché
Tel. +32 22345186
Fax +32 22865899

Mrs Christina WÜHRER
Attaché
Tel. +32 22345179
Fax +32 22865899

Mrs Yasmin SOETOPO
Attaché
Tel. +32 22345187
Fax +32 22865899

Mr Christoph RIEDMANN
Attaché
Tel. +32 22345188
Fax +32 22865899

Mrs Nora KUTZBACH-BERGER
Attaché
Tel. +32 22345183
Fax +32 22865899

Federal Chamber of Labour

Mr Amir Farhang GHOREISHI NIAKI
Counsellor
Tel. +32 22345198
Fax +32 22302973

Mr Frank EY
Tel. +32 22345178
Fax +32 22302973

Mr Christof CESNOVAR
Tel. +32 22345189
Fax +32 22302973

Conference of the Austrian Chamber of Agriculture

Mr Gerfried GRUBER
Attaché
Tel. +32 22345185
Fax +32 22854671

Austrian Confederation of Trade Unions

Mr Oliver RÖPKE
Attaché
Tel. +32 22345175
Fax +32 22311710

Mrs Tanja BUZEK
Tel. +32 22345176
Fax +32 22311710

Mrs Angelika KOLLREIDER
Tel. +32 22345177
Fax +32 22311710

Federation of Austrian Industries

Mr Berthold BERGER
Counsellor
Tel. +32 22350431
Fax +32 22309591

Mrs Ute TEUFELBERGER
Tel. +32 22350434
Fax +32 22309591

Mr Sebastian GRABNER
Tel. +32 22345229
Fax +32 22309591

Mrs Maria Therese LEIN
Tel. +32 22350432
Fax +32 22309591

Austrian Development Agency

Mr Wolfgang LEHOFER
Attaché
Tel. +32 22345481
Fax +32 22356481

Political and Security Committee

HE Mr Andreas WIEDENHOFF
Ambassador, Representative of Austria in the Political and Security Committee of the European Union
Tel. +32 22345202
Fax +32 22356202

Mr Philipp AGATHONOS
First Secretary, Deputy Representative of Austria on the Political and Security Committee of the European Union
Tel. +32 22345293
Fax +32 22356293

Mrs Larissa LASSMANN
First Secretary
Tel. +32 22345194
Fax +32 22356194

Military Committee

Tel. +32 22343850
Fax +32 22343859

Mr Wolfgang WOSOLSOBE
Brigadier
Military Representative of Austria to the Military Committee of the European Union

Mr Klaus JENSCHIK
Colonel
Military Counsellor of Austria to the Military Committee of the European Union

Mr Michael KUGLER
Lieutenant Colonel
Military Counsellor of Austria to the Military Committee of the European Union

Mr Berthold SANDTNER
Major
Military Counsellor of Austria to the European Union Military Committee

Mr Thomas PILLMEIER
Lieutenant Colonel
Military Counsellor of Austria to the Military Committee of the European Union

Mr Anton RESCH
Lieutenant Colonel
Military Counsellor of Austria to the Military Committee of the European Union

PERMANENT REPRESENTATION OF POLAND

Avenue de Tervuren 282-284
B-1150 Brussels
E-mail: mail@plrep.eu
prénom.nom@plrep.eu
Website: http://www.brukselaeu.polemb.net
Tel. +32 27777220, 7777224
Fax +32 27777297, 7777298

HE Mr Jan TOMBIŃSKI
Ambassador Extraordinary and Plenipotentiary
Permanent Representative

Mrs Agnieszka TOMBIŃSKA

HE Mrs Karolina OSTRZYNIEWSKA
Minister Counsellor
Deputy Permanent Representative (Coreper I)

Mr Krzysztof OSTRZYNIEWSKI

HE Mr Jerzy DROŻDŻ
Minister Counsellor
Deputy Permanent Representative (responsible for administration and personnel)

Mrs DROŻDŻ

HE Mrs Beata PEKSA-KRAWIEC
Ambassador
Representative of Poland to the Political and Security Committee (PSC)

Mr Tomasz HUSAK
Third Secretary (Antici)

Mrs HUSAK

Mrs Magdalena CANOWIECKA
First Secretary (Mertens)

External relations policy

Mr Artur KLOPOTOWSKI
Minister Counsellor

Mrs KLOPOTOWSKA

Mr Henryk BILSKI
First Counsellor

Mrs BILSKA

Mrs Urszula PALLASZ
First Counsellor

Mrs Karolina NOWAK
First Secretary

Mrs Małgorzata JANKOWSKA
Second Secretary

Mrs Aleksandra SZCZEPAŃSKA
Second Secretary

Mrs Bogumiła ORDYK
Second Secretary

Political and Security Committee policy

Mr Piotr DZWONEK
First Secretary

Mrs DZWONEK

Mr Lech DRAB
Counsellor

Mrs DRAB

Mr Jan RYKOWSKI
Counsellor

Mr Tomasz ŚMIGIELSKI
First Secretary

Mrs Maryla OTACHEL
First Secretary

Mr Rafał MARCINIAK
First Secretary

Mrs MARCINIAK

Mrs Anna TYSZKIEWICZ
Second Secretary

Mr TYSZKIEWICZ

Institutional and Legal Section

Mr Miroslaw BROILO
Counsellor

Mrs BROILO

Mrs Anna PIESIAK
Second Secretary

Mrs Urszula DROŻDŻ
Attaché

Parliamentary Section

Mr Hubert CZERNIUK
First Secretary

Mr Jacek JANKOWSKI
First Counsellor

Mrs JANKOWSKA

Mrs Magdalena SKRZYŃSKA
Counsellor

Mrs Magdalena SKULIMOWSKA
First Secretary

Agriculture and fisheries

Mr Andrzej BABUCHOWSKI
Minister Counsellor

Mrs BABUCHOWSKA

Mr Andrzej GASOWSKI
First Counsellor

Mr Jan PRANDOTA
First Counsellor

Mrs PRANDOTA

Mr Andrzej KRAWCZYK
First Counsellor

Mrs KRAWCZYK

Mr Kamil OCHMANSKI
First Secretary

Mr Marcin RUCINSKI
Third Secretary

Mrs SIENKO-RUCINSKA

Press, information, culture and audiovisual policy

Mr Kacper CHMIELEWSKI
First Secretary
Spokesperson (Coreper II)

Mrs Magdalena BALCER-CHMIELEWSKA

Mrs Renata BANCARZEWSKA
First Secretary
Deputy Spokesperson (Coreper I)

Mr Grzegorz PRACZYK
First Secretary

Mrs Katarzyna BUDZYŃSKA
Attaché

Justice and home affairs

Mr Janusz GACIARZ
First Counsellor

Mrs Bozena JEKOT
First Counsellor

Mr Maciej LEWANDOWSKI
First Counsellor

Mrs LEWANDOWSKA

Mr Jacek GARSTKA
Counsellor

Mrs GARSTKA

Mr Mariusz BOGUSZEWSKI
First Secretary

Mrs BOGUSZEWSKA

Mr Filip JASINSKI
First Secretary

Mrs JASINSKA

Mr Tadeusz OWCZARSKI
First Secretary

Financial and monetary affairs

Mr Grzegorz RADZIEJEWSKI
Counsellor

Mrs RADZIEJEWSKA

Mr Tomasz MICHALAK
Minister Counsellor

Mrs SIKORSKA-MICHALAK

Mr Damian JAWORSKI
Counsellor

Mrs JAWORSKA

Mr Mariusz KRUKOWSKI
Counsellor

Mrs KRUKOWSKA

Mr Adam SIEKIERSKI
Counsellor

Mrs SIEKIERSKA

Mrs Malgorzata SLIWIŃSKA
Counsellor

Mr SLIWINSKI

Economic and trade affairs

Mrs Małgorzata MIKA-BRYSKA
Minister Counsellor

Mrs Małgorzata WENERSKA-CRAPS
Counsellor

Mr CRAPS

Mrs Katarzyna CHAJEC
Second Secretary

Mr Adam JANCZAK
First Secretary

Mrs JANCZAK

Mrs Patrycja SOBCZAK
Second Secretary

Mrs Joanna BEK
First Secretary

Mr Wojciech SUDOL
First Secretary

Mrs SUDOL

Regional and cohesion policy

Mrs Monika DOŁOWIEC
First Secretary

Mr Marcin GLUCHOWSKI
Second Secretary

Mrs Małgorzata KOZLOWSKA
Expert

Social affairs and employment

Mrs Ewa BOROWCZYK
First Counsellor

Mr Jarosław STREJCZYK
First Counsellor

Mrs Agnieszka WOLOSZYN
First Secretary

Education and research

Mrs Grazyna OMARSKA
Counsellor

Mrs Joanna DOBERSZYC-TOULSALY
First Secretary

Mr Krzysztof KOPYTKO
First Secretary

Environment

Beata WOLCZUK
Second Secretary

Mr WOLCZUK

Mr Olaf KOPCZYNSKI
Second Secretary

Mrs KOPCZYNSKA

Telecommunications and Information Society Unit

Mr Krzysztof WASIEK
First Counsellor

Mrs WASIEK

Transport policy

Mr Lukasz WOJTAS
Counsellor

Mrs WOJTAS

Mr Paweł ROSICKI
Counsellor

Mrs ROSICKA

Mrs Anna KRUKOWSKA
First Secretary

Mr Krzysztof WOJCIECHOWICZ
Second Secretary

Administrative Department

Mr Andrzej SKOWRONSKI
First Secretary

Mr Czesław BAFELTOWSKI
First Secretary

Mrs BAFELTOWSKA

Mrs NOWAK
Attaché

Mr NOWAK

Mr Pawel HARTMANN
Attaché

Mrs Anna ZADROZNA
Third Secretary

Mr ZADROŻNY

PERMANENT REPRESENTATION OF PORTUGAL

Avenue de Cortenbergh 12
B-1040 Brussels
E-mail: reper@reper-portugal.be
Tel. +32 22864211
Fax +32 22310026

HE Mr Manuel LOBO ANTUNES
Ambassador Extraordinary and Plenipotentiary
Permanent Representative

Mrs Maria LOBO ANTUNES

HE Mrs Ana Paula ZACARIAS
Deputy Permanent Representative

HE Mr Carlos DURRANT PAIS
Portugal's Representative to the PSC

Mrs Ana Maria NEVES DURRANT PAIS

Coreper coordination and interinstitutional affairs

Mr Francisco DUARTE LOPES
Counsellor

Mrs Maria Paula PINTO DUARTE LOPES

Mr Hugo SOBRAL
Secretary

Mrs Sara CRESPO
Secretary

Portuguese officials in the European institutions

Mrs Maria José SALAZAR LEITE
Counsellor

Mr João Pedro BASTOS SALAZAR LEITE

External relations, CFSP and ESDP

Mrs Clara BORJA RAMOS
Counsellor

Mr Vasco BRANDÃO RAMOS

Mr António LEÃO ROCHA
Counsellor

Mrs Maria Luísa SOUSA SALVAÇÃO BARRETO LEÃO ROCHA

Mr Paulo DOMINGUES
Secretary

Mrs Carla DA SILVA DOMINGUES

Mr Paulo DE ALMEIDA PEREIRA
Counsellor

Mr Rui BRITO ELVAS
Military Counsellor

Mrs Helena Maria LOUREIRO VASCONCELOS

Mr Nuno CHAVES FERREIRA
Military Counsellor

Middle East, North Africa and Latin America

Mrs Maria José PIRES
Minister Plenipotentiary

Mr Manuel Tomás FERNANDES PEREIRA

ACP Countries

Mrs Carolina QUINA
Counsellor

Mr António SILVA

Africa and development cooperation

Mrs Vera VASCONCELOS ABREU
Counsellor

Mr João MARQUES DE ALMEIDA

Asia

Mrs Isabel VALENTE
Secretary

Eastern Europe and Central Asia, Council of Europe

Mrs Joana ARAÚJO
Secretary

Mr Nuno CHAVES FERREIRA

Western Balkans, central and south-eastern Europe

Mrs Alexandra BILREIRO
Secretary

Mr Henrique P. HENRIQUES

Community programmes — external cooperation, culture, sport and youth affairs

Mrs Patrícia PINCARILHO
Counsellor

Enlargement

Mrs Ana Cristina MELO
Counsellor

Commercial affairs

Mrs Ana Luísa FIGUEIRA
Counsellor

Mr Miguel ALMEIDA ANDRADE

Mrs Susana MENDONÇA
Counsellor

Economic and financial affairs

Mr Francisco BARROS CASTRO
Counsellor

Mrs Maria Isabel MEIRELES DE ANDRADE

Mr Rui MOURATO
Counsellor

Mrs Maria CORTEZ PEREIRA

Mr Celestino CRUZ GERALDES
Counsellor

Mrs Celeste GONÇALVES CRESPO

Mrs Cristina DIAS
Counsellor

Mr Nuno Alexandre COSTA MACHADO

Mr Miguel SILVA PINTO
Counsellor

Mrs Filomena PINTO

Health

Mr Jorge MENEZES
Adviser

Mrs Maria Isabel MENEZES

Research, education and information society

Mrs Carla Alexandra MATIAS SANTOS
Counsellor

Industrial policy, energy, nuclear questions and internal market

Mr Paulo SILVA LOPES
Adviser

Mrs Joan Mary PRINCE

Mr João SANTOS E SILVA
Counsellor

Mrs Fernanda FERREIRA DIAS
Adviser

Mr Paulo FERREIRA DIAS

Mr Joaquim BRANDÃO
Counsellor

Transport and communications

Mrs Ana Margarida SEVERINO
Counsellor

Mr José Carlos PINTO VINCENTE

Mrs Ana Cristina COSTA
Counsellor

Mr António Manuel RAMOS SANTOS

Home affairs and justice

Mrs Constança URBANO DE SOUSA
Counsellor

Mr Matthias CONTZEN

Mr Carlos Alberto MATOS MOREIRA
Counsellor

Mr Paulo CUNHA ALVES
Counsellor

Mrs Filomena RODRIGUES DA CUNHA ALVES

Mrs Claudia FARIA
Counsellor

Mr Gerard VAN DER HEIJDEN

Mrs Raquel CORREIA
Counsellor

Legal affairs

Mrs Patrícia GALVÃO TELES
Counsellor

Mr Tiago SANTOS PEREIRA

Mr Miguel FRANCO E ABREU
Counsellor

Regional policy, Committee of the Regions and Outermost Regions

Mrs Maria Cecília ANTOLIN
Counsellor

Agriculture

Mr Miguel João DE FREITAS
Adviser

Mr Luís Alberto CAIANO
Counsellor

Mrs Maria Paula DA CUNHA GONÇALVES CAIANO

Mrs Rita HORTA
Counsellor

Fisheries

Mr Rui RIBEIRO DO RÓSÁRIO
Counsellor

Social affairs and Economic and Social Committee

Mrs Ana FERREIRA REIS
Counsellor

Environment

Mr Paulo SILVA LEMOS
Counsellor

Mrs Rita FREITAS FERREIRA
Counsellor

Mrs Cristina FALCÃO DE CAMPOS
Counsellor

Spokesperson, press and information

Mr Manuel CANSADO DE CARVALHO
Counsellor

Mrs Joanna DE ALMADA TAVARES DE CARVALHO

Mrs Maria Rui FONSECA
Counsellor

Administration

Mrs Cristina DE SOUSA
Counsellor

Mr Rui CORREIA

Informatics

Mr Pedro ESTEVES PEREIRA
Attaché

Protocol

Mr Reinaldo BARREIROS
Attaché

Thi Cam Van TRAN

PERMANENT REPRESENTATION OF ROMANIA

Rue Montoyer 12
B-1000 Brussels
E-mail: bru@rpro.eu
Website: http://www.ue.mae.ro
Tel. +32 27000640
Fax +32 27000641

HE Mr Mihnea MOTOC
Ambassador Extraordinary and Plenipotentiary
Permanent Representative

HE Mr Marius HIRTE
Minister Adviser
Coreper I Representative

HE Mr Viorel ARDELEANU
Minister Plenipotentiary
Permanent Representative in PSC and WEU

Mrs Sorina ARDELEANU

Coreper coordination

Mrs Alina PĂDEANU
First Secretary (Antici)
E-mail: alina.padeanu@rpro.eu
Tel. +32 27000514

Mrs Ioana BIVOLARU
Second Secretary (Mertens)
E-mail: ioana.bivolaru@rpro.eu
Tel. +32 27000317

Legal and institutional affairs

Mr Ion SIMION
Counsellor
E-mail: ion.simion@rpro.eu
Tel. +32 27000304

Mr Sorin DIMA
First Secretary
E-mail: sorin.dima@rpro.eu
Tel. +32 27000312

Press and communication

Mrs Doris Theodora MIRCEA
Spokesperson, Head of Section
E-mail: doris.mircea@rpro.eu
Tel. +32 27000310

Mrs Brinduşa CHIRIBUŢĂ
Third Secretary
E-mail: brindusa.chiributa@rpro.eu
Tel. +32 27000320

External relations

Mr Cristian OLIMID
Adviser
Deputy Permanent Representative PSC
E-mail: cristian.olimid@rpro.eu
Tel. +32 27000503

Mrs Lavinia OLIMID

Mr Cristian NEGRILĂ
Counsellor
E-mail: cristian.negrila@rpro.eu
Tel. +32 27000501

Mrs Valentina NEGRILĂ

Mrs Gentiana ŞERBU
Counsellor
E-mail: gentiana.serbu@rpro.eu
Tel. +32 27000511

Mrs Mihaela VASIU
First Secretary
E-mail: mihaela.vasiu@rpro.eu
Tel. +32 27000507

Mr Cătălin MIHĂILESCU
Second Secretary
E-mail: catalin.mihailescu@rpro.eu
Tel. +32 27000212

Mrs Amira MIHĂILESCU

Mrs Anda SĂLĂGEAN
Second Secretary
E-mail: anda.salagean@rpro.eu
Tel. +32 27000513

Mrs Brinduşa CHIRIBUŢĂ
Third Secretary
E-mail: brindusa.chiributa@rpro.eu
Tel. +32 27000320

Mrs Iulia MATEI
Third Secretary
E-mail: iulia.matei@rpro.eu
Tel. +32 27000212

Mrs Irina TICA-DIACONU
Third Secretary
E-mail: irina.tica-diaconu@rpro.eu
Tel. +32 27000550

Mr Artur RĂDUCANU
Third Secretary
E-mail: artur.raducanu@rpro.eu
Tel. +32 27000308

Mrs Anca ALEXANDRESCU
Attaché
E-mail: anca.alexandrescu@rpro.eu
Tel. +32 27000603

European Security and Defence Policy (ESDP)

Mr Cristian OLIMID
Counsellor, Head of Section
E-mail: cristian.olimid@rpro.eu
Tel. +32 27000503

Mrs Lavinia OLIMID

Mr Dragos ANDREI
Minister Counsellor
E-mail: dragos.andrei@rpro.eu
Tel. +32 27000505

Mr Mircea MUDURA
Counsellor
E-mail: mircea.mudura@rpro.eu
Tel. +32 27000509

Mrs Viorica MUDURA

Mrs Milica NEACŞU
First Secretary
E-mail: milica.neacsu@rpro.eu
Tel. +32 27000519

Mrs Amira MIHĂILESCU
Second Secretary (Nicolaïdis)
E-mail: amira.mihailescu@rpro.eu
Tel. +32 27000502

Mr Cătălin MIHĂILESCU

Mr Doru HOBJILĂ
Second Secretary
E-mail: doru.hobjila@rpro.eu
Tel. +32 27000512

Mrs Irina TICA-DIACONU
Third Secretary
E-mail: irina.tica-diaconu@rpro.eu
Tel. +32 27000550

Mr Daniel BARBU
Attaché
E-mail: daniel.barbu@rpro.eu
Tel. +32 27000777

Military Representation of Romania to the European Union

Mr Cornel PARANIAC
General
Military Representative
E-mail: cornel.paraniac@rpro.eu
Tel. +32 27079660

Mr Victor GUIDEA
Coordinating Officer
Deputy Military Representative
E-mail: milrep@rpro.eu
Tel. +32 27000508

Mr Gheorghe BALAGIU
Lieutenant Colonel
E-mail: gheorghe.balagiu@rpro.eu
Tel. +32 27000520

Mr Ionel NICOLAE
Lieutenant Colonel
E-mail: ionel.nicolae@rpro.eu
Tel. +32 27000510

Mrs Ionela NICUT
Captain
E-mail: milrep@rpro.eu
Tel. +32 27000510

Trade

Mr Dan DINUTĂ
Minister Adviser (Head of Section)
E-mail: dan.dinuta@rpro.eu
Tel. +32 27000404

Mrs Diana CODAU
Second Secretary
E-mail: diana.codau@rpro.eu
Tel. +32 27000415

Mr Victor GRIGORESCU
Second Secretary
E-mail: victor.grigorescu@rpro.eu
Tel. +32 27000405

Mr Ciprian RUSU
First Secretary (Customs Attaché)
E-mail: customs@risue.org
Tel. +32 27000309

Economic affairs, finance and monetary policies

Mr Marius SPIRIDON
First Secretary
E-mail: marius.spiridon@rpro.eu
Tel. +32 27000316

Mrs Andreea Diana SPIRIDON

Mrs Daniela-Adriana NUȚU
First Secretary
E-mail: adriana.nutu@rpro.eu
Tel. +32 27000306

Mr Dragoş UNGUREANU
First Secretary
E-mail: dragos.ungureanu@rpro.eu
Tel. +32 27000200

Mr Bogdan TAŞNADI
Second Secretary
E-mail: bogdan.tasnadi@rpro.eu
Tel. +32 27000210

Mrs Luminița TAŞNADI

Justice and home affairs

Mrs Anca PRISTAVU
Second Secretary (Head of Section)
E-mail: anca.pristavu@rpro.eu
Tel. +32 27000201

Mrs Aurelia ILIE
Second Secretary
E-mail: aurelia.ilie@rpro.eu
Tel. +32 27000250

Mr Alexandru MAXIMESCU
Third Secretary
E-mail: alexandru.maximescu@rpro.eu
Tel. +32 27000211

Horizontal issues

Mr Ion SERPE
Minister Counsellor
E-mail: ion.serpe@rpro.eu
Tel. +32 27000304

Mrs Carmen IFRIM
Counsellor
E-mail: carmen.ifrim@rpro.eu
Tel. +32 27000314

Mr Gyula BARA
Second Secretary
E-mail: gyula.bara@rpro.eu
Tel. +32 27000303

Mrs Alexandra ROTILEANU
Third Secretary
E-mail: alexandra.rotileanu@rpro.eu
Tel. +32 27000220

Mr Artur RĂDUCANU
Third Secretary
E-mail: artur.raducanu@rpro.eu
Tel. +32 27000308

Mihai ADAMESCU
Third Secretary
E-mail: mihai.adamescu@rpro.eu
Tel. +32 27000318

Employment, social affairs and health

Mrs Roxana ELENA-IONESCU
First Secretary
E-mail: roxana.ionescu@rpro.eu
Tel. +32 27000219

Mrs Silvia OLTEANU
First Secretary
E-mail: silvia.olteanu@rpro.eu
Tel. +32 27000423

Internal market, competitiveness, industrial policy, consumer protection

Mr Ion SIMION
Counsellor
E-mail: ion.simion@rpro.eu
Tel. +32 27000304

Mrs Cosmina MIU
Counsellor
E-mail: cosmina.miu@rpro.eu
Tel. +32 27000413

Mr Cornel MIU

Mihai ADAMESCU
Third Secretary
E-mail: mihai.adamescu@rpro.eu
Tel. +32 27000318

Transport, telecommunications, energy

Mr Razvan Eugen NICOLESCU
Second Secretary (Head of Section)
E-mail: eugen.nicolescu@rpro.eu
Tel. +32 27000307

Mrs Elena POPESCU
Counsellor
E-mail: elena.popescu@rpro.eu
Tel. +32 27000403

Anda MICLE
Third Secretary
E-mail: anda.micle@rpro.eu
Tel. +32 27000300

Mrs Alina BĂBEANU
Third Secretary
E-mail: alina.babeanu@rpro.eu
Tel. +32 27000315

Mr Ramona NITĂ
Third Secretary
E-mail: ramona.nita@rpro.eu
Tel. +32 27000305

Agriculture, fisheries and rural development

Mr Achim IRIMESCU
Counsellor (Head of Section)
E-mail: achim.irimescu@rpro.eu
Tel. +32 27000203

Mrs Mihaela BARBUŞ
Second Secretary
E-mail: mihaela.barbus@rpro.eu
Tel. +32 27000450

Mr Alexandru MARCHIS
Third Secretary
E-mail: alexandru.marchis@rpro.eu
Tel. +32 27000416

Mrs Ana Maria POPA
Third Secretary
E-mail: anamaria.popa@rpro.eu
Tel. +32 27000407

Mr Daniel LICA
First Secretary
E-mail: daniel.lica@rpro.eu
Tel. +32 27000406

Environment

Mrs Violeta DRAGU
Counsellor (Head of Section)
E-mail: violeta.dragu@rpro.eu
Tel. +32 27000218

Mrs Monica OTEL
First Secretary
E-mail: monica.otel@rpro.eu
Tel. +32 27000208

Education, research, youth and culture

Mr Mircea SBÂRNÍ
Counsellor
E-mail: mircea.sbarna@rpro.eu
Tel. +32 27000202

Mrs Ioana RUS
Third Secretary
E-mail: ioana.rus@rpro.eu
Tel. +32 27000209

Carmen HIRTAN
Third Secretary
E-mail: carmen.hirtan@rpro.eu
Tel. +32 27000313

Protocol and administration

Mr Iulian POPESCU
Minister Counsellor
E-mail: iulian.popescu@rpro.eu
Tel. +32 27000602

Mr Constantin VLAD
Financial services
E-mail: financiar@rpro.eu
Tel. +32 27000215

Mr Mihai MIHAI
Protocol
E-mail: mihai.mihai@rpro.eu
Tel. +32 27000207

Mrs Cristina RUSCEA
Administrative services
E-mail: cristina.ruscea@rpro.eu
Tel. +32 27000214

PERMANENT REPRESENTATION OF SLOVENIA

Rue du Commerce 44
B-1000 Brussels
E-mail: spbr ou prénom.nom@gov.si
Media: pr.spbr@gov.si
Website: http://www.mzz.gov.si
Tel. +32 22136300
Fax +32 22136301

HE Mr Igor SENČAR
Ambassador Extraordinary and Plenipotentiary
Permanent Representative

Mrs Tatjana BAJUK SENČAR

HE Mrs Mary Veronika TOVŠAK PLETERSKI
Minister Plenipotentiary
Deputy Permanent Representative

Mr Miran PLETERSKI

HE Mrs Metka IPAVIC
Minister plenipotentiary
PSC Representative

Mr Zoran VUČKOVIĆ

Mr Iztok GRMEK
Minister plenipotentiary
Head of Administration and Secretariat

Mrs Maja DOBNIKAR

Coordination

Mrs Tina VODNIK
(Antici)

Mr Jure VRŠNAK
(Mertens)

Mr Oliver ĐAJIĆ
(Nicolaïdis)

Mr Mihael ZUPANČIČ
(Legal affairs)

Press and protocol

Mrs Maja KOCIJANČIČ
Spokesperson

Mrs Dacha SIMČIČ
(Protocol and organisation)

Relations with the institutions

Mrs Berta MRAK
(Relations with the European Parliament, GAG)

External relations and enlargement

Mrs Tamara WEINGERL POŽAR
(Enlargement)

Mr Damijan SEDAR
(COWEB)

Mrs Petra LANGERHOLC
(COASI)

Mrs Jasna PONIKVAR
(Latin America)

Mr Bogdan BATIČ
(Middle East /Gulf Working Party, MaMa, COMEP, EURO-MED)

Mrs Mateja NORČIČ
(COEST)

Justice and home affairs

Mr Andrej GROŠELJ
(Terrorism, organised crime, Europol)

Mrs Suzana IVANOVIČ
(Visa, Schengen)

Mrs Helena KOROŠEC
(Migration, asylum policy)

Mrs Danica BABIČ
(Civil protection)

Mrs Mateja KRIVEC
(Civil law)

Mrs Jana BAMBIČ
(Justice)

Financial affairs

Mr Alenka JERKIČ
Senior Financial Adviser

Mrs Mojca AMBROŽ
(Budget)

Mrs Mateja JANŠA
(Financial affairs)

Mr Borut FRANJGA
(Customs)

Mr Mitja KOŠMRL
(Taxation)

Mr Miran VATOVEC
(Structural Funds)

Trade and development

Mrs Katarina PETAČ
(Article 133 Committee)

Mrs Martina SKOK
(ACP, Devgen)

Political and Security Committee

Mrs Renata CVELBAR BEK
(RELEX)

Mr Mirko CIGLER
Political Adviser PMG

Mr Ivan HOSTNIK
Defence Adviser PMG

Military Committee

Mr Renato PETRIČ
(EUMC)

Mr Aleš LAZAR
(EVOP)

Mr Samo ZANOŠKAR
(HTF)

Mr Tomaž VENIŠNIK
(Horizontal affairs)

Agriculture and fisheries

Mr Gvido MRAVLJAK
(Agriculture)

Mrs Polona KOLAREK
(Agriculture)

Mrs Alisa TIGANJ
(Fisheries)

Mr Ian KAIN
(Health and plant health control)

Energy, science and telecommunications

Mrs Anamraija JESENKO
(Telecommunications and the information society)

Mr Albin KRALJ
(Research)

Mr Sergej MOŽINA
(Research)

Mrs Mateja MLAKAR
(Competition and growth)

Mrs Edita SAMSA
(Technical harmonisation)

Mr Dušan PŠENIČNIK
(Intellectual property and company law)

Mrs Urška DOLINŠEK
(Energy, Euratom)

Transport

Mr Franc ŽEPIČ
Counsellor (transport)

Mr Darko TRAJANOV
(Maritime transport)

Employment, social affairs and public health

Mrs Maja RIJAVEC
(Employment, social affairs and equal opportunities)

Environment

Mrs Štefanija NOVAK
(Environment)

Culture and Education

Mr Sašo GAZDIĆ
(Cultural and audiovisual affairs)

Mrs Sabina MELAVC
(Education and youth)

PERMANENT REPRESENTATION OF SLOVAKIA

Avenue de Cortenbergh 79
B-1000 Brussels
E-mail: slovakmission@pmsreu.be
Website: http://www.mzv.sk/szbrusel
Tel. +32 27436811
Fax +32 27436888/89

HE Mr Maroš ŠEFČOVIČ
Ambassador Extraordinary and Plenipotentiary
Permanent Representative
Tel. +32 27436800

Mrs Helena ŠEFČOVIČOVÁ

HE Mr Peter JAVORČIK
Counsellor
Deputy Permanent Representative
Tel. +32 27436801

Mrs Gabriela JAVORČÍKOVÁ

Political and Security Committee

HE Mr Ľubomír REHÁK
Ambassador
Permanent Representative to the PSC
Tel. +32 27436861

Mrs Dana REHÁKOVÁ

European Union Military Committee

Mr Jaroslav KUČA
Brigadier
Tel. +32 27072736

Mrs Slávka KUČOVÁ

Coordination

Mrs Alena GAŽÚROVÁ
First Secretary (Antici)
Tel. +32 27436840

Mr Peter BEŇO
Third secretary (Mertens)
Tel. +32 27436842

Administration and Protocol

Mrs Dagmar KOPÁČOVÁ
First Secretary
Tel. +32 27436825

Mr Václav ŠIMON

Press and information

Mrs Zuzana DUTKOVÁ
Attaché
Tel. +32 27436807

European Parliament, institutional matters

Mr Branislav PAVLOVIČ
Third Secretary
Tel. +32 27436805

Lisbon Strategy

Mrs Gabriela SÁBELOVÁ
Third Secretary
Tel. +32 27436796

Enlargement

Mr Marcel BABICZ
First Secretary
Tel. +32 27436897

Legal Affairs, Court of Justice of the European Communities

Mr Tomáš BUCHTA
Third Secretary
Legal Adviser
Tel. +32 27436851

Foreign Affairs, Policy and Security Committee

Mr Peter SEDLÁČEK
First Secretary (RELEX)
Tel. +32 27436870

Mrs Janka SEDLÁČKOVÁ

Mr Ladislav BALLEK
Third Secretary
Tel. +32 27436877

Martin KMOŠENA
First Secretary
Tel. +32 27436803

Mr Marcel BABICZ
Third Secretary
Tel. +32 27436897

Mr Norbert BRADA
Third Secretary
Tel. +32 27436879

Mr Ivan VAŇO
Third Secretary
Tel. +32 27436846

Mrs Simona VAŇOVÁ

Mrs Katarína JURISOVÁ
Third Secretary
Tel. +32 27436845

Mr Tomáš KOZÁK
Third Secretary
Tel. +32 27436804

Mr Michal VANČO
Attaché
Tel. +32 27436834

Mrs Eva VANČOVÁ

Mr Mário NICOLINI
Counsellor (Defence)
Tel. +32 27436875

Mr Martin SKLENÁR
Counsellor (Defence)
Tel. +32 27436873

Home affairs and justice

Mr Ľubomír HANUS
Counsellor
Tel. +32 27436838

Mrs Iveta ZRAKOVÁ
Second Secretary
Tel. +32 27436829

Mr Štefan BALÁZSY
Third Secretary
Tel. +32 27436849

Mrs Eva BALÁZSYOVÁ

Mr Alexander KUNOŠÍK
Third Secretary
Tel. +32 27436852

Mr Michal KOTLÁRIK
Third Secretary
Tel. +32 27436827

Mr Ján JAVORSKÝ

Ecofin

Mrs Andrea ZÁHUMENSKÁ
Third Secretary
Tel. +32 27436830

Mr Jaroslav NÁHLIK
Counsellor
Tel. +32 27436839

Mrs Beáta NÁHLIKOVÁ

Mr Viliam HARVAN
Counsellor
Tel. +32 27436892

Mrs Petra HARVANOVÁ

Mr Vladimír STAŠKO
Second Secretary
Tel. +32 27436812

Mrs Miriam STAŠKOVÁ

Mr Tomáš MAJERČÁK
Third Secretary
Tel. +32 27436869

Agriculture, fisheries

Mr Martin CHUDÝ
First Secretary
Tel. +32 27436810

Mrs Karin MURÁNIOVÁ
Attaché
Tel. +32 27436823

Mr Ján KADEŘÁBEK
Attaché
Tel. +32 27436824

Mrs Tatiana ŠIMONČIČOVÁ
Attaché
Tel. +32 27436880

Trade, internal market, energy, atomic questions

Mrs Judita VANKOVÁ
First Secretary
Tel. +32 27436893

Mr Ľubomír KUCHTA
Counsellor
Tel. +32 27436896

Mrs L'udmila KUCHTOVÁ

Mr Peter MUŠKA
First Secretary
Tel. +32 27436511

Mrs Mária MUŠKOVÁ

Mr Dušan DUŠÁK
First Secretary
Tel. +32 27436843

Mrs Lucia DUŠÁKOVÁ

Richard PAULE
Second Secretary
Tel. +32 27436809

Mrs Gabriela PAULE

Environment

Mrs Katarína MOYZESOVÁ
Third Secretary
Tel. +32 27436819

Mr Norbert KURILLA
Attaché
Tel. +32 27436833

Telecommunications

Mr Anton SMITKA
Counsellor
Tel. +32 27436848

Transport

Mr Kvetoslav KMEC
Second Secretary
Tel. +32 27436891

Mrs KMECOVÁ

Mr Peter BAREK
Counsellor
Tel. +32 27436826

Employment, social policy and health

Mr Pavol JUHÁS
Second Secretary
Tel. +32 27436837

Mr Tomáš ŠEFRANKO
Attaché
Tel. +32 27436882

Mrs Xénia MALÁ
Attaché
Tel. +32 27436795

Mrs Marta MAŠKOVÁ
Third Secretary
Tel. +32 27436847

Regional policy

Mrs Katarína KUKUČKOVÁ TOMKOVÁ
Third Secretary
Tel. +32 27436797

Mr Pavol KUKUČKA

Mr Roman ŽATKO
Counsellor
Tel. +32 27436835

Mrs Jozefína ŽATKOVÁ

Research

Mr Jozef PITEL
First Secretary
Tel. +32 27436808

Mrs Ľubica PITLOVÁ

Education

Mr Ivan HROMADA
Second Secretary
Tel. +32 27436878

Mrs Regina HROMADOVÁ

Culture, audiovisual and intellectual property

Mr Dušan ŠÁNDOR
Second Secretary
Tel. +32 27436859

Mrs Zuzana ŠÁNDOROVÁ

Military Committee

Mr Ján GOCELIAK
Colonel
Tel. +32 27436821

Mrs Táňa GOCELIAKOVÁ

Mr Tibor KRÁLIK
Colonel
Tel. +32 27436864

Juraj HAKAJ
Commander
Tel. +32 27436866

Mr Jaroslav GELETIČ
Commander
Tel. +32 27436875

Mrs Júlia GELETIČOVÁ

Mr Jaroslav BENCA
Tel. +32 27436868

National Security Authority

Mr Miroslaw PÁSTOR
First Secretary
Tel. +32 27436883

Mrs Mária PÁSTOROVÁ

Security

Mr Martin MAŤAS
First Secretary
Tel. +32 27436894

Mrs Jana MAŤASOVÁ

PERMANENT REPRESENTATION OF FINLAND

Rue de Trèves 100
B-1040 Brussels
E-mail: firstname.lastname@formin.fi,
sanomat.eue@formin.fi
Website: http://www.finland.eu
Tel. +32 22878411
Fax +32 22878400

HE Mr Jan STORE
Ambassador Extraordinary and Plenipotentiary
Permanent Representative
Tel. +32 22878422

Mrs Iris STORE

HE Mrs Marja RISLAKKI
Minister
Deputy Permanent Representative
Tel. +32 22878425

Mr Pekka RISLAKKI

Coordination and information

Mrs Marianne HUUSKO-LAMPONEN
Adviser (Antici)
Tel. +32 22878440

Mr Mika KUKKONEN
Second Secretary (Mertens)
Tel. +32 22878496

Mrs Heli KUKKONEN

Parliament

Mrs Reetta HÄRÖNOJA
First Secretary (relations with the European Parliament)
Tel. +32 22878434

Relations with the European institutions, institutional affairs

Mr Henrik RUSO
Counsellor
Tel. +32 22878461

Press relations

Mr Marko RUONALA
Counsellor (press)
Tel. +32 22878472

Interim Political and Security Committee

HE Mrs Anne SIPILÄINEN
Ambassador
Tel. +32 22878485

Mr Olli-Pekka IMMONEN

Mr Antti KASKI
First Secretary (PSC, PMG, Nicolaïdis, coordination)
Tel. +32 22878465

Mrs Anne KEMPPAINEN
Counsellor (RELEX)
Tel. +32 22878514

Mr Claus SCHULTZE

Mr Pete PIIRAINEN
Counsellor (defence policy)
Tel. +32 22878479

Mrs Kaisa-Reetta KARHU
Second Secretary (civilian crisis management and coordination)
Tel. +32 22878498

Juha KARHU

European Defence Agency (EDA)

Mr Olli RUUTU
Adviser (defence policy)
Tel. +32 22878603

Mrs Tania RUUTU

Interim Military Body

Mr Juha KILPIÄ
Major-General
Military Representative
E-mail: juha.kilpia@formin.fi
Tel. +32 22878475

Mrs Mirja KILPIÄ

Mr Sakari MARTIMO
Captain
Deputy Military Representative
E-mail: sakari.martimo@formin.fi
Tel. +32 22878435

Mrs Yvonne MARTIMO

Mr Petteri GRANLUND
Commander
Deputy Military Representative
E-mail: petteri.granlund@formin.fi
Tel. +32 22878565

Mrs Sanna GRANLUND

Headline Goal Task Force (HTF)

Mr Jukka KOTILEHTO
Major
Tel. +32 22878492

Mrs Virpi KORPI

Regional policy

Mrs Kielo KARIOJA-MÄKELÄ
Counsellor
Tel. +32 22878580

Mr Jarmo MÄKELÄ

Commercial policy

Mr Petri PUHAKKA
Counsellor (Article 133 Committee, services)
Tel. +32 22878457

Mrs Outi PUHAKKA

Mr Jouko LEINONEN
Counsellor (Article 133 Committee, EEA, EFTA, Nordic cooperation, Transatlantic relations)
Tel. +32 22878512

Enlargement, central Europe, western Europe

Mrs Miia LAHTI
Second Secretary
Tel. +32 22878444

Legal and institutional affairs

Mrs Henriikka LEPPO
Secretary of Legislation (institutional issues)
Tel. +32 22878448

Mr Johannes LEPPO

Justice and home affairs

Mrs Tiina KANGAS-ALKU
Counsellor (civil law)
Tel. +32 22878431

Mr Lauri ALKU

Mr Matti SARASMAA
Adviser (border security, visas)
Tel. +32 22878527

Mrs Anne SARASMAA

Mr Mikko MONTO
Counsellor (legal cooperation, legal matters, criminal law)
Tel. +32 22879594

Mrs Hanna MONTO

Mrs Hannele TAAVILA
Counsellor (Police cooperation)
Tel. +32 22878504

Mr Jyrki RINNE

Mrs Annikki VANAMO-ALHO
Adviser (home affairs)
Tel. +32 22878420

Civil crisis management

Mrs Kaisa-Reetta KARHU
Second Secretary
Tel. +32 22878498

Mr Juha KARHU

Economic and financial affairs

Mr Tuomas MAJURI
Counsellor (banking and financial matters, statistics)
Tel. +32 22878528

Mrs Pia MAJURI

Mrs Niina PAUTOLA-MOL
Counsellor (economic affairs)
Tel. +32 22878524

Mr Baptiest MOL

Mrs Nina ALATALO
Counsellor (budget)
Tel. +32 22878526

Mrs Marja HOKKANEN
Counsellor (taxation-fiscal system)
Tel. +32 22878451

External relations

Mrs Krista NAPOLA
First Secretary (Western Balkans)
Tel. +32 22878466

Mr Martti NAPOLA

Mrs Lauratuulia LEHTINEN
Second Secretary (development)
Tel. +32 22878572

Mr Lauri HIRVONEN

Mr Claus LINDROOS
First Secretary (Cotonou, ACP, Africa, Food aid)
Tel. +32 22878621

Mrs Annika SUNDBÄCK-LINDROOS

Mrs Laura LINDGREN
Embassy Counsellor (Asia, Latin America)
Tel. +32 22878460

Mrs Johanna BIRKSTEDT
First Secretary (Mediterranean, Middle East, Barcelona process, Persian Gulf)
Tel. +32 22878595

Mr Teemu VASS

Mrs Anne KEMPPAINEN
Counsellor (RELEX)
Tel. +32 22878514

Mr Claus SCHULTZE

Mrs Jaana TECKENBERG
Embassy Counsellor (Russia, CIS, Northern Dimension)
Tel. +32 22878471

Mr Rolf GRÖNHOLM

Culture and education

Mrs Johanna HULKKO
Counsellor (education, vocational education and training, culture, audiovisual services, youth)
Tel. +32 22878525

Harri SYVÄSALMI
Counsellor (gambling, lotteries, sport)
Tel. +32 22878624

Mrs Tiina PERHO

Transport

Mrs Jaana HEIKKINEN
Adviser (road transport, inland waterway transport, TEN-T, maritime transport)
Tel. +32 22878463

Mrs Suvi JÄRVELÄ
Adviser (aviation, rail transport)
Tel. +32 22878538

Mr Tatu TUOMINEN
Counsellor (telecommunications, audiovisual services (technology), information society)
Tel. +32 22878550

Mrs Monica LÖV

Agriculture, forestry and fisheries

Mrs Berit KORPILO
Counsellor (veterinary and phytosanitary issues, food safety)
Tel. +32 22878468

Mr Heikki LEHTINEN
Counsellor (fisheries)
Tel. +32 22878464

Mr Osmo RÖNTY
Adviser (SCA, agriculture, environmental issues, forestry)
Tel. +32 22878432

Mrs Kaisu RÖNTY

Mr Ahti HIRVONEN
Counsellor (SCA, agriculture, forests)
Tel. +32 22878638

Mrs Johanna HIRVONEN

Social policy, labour and employment

Mrs Liisa HEINONEN
Counsellor (employment policies, ECOSOC)
Tel. +32 22878583

Mr Ari VEIJONEN

Mrs Eeva KOLEHMAINEN
Adviser (social security, social protection, health and safety at work, gender equality)
Tel. +32 22878445

Industrial policy, energy, internal market and research

Mr Timo HAAPALEHTO
Adviser (research, Euratom)
Tel. +32 22878429

Mrs Christine SARRETTE

Mrs Liisa HUHTALA
Counsellor (consumer policy, company law, intellectual property rights, public procurement, mutual recognition of diplomas, better regulation, horizontal competiveness issues)
Tel. +32 22878450

Mr Sakke HUHTALA

Mr Kim FYHR
Adviser (energy, industrial policy)
Tel. +32 22878449

Mrs Heli FYHR

Mr Kari VIRTANEN
Adviser (internal market, foodstuffs, tourism)
Tel. +32 22878433

Health and private insurance

Mr Toivo HURME
Adviser (public health, pharmaceuticals, private insurance)
Tel. +32 22878467

Mrs Satu SILVANTO

Customs

Mr Jouko LEMPIÄINEN
Adviser (customs)
Tel. +32 22878438

Mrs Thérèse BLANCHET

Environment

Mrs Ulla-Riitta SOVERI
Counsellor (chemicals, nature conservation, fresh water, environmental information, waste management, 6th EAP)
Tel. +32 22878477

Mrs Tuula VARIS
Counsellor (air quality, marine protection, nature management, climate change)
Tel. +32 22878414

Åland Islands

Mr Andreas BACKFOLK
Counsellor
Tel. +32 22878459

Administration

Mrs Oivi HEINONEN
Counsellor
Tel. +32 22878503

Mr Raino HEINONEN

Mrs Anne MALINEN-WILLIAMS
Administrative Attaché
Tel. +32 22878521

Mr David G. WILLIAMS

Mrs Kirsi MAJANDER
Administrative Attaché
Tel. +32 22878581

PERMANENT REPRESENTATION OF SWEDEN

Square de Meeûs 30
B-1000 Brussels
E-mail: representationen.bryssel@foreign.ministry.se
Tel. +32 22895611
Fax +32 22895600

HE Mr Christian DANIELSSON
Ambassador Extraordinary and Plenipotentiary
Permanent Representative
E-mail: christian.danielsson@foreign.ministry.se
Tel. +32 22895645

Mrs Veronika WAND DANIELSSON

HE Mrs Ulrika BARKLUND LARSSON
Ambassador
Deputy Permanent Representative
E-mail: ulrika.barklund-larsson@foreign.ministry.se
Tel. +32 22895642

Mr Kjell LARSSON

Coordination

Mrs Charlotte MUÑOZ SAMMELIN
Counsellor (Antici)
E-mail: charlotte.sammelin@foreign.ministry.se
Tel. +32 22895621

Mr Miguel MUÑOZ RAMIREZ

Mr Daniel SVENSSON
Counsellor (Mertens)
E-mail: daniel.svensson@foreign.ministry.se
Tel. +32 22895638

Mrs Sophie KUNSH

Mr Mårten WIERUP
Second Secretary (Antici deputy)
E-mail: marten.wierup@foreign.ministry.se
Tel. +32 22895809

Mrs Moa LAGERCRANTZ
Second Secretary (Mertens deputy)
E-mail: moa.lagercrantz@foreign.ministry.se
Tel. +32 22895632

Press and information

Mr Thomas LINDBLOM
Press Advisor
E-mail: thomas.lindblom@foreign.ministry.se
Tel. +32 22895655

Mrs Camilla ÅKESSON LINDBLOM

Foreign and Security Policy Unit

HE Mr Olof SKOOG
Ambassador, Head of Unit
Representative of Sweden to the PSC
Permanent Representative of Sweden to the WEU
E-mail: olof.skoog@foreign.ministry.se
Tel. +32 22895657

Mrs Johanna BRISMAR SKOOG

Mr Carl HARTZELL
Counsellor (Deputy Representative for PSC, WEU, ISS)
E-mail: carl.hartzell@foreign.ministry.se
Tel. +32 22895763

Mrs Mette HARTZELL

Mrs Therese HYDÉN
Counsellor (RELEX, horizontal CFSP questions)
E-mail: therese.hyden@foreign.ministry.se
Tel. +32 22895842

Mr Jonas NILSSON

Mrs Maria WEIMER
Second Secretary (Nicolaïdis)
E-mail: maria.weimer@foreign.ministry.se
Tel. +32 22895622

ESDP/Ministry of Foreign Affairs

Mrs Inger BUXTON
Counsellor (Politico-Military Working Party, security and development)
E-mail: inger.buxton@foreign.ministry.se
Tel. +32 22895677

Mr David BUXTON

Mrs Anna CRAENEN
Adviser (Western Balkans, CARDS, transatlantic relations)
E-mail: anna.craenen@foreign.ministry.se
Tel. +32 22895637

Mr Jan CRAENEN

Mr Mathias GRÖNLUND
Counsellor (customs union (1st pillar), GSP, WCO)
E-mail: mathias.gronlund@foreign.ministry.se
Tel. +32 22895742

Mr Martin HAGSTRÖM
Embassy Counsellor (Eastern Europe, Central Asia, northern dimension, TACIS)
E-mail: martin.hagstrom@foreign.ministry.se
Tel. +32 22895667

Mrs Tania SMIRNOVA

Mrs Anna JARDFELT MELVIN
Counsellor (Mashreq, Maghreb, Middle East)
E-mail: anna.jardfelt@foreign.ministry.se
Tel. +32 22895697

Mr Neil MELVIN

Mr Staffan OCUSTO
Counsellor (civilian crisis management)
E-mail: staffan.ocusto@foreign.ministry.se
Tel. +32 22895646

Mrs Alma-Anethe WESTFAL-OCUSTO

Mrs Marita OLSON
Adviser (international development cooperation)
E-mail: marita.olson@foreign.ministry.se
Tel. +32 22895606

Mr Bennett OLSON

Mrs Charlotta OZAKI MACIAS
Counsellor (Asia)
E-mail: charlotta.ozaki-macias@foreign.ministry.se
Tel. +32 22895746

Mr Nicolas MACIAS

Mr Joakim REITER
Counsellor (Article 133 Committee, MRA, WTO, commercial policy)
E-mail: joakim.reiter@foreign.ministry.se
Tel. +32 22895664

Mrs Anna STRÖMBÄCK REITER

Mr Mikael ANZÉN
First Secretary (EFTA, Article 133 services)
E-mail: mikael.anzen@foreign.ministry.se
Tel. +32 22895874

Mrs Maud FLOTARD ANZÉN

Mr Hans GRUNDBERG
First Secretary (Barcelona process, Mediterranean, Gulf)
E-mail: hans.grundberg@foreign.ministry.se
Tel. +32 22895650

Mrs Alexandra RYDMARK

Mrs Petra LÄRKE
First Secretary (enlargement, Cyprus, Romania, Bulgaria)
E-mail: petra.larke@foreign.ministry.se
Tel. +32 22895673

Mr Magnus LÄRKE

Mr Johan NDISI
First Secretary (Subsaharan Africa, EU/Africa)
E-mail: johan.ndisi@foreign.ministry.se
Tel. +32 22895757

Mrs Linalotta PETRELIUS NDISI

Mrs Fredrike TAMAS HERMELIN
First Secretary (Latin America, transatlantic relations)
E-mail: fredrike.tamas-hermelin@foreign.ministry.se
Tel. +32 22895841

Mr Krystof TAMAS

Mrs Gabriella SAVE
Second Secretary (RELEX deputy)
E-mail: gabriella.save@foreign.ministry.se
Tel. +32 22895864

Mr Ola SOHLSTRÖM
Second Secretary (ACP, European Development Fund)
E-mail: ola.sohlstrom@foreign.ministry.se
Tel. +32 22895704

Mrs Amelie HENRY
Third Secretary (national experts, servants of the institutions)
E-mail: amelie.henry@foreign.ministry.se
Tel. +32 22895722

Mr Mårten GUNNARTZ

ESDP/Ministry of Defence

Mrs Annika ELMGART
Counsellor (Affairs of the Ministry of Defence, Politico-Military Working Group)
E-mail: annika.elmgart@foreign.ministry.se
Tel. +32 22895870

Mr Otto ELMGART

Mrs Sara SIRI
Counsellor (Ministry of Defence civilian affairs, civilian security)
E-mail: sara.siri@foreign.ministry.se
Tel. +32 22895676

Mr Julien SIRI

Mr Christian MADSEN
Counsellor (AED, GAEO, research and defence development)
E-mail: christian.madsen@foreign.ministry.se
Tel. +32 22895831

Mrs Annakarin MADSEN

Mr Stefan ENGDAHL
Rear-Admiral
Military Adviser (Representative of Sweden on the Military Committee of the European Union)
E-mail: stefan.engdahl@foreign.ministry.se
Tel. +32 22895694

Mrs Kerstin ENGDAHL

Mr Christer NORDH
Lieutenant Colonel
Counsellor (Deputy Military Representative to the EU Military Committee, EU Military Committee Working Group, military capability)
E-mail: christer.nordh@foreign.ministry.se
Tel. +32 22895783

Mrs Alda ROLO GALACHO

Mr Lars-Ove ROOS
Lieutenant Colonel
Adviser (Military Working Group, HTF)
E-mail: lars-ove.roos@foreign.ministry.se
Tel. +32 22895832

Mrs Theresa ROOS

European Parliamant, interinstitutional affairs

Mrs Johanna BRISMAR SKOOG
Minister (European Parliament, general affairs)
E-mail: johanna.brismar-skoog@foreign.ministry.se
Tel. +32 22895659

Mr Olof SKOOG

Legal affairs, justice and home affairs, internal market

Mr Nils HÄNNINGER
Adviser (JAI, police cooperation, terrorism, Schengen)
E-mail: nils.hanninger@foreign.ministry.se
Tel. +32 22895604

Mr Jonas HÖGSTRÖM
Counsellor (civil law, consumers' rights, transparency)
E-mail: jonas.hogstrom@foreign.ministry.se
Tel. +32 22895854

Mrs Mirja HÖGSTRÖM

Mrs Mirja HÖGSTRÖM
Counsellor (criminal law, judicial cooperation, intellectual property)
E-mail: mirja.hogstrom@foreign.ministry.se
Tel. +32 22895614

Mr Jonas HÖGSTRÖM

Mr Lars Johan LÖNNBACK
Counsellor (asylum, migration)
E-mail: lars-johan.lonnback@foreign.ministry.se
Tel. +32 22895759

Mrs Patrizia MAURO

Mrs Åsa WEBBER
Counsellor (JHA, Article 36, criminal matters)
E-mail: asa.webber@foreign.ministry.se
Tel. +32 22895615

Mr Paul WEBBER

Mr Jesper KANSBOD
First Secretary (EU law, Court of Justice, internal market, competition)
E-mail: jesper.kansbod@foreign.ministry.se
Tel. +32 22895728

Mrs Anneli KANSBOD

Economic and financial affairs

Mrs Sara ALMER
Adviser (budget, Budget Committee, Agenda 2007)
E-mail: sara.almer@foreign.ministry.se
Tel. +32 22895846

Mr Ivan CARDENAS ARDILES

Mrs Charlotta ERIKSON
Counsellor (financial markets and government procurement)
E-mail: charlotta.erikson@foreign.ministry.se
Tel. +32 22895693

Mrs Åsa JOHANSSON
Counsellor (Ecofin, EMU, financial instruments)
E-mail: asa.johansson@foreign.ministry.se
Tel. +32 22895711

Mrs Gabriela KALM
Adviser (customs (3rd pillar), customs cooperation, WCO)
E-mail: gabriela.kalm@foreign.ministry.se
Tel. +32 22895670

Mr Jan OLSSON
Counsellor (fiscal questions)
E-mail: jan.e.olsson@foreign.ministry.se
Tel. +32 22895647

Mrs Renate DONATH-OLSSON

Mr Ulf REHNBERG
Counsellor (fiscal questions)
E-mail: ulf.rehnberg@foreign.ministry.se
Tel. +32 22895714

Mrs Louise REHNBERG

Mrs Kristina ÅKESSON
Counsellor (EU budget, financial control, auditing)
E-mail: kristina.akesson@foreign.ministry.se
Tel. +32 22895748

Agriculture and fisheries

Mrs Pernilla IVARSSON
Minister (foodstuffs, plant health, seeds, veterinary questions)
E-mail: pernilla.ivarsson@foreign.ministry.se
Tel. +32 22895688

Mr Carl-Johan LINDÉN
Adviser (CAP, SCA)
E-mail: carl-johan.linden@foreign.ministry.se
Tel. +32 22895689

Mrs Maria ROSANDER
Adviser (CAP, SCA)
E-mail: maria.rosander@foreign.ministry.se
Tel. +32 22895654

Mr Bengt LEWIN

Mr Robin ROSENKRANZ
Adviser (fisheries, EFTA/EEA)
E-mail: robin.rosenkranz@foreign.ministry.se
Tel. +32 22895658

Mrs Maria MEYER-ROSENKRANZ

Mrs Mathilda ÅBERG
Counsellor (food, plant protection, seeds)
E-mail: mathilda.aberg@foreign.ministry.se
Tel. +32 22895681

Environment and sustainable development

Mr Ulf BJÖRNHOLM-OTTOSSON
Adviser (waste and recycling, water, vehicles and traffic issues, nature conservation)
E-mail: ulf.bjornholm-ottosson@foreign.ministry.se
Tel. +32 22895602

Mrs Sari BJÖRNHOLM

Mr Gabór SZENDRÖ
Counsellor (atomic affairs, nuclear safety)
E-mail: gabor.szendro@foreign.ministry.se
Tel. +32 22895625

Mrs Beata DOBOSSY

Mrs Zofia TUCINSKA
Adviser (sustainable development, air, chemicals, EU budget for the environment)
E-mail: zofia.tucinska@foreign.ministry.se
Tel. +32 22895729

Mrs Monica TÖRNLUND
Adviser (waste and recycling, water, vehicles and traffic issues, nature conservation)
E-mail: monica. tornlund@foreign.ministry.se
Tel. +32 22895631

Mr Olof REIMER

Health and social affairs

Mr Fredrik MOEN
Counsellor (public health, medicines, alcohol, narcotics)
E-mail: fredrik.moen@foreign.ministry.se
Tel. +32 22895719

Mrs Annika MANSNÉRUS
Counsellor (social affairs, working environment, equality, narcotics)
E-mail: annika.mansnerus@foreign.ministry.se
Tel. +32 22895725

Mr Alexander CARLBERG

Employment

Mr Gustaf LINDGREN
Adviser (Ecosoc, labour law, social dialogue)
E-mail: gustaf.lindgren@foreign.ministry.se
Tel. +32 22895847

Mrs Lena RIPA

Entreprise, energy and communications

Mr Tomas BROLIN
Adviser (railways, air transport)
E-mail: tomas.brolin@foreign.ministry.se
Tel. +32 22895830

Mrs Elisabet BJÖRNFOT

Mrs Anna HALVARSSON
Adviser (railways, air transport)
E-mail: anna.halvarsson@foreign.ministry.se
Tel. +32 22895648

Mrs Sofia JOHANSSON
Adviser (regional policy, Structural Funds, Committee of the Regions, tourism)
E-mail: sofia.johansson@foreign.ministry.se
Tel. +32 22895626

Mrs Kersti KARLSSON
Counsellor (road transport, shipping)
E-mail: kersti.karlsson@foreign.ministry.se
Tel. +32 22895618

Mr Rolf KARLSSON

Mrs Anette PERSSON
Counsellor (energy policy, energy charter)
E-mail: anette.persson@foreign.ministry.se
Tel. +32 22895708

Mr Maths PERSSON

Mr Jörgen SAMUELSSON
Adviser (telecommunications, postal issues, industrial policy, competitiveness)
E-mail: jorgen.samuelsson@foreign.ministry.se
Tel. +32 22895723

Mrs Malin SAMUELSSON

Mr Per TERVAHAUTA
Counsellor (industry)
E-mail: per.tervahauta@foreign.ministry.se
Tel. +32 22895641

Mrs Carolina STEGE

Education, research

Mr Bjarne KIRSEBOM
Minister (research and development)
E-mail: bjarne.kirsebom@foreign.ministry.se
Tel. +32 22895703

Mrs Gunilla JACOBSSON

Mrs Karin HENRIKSSON
Counsellor (education, recognition of diplomas)
E-mail: karin.henriksson@foreign.ministry.se
Tel. +32 22895701

Mr Gary NEWMAN

Culture

Mr Jerker STATTIN
Counsellor (culture, media)
E-mail: jerker.stattin@foreign.ministry.se
Tel. +32 22895635

Mr Bengt STENBERG

Administrative affairs

Mr Thomas VESTIN
Minister (Head of Chancellery)
E-mail: thomas.vestin@foreign.ministry.se
Tel. +32 22895691

Mrs Carina STÅLBERG
Embassy First Secretary (archives)
E-mail: carina.stalberg@foreign.ministry.se
Tel. +32 22895649

Mr Tommy SVENSSON

Mr Lukas UDD
Second Secretary (computer management)
E-mail: lukas.udd@foreign.ministry.se
Tel. +32 22895669

PERMANENT REPRESENTATION OF THE UNITED KINGDOM

Avenue d'Auderghem 10
B-1040 Brussels
E-mail: ukrep@fco.gov.uk
Website: http://www.ukrep.be
Tel. +32 22878211
Fax +32 22878398

HE Mr Kim DARROCH KCMG
Ambassador Extraordinary and Plenipotentiary
Permanent Representative

Mrs DARROCH

HE Mr Andrew LEBRECHT
Deputy Permanent Representative

Mrs LEBRECHT

Mr Richard JONES
Adviser
Political and institutional affairs
Tel. +32 22878272

Mrs Hazel CAMERON
First Secretary (Antici)
Tel. +32 22878285

Miss Ann SWAMPILLAI
First Secretary (Future of Europe)
Tel. +32 22878248

Mrs Juliette BIRD
First Secretary
Tel. +32 22878391

Mrs Victoria COURTNEY
First Secretary (press and information)
Tel. +32 22878206

Miss Helen BOWER
Second Secretary (press and information)
Tel. +32 22878212

Miss Libby DAVIDSON
Counsellor
Tel. +32 486646948

Mr Ed LOCKE
Counsellor
Tel. +32 0476961402

Political and institutional affairs

Mr Paul HEARDMAN
First Secretary
Tel. +32 22878292

Legal affairs

Mrs Sally LANGRISH
Adviser (legal matters)
Tel. +32 22878337

Mrs Alyson KING
First Secretary
Tel. +32 22828932

Mr Gerry REGAN
First Secretary
Tel. +32 22878364

Justice and home affairs

Mr Vijay RANGARAJAN
Counsellor (justice and home affairs)
Tel. +32 22878281

Mrs RANGARAJAN

Mr Phil DOUGLAS
First Secretary
Tel. +32 22878257

Mrs Claire FIELDER
First Secretary
Tel. +32 22878259

Mrs Robin HEALEY
First Secretary
Tel. +32 22878241

Mrs Alexandra KNAPTON
First Secretary
Tel. +32 22878384

Mrs Sally COOK
Second Secretary
Tel. +32 22878916

Mrs Rebecca PUGH
Second Secretary
Tel. +32 22878368

Agricultural affairs

Mr Tim RENDER
Counsellor (agriculture)
Tel. +32 22878254

Mr Steve DAVIES
First Secretary
Tel. +32 22878249

Mr Simon STANNARD
First Secretary
Tel. +32 22878214

Mrs NORTON

Mr David TRIPP
First Secretary
Tel. +32 22878389

Mr Graeme TAYLOR
Second Secretary
Tel. +32 22878286

Mr Nigel BARCLAY
Second Secretary
Tel. +32 22878336

Mr Matthew SABOURIN
Second Secretary
Tel. +32 22878255

Economic and financial affairs, taxation

Mr Michael COLLINS
Counsellor (economic and financial affairs)
Tel. +32 22878264

Mr Robert HARDING
First Secretary (economic and financial affairs)
Tel. +32 22878293

Mr Greg HOUSTON
First Secretary (budget)
Tel. +32 22878283

Mr Jack SCHICKLER
First Secretary (economic and financial affairs)
Tel. +32 22878223

Mr Mikael DOWN
First Secretary (taxation)
Tel. +32 22878378

Mrs Helena OWEN
Second Secretary (budget)
Tel. +32 22878284

Mr Mark ARULIAH
Second Secretary
Tel. +32 22828940

Mrs Clare SHEEHAN
Second Secretary
Tel. +32 22828938

Industrial affairs, transport, energy and internal market

Mrs Catherine BRADLEY
Adviser
Tel. +32 22878240

Mr Antony MANCHESTER
First Secretary
Tel. +32 22878236

Mrs Clelia UHART
First Secretary
Tel. +32 22878295

Mr Bill JONES
First Secretary
Tel. +32 22878253

Mrs JONES

Mr Matthew HOULIHAN
First Secretary
Tel. +32 22878218

Mrs Sarah FRANCIS
First Secretary
Tel. +32 22878302

Mr Andrew EMPSON
Second Secretary
Tel. +32 22878278

Mr Richard HADFIELD
Second Secretary
Tel. +32 22878203

Miss Sayida HUSSAIN
Second Secretary
Tel. +32 22878918

Mr Steve MASON
Second Secretary
Tel. +32 22878925

External relations

HE Mr Tim BARROW
Representative of the United Kingdom to COPSI/EU
Tel. +32 22878319

Mr Angus LAPSLEY
Adviser
Tel. +32 22828921

Mr Martin REYNOLDS
Adviser
Tel. +32 22878235

Mrs Susan MORTIMER
First Secretary (trade)
Tel. +32 22878246

Mrs Tessa HARRIS-HESS
First Secretary
Tel. +32 22878255

Mr Alexander NAQVI
Second Secretary
Tel. +32 22878219

Mrs Claire LAWRENCE
First Secretary
Tel. +32 22878252

Mr Duncan MCCOMBIE
First Secretary
Tel. +32 22878346

Mrs Anna BRADBURY
First Secretary
Tel. +32 22878222

Mr Jonathan HOLYOAK
First Secretary
Tel. +32 22878232

Mrs Felicity ROSE
First Secretary
Tel. +32 22878347

Miss Jaya CHORAYA
Second Secretary
Tel. +32 22878205

Mr James HOW
Second Secretary
Tel. +32 22878239

Mr Charles RAHTZ
Second Secretary
Tel. +32 22878386

Mr David HOGAN-HERN
Second Secretary
Tel. +32 22878256

Mr Lance DOMM
Second Secretary
Tel. +32 22828936

Mr Owen JENKINS
First Secretary
Tel. +32 22878322

Mr Nicholas WOOLLEY
Second Secretary
Tel. +32 22828903

Mrs Alison KERR
First Secretary
Tel. +32 22878307

Mrs Anna DURHAM
Third Secretary
Tel. +32 22878251

Mr Shane JONES
Third Secretary
Tel. +32 22878251

Mrs Maryam TESCHKE-PANAH
First Secretary
Tel. +32 22878386

Mrs Nicola RUTHVEN
Second Secretary
Tel. +32 22878375

Social affairs, environment and regional policy

Mr Tim GREEN
Counsellor
Tel. +32 22878266

Mr Tim HEMMINGS
First Secretary
Tel. +32 22878358

Miss Nicola WEBB
First Secretary
Tel. +32 22878301

Mr Christopher HOBLEY
First Secretary
Tel. +32 22878213

Mr Gian Marco CURRADO
First Secretary
Tel. +32 22878201

Mr John ROWAN
First Secretary
Tel. +32 22878270

Mr Kevin DENCH
Second Secretary
Tel. +32 22878221

Mrs DENCH

Mr Paul CREARY
Second Secretary
Tel. +32 22878351

Miss Rebecca DOWNING
Second Secretary
Tel. +32 22878244

Administrative affairs

Mr Andy GOODWIN
First Secretary
Tel. +32 22878338

Northern Ireland Executive EU Office

Mrs Evelyn CUMMINS
Head of Office
Tel. +32 22901335

Mr Alasdair MACINNES
Deputy Head
Tel. +32 22901334

Mrs Eileen KELLY
First Secretary
Tel. +32 22901342

Mr Noel GRIFFIN
Second Secretary
Tel. +32 22901339

Scottish Executive EU Office

Mr Donald HENDERSON
Head of delegation
Tel. +32 22828331

Mr Ian CAMPBELL
Deputy Director
Tel. +32 22828334

Mr Craig EGNER
First Secretary
Tel. +32 22828333

Mr Barry MCCAFFREY
First Secretary
Tel. +32 22828359

Mr Ed THOMSON
Second Secretary
Tel. +32 22828332

Mr James JOHNSTON
Second Secretary
Tel. +32 22828356

Welsh Assembly EU Office

Mr Desmond CLIFFORD
Head of delegation
Tel. +32 25064480

Mr Andrew AGGETT
First Secretary
Tel. +32 25064482

Mr Steven MCGREGOR
First Secretary
Tel. +32 25064487

Mrs Liz CASSIDY
First Secretary
Tel. +32 25064475

Mr Peredur JOHN
First Secretary
Tel. +32 25064486

Mrs Nia LEWIS
First Secretary
Tel. +32 25064478

Mrs Kathryn WEEKES
Second Secretary
Tel. +32 25064481

Mr James FENWICK
Third Secretary
Tel. +32 25064474

General Secretariat of the Council of the European Union

Rue de la Loi 175
B-1048 Brussels
Website: http://www.consilium.europa.eu
Tel. +32 2281-6111
Fax +32 2281-6934

The Council is assisted by a General Secretariat under the responsibility of a Secretary-General/High Representative for the common foreign and security policy, assisted by a Deputy Secretary-General. The General Secretariat carries out all the necessary work for the activities of the Council, the Permanent Representatives Committee and all the committees and working parties set up within the Council.

Secretary-General/High Representative

Javier SOLANA
Tel. +32 2281-5660

Deputy Secretary-General

Pierre de BOISSIEU
Tel. +32 2281-6215

PRIVATE OFFICE

Enrique MORA
Head of Cabinet of the Secretary-General/High Representative
Director
Tel. +32 2281-5572

Patrice BERGAMINI
Deputy Head of the Secretary-General/High Representative's Cabinet
(CFSP, liaison with the PU, EUSR coordination)
Head of Division
Tel. +32 2281-5571

David GALLOWAY
Head of Cabinet of the Deputy Secretary-General
Director
Tel. +32 2281-6194

Carl HALLERGÅRD
Tel. +32 2281-5437

Ralph KAESSNER
Adviser
Tel. +32 2281-9422

Steven EVERTS
Adviser
Tel. +32 2281-7994

Olivia HOLDSWORTH
Tel. +32 2281-6877

Departments attached to the Secretary-General/High Representative

Personal Representatives of the Secretary-General/High Representative

Annalisa GIANNELLA
Secretary-General's Personal Representative/High Representative for non-proliferation
Director
Tel. +32 2281-8044

Michael MATTHIESSEN
Personal Representative of the Secretary-General/High Representative for the CFSP
Director
Tel. +32 2281-5321

Gilles DE KERCHOVE D'OUSSELGHEM
Personal Representative of the Secretary-General/High Representative for coordinating the fight against terrorism
Director
Tel. +32 2281-7933

Riina KIONKA
Secretary-General's Personal Representative/High Representative for human rights in the area of the CFSC
Head of Unit
Tel. +32 2281-9689

Policy unit (PU)

Helga Maria SCHMID
Director
Tel. +32 2281-5430

European Security and Defence Policy (ESDP) Task Force

Hans Bernhard WEISSERTH
Tel. +32 2281-5848

Mediterranean/Barcelona and Middle East Task Force

Christian JOURET
Tel. +32 2281-5324

Petr HLADIK
Tel. +32 2281-5186

Milton NICOLAIDIS
Tel. +32 2281-7010

Colin SCICLUNA
Tel. +32 2281-3679

Africa Task Force

José Fernando COSTA PEREIRA
Head of Unit
Tel. +32 2281-9734

Eastern Europe and Central Asia Unit (DG E)

Jukka LESKELÄ
Head of Unit
Tel. +32 2281-8528

Nadia ERNZER
Tel. +32 2281-5845

Björn FAGERBERG
Tel. +32 2281-5648

Rasa OSTRAUSKAITE
Tel. +32 2281-6651

Pirkka TAPIOLA
Tel. +32 2281-5846

Asia Task Force

Boguslaw MAJEWSKI
Head of Unit
Tel. +32 2281-6831

Tim EESTERMANS
Tel. +32 2281-5328

Tatania Asenova LEVCEVA
Tel. +32 2281-5715

Razvan Stefan RAB
Tel. +32 2281-5716

Marek REPOVSKY
Tel. +32 2281-7015

Western Balkans and Central Europe Task Force

Stefan LEHNE
Director
Tel. +32 2281-5327

Lothar JASCHKE
Tel. +32 2281-7094

Sabina STADLER
Tel. +32 2281-7416

United Nations and Latin America Task Force

Nicolás PASCUAL DE LA PARTE
Head of Unit
Tel. +32 2281-5322

Horizontal Security Affairs, Conflict Prevention and Human Rights Task Force

György TATÁR
Head of Unit
Tel. +32 2281-5842

Merete BILDE
Tel. +32 2281-6585

Ikaros MOUSHOUTTAS
Tel. +32 2281-5131

Sean O REGAN
Tel. +32 2281-5840

Rein TAMMSAAR
Tel. +32 2281-5232

Military Staff

David LEAKEY
Army Corps General
Director-General of the European Union Military Staff
Tel. +32 2281-5990

Fernando LISTA
Vice-Admiral
Deputy Director-General and Chief of the European Union Military Staff
Tel. +32 22815888

Coordination Unit

Eric BLOMMESTIJN
Colonel
Head of Office
Tel. +32 2281-5961

Chairman, Military Committee Support Unit

Jean-Pol CHAUDRON
Colonel
Head of Office
Tel. +32 2281-5902

Concept Planning Division

Gábor HÓRVATH
Brigadier General
Director
Tel. +32 2281-5954

Alistair SHEPPARD
Colonel
Tel. +32 2281-5950

Pekka HOLOPAINEN
Colonel
Tel. +32 2281-3131

Piotr ROSOLAK
Colonel
Tel. +32 2281-5951

Information Division

Gintaras BAGDONAS
Brigadier General
Director
Tel. +32 2281-5905

Dieter HAAG
Colonel
Tel. +32 2281-5941

Danijel PAVLIC
Colonel
Tel. +32 2281-5944

Fulvio MARANGONI
Colonel
Tel. +32 2281-5937

Operations/Exercises Division

Esa PULKKINEN
Brigadier General
Director
Tel. +32 2281-5906

Antoine DEVAUX
Captain
Tel. +32 2281-9539

Hans FOLMER
Colonel
Tel. +32 2281-3504

Operations Centre Permanent Staff and Watchkeeping Capability

Hans FOLMER
Colonel
Tel. +32 2281-3504

CivMil Cell

Giovanni MANIONE
Brigadier General
Director
Tel. +32 2281-9617

Kaija VANONEN
Tel. +32 2281-8150

Michael AARÖE
Captain
Tel. +32 2281-3530

Eckart KLINK
Colonel
Tel. +32 2281-5936

Logistics Support Division

Michael FINN
Brigadier General
Director
Tel. +32 2281-5915

Indalecio NUÑEZ LACACI
Captain
Tel. +32 2281-5968

Silvio IACONIS
Colonel
Tel. +32 2281-6484

Michael LARSEN
Colonel
Tel. +32 2281-5920

Information and Communication System Division

António CABRAL
Vice-Admiral
Directeur
Tel. +32 2281-5931

Adam PAWLIK
Colonel
Tel. +32 2281-5949

Panagiotis KALIMERIS
Colonel
Tel. +32 2281-4714

Joint Situation Centre of the European Union

William SHAPCOTT
Director
Tel. +32 2281-5824
Fax +32 2281-5853

Interim Civilian Planning and Conduct Capability

Kees Jan René KLOMPENHOUWER
Director
Tel. +32 2281-2629

Katrin Susanna HAGEMANN
Assistant to the Director
Tel. +32 2281-8497

Conduct of Operations Unit

...
Head of Unit
Tel. +32 2281-5462

Kim FREIDBERG
Tel. +32 2281-7729

Birgit LOESER
Tel. +32 2281-7808

Marco SOLAINI
Tel. +32 2281-8166

Daniel ARISTI
Tel. +32 2281-8692

Thomas WIERSING
Tel. +32 2281-9357

Riccardo CHELLERI
Tel. +32 2281-4923

Oliver KNOERICH
Tel. +32 2281-3263

Alexis HUPIN
Tel. +32 2281-2072

Guillermo MARTINEZ ERADES
Tel. +32 2281-2669

Thierry BAUD
Tel. +32 2281-5636

Luigi BRUNO
Tel. +32 2281-2674

Elka ERMENKOVA
Tel. +32 2281-2660

Markus FEILKE
Tel. +32 2281-3614

John HESTER
Tel. +32 2281-5633

Antonio MOLINARO
Tel. +32 2281-2073

Dana PURCARESCU
Tel. +32 2281-7114

Francisco RODRIGUEZ LORENZO
Tel. +32 2281-6985

Janez RUPAR
Tel. +32 2281-7500

Francesco SCANU
Tel. +32 2281-5982

COS/Horizontal Coordination Unit

Matthew REECE
Head of Unit
Tel. +32 2281-5994

Maria Mercedes GARCÍA PÉREZ
Tel. +32 2281-6486

Elena Maria PERESSO
Tel. +32 2281-6753

Francisco ESTEBAN PÉREZ
Tel. +32 2281-5825

Ulf KARLSSON
Tel. +32 2281-9984

Elina PAPADIMOULI
Tel. +32 2281-8427

Mission Support Unit

Silvia BIANCHI
Head of Unit
Tel. +32 2281-7737

Risto NIEMINEN
Tel. +32 2281-2071

Paulo VIDAL
Tel. +32 2281-5802

Veronica SABBAG AFOTA
Tel. +32 2281-2070

Corrado PAMPALONI
Tel. +32 2281-6908

Mari LINNAPUOMI
Tel. +32 2281-3271

Rita Sofia GOMES-PIRES
Tel. +32 2281-5872

Paul KIRWAN
Tel. +32 2281-2581

László SZABÓ
Tel. +32 2281-3289

Ulla BERGQVIST
Tel. +32 2281-8596

Communications Centre (Comcen), consular affairs

Giorgio PORZIO
Head of Unit
Tel. +32 2281-6102

Operational Unit (OPS)

Johnny ENGELL-HANSEN
Tel. +32 2281-8561

Analysis Unit

Lionel POTTIER
Tel. +32 2281-3537

Departments attached to the Secretary-General/High Representative and to the Deputy Secretary-General (1)

Directorate for General Political Questions

Jim CLOOS
Director
Tel. +32 2281-9330

Unit for General Political Questions/ Meetings

Georges ZBYSZEWSKI
Head of Unit
Tel. +32 2281-7659

André GILLISSEN
Tel. +32 2281-8514

Jürgen NEISSE
Coreper I Group 'Mertens'
Tel. +32 2281-7097

Maria Alexandra ALMEIDA
Tel. +32 2281-6313

Anastasia GITONA
Coreper II Group 'Antici'
Tel. +32 2281-4819

Directorate Security Office

Alexandro LEGEIN
Director
Tel. +32 2281-8517, 2281-7277

Internal Audit Unit

...
Head of Unit
Tel. +32 2281-7268

Gertrud QUERTON
Tel. +32 2281-7582

Mohammed AMRI
Tel. +32 2281-5071

Francisco CAMPILLO SANTOS
Tel. +32 2281-6081

Corrado CLEMA
Tel. +32 2281-6487

Luc MASSAUX
Tel. +32 2281-3845

Enrique MORALES MARTIN
Tel. +32 2281-6415

(1) The Head of Cabinet of the Secretary-General/High Representative and the Head of Cabinet of the Deputy Secretary-General ensure links with the departments attached to them.

Data Protection Unit

Pierre Henri VERNHES ([2])
Head of Unit
Tel. +32 2281-9009

Camino YOLDI ERICE
Tel. +32 2281-7009

Infosec Unit (information systems security)

Bartolomeo MANENTI
Head of Unit
Tel. +32 2281-7645

Prevention Service Unit

Guy DHAEYER
Tel. +32 2281-5456

Eric BLEYAERT
Tel. +32 2281-8243

LEGAL SERVICE

Jean-Claude PIRIS
Director-General
Legal Adviser to the Council
Tel. +32 2281-6227

Coordination Unit

Thérèse BLANCHET
Tel. +32 2281-8775

Information, Training and Finance Unit

Christos MAVRAKOS
Head of Unit
Tel. +32 2281-7190

Directorate 1A — Coreper I Areas, Including Coordination and Codecision

Hubert LEGAL
Director
Tel. +32 2281-7322

Eva KARLSSON
Tel. +32 2281-7983

Fernando FLORINDO GIJÓN
Tel. +32 2281-6196

Anna LO MONACO
Tel. +32 2281-6459

Kristien MICHOEL
Tel. +32 2281-5702

Gayle KIMBERLEY
Tel. +32 2281-3782

Co-decision Unit

Aidan FEENEY
Head of Unit
Tel. +32 2281-9284

Jonathan DANCOURT-CAVANAGH
Tel. +32 2281-5800

Jérôme GUICHARD
Tel. +32 2281-7340

Simone O'SULLIVAN
Tel. +32 22819665

Alvaro DE ELERA SAN MIGUEL HURTADO
Tel. +32 2281-2668

Directorate 1B — Coreper I Areas — Enlargement

Jürgen HUBER
Director
Tel. +32 2281-7348

Anna LO MONACO
Tel. +32 2281-6459

Marion SIMM
Tel. +32 2281-5123

Madalena VEIGA
Tel. +32 2281-5329

Gayle KIMBERLEY
Tel. +32 2281-3782

Johannes LEPPO
Tel. +32 2281-8259

Rita LIUDVINAVICIUTE-CORDEIRO
Tel. +32 2281-3781

Inese SULCE
Tel. +32 2281-3780

Directorate 2 — Ecofin, Agriculture and Fisheries

Timothy MIDDLETON
Director
Tel. +32 2281-7919

Moyra SIMS
Tel. +32 2281-7849

Anna-Maria COLAERT
Tel. +32 2281-8365

Matthew MOORE
Tel. +32 2281-9680

Alberto de GREGORIO MERINO
Tel. +32 2281-9353

Andrea WESTERHOF LÖFFLEROVÁ
Tel. +32 2281-3097

Petra MAHNIČ BRUNI
Tel. +32 2281-3784

Directorate 3 — External Relations

Ricardo GOSALBO BONO
Director
Tel. +32 2281-6259

Gert-Jan VAN HEGELSOM
Tel. +32 2281-5747

Michael BISHOP
Tel. +32 2281-8303

Jenő CZUCZAI
Tel. +32 2281-9504

Jan Peter HIX
Tel. +32 2281-7811

Gilles MARHIC
Tel. +32 2281-5023

Bart DRIESSEN
Tel. +32 2281-7398

Emer FINNEGAN
Tel. +32 2281-5283

Eric CHABOUREAU
Tel. +32 2281-5024

Alessandro VITRO
Tel. +32 2281-3783

Frederik NAERT
Tel. +32 2281-8470

Richard SZOSTAK
Tel. +32 2281-3098

Directorate 4 — Institutional Questions, Budget and Staff Regulations

Giorgio MAGANZA
Director
Tel. +32 2281-7950

Micail VITSENTZATOS
Tel. +32 2282-2220

Martin BAUER
Tel. +32 2281-8341

Maria BALTA
Tel. +32 2281-4969

Katarzyna ZIELESKIEWICZ
Tel. +32 2281-5233

Csilla FEKETE
Tel. +32 2281-7751

Directorate 5 — Justice and Home Affairs

Julian SCHUTTE
Director
Tel. +32 2281-6229

Ole PETERSEN
Tel. +32 2281-7169

Jorge MONTEIRO
Tel. +32 2281-8533

Sofia KYRIAKOPOULOU
Tel. +32 2281-8221

([2]) Data Protection Officer

Paloma PLAZA GARCIA
Tel. +32 2281-7261

Zuzana KUPCOVÁ
Tel. +32 2281-5742

Ivan GUROV
Tel. +32 2281-9063

Directorate 6 — Interinstitutional Relations

Marta ARPIO-SANTACRUZ
Director
Tel. +32 2281-6183

Unit 'European Parliament Coordination: Internal Policy; Relations with other Institutions and Agencies '

Hartmut BERGER
Tel. +32 2281-7305

Guiliano CASTELLAN
Tel. +32 2281-5883

Martin KÜCHLER
Tel. +32 2281-8171

Eugenia Elena DUMITRIU-SEGNANA
Tel. +32 2281-2580

Unit 'European Parliament Coordination: External Policy and Plenary Sessions '

Guy MILTON
Head of Unit
Tel. +32 22818519

Roberta GARABELLO
Tel. +32 2281-6041

Micheline JANSSEN
Tel. +32 2281-6316

Sven OTT
Tel. +32 2281-9640

Directorate 7 — Quality of Legislation

Geneviève TUTS
Director
Tel. +32 2281-7474

Resources Unit

Anna Katharina KALBE
Head of Unit
Tel. +32 2281-8249

French section

Marie-Jeanne VERNIER
Tel. +32 2281-7258

Caroline GERKENS
Tel. +32 2281-9648

Frédérique LAMBERT
Tel. +32 2281-7192

Raphaël ZENOU
Tel. +32 2281-7910

Spanish section

Luis ESCOBAR GUERRERO
Tel. +32 2281-9645

Germán RAMOS RUANO
Tel. +32 2281-7812

María Dolores SOUTO IGLESIAS
Tel. +32 2281-5267

José María SUBRA ALFARO
Tel. +32 2281-6079

Swedish section

Jarl MATTSSON
Tel. +32 2281-8638

Isabelle RÅDESTAD
Tel. +32 2281-6656

Anna KILANDER
Tel. +32 2281-9657

Kerstin Sofia MICHELSEN
Tel. +32 2281-5649

Hungarian section

Zsuzsanna FELKAI JANSSEN
Tel. +32 2281-5227

Krisztina HORVÁTH
Tel. +32 2281-9751

Gabriella TÓTH
Tel. +32 2281-2015

Gabriella LODI
Tel. +32 2281-9750

Dutch section

Hessel DAALDER
Tel. +32 2281-7113

Antonio LUCIDI
Tel. +32 2281-7935

Carla VAN DE SCHOOT
Tel. +32 2281-8195

Jesper VAN STEENBERGEN
Tel. +32 2281-5604

Slovenian section

Matei PEDICEK
Tel. +32 2281-5127

Polona SENK
Tel. +32 2281-5211

Ana BRACIC
Tel. +32 2281-5213

Barbara ERNST
Tel. +32 2281-7218

Latvian section

Ilze EGLITE
Tel. +32 2281-5205

Ieva LEJASISAKA
Tel. +32 2281-5147

Dace EIZĀNE
Tel. +32 2281-5209

Romanian section

Doina DITU
Tel. +32 2281-7594

Raluca DUMITRESCU
Tel. +32 2281-3889

Oana Diana DUTESCU
Tel. +32 2281-9628

Ionut-Octavian RĂDULETU
Tel. +32 2281-9624

Quality Unit

Manuela GUGGEIS
Head of Unit
Tel. +32 2281-8359

German section

Arved FICHTELMANN
Tel. +32 2281-6493

Kirsten BACHOUR
Tel. +32 2281-6725

Joachim HERRMANN
Tel. +32 2281-7530

Stefan LECHLER
Tel. +32 2281-7565

Portuguese section

Paulo BORGES
Tel. +32 2281-8371

Maria SACRAMENTO
Tel. +32 2281-6533

José Paulo FERNANDES MARIANO PEGO
Tel. +32 2281-9644

Ilidio José LEMOS TORRES DO VALE VIEIRA
Tel. +32 2281-7879

Danish section

Anne Cecilie ADSERBALLE
Tel. +32 2281-9983

Dorthe SKOV
Tel. +32 2281-6587

Kasper HOLST
Tel. +32 2281-7434

Anne Funch JENSEN
Tel. +32 2281-9335

Slovak section

Nikoleta GLINDOVÁ
Tel. +32 2281-3987

Adriana KAVCOVA
Tel. +32 2281-5198

Beata BRADNANSKA
Tel. +32 2281-3988

Robert SPISIAK
Tel. +32 2281-9304

Polish section

Maciej J. PAWLUSIEWICZ
Tel. +32 2281-5197

Katarzyna ADAMCZYK DELAMARRE
Tel. +32 2281-9649

Inga TCHÓRZEWSKA
Tel. +32 2281-7904

Greek section

Georgios ANGELOPOULOS
Tel. +32 2281-7592

Despina ZAHARIOU
Tel. +32 2281-6608

Ekaterini DESPOTOPOULOU
Tel. +32 2281-5909

Evgenia CHATZIIOAKEIMIDOU
Tel. +32 2281-9646

Lithuanian section

Audrius PAKSAS
Tel. +32 2281-5229

Jurate VAICIUKAITE
Tel. +32 2281-5228

Julius BERNATONIS
Tel. +32 2281-2986

Ieva PANAVAITE
Tel. +32 2281-6323

Follow-up Unit

Christoph SAILE
Head of Unit
Tel. +32 2281-9506

English section

Colin ROBERTSON
Tel. +32 2281-8199

Nelius CAREY
Tel. +32 2281-9639

Simonetta COOK
Tel. +32 2281-6678

Jane Elizabeth GRAF
Tel. +32 2281-8358

Denis O'SULLIVAN
Tel. +32 2281-6200

Irish Team

Francis MANGAN
Tel. +32 2281-2801

Séamus HOWARD
Tel. +32 2281-5608

Finnish section

Heikki ERNO
Tel. +32 2281-6018

Ulla HÄTÖNEN
Tel. +32 2281-6852

Hans GRAHN
Tel. +32 2281-9481

Virpi KOIVU
Tel. +32 2281-6939

Czech section

Jan FALTYS
Tel. +32 2281-3989

Radovan PEKAR
Tel. +32 2281-5212

Stepan HULKA
Tel. +32 2281-5235

Maltese section

Joseph AQUILINA
Tel. +32 2281-3019

Tzeitel SCHUSTER
Tel. +32 2281-5231

Roderick MIFSUD
Tel. +32 2281-8229

Mario SAMMUT
Tel. +32 2281-5350

Joanne SCHEMBRI WORLEY
Tel. +32 2281-3144

Italian section

Constantino DELLA TORRE
Tel. +32 2281-7881

Roberto SPADARO
Tel. +32 2281-7440

Estonian section

Ann STOLFOT
Tel. +32 2281-5202

Mari SUTT
Tel. +32 2281-5204

Edda LINK
Tel. +32 2281-7991

Triin TOBRELUTS
Tel. +32 2281-5149

Bulgarian section

Delyana GICHEVA
Tel. +32 2281-3849

Borislav KARALEEV
Tel. +32 2281-6849

Monika KOPCHEVA
Tel. +32 2281-7489

Maria Ivanova NIKOLOVA
Tel. +32 2281-3887

Corrigenda

Jan-Erik BJÖRKLUND
Tel. +32 2281-8487

Codification

Sara GÓMEZ-REINO
Tel. +32 2281-8331

Kirsti REINARTZ
Tel. +32 2281-7593

DIRECTORATE-GENERAL A – PERSONNEL AND ADMINISTRATION

Vittorio GRIFFO
Director-General
Tel. +32 2281-6540

Frédéric ANTON
Assistant to the Director-General
Tel. +32 2281-8780

Directorate 1A — Human Resources

Dirk SCHILDERS
Director
Tel. +32 2281-9989

Equal Opportunities and Organisational Development

Sally BLISS
Tel. +32 2281-8509

Béatrice ORNSTEDT
Tel. +32 2281-9654

Staffing and Mobility Unit

Björn LARSSON
Head of Unit
Tel. +32 2281-9415

Lotte BERG
Tel. +32 2281-5275

Milena MLAKER
Tel. +32 2281-3901

Luis Jesús PASCUAL
Tel. +32 2281-9781

Training and Development Unit

Rafael GALVEZ VIA
Head of Unit
Tel. +32 2281-9510

Orlando GAMBOA DOS SANTOS
Tel. +32 2281-5495

Carmen GAMBA
Tel. +32 2281-9449

Myriam GOINARD
Tel. +32 2281-7573

Careers and Skills Development Unit

Nessa DELANEY
Head of Unit
Tel. +32 2281-7344

Yvette GUFFENS
Tel. +32 2281-6249

Lena WESTBERG
Tel. +32 2281-9656

Pia GOEBEL
Tel. +32 2281-8568

Aleksandra KRYSZTOFIAK
Tel. +32 2281-8788

Coordination of Human Resources Systems — ITD

Mark MC LOUGHLIN
Tel. +32 2281-8575

Arnaud CRAMAZOU
Tel. +32 2281-7874

Régis FAU
Tel. +32 2281-9658

Internal Communication Unit

Armel PRIEUR
Tel. +32 2281-7628

Georg BIEKÖTTER
Tel. +32 2281-6700

Micheline FOUCART
Tel. +32 2281-6665

Ingrid HVASS
Tel. +32 2281-2762

Directorate 1B — Personnel Administration

Leopold RADAUER
Director
Tel. +32 2281-8915

Assistants to the Director

Laurent BENHAMOU
Tel. +32 2281-9589

Ralf Dieter SALLER
Tel. +32 2281-9816

Medical Service Unit

Dr Manuel GARCÍA PÉREZ
Medical Examiner
Head of Unit
Tel. +32 2281-6970

Dr Johan DE GEEST
Tel. +32 2281-6901

Anne Marie KLEPANDY
Tel. +32 2281-6970

Directorate Advisers Unit

Alain PILETTE
Head of Unit
Tel. +32 2281-8989

Carmen LOPEZ RUIZ
Tel. +32 2281-6876

Paola CASINI
Tel. +32 2281-9437

Cecile REMEUR
Tel. +32 2281-7658

Krzysztof MAJKA
Tel. +32 2281-6845

Matthieu CHAVRIER
Tel. +32 2281-8968

João HEREDIA
Tel. +32 2281-7178

Szilvia SOMOGYI
Tel. +32 2281-9396

Privileges and Immunities and Social Insurance Unit

Daniel DULBECCO
Head of Unit
Tel. +32 2281-7428

Individual Rights Unit

Dirk HELLWIG
Head of Unit
Tel. +32 2281-6958

Philippe DEMONCEAU
Tel. +32 2281-7536

Benjamín MOYA MURCIA
Tel. +32 2281-6075

Thérèse DUVAL-MAILLARD
Tel. +32 2281-7166

Rinaldo PEDRAZZINI
Tel. +32 2281-7866

Anna SWIDA-BRUGGEMAN
Tel. +32 2281-3075

Anna Monika SEKULSKA
Tel. +32 2281-8191

Unit Salaries — Missions

Maarten BOGAARDT
Head of Unit
Tel. +32 2281-7346

Vincent YACOUB
Tel. +32 2281-8721

Daniela CARZANIGA
Tel. +32 2281-9250

Social Unit

Maria Augusta SANTOS
Head of Unit
Tel. +32 2281-7027

Directorate 2 — Conferences, Organisation, Infrastructures

Dominique-Georges MARRO
Director
Tel. +32 2281-6423

Financial Coordination Unit

Sergio ZANGAGLIA
Head of Unit
Tel. +32 2281-8134

Paulo BRANCO
Tel. +32 2281-5484

Albert-Jan JANSEN
Tel. +32 2281-2051

Nofissa EL AKEL STAITI
Tel. +32 2281-7654

Jamila SIMPSON
Tel. +32 2281-7328

Conferences Unit

Petr HRDLICKA
Head of Unit
Tel. +32 2281-7477

Eric THORAVAL
Tel. +32 2281-5432

Bruno PEREIRA LAGOS
Tel. +32 2281-4925

Karel VAN DE WEYER
Tel. +32 2281-8877

Conferences/external relations

Kalliopi PAPASTATHOPOULOU
Tel. +32 2281-7083

Conferences/organisation of official meals

Alain DI FIORE
Tel. +32 2281-8265

Conferences/restaurants

Stefano COCHI
Tel. +32 2281-7583

Travel agency/delegates' expenses

João MARTINS
Tel. +32 2281-8053

Conferences/planning of meetings

Teresa MARTINS
Tel. +32 2281-7825

Conferences/technical equipment/logistics

André COLOT
Tel. +32 2281-6593

Conferences/messengers — Meeting rooms — Receptionists

Albert VANSCHOENWINKEL
Tel. +32 2281-6405

Buildings Unit

Johan BURGERS
Head of Unit
Tel. +32 2281-7174

Administrative and budget management

Nicolas BOURGEOIS
Tel. +32 2281-5874

Property policy and projects

Luigi COVA
Tel. +32 2281-9904

Christian BONTE
Tel. +32 2281-5010

José Maria PEREZ SANTANDER
Tel. +32 2281-3082

Serge KERKHOFS
Tel. +32 2281-8063

Technical equipment and removals

Davy MESOTTEN
Tel. +32 2281-9264

Vincent POLOME
Tel. +32 2281-6679

Central Catering Service

Graziella SCEBBA
Tel. +32 2281-6669

Logistics Unit

Kristin VAN HOOLST
Head of Unit
Tel. +32 2281-5454

Horizontal Issues

Javier LOPEZ ARIZA
Tel. +32 2281-6331

Purchasing

Jean-Claude VANBEVER
Tel. +32 2281-6378

Office furniture and supplies

Eddy CEULEERS
Tel. +32 2281-8906

Drivers

Jean-Claude HUAUX
Tel. +32 2281-7883

Depot

Gian-Salvatore PALMERI
Tel. +32 2281-6049

Directorate 3 — Translation and Document Production

Margarida LACERDA
Director
Tel. +32 2281-7205

Advisers to the Director

Alejandro PÉREZ VIDAL
Tel. +32 2281-6105

René SMEETS
Tel. +32 2281-7589

Resources Unit

Brendan O'BRIEN
Head of Unit
Tel. +32 2281-7717

Elena GARCIA RAMOS
Tel. +32 2281-6298

Juan PALLARES CASADO
Tel. +32 2281-9922

Marjukka SAINE
Tel. +32 2281-8661

Coordination and Production Unit

João CORTEZ
Head of Unit
Tel. +32 2281-7030

Control tower

Riikka IKÄHEIMO
Tel. +32 2281-9194

Alba BELLOTTO
Tel. +32 2281-7867

Language coordination

Andrew UNWIN
Tel. +32 2281-7905

Agreements office

Philip EVANS
Tel. +32 2281-6764

Classified Information Office (CIO)

Gabriel OLIVIER
Tel. +32 2281-6280

Mail

Pedro José PINHO
Tel. +32 2281-8525

Technical production services

Pedro José PINHO
Tel. +32 2281-8525

Language Service — Group A

Astérios ZOIS
Head of Unit
Tel. +32 2281-7691

Katelijn SERLET
Assistant to Head of Unit
Tel. +32 2281-7285

John BEAVEN
Quality control
Tel. +32 2281-5413

Terminology and Documentation

Manuel LEAL
Tel. +32 2281-7588

Bulgarian Language Unit (BG)

Eva GONZÁLEZ
Head of Unit
Tel. +32 2281-8667

...
Quality control

Eija HASSLOEF KOSKELA
Resource management
Tel. +32 2281-1991

...
Coordination

Spanish Language Unit (ES)

Helio GÓMEZ DE MAYORA ROJAS
Head of Unit
Tel. +32 2281-6946

Jorge BINAGHI FASCE
Quality control
Tel. +32 2281-6303

Grazia MARCHESE
Resource management
Tel. +32 2281-7047

Frieke BIEMANS
Coordination
Tel. +32 2281-6103

Czech Language Unit (CS)

David ZELINGER
Head of Unit
Tel. +32 2281-2540

Jiri PLACEK
Quality control
Tel. +32 2281-9774

Lenka NACERADSKA
Resource management
Tel. +32 2281-9697

...
Coordination

German Language Unit (DE)

Karl-Heinz WALKER
Head of Unit
Tel. +32 2281-7412

Dieter KEILER
Quality control
Tel. +32 2281-6761

Maschka Hildegard MÜLLER
Resource management
Tel. +32 2281-7570

Barbara LEUBNER
Coordination
Tel. +32 2281-7806

Greek Language Unit (EL)

Ioannis DIMOLITSAS
Head of Unit
Tel. +32 2281-7323

Angelos TSIRIMOKOS
Quality control
Tel. +32 2281-6758

Carina DE DONCKER
Resource management
Tel. +32 2281-6433

Fani VERGIADOU
Coordination
Tel. +32 2281-3698

English and Irish Language Unit (EN/GA)

Christopher BURDON
Head of Unit
Tel. +32 2281-7615

Fiona COLLIER
Quality control
Tel. +32 2281-7342

Joyce GILABERT
Resource management
Tel. +32 2281-6870

Olga MICHALOPOULOU
Coordination
Tel. +32 2281-6478

Italian Language Unit (IT)

Lauretta SERRA
Head of Unit
Tel. +32 2281-7247

Francesca PIOMBO
Quality control
Tel. +32 2281-6296

Silvia KHAMAL
Resource management
Tel. +32 2281-6828

Roberto SABBATINI
Coordination
Tel. +32 2281-9374

Latvian Language Unit (LV)

Alan SAUNDERS
Head of Unit
Tel. +32 2281-6527

Mareks KOVALEVSKIS
Quality control
Tel. +32 2281-3767

...
Resource management

Inga BARTKEVICA
Coordination
Tel. +32 2281-9761

Lithuanian Language Unit (LT)

Viktorija TICHONOVA-ZURBIENE
Head of Unit
Tel. +32 2281-3765

...
Quality control

...
Resource management

Ruta SAMUOLYTE NAVARDAUSKIENE
Coordination
Tel. +32 2281-2280

Portuguese Language Unit (PT)

Armando GONÇALVES
Head of Unit
Tel. +32 2281-6389

João VASCONCELOS
Quality control
Tel. +32 2281-7025

Roldana LELLI MINGOZZI
Resource management
Tel. +32 2281-7553

Maria Teresa DE MELLO CORREA
Coordination
Tel. +32 2281-6150

Slovak Language Unit (SK)

Eva KRÁTKA
Head of Unit
Tel. +32 2281-3764

...
Quality control

José Carlos LECHADO GARCÍA
Resource management
Tel. +32 2281-8160

...
Coordination

Language Service — Group B

Hendrik BAES
Head of Unit
Tel. +32 2281-7789

Katelijn SERLET
Assistant to Head of Unit
Tel. +32 2281-7285

John BEAVEN
Quality control
Tel. +32 2281-5413

Danish Language Unit (DA)

Annelise TRUELSEN
Head of Unit
Tel. +32 2281-7447

Uffe BRØNS
Quality control
Tel. +32 2281-7908

Grethe SØRENSEN
Resource management
Tel. +32 2281-6835

Lena HULL
Coordination
Tel. +32 2281-8652

Estonian Language Unit (ET)

Heiki PISUKE
Head of Unit
Tel. +32 2281-3968

...
Quality control

...
Resource management

Rita SAGUR
Coordination
Tel. +32 2281-3843

French Language Unit (FR)

Eddie BONESIRE
Head of Unit
Tel. +32 2281-7195

Jean ROOS
Quality control
Tel. +32 2281-7127

Geneviève VALENTE
Resource management
Tel. +32 2281-6848

Maria JOÃO ANTUNES
Coordination
Tel. +32 2281-6950

Hungarian Language Unit (HU)

Agnes TARNAI
Head of Unit
Tel. +32 2281-3938

Zsuzsanna KOVÁCS
Quality control
Tel. +32 2281-2814

Tamas ZAHONYI
Resource management
Tel. +32 2281-6461

...
Coordination

Maltese Language Unit (MT)

Paul SALIBA
Head of Unit
Tel. +32 2281-5196

Joseph CHIRCOP
Quality control
Tel. +32 2281-3623

Chrissoula KITRIMI
Resource management
Tel. +32 2281-7461

Carmelo ZAHRA
Coordination
Tel. +32 2281-3855

Dutch Language Unit (NL)

Mark VAN DE BEEK
Head of Unit
Tel. +32 2281-7432

Patrick WEYMEIS
Quality control
Tel. +32 2281-7448

Jacqueline VERVOORT
Resource management
Tel. +32 2281-8588

Michèle DESMEDT
Coordination
Tel. +32 2281-2408

Polish Language Unit (PL)

Jaroslaw ZACZYKIEWICZ
Head of Unit
Tel. +32 2281-3886

Krzysztof KWASNIEWICZ
Quality control
Tel. +32 2281-3850

...
Resource management

...
Coordination
Tel. +32 2281-7329

Romanian Language Unit (RO)

Stylianos PERRAKIS
Tel. +32 2281-2934

...
Quality control

Ioana VALCU
Resource management
Tel. +32 2281-9671

...
Coordination

Slovene Language Unit (SL)

Bostjan SPORAR
Head of Unit
Tel. +32 2281-3902

Aleksandra KRANER
Quality control
Tel. +32 2281-3001

Marjana BRNE
Resource management
Tel. +32 2281-3005

...
Coordination

Finnish Language Unit (FI)

Pirjo KIVELÄ
Head of Unit
Tel. +32 2281-8636

Hellevi MALM
Quality control
Tel. +32 2281-8644

Risto HELLE
Resource management
Tel. +32 2281-8691

Sirkka HAAPOJA
Coordination
Tel. +32 2281-9788

Swedish Language Unit (SV)

Bertil LUNDGREN
Head of Unit
Tel. +32 2281-8635

Björn WELANDER
Quality control
Tel. +32 2281-8673

Annabelle GAUCI
Resource management
Tel. +32 2281-3658

Gabrielle JURINOVIC
Coordination
Tel. +32 2281-7603

Directorate 4 — Finances

José Antonio MARIGUESA
Director
Tel. +32 2281-6058

Budget Management Unit

Johannes GILBERS
Head of Unit
Tel. +32 2281-9891

Serenella MORELLI
Tel. +32 2281-7568

Nathalie TERRANA
Tel. +32 2281-3285

Mikko LEINONEN
Tel. +32 2281-7899

Cédric BARRA
Tel. +32 2281-9675

Albert NYS
Tel. +32 2281-3259

Projects and Finance Unit

Jacob VRIES
Head of Unit
Tel. +32 2281-5619

Thierry BOUCHER
Tel. +32 2281-6569

André BRISMEZ
Tel. +32 2281-5901

Alain BULON
Tel. +32 2281-6973

Laurent PACCAUD
Tel. +32 2281-2017

Max Frank WATZKE
Tel. +32 2281-2014

Procurement Coordination Unit

Gilles DUVAL
Head of Unit
Tel. +32 2281-8142

Maria LOOSE
Tel. +32 2281-6754

Maurice ROBERT
Tel. +32 2281-7844

Bernard VAN BELLE
Tel. +32 2281-8387

Patrick VANBERGHEN
Tel. +32 2281-5286

Alenka JASCHKE
Tel. +32 2281-8188

Stephanie BROOKS
Tel. +32 2281-8604

Accounting Unit

Piet SCHELLING
Head of Unit
Tel. +32 2281-4967

Gernot DINSE
Tel. +32 2281-5894

Directorate 5 — Information and Communication System (ICS)

Hans-Werner GRENZHÄUSER
Director
Tel. +32 2281-6462

Management Supervision and Administration

Antonio RUBIO
Tel. +32 2281-6574

Thierry DALOZE
Tel. +32 2281-9186

Jan PLAS
Tel. +32 2281-9814

Lluis JAUME PUJOL
Tel. +32 2281-6923

Security of Sensitive Information and Communication Systems

Sébastien LEONNET
Head of Unit
Tel. +32 2281-5538

Administration Solutions Unit

Jean-Marie VANDEPUTTE
Head of Unit
Tel. +32 2281-7200

Gerd HOLZHAUER
Tel. +32 2281-5494

Frederik DUYM
Tel. +32 2281-6660

Fabrice DREZET
Tel. +32 2281-9390

Christophe THIERRY
Tel. +32 2281-9495

Production Solutions Unit

Philippe VLEMINCKX
Head of Unit
Tel. +32 2281-7138

Pierre Dominique COTTE
Tel. +32 2281-6253

Nikos GIANNOPOULOS
Tel. +32 2281-4899

Achilleas KARRAS
Tel. +32 2281-5317

Wout DEKEYSER
Tel. +32 2281-9151

Nicola KUBICECK
Tel. +32 2281-8536

Bénédicte LAMALLE
Tel. +32 2281-8204

Guido FEYAERTS
Tel. +32 2281-9281

Johan LAMMERS
Tel. +32 2281-8609

Benedikt LUYCKX
Tel. +32 2281-6281

Macintosh Solutions Unit

Erik SCHULTZ-NIELSEN
Head of Unit
Tel. +32 2281-7372

Networks and Telecommunications Unit

Daniel SPRENGERS
Head of Unit
Tel. +32 2281-7399

Kalenga D'ALMEIDA
Tel. +32 2281-5460

Paul GORDEBEKE
Tel. +32 2281-6762

Cuong LY
Tel. +32 2281-9188

Jean-Guy HOTTIAUX
Tel. +32 2281-5955

Laurent CLAISSE
Tel. +32 2281-2030

Marco NERVI
Tel. +32 2281-5598

Marc VAN DEN BRANDE
Tel. +32 2281-6062

Donato CURIONI
Tel. +32 2281-9581

Dietmar WICHERT
Tel. +32 2281-7968

Help desk

Chris MERCKX
Head of Unit
Tel. +32 2281-8168

Frank HOOGERVORST
Deputy Head of Unit
Tel. +32 2281-9936

Jan STUER
Tel. +32 2281-2871

Henrique COELHO
Tel. +32 2281-8167

Didier VAN ELDEREN
Tel. +32 2281-6178

Luciano GISSI
Tel. +32 2281-8110

Salvatore CORLIANO
Tel. +32 2281-6815

Johan COENE
Tel. +32 2281-8242

Isabel RAMOS
Tel. +32 2281-7102

DIRECTORATE-GENERAL B – AGRICULTURE AND FISHERIES

Ángel BOIXAREU CARRERA
Director-General
Tel. +32 2281-6234

Catherine TYLIACOS
Tel. +32 2281-5245

Antonio ATAZ
Tel. +32 2281-4964

Pilar VELAZQUEZ
Tel. +32 2281-6628

Raluca IVĂNESCU
Tel. +32 2281-3158

Directorate 1 — Market organisations, veterinary and zootechnical questions including international aspects

Luigi MAZZASCHI
Director
Tel. +32 2281-7571

Unit 1A — Animal products and veterinary and zootechnical questions (including international aspects affecting these sectors)

Andreas LERNHART
Head of Unit
Tel. +32 2281-6241

Laurent TRUQUET
Tel. +32 2281-8323

Jean RECALDE
Tel. +32 2281-9440

Outi TYNI
Tel. +32 2281-2770

Unit 1B — International and horizontal aspects of the CAP, particularly direct support and plant products

Paul REIDERMAN
Head of Unit
Tel. +32 2281-8704

Stella THEODOSSIADIS
Tel. +32 2281-8327

Elizabeth WILLOCKS
Tel. +32 2281-6216

Jean-Pierre SABSOUB
Tel. +32 2281-7228

Directorate 2 — Agricultural structures, rural development, agromonetary and agrofinancial issues, phytosanitary matters, organic products, food quality, GMOs, codex alimentarius, plant protection

Andrä RUPPRECHTER
Director
Tel. +32 2281-8422

Unit 2A — Financial and agromonetary issues, reinforcement of supervision, national aid, forestry, agricultural structures and statistics, rural development, agroenvironment, genetic resources

Mariano ABAD MENÉNDEZ
Head of Unit
Tel. +32 2281-5093

Christina STRÖMHOLM
Tel. +32 2281-6004

Robert DAUTZENBERG
Tel. +32 2281-7089

Margus ALVER
Tel. +32 2281-3870

Unit 2B — Food security, GMOs, Codex Alimentarius, food quality, pesticide residues, plant protection, organic production

César CORTES
Head of Unit
Tel. +32 2281-6114

Kari TÖLLIKKÖ
Tel. +32 2281-7841

Directorate 3 — Fisheries, including external relations

Frank WALL
Director
Tel. +32 2281-8055

Unit 3A — General matters; structural policy; market organisation; the Mediterranean; relations with countries in Africa, the Indian Ocean and Latin America; Antarctica

Janusz BIELECKI
Head of Unit
Tel. +32 2281-6003

Klavs SKOVSHOLM
Tel. +32 2281-8379

Unit 3B — Resource management and conservation; monitoring of fishery activities; relations with countries in northern and eastern Europe and North America; international organisations; North Atlantic and Baltic Sea; research

Luís TEIXEIRA DA COSTA
Head of Unit
Tel. +32 2281-9808

Jeremy RAND
Tel. +32 2281-5606

Gloria DE LA CORTE RODRIGUEZ
Tel. +32 2281-6561

DIRECTORATE-GENERAL C – COMPETITIVENESS, INNOVATION AND RESEARCH, INDUSTRY AND INFORMATION SOCIETY, INTERNAL MARKET, COMPETITION AND CUSTOMS, TRANSPORT, ENERGY

Klaus GRETSCHMANN
Director-General
Tel. +32 2281-5550

'Policy and politics of energy, including atomic questions' Unit

Jean-Paul DECAESTECKER
Head of Unit
Tel. +32 2281-6807

Ulrike RACKOW
Tel. +32 2281-7504

Aris TEKELENBURG
Tel. +32 2281-5511

Gintautas BARANAUSKAS
Tel. +32 2281-6727

Coordination cell, horizontal questions and management

Anastassios PAPADOPOULOS
Tel. +32 2281-7033

Katrin EITEL
Tel. +32 2281-6205

Gabriela HARTIG
Tel. +32 2281-6442

Directorate 1 — Internal market — competition — customs union

Anders OLANDER
Director
Tel. +32 2281-6392

Unit 1A — Internal market (four freedoms, better regulation, technical harmonisation)

Ana RAMÍREZ FUEYO
Head of Unit
Tel. +32 2281-7004

Dimitros MANTZEVELAKIS
Tel. +32 2281-7995

Lars Erik SVENSSON
Tel. +32 2281-7853

Andreas WEIDA
Tel. +32 2281-8605

Corinne DREYFUS POLITRONACCI
Tel. +32 2281-3795

Gérard TAQUIN
Tel. +32 2281-9865

Peter AGIUS
Tel. +32 2281-5236

Unit 1B — Competition, customs union — company law — intellectual property — public procurement

Klaus SCHWAB
Head of Unit
Tel. +32 2281-7293

Leonidas KARAMOUNTZOS
Tel. +32 2281-8546

Vassilios KANARAS
Tel. +32 2281-5170

Philippe LEFÉBURE
Tel. +32 2281-8494

Eleonora BOTAR
Tel. +32 2281-9359

Directorate 2 — Competitiveness — Lisbon strategy — industry — research — information society — electronic communications

Jiří BURIÁNEK
Director
Tel. +32 2281-7215

Unit 2A — Competitiveness, Lisbon strategy, industry

Thomas BRANDTNER
Head of Unit
Tel. +32 2281-7072

Erwin van RIJ
Tel. +32 2281-6943

Frits SMULDERS
Tel. +32 2281-5586

Grazia Mattea TARGA
Tel. +32 2281-9350

Catherine COLLART
Tel. +32 2281-6080

Unit 2B — Research, innovation, information society

Eva VEIVO
Head of Unit
Tel. +32 2281-9588

Kimmo PEIPPO
Tel. +32 2281-7363

Huibert VAN WAGENSVELD
Tel. +32 2281-7044

Elissavet KAPNOPOULOU
Tel. +32 2281-5066

Marko FERBAR
Tel. +32 2281-9388

Ulla MESIÄ
Tel. +32 2281-7914

Directorate 3 — Transport policy

Elisabeth ALTEKÖSTER
Director
Tel. +32 2281-9770

Unit 3A — Land, maritime and air transport, Galileo

Paulo OLIVEIRA
Head of Unit
Tel. +32 2281-6619

Maria SEVDALI
Tel. +32 2281-7091

Kai STOLZENBURG
Tel. +32 2281-7693

Göran WELIN
Tel. +32 2281-6664

Thomas GLÖCKEL
Tel. +32 2281-5891

Victor HOLLEBOOM
Tel. +32 2281-9389

Simon BRAIN
Tel. +32 2281-7631

Peter ASANGER
Tel. +32 2281-5109

DIRECTORATE-GENERAL E – EXTERNAL AND POLITICAL-MILITARY AFFAIRS

Robert COOPER
Director-General
Tel. +32 2281-8552

Coordination Unit

Cesira D'ANIELLO
Head of Unit
Tel. +32 2281-8253

Coordination of the Political and Security Committee (PSC)

Elina DZALBE
Tel. +32 2281-7381

Saskia MATL
Tel. +32 2281-7341

Bruno SCHOLL
Tel. +32 2281-7213

Group of Advisers RELEX

Francesco FINI
Tel. +32 2281-9474

Jaroslaw TIMOFIEJUK
Tel. +32 2281-7605

Ineke VAN ROOIJEN
Tel. +32 2281-6332

Maura CLUNE
Tel. +32 2281-7087

Administration and personnel — Working methods — Training — Political dialogue

Ana Maria ANSELMO
Tel. +32 2281-8111

Filomena ANTUNES
Tel. +32 2281-8268

Stein VERSCHELDEN
Tel. +32 2281-5179

Human Rights Unit

Riina KIONKA
Personal Representative of the Secretary-General/ High Representative for human rights
Head of Unit
Tel. +32 2281-9689

Claudia GINTERSDORFER
Tel. +32 2281-6328

Aymeric DUPONT
Tel. +32 2281-6817

Katariina LEINONEN
Tel. +32 2281-8179

Marcela-Blanka NOVÁKOVÁ
Tel. +32 2281-4440

Audrone PERKAUSKIENE
Tel. +32 2281-9825

Maria João BOURBON
Tel. +32 2281-7835

Enlargement Unit

Christos KATHARIOS
Head of Unit
Tel. +32 2281-7567

Enlargement

Fernando CRIADO-ALONSO
Tel. +32 2281-6255

Anders KJELLGREN
Tel. +32 2281-5801

Lucie SAMCOVÁ
Tel. +32 2281-7427

Gabriele SCARAMUCCI
Tel. +32 2281-6447

Jaana TEDDER
Tel. +32 2281-9796

Directorate 'Development and ACP; multilateral economic affairs and non-EU western Europe'

Paul CULLEY
Director
Tel. +32 2281-6197

Development and ACP Unit

Walpurga SPECKBACHER
Head of Unit
Tel. +32 2281-5240

1. Development cooperation — CDI/CTA — Food aid — United Nations Conferences on Commodities Development

Andres TOBIAS Y RUBIO
Tel. +32 2281-7006

Jan VAN ELST
Tel. +32 2281-8252

2. ACP/OCT — Generalised system of preferences

Gianluigi FAURE
Tel. +32 2281-6468

Piotr KRYGIEL
Tel. +32 2281-3775

Pierpaolo SETTEMBRI
Tel. +32 2281-5457

Alice COSTA
Tel. +32 2281-6948

Unit for multilateral economic affairs and non-EU Western Europe

Massimo PARNISARI
Head of Unit
Tel. +32 2281-8316

1. WTO — Trade policy, textiles agreements

Luisa BALSELLS TRAVER
Tel. +32 2281-4943

Bert HOFMANN
Tel. +32 2281-8098

Olli MATTILA
Tel. +32 2281-8357

2. Commercial policy instruments, national cooperation agreements, ECSC agreements, shipbuilding, reports from commercial counsellors, fairs and exhibitions, OECD

Jacob VISSCHER
Tel. +32 2281-7183

Agnieszka CZARNECKA
Tel. +32 2281-7538

3. EEA/EFTA, Switzerland, Faroe Islands, Iceland, Andorra, San Marino, Norway, Liechtenstein, Monaco, Holy See

Bärbel DÜRHAEGER
Tel. +32 2281-6763

Directorate — 'America, United Nations, human rights and counterterrorism'

Marek GRELA
Director
Tel. +32 2281-6385

1. Transatlantic relations

Margarita COMAMALA LANA
Tel. +32 2281-7039

Rory DOMM
Tel. +32 2281-6343

Christiane HOEHN
Tel. +32 2281-5380

2. United Nations — Public international law

Massimo BIANCHI
Tel. +32 2281-8555

Rafael DE BUSTAMANTE TELLO
Tel. +32 2281-5190

Morten KNUDSEN
Tel. +32 2281-7418

3. Latin America

Blanca AUSEJO MARTINEZ
Tel. +32 2281-7012

Karl BUCK
Tel. +32 2281-7574

Nicolás PASCUAL DE LA PARTE (3)
Tel. +32 2281-5322

Horizontal Issues

Ignacio DIEZ PARRA
Tel. +32 2281-8313

Ran VAN REEDT DORTLAND
Tel. +32 2281-8042

Catherine MACDONALD
Tel. +32 2281-9559

Middle East, Mediterranean Region Unit

Christian JOURET (4)
Head of Unit
Tel. +32 2281-5324

Wolfgang BÄRWINKEL
Tel. +32 2281-8241

Maja BOZOVIC
Tel. +32 2281-7485

Didier COSSÉ
Tel. +32 2281-7758

John GATT-RUTTER
Tel. +32 2281-6086

Petr HLADIK (5)
Tel. +32 2281-5186

Lene HOVE
Tel. +32 2281-8472

Sophie KISLING
Tel. +32 2281-7785

Milton NICOLAIDIS (6)
Tel. +32 2281-7010

(3) Policy Unit
(4) Policy Unit
(5) Policy Unit
(6) Policy Unit

Roberto OLMI
Tel. +32 2281-6778

Colin SCICLUNA (7)
Tel. +32 2281-3679

Alexander ZAFIRIOU
Tel. +32 2281-9121

Unit Africa

José Fernando Alves da COSTA PEREIRA
Head of Unit
Tel. +32 2281-9734

Peter CLAUSEN
Tel. +32 2281-7356

Andreas FISCHER-BARNICOL
Tel. +32 2281-3684

Marie-Luise LINDORFER
Tel. +32 2281-9280

Susanne NIELSEN
Tel. +32 2281-4394

Sandra PAESEN
Tel. +32 2281-5804

Ragnheidur ROUBINEAU
Tel. +32 2281-7135

Asia and Oceania Unit

Boguslaw MAJEWSKI
Head of Unit
Tel. +32 2281-6831

Tim EESTERMANS (8)
Tel. +32 2281-5328

Morgan MC SWINEY (9)
Tel. +32 2281-5482

Francesco PRESUTTI
Tel. +32 2281-6333

Razvan Stefan RAB (10)
Tel. +32 2281-5716

Marek REPOVSKY (11)
Tel. +32 2281-7015

Leo SCHULTE-NORDOLT
Tel. +32 2281-8483

Directorate — Western Balkans region, eastern Europe and central Asia

...
Director

Western Balkans Unit

Jonas JONSSON
Head of Unit
Tel. +32 2281-4361

Anna-Maria BOURA
Tel. +32 2281-7049

(7) Policy Unit
(8) Policy Unit
(9) Policy Unit
(10) Policy Unit
(11) Policy Unit

Benjamin CRAMPTON
Tel. +32 2281-9340

Lothar JASCHKE (12)
Tel. +32 2281-7094

Terkel PETERSEN
Tel. +32 2281-7034

Sabina STADLER (13)
Tel. +32 2281-7416

Johanna STRÖMQUIST
Tel. +32 2281-8036

Annika WEIDEMANN
Tel. +32 2281-8334

Véronique JEANGILLE
Tel. +32 2281-7985

Eastern Europe and Central Asia Unit

Jukka LESKELÄ
Head of Unit
Tel. +32 2281-8528

David JOHNS
Tel. +32 2281-8600

Baiba ALEKSEJUKA
Tel. +32 2281-9767

Ausra ALELIUNAITE
Tel. +32 2281-6938

Gints APALS (14)
Tel. +32 2281-5501

Paulo BARROSO SIMOES
Tel. +32 2281-5373

Nadia ERNZER (15)
Tel. +32 2281-5845

Björn FAGERBERG (16)
Tel. +32 2281-5648

Tatiana LEVCEVA (17)
Tel. +32 2281-5715

Viktoria LÖVENBERG
Tel. +32 2281-5122

Rasa OSTRAUSKAITE (18)
Tel. +32 2281-6651

Eleftheria PERTZINIDOU
Tel. +32 2281-7828

Kristi RAIK
Tel. +32 2281-4427

Pirkka TAPIOLA (19)
Tel. +32 2281-5846

Stefan TRESSING
Tel. +32 2281-8548

Anne-Marie FEVE
Tel. +32 2281-6443

(12) Policy Unit
(13) Policy Unit
(14) Policy Unit
(15) Policy Unit
(16) Policy Unit
(17) Policy Unit
(18) Policy Unit
(19) Policy Unit

Directorate 8 — Defence aspects

Claude-France ARNOULD
Director
Tel. +32 2281-6185

Defence Policy and Capabilities Unit

Alda SILVEIRA REIS
Head of Unit
Tel. +32 2281-6093

Jan ALHADEFF
Tel. +32 2281-5799

Helena BOGUSLAWSKA
Tel. +32 2281-5366

Patrick CHATARD MOULIN
Tel. +32 2281-8251

Dirk DUBOIS
Tel. +32 2281-2633

Hans Joachim HOLSTEIN
Tel. +32 2281-8518

Patrick LANGLOIS
Tel. +32 2281-5907

Dan TRIFANESCU
Tel. +32 2281-2632

Hans Bernhard WEISSERTH (20)
Tel. +32 2281-5848

Marie-Pierre DEVROEDT
Tel. +32 2281-6746

Operations and Exercises Unit

Didier LENOIR
Head of Unit
Tel. +32 2281-5675

Sébastien BERGEON
Tel. +32 2281-7082

Gérard DEJOUE
Tel. +32 2281-4810

Patrick GEYSEN
Tel. +32 2281-9604

Uwe HARMS
Tel. +32 2281-5012

Ken HUME
Tel. +32 2281-5108

Teresa MÚGICA INCIARTE
Tel. +32 2281-7037

Graham MUIR
Tel. +32 2281-7720

Bernard RAMBAUD
Tel. +32 2281-5158

Patrick VANHEES
Tel. +32 2281-2598

Marina VRAILA
Tel. +32 2281-6010

Catharina WALE GRUNDITZ
Tel. +32 2281-3706

(20) Policy Unit

Directorate 'Civilian crisis management'

Mika-Markus LEINONEN
Director
Tel. +32 2281-9383

Horizontal Issues Unit

Veronica CODY
Head of Unit
Tel. +32 2281-8543

Johannes SCHACHINGER
Tel. +32 2281-3699

Preben AAMANN
Tel. +32 2281-3723

Dorata EGGERT
Tel. +32 2281-3674

Timo RANTA
Tel. +32 2281-3723

Rainer RUGE
Tel. +32 2281-9301

Michel SAVARY
Tel. +32 2281-8954

Colin STEINBACH
Tel. +32 2281-8953

Antoinette KEULEN
Tel. +32 2281-7786

Operations Unit

Antonio TANCA
Head of Unit
Tel. +32 2281-8601

Gerrit BAUWENS
Tel. +32 2281-3270

Hadewych HAZELZET
Tel. +32 2281-3683

Peter HEDLING
Tel. +32 2281-7609

Radek KHOL
Tel. +32 2281-4432

Joël SCHUYER
Tel. +32 2281-7731

Satu SEPPÄNEN
Tel. +32 2281-9914

Office of the personal representative of the High Representative for matters of non-proliferation ([21])

Arms control, disarmament, non-proliferation

Exportation of conventional arms, including: COARM and code of conduct, disarmament, including CODUN, non-proliferation, including CONOP

Annalisa GIANNELLA
Personal Representative of the Secretary General/ High Representative
Director
Tel. +32 2281-8044

Andreas STRUB
Tel. +32 2281-8321

Rosemary CHABANSKI
Tel. +32 2281-6893

Fabio DELLA PIAZZA
Tel. +32 2281-6122

Anne KEMPPAINEN
Tel. +32 2281-5642

Stephan KLEMENT
Tel. +32 2281-8353

Tomas REYES ORTEGA
Tel. +32 2281-3996

Zuzana SUTIAKOVÁ
Tel. +32 2281-9587

Daniel VAN ASSCHE
Tel. +32 2281-8958

Geneva — Office for Liaison with the European Office of the United Nations

Dimitris ILIOPOULOS
Director
Head of Liaison Office
Tel. +41 229197401

Guus HOUTTUIN
Head of Unit
Tel. +41 229197402

WTO, human rights (in particular CHR), humanitarian affairs (HCR, ICRC). disarmament, WHO, ILO, UNCTAD, UNECE, International Telecommunications Union (ITU), WIPO

Bruno HANSES
Tel. +41 229197405

Georgios KRITIKOS
Tel. +41 229197403

Nicole RECKINGER
Tel. +41 229197406

Leonor VIEIRA SOUSA
Tel. +41 229197442

Colette JEMAA
Tel. +41 229197407

New York — United Nations Liaison Office

Pedro SERRANO DE HARO
Director
Head of Liaison Office
Tel. +1 2122928601

Stephan MARQUARDT
Tel. +1 2122928603

Per LAGERGREN
Tel. +1 2122928619

Stefano TOMAT
Tel. +1 2122928612

Friederike TSCHAMPA
Tel. +1 2122928604

Military Adviser to the EU

Fergus BUSHELL
Tel. +1 2122928606

Security, protocol

Erik VANDEPERRE
Tel. +1 2122928607

Finance and administration

Keld THOMSEN
Tel. +1 2122928611

DIRECTORATE-GENERAL F – PRESS, COMMUNICATION, PROTOCOL

Marc LEPOIVRE
Director-General
Head of Protocol
Tel. +32 2281-8267

Coordination, personnel and administrative management

Loreto ROSAS VALLE
Tel. +32 2281-6454

Protocol

Cristina BERTACCA
Tel. +32 2281-6438

Budgetary and financial Management

Gerda DAIDONE
Tel. +32 2281-7168

Information policy

Vincenzo LE VOCI
Tel. +32 2281-6930

Business Continuity Planning (BCP)

Siegfried VAN DEN ENDEN
Tel. +32 2281-6308

Philip MEULENBERGHS
Tel. +32 2281-8034

([21]) Reporting directly to the High representative.

Unit 1 — Press

Nicolas KERLEROUX
Head of Unit
Tel. +32 2281-8239

Press Information

General affairs and external relations, IGC, security and defence

Jesús CARMONA NUÑEZ
Tel. +32 2281-9548

General affairs, external relations, economic and financial affairs, development cooperation

François HEAD
Tel. +32 2281-6083

Security and defence policy

Stavros PETROPOULOS
Tel. +32 2281-8348

Céline RUIZ
Tel. +32 2281-9333

Justice and home affairs; coverage of press issues relating to coordination in countering terrorism

Jesús CARMONA NUÑEZ
Tel. +32 2281-9548

Agriculture and fisheries; budget, employment and social policy; health and consumer affairs

Carole MICMACHER-GRANDCOLAS
Tel. +32 2281-5389

Jérôme UNTERHUBER
Tel. +32 2281-5394

Competitiveness (internal market, industry and research); environment; transport, telecommunications and energy; education, youth affairs and culture

Victor FLAVIÁN
Tel. +32 2281-6715

Miriam VANCOVA
Tel. +32 2281-9776

Susanne KIEFER
Tel. +32 2281-9442

Research and documentation

Reinhard SCHMIDT
Tel. +32 2281-8847

Helena GOMES
Tel. +32 2281-7040

Evi LIASKOU
Tel. +32 2281-5272

Bo LAURSEN
Tel. +32 2281-5445

Crisis management mechanisms and coordination of the open sessions of the Council

Dana MANESCU
Tel. +32 2281-4477

Press and Audiovisual Centre

Coreper II/European Council

Margarete GILOT-KÖHLER
Tel. +32 2281-6550

Coreper I/Photography Unit/European Council

Valerie GOLDSMITH
Tel. +32 2281-8969

Media

Isabelle BRUSSELMANS
Tel. +32 2281-5713

Laura DI ROSA
Tel. +32 2281-7367

Media Monitoring

Johan SLOTBOOM
Tel. +32 2281-5505
Fax +32 2281-5335

Spokesperson to the Secretary-General/High Representative for common foreign and security policy

Cristina GALLACH ([22])
Head of Unit
Tel. +32 2281-6467/5151/5150
Fax +32 2281-5694

Mary BRAZIER
Assistant to the Spokesperson
Tel. +32 2281-5183

Alain PLUCKERS
Assistant to the Spokesperson
Tel. +32 2281-6217

Unit 2 — Communication

Karel JEZEK
Head of Unit
Tel. +32 2281-8783
Fax +32 2281-5333

Internet

Richard HUK
Tel. +32 2281-3586
Fax +32 2281-5333

Publications, documentation

Jorge TAVARES DA SILVA
Tel. +32 2281-8180
Fax +32 2281-5334

Visits, public events, information for the public

Sari HÄNNINEN
Tel. +32 2281-8693
Fax +32 2281-6609

Unit 3 — Transparency, Official Journal, archives, libraries

Ramón JIMÉNEZ FRAILE
Head of Unit
Tel. +32 2281-6176
Fax +32 2281-5333

Transparency, access to documents

Jakob THOMSEN
Tel. +32 2281-9417
Fax +32 2281-6361

Official Journal

Eva Maria MAURER
Tel. +32 2281-9956

Central archives

Michel WEYSSOW
Tel. +32 2281-5671
Fax +32 2281-8124

Libraries

Riitta TINGANDER
Tel. +32 2281-6541
Fax +32 2281-8174

DIRECTORATE-GENERAL G – ECONOMIC AND SOCIAL AFFAIRS

Carsten PILLATH
Director-General
Tel. +32 2281-6213

Directorate 1 — Economic and regional affairs

Petr BLIZKOVSKY
Director
Tel. +32 2281-5130

Economic and regional policy, export credits

Pedro SAN JOSÉ
Tel. +32 2281-8266

Kyle GALLER
Tel. +32 2281-7298

Agnieszka BARTOL
Tel. +32 2281-6694

Unit 1B — Tax policy and export credits

Servatius VAN THIEL
Head of Unit
Tel. +32 2281-6617

Glykéria MARKOPOULIOTOU
Tel. +32 2281-6899

Liam O'LUANAIGH
Tel. +32 2281-7357

([22]) Attached to the Secretary-General/High Representative.

Marius VASCEGA
Tel. +32 2281-8715

Monique DERELOU
Tel. +32 2281-6557

Unit 1C — Financial services

Bodil S. NIELSEN
Head of Unit
Tel. +32 2281-6195

Tomas BRÄNNSTRÖM
Tel. +32 2281-9416

Jean-Luc FILIPPINI
Tel. +32 2281-5622

Carlos SOARES
Tel. +32 2281-9419

Agnieszka BARTOL
Tel. +32 2281-6694

Directorate 2 — Social affairs

Unit 2A — Employment and social policy

Andrew GEORGE
Head of Unit
Tel. +32 2281-7354

Employment, health and safety at work

Mervi HIETANEN
Tel. +32 2281-8197

Working conditions, gender equality, non-discrimination

Philip LANDON
Tel. +32 2281-4966

Social security, social protection, fight against poverty and social exclusion, employee representation in undertakings

Muriel DE PUIFFERRAT
Tel. +32 2281-8135

Demography, family policy, statistics, consultative committees

Petra CERNA
Tel. +32 2281-3084

Directorate 3 — Budget and financial regulations

François VAN HÖVELL
Director
Tel. +32 2281-7268

Unit 3A — Budget/finance

Jean-Paul GROSSIR
Head of Unit
Tel. +32 2281-8118

Marjatta MÄKINEN
Tel. +32 2281-8658

Ilkka SAARILAHTI
Tel. +32 2281-5524

Tobias PABSCH
Tel. +32 2281-6235

Piera GHIGNONE
Tel. +32 2281-5886

Carmen RAGIONE
Tel. +32 2281-4815

Bostjan KRASOVEC
Tel. +32 2281-8779

DIRECTORATE-GENERAL H – JUSTICE AND HOME AFFAIRS

Ivan BIZJAK
Director-General
Tel. +32 2281-8505

Rafael FERNÁNDEZ-PITA Y GONZÁLEZ
Deputy Director-General
Tel. +32 2281-9889

Coordination team

Wouter van de RIJT
Tel. +32 2281-5416

Bernard PHILIPPART
Tel. +32 2281-9619

Stephan BROCZA
Tel. +32 2281-7245

Secretariat for data protection (Schengen, customs, Europol)

Peter MICHAEL
Tel. +32 2281-5026

Directorate 1 — Asylum, visas, immigration, frontiers

Paul HICKEY
Director
Tel. +32 2281-6546

Unit 1A — Visas, frontiers

Bent MEJBORN
Head of Unit
Tel. +32 2281-6722

Pascal ROELANDTS
Tel. +32 2281-6800

Magdalena MARTINEZ-ALMEIDA
Tel. +32 2281-6219

Giovanna GIGLIO
Tel. +32 2281-5545

Manfred LAVICKA
Tel. +32 2281-5536

Dorothy SUTHERLAND
Tel. +32 2281-9932

Unit 1B — Asylum and immigration

Guillermo TRONCOSO GONZÁLEZ
Head of Unit
Tel. +32 2281-8217

Paolo Martino COSSU
Tel. +32 2281-8113

Gavriil KAMPOUROGLOU
Tel. +32 2281-4948

Directorate 2 — Judicial cooperation in civil and criminal matters

Leonardo SCHIAVO
Director
Tel. +32 22815575

Unit 2A — Judicial cooperation in civil matters

Fernando Rui PAULINO PEREIRA
Head of Unit
Tel. +32 2281-6621

Bente SØRENSEN
Tel. +32 2281-8099

Fabien CADET
Tel. +32 2281-5291

Kristi RABA
Tel. +32 2281-8902

Maïlys RAMONATXO
Tel. +32 2281-9458

Unit 2B — Criminal judicial cooperation

Hans NILSSON
Head of Unit
Tel. +32 2281-7915

Irene SIMANTONI
Tel. +32 2281-7702

Steven CRAS
Tel. +32 2281-5483

Guy STESSENS
Tel. +32 2281-6711

Anna Halina LIPSKA
Tel. +32 2281-9515

Directorate 3 — Police and customs cooperation, Schengen

Roland GENSON
Director
Tel. +32 2281-5822

Unit 3A — Police and customs cooperation

Nathalie PENSAERT
Head of Unit
Tel. +32 2281-5425

Erwin BUYSSENS
Tel. +32 2281-5397

Zuzana HORVATHOVA
Tel. +32 2281-3945

Ave POOM
Tel. +32 2281-9664

Unit 3B — Schengen

Luc VANDAMME
Head of Unit
Tel. +32 2281-5399

Gerrit HUYBREGHTS
Tel. +32 2281-6712

Laetitia BOT
Tel. +32 2281-8981

Jacinto DA SILVA SANTOS
Tel. +32 2281-5255

Klaus-Dieter RUDOLPH
Tel. +32 2281-3998

Directorate 4 — Civil protection

Sabine EHMKE-GENDRON
Director
Tel. +32 2281-8569

Christian FRØIK
Tel. +32 2281-6381

Leni RIKKONEN-LE VILLAIN
Tel. +32 2281-8723

Joanna JASKOWIAK
Tel. +32 2281-3607

DIRECTORATE-GENERAL I – PROTECTION OF THE ENVIRONMENT AND CONSUMERS, HEALTH, FOODSTUFFS, EDUCATION, YOUTH, CULTURE, AUDIOVISUAL AFFAIRS

Jaroslaw PIETRAS
Director-General
Tel. +32 2281-7421

Environment Unit

Wolfgang PLOCH
Head of Unit
Tel. +32 2281-7771

Chiara MANTEGAZZINI
Tel. +32 2281-4949

Joaquim MARINHO DE BASTOS
Tel. +32 2281-6072

Maria MAROTTA
Tel. +32 2281-6225

Simon COATES
Tel. +32 2281-5768

Inès HEMPEL
Tel. +32 2281-5688

Aikaterini-Zoi VARFI
Tel. +32 2281-9760

Maurizio DI LULLO
Tel. +32 2281-6579

Yves-Marie LEONET
Tel. +32 2281-6087

Monica SILVA
Tel. +32 2281-9356

Martin SALVET
Tel. +32 2281-4796

Directorate 2 — Education, youth, culture, audiovisual affairs, health, consumers, foodstuffs

Sándor SZABÓ
Director
Tel. +32 2281-8841

Unit 2B — Health, consumers, foodstuffs

Juraj SYKORA
Tel. +32 2281-9385

Enrique ESTELLER ALBERICH
Tel. +32 2281-5724

Laurent LABOURÉ
Tel. +32 2281-7400

Maria Paula MARQUES
Tel. +32 2281-8716

Unit 2A — Education, youth, culture, audiovisual affairs

Luc LAPERE
Head of Unit
Tel. +32 2281-6640

Graham NEQUEST
Tel. +32 2281-7267

Nicholas PLATTEN
Tel. +32 2281-7431

Anu POTISEPP
Tel. +32 2281-9777

Association Councils

EU–ALGERIA ASSOCIATION COUNCIL

Diplomatic representation of Algeria

Chancellerie:
Avenue Molière 209
B-1050 Brussels
Tel. +32 23435078
Fax +32 23435168

HE Mr Halim BENATTALLAH
Ambassador
Head of Mission (EC, Euratom)

Secretariat of the Association Council

Rue de la Loi 175
B-1048 Brussels

The Secretariat is run jointly by an official of the Algerian Government and a Community official.

For the Community side, the Co-Secretary is Mr Milton Nicolaidis, and for the Algerian side, Mr Fawzi DIB.

EU–EGYPT ASSOCIATION COUNCIL

Diplomatic representation of Egypt

Chancellerie:
Avenue de l'Uruguay 19
B-1000 Brussels
Tel. +32 26635800
Fax +32 26755888

HE Mr Mahmoud KAREM
Ambassador
Head of Mission (EC, Euratom)

Secretariat of the Association Council

Rue de la Loi 175
B-1048 Brussels

The Secretariat is run jointly by an official of the Egyptian Government and a Community official.

For the Community side, the Co-Secretary is Mr Roberto OLMI, and for the Egyptian side, Mr Kamel GALAL.

EU–LEBANON ASSOCIATION COUNCIL

Diplomatic representation of Lebanon

Chancellerie:
Rue Guillaume Stocq 2
B-1050 Brussels
Tel. +32 26457760
Fax +32 26457769

HE Mr Adnan MANSOU
Ambassador
Head of Mission (EC, Euratom)

Secretariat of the Association Council

Rue de la Loi 175
B-1048 Brussels

The Secretariat is run jointly by an official of the Egyptian Government and a Community official.

For the Community side, the Co-Secretary is Mr Roberto OLMI, and for the Lebanese side, Mrs Joanna AZZI.

ASSOCIATION COUNCIL WITH TUNISIA

Diplomatic representation of Tunisia

Chancellerie:
Avenue de Tervuren 278
B-1150 Brussels
Tel. +32 27717395
Fax +32 27719433

HE Mr Abdessalem HETIRA
Ambassador
Head of Representation (EEC)
Head of Mission (Euratom)

Secretariat of the Association Council

Rue de la Loi 175
B-1048 Brussels

The Secretariat is run jointly by an official of the Tunisian Government and a Community official.

For the Community side, the Co-Secretary is Mr Milton Nicolaidis, and for the Tunisian side, Mr Ridha AZAIEZ.

ASSOCIATION COUNCIL WITH MOROCCO

Diplomatic representation of Morocco

Chancellerie:
Avenue F. D. Roosevelt 2
B-1050 Brussels
Tel. +32 26263410
Fax +32 26263434

HE Mr Menouar ALEM
Ambassador
Head of Representation (EEC)
Head of Mission (EC)

Secretariat of the Association Council

Rue de la Loi 175
B-1048 Brussels

The Secretariat is run jointly by an official of the Moroccan Government and a Community official.

For the Community side, the Co-Secretary is Mr Milton Nicolaidis, and for the Moroccan side, Mr Nacim TOUROUGUI.

ASSOCIATION COUNCIL WITH ISRAEL

Diplomatic representation of Israel

Chancellerie:
Avenue de l'Observatoire 40
B-1180 Brussels
Tel. +32 23735500
Fax +32 23735677

HE Mr Ran CURIEL
Ambassador
Head of Mission (EEC, ECSC, Euratom)

Secretariat of the Association Council

Rue de la Loi 175
B-1048 Brussels
The Secretariat is run jointly by an official oft he Israeli Government and a Community official.

For the Community side, the Co-Secretary is Mr Petr Hladik, and for the Israeli side, Mr Zvi TAL.

EEC–TURKEY ASSOCIATION COUNCIL

Diplomatic representation of Turkey

Chancellerie:
Rue Montoyer 4
B-1000 Brussels
Tel. +32 22896240
Fax +32 25110450

HE Mr Volkan BOZKIR
Ambassador
Permanent Delegate

Secretariat of the Association Council

Rue de la Loi 175
B-1048 Brussels
The Secretariat is run jointly by an official of the Turkish Government and a Community official.

For the Community side, the Co-Secretary of the Association Council is Mr Gabriele SCARAMUCCI, Principal Administrator of the General Secretariat of the Council of the European Union. For the Turkish side the Co-Secretary is Ms Deniz EKE, First Secretary of the Turkish Mission.
The Association Council is assisted by an Association Committee, whose task is to prepare the Council's proceedings and to ensure the continuing cooperation necessary for the proper functioning of the agreement. This Committee is composed of representatives of the members of the Association Council.

ASSOCIATION COUNCIL WITH JORDAN

Diplomatic representation of Jordan

Chancellerie:
Avenue F. D. Roosevelt 104
B-1050 Brussels
Tel. +32 26407755
Fax +32 26402796

HE Mr Ahmad K. MASA'DEH
Ambassador
Head of Mission (EC, Euratom)

Secretariat of the Association Council

Rue de la Loi 175
B-1048 Brussels

The Secretariat is run jointly by an official of the Jordanian Government and a Community official.

For the Community side, the Co-Secretary is M. Petr Hladik, and for the Jordanian side, Mr Hamzeh AL-SHRIEDEH.

Cooperation Councils

COOPERATION COUNCIL EUROPEAN COMMUNITY–SOUTH AFRICA

Diplomatic representation of South Africa

HE Mr Anil SOOKLAL ([23])
Ambassador
Head of the Mission of the Republic of South Africa to the European Communities
Rue de la Loi 26 (Box 14/15)
B-1040 Brussels
Tel. +32 22854460
Fax +32 22854487

Cooperation Council Secretariat

Rue de la Loi 175
B-1048 Brussels
Tel. +32 22816111
An official of the General Secretariat of the Council of the European Union and an official of the South African Government act jointly as Secretaries of the Cooperation Council.

EEC–SYRIA COOPERATION COUNCIL

Diplomatic representation of Syria

Chancellerie:
Avenue F. D. Roosevelt 3
B-1050 Brussels
Tel. +32 25541921
Fax +32 26464018

HE Mr ...
Ambassador
Head of Mission (EC, Euratom)

Secretariat of the Cooperation Council

Rue de la Loi 175
B-1048 Brussels
The Secretariat is run jointly by an official of the Syrian Government and a Community official.

The office of President of the Cooperation Council is held alternately by the contracting parties.

The Cooperation Council may decide to set up any committee that can assist it in carrying out its duties.

([23]) In the process of accreditation.

Council of Ministers of the African, Caribbean and Pacific (ACP) States – European Community

The ACP-EC Council of Ministers comprises, on the one hand, the members of the Council of the European Union and members of the Commission of the European Communities and, on the other, a member of the government of each ACP Member State.

The office of President of the Council is held alternately by a member of the Council of the European Union (from 1 October to 31 March) and by a member of the government of an ACP State (from 1 April to 30 September).

The Committee of Ambassadors comprises, on the one hand, the permanent representative of each Member State to the European Union and a representative of the Commission, and, on the other, the head of mission of each ACP State to the European Union.

The office of Chairman of the Committee is held alternately by a permanent representative of a Member State and a head of mission representing an ACP State.

The Development Finance Cooperation Committee meets every three months and comprises, on a basis of parity, representatives of the ACP States and the Community or their authorised representatives. It meets at ministerial level whenever one of the parties so requests, at least once a year.

The office of Chairman of the Committee is held alternately by a representative of the Community and by an ACP representative.

The Cotonou Agreement also sets up a Joint Ministerial Trade Committee comprising, on the one hand, a minister from each of the Member States of the European Community and a member of the Commission of the European Communities and, on the other, 18 ministers from the ACP States.

The office of Chairman of the Trade Committee is held alternately for six-month periods by a member of the Commission on behalf of the European Community and by a representative of the ACP States.

The Secretariat of the Council of Ministers, the Committee of Ambassadors, committees, sub-committees and working groups, the Development Finance Cooperation Committee and the Joint Trade Committee is run jointly by two secretaries who are appointed after joint consultation, one by the ACP States and the other by the Community.

Secretariat of the ACP-EC Council of Ministers

Rue de la Loi 175
B-1048 Brussels
Tel. +32 22816111

Mr Paul CULLEY
Director at the General Secretariat of the Council
Co-Secretary

HE Sir John R. KAPUTIN
Secretary-General of the group of ACP countries
Co-Secretary

General Secretariat of the ACP Group of States

Avenue Georges-Henri 451
B-1200 Brussels
Tel. +32 27430600

Centre for the Development of Enterprise (CDE)

Avenue Herrmann Debroux 52
B-1160 Brussels
Tel. +32 26791811
The Centre for the Development of Enterprise, which is covered by Article 2 of Annex III to the Cotonou Agreement, aims to assist private ACP enterprises to become more competitive in all sectors of the economy.

Mabousso THIAM
Director

Technical Centre for Agricultural and Rural Cooperation 'De Rietkampen'

Postbus 380
6700 AJ Wageningen
Netherlands
Tel. +31 317467100
The Technical Centre for Agriculture and Rural Cooperation (Article 3 of Annex III to the Cotonou Agreement), placed under the authority of the Committee of Ambassadors, is at the disposal of the ACP States' authorities responsible for agricultural development in order to provide them with better access to information and innovations in the spheres of agricultural and rural development.

Mr Hansjörg NEUN
Director

REPRESENTATIONS OF THE AFRICAN, CARIBBEAN AND PACIFIC STATES

Angola

HE Mr Toko DIAKENGA SERÃO
Head of the Mission of the Republic of Angola to the European Communities
Rue Franz Merjay 182
B-1050 Brussels
Tel. +32 23461872/80
Fax +32 23440894

Antigua and Barbuda

...
Ambassador Extraordinary and Plenipotentiary
Head of the Mission of Antigua and Barbuda
Rue de Livourne 42
B-1000 Brussels
Tel. +32 25342611, 25441802
Fax +32 25394009

Bahamas (The)

HE Mr Paul H. FARQUHARSON
Ambassador Extraordinary and Plenipotentiary
Head of the Mission of the Commonwealth of the Bahamas to the European Communities
10 Chesterfield Street
London W1X 8AH
United Kingdom
E-mail: information@bahamashclondon.net
Tel. +44 1714084488
Fax +44 1714999937

Barbados

Errol HUMPHREY
Ambassador Extraordinary and Plenipotentiary
Head of the Barbadian Mission to the European Communities
Avenue Franklin Roosevelt 100
B-1050 Brussels
Tel. +32 27321737
Fax +32 27323266

Belize

HE Mrs Audrey Joy GRANT [24]
Ambassador Extraordinary and Plenipotentiary
Head of the Mission of Belize to the European Communities
Boulevard Brand Whitlock 136
B-1200 Brussels
Tel. +32 27326204
Fax +32 27326246

Benin

HE Mr ...
Ambassador Extraordinary and Plenipotentiary
Head of the Mission of the Republic of Benin to the European Communities
Avenue de l'Observatoire 5
B-1180 Brussels
Tel. +32 23750674
Fax +32 23758326

[24] Accreditation in progress.

Botswana

HE Mrs Claurinah Tshenolo MODISE
Ambassador Extraordinary and Plenipotentiary
Head of the Mission of the Republic of Botswana to the European Communities
Avenue de Tervuren 169
B-1150 Brussels
Tel. +32 27352070
Fax +32 27356318

Burkina Faso

HE Mr Kadré Désiré OUEDRAGO
Ambassador Extraordinary and Plenipotentiary
Head of the Mission of Burkina Faso to the European Communities
Place Guy d'Arezzo 16
B-1180 Brussels
Tel. +32 23459911, 23459912
Fax +32 23450612

Burundi

HE Mr Laurent KAVAKURE
Ambassador Extraordinary and Plenipotentiary
Head of the Mission of the Republic of Burundi to the European Communities
Square Marie-Louise 46
B-1000 Brussels
Tel. +32 22304535, 22304548
Fax +32 22307883

Cameroon

HE Mr Daniel EVINA ABE'E [25]
Ambassador Extraordinary and Plenipotentiary
Mission of the Republic of Cameroon to the European Communities
Avenue Brugmann 131-133
B-1190 Brussels
Tel. +32 23451870
Fax +32 23445735

Cap Verde

HE Mr Fernando Wahnon FERREIRA
Ambassador Extraordinary and Plenipotentiary
Head of the Mission of the Republic of Cape Verde to the European Communities
Avenue Jeanne 29
B-1050 Brussels
Tel. +32 26436270
Fax +32 26463385

Central African Republic

HE Mr Abel SABONO
Ambassador Extraordinary and Plenipotentiary
Head of the Mission of the Central African Republic to the European Communities
Boulevard Lambermont 416
B-1030 Brussels
Tel. +32 22422880
Fax +32 23531674

[25] Accreditation in progress.

Chad

HE Mr Maïtine DJOUMBE
Ambassador Extraordinary and Plenipotentiary
Head of the Mission of the Republic of Chad to the European Communities
Boulevard Lambermont 52
B-1030 Brussels
Tel. +32 22151975
Fax +32 22163526

Commonwealth of Dominica

HE Mrs Shirley SKERRIT-ANDREW [26]
Ambassador Extraordinary and Plenipotentiary
Head of the Mission of the Commonwealth of Dominica to the European Communities
Rue de Livourne 42
B-1000 Brussels
Tel. +32 25342611, 25441802
Fax +32 25394009

Comoros

... [27]
Ambassador Extraordinary and Plenipotentiary
Head of the Mission of the Islamic Federal Republic of the Comoros to the European Communities
Rue Berthelot 163
B-1190 Brussels
Tel. +32 27795838
Fax +32 27795838

Congo

HE Mr Roger Julien MENGA [28]
Ambassador Extraordinary and Plenipotentiary
Head of the Mission of the Republic of Congo to the European Communities
Avenue F. D. Roosevelt 16
B-1050 Brussels
Tel. +32 26483856
Fax +32 26484213

Cook Islands

HE Mr Todd McCLAY
Ambassador
Head of the Mission of the Cook Islands
Rue Berckmans 10
B-1060 Brussels
Tel. +32 25341000
Fax +32 25341001

Côte d'Ivoire

HE Mrs Marie GOSSET
Ambassador Extraordinary and Plenipotentiary
Head of the Mission of the Republic of Côte d'Ivoire to the European Communities
Avenue F. D. Roosevelt 234
B-1050 Brussels
Tel. +32 26729577, 26722357
Fax +32 26720491

[26] Accreditation in progress.
[27] Accreditation in progress.
[28] Accreditation in progress.

Democratic Republic of the Congo

HE Mr Corneille YAMBU-A-NGOYI
Ambassador Extraordinary and Plenipotentiary
Head of the Mission of the Democratic Republic of the Congo to the European Union
Avenue de Foestraets 6
B-1180 Brussels
Tel. +32 25136610, 25134360
Fax +32 25140403

Djibouti

HE Mr Mohamed MOUSSA CHEHEM
Ambassador Extraordinary and Plenipotentiary
Head of the Mission of the Republic of Djibouti to the European Communities
Avenue Franklin Roosevelt 204
B-1050 Brussels
Tel. +32 23476967
Fax +32 23476963

Dominican Republic

HE Mr Federico Alberto CUELLO CAMILO
Ambassador Extraordinary and Plenipotentiary
Head of the Mission of the Dominican Republic to the European Communities
Avenue Louise 130 A
B-1050 Brussels
Tel. +32 23464935
Fax +32 23465152

East Timor

HE Mrs Maria Natália GUTERRES VIEGAS CARRASCALÃO [29]
Ambassador Extraordinary and Plenipotentiary
Head of the Mission of the Democratic Republic of Timor Leste to the European Communities
PO Box 198
B-1040 Brussels
Tel. +32 22800096
Fax +32 22800277

Eritrea

HE Mr Girma Asmerom TESFAY
Ambassador Extraordinary and Plenipotetiary
Head of the Mission of the State of Eritrea to the European Communities
Avenue Wolvendael 15-17
B-1180 Brussels
Tel. +32 23744434
Fax +32 23720730

Equatorial Guinea

HE Mr Victorino Nka OBIANG MAYE
Ambassador Extraordinary and Plenipotentiary
Head of the Mission of the Republic of Equatorial Guinea to the European Communities
Place Guy d'Arezzo 6
B-1180 Brussels
Tel. +32 23462509
Fax +32 23463309

([29]) Accreditation in progress.

Federal Democratic Republic of Ethiopia

HE Mr Ato Berhane GEBRE-CHRISTOS
Ambassador Extraordinary and Plenipotentiary
Head of the Mission of the Federal Democratic Republic of Ethiopia to the European Communities
Avenue de Tervuren 231
B-1150 Brussels
Tel. +32 27713294, 27713590
Fax +32 27714914

Federated States of Micronesia

c/o Permanent Representative of the Federated States of Micronesia to the United Nations
820 Second Avenue, Suite 17A
N.Y. 10017 New York
Tel. +1 212697-8370
Fax +1 212697-8295

Gabon

HE Mr René MAKONGO
Ambassador Extraordinary and Plenipotentiary
Head of the Mission of the Gabonese Republic to the European Communities
Avenue Winston Churchill 112
B-1180 Brussels
Tel. +32 23406210
Fax +32 23464669

Gambia

HE Mr Mamour JAGNE A. [30]
Ambassador Extraordinary and Plenipotentiary
Mission of the Republic of the Gambia to the European Communities
Avenue F. D. Roosevelt 126
B-1050 Brussels
Tel. +32 26401049
Fax +32 26464689

Ghana

HE Mrs Nana BEMA KUMI
Ambassador Extraordinary and Plenipotentiary
Head of the Mission of the Republic of Ghana to the European Communities
Boulevard Général Wahis 7
B-1030 Brussels
Tel. +32 27058220
Fax +32 27056653

Grenada

HE Mr Stephen FLETCHER [31]
Ambassador Extraordinary and Plenipotentiary
Head of the Mission of Grenada to the European Communities
Rue de Laeken 123
B-1000 Brussels
Tel. +32 22237298
Fax +32 22237307

([30]) Accreditation in progress.
([31]) Accreditation in progress.

Guinea

Ahmed Tidiane SAKHO
Ambassador Extraordinary and Plenipotentiary
Head of the Mission of the Republic of Guinea to the European Communities
Boulevard Auguste Reyers 108
B-1030 Brussels
Tel. +32 27710126
Fax +32 27626036

Guinea-Bissau

HE Mr Henrique Adriano DA SILVA
Ambassador Extraordinary and Plenipotentiary
Mission of the Republic of Guinea-Bissau to the European Communities
Avenue F.D. Roosevelt 70
B-1050 Brussels
Tel. +32 22905181
Fax +32 22905156

Guyana

HE Mr Patrick Ignatius GOMES
Ambassador Extraordinary and Plenipotentiary
Head of the Mission of the cooperative Republic of Guyana to the European Communities
Avenue du Brésil 12
B-1000 Brussels
Tel. +32 26756216, 26756312
Fax +32 26756331

Haïti

HE Mr Raymond LAFONTANT [32]
Ambassador Extraordinary and Plenipotentiary
Head of the Mission of the Republic of Haiti to the European Communities
Chaussée de Charleroi 139
B-1060 Brussels
Tel. +32 26497381, 26496247
Fax +32 26406080

Independent State of Samoa

HE Mr Tuala Falani CHAN TUNG
Ambassador Extraordinary and Plenipotentiary
Head of the Mission of the Independent State of Samoa to the European Communities
Avenue de l'Orée 20
B-1000 Brussels
Tel. +32 26608454
Fax +32 26750336

Jamaica

HE Mrs Marcia Yvette GILBERT-ROBERTS
Ambassador Extraordinary and Plenipotentiary
Head of the Mission of Jamaica to the European Communities
Avenue Hansen-Soulie 77B
B-1040 Brussels
Tel. +32 22301170
Fax +32 22346969

([32]) Accreditation in progress.

Kenya

HE Mr Marx Gad NJUGUNA KAHENDE [33]
Ambassador Extraordinary and Plenipotentiary
Head of the Mission of the Republic of Kenya to the European Communities
Avenue Winston Churchill 208
B-1180 Brussels
Tel. +32 23401040
Fax +32 23401050, 26881551

Kingdom of Lesotho

HE Mrs Mamoruti TIHELI
Ambassador Extraordinary and Plenipotentiary
Head of the Mission of the Kingdom of Lesotho to the European Communities
Boulevard Général Wahis 45
B-1030 Brussels
Belgique
Tel. +32 27053976
Fax +32 27056779

Liberia

HE Ms Youngor Sevelee TELEWODA
Ambassador Extraordinary and Plenipotentiary
Mission of the Republic of Liberia to the European Communities
Avenue du Château 50
B-1081 Brussels
Tel. +32 24110112
Fax +32 24110912

Madagascar

HE Mr Jeannot RAKOTOMALALA
Ambassador Extraordinary and Plenipotentiary
Head of the Mission of the Democratic Republic of Madagascar to the European Communities
Avenue de Tervuren 276
B-1150 Brussels
Tel. +32 27701726
Fax +32 27723731

Malawi

HE Ms Brave Rona NDISALE
Ambassador Extraordinary and Plenipotentiary
Head of the Mission of the Republic of Malawi to the European Communities
Avenue Hermann-Debroux 46
B-1160 Brussels
Tel. +32 22310980
Fax +32 22311066

Mali

HE Mr Ibraham Bocar BA
Ambassador Extraordinary and Plenipotentiary
Head of the Mission of the Republic of Mali to the European Communities
Avenue Molière 487
B-1050 Brussels
Tel. +32 23457432, 23457589
Fax +32 23445700

[33] Accreditation in progress.

Marshall Islands

c/o Permanent Representative of the Republic of the Marshall Island to the United Nations
800 Second Avenue, 18th floor
N.Y. 10017 New York
Tel. +1 212983-3040
Fax +1 212983-3202

Mauritania

HE Mr Moulaye OULD MOHAMED LAGHDAF
Ambassador Extraordinary and Plenipotentiary
Head of the Mission of the Islamic Republic of Mauritania to the European Communities
Avenue de la Colombie 6
B-1000 Brussels
Tel. +32 26724747, 26721802
Fax +32 26722051

Mauritius

HE Mr Sutiawan GUNESSEE
Ambassador Extraordinary and Plenipotentiary
Head of the Mission of Mauritius to the European Communities
Rue des Bollandistes 68
B-1040 Brussels
Tel. +32 27339988, 27339989
Fax +32 27344021

Mozambique

HE Mrs Maria Manuela DOS SANTOS LUCAS
Ambassador Extraordinary and Plenipotentiary
Head of the Mission of the Republic of Mozambique to the European Communities
Boulevard Saint-Michel 97
B-1040 Brussels
Tel. +32 27362564
Fax +32 27320664

Namibia

HE Mr Hanno Burkhard RUMPF
Ambassador Extraordinary and Plenipotentiary
Head of the Mission of the Republic of Namibia to the European Communities
Avenue de Tervuren 454
B-1150 Brussels
Tel. +32 227711410
Fax +32 227719689

Nauru

c/o Permanent Representative of the Republic of Nauru to the United Nations
800 Second Avenue, Suite 400D
N.Y.10017 New York
Tel. +1 212937-0074
Fax +1 212937-0079

Niger

HE Mr Abdou ABARRY
Ambassador Extraordinary and Plenipotentiary
Head of the Mission of the Republic of Niger to the European Communities
Avenue F. D. Roosevelt 78
B-1050 Brussels
Tel. +32 26485960
Fax +32 26487958

Nigeria

HE Mr Usman Alhaji BARAYA
Ambassador Extraordinary and Plenipotentiary
Head of the Mission of the Federal Republic of Nigeria to the European Communities
Avenue de Tervuren 288
B-1150 Brussels
Tel. +32 27629831, 27629832
Fax +32 27623763

Niue

HE Mr Todd McCLAY
Ambassador Extraordinary and Plenipotentiary
Head of the Mission of the Republic of Niue to the European Communities
Rue Berckmans 10
B-1060 Brussels
Tel. +32 25341000
Fax +32 25341001

Papua New Guinea

HE Mr Peter Pulkiye MAGINDE [34]
Ambassador Extraordinary and Plenipotentiary
Head of the Mission of the Independent State of Papua New Guinea to the European Communities
Avenue de Tervuren 430
B-1150 Brussels
Tel. +32 27790609
Fax +32 27727088

Republic of Fiji Island

HE Mr Ratu Seremaia Tuinausori CAVUILATI
Ambassador Extraordinary and Plenipotentiary
Head of the Mission of Fiji to the European Communities
Square Plasky, 92-94, 5th floor
B-1030 Brussels
Tel. +32 27369050
Fax +32 27361458

Republic of Kiribati

HE Mr Teburo TITO
Chief Minister
Ministry of Foreign Affairs
PO Box 68
Bairiki Tarawa
Republic of Kiribati
Fax +686 21466
Telex FORMIN TARAWA

Republic of Palau

PO Box No 100
Koror
Republic of Palau

Republic of Seychelles

HE Mr Barry FAURE
Ambassador Extraordinary and Plenipotentiary
Head of the Mission of the Republic of Seychelles to the European Communities
Boulevard Saint Michel, 28 Bte 5
B-1040 Brussels
Tel. +32 27336055
Fax +32 27326022

[34] Accreditation in progress.

Republic of Sierra Leone

HE Mr Christian Sheka KARGBO
Ambassador Extraordinary and Plenipotentiary
Head of the Mission of the Republic of Sierra Leone to the European Communities
Avenue de Tervuren 410
B-1150 Brussels
Tel. +32 27710053
Fax +32 27718230

Republic of South Africa

HE Mr Anil SOOKLAL
Ambassador Extraordinary and Plenipotentiary
Head of the Mission of the Republic of South Africa to the European Communities
Rue Montoyer 17-19B
B-1000 Brussels
Tel. +32 22854400
Fax +32 22854402

Republic of Sudan

HE Mr Najeib EL Kheir Abdel WAHAB
Ambassador Extraordinary and Plenipotentiary
Head of the Mission of the Republic of Sudan to the European Communities
Avenue F. D. Roosevelt 124
B-1050 Brussels
Tel. +32 26479494, 26475159
Fax +32 26483499

Republic of Trinidad and Tobago

HE Mr Gerald THOMPSON (35)
Ambassador Extraordinary and Plenipotentiary
Head of the Mission of the Republic of Trinidad and Tobago to the European Communities
Avenue de la Faisanderie 14
B-1150 Brussels
Tel. +32 27629415, 27629400
Fax +32 27722783

Rwanda

HE Mr Joseph BONESHA
Ambassador Extraordinary and Plenipotentiary
Head of the Mission of the Republic of Rwanda to the European Communities
Avenue des Fleurs 1
B-1150 Brussels
Tel. +32 27630721, 27630702, 27630705
Fax +32 27630753

Saint Kitts and Nevis

HE Mrs Shirley SKERRIT-ANDREW (36)
Ambassador Extraordinary and Plenipotentiary
Head of the Mission of Saint Kitts and Nevis to the European Communities
Rue de Livourne 42
B-1000 Brussels
Tel. +32 25342611, 25441802
Fax +32 25394009

(35) Accreditation in progress.
(36) Accreditation in progress.
(37) Accreditation in progress.

Saint Lucia

HE Mrs Shirley SKERRIT-ANDREW (37)
Ambassador Extraordinary and Plenipotentiary
Head of the Mission of Saint Lucia to the European Communities
Rue de Livourne 42
B-1000 Brussels
Tel. +32 25342611, 25441802
Fax +32 25394009

Saint Vincent and the Grenadines

HE Mrs Shirley SKERRIT-ANDREW (38)
Ambassador Extraordinary and Plenipotentiary
Head of the Mission of Saint Vincent and the Grenadines to the European Communities
Rue de Livourne 42
B-1000 Brussels
Tel. +32 25342611, 25441802
Fax +32 25394009

São Tomé and Príncipe

Carlos Gustavo DOS ANJOS (39)
Ambassador
Head of the Mission of the Democratic Republic of São Tomé and Príncipe to the European Communities
Avenue de Tervuren 175
B-1150 Brussels
Tel. +32 27348966
Fax +32 27348815

Secretariat of ACP

HE Sir John R. KAPUTIN
Secretary-General of the African, Caribbean and Pacific Group of States
Avenue Georges-Henri 451
B-1200 Brussels
Tel. +32 27430600
Fax +32 27355573

Senegal

HE Mr ...
Ambassador Extraordinary and Plenipotentiary
Head of the Mission of the Republic of Senegal to the European Communities
Avenue F. D. Roosevelt 196
B-1050 Brussels
Tel. +32 26730097
Fax +32 26750460

Solomon Islands

HE Mr Joseph MA'AHANUA
Ambassador Extraordinary and Plenipotentary
Head of the Mission of the Solomon Islands to the European Communities
Avenue Edouard Lacomble 17
B-1040 Brussels
Tel. +32 27327085
Fax +32 27326885

Somalia

p.m.
Mission of the Somali Democratic Republic to the European Communities

(38) Accreditation in progress.
(39) Accreditation in progress.

Suriname

HE Mr Gerard Otmar HIWAT
Ambassador Extraordinary and Plenipotentiary
Head of the Mission of the Republic of Suriname to the European Communities
Avenue Louise 379, boîte 20
B-1050 Brussels
Tel. +32 26401172
Fax +32 26463962

Swaziland

HE Mr Solomon Mnukwa DLAMINI
Ambassador Extraordinary and Plenipotentiary
Head of the Mission of the Kingdom of Swaziland to the European Communities
Avenue Winston Churchill 188
B-1180 Brussels
Tel. +32 23474771
Fax +32 23474623

Tanzania

HE Mr Simon Uforosia Ralph MLAY
Ambassador Extraordinary and Plenipotentiary
Head of the Mission of the United Republic of Tanzania to the European Communities
Avenue F.D. Roosevelt 72
B-1050 Brussels
Tel. +32 26406500
Fax +32 26468026

Togo

HE Mr Félix Kodjo SAGBO
Ambassador Extraordinary and Plenipotentiary
Head of the Mission of the Togolese Republic to the European Communities
Avenue de Tervuren 264
B-1150 Brussels
Tel. +32 27701791, 27705563
Fax +32 27715075

Tonga

HE Mr Sione Ngongo KIOA
Ambassador Extraordinary and Plenipotentiary
Head of the Mission of the Kingdom of Tonga to the European Communities
36 Molyneux street
London W1H 6AB
United Kingdom
Tel. +44 2077245828
Fax +44 2077239074

Tuvalu

HE Mr Panapasi NELESONE
Head of the Mission of Tuvalu to the European Union
Suva
Fiji
Tel. +679 301023
Fax +679 308479

Republic of Uganda

HE Mr Stephen Tinkasimire Kapimpina KATENTA-APULI
Ambassador Extraordinary and Plenipotentiary
Head of the Mission of the Republic of Uganda to the European Communities
Avenue de Tervuren 317
B-1150 Brussels
Tel. +32 27625825
Fax +32 27630438

Vanuatu

HE Mr Roy Mickey JOY
Ambassador Extraordinary and Plenipotentiary
Head of the Mission of the Republic of Vanuatu to the European Communities
Avenue de Tervuren 380 — Chemin de Ronde
B-1150 Brussels
Tel. +32 27717494
Fax +32 27717494

Zambia

HE Mr Muyambo SIPANGULE
Ambassador Extraordinary and Plenipotentiary
Head of the Mission of the Republic of Zambia to the European Communities
Avenue Molière 469
B-1050 Brussels
Tel. +32 23435649
Fax +32 23474333

Zimbabwe

HE Mr Gift PUNUNGWE
Ambassador Extraordinary and Plenipotentiary
Head of the Mission of the Republic of Zimbabwe to the European Communities
Square Josephine Charlotte 11
B-1200 Brussels
Tel. +32 27625808
Fax +32 27629605

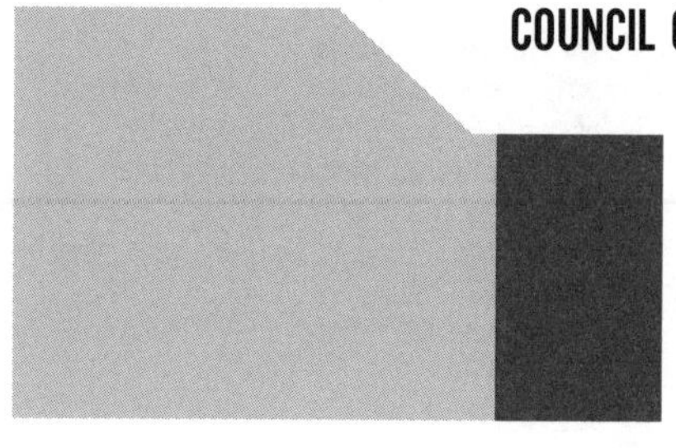

Committee of Senior Officials on Scientific and Technical Research (COST)

The Committee of Senior Officials is currently composed of representatives of 35 States [40].

The tasks of the Committee are to prepare the general strategy of COST cooperation, to select and prepare the various projects and elaborate the agreements relating to them. It is also responsible for managing the COST fund, appointing project coordinators and experts and setting up subcommittees.

It is composed of representatives of each participating State and of representatives of the Commission of the European Communities. Its secretariat is provided by the General Secretariat of the Council, which also provides the secretariat for the horizontal subcommittees, and in particular for the Working Party on Legal, Administrative and Financial Questions (JAF Working Party).

President

Prof. Dr. Francesco FEDI
Via Paolo Bentivoglio 29 B
I-00165 Rome
E-mail: francesco.fedi@tiscali.it
Tel. +39 0639387241
Fax +39 0639389651

Vice-President

Mr John BARTZIS
University of West Macedonia
Department of Engineering and Management of Energy Resources
Sialvera and Bakola Str.
EL-50100
E-mail: bartzis@uowm.gr
Tel. +30 2461056620
Fax +30 2461021730

COST Secretariat

General Secretariat of the Council of the European Union
Rue de la Loi 175
B-1048 Brussels
E-mail: cost@consilium.europa.eu
Tel. +32 22816896
Fax +32 22818551

Mr Kimmo PEIPPO
Tel. +32 22817363

Mrs Ulla MESIÄ
Tel. +32 22817914

[40] Austria, Belgium, Bulgaria, Croatia, Cyprus, Czech Republic, Denmark, Estonia, Finland, France, Germany, Greece, Hungary, Iceland, Ireland, Italy, Latvia, Lithuania, Luxembourg, Former Yugoslav Republic of Macedonia, Malta, Netherlands, Norway, Poland, Portugal, Romania, Serbia, Slovakia, Slovenia, Spain, Sweden, Switzerland, Turkey, United Kingdom and Israel as a cooperating State.

Community institutions, bodies and agencies

EUROPEAN COMMISSION

EUROPEAN COMMISSION

The Commission

B-1049 Brussels
Website: http://europa.eu/
Tel. +32 229-91111 (operator)
Fax +32 229 + extension

Cabinet of the President, José Manuel Barroso

José Manuel BARROSO
President
Tel. +32 229-88150, 88152

João VALE DE ALMEIDA
Head of Cabinet
Tel. +32 229-65664

Jean-Claude THEBAULT
Deputy Head of Cabinet
Tel. +32 229-50169, 92894

Sabine WEYAND
Expert attached to the Office
Tel. +32 229-60143

Cabinet of Margot Wallström — Institutional Relations and Communication Strategy

Margot WALLSTRÖM
Vice-President
Tel. +32 229-81800, 20568

Christian LEFFLER
Head of Cabinet
Tel. +32 229-50502, 86435

Patrick COSTELLO
Deputy Head of Cabinet
Tel. +32 229-99529

Cabinet of Günter Verheugen — Enterprise and Industry

Günter VERHEUGEN
Vice-President
Tel. +32 229-81100, 93869

Petra ERLER
Head of Cabinet
Tel. +32 229-81109

Simon MORDUE
Deputy Head of Cabinet
Tel. +32 229-84970, 81116

Cabinet of Jacques Barrot — Transport

Jacques BARROT
Vice-President
Tel. +32 229-81500, 81506

Kerstin JORNA
Head of Cabinet
Tel. +32 229-61326, 20832

Laurent MUSCHEL
Deputy Head of Cabinet
Tel. +32 229-94708, 65636

Cabinet of Siim Kallas — Administrative Affairs, Audit and Anti-Fraud

Siim KALLAS
Vice-President
Tel. +32 229-88762, 88763

Henrik HOLOLEI
Head of Cabinet
Tel. +32 229-88764, 88765

Kristian SCHMIDT
Deputy Head of Cabinet
Tel. +32 229-88769, 88768

Cabinet of Antonio Tajani — Transport

Antonio TAJANI
Vice-President
Tel. +32 229-57564, 57650

Antonio PRETO
Head of Cabinet
Tel. +32 229-81973

Diego CANGA FANO
Deputy Head of Cabinet
Tel. +32 229-57252

Cabinet of Viviane Reding — Information Society and the Media

Viviane REDING
Member of the Commission
Tel. +32 229-81600, 58992

Rudolf STROHMEIER
Head of Cabinet
Tel. +32 229-62341, 81092

Viviane HOFFMANN
Deputy Head of Cabinet
Tel. +32 229-60305, 56734

Cabinet of Stavros Dimas — Environment

Stavros DIMAS
Member of the Commission
Tel. +32 229-82000, 82001

Nancy KONTOU
Head of Cabinet
Tel. +32 229-61989, 82003

John QUINN
Deputy Head of Cabinet
Tel. +32 229-54706

Cabinet of Joaquín Almunia — Economic and Monetary Affairs

Joaquín ALMUNIA
Member of the Commission
Tel. +32 229-80900, 80901

Gerassimos THOMAS
Head of Cabinet
Tel. +32 229-93442, 80903

Antoine QUERO MUSSOT
Deputy Head of Cabinet
Tel. +32 229-69438, 21138

Cabinet of Danuta Hübner — Regional Policy

Danuta HÜBNER
Member of the Commission
Tel. +32 229-88625, 88626

Marc LEMAÎTRE
Head of Cabinet
Tel. +32 229-90902, 59993

Marta CYGAN
Deputy Head of Cabinet
Tel. +32 229-59927, 98438

Cabinet of Joe Borg — Fisheries and Maritime Affairs

Joe BORG
Member of the Commission
Tel. +32 229-88685, 88688

Michael KOEHLER
Head of Cabinet
Tel. +32 229-90753, 62549

Johanna DARMANIN
Deputy Head of Cabinet
Tel. +32 229-88689

Cabinet of Dalia Grybauskaitė — Financial Programming and Budget

Dalia GRYBAUSKAITĖ
Member of the Commission
Tel. +32 229-88731, 80191

Stephen QUEST
Head of Cabinet
Tel. +32 229-65897

Lina ADAKAUSKIENE
Deputy Head of Cabinet
Tel. +32 229-20737, 55211

Cabinet of Janez Potočnik — Science and Research

Janez POTOČNIK
Member of the Commission
Tel. +32 229-88670, 88671

Kurt VANDENBERGHE
Head of Cabinet
Tel. +32 229-69207, 63601

Waldemar KUETT
Deputy Head of Cabinet
Tel. +32 229-94145

Cabinet of Ján Figel — Education, Training and Culture

Ján FIGEĽ
Member of the Commission
Tel. +32 229-88716, 88719

Miroslav ADAMIS
Head of Cabinet
Tel. +32 229-20836, 86574

Margarida GAMEIRO
Deputy Head of Cabinet
Tel. +32 229-65862, 57834

Cabinet of Markos Kyprianou — Health

Androulla VASSILIOU
Member of the Commission
Tel. +32 229-88700, 20806

Philippe BRUNET
Head of Cabinet
Tel. +32 229-54128

Despina SPANOU
Deputy Head of Cabinet
Tel. +32 229-20807

Cabinet of Olli Rehn — Enlargement

Olli REHN
Member of the Commission
Tel. +32 229-57957, 51440

Timo PESONEN
Head of Cabinet
Tel. +32 229-57995, 60637

Myriam FERRAN-VERGER
Deputy Head of Cabinet
Tel. +32 229-69119, 62825

Cabinet of Louis Michel — Development and Humanitarian Aid

Louis MICHEL
Member of the Commission
Tel. +32 229-59600, 65159

Koen DOENS
Head of Cabinet
Tel. +32 229-63684

Hervé DELPHIN
Deputy Head of Cabinet
Tel. +32 229-51820

Cabinet of László Kovács — Taxation and Customs Union

László KOVÁCS
Member of the Commission
Tel. +32 229-88400, 87862

Stephen BILL
Head of Cabinet
Tel. +32 229-57883, 95752

Anabela GAGO
Deputy Head of Cabinet
Tel. +32 229-61022, 68806

Cabinet of Neelie Kroes — Competition

Neelie KROES
Member of the Commission
Tel. +32 229-92400, 84977

Anthony WHELAN
Head of Cabinet
Tel. +32 229-50941, 64029

Lorena BOIX ALONSO
Deputy Head of Cabinet
Tel. +32 229-90009

Cabinet of Mariann Fischer Boel — Agriculture and Rural Development

Mariann FISCHER BOEL
Member of the Commission
Tel. +32 229-93400, 87874

Poul-Skytte CHRISTOFFERSEN
Head of Cabinet
Tel. +32 229-63532, 66889

Klaus-Dieter BORCHARDT
Deputy Head of Cabinet
Tel. +32 229-94011, 51377

Cabinet of Benita Ferrero-Waldner — External Relations and European Neighbourhood Policy

Benita FERRERO-WALDNER
Member of the Commission
Tel. +32 229-94900, 93220

Patrick CHILD
Head of Cabinet
Tel. +32 229-69750, 96966

Vincent GUEREND
Deputy Head of Cabinet
Tel. +32 229-59631, 50397

Cabinet of Charlie McCreevy — Internal Market and Services

Charlie McCREEVY
Member of the Commission
Tel. +32 229-88040, 67126

Martin POWER
Head of Cabinet
Tel. +32 229-55436

Nathalie DE BASALDUA LEMARCHAND
Deputy Head of Cabinet
Tel. +32 229-56189, 54564

Cabinet of Vladimir Špidla — Employment, Social Affairs and Equal Opportunities

Vladimír ŠPIDLA
Member of the Commission
Tel. +32 229-88530, 81729

Kristin SCHREIBER
Head of Cabinet
Tel. +32 229-65823, 80717

Stéphane OUAKI
Deputy Head of Cabinet
Tel. +32 229-67286, 50446

Cabinet of Baroness Catherine Ashton — Trade

Catherine ASHTON
Member of the Commission
Tel. +32 229-88590, 57693

Julian KING
Head of Cabinet
Tel. +32 229-68621, 69202

Éric PETERS
Deputy Head of Cabinet
Tel. +32 229-51873, 86999

Cabinet of Andris Piebalgs — Energy

Andris PIEBALGS
Member of the Commission
Tel. +32 229-88747, 80507

Andris KESTERIS
Head of Cabinet
Tel. +32 229-21318

Stina SOEWARTA
Deputy Head of Cabinet
Tel. +32 229-91940, 62613

Cabinet of Meglena Kuneva — Consumer Protection

Meglena KUNEVA
Member of the Commission
Tel. +32 229-93384, 93684

John BELL
Head of Cabinet
Tel. +32 229-91940, 62613

Kristian HEDBERG
Deputy Head of Cabinet
Tel. +32 229-55164, 94958

Cabinet of Leonard Orban — Multilingualism

Leonard ORBAN
Member of the Commission
Tel. +32 229-94624, 94705

Patricia BUGNOT
Head of Cabinet
Tel. +32 229-50731, 52832

Jochen RICHTER
Deputy Head of Cabinet
Tel. +32 229-85334, 85335

SECRETARIAT-GENERAL

B-1049 Brussels
Tel. +32 229-91111 (operator)

Bâtiment Jean Monnet
Rue Alcide De Gasperi
L-2920 Luxembourg
Tel. +352 4301-1 (operator)
Tel. +352 4301 + extension

Catherine DAY
Secretary-General
Tel. +32 229-58312, 90725

Hervé JOUANJEAN
Deputy Secretary-General
Tel. +32 229-92210, 61888

Alexander ITALIANER
Deputy Secretary-General
(with particular responsibility for Directorates A, B, C, and G)
Tel. +32 229-94393, 90860

Olivier BAILLY
Assistant to the Director-General
Tel. +32 229-68717, 67021

Elizabeth GOLBERG
Adviser
Tel. +32 229-92021, 84108

Internal audit

Gianluca PECCHI
Head of Unit
Tel. +32 229-98666, 59879

Reporting directly to the Deputy Secretary-General

Mercedes DE SOLA DOMINGO
Chief Adviser
Tel. +32 229-56272

Pedro CYMBRON
Adviser
Tel. +32 229-90117, 60870

Data Protection Office

Philippe RENAUDIERE
Head of Unit
Tel. +32 229-68750, 53488

Protocol service

Jacques DE BAENST
Director
Tel. +32 229-52325, 53359

Directorate R — Resources and General Matters

Gianmarco DI VITA
Director
Tel. +32 229-68846, 68121

1. Programming and resources

Henrik KERSTING
Head of Unit
Tel. +32 229-64900, 69595

2. Mail and document management

Arthur POOLEY
Head of Unit
Tel. +32 229-56806, 87917

3. Information technology

Eric MULLER
Head of Unit
Tel. +32 229-52257, 61196

4. Information and databases

Martine ROZET
Head of Unit
Tel. +32 229-54791, 61320

Directorate A — Registry and Commission Decision-Making Process

Jordi AYET PUIGARNAU
Director
Tel. +32 229-51528, 52449

1. Advice, developments and logistics

François KODECK
Head of Unit
Tel. +32 229-57435, 69522

2. Oral procedures

François GENISSON
Head of Unit
Tel. +32 229-58036

3. Written, empowerment and delegation procedures, external transmission

Karl VON KEMPIS
Head of Unit
Tel. +32 229-68809, 96037

Directorate B — Better Regulation and Administration

Hubert SZLASZEWSKI
Director
Tel. +32 229-95171, 63156

1. Administrative modernisation

Peter HANDLEY
Head of Unit
Tel. +32 229-62430, 62142

2. APC audit

Friedrich BRAEUER
Head of Unit
Tel. +32 229-96070, 55115

3. Crisis management

Emanuela BELLAN
Head of Unit
Tel. +32 229-53134, 52567

4. Public service ethics

Donatienne CLAEYS BOUUAERT
Head of Unit
Tel. +32 229-62659, 61393

Directorate C — Better Regulation, Programming and Impact Assessment

Marianne KLINGBEIL
Director
Tel. +32 229-60493, 90174

José CANDELA CASTILLO
Adviser
Tel. +32 229-52090, 91245

1. Strategic planning and programming

Pascal LEARDINI
Head of Unit
Tel. +32 229-61306, 60401

2. Better regulation and impact assessment

John WATSON
Head of Unit
Tel. +32 229-64166, 52291

Directorate D — Better Regulation and Coordination

Michel SERVOZ
Director
Tel. +32 229-56891, 93675

1. Strategic objective — Prosperity

Gerrit Gerard DE GRAAF
Head of Unit
Tel. +32 229-68466, 59434

2. Strategic objective — Solidarity

Marcel HAAG
Head of Unit
Tel. +32 229-68605, 63832

3. Strategic objective — Security and external responsibility and presidential briefings

Florika FINK-HOOIJER
Head of Unit
Tel. +32 229-64968, 62556

Directorate E — Better Regulation and Institutional Matters

Jens NYMAND CHRISTENSEN
Director
Tel. +32 229-93317, 62598

1. Institutional questions

Mario-Paulo TENREIRO
Head of Unit
Tel. +32 229-51367, 90319

2. Application of Community law

Jonathon STOODLEY
Head of Unit
Tel. +32 229-69335, 62179

3. Transparency, relations with stakeholders and external organisations

Gerard LEGRIS
Head of Unit
Tel. +32 229-99406, 85156

Directorate F — Relations with the Council

Gustaaf BORCHARDT
Director
Tel. +32 229-66583, 66670

1. Coreper I

Maria-Christina RUSSO
Head of Unit
Tel. +32 229-55975, 62714

2. Coreper II — G7/G8

Joost KORTE
Head of Unit
Tel. +32 229-65900

3. Co-decision

Una O'DWYER
Head of Unit
Tel. +32 229-60956, 87210

Directorate G — Relations with the European Parliament, the European Ombudsman, the European Economic and Social Committee, the Committee of the Regions and National Parliaments

Fernando FRUTUOSO MELO
Director
Tel. +32 229-93145, 51013

1. Coordination — European Parliament internal policies

Lars MITEK PEDERSEN
Head of Unit
Tel. +32 229-54924

2. Coordination — European Parliament external policies

Ewa SZYMANSKA
Head of Unit
Tel. +32 229-60513, 84616

3. European Economic and Social Committee, Committee of the Regions, European Ombudsman and national parliaments

Panayotis ANASTOPOULOS
Head of Unit
Tel. +32 229-58141, 99089

Principal Adviser Institutional Questions

Paolo PONZANO
Chief Adviser
Tel. +32 229-51934, 98744

LEGAL SERVICE

B-1049 Brussels
Tel. +32 229-91111 (operator)
+32 229 + extension

Claire-Françoise DURAND
Director-General
Tel. +32 229-51192, 59168

Francisco SANTAOLALLA GADEA
Deputy Director-General (acting)
Tel. +32 229-61956, 51399

William O'LEARY
Assistant to the Director-General
Tel. +32 229-66221, 52934

Paolo STANCANELLI
Assistant to the Director-General
Tel. +32 229-61808, 92704

Directorate CJ– Legal Advisers

Principal Legal Advisers

Bevis CLARKE-SMITH
Principal Legal Adviser
Tel. +32 229-52828, 53462

Frank BENYON
Principal Legal Adviser
Tel. +32 229-58241, 65788

Thomas VAN RIJN
Principal Legal Adviser
Tel. +32 229-51818, 59864

Francisco SANTAOLALLA GADEA
Principal Legal Adviser
Tel. +32 229-956, 51399

Jürgen GRUNWALD
Principal Legal Adviser
Tel. +32 229-58263, 58991

Theofanis CHRISTOFOROU
Principal Legal Adviser
Tel. +32 229-50168, 51904

Hans HARTVIG
Principal Legal Adviser
Tel. +32 229-51065, 69500

Eugenio DE MARCH
Principal Legal Adviser
Tel. +32 229-56368, 59710

Eva KRUZIKOVA
Principal Legal Adviser
Tel. +32 229-90785, 52831

Patrick HETSCH
Principal Legal Adviser
Tel. +32 229-51151, 50887

Marc VAN HOOF
Principal Legal Adviser
Tel. +32 229-50625, 68315

Bernardus SMULDERS
Principal Legal Adviser
Tel. +32 229-55299, 96090

Ulrich WOELKER
Principal Legal Adviser
Tel. +32 229-62268, 52831

Alain VAN SOLINGE
Principal Legal Adviser (acting)
Tel. +32 229-55854, 60068

Éric WHITE
Principal Legal Adviser (acting)
Tel. +32 229-54856, 66908

Enrico TRAVERSA
Principal Legal Adviser (acting)
Tel. +32 229-55921, 65788

Legal Advisers

Hans CROSSLAND
Legal Adviser
Tel. +32 229-55746, 85090

Enrico TRAVERSA
Legal Adviser
Tel. +32 229-55921, 65788

Peter OLIVER
Legal Adviser
Tel. +32 229-66339, 54975

Karen BANKS
Legal Adviser
Tel. +32 229-52824

Michel NOLIN
Legal Adviser
Tel. +32 229-55094, 85237

Richard LYAL
Legal Adviser
Tel. +32 229-54814, 58991

Vittorio DI BUCCI
Legal Adviser
Tel. +32 22729-57900, 53684

Julian CURRALL
Legal Adviser
Tel. +32 229-57900, 53684

Mary Carmel O'REILLY
Legal Adviser
Tel. +32 229-66067, 91554

Christopher DOCKSEY
Legal Adviser
Tel. +32 229-55717, 91554

Dominique MAIDANI
Legal Adviser
Tel. +32 229-94913, 65653

Maria CONDOU
Legal Adviser
Tel. +32 229-58342

Anne-Marie ROUCHAUD-JOET
Legal Adviser
Tel. +32 229-58501, 92983

Pieter VAN NUFFEL
Legal Adviser
Tel. +32 229-50029, 50887

Elsa Christina TUFVESSON
Legal Adviser
Tel. +32 229-59203, 66908

Gérard ROZET
Legal Adviser
Tel. +32 229-57218, 67847

Viktor KREUSCHITZ
Legal Adviser
Tel. +32 229-95369, 56289

Raimund RAITH
Legal Adviser
Tel. +32 229-93095, 67875

Éric WHITE
Legal Adviser
Tel. +32 229-54856, 66908

Members of the Legal Service

Paul LAFILI
Adviser (ad personam)
Tel. +32 229-52364

Legal Revisers Group

Paul LAFILI
Head of the Legal Revisers Group
Tel. +32 229-52364, 67007

COMMUNICATION DG

Rue de la Loi 200
B-1040 Brussels
Tel. +32 229-91111 (operator)

Claus SØRENSEN
Director-General
Tel. +32 229-86644, 66432

Reporting directly to the Director-General

Dimitri BARUA
Assistant to the Director-General
Tel. +32 229-98821, 53984

Panayotis CARVOUNIS
Deputy Director-General
Tel. +32 229-52173, 95693

Audit

Edwin CROONEN
Head of Unit
Tel. +32 229-61867, 53799

Spokespersons' Service

Johannes LAITENBERGER
Director
Tel. +32 229-65745, 56798

Spokespersons' coordination and planning

Pia AHRENKILDE HANSEN
Head of Unit
Tel. +32 229-53070, 86659

Spokespersons' group

...

Directorate A — Strategy

Tamás SZŰCS
Director
Tel. +32 229-88656, 50427

Marios CAMHIS
Adviser
Tel. +32 229-56882

1. General matters and Interinstitutional relations

Marc JORNA
Head of Unit
Tel. +32 229-63380, 91640

2. Communication: Projects and strategies

Alain DUMORT
Head of Unit
Tel. +32 229-53849, 99003

3. Communication: Research and political analysis

Antonis PAPACOSTAS
Head of Unit
Tel. +32 229-59967, 90327

Directorate B — Representations

Lieve FRANSEN
Director
Tel. +32 229-63698, 60159

Karl DOUTLIK
Adviser
Tel. +32 229-81472

1. Geographical coordination

Georgios MARKOPOULIOTIS
Head of Unit
Tel. +32 229-92974, 94909

2. Thematic support

Paavo PALK
Head of Unit
Tel. +32 229-85153

Athens — Representation in Greece

Ierotheos PAPADOPOULOS
Head of representation
Tel. *80600

Berlin — Representation in Germany

Dietlind JERING
Head of Representation (acting)
Tel. *80601

Bratislava — Representation in Slovakia

Andrea MATISOVA
Head of representation
Tel. *80951

Brussels — Representation in Belgium

Willy HELIN
Head of representation
Tel. +32 229-84228, 58356

Bucharest — Representation in Romania

Niculae IDU
Head of representation
Tel. *80875

Budapest — Representation in Hungary

Gábor GYÖRGY
Head of representation
Tel. *80388

Copenhagen — Representation in Denmark

Jan SCHMIDT
Head of representation
Tel. *80604

Dublin — Representation in Ireland

Martin TERRITT
Head of representation
Tel. *80605

Helsinki — Representation in Finland

Eikka KOSONEN
Head of representation
Tel. *80809

The Hague — Representation in the Netherlands

Ludolf VAN HASSELT
Head of representation
Tel. *80608

Valetta — Representation in Malta

Joanna DRAKE
Head of representation
Tel. *81947200

Lisbon — Representation in Portugal

Margarida MARQUES
Head of representation
Tel. *80699

Ljubljana — Representation in Slovenia

Mihaela ZUPANCIC
Head of representation
Tel. *80894

London — Representation in the United Kingdom

Sarah LAMBERT
Head of Representation (acting)
Tel. *806091921

Luxembourg — Representation in Luxembourg

Ernst MOUTSCHEN
Head of representation
Tel. +352 4301-32925, 34925

Madrid — Representation in Spain

José GONZALEZ VALLVE
Head of representation
Tel. *80700

Nicosia — Representation in Cyprus

Androulla KAMINARA
Head of representation
Tel. *80418

Paris — Representation in France

Yves GAZZO
Head of representation
Tel. *80612

Marseille — Regional office in France

Blandine PELLISTRANDI
Head of representation
Tel. *80467

Prague — Representation in the Czech Republic

Irena MOOZOVA
Head of representation
Tel. *80563

Riga — Representation in Latvia

Iveta SULCA
Head of representation
Tel. *81209

Rome — Representation in Italy

Pier Virgilio DASTOLI
Head of representation
Tel. *80950

Sofia — Representation in Bulgaria

Zinaida ZLATANOVA
Head of representation
Tel. *80566

Stockholm — Representation in Sweden

Tallinn — Representation in Estonia

Toivo KLAAR
Head of representation
Tel. *81182

Warsaw — Representation in Poland

Roza THUN UND HOHENSTEIN, GRAEFIN VON
Head of representation
Tel. *80567

Vienna — Representation in Austria

Richard KUEHNEL
Head of representation
Tel. +32 229-59456, 81716

Vilnius — Representation in Lithuania

Kestutis SADAUSKAS
Head of representation
Tel. *81189

Directorate C — Multimedia Communication

Ylva TIVEUS
Director
Tel. +32 229-66673, 69347

Thierry VISSOL
Adviser
Tel. +32 229-94418, 95448

1. Audiovisual Service

Fabrizia DE ROSA
Head of Unit
Tel. +32 229-93739, 99426

2. Web and contact centre

Bruno FETELIAN
Head of Unit
Tel. +32 229-67255

3. Editorial content and support

Stefaan DE RYNCK
Head of Unit
Tel. +32 229-63421

Directorate D — Resources

Jean-Pierre VANDERSTEEN
Director
Tel. +32 229-86170, 69584

1. Planning and budget

Benoît WORINGER
Head of Unit
Tel. +32 229-63498, 63501

2. Management and human resources

Bernard CAISSO
Head of Unit
Tel. +32 229-57659

3. Finance and infrastructure

Giuseppe MENCHI
Head of Unit
Tel. +32 229-61193, 92640

4. Control and evaluation

Jean-Jacques CHAMLA
Head of Unit
Tel. +32 229-57823, 81206

5. Information technology

José TORCATO
Head of Unit
Tel. +32 229-63537, 90798

BUREAU OF EUROPEAN POLICY ADVISERS

Rue de la Loi 200
B-1040 Brussels

Vitor GASPAR
Director
Tel. +32 229-66388, 96264

Vitor GASPAR
Director-General (acting)
Tel. +32 229-66388, 96264

Tassos BELESSIOTIS
Adviser
Tel. +32 229-93410

Ana MELICH JUSTE
Adviser
Tel. +32 229-99172, 57118

Agnes HUBERT
Adviser
Tel. +32 229-58889, 57118

Jorge CESAR DAS NEVES
Adviser
Tel. +32 229-64248

Thierry BECHET
Adviser
Tel. +32 229-95381

Peter DUN
Adviser
Tel. +32 229-53881

Jozef KONINGS
Adviser
Tel. +32 229-86833

Coordination

Paola COLOMBO
Head of Unit
Tel. +32 229-90750, 51490

Economic area

Political area

Jonas CONDOMINES BERAUD
Chief Adviser
Tel. +32 229-80065, 55790

Societal area

Maria Da Garca CARVALHO
Chief Adviser
Tel. +32 229-81078

Avenue de Beaulieu 1
B-1160 Brussels
Tel. +32 229-91111 (operator)

Bâtiment Wagner
Rue Alcide De Gasperi
L-2920 Luxembourg

Marco BUTI
Director-General
Tel. +32 262246, 96261

Björn DOEHRING
Assistant to the Director-General
Tel. +32 229-98160

Peter GRASMANN
Head of Unit (seconded)
Tel. +32 229-93417

Jean-Marie MAGNETTE
Head of Unit (seconded)
Tel. +352 4301-36261, 36018

Klaus REGLING
Adviser hors classe
Tel. +32 229-94366, 94360

Reporting directly to the Director-General

Peter BASCH
Chief Adviser
Tel. +352 4301-32514, 36229

Internal audit [1]

Tony MURPHY
Head of Unit
Tel. +352 4301-36113, 35110

BERD (Director responsible for relations with the EBRD)

Vassili LELAKIS
Director (responsible for relations with the EBRD)
Tel. +32 294415, 63553

Directorate EFC.EPC — Secretary of the Economic and Financial Committee and the Economic Policy Committee

Odile RENAUD-BASSO
Director
(Secretary of the Economic and Financial Committee and of the Economic Policy Committee)
Tel. +32 229-94361, 93303

Loukas STEMITSIOTIS
Director (acting)
Tel. +32 229-93366, 93303

1. Coordination of the Secretariat of the EFC and EPC

Stefan PFLUEGER
Head of Unit
Tel. +32 229-93413, 88635

Directorate A — Economic Studies and Research

Istvan Pal SZEKELY
Director
Tel. +32 229-58674, 61273

Marco BUTI
Deputy Director-General
Tel. +32 229-62246, 96261

Karl PICHELMANN
Adviser
Tel. +32 229-93365, 95406

Paul Joseph VAN DEN NOORD
Economic adviser
Tel. +32 229-60074, 61273

Johan BARAS
Economic adviser
Tel. +32 229-91996, 93868

Heikki OKSANEN
Adviser
Tel. +32 229-59326, 93492

Jon Lars JONUNG
Adviser
Tel. +32 229-94562, 51954

Joao NOGUEIRA MARTINS
Adviser
Tel. +32 229-93457

1. Econometric models and medium-term studies

Werner ROEGER
Head of Unit
Tel. +32 229-93362, 65265

2. Economic databases and statistical coordination

Frank SCHÖNBORN
Head of Unit
Tel. +32 229-93358, 91031

3. Business surveys

Gabriele GIUDICE
Head of Unit
Tel. +32 229-63654

4. Forecasts and economic situation

Annika MELANDER
Head of Unit
Tel. +32 229-67158, 85780

5. Economic studies and research

Kristine VLAGSMA
Head of Unit
Tel. +32 229-87328, 81343

Directorate B — Economic Service and Structural Reforms

Gert-Jan KOOPMAN
Director
Tel. +32 229-93381, 71231

1. Coordination of structural reforms and of the economic service

John SHEEHY
Head of Unit (acting)
Tel. +32 229-93399

2. Product market reforms

Fabienne ILZKOVITZ
Head of Unit
Tel. +32 229-93379, 97744

3. Labour market reforms

Giuseppe CARONE
Head of Unit
Tel. +32 229-92295, 60593

4. Reforms under the sustainable development strategy

Nathalie DARNAUT
Head of Unit
Tel. +32 229-66575, 93579

Directorate C — Macroeconomy of the Euro Area and the EU

Servaas DEROOSE
Director
Tel. +32 229-94375, 94424

1. Economy of the euro area and EMU

Reinhard FELKE
Head of Unit
Tel. +32 229-94582

2. Public finances in the euro area and the EU

Lucio PENCH
Head of Unit
Tel. +32 229-93433, 59131

3. Monetary and exchange rate policy of the euro area and the other Member States, ERM II and euro adoption

Massimo SUARDI
Head of Unit
Tel. +32 229-67171, 95360

[1] Unit located in Luxembourg.

4. Macro-financial developments, financial stability and integration

John BERRIGAN
Head of Unit
Tel. +32 229-93580, 58940

5. Euro cash, consumer financial services analysis, EMU legal and institutional questions

Benjamin ANGEL
Head of Unit
Tel. +32 229-69785, 67214

Directorate D — International Economic and Financial Affairs

Antonio DE LECEA FLORES DE LEMUS
Director
Tel. +32 229-61411, 94421

Daniel DACO
Adviser
Tel. *80352

1. Economic affairs within the candidate countries and the Western Balkans, economic policy related to enlargement

José LEANDRO
Head of Unit
Tel. +32 229-95430, 86468

2. Economies of America and Asia, and main international economic institutions and fora

Moreno BERTOLDI
Head of Unit
Tel. +32 229-84702, 66764

3. Economic affairs within the Mediterranean countries, Russia and the newly independent States, economic aspects of neighbourhood policy

Loukas STEMITSIOTIS
Head of Unit
Tel. +32 229-93366, 93303

4. Horizontal issues and coordination of financial assistance, development policy, links with multilateral banks

Carole GARNIER
Head of Unit
Tel. +32 229-94358, 93119

5. International economic aspects of globalisation

Declan COSTELLO
Head of Unit
Tel. +32 229-93375, 65478

Directorate F — Economies of the Member States I

Jürgen KRÖGER
Director
Tel. +32 229-93488, 94399

Mary MCCARTHY
Economic adviser
Tel. +32 229-93493

1. Ireland, Italy, Malta, Slovenia

Charlotte VAN HOOOYDONK
Head of Unit
Tel. +32 229-69607

2. Denmark, Germany, Finland, Austria, Sweden

Georg BUSCH
Head of Unit
Tel. +32 229-94355, 54636

3. Bulgaria, Greece, Spain, Cyprus, Portugal

Carlos MARTINEZ-MONGAY
Head of Unit
Tel. +32 229-61228, 62851

4. Coordination of country-specific policy surveillance

Peter WEISS
Head of Unit
Tel. +32 229-54350, 58466

Directorate G — Economies of the Member States II

Elena FLORES GUAL
Director
Tel. +32 229-93461, 86495

1. Estonia, Latvia, Lithuania, United Kingdom

José ROBLEDO FRAGA
Head of Unit
Tel. +32 229-56664, 93407

2. Belgium, France, Luxembourg, Hungary, Netherlands

Barbara KAUFFMANN
Head of Unit
Tel. +32 229-93489

3. Czech Republic, Poland, Romania, Slovakia

Filip KEEREMAN
Head of Unit
Tel. +32 229-93490, 53035

Directorate L — Financial Operations, Programme Management and Liaison with the EIB Group

1. Liaison with the EIB group and new financial instruments

Giorgio CHIARION CASONI
Head of Unit (acting)
Tel. +352 4301-36404, 36018

2. EIF programme management

James MC GING
Head of Unit
Tel. +352 4301-36129, 36349

3. Lending and IFI programme management

Javier GARCIA LON
Head of Unit
Tel. +352 4301-36372, 33150

4. Accounting and risk management

Peter REICHEL
Head of Unit
Tel. +352 4301-36443, 36229

5. Liquidity, borrowing and guarantee fund

Herbert BARTH
Head of Unit
Tel. +352 4301-36182, 33716

6. Coordination, planning and legal affairs

Burkhard SCHMIDT
Head of Unit
Tel. +352 4301-36150, 33050

Directorate R — Resources

Linda CORUGEDO STENEBERG
Director
Tel. +32 229-96383, 58622

Christian GHYMERS
Adviser
Tel. +32 229-56227, 63553

Francesco CONTESSO
Adviser
Tel. +32 229-95965

1. Human resources and administration

Joost KUHLMANN
Head of Unit
Tel. +32 229-93348, 59180

2. Financial management and control

Johan VERHAEVEN
Head of Unit
Tel. +32 229-93443, 81202

3. Strategic programming and control, interinstitutional relations

Jean-Pierre RAES
Head of Unit
Tel. +32 229-56056, 58971

4. External communication

Stefan APPEL
Head of Unit (acting)
Tel. +32 229-54596

5. Management of IT resources

Tomasz Jaroslaw PIETRZAK
Head of Unit
Tel. +32 229-94392, 94397

ENTERPRISE AND INDUSTRY DG

Avenue d'Auderghem 45
B-1049 Brussels
Tel. +32 229-91111 (operator)
Fax +32 229-69930

Heinz ZOUREK
Director-General
Tel. +32 229-91604, 58643

Françoise LE BAIL
Deputy Director-General
(responsible for Directorates B and G)
Tel. +32 229-92243, 58063

Stéphane MAIL FOUILLEUL
Assistant to the Director-General
Tel. +32 229-95050, 86518

Claus GIERING
Assistant to the Director-General
Tel. +32 229-60389

Reporting directly to the Director-General

Internal audit

Reinder VAN DER ZEE
Head of Unit
Tel. +32 229-65734, 80494

Directorate R — Resources and Communication

Colette COTTER
Director
Tel. +32 229-59668, 65611

1. Financial resources

Lluis PRATS
Head of Unit
Tel. +32 229-66994, 50414

2. Human resources

Robert Bruno PRAGNELL
Head of Unit
Tel. +32 229-91100, 64468

3. Informatics

Wilfried BEURMS
Head of Unit
Tel. +32 229-67357

4. Communication and information

Sjoukje-Sandra KRAMER
Head of Unit
Tel. +32 229-55541, 52714

Coordination, planning and international affairs

John FARNELL
Director
Tel. +32 229-56397, 81115

Andreas MENIDIATIS
Adviser
Tel. +32 229-55388

1. General coordination

Peter WAGNER
Head of Unit
Tel. +32 229-65498, 56833

2. International affairs

Christian SIEBERT
Head of Unit
Tel. +32 229-66244, 68059

3. Interinstitutional relations

Stéphane LEBRUN
Head of Unit
Tel. +32 229-62530, 54457

4. Planning and management

Peter WRAGG
Head of Unit
Tel. +32 229-60126

Directorate B — Industrial Policy and Economic Reforms

Viola GROEBNER
Director
Tel. +32 229-90078, 50411

1. Sustainable industrial policy

Didier HERBERT
Head of Unit
Tel. +32 229-90087, 68112

2. Development of industrial policy

Manfred BERGMANN
Head of Unit
Tel. +32 229-93479

3. Lisbon coordination and economic reforms

Outi SLOTBOOM
Head of Unit
Tel. +32 229-67296, 95645

4. Economic analysis and evaluation

Andrzej RUDKA
Head of Unit
Tel. +32 229-91331, 54939

5. Impact assessment and administrative burden reduction programme

Geneviève PONS-DELADRIÈRE
Head of Unit
Tel. +32 229-56460, 52388

Directorate C — Regulatory Policy

Ghyslaine GUISOLPHE
Director (acting)
Tel. +32 229-51860, 58042

Joanna SZYCHOWSKA
Adviser
Tel. +32 229-88632, 56497

1. Regulatory approach for the free circulation of goods

Jacques McMILLAN
Head of Unit
Tel. +32 229-52475, 84430

2. Application of Articles 28-30 EC

Maciej GORKA
Head of Unit
Tel. +32 229-54714, 88390

3. Notification of technical regulations

Ghyslaine GUISOLPHE
Head of Unit
Tel. +32 229-51860, 58042

4. Internal market and simplification

Liliana BRYKMAN
Head of Unit
Tel. +32 229-90025, 87910

Directorate D — Innovation Policy

Jean-Noël DURVY
Director
Tel. +32 229-63582, 69512

1. Innovation policy development

Peter DROELL
Head of Unit
Tel. +32 229-90348, 84454

2. Support for innovation

Reinhard BÜSCHER
Head of Unit
Tel. +32 229-59906, 58118

3. Financing innovation and SMEs

Per-Ove ENGELBRECHT
Head of Unit
Tel. +32 229-92149, 97646

4. ICT for competitiveness and innovation

Constantin ANDROPOULOS
Head of Unit
Tel. +32 229-56601, 50963

Directorate E — Promotion of SMEs' Competitiveness

Maive RUTE
Director
Tel. +32 229-59159, 64584

Josef Christian WEINBERGER
Adviser
Tel. +32 229-55305, 64584

Marko CURAVIC
Adviser
Tel. +32 229-87425

1. Entrepreneurship

Reinhard KLEIN
Head of Unit
Tel. +32 229-69700, 84461

2. Business cooperation and Community business support network development

Jean-François AGUINAGA
Head of Unit
Tel. +32 229-51442, 65048

3. Crafts, small businesses, cooperatives and mutuals

Sylvia VLAEMINCK
Head of Unit
Tel. +32 229-56385, 58726

4. SME policy development

Mechthild WOERSDOERFER
Head of Unit
Tel. +32 229-90030, 53886

Directorate F — Consumer Goods

Georgette LALIS
Director
Tel. +32 229-87930, 51258

Cornelis BREKELMANS
Adviser
Tel. +32 229-56600

1. Automotive industry

Philippe JEAN
Head of Unit
Tel. +32 229-50539, 58173

2. Pharmaceuticals

Martin TERBERGER
Head of Unit
Tel. +32 229-53986, 95699

3. Cosmetics and medical devices

Sabine LECRENIER
Head of Unit
Tel. +32 229-55738, 95820

4. Food industry

Michel COOMANS
Head of Unit
Tel. +32 229-68148, 58296

5. Competitiveness in the pharmaceuticals industry and biotechnology

Giulia DEL BRENNA
Head of Unit
Tel. +32 229-58090

Directorate G — Chemicals, Metals, Forest-based and Textile Industries

Gwenole COZIGOU
Director
Tel. +32 229-51304, 52838

Michel CATINAT
Adviser
Tel. +32 229-69529, 54623

1. REACH

Graham WILLMOTT
Head of Unit (acting)
Tel. +32 229-52056, 65253

2. Chemicals

Klaus BEREND
Head of Unit
Tel. +32 229-94860, 68938

3. Steel, non-ferrous metals, minerals and mineral products

Abraao CARVALHO
Head of Unit
Tel. +32 229-57397, 59477

4. Textiles, fashion and forest-based industries

Luis GIRAO
Head of Unit
Tel. +32 229-92216, 67225

Directorate H — Aerospace, GMES, Security and Defence

Paul WEISSENBERG
Director
Tel. +32 229-63358, 94706

1. Aerospace, defence and maritime industries

Luigi VITIELLO
Head of Unit (acting)
Tel. +32 229-53217, 95158

2. Space policy and coordination

Stefan NONNEMAN
Head of Unit
Tel. +32 229-84262, 50576

3. Space research and development

Reinhard SCHULTE-BRAUCKS
Head of Unit
Tel. +32 229-55882

4. Security research and development

Marco MALACARNE
Head of Unit
Tel. +32 229-55277, 67869

5. GMES Bureau

Valère MOUTARLIER
Head of Unit
Tel. +32 229-62162, 69967

6. Administration, finance and communication

Segundo Augusto GONZALEZ HERNANDEZ
Head of Unit
Tel. +32 229-66319

Directorate I — New Approach Industries, Tourism and CSR

Pedro ORTUN SILVAN
Director
Tel. +32 229-52084, 57805

Kim HOLMSTRÖM
Adviser
Tel. +32 229-91852

Norbert ANSELMANN
Adviser
Tel. +32 229-95672

1. Tourism

Francesco IANNIELLO
Head of Unit
Tel. +32 229-55155, 96345

2. International regulatory agreements, toys safety, CSR

Luis MONTOYA
Head of Unit
Tel. +32 229-62592, 94912

3. Standardisation

Renate WEISSENHORN
Head of Unit
Tel. +32 229-52014, 86317

4. Mechanical, electrical and telecom equipment

Alexandra JOUR-SCHROEDER
Head of Unit
Tel. +32 229-51553, 56008

5. Construction, pressure equipment, metrology

Vicente LEOZ ARGUELLES
Head of Unit
Tel. +32 229-51225, 59948

COMPETITION DG

Rue Joseph II 70
B-1000 Brussels
Tel. +32 229-91111 (operator)

Philip LOWE
Director-General
Tel. +32 229-65040, 54562

Thomas DEISENHOFER
Assistant to the Director-General
Tel. +32 229-85081, 86597

Inge BERNAERTS
Assistant to the Director-General
Tel. +32 229-51888, 21098

Nadia Maria CALVINO SANTAMARIA
Deputy Director-General
(with responsibility for mergers and antitrust)
Tel. +32 229-55067

Lowri EVANS
Deputy Director-General
(with responsibility for operations)
Tel. +32 229-65029

Émil PAULIS
Deputy Director-General (acting)
Tel. +32 229-65033, 65574

Herbert UNGERER
Deputy Director-General
(responsible for State aid)
Tel. +32 229-68623

Juan RIVIERE Y MARTÍ
Adviser
Tel. +32 229-51146

Claude RAKOVSKY
Adviser
Tel. +32 229-55389

Kris DEKEYSER
Head of the Task Force
Tel. +32 229-54206, 80336

Reporting directly to the Director-General

Rosalind BUFTON
Hearing Officer
Tel. +32 229-64116

Damien NEVEN
Chief Economist
Tel. +32 229-87312

1. Communications policy and interinstitutional relations

Kevin COATES
Head of Unit
Tel. +32 229-59758

2. Support for antitrust and merger case

Guillaume LORIOT
Head of Unit
Tel. +32 229-84988, 88592

3. Support for cases of State aid

Nicola PESARESI
Head of Unit
Tel. +32 229-92906, 95033

4. Strategy and delivery

Anna COLUCCI
Head of Unit (acting)
Tel. +32 229-68319, 54104

Directorate A — Policy and Strategy

Carles ESTEVA MOSSO
Director (acting)
Tel. +32 229-69721, 87997

Dietrich KLEEMANN
Adviser
Tel. +32 229-65031, 54133

Juan RIVIERE Y MARTÍ
Adviser
Tel. +32 229-51146

1. Private enforcement

Carles ESTEVA MOSSO
Head of Unit
Tel. +32 229-69721, 87997

2. Antitrust and mergers policy and scrutiny

Claude RAKOVSKY
Head of Unit
Tel. +32 229-55389

3. State-aids policy and scrutiny

Alain ALEXIS
Head of Unit
Tel. +32 229-55303, 81808

4. European competition network

Alès MUSIL
Head of Unit
Tel. +32 229-92204

5. International relations

Dominique VAN DER WEE
Head of Unit
Tel. +32 229-60216

6. Consumer liaison

Zsuzsanna JAMBOR
Head of Unit
Tel. +32 229-87436, 90797

Directorate B — Markets and Cases I: Energy and Environment

Éric VAN GINDERACHTER
Director (acting)
Tel. +32 229-54427, 98634

1. Antitrust: Energy, environment

Céline GAUER
Head of Unit
Tel. +32 229-63919, 54850

2. State aid

Éric VAN GINDERACHTER
Head of Unit
Tel. +32 229-54427, 98634

3. Mergers

Dan SJOBLOM
Head of Unit
Tel. +32 229-67964, 60614

Directorate C — Markets and Cases II: Information, Communication and Media

Cecilio MADERO VILLAREJO
Director
Tel. +32 229-60949, 53966

1. Antitrust: Telecommunications

Joachim LUECKING
Head of Unit
Tel. +32 229-66545, 93260

2. Antitrust: Media

Gerald MIERSCH
Head of Unit (acting)
Tel. +32 229-96504

3. Antitrust: IT, Internet and consumer electronics

Per HELLSTROM
Head of Unit
Tel. +32 229-66935, 90590

4. State aid

Wouter PIEKE
Head of Unit
Tel. +32 229-59824, 67267

5. Mergers

Sophie MOONEN
Head of Unit (acting)
Tel. +32 229-81807

Directorate D — Markets and Cases III: Financial Services and Health-related Markets

Irmfried SCHWIMANN
Director (acting)
Tel. +32 229-67002

1. Antitrust: Payment systems

Irmfried SCHWIMANN
Head of Unit
Tel. +32 229-67002

2. Antitrust: Financial services

Tatjana VERRIER
Head of Unit
Tel. +32 229-92535

Silke OBST
Head of Unit (acting)
Tel. +32 229-84643

3. State aids

María Blanca RODRÍGUEZ GALINDO
Head of Unit
Tel. +32 229-52920, 67725

4. Mergers

Johannes LUEBKING
Head of Unit
Tel. +32 229-59851, 95592

Directorate E — Markets and Cases IV: Basic Industries, Manufacturing and Agriculture

Pal CSISZAR
Director
Tel. +32 229-84669, 98518

Yves DEVELLENNES
Adviser
Tel. +32 229-51590, 68611

2. Antitrust: Consumer goods, basic industry, agriculture and manufacturing

Paolo CESARINI
Head of Unit
Tel. +32 229-51286, 86982

3. State aids: Industrial restructuring

Karl SOUKUP
Head of Unit
Tel. +32 229-67442, 21409

4. Mergers

Maria REHBINDER
Head of Unit
Tel. +32 229-90007, 59232

Directorate F — Markets and Cases V: Transport, Post and Other Services

Olivier GUERSENT
Director (acting)
Tel. +32 229-65414, 98799

1. Antitrust: Transport and post

Linsey MC CALLUM
Head of Unit
Tel. +32 229-90122, 87129

2. Antitrust: Other services

Georg-Klaus DE BRONETT
Head of Unit
Tel. +32 229-59268, 58315

3. State aids

Joaquin FERNANDEZ MARTIN
Head of Unit
Tel. +32 229-51041, 60879

4. Mergers

Olivier GUERSENT
Head of Unit
Tel. +32 229-65414, 98799

Directorate G — Cartels

Kirtikumar MEHTA
Director
Tel. +32 229-57389, 90183

1. Cartels I

Paul MALRIC-SMITH
Head of Unit
Tel. +32 229-59675, 64903

2. Cartels II

Dirk VAN ERPS
Head of Unit
Tel. +32 229-66080, 96439

3. Cartels III

Jaroslaw POREJSKI
Head of Unit
Tel. +32 229-87440, 66634

4. Cartels IV

Ewoud SAKKERS
Head of Unit
Tel. +32 229-66352, 50559

5. Cartels V

Malgorzata Hanna JOUVE-MAKOWSKA
Head of Unit
Tel. +32 229-92407

6. Cartels — Transaction procedures

Flavio LAINA
Head of Unit
Tel. +32 229-69669, 50658

Directorate H — State Aid: Cohesion, R&D&I and Enforcement

Humbert DRABBE
Director
Tel. +32 229-50060, 67991

1. Regional aid

Robert HANKIN
Head of Unit
Tel. +32 229-59773, 81366

2. R & D, innovation and risk capital

Jorma PIHLATIE
Head of Unit
Tel. +32 229-53607, 98651

3. State aid network and transparency

Wolfgang MEDERER
Head of Unit
Tel. +32 229-53584, 54449

4. Enforcement and procedural reform

Barbara BRANDTNER
Head of Unit
Tel. +32 229-51563, 53020

Directorate R — Registry and Resources

Isabelle BENOLIEL
Director
Tel. +32 229-60198, 59090

1. Document management

Corinne DUSSART-LEFRET
Head of Unit
Tel. +32 229-61223, 52814

2. Resources

Joos STRAGIER
Head of Unit
Tel. +32 229-52482

3. Information technology

Manuel PEREZ ESPIN
Head of Unit
Tel. +32 229-61691, 80259

EMPLOYMENT, SOCIAL AFFAIRS AND EQUAL OPPORTUNITIES DG

B-1049 Brussels
Tel. +32 22991111 (operator)
Tel. +32 229 + extension

Euroforum 1
10, rue Robert Stumper
L-2557 Luxembourg
Tel. +352 4301-1 (operator)
Tel. +352 4301 + extension

Nikolaus VAN DER PAS
Director-General
Tel. +32 229-68308, 90482

Eleni SAMUEL
Deputy Director-General
Tel. +32 229-84001, 90664

Raymond MAES
Assistant to the Director-General
Tel. +32 229-95283, 53625

David DION
Assistant to the Director-General
Tel. +32 229-88269, 90482

Reporting directly to the Director-General

1. General coordination, interinstitutional relations

Nicolas GIBERT-MORIN
Head of Unit
Tel. +32 229-91120, 87958

2. Internal audit

Carlo PETTINELLI
Head of Unit
Tel. +32 229-94037, 65130

3. Evaluation and impact assessment

Antonella SCHULTE-BRAUCKS
Head of Unit
Tel. +32 229-57159, 59214

Directorate A — ESF, Monitoring of Corresponding National Policies I, Coordination

David COYNE
Director
Tel. +32 229-55741, 65760

1. ESF coordination

Thomas BENDER
Head of Unit
Tel. +32 229-69917, 62357

2. Bulgaria, Croatia, Hungary, Netherlands

Filip BUSZ
Head of Unit
Tel. +32 229-90923, 64670

3. Germany, Austria, Slovenia

Franz-Peter VEITS
Head of Unit (acting)
Tel. +32 229-95411

4. Luxembourg, Portugal, Czech Republic

Horacio BARATA
Head of Unit (acting)
Tel. +32 229-51641

Szilard TAMAS
Head of Unit
Tel. +32 229-63560, 59145

Directorate B — ESF, Monitoring of Corresponding National Policies II

Peter STUB JØRGENSEN
Director
Tel. +32 229-86000, 96446

1. Italy, Malta, Romania, the former Yugoslav Republic of Macedonia

Philippe HATT
Head of Unit
Tel. +32 229-56701, 86215

2. Belgium, France, Slovakia

Aurelio CECILIO
Head of Unit
Tel. +32 229-62806, 92264

3. Estonia, Finland, Lithuania, Sweden

Michel LAINE
Head of Unit
Tel. +32 229-58138, 50392

4. Transnationality, EGF (European Globalisation Adjustment Fund)

Walter FABER
Head of Unit
Tel. +32 229-50377, 90502

Directorate C — ESF, Monitoring of Corresponding National Policies III

Peter Stub JØRGENSEN
Director (acting)
Tel. +32 229-86000, 96446

1. Ireland, Latvia, United Kingdom

Santiago LORANCA-GARCIA
Head of Unit
Tel. +32 229-66800, 95600

2. Cyprus, Greece, Poland

Georges KINTZELE
Head of Unit
Tel. +32 229-52539, 84323

3. Denmark, Spain, Turkey

Lucio BATTISTOTTI
Head of Unit
Tel. +32 229-85799, 88466

4. Article 6 ESF, ECSC, CELFI, ESF archives

Brendan SINNOTT
Head of Unit
Tel. +32 229-58688, 53114

Directorate D — Employment, Lisbon Strategy, International Affairs

Xavier PRATS-MONNE
Director
Tel. +32 229-61230, 59144

Constantinos FOTAKIS
Adviser
Tel. +32 229-50206

1. Employment analysis

Radek MALY
Head of Unit
Tel. +32 229-20868, 60837

2. European employment strategy, CSR, local development

Robert STRAUSS
Head of Unit
Tel. +32 229-60531, 84257

3. Employment services, mobility

Wallis GOELEN
Head of Unit
Tel. +32 229-51827, 58495

4. International affairs, enlargement

Michael MORASS
Head of Unit (acting)
Tel. +32 229-66433, 52119

Directorate E — Social Protection and Integration

Jérôme VIGNON
Director
Tel. +32 229-54602, 68344

Robertus CORNELISSEN
Adviser
Tel. +32 229-57667, 86979

1. Social and demographic analysis

Ralf JACOB
Head of Unit
Tel. +32 229-90483, 87553

2. Inclusion, social policy aspects of migration, streamlining of social policies

Antonia CARPARELLI
Head of Unit
Tel. +32 229-93428, 69410

3. Coordination of social security schemes, free movement of workers

Jackie MORIN
Head of Unit
Tel. +32 229-61145, 68996

4. Social protection, social services

Georg FISCHER
Head of Unit
Tel. +32 229-92118, 87167

Directorate F — Social Dialogue, Social Rights, Working Conditions, Adaptation to Change

Armindo SILVA
Director (acting)
Tel. +32 229-60231

1. Social dialogue, industrial relations

Jean-Paul TRICART
Head of Unit
Tel. +32 229-90511, 53280

2. Labour law

Armindo SILVA
Head of Unit
Tel. +32 229-60231

3. Working conditions, adaptation to change

Jean-François LEBRUN
Head of Unit
Tel. +32 229-92274, 66584

4. Health, safety and hygiene at work

Costas CONSTANTINOU
Head of Unit
Tel. +352 4301-31833

Directorate G — Equality between Men and Women, Action against Discrimination, Civil Society

Belinda PYKE
Director
Tel. +32 229-61673, 66369

1. Equality between men and women

Fay DEVONIC
Head of Unit
Tel. +32 229-56151, 81053

2. Equality, action against discrimination, legal questions

Daniela BANKIER
Head of Unit
Tel. +32 229-81708, 62317

3. Integration of people with disabilities

Johan TEN GEUZENDAM
Head of Unit
Tel. +32 229-57829, 88232

4. Action against discrimination, civil society

Erik Stefan OLSSON
Head of Unit
Tel. +32 229-53569, 84164

Directorate H — Resources, Communication

Marie DONNELLY
Director
Tel. +32 229-60332, 91601

Paul GLYNN
Adviser
Tel. +32 229-50183, 63100

1. Personnel, administration

Johan DUMAS
Head of Unit (acting)
Tel. +32 229-95757, 88667

2. Budget, financial coordination, SPP

Olivier ROULAND
Head of Unit
Tel. +32 229-66218, 84463

3. Communication, CAD

Joseph JAMAR
Head of Unit
Tel. +32 229-52082, 55375

4. Information technologies

Wolfgang SCHOBESBERGER
Head of Unit
Tel. +32 229-51864, 65429

Directorate I — Audit, Controls, Evaluation

Viktorija SMATKO-ABAZA
Director
Tel. +32 229-94537, 86813

1. *Ex-ante* control, relations with the control authorities

Franck SEBERT
Head of Unit
Tel. +32 229-69590, 87919

2. *Ex-post* control of direct management expenditure

Vincent WIDDERSHOVEN
Head of Unit
Tel. +32 229-53330, 65629

3. ESF audits: Horizontal issues

Themistoklis GALEROS
Head of Unit
Tel. +32 229-57548, 94821

4. ESF audits

Anni HELLMAN
Head of Unit
Tel. +32 229-99041, 51306

Rue de la Loi 130
B-1049 Brussels
Tel. +32 229-91111
Fax +32 229-50130

Jean-Luc DEMARTY
Director-General
Tel. +32 229-56126, 67336

Jerzy Bogdan PLEWA
Deputy Director-General
(with responsibility for Directorates A and B)
Tel. +32 229-80125, 59485

Lars HOELGAARD
Deputy Director-General
(responsible for Directorates C and D)
Tel. +32 229-63314, 62615

Loretta DORMAL-MARINO
Deputy Director-General
(responsible for Directorates E, F, G and H)
Tel. +32 229-58603, 55095

Prosper DE WINNE
Deputy Director-General
(responsible for Directorates I, J and K)
Tel. +32 229-56394, 51331

João ONOFRE ANTAS GONCALVES
Assistant to the Director-General
Tel. +32 229-69788, 59392

Willi SCHULZ-GREVE
Assistant to the Director-General
Tel. +32 229-60945, 57566

Reporting directly to the Director-General

Internal audit

Paul WEBB
Head of Unit
Tel. +32 229-54533, 65708

Directorate A — International Affairs I, in particular Multilateral Negotiations

Nikiforos SIVENAS
Director
Tel. +32 229-59662, 94338

1. WTO (World Trade Organisation)

Norbert NORRIS
Head of Unit
Tel. +32 229-90126, 84724

2. Industrialised countries, OECD

Michael ERHART
Head of Unit
Tel. +32 259617, 95627

3. ACP and South Africa, FAO, food aid

Léonard MIZZI
Head of Unit
Tel. +32 229-80477, 93023

Directorate B — International Affairs II, in particular Enlargement

Aldo LONGO
Director
Tel. +32 229-56690, 53251

Isabelle PEUTZ
Adviser
Tel. +32 229-52331, 56756

1. Latin America, Asia other than OECD members

Jesús ZORRILLA TORRAS
Head of Unit
Tel. +32 229-67445, 50047

2. Enlargement

Dusan CHRENEK
Head of Unit
Tel. +32 229-86035, 58939

3. European neighbourhood policy, EFTA

Nicolas VERLET
Head of Unit
Tel. +32 229-61508, 59874

Directorate C — Economics of Agricultural Markets (and CMO)

Russell MILDON
Director
Tel. +32 229-53224, 92096

1. Horizontal matters concerning the single CMO

Elisabetta SIRACUSA
Head of Unit
Tel. +32 229-94234, 95107

2. Olive oil, horticultural products

Tomás GARCÍA AZCÁRATE
Head of Unit
Tel. +32 229-53317, 56150

3. Wine, alcohol, tobacco, seeds and hops

Emmanuel JACQUIN
Head of Unit
Tel. +32 229-55798, 92328

4. Animal products

Juan Luis FERNÁNDEZ MARTÍN
Head of Unit
Tel. +32 229-62750, 87135

5. Arable crops, sugar, fibre plants, animal feed

Bruno BUFFARIA
Head of Unit
Tel. +32 229-63144, 99613

Directorate D — Direct Support, Market Measures, Promotion

Hermanus VERSTEIJLEN
Director
Tel. +32 229-59527, 56370

1. Direct support

Jean-Jacques JAFFRELOT
Head of Unit
Tel. +32 229-52836, 61486

2. Management of market measures

Willy SCHOOFS
Head of Unit
Tel. +32 229-57039, 63371

3. Cross-compliance, food and feed legislation, POSEI

Aymeric BERLING
Head of Unit (acting)
Tel. +32 229-91218

4. Promotion of agricultural products

Michele OTTATI
Head of Unit
Tel. +32 229-58402, 51273

Directorate E — Rural Development Programmes I

Pedro TARNO
Director (acting)
Tel. +32 229-59364, 50218

1. Belgium, France, Luxembourg, Netherlands

Pedro TARNO
Head of Unit
Tel. +32 229-59364, 50218

2. Cyprus, Greece, Ireland, United Kingdom

Adelina DOS REIS
Head of Unit
Tel. +32 229-61454, 53202

3. Denmark, Lithuania, Poland

Evangelos DIVARIS
Head of Unit (acting)
Tel. +32 229-61163, 56686

4. Hungary, Italy, Malta

Robertus PETERS
Head of Unit
Tel. +32 229-62624, 56785

Directorate F — Rural Development Programmes II

Antonis CONSTANTINOU
Director
Tel. +32 229-52638, 52642

1. Portugal, Spain

Pedro RAMIREZ GRANADOS
Head of Unit (acting)
Tel. +32 229-58817, 60004

2. Estonia, Finland, Latvia, Sweden

Soeren KISSMEYER-NIELSEN
Head of Unit
Tel. +32 229-53295, 56464

3. Austria, Germany, Slovenia

Peter BOKOR
Head of Unit
Tel. +32 229-97889, 50439

4. Bulgaria, Czech Republic, Romania, Slovakia

Irini PAPADIMITRIOU
Head of Unit
Tel. +32 229-59127, 58390

Directorate F — Horizontal Aspects of Rural Development

José SOUSA UVA
Director
Tel. +32 229-59318, 50653

1. Consistency of rural development

Josefine LORIZ-HOFFMANN
Head of Unit
Tel. +32 229-57977, 61081

2. Financial coordination of rural development

Felix LOZANO GALLEGO
Head of Unit
Tel. +32 229-59542, 55403

3. European network and monitoring of rural development policy

John LOUGHEED
Head of Unit
Tel. +32 229-57306, 56829

4. Pre-accession assistance to agriculture and rural development

Kaj MORTENSEN
Head of Unit
Tel. +32 22729-64786, 96496

Directorate H — Sustainability and Quality of Agriculture and Rural Development

María Angeles BENITEZ SALAS
Director
Tel. +32 229-95472, 60732

1. Environment, GMOs and genetic resources

Martin SCHEELE
Head of Unit
Tel. +32 229-63970, 56689

2. Agricultural product quality policy

Keijo HYVONEN
Head of Unit
Tel. +32 229-96335, 62084

3. Organic farming

Jean-François HULOT
Head of Unit
Tel. +32 229-52991, 80154

4. Bioenergy, biomass, forestry and climatic change

Hilkka SUMMA
Head of Unit
Tel. +32 229-95093, 69909

Directorate I — Resource Management

Monique PARIAT
Director
Tel. +32 229-53188, 58651

Prosper DE WINNE
Deputy Director-General
Tel. +32 229-56394, 51331

Bernard VANDERHAEGHEN
Adviser
Tel. +32 229-53975

1. Budget management

Christina BORCHMANN
Head of Unit
Tel. +32 229-53259

2. Assistance and central financial control

Yves HERIN
Head of Unit
Tel. +32 229-59230, 91620

3. Information technology

Javier Juan PUIG SAQUÉS
Head of Unit
Tel. +32 229-68989, 56791

4. Financial management of EAGGF

Susanne NIKOLAJSEN
Head of Unit
Tel. +32 229-58079, 55524

5. Personnel and administration

Markus HOLZER
Head of Unit
Tel. +32 229-51795, 88245

6. Management by activities, relations with the Court of Auditors

Georg HAEUSLER
Head of Unit
Tel. +32 229-61082, 91981

Directorate J — Audit of Agricultural Expenditure

Wolfgang BURTSCHER
Director
Tel. +32 229-96898, 60968

Gerrit VERHELST
Adviser
Tel. +32 229-52440

1. Coordination of horizontal questions concerning the clearance of accounts

Michael NIEJAHR
Head of Unit
Tel. +32 229-69576, 93243

2. Audit of expenditure on market measures

Malcolm SLADE
Head of Unit
Tel. +32 229-57105, 61131

3. Audit of direct aid

Richard ETIEVANT
Head of Unit
Tel. +32 229-94468, 60156

4. Audit of expenditure on rural development and IPARD

Cornelia OVERBEEKE
Head of Unit
Tel. +32 229-98926, 20790

5. Financial audit

Anders EGONSON
Head of Unit
Tel. +32 229-57664, 55910

Directorate K — Relations with Other Institutions, Communication and Documentation

Gerard KIELY
Director (acting)
Tel. +32 229-87427, 56777

1. Internal and external communication

Johann Erwin BARTH
Head of Unit
Tel. +32 229-56363, 69752

2. Document management, security, protection of personal data

Maciej KUCZYNSKI
Head of Unit
Tel. +32 229-96941, 80579

3. Relations with the other Community institutions and agricultural NGOs

Gérard KIELY
Head of Unit
Tel. +32 229-87427, 56777

Directorate L — Economic Analysis, Perspectives and Evaluations

John BENSTED-SMITH
Director
Tel. +32 229-57443, 61261

Panayotis LEBESSIS
Adviser
Tel. +32 229-51932, 87186

1. Agricultural policy and perspectives

Anastassios HANIOTIS
Head of Unit
Tel. +32 229-91381, 56119

2. Economic analysis of EU agriculture

Pierre BASCOU
Head of Unit
Tel. +32 229-50846, 58397

3. Microeconomic analysis of EU agricultural holdings

Efthimios BOKIAS
Head of Unit (acting)
Tel. +32 229-62023, 51334

4. Evaluation of measures applicable to agriculture, studies

Leopold MAIER
Head of Unit
Tel. +32 229-98195, 56866

5. Agricultural trade policy analysis

Flavio COTURNI
Head of Unit
Tel. +32 229-67585

Directorate H — Agricultural Legislation

Rudolf MOEGELE
Director
Tel. +32 229-62930, 86832

1. Agricultural law, simplification

Nathalie SAUZE-VANDEVYVER
Head of Unit
Tel. +32 229-54765, 59068

2. Competition

Susana MARAZUELA AZPIROZ
Head of Unit
Tel. +32 229-65725

3. Supervision of the application of agricultural legislation, infringements and complaints

Kristine LILJEBERG
Head of Unit
Tel. +32 229-84630, 57161

4. Coordination of procedures and joint secretariat of management committees

Katrien BERBERS
Head of Unit
Tel. +32 229-58455, 84520

ENERGY AND TRANSPORT DG

Rue Demot 24-28
B-1040 Brussels
Tel. +32 229-91111 (operator)

Euroforum 1
10, rue Robert Stumper
L-2557 Luxembourg
Tel. +352 4301-1 (operator)
Tel. +352 4301 + extension

Euroforum 2
2, rue Henri M. Schnadt
L-2530 Luxembourg

Alfred Matthias RUETE
Director-General
Tel. +32 229-50734, 52386

Claire DEPRÉ
Assistant to the Director-General
Tel. +32 229-98463, 95264

Eddy LIÈGEOIS
Assistant to the Director-General
Tel. +32 229-51839, 95264

Filip CORNELIS
Assistant to the Director-General
Tel. +32 229-69219, 85135

Fabrizio BARBASO
Deputy Director-General
Coordination of Directorates C and D
Tel. +32 229-56739, 52500

Zoltan KAZATSAY
Deputy Director-General
Coordination of Directorates B, E, F and G
Tel. +32 229-59172, 58316

Dirk VAN VRECKEM
Adviser
Tel. +32 229-68439, 56344

Dominique RISTORI
Deputy Director-General
Coordination of nuclear activities, supervision of Directorates H and I
Tel. +352 4301-32047

Nina COMMEAU-YANNOUSSIS
Adviser
Tel. +32 229-67249

Reporting directly to the Director-General

Herman NACKAERTS
Head of Unit (seconded)

Alfonso GONZALEZ FINAT
Head of the Task Force
Tel. +32 229-68287, 58876

Internal audit

Alessandro D'ATRI
Head of Unit
Tel. +32 229-59301

Directorate A — Internal Market and Sustainability

Anne HOUTMAN
Director
Tel. +32 229-59628, 92627

1. Economic analysis, impact assessment, evaluation and climate change

Sandro SANTAMATO
Head of Unit
Tel. +32 229-93447, 94384

2. Internal market and competition

Jean-Louis COLSON
Head of Unit
Tel. +32 229-60995, 88565

3. Services of general economic interest, users' rights and infringements

Anne HOUTMAN
Head of Unit (acting)
Tel. +32 229-59628, 92627

4. Clean transport and urban transport

Eleni KOPANEZOU
Head of Unit
Tel. +32 229-96768, 68694

Directorate B — Trans-European Networks (TEN), Energy and Transport

Jonathan SCHEELE
Director
Tel. +32 229-57984, 68289

1. International transport relations and trans-European transport network policy

Jean-Éric PAQUET
Head of Unit
Tel. +32 229-81426, 53776

2. Coordination of TEN-T priority projects

Jean-Éric PAQUET
Head of Unit (acting)
Tel. +32 229-81426, 53776

3. Logistics, co-modality, inland waterways, motorways of the sea and Marco Polo

Bernard VAN HOUTTE
Head of Unit
Tel. +32 229-50494

Roberto FERRAVANTE
Head of Unit (acting)
Tel. +32 229-69250

Directorate C — Security of Supply, the Market in Energy

Heinz HILBRECHT
Director
Tel. +32 229-68174, 65356

Derek TAYLOR
Adviser
Tel. +32 229-53401, 61160

Cristóbal BURGOS ALONSO
Adviser
Tel. +32 229-62350, 61160

1. Energy policy and security of supply

Jean-Arnold VINOIS
Head of Unit
Tel. +32 229-68475, 97803

2. Electricity and gas

Ana ARANA ANTELO
Head of Unit
Tel. +32 229-64263, 54325

3. Coal and oil

Jan PANEK
Head of Unit
Tel. +32 229-69955, 65396

4. Observatory for the energy market

Christine BERG
Head of Unit
Tel. +32 229-91922, 99701

Directorate D — New and Renewable Sources of Energy, Energy Efficiency and Innovation

Christopher JONES
Director
Tel. +32 229-65030

Karl KELLNER
Adviser
Tel. +32 229-52410, 60019

1. Regulatory policy, promotion of new energy sources, demand management and energy efficiency

Hans VAN STEEN
Head of Unit
Tel. +32 229-53798, 50369

2. Energy technologies and research coordination

Stefan TOSTMANN
Head of Unit
Tel. +32 229-68833, 61374

3. Energy efficiency of products and 'Intelligent Energy — Europe'

André BRISAER
Head of Unit
Tel. +32 229-68236, 60904

4. Energy efficiency

Pirjo-Liisa KOSKIMAKI
Head of Unit
Tel. +32 229-51640

Directorate E — Inland Transport

Enrico GRILLO PASQUARELLI
Director
Tel. +32 229-56203, 60369

1. Land transport policy

Geza Szabolcs SCHMIDT
Head of Unit
Tel. +32 229-69958, 97661

2. Rail transport and inter-operability

Maurizio CASTELLETTI
Head of Unit
Tel. +32 229-91915, 60535

3. Road safety

Isabelle KARDACZ
Head of Unit
Tel. +32 229-59666

4. Security of land transport and dangerous goods

Wolfgang ELSNER
Head of Unit
Tel. +32 229-68476, 64807

Directorate F — Air Transport

Daniel CALLEJA CRESPO
Director
Tel. +32 229-61386, 60102

1. Internal market, air transport agreements and multilateral relations

Olivier ONIDI
Head of Unit
Tel. +32 229-56040, 55971

2. Single sky and modernisation of air traffic control

Luc TYTGAT
Head of Unit
Tel. +32 229-68430, 84349

3. Air safety

Roberto SALVARANI
Head of Unit
Tel. +32 229-68482, 71703

4. Infrastructure and airports

Rodrigo VILA DE BENAVENT
Head of Unit
Tel. +32 229-68828, 59366

5. Aviation security

Eckard SEEBOHM
Head of Unit
Tel. +32 229-68414, 68080

Directorate G — Maritime Transport, Galileo and Intelligent Transport

Fotis KARAMITSOS
Director
Tel. +32 229-63461, 81744

Willem De RUITER
Adviser
Tel. +32 229-63461, 81744

1. Maritime transport policy: Regulatory questions, maritime safety and seafarers

Philippe BURGHELLE-VERNET
Head of Unit
Tel. +32 229-51799, 50561

2. Maritime transport and ports policy; maritime security

Dimitrios THEOLOGITIS
Head of Unit
Tel. +32 229-95582, 68464

3. EU satellite navigation programmes: Infrastructure, deployment and operation

Paul VERHOEF
Head of Unit
Tel. +32 229-51067, 65093

4. EU satellite navigation programmes: Applications, intelligent transport systems (ITS)

Edgar THIELMANN
Head of Unit
Tel. +32 229-54615, 96736

5. EU satellite navigation programmes: Legal and financial aspects

Fotis KARAMITSOS
Head of Unit (acting)
Tel. +32 229-63461, 81744

Directorate H — Nuclear Energy (2)

Peter FAROSS
Director
Tel. +352 4301-34342
Tel. +32 229-53502

(2) Staff based in Luxembourg.

1. Legal questions and Euratom coordination, international relations

Massimo GARRIBBA
Head of Unit
Tel. +352 4301-33861, 35784

2. Nuclear energy, transport, decommissioning and waste management

Ute BLOHM-HIEBER
Head of Unit
Tel. +352 4301-34151, 33715

3. Nuclear accountancy, methods and evaluation

Stamatios TSALAS
Head of Unit
Tel. +352 4301-37147, 35915

Sotiris SYNETOS
Head of Unit (acting)
Tel. +352 4301-37150, 32778

4. Radiation protection

Augustin JANSSENS
Head of Unit
Tel. +352 4301-36395, 32192

Directorate I — Nuclear Safeguards (3)

Stamatios TSALAS
Director (acting)
Tel. +352 4301-37147, 35915

1. Design, planning and evaluation of inspections, logistical support

Maurizio BOELLA
Head of Unit
Tel. +352 4301-37125, 32034

2. Inspections, reprocessing plants

Paul MEYLEMANS
Head of Unit
Tel. +352 4301-36524, 32175

3. Verification of production and enrichment plants

Eva ADRIAN
Head of Unit
Tel. +352 4301-36946, 32224

4. Verification of reactors and of storage and other facilities

Pavel JIRSA
Head of Unit
Tel. +352 4301-34860

(3) Staff based in Luxembourg.
(4) Attached for administrative purposes to the Energy and Transport DG.

ESA — Euratom Supply Agency (4)

B-1049 Brussels
Tel. +32 229-91111 (operator)
Tel. +32 229 + extension

Christian CLEUTINX
Director
Tel. +352 4301-36236
Tel. +32 229-69662

Ivo ALEHNO
Head of Unit
Tel. +352 4301-36738, 31974

Directorate P — General Policy

Marjeta JAGER
Director
Tel. +32 229-80322, 61169

1. Planning and coordination, interinstitutional relations

Ricardo PASCUAL BREMON
Head of Unit
Tel. +32 229-61383, 58915

2. Information and communication, document management

Marie WOLFCARIUS
Head of Unit
Tel. +32 229-59120, 71692

3. International energy relations, enlargement

Paula ABREU MARQUES
Head of Unit (acting)
Tel. +32 229-53805, 57751

Directorate R — Resources

Augusto BONUCCI
Director
Tel. +32 229-93197, 69504

1. Financial resources and coordination of agencies

Carlos FILIPE
Head of Unit
Tel. +32 229-60862

2. Human resources

Sian PROUT
Head of Unit
Tel. +32 229-68240

3. Financial management

Jean-Claude MERCIOL
Head of Unit
Tel. +32 229-53504, 85246

4. Informatics and logistics

André MAMBOURG
Head of Unit
Tel. +32 229-69222, 91833

5. Financial audit

Jean-Claude MERCIOL
Head of Unit
Tel. +32 229-53504, 85246

Directorate T — TEN-T Executive Agency

Dirk BECKERS
Director (seconded)
Tel. +32 229-54261, 53125

1. Resources

Marcos ROMAN PARRA
Head of Unit (seconded)
Tel. +32 229-55492, 96906

2. Rail and road transport

Ionnis GIOGKARAKIS-ARGYROPOULOS
Head of Unit (seconded)
Tel. +32 229-66283, 53262

3. Air and waterborne transport, logistics, innovation and co-modality

Christopher NORTH
Head of Unit (seconded)
Tel. +32 229-68336, 69109

ENVIRONMENT DG

Avenue de Beaulieu 5
B-1160 Brussels
Tel. +32 229-91111 (operator)

Bâtiment Jean Monnet
L-2920 Luxembourg
Tel. +352 4301-1 (operator)
Tel. +352 4301 + extension

Karl-Friedrich FALKENBERG
Director-General
Tel. +32 229-92220, 56657

Bettina DOESER
Assistant to the Director-General
Tel. +32 229-67050

Reporting directly to the Director-General

Nicolas THERY
Chief Adviser
Tel. +32 229-84240, 63396

Mogens CARL
Adviser hors classe
Tel. +32 229-92205, 65738

1. Strategic planning and evaluation

Nicholas BANFIELD
Head of Unit
Tel. +32 229-68761, 57250

2. Legislation and other interinstitutional activities

Paulus BROUWER
Head of Unit
Tel. +32 229-54125, 50309

3. Internal audit

Jan Julius GROENENDAAL
Head of Unit
Tel. +32 229-92271, 60931

Directorate A — Communication, Legal Affairs and Civil Protection

Pia BUCELLA
Director
Tel. +32 229-57099.51443

1. Communication and governance

Nicholas HANLEY
Head of Unit
Tel. +32 229-68703, 59705

Anna VOPEL
Head of Unit (acting)
Tel. +32 229-69175, 94191

2. Infringements

Julio GARCIA BURGUES
Head of Unit
Tel. +32 229-68763, 85017

3. Civil protection

Hervé MARTIN
Head of Unit
Tel. +32 229-65444, 85642

Directorate B — Protecting the Natural Environment

Ladislav MIKO
Director
Tel. +32 229-87237, 68797

Robert FLIES
Adviser
Tel. +32 229-57979, 81963

1. Agriculture and soil

Michael HAMELL
Head of Unit
Tel. +32 229-59826, 99292

2. Nature and biodiversity

Stefan LEINER
Head of Unit (acting)
Tel. +32 229-95068, 61179

3. Biotechnology, pesticides and health

Chantal BRUETSCHY
Head of Unit
Tel. +32 229-62362, 80751

Directorate C — Climate Change and Air

Jos DELBEKE
Director (acting)
Tel. +32 229-68804

1. Climate strategy, international negotiation and monitoring of EU action

Artur RUNGE-METZGER
Head of Unit
Tel. +32 229-56898, 68844

2. Market-based instruments including greenhouse gas emissions trading

Yvon SLINGENBERG
Head of Unit
Tel. +32 229-92036, 69361

3. Clean air and transport

Stefan MOSER
Head of Unit (acting)
Tel. +32 229-65880, 56213

4. Industrial emissions and protection of the ozone layer

Marianne WENNING
Head of Unit
Tel. +32 229-55943, 85448

5. Energy and environment

Piotr Jaroslaw TULEJ
Head of Unit
Tel. +32 229-99732, 55141

Directorate D — Water, Chemicals and Cohesion

Peter GAMMELTOFT
Director (acting)
Tel. +32 229-68695, 52205

Eva HELLSTEN
Adviser
Tel. +32 229-96765, 69151

1. Chemicals

Astrid SCHOMAKER
Head of Unit
Tel. +32 229-69641, 51511

2. Protection of water and the marine environment [5]

Peter GAMMELTOFT
Head of Unit
Tel. +32 229-68695, 52205

3. Cohesion policy and environmental impact assessments

Georges-Stavros KREMLIS
Head of Unit
Tel. +32 229-66526, 90409

Directorate E — International Affairs and LIFE

Soledad BLANCO MANGUDO
Director
Tel. +32 229-95182, 53774

Jill HANNA
Adviser
Tel. +32 229-53232, 56117

1. International environmental governance and developing countries

François WAKENHUT
Head of Unit
Tel. +32 229-65380, 68712

2. Environmental agreements and trade

Hugo SCHALLY
Head of Unit
Tel. +32 229-58569, 93164

3. Enlargement and neighbouring countries

Claude ROUAM
Head of Unit
Tel. +32 229-57994, 87607

4. LIFE

Philip OWEN
Head of Unit
Tel. +32 229-65562, 56667

Directorate F — Resources

Hans DE JONG
Director (acting)
Tel. +32 229-51347, 90390

1. Human resources and administration

Hans DE JONG
Head of Unit
Tel. +32 229-51347, 90390

2. Finance

François CASANA
Head of Unit
Tel. +32 229-51978, 81436

3. Information technology

Martin GRITSCH
Head of Unit
Tel. +32 229-59467, 54680

4. Financial processing and assistance

Angelo SALSI
Head of Unit
Tel. +32 229-69376, 68277

Directorate G — Sustainable Development and Integration

Timo MÄKELÄ
Director
Tel. +32 229-62634, 60180

Herbert AICHINGER
Adviser
Tel. +32 229-66954, 60180

1. Sustainable development and economic analysis

Robin MIEGE
Head of Unit
Tel. +32 229-58043, 68180

2. Environment and industry

Pavel MISIGA
Head of Unit
Tel. +32 229-94420, 68461

3. Research, science and innovation

Ian CLARK
Head of Unit
Tel. +32 229-69094, 52787

4. Production, consumption and waste

Klaus KOEGLER
Head of Unit
Tel. +32 229-62379, 56312

RESEARCH DG

Rue du Champ de Mars 21
B-1050 Brussels
Tel. +32 229-91111 (operator)

José Manuel SILVA RODRÍGUEZ
Director-General
Tel. +32 229-51910, 53274

Doriane GIVORD-STRASSEL
Assistant to the Director-General
Tel. +32 229-50799, 87748

Ann-Sofie RONNLUND
Assistant to the Director-General
Tel. +32 229-53581

Daniel JACOB
Deputy Director-General
with responsibility for Directorates F, H, S and T
Tel. +32 229-59870, 60690

Zoran STANČIČ
Deputy Director-General
with responsibility for Directorates E, G, I, J and K
Tel. +32 229-62475, 87550

Anneli PAULI
Deputy Director-General
with responsibility for Directorates B, C, D and L
Tel. +32 229-54055

Graham STROUD
Head of Unit (seconded)
Tel. +32 229-53825, 61644

Marc TACHELET
Head of Unit (seconded)
Tel. +32 229-67827
Tel. +352 4301-36616

Michel ANDRÉ
Adviser (responsible for research policy matters)
Tel. +32 229-60781

Nicolas SABATIER
Adviser (with responsibility for analysing the new financial instruments)
Tel. +32 229-67131

...
Principal Adviser (with responsibility for thermonuclear fusion)

...
Principal Adviser (with responsibility for economic questions)

1. Internal audit

José CARBAJALES
Head of Unit (acting)
Tel. +32 229-58379

[5] Unit provisionally under the supervision of Prudencio Perera

Directorate A — Inter-institutional and Legal Matters, Framework Programme

Clara DE LA TORRE
Director
Tel. +32 229-95827

1. Interinstitutional relations and coordination of the framework programme

Brendan HAWDON
Head of Unit (acting)
Tel. +32 229-63750, 80307

2. Legal matters

Liliane DE WOLF
Head of Unit
Tel. +32 229-61073, 81216

3. Evaluation and monitoring of programme

Peter FISCH
Head of Unit
Tel. +32 229-52468, 94740

4. External audit

Marc BELLENS
Head of Unit
Tel. +32 229-50942, 71850

5. Implementation of audit certification policy and outsourced audits

Philippe COENJAARTS
Head of Unit
Tel. +32 229-67095, 53801

6. Definition of management processes

Antonio MICELI
Head of Unit
Tel. +32 229-63783, 98213

Information Technology Planning Office (ITPO)

Augusto BURGUENO ARJONA
Head of the Task Force
Tel. +32 229-92471

Directorate B — European Research Area: Research Programmes and Capacity

Robert-Jan SMITS
Director
Tel. +32 229-63296, 94919

Leonidas KARAPIPERIS
Adviser (with responsibility for new initiatives in connection with the ERA)
Tel. +32 229-53243

1. Coordination of national research programmes, joint programming and major European initiatives

Étienne MAGNIEN
Head of Unit
Tel. +32 229-59347, 98646

2. Policy analysis

Ugur MULDUR
Head of Unit
Tel. +32 229-65604

3. Research infrastructure

Hervé PERO
Head of Unit
Tel. +32 229-61232, 96416

4. Regions of knowledge and research potential

Jean-David MALO
Head of Unit
Tel. +32 229-93842, 84599

5. Administration and finance

Michael SUCKER
Head of Unit
Tel. +32 229-90175, 50614

Directorate C — European Research Area: Knowledge-based Economy

Isi SARAGOSSI
Director
Tel. +32 229-55517, 54160

Jocelyne GAUDIN
Adviser (for relations with other Community policies)
Tel. +32 229-50976, 51263

1. European Research Area policy

James GAVIGAN
Head of Unit
Tel. +32 229-60708, 90227

2. Private investment and technology platforms

Tiit JURIMAE
Head of Unit
Tel. +32 229-92059, 71501

3. Economic analysis and national policy for research, Lisbon strategy

Pierre VIGIER
Head of Unit
Tel. +32 229-62318, 60604

4. Universities and researchers

Stefaan HERMANS
Head of Unit
Tel. +32 229-69288, 51356

Directorate D — International Cooperation

Mary MINCH
Director
Tel. +32 229-61651, 60105

Georges PAPAGEORGIOU
Non-structural adviser assigned to a delegation
Tel. *80352

Laurent BOCHEREAU
Non-structural adviser assigned to a delegation
Tel. *80615

Robert KRENGEL
Non-structural adviser assigned to a delegation
Tel. +32 229-63892, 94450

Rudolf MEIJER
Adviser (Russia, eastern Europe and associated states)
Tel. +32 229-68954

1. International dimension of the framework programme

Alessandro DAMIANI
Head of Unit
Tel. +32 229-80120, 53059

2. Analysis and monitoring of research policies around the world

Sieglinde GRUBER
Head of Unit
Tel. +32 229-84342, 94028

3. Specific international cooperation activities

Robert BURMANJER
Head of Unit
Tel. +32 229-68949, 92559

4. Administration and finance

Alexis LONCKE
Head of Unit
Tel. +32 229-93805, 84937

Directorate E — Biotechnology, Food Processing Industry

Timothy HALL
Director (acting)
Tel. +32 229-52808, 50642

1. Horizontal aspects and coordination

Line MATTHIESSEN-GUYADER
Head of Unit
Tel. +32 229-52853, 98972

2. Biotechnology

Alfredo AGUILAR ROMANILLOS
Head of Unit
Tel. +32 229-61481, 60779

3. Food, health, well-being

Antonio DI GIULIO
Head of Unit
Tel. +32 229-52212, 95886

4. Agriculture, forests, fishing, aquaculture

Timothy HALL
Head of Unit
Tel. +32 229-52808, 50642

5. Administration and finance

Patrice LEMAÎTRE
Head of Unit
Tel. +32 229-61464, 81066

Directorate F — Health

Manuel HALLEN
Director (acting)
Tel. +32 229-57407, 53582

1. Horizontal aspects and coordination

Stéphane HOGAN
Head of Unit
Tel. +32 229-62965, 98777

2. Medical and public health research

Manuel HALLEN
Head of Unit
Tel. +32 229-57407, 53582

3. Infectious diseases

Alain VANVOSSEL
Head of Unit
Tel. +32 229-62578, 91185

4. Genomics and systems biology

Patrik KOLAR
Head of Unit
Tel. +32 229-85161, 61755

5. Health biotechnology

Arnd HOEVELER
Head of Unit
Tel. +32 229-56801, 66984

6. Administration and finance

Georgios ZISIMATOS
Head of Unit
Tel. +32 229-67038

Directorate G — Industrial Technologies

Herbert VON BOSE
Director
Tel. +32 229-59074, 60193

Hélène CHRAYE
Adviser
Tel. +32 229-89469, 85471

1. Horizontal aspects and coordination

Michel POIREAU
Head of Unit
Tel. +32 229-51411, 87803

2. New generation products

José-Lorenzo VALLES
Head of Unit
Tel. +32 229-91757, 83125

3. Value-added materials

Renzo TOMELLINI
Head of Unit
Tel. +32 229-60136, 86150

4. Nano S & T, convergent science and technology

Christos TOKAMANIS
Head of Unit
Tel. +32 229-59565, 65579

5. Administration and finance

Tibor Gyula DOKA
Head of Unit
Tel. +32 229-96234, 88166

Directorate H — Transport

András SIEGLER
Director
Tel. +32 229-80182, 88322

1. Horizontal aspects and coordination

Arnoldas MILUKAS
Head of Unit
Tel. +32 229-98414, 67965

2. Surface transport

Luisa PRISTA
Head of Unit
Tel. +32 229-61598, 51402

3. Aeronautics

Liam BRESLIN
Head of Unit
Tel. +32 229-75991, 50477

4. Administration and finance

Udo HEIDER
Head of Unit
Tel. +32 229-51892, 59281

Directorate I — Environment

Manuela SOARES
Director
Tel. +32 229-62148, 68958

1. Horizontal aspects and coordination

Birgit DE BOISSEZON
Head of Unit
Tel. +32 229-94715, 90606

2. Sustainable development

Nicole DEWANDRE
Head of Unit
Tel. +32 229-94925, 99598

3. Environmental technology, pollution prevention

Andrea TILCHE
Head of Unit
Tel. +32 229-96342, 50415

4. Management of natural resources

Pierre MATHY
Head of Unit
Tel. +32 229-58160, 65379

5. Climate change and environmental risks

Elisabeth LIPIATOU
Head of Unit
Tel. +32 229-66286, 81142

6. Administration and finance

Mireille DELPRAT
Head of Unit
Tel. +32 229-51564

Directorate J — Energy (Euratom)

Octavio QUINTANA TRIAS
Director
Tel. +32 229-89330, 85029

1. Horizontal aspects and coordination

Angél PEREZ SAINZ
Head of Unit
Tel. +32 229-61596, 65151

2. Fission

Simon WEBSTER
Head of Unit
Tel. +32 229-90442, 66379

3. Joint development of fusion

Serge PAIDASSI
Head of Unit (acting)
Tel. +32 229-58350, 92887

4. Fusion association agreements

Yvan CAPOUET
Head of Unit
Tel. +32 229-54058, 92791

5. Administration and finance

Eduard RILLE
Head of Unit
Tel. +32 229-54683, 66381

Directorate K — Energy

Raffaele LIBERALI
Director
Tel. +32 229-58673, 58879

1. Horizontal aspects and coordination

María DE AIRES SOARES
Head of Unit
Tel. +32 229-57778, 87922

2. Conversion system and energy transport

Wiktor RALDOW
Head of Unit
Tel. +32 229-93163, 58973

3. New and renewable energy sources

Bruno SCHMITZ
Head of Unit
Tel. +32 229-50514, 58089

4. Research Fund for Coal and Steel

Michel ANDRIEU
Head of Unit (acting)
Tel. +32 229-87053

5. Administration and finance

Istvan Laszlo NARAI
Head of Unit
Tel. +32 229-66348, 85855

Directorate L — Science, Economy and Society

Jean-Michel BAER
Director
Tel. +32 229-81445, 57549

Paraskevas CARACOSTAS
Adviser
Tel. +32 229-50888, 65853

1. Horizontal aspects and coordination

Dimitri CORPAKIS
Head of Unit
Tel. +32 229-68445, 54281

2. Research in the economic, social sciences and humanities

Pierre VALETTE
Head of Unit
Tel. +32 229-56356, 97823

3. Governance and ethics

Péteris ZILGALVIS
Head of Unit
Tel. +32 229-50935, 58294

4. Scientific culture and gender issues

Johannes KLUMPERS
Head of Unit
Tel. +32 229-60911, 95287

5. Communication

José Pablo AMOR ECHEVERRI
Head of Unit
Tel. +32 229-80167, 94359

6. Administration and finance

Thomas ARNOLD
Head of Unit
Tel. +32 229-94062, 98843

Directorate R — Resources

Franco BISCONTIN
Director
Tel. +32 229-67122, 80962

1. Personal policy

Francine GOFFAUX
Head of Unit (acting)
Tel. +32 229-91613, 87524

2. Budget and financial services

Priscilla FERNANDEZ CANADAS
Head of Unit
Tel. +32 229-55945, 88122

3. Strategic planning and programming

Gilles LAROCHE
Head of Unit
Tel. +32 229-91122, 62092

4. IT management

Georgios VLAHOPOULOS
Head of Unit
Tel. +32 229-62352, 58033

5. Risk management

José Antonio LOPEZ SANCHEZ
Head of Unit
Tel. +32 229-90105, 55551

6. Internal information, document management, procedures, ISC and office allocation

Francine GOFFAUX
Head of Unit
Tel. +32 229-91613, 87524

7. Management of debt and guarantee fund

Peter BAADER
Head of Unit (acting)
Tel. +32 229-84200

Directorate S — Implementation of the 'Ideas' Programme

Jack METTHEY
Director
Tel. +32 229-68870, 68318

1. Strategic matters and relations with the Scientific Council

William CANNELL
Head of Unit
Tel. +32 229-60952, 97795

2. Management of the 'Ideas' programme

Gabor MIHALY NAGY
Head of Unit
Tel. +32 229-68367, 85729

3. Administration and finance

Martin BOHLE
Head of Unit
Tel. +32 229-58111, 92830

Directorate T — Implementation of Activities to Outsource

Theodius LENNON
Director
Tel. +32 229-59986, 55404

Barbara RHODE
Adviser
Tel. +32 229-59888

1. Implementation of outsourcing

John CLAXTON
Head of Unit (acting)
Tel. +32 229-84375

2. Marie Curie actions: Fellowships

Georges BINGEN
Head of Unit
Tel. +32 229-69418, 97780

3. Marie Curie actions: Networks

Maria Begona ARANO
Head of Unit
Tel. +32 229-92040, 95089

4. SMEs

Bernd REICHERT
Head of Unit
Tel. +32 229-54617, 99228

5. Framework programme logistics

Alan HAIGH
Head of Unit
Tel. +32 229-65749, 88536

6. Administration and finance

Jochen BRODERSEN
Adviser (acting)
Tel. +32 229-56958

Rue de la Loi 200
B-1049 Brussels
Tel. +32 229-91111 (operator)
Fax +32 229-50146

Roland SCHENKEL
Director-General
Tel. +32 229-99840, 61490

Roland SCHENKEL
Deputy Director-General (acting)
Tel. +32 229-99840, 61490

Anneli PAULI
Deputy Director-General (handover)
Tel. +32 229-54055, 56260

Jan MUELLER
Assistant to the Director-General

Pierre FRIGOLA
Adviser
Tel. +32 229-59070, 53112

Marc BECQUET
Head of Unit
Tel. +32 229-93181, 80276

Piedad GARCIA DE LA RASILLA Y PINEDA
Adviser
Tel. +32 229-50146

1. Internal audit

Jacques VAN OOST
Head of Unit
Tel. +32 229-68523, 97618

2. Evaluation

Pieter VAN NES
Head of Unit
Tel. +32 229-60191, 58687

Directorate A — Programmes and Stakeholder Relations

Rue de la Loi 200/Wetstraat 200
B-1049 Brussels
Tel. +32 229-91111 (operator)
Fax +32 22950146

Krzysztof MARUSZEWSKI
Director
Tel. +32 229-99158, 99193

Steven EISENREICH
Adviser
Tel. +32 229-93744

...
Adviser
Relations with the Council, the European Parliament and the Member States

1. Work programme

Jean-Paul MALINGREAU
Head of Unit
Tel. +32 229-69433, 98416

2. Intellectual property and scientific cooperation

Géraldine BARRY
Head of Unit
Tel. +32 229-90266, 55261

3. Relations with customers and stakeholders

Giancarlo CARATTI DI LANZACCO
Head of Unit
Tel. +32 229-61516, 51902

4. Internal and external communication

Ulla ENGELMANN
Head of Unit
Tel. +32 229-57624, 68102

5. Management support

Jean-Pierre MICHEL
Head of Unit
Tel. +32 229-99363, 53701

6. Euratom work programme

Didier HAAS
Head of Unit
Tel. +32 229-92642

Directorate B — Management of Resources

Margaret Megan RICHARDS
Director
Tel. +32 229-62443, 87176

1. Human resources (Ispra)

Emanuela ROSSI
Head of Unit
Tel. +39 0332789981/9650

2. Budget and resource programming (Brussels)

Eric FISCHER
Head of Unit
Tel. +32 229-58683, 66308

3. Analytical accounting and finances (Ispra)

Peter CHURCHILL
Head of Unit
Tel. +32 229-65031

4. Corporate planning, monitoring and internal control (Ispra)

Kenneth WEAVING
Head of Unit
Tel. +32 229-69770

5. Training (Ispra)

Ilze BALTMANE
Head of Unit
Tel. +39 0332786379

Directorate C — ISPRA Site Directorate

I-21020 Ispra (Varese)
Tel. +39 0332789111
Fax +39 0332789045

David WILKINSON
Director
Tel. +39 0332786750

1. Decommissioning and management of nuclear installations

Celso OSIMANI
Head of Unit
Tel. +39 0332789829/5077

2. Health, industrial safety and hygiene

Danielle DEPIESSE
Head of Unit
Tel. +39 0332786775/9284

3. Social services

Raymond CRANDON
Head of Unit
Tel. +39 0332789828/6148

4. Site maintenance

Giacinto TARTAGLIA
Head of Unit
Tel. +39 0332789338

5. Informatics, networks and library

Marc WILIKENS
Head of Unit
Tel. +39 0332789737

6. Management support

Marinus STROOSNIJDER
Head of Unit
Tel. +39 0332785281

7. Logistics and security

Antonios KOLETSOS
Head of Unit
Tel. +39 0332786100

8. Site development

Dolf VAN HATTEM
Head of Unit
Tel. +39 0332789541

9. Asset management

Iain FORMOSA
Head of Unit
Tel. +39 0332786091

Directorate D — Institute for Reference Materials and Measurements (Geel)

Steenweg op Retie
B-2240 Geel
Tel. +32 1457-1211
Fax +32 1458-4273

Alejandro HERRERO MOLINA
Director
Tel. +32 1457-1292, 1293

1. Management support

Marc WELLENS
Head of Unit
Tel. +32 1457-1327, 1864

2. Reference materials

Hendrik EMONS
Head of Unit
Tel. +32 1457-1722, 1548

3. Infrastructure and site management

Colin WOODWARD
Head of Unit
Tel. +32 1457-1585

4. Isotope measurement

Philip TAYLOR
Head of Unit
Tel. +32 1457-1605, 1608

5. Neutron physics

Peter RULLHUSEN
Head of Unit
Tel. +32 1457-1476, 1862

6. Informatics and electronics

Bartel MEERSMAN
Head of Unit
Tel. +32 1457-1404, 1539

7. Institute development and programme management

Doris FLORIAN
Head of Unit
Tel. +32 1457-1272, 1584

8. Food safety and quality

Franz ULBERTH
Head of Unit
Tel. +32 1457-1316, 1783

Directorate E — Institute for Transuranium Elements (Karlsruhe)

Postfach 2340
D-76125 Karlsruhe
Tel. +49 7247951-0
Fax +49 7247951-590

Thomas FANGHAENEL
Director
Tel. +49 7247951-350, 591

1. Management support

Jean-François BABELOT
Head of Unit
Tel. +49 7247951-352, 590

2. Hot cells

Vincenzo RONDINELLA
Head of Unit
Tel. +49 7247951-279, 447

3. Materials research

Rudy KONINGS
Head of Unit
Tel. +49 7247951-391, 99391

4. Nuclear fuels

Joseph SOMERS
Head of Unit
Tel. +49 7247951-359, 599

5. Nuclear chemistry

Jean-Paul GLATZ
Head of Unit
Tel. +49 7247951-321, 588

6. Actinides research

Roberto CACIUFFO
Head of Unit
Tel. +49 7247951-382, 599

7. Nuclear security

Werner WAGNER
Head of Unit
Tel. +49 7247951-330, 611

8. Applied safeguards laboratory

Klaus LÜTZENKIRCHEN
Head of Unit
Tel. +49 7247951-424, 99424

Directorate F — Institute for Energy (Petten)

Westerduinweg 3
Postbus Nr. 2
1755 ZG Petten (N.-H.)
Netherlands
Tel. +31 224565656
Fax +31 224563393

Giovanni DE SANTI
Director
Tel. +31 224565401/5601

Roger HURST
Adviser (responsible for science strategy)
Tel. +31 224565219/5621

1. Management support

Josephina PIJLS
Head of Unit
Tel. +31 224565332/5602

2. Cleaner energy

Marc STEEN
Head of Unit
Tel. +31 224565271/5630

3. Energy security

Roberto MAY
Head of Unit
Tel. +31 224565121/5615

4. Safety of future nuclear reactors

Luigi DEBARBERIS
Head of Unit (acting)
Tel. +31 224565130/5130

5. Safety of present nuclear reactors

Michel BIETH
Head of Unit
Tel. +31 224565157

6. Programme management and support

Juha-Pekka HIRVONEN
Head of Unit
Tel. +31 224565208/5210

7. Energy systems evaluation

Estathios PETEVES
Head of Unit
Tel. +31 224565245/5648

8. Renewable energies (Ispra)

Heinz OSSENBRINK
Head of Unit
Tel. +39 033278-9196/9268

Directorate G — Institute for the Protection and Security of the Citizen (Ispra)

I-21020 Ispra (Varese)
Tel. +39 033278-9111
Fax +39 033278-9923

Stephan LECHNER
Director
Tel. +39 033278-9947, 9923

Gerald VOLLMER
Adviser

1. Management support

James GRAY
Head of Unit
Tel. +39 033278-5875, 9682

2. Support for external security

Delilah AL KHUDHAIRY
Head of Unit
Tel. +39 033278-5696, 5154

3. Agriculture

Jacques DELINCÉ
Head of Unit
Tel. +39 033278-5579, 5162

4. Maritime affairs

Thomas BARBAS
Head of Unit (acting)
Tel. +39 033278-9512, 9156

5. European laboratory for structural assessment

Michel GERADIN
Head of Unit
Tel. +39 033278-9989, 9562

6. Sensors, radar technologies and cybersecurity

Alois SIEBER
Head of Unit
Tel. +39 033278-9089, 5469

7. Traceability and vulnerability assessment

Thomas HARTUNG
Head of Unit
Tel. +39 033278-5939, 5145

8. Nuclear safeguards

Willem JANSSENS
Head of Unit
Tel. +39 033278-9939, 9185

9. Econometrics and statistical support to anti-fraud

Andrea SALTELLI
Head of Unit
Tel. +39 033278-6391, 5733

Directorate H — Institute for Environment and Sustainability (Ispra)

I-21020 Ispra (Varese)
Tel. +39 033278-9111
Fax +39 033278-9222

Leendert HORDIJK
Director
Tel. +39 033278-6680, 9222

Peter PART
Adviser (in charge of health and environment interactions)
Tel. +39 033278-5496, 6292

1. Management support

Neil HUBBARD
Head of Unit
Tel. +39 033278-5725, 9816

2. Climate change

Frank RAES
Head of Unit
Tel. +39 033278-9958, 5704

Franciscus DENTENER
Head of Unit (acting)
Tel. +39 0332786392, 5837

3. Global environment monitoring

Alan BELWARD
Head of Unit
Tel. +39 033278-9298, 9073

4. Transport and air quality

Alois KRASENBRINK
Head of Unit (acting)
Tel. +39 033278-5474, 9259

5. Rural, water and ecosystem resources

Giovanni BIDOGLIO
Head of Unit
Tel. +39 033278-9383, 5537

6. Spatial data infrastructures

Alessandro ANNONI
Head of Unit
Tel. +39 033278-6166, 6086

7. Land management and natural hazards

Guido SCHMUCK
Head of Unit
Tel. +39 033278-9514, 5230

Directorate I — Institute for Health and Consumer Protection (Ispra)

I-21020 Ispra (Varese)
Tel. +39 033278-9111
Fax +39 033278-9536

Elke ANKLAM
Director
Tel. +39 033278-5151, 9059

1. Management support

Clemens WITTWEHR
Head of Unit (acting)
Tel. +39 033278-9028, 5730

2. *In-vitro* toxicology

Joachim KREYSA
Head of Unit
Tel. +39 033278-6735, 6297

3. Consumer products safety and quality

Ana PAYA PEREZ
Head of Unit (acting)
Tel. +39 033278-5414, 9963

4. Nanotechnology and molecular imaging

Hermann STAMM
Head of Unit
Tel. +39 033278-9030, 5388

5. Physical and chemical exposure

Dimitrios KOTZIAS
Head of Unit
Tel. +39 033278-5950, 9453

6. Biotechnology and GMOs

Guy VAN DEN EEDE
Head of Unit
Tel. +39 033278-5239, 5483

Directorate J — Institute for Prospective Technological Studies (Seville)

World Trade Center
Isla de la Cartuja s/n
E-41092 Sevilla
Tel. +34 95448-8273
Fax +34 95448-8274

Peter KIND
Director
Tel. +34 95448-8273, 8274

Jean-Claude BURGELMAN
Adviser
Tel. +32 229-80006

1. Management support

Maria Asunción RUBIRALTA CASAS
Head of Unit
Tel. +34 95448-8389, 8300

2. Competitiveness and sustainability

Szabolcs SZEKERES
Head of Unit
Tel. +34 95448-8335, 8235

3. Knowledge in the service of growth

Xabier GOENAGA BELDARRAIN
Head of Unit
Tel. +34 95448-8382, 8326

4. Information society

David BROSTER
Head of Unit
Tel. +34 95448-8496, 8208

5. Agriculture and biological sciences in the economy

Per SØRUP
Head of Unit
Tel. +34 95448-8320, 8252

INFORMATION SOCIETY AND MEDIA DG

Avenue de Beaulieu
B-1049 Brussels
Tel. +32 229-91111 (operator)
Tel. +32 229 + extension

10, rue Robert Stumper
L-2557 Luxembourg
Tel. +352 4301-1 (operator)
Tel. +352 4301 + extension

Fabio COLASANTI
Director-General
Tel. +32 229-94374, 51586

Maria Ana JARA DE CARVALHO
Assistant to the Director-General
Tel. +32 229-94374, 54518

Hervé DUPUY
Assistant to the Director-General
Tel. +32 229-95258

Simon BENSASSON
Adviser (with special responsibility for international aspects of Internet governance and the Secretariat of the ICANN Governmental Advisory Committee (GAC))
Tel. +32 229-68066

Wolfgang STREITENBERGER
Adviser
Tel. +32 229-84426, 60213

Pierrette PELHATE
Adviser
Tel. +32 229-69633

Reporting directly to the Director-General

Internal audit

Fernando SENDRA PALMER
Head of Unit
Tel. +32 229-54324

Reporting directly to the Deputy Director-General

Antti Ilmari PELTOMAKI
Deputy Director-General
Tel. +32 229-52847, 61642

Detlef ECKERT
Adviser
Tel. +32 229-63197

Ruprecht NIEPOLD
Adviser
Tel. +32 229-68955, 86142

...
Adviser (with special responsibility for monitoring world policies on telecommunications and the information society and developments in network technologies)

Directorate R — Resources

Anne BUCHER
Director
Tel. +32 229-93456, 51241

1. Human resources

Christian DUBS
Head of Unit
Tel. +32 229-59777, 80896

2. Budgetary resources

Joaquín PÉREZ ECHAGÜE
Head of Unit
Tel. +32 229-93685, 68120

3. Information systems development and support

Yves PATERNOSTER
Head of Unit
Tel. +32 229-58355, 94410

4. Information technology infrastructure and services (6)

Hervé DE SADELEER
Head of Unit
Tel. +32 229-91687, 72911

Directorate S — General Affairs

Walter SCHWARZENBRUNNER
Director
Tel. +32 229-92270, 63513

1. Planning, coordination and interinstitutional relations

Enrico FORTI
Head of Unit
Tel. +32 229-65172, 86563

2. Management support

Armand RAUCH
Head of Unit
Tel. +32 229-62737, 61250

3. Information and communication

Marie Sixtine BOUYGUES
Head of Unit
Tel. +32 229-51718, 68567

4. Legal aspects

Ziga BAHOVEC
Head of Unit
Tel. +32 229-88284, 68209

5. External audit

Freddy DEZEURE
Head of Unit
Tel. +32 229-59805, 57223

Directorate A — Audiovisual, Media, Internet

Gregory PAULGER
Director
Tel. +32 229-99434, 58538

1. Audiovisual and media policies

Jean-Éric DE COCKBORNE
Head of Unit
Tel. +32 229-68632, 81086

2. MEDIA programme and media literacy

Aviva SILVER
Head of Unit
Tel. +32 229-52290, 97851

3. Internet; network and information security

Fritz Michael NIEBEL
Head of Unit
Tel. +32 229-60705, 52753

4. International relations

Jean-François SOUPIZET
Head of Unit
Tel. +32 229-68964, 52337

(6) Part of this unit is based in Luxembourg.

Directorate B — Electronic Communications Policy

Bernd LANGEHEINE
Director
Tel. +32 229-91855, 68988

1. Policy development

Peter RODFORD
Head of Unit
Tel. +32 229-90015

2. Implementation of regulatory framework (I)

Paraskevi MICHOU
Head of Unit
Tel. +32 229-53437, 84810

3. Implementation of regulatory framework (II)

George PAPAPAVLOU
Head of Unit
Tel. +32 229-54990, 60782

Wolf-Dietrich GRUSSMANN
Head of Unit
Tel. +32 229-58559, 68500

4. Radio spectrum policy

Pearse O'DONOHUE
Head of Unit
Tel. +32 229-91280, 50613

5. Procedures related to national regulatory measures

Reinald KRUEGER
Head of Unit
Tel. +32 229-61555, 93260

Directorate C — Lisbon Strategy and Policies for the Information Society

Susan BINNS
Director

Morten MOLLER
Director (acting)
Tel. +32 229-63526, 58095

Stephan PASCALL
Adviser
Tel. +32 229-68178, 63667

1. Lisbon strategy and i2010

Kenneth DUCATEL
Head of Unit
Tel. +32 229-56867

2. Strategy for ICT research and innovation

Khalil ROUHANA
Head of Unit
Tel. +32 229-54077, 96902

3. Evaluation and monitoring

Constantin PALEOLOGOS
Head of Unit (acting)
Tel. +32 229-68972, 97652

4. Economic and statistical analyses

Lucilla SIOLI
Head of Unit (acting)
Tel. +32 229-51262, 58340

5. Operations for ICT research and innovation

Morten MOLLER
Head of Unit
Tel. +32 229-63526, 58095

Directorate D — Converged Networks and Services

João Augusto DA SILVA
Director
Tel. +32 229-63417, 63541

1. Future networks

Rainer ZIMMERMANN
Head of Unit
Tel. +32 229-68110, 59464

2. Networked media systems

Luis RODRÍGUEZ-ROSELLÓ
Head of Unit
Tel. +32 229-63406, 87397

3. Software and service architectures and infrastructures

Jesús VILLASANTE
Head of Unit
Tel. +32 229-63521, 89302

4. Networked Enterprise and Radio Frequency Identification (RFID)

Gérald SANTUCCI
Head of Unit
Tel. +32 229-68963, 69351

5. Administration and finance

Ioannis MALEKOS
Head of Unit
Tel. +32 229-52902, 92091

Directorate E — Digital Content and Cognitive Systems (7)

Horst FORSTER
Director
Tel. +352 4301-32123, 38806
Tel. +32 229-68057

(7) Luxembourg.

1. Language technologies, machine translation

Roberto CENCIONI
Head of Unit
Tel. +352 4301-32859, 38056

2. Technologies for information management

Marta NAGY-ROTHENGASS
Head of Unit
Tel. +352 4301-31680

3. Cultural heritage and technology-enhanced learning

Patricia MANSON
Head of Unit
Tel. +352 4301-33261, 37307

4. Access to information

Javier HERNANDEZ-ROS
Head of Unit
Tel. +352 4301-34533, 33349

5. Cognitive systems, interaction, robotics

Libor KRAL
Head of Unit
Tel. +352 4301-35878, 33528

6. *e*Content and safer Internet

Richard SWETENHAM
Head of Unit
Tel. +352 4301-32400, 32963

7. Administration and finance

Peter BEUSELING
Head of Unit
Tel. +352 4301-35590, 36623

Directorate F — Emerging Technologies and Infrastructures

Mario CAMPOLARGO
Director
Tel. +32 229-63479, 68578

1. Future and emerging technologies (FET), proactive

Wolfgang BOCH
Head of Unit
Tel. +32 229-63591, 94575

2. Future and emerging technologies (FET), open

Alès FIALA
Head of Unit
Tel. +32 229-64787, 61645

3. GEANT and e-infrastructures

Konstantinos GLINOS
Head of Unit
Tel. +32 229-69577, 68072

4. New infrastructure paradigms and experimental facilities

Per Goeran BLIXT
Head of Unit
Tel. +32 229-68048, 84534

5. Trust and security

Jacobus BUS
Head of Unit
Tel. +32 229-68116, 66818

6. Administration and finance

Johannes MACHNIK
Head of Unit
Tel. +32 229-68579, 71966

Ralf HANSEN
Head of Unit (acting)
Tel. +32 229-68153, 71966

Directorate G — Components and Systems

Thierry VAN DER PYL
Director
Tel. +32 229-68105

1. Nanoelectronics

Dirk BEERNAERT
Head of Unit
Tel. +32 229-68020, 80532

2. Microsystems

Augusto DE ALBUQUERQUE
Head of Unit
Tel. +32 229-63476, 68661

3. Embedded systems and control

José COTTA
Head of Unit
Tel. +32 229-66407, 66408

4. Information and communication technologies (ICT) for transport

André VITS
Head of Unit
Tel. +32 229-63523, 56771

Aulis JAASKELAINEN
Head of Unit (acting)
Tel. +32 229-65459

5. Photonics

John MAGAN
Head of Unit (acting)
Tel. +32 229-61204, 55846

6. Administration and finance

Massimo LUCIOLLI
Head of Unit
Tel. +32 229-94346, 69404

Directorate H — ICT Addressing Societal Challenges

Gérard COMYN
Director (acting)
Tel. +32 229-94346, 66949

Bror SALMELIN
Adviser
Tel. +32 229-69564, 97635

1. Information and communication technologies (ICT) for health

Gérard COMYN
Head of Unit
Tel. +32 229-93346, 66949

2. ICT for government and public services

Mechthild ROHEN
Head of Unit
Tel. +32 229-63674

3. ICT for inclusion

Paul TIMMERS
Head of Unit
Tel. +32 229-90245, 95390

Miguel GONZALEZ-SANCHO BODERO
Head of Unit (acting)
Tel. +32 229-52918

4. ICT for sustainable growth

Colette MALONEY
Head of Unit
Tel. +32 229-69082

5. Administration and finance

Willy VAN PUYMBROECK
Head of Unit
Tel. +32 229-68138, 87586

MARITIME AFFAIRS AND FISHERIES DG

Rue Joseph II 99
B-1000 Brussels
Tel. +32 229-91111 (operator)
Tel. +32 229 + extension

Fokion FOTIADIS
Director-General
Tel. +32 229-92302, 86407

Gilles BERTRAND
Assistant to the Director-General
Tel. +32 229-55512, 86407

Harm KOSTER
Head of Unit (seconded)
Tel. +32 229-50235, 60009

Constantin-Nikolas VAMVAKAS
Adviser
Tel. +32 229-55784, 50355

Ole TOUGAARD
Adviser
Tel. +32 229-52209, 60009

Reporting directly to the Director-General

Internal audit

Maritime Policy Task Force

John RICHARDSON
Head of the Task Force
Tel. +32 229-80610, 57007

Paul NEMITZ
Adviser
Tel. +32 229-69135, 87701

Directorate A — Policy Development and Coordination

César DEBÉN ALFONSO
Director
Tel. +32 229-93224, 52402

Poul DEGNBOL
Adviser
Tel. +32 229-57316, 85808

Giorgio GALLIZIOLI
Adviser
Tel. +32 229-55047

1. Maritime policy

Paul NEMITZ
Head of Unit
Tel. +32 229-69135, 87701

2. Common fisheries policy and aquaculture

Ernesto PENAS LADO
Head of Unit
Tel. +32 229-63744, 84661

3. Structural policy and economic analysis

Alberto SPAGNOLLI
Head of Unit
Tel. +32 229-63859, 52390

4. Fisheries control policy

Valérie LAINE
Head of Unit
Tel. +32 229-65341, 67576

Directorate B — International Affairs and Markets

Pierre AMILHAT
Director
Tel. +32 229-75879, 92054

1. International affairs, law of the sea and regional fisheries organisations

Constantin ALEXANDROU
Head of Unit
Tel. +32 229-69493, 85479

2. Fisheries control in international waters

Willem BRUGGE
Head of Unit
Tel. +32 229-55137, 94776

3. Bilateral agreements

Fabrizio DONATELLA
Head of Unit
Tel. +32 229-68038, 95760

4. Trade and markets

Christian RAMBAUD
Head of Unit
Tel. +32 229-60545, 50345

Directorate C — Atlantic, Outermost Regions and Arctic

Reinhard PRIEBE
Director
Tel. +32 229-50161, 54989

Armando ASTUDILLO GONZALEZ
Adviser
Tel. +32 229-61191

Edward SPENCER
Adviser
Tel. +32 229-56858, 57450

1. Maritime policy — Atlantic, outermost regions and Arctic

Everardus HARTOG
Head of Unit
Tel. +32 229-90084, 63364

2. Fisheries conservation and control — Atlantic and outermost regions

María de la Fuensant CANDELA CASTILLO
Head of Unit
Tel. +32 229-57753, 62549

3. Structural actions: Ireland, Spain, France, Portugal and United Kingdom; horizontal management of data collection

Veronika VEITS
Head of Unit
Tel. +32 229-67224, 61303

Directorate D — Mediterranean and Black Sea

John MALLETT
Director (acting)
Tel. +32 229-52100, 57280

1. Maritime policy — Mediterranean and Black Sea

Fabrizia BENINI
Head of Unit
Tel. +32 229-66417

2. Fisheries conservation and control — Mediterranean and Black Sea and horizontal management of fisheries data

John MALLETT
Head of Unit
Tel. +32 229-52100, 57280

3. Structural actions: Bulgaria, Greece, Italy, Cyprus, Malta, Romania, Slovenia

Chiara GARIAZZO
Head of Unit
Tel. +32 229-99255, 99076

Directorate E — Baltic Sea, North Sea and Landlocked Member States

Olle HAGSTROM
Adviser
Tel. +32 229-92116, 52666

Stephanos SAMARAS
Director (acting)
Tel. +32 229-58834, 82017

1. Maritime policy — Baltic and North Sea

Pierre SCHELLEKENS
Head of Unit
Tel. +32 229-53528, 54027

2. Fisheries conservation and control — Baltic and North Sea

Jean-Claude CUEFF
Head of Unit
Tel. +32 229-51292, 90447

3. Structural actions: Belgium, Denmark, Germany, Estonia, Latvia, Lithuania, the Netherlands, Poland, Finland, Sweden and landlocked Member States

Stéphanos SAMARAS
Head of Unit
Tel. +32 229-58834, 82017

Directorate F — Resources

Daniela GHEORGHE
Director
Tel. +32 229-54619, 91995

Ilona JEPSENA
Adviser
Tel. +32 229-69149, 67148

1. Budget, public procurement and control

Mark JOHNSTON
Head of Unit
Tel. +32 229-68513, 94100

2. Information, communication, interinstitutional relations, evaluation and programming

Emmanouil-Georgios PAPAIOANNOU
Head of Unit
Tel. +32 229-69988, 87080

3. Human resources, IT and document management

Agnès LINDEMANS-MAES
Head of Unit
Tel. +32 229-60528, 50019

4. Legal matters

Friedrich WIELAND
Head of Unit
Tel. +32 229-63205, 51674

INTERNAL MARKET AND SERVICES DG

Rue de Spa
B-1000 Brussels
Tel. +32 229-91111 (operator)
Tel. +32 229 + extension

Jorgen HOLMQUIST
Director-General
Tel. +32 229-55192, 65192

Thierry STOLL
Deputy Director-General
Tel. +32 229-52438, 94970

David WRIGHT
Deputy Director-General
Tel. +32 229-58626, 60921

Sven GENTNER
Assistant to the Director-General
Tel. +32 229-53751

Florence FRANÇOIS-PONCET
Assistant to the Director-General
Tel. +32 229-93816

Peter SMITH
Adviser
Tel. +32 229-53994

Directorate A — Planning, Administrative Support and Communication

Panayotis STAMATOPOULOS
Director (acting)
Tel. +32 229-61772, 57999

1. Human and financial resources

Olivier SALLES
Head of Unit
Tel. +32 229-56954, 96351

2. Programming and planning

Matthew KING
Head of Unit
Tel. +32 229-55077, 80680

3. Information technology and document handling

Fernando TOLEDANO
Head of Unit
Tel. +32 229-68177

4. Internal and external communication

Panayotis STAMATOPOULOS
Head of Unit
Tel. +32 229-61772, 57999

Directorate B — Horizontal Policy Development

Emer DALY
Director
Tel. +32 229-60503, 53231

Dag Sverker Håkan ANDER
Adviser
Tel. +32 229-63104

1. Development and coordination of internal market policy

Bernhard FRIESS
Head of Unit
Tel. +32 229-56038, 54610

2. Better regulation cycle: Impact assessment and evaluation

Werner STENGG
Head of Unit
Tel. +32 229-69159, 91124

3. Better regulation cycle: Legal aspects

Henrik MORCH
Head of Unit
Tel. +32 229-50766, 85725

4. Internal market: External dimension

Anthony DEMPSEY
Head of Unit
Tel. +32 229-57357, 94736

Directorate C — Public Procurement Policy

Bertrand CARSIN
Director
Tel. +32 229-55795, 51916

1. Economic and international dimension of public procurement policy, e-procurement

Erik NOOTEBOOM
Head of Unit
Tel. +32 229-60348, 54209

2. Formulation and enforcement of public procurement law I ([8])

Matthias PETSCHKE
Head of Unit
Tel. +32 229-66867, 87322

3. Formulation and enforcement of public procurement law II ([9])

Ugo BASSI
Head of Unit
Tel. +32 229-53118, 84925

([8]) For BE, CY, FR, EL, HU, IE, LU, LT, LV, PT, PL, ES, UK.
([9]) For AT, CZ, DK, EE, FI, DE, IT, MT, NL, SE, SK, SI.

Directorate D — Knowledge-based Economy

Margot FRÖHLINGER
Director
Tel. +32 229-59350, 51783

1. Copyright and knowledge-based economy

Tilman LUEDER
Head of Unit
Tel. +32 229-91548, 50242

2. Industrial property

Oliver VARHELYI
Head of Unit
Tel. +32 229-55536, 97979

3. Enforcement of industrial and intellectual property rights

Alvydas STANCIKAS
Head of Unit
Tel. +32 229-63857, 84614

4. Regulated professions

Pamela BRUMTER-CORET
Head of Unit
Tel. +32 229-59408, 93757

Directorate E — Services

Guido BERARDIS
Director
Tel. +32 229-94012, 63511

1. Services I

Maria MARTIN-PRAT DE ABREU
Head of Unit (acting)
Tel. +32 229-65157, 50483

2. Services II

Jean BERGEVIN
Head of Unit
Tel. +32 229-51639, 63075

3. Administrative cooperation and Member States' networks

Nicholas LEAPMAN
Head of Unit
Tel. +32 229-51266, 51495

4. Postal services

Peter Jörg REINBOTHE
Head of Unit
Tel. +32 229-55323, 59427

Directorate F — Free Movement of Capital, Company Law and Corporate Governance

Pierre DELSAUX
Director
Tel. +32 229-65472, 69787

Piotr MADZIAR
Adviser
Tel. +32 229-50869

1. Free movement of capital and financial integration

Francisco de Asís CABALLERO SANZ
Head of Unit
Tel. +32 229-51168

2. Company law, corporate governance and financial crime

Claire BURY
Head of Unit
Tel. +32 229-60499, 89305

3. Accounting

Johannes HOOIJER
Head of Unit
Tel. +32 229-55885, 65199

4. Auditing

Jurgen TIEDJE
Head of Unit
Tel. +32 229-50525, 96094

Directorate G — Financial Services Policy and Financial Markets

Emil PAULIS
Director
Tel. +32 229-65033, 65574

1. Financial services policy

Martin MERLIN
Head of Unit
Tel. +32 229-58947

2. Financial markets infrastructure

Mario NAVA
Head of Unit
Tel. +32 229-64235, 80346

3. Securities markets

María VELENTZA
Head of Unit
Tel. +32 229-51723, 57546

4. Asset management

Niall BOHAN
Head of Unit
Tel. +32 229-63007, 21079

Directorate H — Financial Institutions

Elemer TERTAK
Director
Tel. +32 229-80967, 93254

1. Banking and financial conglomerates

Patrick PEARSON
Head of Unit
Tel. +32 229-55758, 50455

2. Insurance and pensions

Karel VAN HULLE
Head of Unit
Tel. +32 229-57954, 62258

3. Retail issues, consumer policy and payment systems

Jean-Yves MUYLLE
Head of Unit
Tel. +32 229-67537

REGIONAL POLICY DG

B-1049 Brussels
Tel. +32 229-91111 (operator)
Tel. +32 229 + extension

Dirk AHNER
Director-General
Tel. +32 229-57555, 59472

Mikel LANDABASO ALVAREZ
Assistant to the Director-General
Tel. +32 229-65256, 96347

Reporting directly to the Director-General

Katarina MATHERNOVA
Deputy Director-General
(development, coordination and communication of cohesion policy)
Tel. +32 229-69508, 98834

Michele PASCA-RAYMONDO
Deputy Director-General
(convergence, competitiveness and cross-border programmes)
Tel. +32 229-56447, 94829

Willebrordus SLUIJTERS
Adviser
Tel. +32 229-54667, 62203

1. Internal audit and advice

Sandrine DE BUGGENOMS
Head of Unit
Tel. +32 229-98529, 85886

Directorate A — Resources

Vittoria ALLIATA DI VILLAFRANCA
Director
Tel. +32 229-58386, 65501

1. Strategic planning and programming, internal control, simplification, document management

Pascale WOLFCARIUS
Head of Unit
Tel. +32 229-91538, 61484

2. Human resources and training

Hendrikus VOOGES
Head of Unit
Tel. +32 229-68108, 96695

3. Financial and budget management

Charles GROUTAGE
Head of Unit
Tel. +32 229-91090, 62203

4. Information technology

Christophe DE LASSUS SAINT GENIES
Head of Unit
Tel. +32 229-98849, 62456

Directorate B — Communication, Information, Relations with Third Countries, Coordination of Outermost Regions, Legal Advice

Ronald HALL
Director
Tel. +32 229-54401, 95425

1. Communication, information, relations with third countries

Raphael GOULET
Head of Unit
Tel. +32 229-92470, 98772

2. Coordination of outermost regions

Ana LAISSY
Head of Unit
Tel. +32 229-53258

3. Legal advice, procedures

Charles GRANT
Head of Unit (acting)
Tel. +32 229-96865, 87998

Directorate C — Policy Development

Natalija KAZLAUSKIENE
Director
Tel. +32 229-59387, 54955

1. Conception, forward studies, impact assessment

Peter BERKOWITZ
Head of Unit
Tel. +32 229-62017, 50598

2. Urban development, territorial cohesion

Wladyslaw PISKORZ
Head of Unit
Tel. +32 229-88639, 65437

3. Economic and quantitative analysis, additionality

Nicola DE MICHELIS
Head of Unit
Tel. +32 229-55230, 91957

4. Evaluation

Veronica GAFFEY
Head of Unit
Tel. +32 229-69596, 85661

Directorate D — Policy Coordination

Rudolf NIESSLER
Director
Tel. +32 229-95280, 95739

1. Programme coordination, relations with other institutions and NGOs, accession negotiations, Solidarity Fund

Bernard LANGE
Head of Unit
Tel. +32 229-51709, 64809

2. Thematic coordination, innovation

John WALSH
Head of Unit (acting)
Tel. +32 229-66061

3. Financial engineering

Dorota Kalina ZALIWSKA
Head of Unit
Tel. +32 229-66943, 85707

Directorate E — Territorial Cooperation, Belgium, France, Ireland, Luxembourg, United Kingdom

José PALMA ANDRÉS
Director
Tel. +32 229-51531, 59578

1. Territorial cooperation

Colin WOLFE
Head of Unit
Tel. +32 229-90516, 64822

2. Ireland, United Kingdom

Jonathan DENNESS
Head of Unit (acting)
Tel. +32 229-65038, 66975

3. Belgium, France and Luxembourg

Germán GRANDA
Head of Unit
Tel. +32 229-92992, 96899

Directorate F — Austria, Czech Republic, Germany, Hungary, Netherlands, Slovakia, Slovenia

Alejandro CHECCHI LANG
Director
Tel. +32 229-56838, 94595

1. Germany and the Netherlands

Christopher TODD
Head of Unit
Tel. +32 229-52776, 53002

2. Czech Republic

Jacobus ENGWEGEN
Head of Unit
Tel. +32 229-56449, 80363

3. Slovakia

Sabine BOURDY
Head of Unit
Tel. +32 229-80291, 55563

4. Austria and Slovenia

Marc BOTMAN
Head of Unit
Tel. +32 229-63895, 51690

5. Hungary

Marco ORANI
Head of Unit
Tel. +32 229-57086, 56824

Directorate G — Italy, Malta, Portugal, Spain

Raoul PRADO
Director
Tel. +32 229-69646, 86164

1. Spain

Michel-Éric DUFEIL
Head of Unit
Tel. +32 229-60490

2. Portugal

Rory MC KENNA
Head of Unit
Tel. +32 229-55510, 51203

3. Italy and Malta

Patrick AMBLARD
Head of Unit
Tel. +32 229-56482, 80356

Directorate H — Denmark, Estonia, Finland, Latvia, Lithuania, Poland, Sweden

Manfred BESCHEL
Director (acting)
Tel. +32 229-53529, 93556

1. Poland

Manfred BESCHEL
Head of Unit
Tel. +32 229-53529, 93556

2. Estonia, Finland and Latvia

Alain ROGGERI
Head of Unit
Tel. +32 229-58368, 69883

3. Lithuania, Sweden and Denmark

Judit TOROKNE ROZSA
Head of Unit

Directorate I — Bulgaria, Cyprus, Greece, Romania, IPA/ISPA

Jean-Marie SEYLER
Director
Tel. +32 229-54681, 53589

1. Romania

Anastassios BOUGAS
Head of Unit
Tel. +32 229-61078, 87757

2. Bulgaria

Renaldo MANDMETS
Head of Unit
Tel. +32 229-94535, 88527

3. Greece and Cyprus

Jacques PONCET
Head of Unit
Tel. +32 229-56142, 51850

4. IPA/ISPA

Erich UNTERWURZACHER
Head of Unit
Tel. +32 229-66721, 93964

Directorate J — Audit

Nicholas MARTYN
Director
Tel. +32 229-62941, 58059

1. Coordination, relations with the Court of Auditors and OLAF

Androulla IOANNOU
Head of Unit
Tel. +32 229-61794, 83150

2. Control and Audit I

Lena ANDERSSON PENCH
Head of Unit
Tel. +32 229-59819, 99942

3. Control and Audit II

Andrea MAIRATE
Head of Unit
Tel. +32 229-50298, 87634

4. Control and Audit III

Aderito PINTO
Head of Unit
Tel. +32 229-59781, 67041

TAXATION AND CUSTOMS UNION DG

Rue Montoyer 59
B-1000 Brussels
Tel. +32 229-91111 (operator)

Robert VERRUE
Director-General
Tel. +32 229-54376, 66914

Lilian BERTIN
Assistant to the Director-General
Tel. *80615

Pierre FAUCHERAND
Adviser
Tel. *80856

Reporting directly to the Director-General

Management of human and financial resources

Jean-Louis VERGNOLLE
Head of Unit
Tel. +32 229-63332, 65688

Directorate A — Coordination and Programmes

Marinus DE GRAAFF
Director
Tel. +32 229-52025, 60587

1. Relations with the institutions, internal coordination, strategic planning

Sabine HENZLER
Head of Unit
Tel. +32 229-92441, 54536

2. Information, training, management of programmes

Iosif DASCALU
Head of Unit
Tel. +32 229-58267, 59887

3. Customs and taxation — Trans-European systems

Paul-Hervé THEUNISSEN
Head of Unit
Tel. +32 229-63095, 94013

4. Customs and taxation — Automated services

Theodoros VASSILIADIS
Head of Unit
Tel. +32 229-61739, 63268

Directorate B — International Affairs and Tariff Matters

Antonis KASTRISSIANAKIS
Director
Tel. +32 229-57380, 58840

1. International affairs 1 — International bilateral agreements and multilateral organisations

Peter KOVACS
Head of Unit
Tel. +32 229-71918, 85238

2. Strategy, political and economic forward studies, evaluation

Bernard GRAND
Head of Unit
Tel. +32 229-55347, 56182

3. Convention of SH, combined nomenclature, tariff classification

Kristian VANGRIEKEN
Head of Unit
Tel. +32 229-65452, 51706

4. Tariff economics, relief from customs duties, TARIC, outermost regions

Tomas KUCIREK
Head of Unit
Tel. +32 229-53616, 52586

5. International affairs 2 — Candidate and neighbouring countries

Eva Ann UUSTALU
Head of Unit
Tel. +32 229-68708

Directorate C — Customs Policy

Miroslaw ZIELINSKI
Director
Tel. +32 229-53050, 62064

1. Customs policy and electronic customs

Maria Manuela CABRAL
Head of Unit
Tel. +32 229-54259/55213

2. General legislation and uniform application of customs law

Jean-Michel GRAVE
Head of Unit
Tel. +32 229-51520, 96931

3. Risk management, security and specific controls

John PULFORD
Head of Unit
Tel. +32 229-58183, 92550

John TAYLOR
Head of Unit (acting)
Tel. +32 229-59671

4. Customs procedures

Karl Michael LUX
Head of Unit
Tel. +32 229-54257, 64934

5. Origin, customs valuation and trade facilitation

Pierre-Jacques LARRIEU
Head of Unit
Tel. +32 229-59489

Directorate D — Indirect Taxation and Tax Administration

Alexander WIEDOW
Director
Tel. +32 229-53605

1. VAT and other turnover taxes

Rolf DIEMER
Head of Unit
Tel. +32 229-61075, 58522

2. Excise duties and transport, environment and energy taxes

Thomas CARROLL
Head of Unit
Tel. +32 229-55842, 59116

3. Control of the application of Community legislation and state aid/ indirect taxes

Micole WIEME
Head of Unit
Tel. +32 229-58262, 95455

4. Administrative cooperation and fight against fiscal fraud

Donato RAPONI
Head of Unit
Tel. +32 229-56307, 96973

Directorate E — Analyses and Tax Policies

Philip KERMODE
Director
Tel. +32 229-61371, 85115

1. Analysis and coordination of tax policies

Philip KERMODE
Head of Unit (acting)
Tel. +32 229-61371, 85115

2. Direct tax legislation

Kerstin MALMER
Head of Unit
Tel. +32 229-52448, 57636

3. Control of the application of Community legislation and state aid/ direct taxation

Bernardus ZUIJDENDORP
Head of Unit
Tel. +32 229-60321, 58117

4. Economic aspects of taxation

Jean-Pierre DE LAET
Head of Unit
Tel. +32 229-60605, 94010

Common Consolidated Corporate Tax Base Task Force

Thomas NEALE
Head of the Task Force
Tel. +32 229-54705, 57906

EDUCATION AND CULTURE DG

Rue de la Loi 200
B-1049 Brussels
Tel. +32 229-91111 (operator)

11, rue Alphonse Weicker
L-2721 Luxembourg
Tel. +352 4301-1 (operator)
Tel. 4301 + extension

Odile QUINTIN
Director-General
Tel. +32 229-92277, 92278

Denis CROWLEY
Assistant to the Director-General
Tel. +32 229-95943

Walter ZAMPIERI
Assistant to the Director-General
Tel. +32 229-98974, 53113

Principal Counsellors

Gilbert GASCARD
Chief Adviser
Tel. +32 229-50017, 62528

David WHITE
Chief Adviser
Tel. +32 229-55724, 62877

Reporting directly to the Director-General

Gilbert GASCARD
Chief Adviser
Tel. +32 229-50017, 62528

1. Policy and interinstitutional coordination

Adam TYSON
Head of Unit
Tel. +32 229-66056, 54958

2. Internal audit (IAC)

Armin BOSCH
Head of Unit
Tel. +32 229-91295, 69986

Directorate A — Lifelong Learning: Horizontal Lisbon Policy Issues and International Affairs

Gordon CLARK
Director (acting)
Tel. +32 229-62929, 63350

Maruja GUTIÉRREZ DÍAZ
Adviser
Tel. +32 229-56346, 58148

1. Lifelong learning: Contribution to the Lisbon process

Gordon CLARK
Head of Unit
Tel. +32 229-62929, 63350

2. European Institute of Innovation and Technology

Lucia RECALDE LANGARICA
Head of Unit (acting)
Tel. +32 229-91281/65375

3. Jean Monnet, university/business partnerships, relations with the agencies

Belen BERNALDO DE QUIROS
Head of Unit
Tel. +32 229-60312, 86429

4. Analysis and studies

Anders HINGEL
Head of Unit
Tel. +32 229-60555, 56970

5. Cooperation and international programmes

Klaus HAUPT
Head of Unit (acting)
Tel. +32 229-69923/81619

Directorate B — Lifelong Learning: Policies and Programme

Helene CLARK
Director
Tel. +32 229-52957/88285

Monika SOPHANSAYNE HOLIK
Head of Unit (seconded)
Tel. +32 229-85807, 61655

1. Coordination of the 'Lifelong learning' programme

Sergio CORTI
Head of Unit
Tel. +32 229-93926, 56392

2. School education; 'Comenius'

Adam POKORNY
Head of Unit
Tel. +32 229-63988/91545

3. Higher education; 'Erasmus'

Barbara NOLAN
Head of Unit
Tel. +32 229-60755/93837

4. Adult education; 'Grundtvig'

Marta FERREIRA-LOURENÇO
Head of Unit
Tel. +32 229-62658/95488

5. Professional training; 'Leonardo da Vinci'

João DELGADO
Head of Unit
Tel. +32 229-53781/61123

Directorate C — Culture, Multilingualism and Communication

Vladimir SUCHA
Director
Tel. +32 229-95548

1. Culture policy and intercultural dialogue

Xavier TROUSSARD
Head of Unit
Tel. +32 229-99126/98792

2. 'Culture' programme and actions

Ann BRANCH
Head of Unit
Tel. +32 229-85340

3. Communication and valorisation

Karel BARTAK
Head of Unit
Tel. +32 229-50695, 67983

4. Central library of the Commission

Roberta PERSICHELLI SCOLA
Head of Unit
Tel. +32 229-50428, 52982

5. Multilingualism policy

Harald HARTUNG
Head of Unit
Tel. +32 229-65450, 86309

Directorate D — Youth, Sport and Citizenship

Pierre MAIRESSE
Director
Tel. +32 229-62009, 62024

1. Youth policy

Sergej KOPERDAK
Head of Unit
Tel. +32 229-69375

2. 'Youth in action'

Pascal LEJEUNE
Head of Unit
Tel. +32 229-50883, 51561

3. Sport

Michal KREJZA
Head of Unit
Tel. +32 229-87423/51135

4. Citizenship policy; 'Europe for citizens'

Risto RAIVIO
Head of Unit
Tel. +32 229-51311, 54919

5. Visits to the Commission

Jaime ANDREU ROMEO
Head of Unit
Tel. +32 229-99252/80876

Directorate R — Resources

António SILVA MENDES
Director
Tel. +32 229-65094, 56687

1. Human resources, internal communication and support to management

Bertrand DELPEUCH
Head of Unit
Tel. +32 229-68711, 67487

2. Programming, budget and evaluation; supervision of EACEA

Bernard NAUDTS
Head of Unit
Tel. +32 229-61537, 63786

3. Accounting and centralised financial management

Bruno KRÖLLER
Head of Unit
Tel. +32 229-59632, 60229

4. Quality of financial management

Johan SIJBENGA
Head of Unit
Tel. +32 229-59106, 66854

5. Informatics resources

Simon SMITH
Head of Unit
Tel. +32 229-68274, 84761

6. Document management, logistical support and traineeships

Jean HERDIES
Head of Unit
Tel. +32 229-61529

HEALTH AND CONSUMERS DG

Rue Breydel 4
B-1049 Brussels
Tel. +32 229-91111 (operator)

L-2920 Luxembourg
Tel. +352 4301-1 (operator)
Tel. +352 4301 + extension

Paul Robert MADELIN
Director-General
Tel. +32 229-63338, 99090

Isabelle BÉNOLIEL
Chief Adviser
Tel. +32 229-60198, 96326

Jan-Peter PAUL
Adviser (reporting directly to the Deputy Director-General)
Tel. +32 229-95064, 66475

Jacques GENNATAS
Adviser (reporting directly to the Deputy Director-General)
Tel. +32 229-59713, 66475

Luc BRIOL
Head of Unit (seconded)
Tel. +352 4301-34450, 37516

Reporting directly to the Director-General

Isabel DE LA MATA
Chief Adviser
Tel. +352 4301-31454, 33988

1. Audit and evaluation

Christophe BERTRAND
Head of Unit
Tel. +32 229-99524

2. Strategy and analysis

María IGLESIA GOMEZ
Head of Unit
Tel. +32 229-53036, 80359

Reporting directly to the Deputy Director-General

Paola TESTORI COGGI
Deputy Director-General
Tel. +32 229-53430

3. Science and stakeholder relations

Robert VANHOORDE
Head of Unit
Tel. +32 229-59928, 63696

4. Veterinary control programmes

James MOYNAGH
Head of Unit
Tel. +32 229-58086, 84530

Directorate A — General Affairs

Robert SHOTTON
Director
Tel. +32 229-56965

Daniel JANSSENS
Director (acting)
Tel. +32 229-51220/51801

David Matthew HUDSON
Adviser
Tel. +32 229-64671, 62465

1. Institutional relations and communication

Éric THÉVENARD
Head of Unit
Tel. +32 229-69966, 21394

2. Legal affairs

Demetris VRYONIDES
Head of Unit
Tel. +32 229-94052, 93600

3. Finance and planning

Daniel JANSSENS
Head of Unit
Tel. +32 229-51220, 51801

4. Information systems

Philippe LOOPUYT
Head of Unit
Tel. +32 229-90572

5. Human resources

Tapani PIHA
Head of Unit
Tel. +32 229-85487/85347

6. Administrative affairs Grange

Serge CHRISTIANE
Head of Unit
Tel. +32 229-70719

Directorate B — Consumer Affairs

Jacqueline MINOR
Director
Tel. +32 229-57226, 69069

1. Consumer markets

David MAIR
Head of Unit
Tel. +32 229-50489, 69736

2. Consumer contracts and marketing law

Guiseppe ABBAMONTE
Head of Unit
Tel. +32 229-93573/54443

3. Product and service safety

Stefano SORO
Head of Unit
Tel. +32 229-67543, 64742

4. Financial services and redress

Dirk STAUDENMAYER
Head of Unit
Tel. +32 229-54552/60649

5. Enforcement and European consumer centres

Tamas Andras MOLNAR
Head of Unit
Tel. +32 229-52319, 65267

6. Consumer strategy, representation and international relations

Carina TORNBLOM-SELT
Head of Unit
Tel. +32 229-90804

Directorate C — Public Health and Risk Assessment

Bâtiment EUFO
L-2920 Luxembourg

Andrzej Jan RYS
Director
Tel. +352 4301-32719, 35640

1. Health programme, communication and knowledge management

Jose Ramon BIOSCA DE SAGASTUY
Head of Unit
Tel. +352 4301-34988, 38947

2. Health information

Nicholas FAHY
Head of Unit
Tel. +352 4301-38816

3. Health threats

John RYAN
Head of Unit
Tel. +352 4301-34658, 34370

4. Health determinants

Michael HUEBEL
Head of Unit
Tel. +352 4301-34023, 36620

5. Health strategy and health systems

Bernard MERKEL
Head of Unit
Tel. +32 229-92100, 86855

6. Health law and international

Patricia BRUNKO
Head of Unit (acting)
Tel. +32 229-62587/96882

7. Risk assessment

Bernardo DELOGU
Head of Unit
Tel. +32 229-90351, 95979

Directorate D — Animal Health and Welfare

Bernard VAN GOETHEM
Director
Tel. +32 229-53143, 68546

Michael SCANNELL
Adviser
Tel. +32 229-93364, 67532

Jacky LE GOSLES
Adviser
Tel. +32 229-63201

1. Animal health and standing committees

Alberto LADDOMADA
Head of Unit
Tel. +32 229-95835, 65207

2. Feed

Willem PENNING
Head of Unit
Tel. +32 229-55651, 54661

3. International questions (multilateral)

Jérôme LEPEINTRE
Head of Unit (acting)
Tel. +32 229-93701

4. International questions (bilateral)

Paul VAN GELDROP
Head of Unit
Tel. +32 229-50513, 68022

5. Animal welfare

Andrea GAVINELLI
Head of Unit
Tel. +32 229-66426, 65041

Directorate E — Safety of the Food Chain

Éric POUDELET
Director
Tel. +32 229-55207/55783

1. Biotechnology and plant health

Michael FLUEH
Head of Unit
Tel. +32 229-92257/92258

2. Hygiene, training and alert system

Koen VAN DYCK
Head of Unit (acting)
Tel. +32 229-84334

3. Chemicals, contaminants, pesticides

Patricia BRUNKO
Head of Unit
Tel. +32 229-62587, 96882

4. Food law, nutrition and labelling

Basil MATHIOUDAKIS
Head of Unit
Tel. +32 229-59182, 90142

5. Enforcement

Carmen GARAU
Head of Unit
Tel. +32 229-58937, 93600

Directorate F — Food and Veterinary Office

Food and Veterinary Office
Grange
Dunsany
Co. Meath
Ireland
Tel. +353 469061700
Fax +353 469061879

Michael Colm GAYNOR
Director
Tel. +32 229-70858, 70892

1. Country profiles, coordination of follow-up

Hugh QUIGLEY
Head of Unit
Tel. +32 229-70730, 70790

2. Food of animal origin: Mammals

Sabine JUELICHER
Head of Unit
Tel. +32 229-70834

3. Food of animal origin: Birds and fish

Carlos ÁLVAREZ ANTOLÍNEZ
Head of Unit
Tel. +32 229-70778

4. Food of plant origin: Plant health, processing and distribution

Nandor Miklos PETE
Head of Unit
Tel. +32 229-70802

5. Animal nutrition, import controls, residues

Kenneth ELLIOTT
Head of Unit (acting)
Tel. +32 229-70837

6. Animal health and welfare

Andrew WILSON
Head of Unit
Tel. +32 229-70786

7. Quality, planning and development

Franciscus ANDRIESSEN
Head of Unit
Tel. +32 229-70714, 70991

JUSTICE, FREEDOM AND SECURITY DG

Rue de Luxembourg 46
B-1050 Brussels
Tel. +32 229-91111 (operator)

Jonathan FAULL
Director-General
Tel. +32 229-58658, 86269

Chiara ADAMO
Assistant to the Director-General
Tel. +32 229-96797, 54327

Telmo BALTAZAR
Assistant to the Director-General
Tel. +32 229-81384, 87085

Diane SCHMITT
Adviser
Tel. +32 229-60736

Reporting directly to the Director-General

Internal audit

Joseph O'NEILL
Head of Unit
Tel. +32 229-60506, 54821

Directorate A — General Affairs

Tung-Lai MARGUE
Director
Tel. +32 229-54437, 54494

1. Strategic policy, evaluation and institutional affairs

Nicola ANNECCHINO
Head of Unit
Tel. +32 229-61870, 58854

2. External relations and enlargement

Luigi SORECA
Head of Unit
Tel. +32 229-62116, 58854

3. Human resources management and IT

Beate GMINDER
Head of Unit
Tel. +32 229-65694, 86596

4. Budget and control

Frédéric KNECHCIAK
Head of Unit
Tel. +32 229-62938, 58624

5. Communication

Nathalie CRESTE
Head of Unit
Tel. +32 229-81027, 58637

Directorate B — Immigration, Asylum and Borders

Jean-Louis DE BROUWER
Director (acting)
Tel. +32 229-61964, 55236

1. Immigration and integration

Martin SCHIEFFER
Head of Unit (acting)
Tel. +32 229-91313/76130

2. Asylum

Angela MARTINI
Head of Unit (acting)
Tel. +32 229-94253

3. International aspects of migration and visa policy

Peter BOSCH
Head of Unit (acting)
Tel. +32 229-62109

4. Financial support — Immigration and asylum

Muriel GUIN
Head of Unit
Tel. +32 229-60013, 88094

Directorate C — Migration and Borders

Jean-Louis DE BROUWER
Director
Tel. +32 229-61964, 55236

1. Border management and return policy

Joannes DE CEUSTER
Head of Unit
Tel. +32 229-61072, 84064

2. IT projects: Infrastructure and legal issues

Frank PAUL
Head of Unit
Tel. +32 229-54875, 85096

3. Large-scale IT systems and biometrics

Bernardus KLOPPENBORG
Head of Unit (acting)
Tel. +32 229-87540/76129

4. Financial support — Migration and borders

Frank ANTOINE-POIREL
Head of Unit (acting)
Tel. +32 229-53163

Directorate D — Fundamental Rights and Citizenship

Francisco FONSECA MORILLO
Director (acting)
Tel. +32 229-56845, 86546

1. Fundamental rights and protection of minors

Ernesto BIANCHI
Head of Unit
Tel. +32 229-94316, 56832

2. Citizenship

Ernesto BIANCHI
Head of Unit (acting)
Tel. +32 229-94316, 56832

3. Anti-drugs policy

Carel EDWARDS
Head of Unit
Tel. +32 229-59538, 57961

4. Financial support — Fundamental rights and citizenship

Renatas MAZEIKA
Head of Unit
Tel. +32 229-62152

5. Data protection

Alain BRUN
Head of Unit
Tel. +32 229-65381, 51287

Directorate E — Justice

Francisco FONSECA MORILLO
Director
Tel. +32 229-56845, 86546

1. General justice and e-justice issues

Lina PAPAMICHALOPOULOU
Head of Unit (acting)
Tel. +32 229-86493, 56146

2. Civil justice

Salla SAASTAMOINEN
Head of Unit
Tel. +32 229-69463, 56567

3. Criminal justice

Peter Jozsef CSONKA
Head of Unit
Tel. +32 229-66563, 57700

4. Financial support — Justice

Lina PAPAMICHALOPOULOU
Head of Unit
Tel. +32 229-86493, 56146

Directorate F — Security

Lotte KNUDSEN
Director (acting)
Tel. +32 229-58066, 57515

1. Fight against terrorism

Lotte KNUDSEN
Head of Unit
Tel. +32 229-58066, 57515

2. Combating organised crime

Jakub BORATYNSKI
Head of Unit
Tel. +32 229-69452/57515

3. Police cooperation and access to information

Joaquim NUNES DE ALMEIDA
Head of Unit
Tel. +32 229-55428, 88099

4. Financial support — Security

Patrick TROUSSON
Head of Unit (acting)
Tel. +32 229-65803, 88058

Rue de la Loi 170
B-1040 Brussels
Tel. +32 229-91111 (operator)

Eneko LANDÁBURU
Director-General
Tel. +32 229-51968, 62211

Karel KOVANDA
Deputy Director-General (CFSP, multilateral relations and North America, east Asia, Australia, New Zealand, EEA, EFTA Directorates A, B and C)
Tel. +32 229-80765, 58324

Hugues MINGARELLI
Deputy Director-General (European neighbourhood policy, relations with eastern Europe, the southern Caucasus and central Asia, the Middle East and the southern Mediterranean (Directorates D, E and F))
Tel. +32 229-99180, 61220

Joao AGUIAR MACHADO
Deputy Director-General (Asia and Latin America, (Directorates G and H))
Tel. +32 229-96310, 60543

Stefano SANNINO
Acting Deputy Director-General (Asia and Latin America (Directorates G and H))
Tel. +32 229-91720

Jean-Marc PISANI
Assistant to the Director-General
Tel. +32 229-95401, 54832

Luisella PAVAN-WOOLFE
Chief Adviser
Tel. +32 229-56638, 95519

Tomasz KOZLOWSKI
Chief Adviser
Tel. +32 229-58926

János HERMAN
Principal Adviser (European neighbourhood policy)
Tel. +32 229-67321, 67370

Peter HUGHES
Adviser
Tel. +32 229-87656

Andriaan VAN DER MEER
Adviser
Tel. *81962

Audit

Francis CLERGEAUD
Head of Unit (seconded)
Tel. +32 229-95585

Directorate A — Crisis Platform, Policy Coordination in Common Foreign and Security Policy (CFSP)

Richard WRIGHT
Director
Tel. +32 229-88598, 90794

1. European correspondent

Helen CAMPBELL
Head of Unit
Tel. +32 229-60172, 57614

2. Crisis response and peacebuilding

Genoveva RUIZ CALAVERA
Head of Unit
Tel. +32 229-50793/94890

3. CFSP operations

Juha AUVINEN
Head of Unit
Tel. +32 229-91072/81125

4. Security policy

Lars-Gunnar WIGEMARK
Head of Unit
Tel. +32 229-52607, 88654

Directorate B — Multilateral Relations and Human Rights

Véronique ARNAULT
Director
Tel. +32 229-90006, 80248

1. Human rights and democratisation

Rolf TIMANS
Head of Unit
Tel. +32 229-87404

2. United Nations, Treaties office

Karen FOGG
Head of Unit
Tel. +32 229-66181, 92687

3. OSCE and the Council of Europe

Gilbert DUBOIS
Head of Unit
Tel. +32 229-57550

Directorate C — North America, East Asia, Australia, New Zealand, EEA, EFTA, San Marino, Andorra and Monaco

Alan SEATTER
Director
Tel. +32 229-54998, 52348

1. United States, Canada

Marc VANHEUKELEN
Head of Unit
Tel. +32 229-98502, 63070

2. Japan, Korea, Australia, New Zealand

Gerhard LOHAN
Head of Unit
Tel. +32 229-91264

Jonathan HATWELL
Head of Unit (acting)
Tel. +32 229-56108/88072

3. EEA, EFTA, San Marino, Andorra, Monaco

Matthias BRINKMANN
Head of Unit
Tel. +32 229-56036, 90096

Directorate D — European Neighbourhood Policy Coordination

Rutger WISSELS
Director
Tel. +32 229-93482, 60971

1. ENP general coordination

John O'ROURKE
Head of Unit
Tel. +32 229-90564, 59280

2. Sectoral ENP coordination

Andreas HERDINA
Head of Unit
Tel. +32 229-69881, 93613

Pierre NAGY
Head of Unit (acting)
Tel. +32 229-53394

Directorate E — Eastern Europe, Southern Caucasus, Central Asian Republics

Gunnar WIEGAND
Director
Tel. +32 229-63110, 90451

1. Russia and Northern Dimension policy

Hilde HARDEMAN
Head of Unit
Tel. +32 229-65077

2. Ukraine, Belarus, Moldova and southern Caucasus

John KJAER
Head of Unit
Tel. +32 229-95504

3. Central Asia

Victor ANDRES MALDONADO
Head of Unit
Tel. +32 229-67420, 53629

Directorate F — Middle East, South Mediterranean

Tomas DUPLA DEL MORAL
Director
Tel. +32 229-92313, 67421

1. Euromed and regional issues

Leonello GABRICI
Head of Unit
Tel. +32 229-65947

2. Gulf countries, Iran, Iraq and Yemen

Patricia LLOMBART CUSSAC
Head of Unit
Tel. +32 229-90964, 92386

3. Near East

Leonidas TEZAPSIDIS
Head of Unit
Tel. +32 229-80067

4. Maghreb

Manfredo FANTI
Head of Unit (acting)
Tel. +32 229-54432

Directorate G — Latin America

Stefano SANNINO
Director
Tel. +32 229-91720

1. Horizontal matters

Marie-Anne CONINSX
Head of Unit
Tel. +32 229-57297, 68544

2. Mexico, Central America

Petros MAVROMICHALIS
Head of Unit
Tel. +32 229-94443, 66567

3. Andean Community

Rafael GELABERT ROTGER
Head of Unit
Tel. +32 229-92354, 92360

4. Mercosur, Chile

Angel CARRO CASTRILLO
Head of Unit
Tel. +32 229-62477, 90829

Directorate H — Asia (except Japan and Korea)

James MORAN
Director
Tel. +32 229-92232, 90734

Andrew Thomas ROE
Adviser
Tel. +32 229-55582

1. Horizontal matters

Jozsef MOLNAR
Head of Unit
Tel. +32 229-86592, 92426

2. China, Hong Kong, Macao, Taiwan, Mongolia

Franz JESSEN
Head of Unit
Tel. +32 229-87028, 53305

3. India, Bhutan, Nepal

Jean-Christian REMOND
Head of Unit
Tel. +32 229-90153, 53275

4. Pakistan, Afghanistan, Sri Lanka, Bangladesh, Maldives

David TIRR
Head of Unit
Tel. +32 229-90181, 61439

5. South-east Asia

Seamus GILLESPIE
Head of Unit
Tel. +32 229-61791, 65606

Directorate I — Headquarters' Resources, Information, Interinstitutional Relations

David LIPMAN
Director
Tel. +32 229-90755, 90655

Christian BRUMTER
Adviser
Tel. +32 229-58918/90655

Styliani ZERVOUDAKI
Adviser
Tel. +32 229-68325, 66689

1. Human resources and administration

Carmen RUIZ SERRANO
Head of Unit
Tel. +32 229-98708, 93576

2. Financial and budgetary matters, relations with the Court of Auditors

Gary MILLER
Head of Unit
Tel. +32 229-57046, 92041

3. Information technology resources and document management

Michael KEYMOLEN
Head of Unit
Tel. +32 229-53788, 51576

4. Interinstitutional relations

Reinhold HACK
Head of Unit
Tel. +32 229-51345

5. Information and communication

David RINGROSE
Head of Unit
Tel. +32 229-93913/51545

Directorate K — External Service

Thierry DE SAINT MAURICE
Director
Tel. +32 229-54727, 65526

Daniel VAN DER SPREE
Adviser
Tel. +32 229-61730

1. Coordination and programming of activities, human and budgetary resources

Ian BOAG
Head of Unit
Tel. +32 229-86533

David O'NEILL
Head of Unit (acting)
Tel. +32 229-62936

2. Ex-post control

Marcel VAN OPSTAL
Head of Unit
Tel. +32 229-64197, 63224

3. Career of officials and contract agents

Rhoda Anette MANDLER
Head of Unit
Tel. +32 229-91649, 88177

4. Rights and obligations of officials and contract agents

Agnes DEMASSIEUX
Head of Unit
Tel. +32 229-50329, 50366

5. Local staff

Girolama NOTARANGELO
Head of Unit
Tel. +32 229-52592, 60712

6. Development of external services: exchanges with Member States, training, protocol and diplomatic questions

Catherine THEODOROU-KALOGIROU
Head of Unit
Tel. +32 229-51833, 68914

7. Infrastructure and security

Fernando PEREZ JIMENEZ
Head of Unit
Tel. +32 229-95225, 68094

8. Prevention and crisis management — Protection

Alberto HASSON
Head of Unit
Tel. +32 229-55800, 94239

9. Informatics

Philippe RUYS
Head of Unit
Tel. +32 229-57020, 52609

Directorate L — Strategy, Coordination and Analysis

Gerhard SABATHIL
Director
Tel. +32 229-63188

Philippe WILLAERT
Adviser
Tel. +32 229-50353, 57128

1. Inspection of delegations

Michael GRAHAM
Head of Unit
Tel. +32 229-69028, 56456

2. Research and forecasting

Alar John Rudolf OLLJUM
Head of Unit
Tel. +32 229-88380, 92353

3. Coordination and analysis

Andrew STANDLEY
Head of Unit
Tel. +32 229-67426, 54042

TRADE DG

Rue de la Loi 200
B-1049 Brussels
Tel. +32 229-91111 (operator)

David O'SULLIVAN
Director-General
Tel. +32 229-50948/50098

Maud LABAT
Assistant to the Director-General
Tel. +32 229-53825, 98268, 98880

João AGUIAR MACHADO
Deputy Director-General
Tel. +32 229-96310/60543

Péter BALÁZS
Deputy Director-General
Tel. +32 229-95168, 90158

Coordination policy

Peter SANDLER
Head of Unit
Tel. +32 229-68645, 52059

Directorate A — Resources and Economic Analysis

Jens SCHAPS
Director
Tel. +32 229-53034, 56399

1. Resources and strategic planning

Anders JESSEN
Head of Unit
Tel. +32 229-92457, 92242

2. Chief Economist

Gaspar FRONTINI CATTIVELLO
Head of Unit
Tel. +32 229-92682, 53942

3. Informatics

Ricardo AGUDO VIVAS
Head of Unit
Tel. +32 229-63509, 95675

Philippe RUYS
Head of Unit (handover)
Tel. +32 229-57020, 52609

Directorate B — Services and Investment, Bilateral Trade Relations

Raffaele PETRICCIONE
Director
Tel. +32 229-61666, 90051

1. Services and investment

Petros SOURMELIS
Head of Unit
Tel. +32 229-87935, 95259

2. Trade relations with the Far East

Maria Helena KONIG
Head of Unit
Tel. +32 229-60205, 52267

3. Trade relations with the Americas

Rupert SCHLEGELMILCH
Head of Unit
Tel. +32 229-85548, 53194

Directorate C — Sustainable Development, Bilateral Trade Relations

Ignacio GARCÍA BERCERO
Director
Tel. +32 229-95661, 58718

1. Sustainable development and SPS issues

Ditte JORGENSEN
Head of Unit
Tel. +32 229-62496, 53081

2. Trade relations with Euromed and the Middle East

Olivier DE LAROUSSILHE
Head of Unit
Tel. +32 229-68502, 51320

3. Trade relations with south Asia, Korea and ASEAN

Philippe MEYER
Head of Unit
Tel. +32 229-51891, 96165

Directorate D — Development and EPAs

Peter THOMPSON
Director
Tel. +32 229-67584, 65640

Roelof PLIJTER
Adviser
Tel. +32 229-68347

1. Trade and development

Andra KOKE
Head of Unit
Tel. +32 229-67998, 85136

2. Economic partnership agreements 1

Claude MAERTEN
Head of Unit
Tel. +32 229-61197, 51099

3. Economic partnership agreements 2

Jacques WUNENBURGER
Head of Unit
Tel. +32 229-64857, 59246

Directorate E — Public Procurement and Intellectual Property, Bilateral Trade Relations

Ewa SYNOWIEC
Director
Tel. +32 229-93810, 92209

1. Europe (non-EU) and central Asia

Leopoldo RUBINACCI
Head of Unit
Tel. +32 229-90303, 61287

2. Public procurement, intellectual property

Luc DEVIGNE
Head of Unit
Tel. +32 229-91873, 86396

Directorate F — WTO Affairs, OECD and Food-related Sectors

Signe RATSO
Director
Tel. +32 229-93776, 86135

1. OMC, OCDE and dual use

Denis REDONNET
Head of Unit
Tel. +32 229-55424

2. Legal aspects of trade policy

Jean-François BRAKELAND
Head of Unit
Tel. +32 229-53918, 21375

Martin LUKAS
Head of Unit (acting)
Tel. +32 229-54506

3. Food-related sectors

Zoltan SOMOGYI
Head of Unit
Tel. +32 229-61237, 68332

Directorate G — Market Access and Industry

Fritz-Harald WENIG
Director
Tel. +32 229-58684, 96169

Peter KLEIN
Director (acting)
Tel. +32 229-57448, 52601

1. Market access

Manuela GELENG
Head of Unit (acting)
Tel. +32 229-62102

2. Industrial sectors

Peter KLEIN
Head of Unit
Tel. +32 229-57448, 52601

3. Tariff and non-tariff industrial negotiations

Fernando PERREAU DE PINNINCK
Head of Unit
Tel. +32 229-61932, 99782

Directorate H — Trade Defence

Stefaan DEPYPERE
Director
Tel. +32 229-90713

Gerhard WELGE
Adviser
Tel. +32 229-68162, 86394

1. General policy, WTO relations

Neil MACDONALD
Head of Unit
Tel. +32 229-57536, 61929

2. Investigations I: Relations with Member States and industry for commercial defence affairs

Thinam JAKOB
Head of Unit
Tel. +32 229-62933, 94275

3. Investigations II: Anti-circumventions

Demos SPATHARIS
Head of Unit
Tel. +32 229-96839, 86394

4. Investigations III: Monitoring of implementation

Piotr OGONOWSKI
Head of Unit
Tel. +32 229-90958

5. Investigations IV: Relations with third countries for commercial defence affairs

Wolfgang MÜLLER
Head of Unit
Tel. +32 229-63010, 91054

6. Investigations V: Administrative matters

Claudia DE CESARIS
Head of Unit
Tel. +32 229-61733, 53470

Hearing Officer

Dominique AVOT
Head of Unit
Tel. +32 229-95102, 99164

Directorate R — Resource Management

Stefaan DEPYPERE
Director
Tel. +32 229-90713, 91027

1. Resources and strategic planning

Anders JESSEN
Head of Unit
Tel. +32 229-92457, 92242

2. Information technology

Ricardo AGUDO VIVAS
Head of Unit
Tel. +32 229-63509

DEVELOPMENT DG

Rue de la Science 15
B-1040 Brussels
Tel. +32 229-91111 (operator)

Stefano MANSERVISI
Director-General
Tel. +32 229-57169, 90417

Philippe LATRICHE
Assistant to the Director-General
Tel. +32 229-93215, 89339

Bernard PETIT
Deputy Director-General
Tel. +32 229-93255, 92898

Anders HENRIKSSON
Chief Adviser
Tel. *80372

Klaas EHBETS
Adviser
Tel. +32 229-92634

1. Internal audit

Walter FARRUGIA
Head of Unit
Tel. +32 229-84280, 92855

2. EU and ACP institutional relations and civil society

Alexander BAUM
Head of Unit
Tel. +32 229-93000, 62961

3. Resources

Chantal GRAYKOWSKI-MASSANGIOLI
Head of Unit
Tel. +32 229-92674, 68446

Directorate A — General Matters and Operational Support

Maciej POPOWSKI
Director
Tel. +32 229-93238, 92635

1. Forward-looking studies and policy coherence

Françoise MOREAU
Head of Unit
Tel. +32 229-90772, 93200

2. Aid effectiveness and relations with Member States and EEA states

Olivier LUYCKX
Head of Unit
Tel. +32 229-64110, 95960

3. Relations with international organisations and non-EU states

Peter CRAIG MCQUAIDE
Head of Unit
Tel. +32 229-92784, 98877

4. Information, communication and IT

Ian BARBER
Head of Unit
Tel. +32 229-52365, 54210

Directorate B — Development Policy and Sectoral Questions

Luis RIERA FIGUERAS
Director
Tel. +32 229-65068, 51810

1. Economic development: Infrastructure and communication networks, trade and regional integration

Antonio GARCÍA FRAGIO
Head of Unit
Tel. +32 229-93295, 93296

2. Sustainable management of natural resources

Philip MIKOS
Head of Unit
Tel. +32 229-93047, 54601

3. Human development, social cohesion and employment

Irene HOREJS
Head of Unit
Tel. +32 229-61302, 92548

Directorate C — ACP I — General Affairs

Klaus RUDISCHHAUSER
Director
Tel. +32 229-90421, 56506

1. Aid programming and management

Jean-Pierre REYMONDET-COMMOY
Head of Unit
Tel. +32 229-91609, 95588

Leandro MERCADE LLORDACHS
Adviser (ad personam)
Tel. +32 229-66519

2. Pan-African issues and institutions, governance and migration

Philippe DARMUZEY
Head of Unit
Tel. +32 229-65592, 69321

3. Economic governance and budget support

Marinus BAAN
Head of Unit
Tel. +32 229-63700

Directorate D — ACP II — West and Central Africa, Caribbean and OCTs

Manuel LOPEZ BLANCO
Director
Tel. +32 229-93230, 91186

1. Relations with the countries and the region of the Caribbean and the OCTs

John CALOGHIROU
Head of Unit
Tel. +32 229-93281, 54559

2. Relations with the countries and the region of west Africa

Patrick SPIRLET
Head of Unit (acting)
Tel. +32 229-60898, 67977

3. Relations with the countries and the region of central Africa and the Great Lakes

Elisabeth TISON
Head of Unit
Tel. +32 229-92766, 91669

Directorate E — ACP III — Horn of Africa, East and Southern Africa, Indian Ocean and Pacific

Roger MOORE
Director
Tel. +32 229-92672, 99812

1. Relations with the countries and the region of the Pacific

Ranieri SABATUCCI
Head of Unit
Tel. +32 229-92936, 90999

2. Relations with the countries and the regions of the Horn of Africa, East Africa and the Indian Ocean

Jeremy LESTER
Head of Unit
Tel. +32 229-53760, 88189

3. Relations with the countries and the region of southern Africa

Giorgio COCCHI
Head of Unit (acting)
Tel. +32 229-92530

ENLARGEMENT DG

Rue de la Loi 200
B-1049 Brussels

Michael LEIGH
Director-General
Tel. +32 229-58236/81748

Jan TRUSZCZYNSKI
Deputy Director-General
Tel. +32 229-98754, 67826

Mark Lawrence MEREDITH
Assistant to the Director-General
Tel. +32 229-57538, 92350

Reporting directly to the Director-General

Internal audit capability

Imre CROUY-CHANEL
Head of Unit
Tel. +32 229-86032/59260

Task Force: Phasing out AER

Rony SABAH
Head of the Task Force
Tel. +32 229-92979

Directorate A — Enlargement Policy and Communication

Timo SUMMA
Director
Tel. +32 229-91671, 21836

Alain SERVANTIE
Adviser
Tel. +32 229-98933, 53269

1. Enlargement strategy

Axel WALLDEN
Head of Unit
Tel. +32 229-66942/61350

2. Information, communication

Gisela GAUGGEL-ROBINSON
Head of Unit
Tel. +32 229-61146/92736

3. Task Force: Turkish Cypriot Community

Andrew RASBASH
Head of Unit
Tel. +32 229-59243/58845

Directorate B — Croatia, the Former Yugoslav Republic of Macedonia, Turkey

Dirk LANGE
Director (acting)
Tel. +32 229-52837/57988

Vaclav DE LOBKOWICZ
Adviser
Tel. +32 229-55176, 50552

1. Croatia

Dirk LANGE
Head of Unit
Tel. +32 229-52837/57988

2. The former Yugoslav Republic of Macedonia

Martin DAWSON
Head of Unit (acting)
Tel. +32 229-85010

3. Turkey

Jean-Christophe FILORI
Head of Unit
Tel. +32 229-65660

Directorate C — Albania, Bosnia and Herzegovina, Montenegro, Serbia, Kosovo Issues

Pierre MIREL
Director
Tel. +32 229-56172, 56349

1. Albania, Bosnia and Herzegovina

Paola PAMPALONI
Head of Unit
Tel. +32 229-63825/62602

2. Montenegro, Serbia

Thérèse SOBIESKI
Head of Unit
Tel. +32 229-90225/84414

3. Kosovo issues

Ruud VAN ENK
Head of Unit (acting)
Tel. +32 229-80136

4. Albania, Montenegro

Vassilis MARAGOS
Head of Unit (acting)
Tel. +32 229-57198

Directorate D — Financial Instruments and Regional Programmes

Timo SUMMA
Director (acting)
Tel. +32 229-91671, 21836

1. Financial instruments and contracts

André LYS
Head of Unit
Tel. +32 229-66681

2. Post-accession financial assistance

Jaime GARCÍA LOMBARDERO
Head of Unit
Tel. +32 229-57799, 59266

3. Regional programmes

Sture Yngve ENGSTROM
Head of Unit
Tel. +32 229-99668, 63392

4. Institution building, TAIEX, twinning

Morten JUNG-OLSEN
Head of Unit
Tel. +32 229-91999, 60972

Directorate E — Resources

Gerhard SCHUMANN-HITZLER
Director
Tel. +32 229-62423, 81155

Göran SEGERLUND
Adviser
Tel. +32 229-92055/58662

1. Strategic planning, internal control and information technology

Adriano ZILHÃO
Head of Unit
Tel. +32 229-93873, 71872

2. Human resources

Michaela DI BUCCI
Head of Unit
Tel. +32 229-96284

3. Financial execution

Daniel HACHEZ
Head of Unit
Tel. +32 229-63708, 66156

4. Operational audit and evaluation

Michael BERRISFORD
Head of Unit
Tel. +32 229-66480/96422

EUROPEAID

Rue de la Loi 41
B-1040 Brussels
Tel. +32 229-65802, 93520

Jacobus RICHELLE
Director-General
Tel. +32 229-63638, 87533

Laurent SARAZIN
Assistant to the Director-General
Tel. +32 229-99621, 66492

Emma TOLEDANO LAREDO
Assistant to the Director-General
Tel. +32 229-66204, 66492

Androulla KAMINARA
Principal Adviser (position during a secondment within the institution)
Tel. *80418

Reporting directly to the Director-General

1. Organisation strategies, efficiency of aid and relations with donors

Luc BAGUR
Head of Unit
Tel. +32 229-91845, 56509

2. Internal auditing

Ole SCOTT-LARSEN
Head of Unit
Tel. +32 229-92722, 54124

3. Evaluation

Jean-Louis CHOMEL
Head of Unit
Tel. +32 229-62939, 66485

4. Information, communication and relations with the public

Philippe LOOP
Head of Unit
Tel. +32 229-93720, 84720

Reporting directly to the Deputy Director-General

Richard WEBER
Deputy Director-General
Tel. +32 229-53055, 97847

Directorate A — Europe, Southern Mediterranean, Middle East and Neighbourhood Policy

Markus CORNARO
Director
Tel. +32 229-95424, 99418

1. Geographical coordination and supervision for Europe

Barbara LUECKE
Head of Unit
Tel. +32 229-63223, 98574

2. Geographical coordination and supervision for the Mediterranean and Middle East

Johannes DUYNHOUWER
Head of Unit
Tel. +32 229-90721, 66347

3. Centralised operations for Europe, the Mediterranean and Middle East

Carla MONTESI
Head of Unit
Tel. +32 229-61453, 56972

4. Nuclear safety

Jean-Paul JOULIA
Head of Unit
Tel. +32 229-57210, 86635

5. Finance, contracts and audit for Europe, the Mediterranean and Middle East

Jean-Louis VILLE
Head of Unit
Tel. +32 229-62256, 62498

6. Multi-country programmes

Juan DE LA CABALLERIA CRUZ
Head of Unit
Tel. +32 229-59123, 55924

Directorate B — Latin America

Alexandra CAS GRANJE
Director
Tel. +32 229-56269, 85653

1. Geographical coordination and supervision for Latin America

Jaime REIS CONDE
Head of Unit
Tel. +32 229-66879, 85255

2. Centralised operations for Latin America

Basile PAPADOPOULOS
Director
Tel. +32 229-92608

3. Financing, contracts and audit for Latin America

Fermin, J. MELENDRO ARNAIZ
Head of Unit
Tel. +32 229-62501, 52203

Directorate C — Sub-Saharan Africa, Caribbean (ACP) and the Pacific

Gary QUINCE
Director
Tel. +32 229-54859, 50931

1. Coordination and supervision for the ACP countries

José Luis TRIMIÑO PEREZ
Head of Unit
Tel. +32 229-90823, 93290

2. Coordination and supervision for the ACP countries

Mikael BARFOD
Head of Unit
Tel. +32 229-54278, 63101

3. Coordination between ACP countries and OCTs, pan-African issues and horizontal aspects

Gerardus GIELEN
Head of Unit
Tel. +32 229-95238

4. Centralised operations for the ACP countries

Raul MATEUS PAULA
Head of Unit
Tel. +32 229-59278, 58616

5. Finance, contracts and audit for the ACP countries

Carlo EICH
Head of Unit
Tel. +32 229-57864, 54265

6. African Union and support for peace

Chantal HEBBERECHT
Head of Unit
Tel. +32 229-92577, 73714

7. Support for water and energy

Carla OSORIO
Head of Unit
Tel. +32 229-51084, 50485

Directorate D — Asia and Central Asia

Dirk MEGANCK
Director
Tel. +32 229-61380, 59438

1. Geographical coordination and supervision for Asia and central Asia

Beata KOLECKA
Head of Unit
Tel. +32 229-67371, 51040

2. Centralised operations for Asia and central Asia

William HANNA
Head of Unit
Tel. +32 229-90430, 54273

3. Finance, contracts and audit for Asia and central Asia

Paul CEUNINCK
Head of Unit (acting)
Tel. +32 229-52179

Directorate E — Quality of Operations

Francesca MOSCA
Director
Tel. +32 229-68575

Guy DOUCET
Adviser
Tel. +32 229-60739

1. Macro-economic support

Jürgen LOVASZ
Head of Unit (acting)
Tel. +32 229-69189

2. Business, trade and regional integration

Jan TEN BLOEMENDAL
Head of Unit
Tel. +32 229-92817, 90806

3. Social and human development and migration

Hélène BOURGADE
Head of Unit
Tel. +32 229-54278, 62891

4. Government, security and human rights

Dominique DELLICOUR
Head of Unit
Tel. +32 229-55937, 95087

5. Quality control systems and methodologies

Wojciech LUBOWIECKI
Head of Unit
Tel. +32 229-98426

6. Natural resources

Jean-Pierre HALKIN
Head of Unit
Tel. +32 229-57042, 53319

7. Infrastructures

Jean-Louis LACUBE
Head of Unit
Tel. +32 229-69166, 93022

Directorate F — Thematic Operations

Aristotelis BOURATSIS
Director
Tel. +32 229-99244, 90853

1. Relations with civil society, coordination

Angelo BAGLIO
Head of Unit
Tel. +32 229-57276

2. Central management of thematic budgetary lines PA RELEX

Sari SUOMALAINEN
Head of Unit
Tel. +32 229-64544, 88528

3. Central management of thematic budget lines PA DEV

Roberto RIDOLFI
Head of Unit
Tel. +32 229-65314, 67997

4. Finance, contracts and audit for thematic budgetary lines

Hans STAUSBOLL
Head of Unit
Tel. +32 229-91681, 90745

Françoise COLLET
Head of the Task Force
Tel. +32 229-90060

Directorate G — Resources

Constantin STATHOPOULOS
Director
Tel. +32 229-52463, 53837

1. Programming and budgetary matters

José IZARRA AGUADO
Head of Unit
Tel. +32 229-92818, 59460

2. Coordination of ICS and methodology for *ex-post* controls and auditing

Fabienne LEVY
Head of Unit
Tel. +32 229-94002, 98717

3. Human resources

Martine LÊVEQUE
Head of Unit
Tel. +32 229-86350, 67509

4. Training and knowledge management

Gerard VAN BILZEN
Head of Unit
Tel. +32 229-63991, 97758

5. Information systems, office automation

Fernando CENTURIONE
Head of Unit
Tel. +32 229-99336

6. Documents management and office infrastructures

Jolita BUTKEVICIENE
Head of Unit
Tel. +32 229-59279, 60394

7. Financial and contractual questions and legal affairs

Denis SALORD
Head of Unit
Tel. +32 229-56047

8. Relations with the Council, the European Parliament and international organisations, Secretariat of the Management Committees

Martyn PENNINGTON
Head of Unit
Tel. +32 229-92597, 99654

HUMANITARIAN AID DG (ECHO)

Rue d'Arlon 88
B-1040 Brussels
Tel. +32 229-91111 (operator)
Fax +32 229-54544

Peter ZANGL
Director-General
Tel. +32 229-54147, 61293

Reporting directly to the Director-General

Policy strategy and evaluation questions

Johannes LUCHNER
Head of Unit
Tel. +32 229-68811, 58550

Directorate A — Operations

Steffen STENBERG-JENSEN
Director
Tel. +32 229-92740, 55998

1. Africa, Caribbean and Pacific countries

Cornelis WITTEBROOD
Head of Unit
Tel. +32 229-57312, 57562

2. Central and eastern Europe, NIS, Mediterranean, Middle East

Jean-Claude HEYRAUD
Head of Unit
Tel. +32 229-69471, 96279

3. Asia and Latin America

Esko KENTRSCHYNSKYJ
Head of Unit
Tel. +32 229-53420, 60260

4. Food aid and preparation for catastrophes

Jan-Artur SIENCZEWSKI
Head of Unit
Tel. +32 229-61949, 65560

5. Information and communication

Simon HORNER
Head of Unit
Tel. +32 229-92996, 54400

Directorate B — Support for Operations

1. Budget, audit, IRM, document management

Vijay BHARDWAJ
Head of Unit
Tel. +32 229-90889, 56587

2. Financial management, legal and procedural affairs

Herman MOSSELMANS
Head of Unit
Tel. +32 229-56704, 58419

3. Human resources

René GUTH
Head of Unit
Tel. +32 229-63749, 61652

EUROSTAT

Bâtiment Bech
11, rue Alphonse Weicker
L-2721 Luxembourg
Tel. +352 4301-1 (operator)
Tel. +352 4301 + extension

Walter RADERMACHER
Director-General
Tel. +352 4301-31748

Marie BOHATA
Deputy Director-General
Tel. +352 4301-37630, 32033

Reporting directly to the Director-General

Annika NÄSLUND FOGELBERG
Assistant to the Director-General
Tel. +352 4301-33055, 33537

Klaus REEH
Adviser
Tel. +352 4301-33523

Daniel DEFAYS
Adviser
Tel. +352 4301-32854, 34190

Robert VAN DER STAR
Adviser
Tel. +352 4301-36374

Guillermo DAVILA MURO
Adviser
Tel. +32 229-93434, 53967

Internal audit

Véronique WASBAUER
Head of Unit
Tel. +352 4301-38102, 35010

Reporting directly to the Deputy Director-General

Statistical governance, quality and evaluation

Antonio BAIGORRI MATAMALA
Head of Unit
Tel. +352 4301-35564, 34066

Directorate A — Resources

Roland LANE
Director (acting)
Tel. +352 4301-34675, 36216

1. Personnel

Roland LANE
Head of Unit
Tel. +352 4301-34675, 36216

2. Planning and reporting

Efstratios CHATZIDOUKAKIS
Head of Unit
Tel. +352 4301-36197, 37141

3. Budgetary matters

Marguerite Christine COIN
Head of Unit
Tel. +352 4301-33722, 34821

4. Legal, institutional and international affairs

Pierre BISCHOFF
Head of Unit
Tel. +352 4301-38561, 34116

5. Communication

Philippe BAUTIER
Head of Unit
Tel. +352 4301-33556

6. Training and document administration

Athanassia CHRISSANTHAKI
Head of Unit
Tel. +352 4301-32087, 37274

Directorate B — Statistical Methods and Tools, Dissemination

Pedro DÍAZ MUÑOZ
Director
Tel. +352 4301-35474, 33821

1. IT systems for statistical production

Adam WRONSKI
Head of Unit
Tel. +352 4301-35285

2. IT infrastructure

Wolfgang KNÜPPEL
Head of Unit
Tel. +352 4301-33221, 34769

3. Statistical information technologies

John ALLEN
Head of Unit
Tel. +352 4301-37291, 32571

4. Reference databases

August GÖTZFRIED
Head of Unit
Tel. +352 4301-34432, 32008

5. Methodology and research

Rainer MUTHMANN
Head of Unit
Tel. +352 4301-37260, 36362

6. Dissemination

Günter SCHÄFER
Head of Unit
Tel. +352 4301-33566, 32581

Directorate C — National and European Accounts

Laurs NØRLUND
Director
Tel. +352 4301-36850, 37209

Maria-Helena FIGUEIRA
Director (acting)
Tel. +352 4301-34730, 31598

Francisco SOBRINO VAZQUEZ
Adviser
Tel. +352 4301-34919

1. National accounts: Methodology and analysis

Gallo GUEYE
Head of Unit
Tel. +352 4301-34859, 31942

2. National accounts: Production

Roberto BARCELLAN
Head of Unit
Tel. +352 4301-35802, 34245

3. Public finance

Luca ASCOLI
Head of Unit
Tel. +352 4301-32707, 36226

4. Balance of payments

Maria-Helena FIGUEIRA
Head of Unit
Tel. +352 4301-34730, 31598

5. Validation of public accounts

Eduardo BARREDO CAPELOT
Head of Unit
Tel. +352 4301-35402, 32473

Directorate D — Economic and Regional Statistics

Inna STEINBUKA
Director
Tel. +352 4301-32372

Marie BOHATA
Director (acting)
Tel. +352 4301-37630, 32033

1. Key indicators for European policies

Nikolaus WURM
Head of Unit
Tel. +352 4301-33589, 34322

2. Regional indicators and geographical information

Roger CUBITT
Head of Unit
Tel. +352 4301-33088, 35647

Berthold FELDMANN
Head of Unit (acting)
Tel. +352 4301-34401/35647

3. Short-term statistics

Brian NEWSON
Head of Unit
Tel. +352 4301-32086, 35257

4. Price statistics

Alexandre MAKARONIDIS
Head of Unit
Tel. +352 4301-34792, 38137

5. Remuneration and pensions

Jean-Claude ROMAN
Head of Unit
Tel. +352 4301-33548, 34191

Directorate E — Agriculture and Environment Statistics, Statistical Cooperation

Pieter EVERAERS
Director
Tel. +352 4301-36847

1. Farms, agro-environment and rural development

Johan SELENIUS
Head of Unit (acting)
Tel. +352 4301-37322, 36475

2. Agricultural and fisheries statistics

Marcel ERNENS
Head of Unit
Tel. +352 4301-34115

3. Environmental statistics and accounts

Gilles DECAND
Head of Unit
Tel. +352 4301-33411, 37242

4. Statistical cooperation with European and Mediterranean countries

Arunas BUTKEVICIUS
Head of Unit
Tel. +352 4301-35693, 31550

5. International statistical cooperation

James WHITWORTH
Head of Unit
Tel. +352 4301-36857, 34830

Directorate F — Social Statistics and Information Society

Michel GLAUDE
Director
Tel. +352 4301-36848, 33010

1. Demographic and migration statistics

Bettina KNAUTH
Head of Unit
Tel. +352 4301-32969, 32751

2. Labour market statistics

Joachim RECKTENWALD
Head of Unit
Tel. +352 4301-34103, 33188

3. Living conditions and social protection statistics

Anne CLEMENCEAU
Head of Unit
Tel. +352 4301-34880, 36707

4. Education, science and culture statistics

Jean-Louis MERCY
Head of Unit
Tel. +352 4301-34862, 37342

5. Health and food safety statistics

Marleen DE SMEDT
Head of Unit
Tel. +352 4301-33673

6. Information society and tourism statistics

Michail SKALIOTIS
Head of Unit
Tel. +352 4301-32011, 34953

Directorate G — Business Statistics

Peter BEKX
Director
Tel. +352 4301-36603, 35585

1. Structural business statistics

Inger OEHMAN
Head of Unit
Tel. +352 4301-37286, 34690

2. International trade statistics: Methodology and classifications

Ales CAPEK
Head of Unit
Tel. +352 4301-36045, 34304

3. International trade statistics: Production

Jan PLANOVSKY
Head of Unit
Tel. +352 4301-35551

4. Energy statistics

Peter TAVOULARIDIS
Head of Unit
Tel. +352 4301-33023, 32040

5. Transport statistics

Ovidio CROCICCHI
Head of Unit
Tel. +352 4301-33608, 34190

PERSONNEL AND ADMINISTRATION DG

Rue de la Loi 200
B-1040 Brussels
Tel. +32 229-91111 (operator)

Bâtiment Jean Monnet
L-2920 Luxembourg
Tel. +352 4301-1 (operator)
Tel. +352 4301 + extension

Claude CHÊNE
Director-General
Tel. +32 229-52437, 52965

Irène SOUKA
Deputy Director-General
Tel. +32 229-57206, 95313

Reporting directly to the Director-General

Christian LINDER
Assistant to the Director-General
Tel. +32 229-86917, 91385

Christian LEVASSEUR
Assistant to the Director-General
Tel. +32 229-65580/91385

1. Audit

Roberto CARLINI
Head of Unit
Tel. +32 229-64512

2. Coordination and policy of the Luxembourg site

Alberto KOZLIK
Head of Unit
Tel. +352 4301-33653, 33458

Principal Adviser in charge of security matters

Frank ASBECK
Chief Adviser

Principal Adviser for administrative reform

Gabrielle CLOTUCHE
Chief Adviser
Tel. +352 4301-87774

Adviser responsible for the financial irregularities panel

Erik HALSKOV
Adviser
Tel. +32 229-62451, 94959

Principal Advisers

Daniel BYK
Principal Adviser (reporting to the Director-General)
Tel. +352 4301-32048

Piet VERLEYSEN
Chief Adviser
Tel. +352 4301-32048, 237928

Permanent rapporteur to the CCA

Hendrik POST
Permanent Rapporteur
Tel. +32 229-66606, 85644

Renaud DENUIT
Adviser
Tel. +32 229-56607, 50464

CCN procedures

Valentina SUPERTI
Head of Unit
Tel. +32 229-65403, 69405

Adviser for organisation and control

...
Adviser (with responsibility for organisation and control)

Directorate A — Staff and Careers

Irène SOUKA
Director (acting)
Tel. +32 229-57206, 95313

1. General policy, agencies and coordination

Enrico Maria ARMANI
Head of Unit
Tel. +32 229-93371

2. SCOP: Career guidance and development of human resources management

Fernando GARCÍA FERREIRO
Head of Unit
Tel. +32 229-50283, 59880

3. Learning and development

Norman JARDINE
Head of Unit
Tel. +32 229-92852, 86528

4. Officials and external staff: Administrative procedures

Jacky MARTEAU
Head of Unit
Tel. +32 229-55264/65386

5. Organisation chart and management staff

Matthias WILL
Head of Unit
Tel. +32 229-57387, 59615

6. Career structure, evaluation and promotions

Christian LEVASSEUR
Head of Unit
Tel. +32 229-65580/91385

Jacky MARTEAU
Head of Unit (handover)
Tel. +32 229-55264/65386

Directorate B — Staff Regulations: Policy, Management and Advisory Services

Bernhard JANSEN
Director
Tel. +32 229-57604, 85798

Adrian BARNETT
Legal Adviser
Tel. +32 229-52190

1. Legal issues and questions relating to the Staff Regulations, relations with the institutions

Marta PASCUA MATEO
Head of Unit (acting)
Tel. +32 229-88586

2. Complaints

Massimo BABICH
Head of Unit (acting)
Tel. +32 229-56612, 50663

3. Conditions of employment, non-pecuniary rights and obligations, ADMINFO

Jean-Pierre GRILLO
Head of Unit
Tel. +32 229-51325

4. Equal opportunities and non-discrimination

Emanuelle GRANGE
Head of Unit
Tel. +32 229-58795, 57422

5. Social dialogue, enlargement and relations with national public administrations

Hans-Georg GERSTENLAUER
Head of Unit
Tel. +32 229-84058, 57594

Directorate C — Social Welfare and Health Policies

Marco-Umberto MORICCA
Director
Tel. +32 229-61654/53905

1. Social welfare policy

Gail KENT
Head of Unit
Tel. +32 229-91945, 85056

2. Medical service and social psychological interventions: Brussels

Giovanni FRACCHIA
Head of Unit
Tel. +32 229-55006/54232

Dr Serve DOLMANS
Adviser
Tel. +32 229-53906, 61210

3. Medical service and social psychological interventions: Luxembourg

Dr Thierry JADOT
Head of Unit
Tel. +352 4301-32592/32588

Directorate D — Resources, Coordination and Communication, Relations with the Offices

Alain SCRIBAN
Director
Tel. +32 229-63343, 56309

Patrice MARCELLI
Adviser (data protection and computer security)
Tel. +32 229-52556

1. Budget and contractual support

Hendrik VANTILBORGH
Head of Unit
Tel. +32 229-55521, 53268

2. Strategic planning and evaluation, relations with the institutions and the offices

Daniele DOTTO
Head of Unit
Tel. +32 229-62701, 55276

3. ADMIN human and financial resources, IAS, Cabinets cell

Sophie BEERNAERTS
Head of Unit
Tel. +32 229-66315, 88667

4. European Schools

Christiane BARDOUX
Head of Unit
Tel. +32 229-54547, 62584

5. Communication and information management

Janette SINCLAIR
Head of Unit
Tel. +32 229-66674, 92164

Directorate DS — Security

Stephen HUTCHINS
Director
Tel. +32 229-56168, 64277

Marc BECQUET
Adviser (seconded)
Tel. +32 229-93181/80276

1. Protection and crisis management

Richard SONNENSCHEIN
Head of Unit
Tel. +32 229-87253

2. Security intelligence and external liaison

Eduardo CANO ROMERA
Head of Unit
Tel. +32 229-61502, 94828

3. Inspection and advisory services

Audrius NAVIKAS
Head of Unit
Tel. +32 229-58716, 92283

4. Guards, equipment and security controls, access controls

Claude CHAMPETTER
Head of Unit
Tel. +32 229-62099, 56654

5. Coordination and IT security

Guido VERVAET
Head of Unit
Tel. +32 229-59224

6. Health and safety at work

Antonio CALVO ALONSO-CORTES
Head of Unit
Tel. +32 229-51015, 51190

Directorate IDOC — Investigation and Disciplinary Office of the Commission

Michel MAGNIER
Director
Tel. +32 229-56199, 57107

1. Investigations and discipline: Compliance with financial obligations

René SLOOTJES
Head of Unit (acting)
Tel. +32 229-56559/57107

2. Investigations and discipline: Compliance with non-financial statutory obligations

René SLOOTJES
Head of Unit
Tel. +32 229-56559/57107

INFORMATICS DG

Rue Alcide de Gasperi
L-2920 Luxembourg
Tel. +352 4301-1 (operator)
Tel. +352 4301 + extension

Avenue de Cortenbergh 6
B-1040 Brussels
Tel. +32 229 + extension

Francisco GARCÍA MORÁN
Director-General
Tel. +352 4301-34561, 34301

Frederic FIMEYER
Assistant to the Director-General
Tel. +32 229-95296, 50529

Reporting directly to the Director-General

Online administration systems (IDABC)

Karel DE VRIENDT
Head of Unit
Tel. +32 229-68563, 84917

Directorate A — Central Infrastructure Services and Solutions

Christos ELLINIDES
Director
Tel. +352 4301-30271
Tel. +32 229-88476

1. Corporate support and training services

Georges TE KOLSTE
Head of Unit
Tel. +32 229-64735
Tel. +352 4301-34237

2. Corporate infrastructure solutions (LUX)

Giorgio BENALI
Head of Unit
Tel. +352 4301-33680/34405

3. Corporate infrastructure solutions for information systems

José MARÍN NAVARRO
Head of Unit
Tel. +352 4301-34531, 34405

Directorate B — Information Systems

Declan DEASY
Director
Tel. +32 229-63715, 57837

1. Information systems for document management and corporate decision-making processes

Philippe BIERLAIRE
Head of Unit
Tel. +32 229-94682/60574

Angelo TOSETTI
Head of Unit (handover)
Tel. +32 229-68924/71930

2. e-Commission, interoperability, architecture and methods

Franck NOËL
Head of Unit (acting)
Tel. +32 229-62112/87059

3. Information systems for human resource management

Philippe BIERLAIRE
Head of Unit (acting)
Tel. +32 229-94682/60574

4. Information systems for planning, financial and document management

Angelo TOSETTI
Head of Unit
Tel. +32 229-68924, 71930

Directorate C — Infrastructure Services Provision

Marcel JORTAY
Director
Tel. +352 4301-34235, 35041

1. Information system hosting services

Patrick DE CONINCK
Head of Unit
Tel. +352 4301-34551, 34237

2. Corporate infrastructure services

Marc FEIDT
Head of Unit
Tel. +352 4301-33104, 37486

3. Corporate ICT infrastructure users proximity services

Margarida ABECASIS
Head of Unit
Tel. +32 229-59999, 96495

Jean-Pierre LAMBOT
Head of Unit (handover)
Tel. +32 229-60201, 52640

4. Infrastructure services coordination and customer relations

Jean-Pierre LAMBOT
Head of Unit
Tel. +32 229-60201, 52640

Directorate R — Resources and Logistics

Arturo CABALLERO BASSEDAS
Director
Tel. +32 229-53974, 69626

1. Planning and resources

Francis PELTGEN
Head of Unit
Tel. +32 229-50907, 57584

2. Finance and contracts

José BILBAO ZABALA
Head of Unit
Tel. +32 229-52544, 67092

3. Logistics

Philippe BELLOSSI
Head of Unit
Tel. +32 229-96501

Adviser Principal

Rocco TANZILLI
Chief Adviser
Tel. +352 4301-38337

BUDGET DG

Avenue d'Auderghem 45
B-1049 Brussels
Tel. +32 229-91111 (operator)

Bâtiment Jean Monnet
L-2920 Luxembourg
Tel. +352 4301-1 (operator)
Tel. +352 4301 + extension

Luis ROMERO REQUENA
Director-General
Tel. +32 229-95150, 62353

Ico WEDEL-GOEDENS
Assistant to the Director-General
Tel. +32 229-57327, 96680

Brian GRAY
Deputy Director-General responsible for Directorate C and Unit 1, Commission Accounting Officer
Tel. +32 229-54627

Pierre MERIGUET
Adviser
Tel. +32 229-54234, 93150

Reporting directly to the Director-General

1. Discharge procedure, parliamentary questions, relations with the ECA and the COCOBU

Elisabeth WERNER
Head of Unit
Tel. +32 229-59506, 50441

2. Internal audit capability

Ekaterini PHILANIOTOU
Head of Unit
Tel. +32 229-57825, 99858

Directorate A — Expenditure

Silvano PRESA
Director
Tel. +32 229-52221, 53931

1. Budgetary procedures and synthesis, ABB and relations with the COBU

Philippe JOURET
Head of Unit
Tel. +32 229-65768, 53517

2. CAP and structural policies

Philippe BERTRAND
Head of Unit
Tel. +32 229-61823, 94297

3. Internal policies

Jacques SANT'ANA CALAZANS
Head of Unit
Tel. +32 229-56300, 88035

4. External policies

Jacques VONTHRON
Head of Unit
Tel. +32 229-52983, 87690

5. Administrative appropriations and allocation of IT resources

Luca DALPOZZO
Head of Unit
Tel. +32 229-51771, 62384

6. Allocation of human resources

Agnes MONFRET
Head of Unit
Tel. +32 229-65402, 68044

7. Monitoring and reporting on budget implementation

Yiannakis ASIMAKIS
Head of Unit
Tel. +32 229-68752, 87925

Directorate B — Own Resources, Evaluation and Financial Programming

Stefan LEHNER
Director
Tel. +32 229-93383, 94984

1. Multiannual financial framework, funding systems and forecasts, budgetary aspects of enlargement

Johan UREEL
Head of Unit (acting)
Tel. +32 229-66609, 92973

2. Revenue management

José MADEIRA
Head of Unit
Tel. +32 229-65440

3. Control of traditional own resources and support for candidate countries

Antti SUORTTI
Head of Unit
Tel. +32 229-67258

4. Control of VAT- and GNP-based resources and ACOR secretariat

Robert GIELISSE
Head of Unit
Tel. +32 229-59649, 65458

5. Evaluation

Svend JAKOBSEN
Head of Unit
Tel. +32 229-60774, 96561

Directorate C — Budget Execution (General Budget and EDF) [10]

Ciaran SPILLANE
Director
Tel. +32 229-81263, 51534

1. Treasury management

Willy HOEBEECK
Head of Unit
Tel. +32 229-54075

2. Accounting

María Rosa ALDEA BUSQUETS
Head of Unit
Tel. +32 229-50848, 56062

3. Accounting and budget execution

Enrique LOBERA ARGUELLES
Head of Unit
Tel. +32 229-63085, 61899

4. Financial reporting and validation of local systems

Joseph MURRAN
Head of Unit
Tel. +32 229-58338, 51534

5. Recovery of entitlements

Marc EKELMANS
Head of Unit
Tel. +32 229-56873, 62606

Directorate D — Central Financial Service

Philippe TAVERNE
Director
Tel. +32 229-53590, 87442

1. Financial regulations

Paraskevi GILCHRIST
Head of Unit
Tel. +32 229-51018, 59895

[10] Coordinated by the Deputy Director-General.

2. Procurement, contracts and grants

...
Head of Unit

3. Financial procedures and control systems

Adrian WINDOW
Head of Unit
Tel. +32 229-52271, 87442

4. BudgWeb, financial training, helpdesk for institutions and agencies

Stephen COLLINS
Head of Unit
Tel. +32 229-98436, 66633

5. User management of financial information systems

Dirk LAPAGE
Head of Unit
Tel. +32 229-61982, 92989

Directorate R — Resources

Éric PARADIS
Director
Tel. +32 229-59811, 58855

1. Information and communication

Éric MAMER
Head of Unit
Tel. +32 229-94073, 96635

2. General coordination, human and budget resources

Jean-Pierre BUISSERET
Head of Unit
Tel. +32 229-54803, 65496

3. Financial information systems

Claude NAHON
Head of Unit
Tel. +32 229-99307, 58855

4. IT infrastructure and user support

André PENING
Head of Unit
Tel. +32 229-69705, 67534

INTERNAL AUDIT SERVICE

Rue de la Loi 200
B-1049 Brussels
E-mail: ias-europa@ec.europa.eu

Walter DEFFAA
Director-General (Internal Auditor of the Commission)
Tel. +32 229-57752, 56640

Directorate A — Horizontal Affairs

Agnieszka Ewa KAZMIERCZAK
Director
Tel. +32 229-90868, 93280

1. Coordination and Communication

Gérard EMION
Head of Unit (acting)
Tel. +32 229-50319

2. Regulatory agencies

Bernard MAGENHANN
Head of Unit
Tel. +32 229-99482

Directorate B — Audit Process

Francisco MERCHÁN CANTOS
Director
Tel. +32 229-96730, 54915

1. Audit Supervisor 1

Cristiana GIACOBBO
Audit Supervisor
Tel. +32 229-95085, 55972

2. Audit Supervisor 2

Jeffrey MASON
Audit Supervisor
Tel. +32 229-58969, 54713

Pascal HALLEZ
Audit Supervisor (handover)
Tel. +32 229-52948, 69672

3. Audit Supervisor 3

Laura CANDELORO
Audit Supervisor
Tel. +32 229-84542

4. Audit Supervisor 4

Pascal HALLEZ
Audit Supervisor
Tel. +32 229-52948, 69672

5. Audit Supervisor 5

Benoît VERMEERSCH
Audit Supervisor
Tel. +32 229-85810, 69672

EUROPEAN ANTI-FRAUD OFFICE

Rue Joseph II 30
B-1000 Brussels
Tel. +32 229-91111 (operator)
Fax +32 229-60853

Franz-Hermann BRÜNER
Director-General
Tel. +32 229-69063, 62976

Sébastien COMBEAUD
Assistant to the Director-General
Tel. +32 229-51338, 53476

Barbel HEINKELMANN
Assistant to the Director-General
Tel. +32 229-98730, 53476

Alberto PERDUCA
Chief Adviser
Tel. +32 229-58508, 52629

Paul Lachal ROBERTS
Adviser (acting)
Tel. +32 229-98514, 59526

Wolfgang HETZER
Adviser (acting)
Tel. +32 229-94992

Reporting directly to the Director-General

Secretariat of the Supervisory Committee

Eberhard BRANDT
Head of Unit
Tel. +32 229-59969, 86422

Directorate A — Investigations and Operations

Thierry CRETIN
Director (acting)
Tel. +32 229-98768, 62764

Marco PECORARO
Adviser
Tel. +32 229-51350

1. Internal investigations: European institutions

Thierry CRETIN
Head of Unit (acting)
Tel. +32 229-98768, 62764

2. Internal/external investigations: EU bodies

Philippe ULLMANN
Head of Unit (acting)
Tel. +32 229-84036, 67042

3. Direct expenditure and external aid

Marco PECORARO
Head of Unit (acting)
Tel. +32 229-51350

4. External aid

Johan VLOGAERT
Tel. +32 229-98766, 55944

Directorate B — Investigations and Operations II

Ian WALTON-GEORGE
Director
Tel. +32 229-95247, 51485

1. Agriculture

Elisabeth SPERBER
Head of Unit
Tel. +32 229-59574, 66802

2. Customs I

David MURPHY
Head of Unit (acting)
Tel. +32 229-65873, 54826

3. Customs II

Austin ROWAN
Head of Unit (acting)
Tel. +32 229-63141, 87115

4. Structural measures

James SWEENEY
Head of Unit (acting)
Tel. +32 229-56037, 63951

Directorate C — Operational and Policy Support

Kjell LARSSON
Director
Tel. +32 229-99067, 65171

1. Judicial and legal advice

Joaquin GONZALEZ GONZALEZ
Head of Unit
Tel. +32 229-91466, 96968

2. Fraud prevention and intelligence

Johan KHOUW
Head of Unit
Tel. +32 229-95946, 54927

3. Mutual assistance and intelligence

Eddy WEYNS
Head of Unit
Tel. +32 229-51134, 58199

4. Operational intelligence

Mika MAKELA
Head of Unit
Tel. +32 229-57785, 85391

5. Protection of the euro and management of the Hercule and Pericles programmes

Yannis XENAKIS
Head of Unit
Tel. +32 229-93483, 51534

Directorate D — General Affairs

Nicholas ILETT
Director
Tel. +32 229-84986, 94036

1. Spokesman, communication and public relations

Alessandro BUTTICE
Head of Unit
Tel. +32 229-65425, 67547

2. Legislation and legal affairs

Lothar KUHL
Head of Unit
Tel. +32 229-63925, 80284

3. Interinstitutional and external relations

Margarete HOFMANN
Head of Unit
Tel. +32 229-81710, 56949

4. General policy and planning

Nicholas ILETT
Head of Unit (acting)
Tel. +32 229-84986, 94036

5. Administration and human resources

Paolo MILLICH
Head of Unit
Tel. +32 229-54410, 55859

6. Budget

Jean-Philippe LIENARD
Head of Unit (acting)
Tel. +32 229-54083, 67078

7. Training, programme implementation

Agnes HORVATH
Head of Unit
Tel. +32 229-84480, 98566

8. Information services

Harald SONNBERGER
Head of Unit
Tel. +32 229-55245, 84996

INTERPRETATION DG

Avenue de Cortenbergh 107
B-1040 Brussels
Tel. +32 229-91111 (operator)

Marco BENEDETTI
Director-General
Tel. +32 229-57058, 60947

Pernilla SJOLIN
Assistant to the Director-General
Tel. +32 229-80013, 55631

David WALKER
Chief Adviser
Tel. +32 229-99300, 67515

Johan BODDIN
Adviser
Tel. +32 229-84494

Reporting directly to the Director-General

1. Audit

Valérie DE LEEUW
Head of Unit (acting)
Tel. +32 229-87446, 87338

2. Communication and information

Ian ANDERSEN
Head of Unit
Tel. +32 229-54024, 99866

Directorate A — Interpreters

Brian FOX
Director
Tel. +32 229-55416, 60174

Interpretation Department I

Luisa CASTELLANI
Head of Language Department
Tel. +32 229-98265, 96253

1. Czech interpretation

Roderick JONES
Head of Unit
Tel. +32 229-80012, 21540

2. French interpretation

....
Head of Unit

3. Lithuanian interpretation

Vytautas VAISNORAS
Head of Unit (acting)
Tel. +32 229-91766, 21540

4. Swedish interpretation

Nuria BONEL CANADELL
Head of Unit
Tel. +32 229-88886, 96253

Interpretation Department II

Irène JANSEN
Head of Language Department
Tel. +32 229-87039, 21540

5. German interpretation

...
Head of Unit

6. Estonian interpretation

Karl LEPA
Head of Unit
Tel. +32 229-91836

7. Hungarian interpretation

Peter AAGAARD
Head of Unit
Tel. +32 229-80011, 21541

8. Finnish interpretation

Veijo KRUTH
Head of Unit
Tel. +32 229-53786, 21541

Interpretation Department III

Ursula PAULINI-SMITH
Head of Language Department
Tel. +32 229-87038, 21541

9. English interpretation

David SMITH
Head of Unit
Tel. +32 229-96515, 21542

10. Latvian interpretation

Ieva ZAUBERGA
Head of Unit
Tel. +32 229-91975

11. Portuguese interpretation

Luís MACHADO
Head of Unit
Tel. +32 229-66518, 21542

12. Slovak interpretation

Annica ÖSTLUND
Head of Unit
Tel. +32 229-95212, 21542

Interpretation Department IV

Terence CLOUGH
Head of Language Department
Tel. +32 229-56631

13. Danish interpretation

Lisbet KROGAGER
Head of Unit
Tel. +32 229-51274, 21543

14. Italian interpretation

Elisabeth LADERCHI
Head of Unit
Tel. +32 229-80015, 21543

15. Dutch interpretation

Annechiene DE MEY
Head of Unit
Tel. +32 229-87031, 21543

16. Slovenian interpretation

Marjanca RUPNIK
Head of Unit (acting)
Tel. +32 229-91998, 21543

Interpretation Department V

Preben SAUGSTRUP
Head of Language Department
Tel. +32 229-90650, 86244

17. Greek interpretation

Alexandra PANAGAKOU
Head of Unit
Tel. +32 229-59319, 66822

18. Spanish interpretation

Manuel VALDIVIA BENZAL
Head of Unit
Tel. +32 229-95412, 66822

19. Maltese interpretation

Peter MIFSUD
Head of Unit (acting)
Tel. +32 229-92237, 66822

20. Polish interpretation

Felizitas KIECHL
Head of Unit
Tel. +32 229-80014, 66822

21. Bulgarian interpretation

Ekaterina DRAGANOVA-TCHORBANOVA
Head of Unit (acting)
Tel. +32 229-91791, 96253

22. Romanian interpretation

Maria KOROKNAI
Head of Unit (acting)
Tel. +32 229-92128

Directorate B — Administration and Resources

Carlos ALEGRÍA
Director
Tel. +32 229-63394, 52900

Jorge CURELL GOTOR
Adviser
Tel. +32 229-90478, 55794

1. Management support, evaluation and IT systems

Emilio DALMONTE
Head of Unit
Tel. +32 229-94021, 59004

2. Strategic planning, budget and financial management

José Manuel BASTOS
Head of Unit
Tel. +32 229-68111, 58139

3. Personnel and general administration

Christopher CURRAN
Head of Unit
Tel. +32 229-62407, 50752

4. Joint management of conference interpreters

Elisabeth EGELUND
Head of Unit
Tel. +32 229-59057, 69732

Directorate C — Organisation of Interpretation

Ann D'HAEN BERTIER
Director
Tel. +32 229-50993, 54218

1. Multilingualism and interpreter training support

Wolter WITTEVEEN
Head of Unit
Tel. +32 229-53087

2. Programming of interpretation

David BAKER
Head of Unit
Tel. +32 229-85078

3. Professional coaching for interpreters

Claude DURAND
Head of Unit
Tel. +32 229-69196, 67469

Directorate D — Conferences

Jupp HAMACHER
Director
Tel. +32 229-52555, 90119

1. Conference organisation

Isabella QUATTROCCHI
Head of Unit
Tel. +32 229-58329, 68652

2. Meeting infrastructure

Didier HESPEL
Head of Unit
Tel. +32 229-59052

3. Conference technology

José ESTEBAN CAUSO
Head of Unit
Tel. +32 229-90562

TRANSLATION DG

Rue de Genève 1
B-1140 Brussels
Tel. +32 229-91111 (operator)

Bâtiment Jean Monnet
L-2920 Luxembourg
Tel. +352 4301-1 (operator)
Tel. +352 4301 + extension

Karl-Johan LÖNNROTH
Chairman of the Administrative Board
Director-General
Tel. +352 4301-37825, 30284

Markku SORMUNEN
Adviser

Reporting directly to the Director-General

Translation Centre

...

1. Audit

Anne GRISARD
Head of Unit
Tel. +32 229-84103, 92414

2. Communication and information

Andrea DAHMEN
Head of Unit
Tel. +32 229-60486, 54668

3. Legal, interinstitutional and international affairs

Milvia VAN RIJ-BRIZZI
Head of Unit
Tel. +32 229-90191, 51721

Directorate A — Translation

Inga ROTH
Director
Tel. +352 4301-35871

DA. Danish-Language Department

Svend BECH
Head of Language Department
Tel. +32 229-56563, 58990

1. Danish-Language Unit 1

Anne-Grethe MIKKELSEN
Head of Unit (acting)
Tel. +32 229-95163

2. Danish-Language Unit 2

Derrick OLESEN
Head of Unit
Tel. +32 229-58460, 58901

3. Danish-Language Unit 3

Bodil FRANSSEN
Head of Unit
Tel. +352 4301-32303

ET. Estonian-Language Department

Merit-Ene ILJA
Head of Language Department
Tel. +352 4301-32441, 38060

1. Estonian-Language Unit 1

Epp VIHTERPAL
Head of Unit
Tel. +352 4301-35576, 36510

2. Estonian-Language Unit 2

Leila ANUPOLD
Head of Unit
Tel. +352 4301-37473

3. Estonian-Language Unit 3

Hiie TAMM
Head of Unit (acting)
Tel. +352 4301-37754, 32518

FI. Finnish-Language Department

Risto NIEMINEN
Head of Language Department
Tel. +32 229-59135, 67823

1. Finnish-Language Unit 1

Tiina LOHIKKO
Head of Unit
Tel. +32 229-95279, 62641

2. Finnish-Language Unit 2

Paula OVASKA-ROMANO
Head of Unit
Tel. +32 229-52403, 65186

3. Finnish-Language Unit 3

Marja KALLIOPUSKA
Head of Unit
Tel. +352 4301-32166

Liisa BAECKMAN
Head of Unit (acting)
Tel. +352 4301-32466

HU. Hungarian-Language Department

Miklós András MÁTYÁSSY
Head of Language Department
Tel. +352 4301-34068, 34774

1. Hungarian-Language Unit 1

Balint VANYI
Head of Unit
Tel. +352 4301-33603, 34417

2. Hungarian-Language Unit 2

Ildiko FABER
Head of Unit (acting)
Tel. +352 4301-35731, 34056

3. Hungarian-Language Unit 3

Sandor KOVACS
Head of Unit
Tel. +352 4301-31654

LT. Lithuanian-Language Department

Anna WALLEN
Head of Language Department (acting)
Tel. +32 229-61512, 69601

1. Lithuanian-Language Unit 1

Zivile ALEKSONYTE-CORMIER
Head of Unit (acting)
Tel. +352 4301-36181, 33795

2. Lithuanian-Language Unit 2

Rita DEDONIENE
Head of Unit
Tel. +352 4301-37844, 33972

3. Lithuanian-Language Unit 3

Vitalija SPOKIENE
Head of Unit
Tel. +352 4301-37847, 32481

LV. Latvian-Language Department

Bodil FRANSSEN
Head of Language Department (acting)
Tel. +352 4301-32303

1. Latvian-Language Unit 1

Uldis PRIEDE
Head of Unit
Tel. +352 4301-37850

2. Latvian-Language Unit 2

Iveta RANCANE-ABARTE
Head of Unit (acting)
Tel. +352 4301-37596, 32846

3. Latvian-Language Unit 3

Valda Selga LIEPINA
Head of Unit
Tel. +352 4301-34388, 34166

PL. Polish-Language Department

Helena LATOMSKI
Head of Language Department
Tel. +352 4301-35296, 36566

1. Polish-Language Unit 1

Justyna BUMBUL
Head of Unit (acting)
Tel. +352 4301-36992

2. Polish-Language Unit 2

Miroslaw SZPAKOWSKI
Head of Unit
Tel. +352 4301-34303, 36637

3. Polish-Language Unit 3

Klaudia Liliana ZAGOROWICZ
Head of Unit
Tel. +352 4301-32574, 38371

SV. Swedish-Language Department

Annette MARINO
Head of Language Department
Tel. +32 229-53083, 91658

1. Swedish-Language Unit 1

Anna WALLEN
Head of Unit
Tel. +32 229-61512, 69601

Monika SODERHOLM
Head of Unit (acting)
Tel. +32 229-59160, 50009

2. Swedish-Language Unit 2

Andreas LARSSON
Head of Unit
Tel. +32 229-59151, 92429

3. Swedish-Language Unit 3

Hans Anders CALMFORS
Head of Unit
Tel. +352 4301-31645

Directorate B — Translation

George VLACHOPOULOS
Director
Tel. +32 229-58618, 51003

DE. German-Language Department

Margret HEIMBECK MEYER-LOHSE
Head of Language Department
Tel. +352 4301-32341
Tel. +32 229-55934

1. German-Language Unit 1

Myriam LAURENT-GATZ
Head of Unit
Tel. +32 229-52820, 60757

2. German-Language Unit 2

Raymond REGH
Head of Unit
Tel. +32 229-50913, 56049

3. German-Language Unit 3

Robert WURZLER
Head of Unit
Tel. +32 229-50192, 52241

4. German-Language Unit 4

Raimund BERNERS
Head of Unit
Tel. +32 229-94626, 59037

5. German-Language Unit 5

Werner GRUNEWALD
Head of Unit
Tel. +352 4301-33280, 34244

6. German-Language Unit 6

Achim BLATT
Head of Unit
Tel. +352 4301-32257, 33193

EN. English-Language Department

Klaus MEYER-KOEKEN
Head of Language Department
Tel. +32 229-52234, 51895

1. English-Language Unit 1

Martin TURLEY
Head of Unit (acting)
Tel. +32 229-55253

2. English-Language Unit 2

William FRASER
Head of Unit
Tel. +32 229-61031, 53213

3. English-Language Unit 3

Niall FINN
Head of Unit
Tel. +352 4301-32450, 32444

FR. French-Language Department

René FOUCART
Head of Language Department
Tel. +32 229-51284, 62163

1. French-Language Unit 1

Isabelle TRANCHANT
Head of Unit
Tel. +32 229-56196, 50089

2. French-Language Unit 2

Marc CHAMPION
Head of Unit
Tel. +32 229-95211

3. French-Language Unit 3

Ludovic LAPORTE
Head of Unit
Tel. +32 229-51757, 54722

4. French-Language Unit 4

Jean-Louis COBBAERT
Head of Unit
Tel. +32 229-56812, 65811

5. French-Language Unit 5

Michel BAUT
Head of Unit
Tel. +352 4301-32627

6. French-Language Unit 6

Armand SPODEN
Head of Unit
Tel. +352 4301-33961

IE. Irish-Language Unit

Donal CAREY
Head of Unit (acting)
Tel. +32 229-65642, 57800

NL. Dutch-Language Department

Ludovicus DE PRINS
Head of Language Department
Tel. +352 4301-32539, 32498

Jean-Pierre STERCK
Head of Language Department (acting)
Tel. +32 229-58163, 55462

Derk HUIZING
Adviser
Tel. +32 229-51834, 50436

1. Dutch-Language Unit 1

Jean-Pierre STERCK
Head of Unit
Tel. +32 229-58163, 55462

Marc DE REU
Head of Unit (acting)
Tel. +32 229-56560, 55462

2. Dutch-Language Unit 2

Luc VERDEGEM
Head of Unit
Tel. +32 229-59554

3. Dutch-Language Unit 3

Dirk STOCKMANS
Head of Unit
Tel. +352 4301-32610, 32343

BG. Bulgarian Language Department

Ludovicus DE PRINS
Head of Language Department (acting)
Tel. +352 4301-32539, 32498

1. Bulgarian-Language Unit 1

Stig OLSEN
Head of Unit (seconded)
Tel. +32 229-51410, 54322

2. Bulgarian-Language Unit 2

Nikolai BOYADJIEV
Head of Unit (acting)
Tel. +352 4301-35736, 37028

3. Bulgarian-Language Unit 3

Ralitza MIHOVA
Head of Unit (acting)
Tel. +352 4301-33617, 38815

RO. Romanian-Language Department

Merit-Ene ILJA
Head of Language Department (acting)
Tel. +352 4301-32441, 38060

1. Romanian-Language Unit 1

Monica STEEN
Head of Unit (seconded)
Tel. +32 229-56705, 69783

2. Romanian-Language Unit 2

Cristian PAVALUCA
Head of Unit (acting)
Tel. +352 4301-37023

3. Romanian-Language Unit 3

Daniel NECSA
Head of Unit (acting)
Tel. +352 4301-38290

Directorate C — Translation: Brussels

Gurli HAUSCHILDT
Director
Tel. +352 4301-38993, 32250

CS. Czech-Language Department

Basile KOUTSIVITIS
Head of Language Department (acting)
Tel. +32 229-58478, 61592

1. Czech-Language Unit 1

Vladimir DRABEK
Head of Unit
Tel. +352 4301-32712, 38848

2. Czech-Language Unit 2

Otto PACHOLIK
Head of Unit
Tel. +352 4301-36523, 38145

3. Czech-Language Unit 3

Jakub CHÁB
Head of Unit
Tel. +352 4301-37842, 34186

EL. Greek-Language Department

Basile KOUTSIVITIS
Head of Language Department
Tel. +32 229-58478, 61592

Athanassios ANTOULAS
Adviser
Tel. +32 229-58381

1. Greek-Language Unit 1

Georgios HANIOTAKIS
Head of Unit
Tel. +32 229-67512, 50408

2. Greek-Language Unit 2

Dimitrios CHRONOPOULOS
Head of Unit
Tel. +32 229-60095, 50825

3. Greek-Language Unit 3

Spiridon BOCOLINIS
Head of Unit
Tel. +352 4301-32328

ES. Spanish-Language Department

Juan MARTINEZ GUILLEN
Head of Language Department
Tel. +32 229-62710

1. Spanish-Language Unit 1

María-José GONZÁLEZ GAYOSO
Head of Unit
Tel. +32 229-54709, 61697

2. Spanish-Language Unit 2

Xavier HUGUET
Head of Unit
Tel. +32 229-60877, 53732

3. Spanish-Language Unit 3

Francisco VALERI
Head of Unit
Tel. +352 4301-34712, 37087

IT. Italian-Language Department

Luigi VESENTINI
Head of Language Department
Tel. +32 229-53373, 52414

1. Italian-Language Unit 1

Italo RUBINO
Head of Unit
Tel. +32 229-62593, 69272

2. Italian-Language Unit 2

Elisa RANUCCI-FISCHER
Head of Unit
Tel. +32 229-57345, 61382

3. Italian-Language Unit 3

Cristiano Maria GAMBARI
Head of Unit
Tel. +352 4301-32881

MT. Maltese-Language Department

Francisco VALERI
Head of Language Department (acting)
Tel. +352 4301-34712, 37087

1. Maltese-Language Unit 1

Helga Josette ZAHRA
Head of Unit
Tel. +352 4301-34496, 35615

2. Maltese-Language Unit 2

Joseph CARUANA
Head of Unit
Tel. +352 4301-37280, 36567

3. Maltese-Language Unit 3

Carmel ATTARD
Head of Unit
Tel. +352 4301-38022, 37518

PT. Portuguese-Language Department

Manuel de OLIVEIRA BARATA
Head of Language Department
Tel. +32 229-60476, 60412

Maria MACHADO
Adviser
Tel. +32 229-61025
Tel. +352 4301-36758

1. Portuguese-Language Unit 1

Maria Cristina de PRETER
Head of Unit
Tel. +32 229-59323, 54289

2. Portuguese-Language Unit 2

Peter SOARES PINTO
Head of Unit
Tel. +32 229-60473, 50662

3. Portuguese-Language Unit 3

Jorge HOMEM
Head of Unit
Tel. +352 4301-32546, 32526

SK. Slovak-Language Department

Luigi VESENTINI
Head of Language Department (acting)
Tel. +32 229-53373, 52414

1. Slovak-Language Unit 1

Jan SALGOVIC
Head of Unit
Tel. +352 4301-34997, 37765

2. Slovak-Language Unit 2

Daniel KLUVANEC
Head of Unit
Tel. +352 4301-32768, 34455

3. Slovak-Language Unit 3

Eva BENOVA
Head of Unit
Tel. +352 4301-33290, 30016

SL. Slovenian-Language Department

Maria MACHADO
Head of Language Department (acting)
Tel. +32 229-61025
Tel. +352 4301-36758

1. Slovenian-Language Unit 1

Jan BEDNARICH
Head of Unit (acting)
Tel. +352 4301-36963

2. Slovenian-Language Unit 2

Igor RECNIK
Head of Unit (acting)
Tel. +352 4301-37873, 32882

3. Slovenian-Language Unit 3

Mojca BOLTIN
Head of Unit (acting)
Tel. +352 4301-36648, 33927

Directorate D — Transversal Linguistic Services

Filip MAJCEN
Director
Tel. +32 229-58728
Tel. +352 4301-35854

1. Field offices and relations with representations

Carole ORY
Head of Unit
Tel. +32 229-51930, 80179

2. Web translation

Ewa ROSSING
Head of Unit
Tel. +32 229-50152, 56702

3. Library, terminology and translation support

Konstantinos ZACHARIS
Head of Unit (acting)
Tel. +352 4301-33460/37170

4. Editing

Paul Andrew STRICKLAND
Head of Unit
Tel. +32 229-58808/50736

Directorate R — Resources

Gertrud INGESTAD
Director (acting)
Tel. +32 229-90515, 67465

1. Human resources

Alicia FRACCHIA-FERNANDEZ
Tel. +32 229-64873, 52798

2. Financial resources

Marco PANIGALLI
Head of Unit
Tel. +32 229-54441

3. Informatics [11]

Josep BONET
Head of Unit
Tel. +352 4301-34759, 36238

4. Training

Gertrud INGESTAD
Head of Unit
Tel. +32 229-90515, 67465

Annette MARINO
Head of Unit (acting)
Tel. +32 229-53083, 91658

5. Internal administrative matters

Paschalis PAPACHRISTOPOULOS
Head of Unit
Tel. +32 229-50820, 50048

Directorate S — Translation Strategy and Multilingualism

Francisco DE VICENTE FERNÁNDEZ
Director
Tel. +32 229-60094, 61024

Cornelis VAN DER HORST
Adviser
Tel. +352 4301-32397

Hubert PAESMANS
Adviser
Tel. +352 4301-32551/34357

1. Demand management

Marta MANTE BARTRA
Head of Unit
Tel. +32 229-63126, 93582

2. External translation

Klaus AHREND
Head of Unit
Tel. +32 229-56610, 94741

3. Translation studies and multilingualism

Miguel Angel NAVARRETE MOLINA
Head of Unit (acting)
Tel. +32 229-56539, 85453

4. Evaluation and analysis

Christian BASTIEN
Head of Unit
Tel. +352 4301-34688, 34346

[11] Unit located in Luxembourg.

PUBLICATIONS OFFICE

2, rue Mercier
L-2985 Luxembourg
Luxembourg
Tel. +352 2929-1 (operator)
Fax +352 2929-44619

Martine REICHERTS
Director-General
Tel. +352 2929-42220
Tel. +32 229-90954

Albrecht BERGER
Adviser (responsible for the secretariat of interinstitutional committees)
Rue de la Loi 86
B-1049 Brussels
Tel. +32 229-57552, 21416

Reporting directly to the Director-General

1. Evaluation, control and future developments

László SZABÓ
Head of Unit
Tel. +352 2929-44195

2. Publishing policy

Serge BRACK
Head of Unit
Tel. +352 2929-42568
Tel. +32 229-53124

3. CORDIS

Philippe LEBAUBE
Head of Unit
Tel. +352 2929-42855

Directorate R — Resources

Bernard REYNOLDS
Director
Tel. +352 2929-42090

1. Human resources

Lucia CECCARELLI
Head of Unit
Tel. +352 2929-42890

2. Calls for tender and contracts

António CARNEIRO
Head of Unit
Tel. +352 2929-42310

3. Finances

June LOWERY-KINGSTON
Head of Unit
Tel. +352 2929-42706

4. Infrastructures

Kurt KOENIG
Head of Unit
Tel. +352 2929-44070

5. IT projects

Saša PREŠERN
Head of Unit
Tel. +352 2929-44591

Directorate A — Official Journal and Access to Law

Yves STEINITZ
Director (acting)
Tel. +352 2929-44567

1. EUR-Lex

Yves STEINITZ
Head of Unit
Tel. +352 2929-44567

2. Unit A2 — Production coordination

Friedrich DÖLL
Head of Unit
Tel. +352 2929-42050

3. Quality control

Wojciech KALAMARZ
Head of Unit
Tel. +352 2929-44415

4. TED

Antonio REIS
Head of Unit (acting)
Tel. +352 2929-42970

5. Legal and documentary issues, consolidation and copyright

Pascale BERTELOOT
Head of Unit
Tel. +352 2929-42110

Directorate B — Publications and Dissemination

Danielle SAFFAR
Director
Tel. +352 2929-44969

1. Cross-media publishing

John YOUNG
Head of Unit
Tel. +352 2929-44399

2. Editorial services

Fabian DIEGO LUIS
Head of Unit
Tel. +352 2929-42487

3. Promotion and dissemination

Michel LANGLAIS
Head of Unit
Tel. +352 2929-42905

4. Customer relations

Thierry DAMAN
Head of Unit
Tel. +32 229-54733, 62422

5. EU Bookshop

Silke STAPEL
Head of Unit
Tel. +352 2929-44608

OFFICE FOR INFRASTRUCTURE AND LOGISTICS IN BRUSSELS

Rue d'Arlon 88
B-1040 Brussels
Tel. +32 229-57641
Fax +32 229-56278

Gábor ZUPKO
Director
Tel. +32 229-87142, 68192

Thomas ZIOLKOWSKI
Adviser
Tel. +32 229-50767

Jean-Claude SCHUTZ
Adviser
Tel. +32 229-95658

1. Programming, resources, internal control coordination and horizontal matters

Mariana SAUDE
Head of Unit
Tel. +32 229-63204, 61381

2. Finance and public procurement

Daniel GERMAIN
Head of Unit
Tel. +32 229-52501, 86156

Property management

Marc MOULIGNEAU
Head of Office Department
Tel. +32 229-56731, 65904

1. Implementation of buildings policy

Konstantin KONSTANTINOU
Head of Unit
Tel. +32 229-63818, 80063

2. Technical services

Reinier LANNEAU
Head of Unit
Tel. +32 229-61632, 64017

3. Safety, health and comfort at work

Franz TSCHISMAROV
Head of Unit
Tel. +32 229-57284, 98341

4. Property projects

Peter BENUSKA
Head of Unit
Tel. +32 229-81321

Logistics and services

Erik HALSKOV
Head of Office Department
Tel. +32 229-62451

1. Historical archives, mail, reproduction

Frank BRADY
Head of Unit
Tel. +32 229-52062, 54962

2. Well-being services

Thierry VINOIS
Head of Unit
Tel. +32 229-63091, 65433

3. Mobility and supplies

Leszek Janusz MADEJA
Head of Unit
Tel. +32 229-63455, 88502

OFFICE FOR THE ADMINISTRATION AND PAYMENT OF INDIVIDUAL ENTITLEMENTS

Rue de la Science 27
B-1049 Brussels
Tel. +32 229-91111 (operator)

Dominique DESHAYES
Director
Tel. +32 229-56156, 86432

1. Salaries and administration of individual rights

Gabriel MARTINEAU
Head of Unit
Tel. +32 229-92336, 69789

2. Missions

Giuseppe SCOGNAMIGLIO
Head of Unit
Tel. +32 229-52799, 62196

3. Sickness and accident insurance

Ludovic PROMELLE
Head of Unit
Tel. +32 229-54451, 50193

4. Pensions

José LUIS SANUDO
Head of Unit
Tel. +32 229-56060, 60591

5. PMO: Luxembourg

François AUGENDRE
Head of Unit
Tel. +352 4301-34399

6. PMO: Ispra

Gilda CAPUANO
Head of Unit
Tel. +39 0332789574

7. Research and forecasting

Pieter KERSTENS
Head of Unit
Tel. +32 229-95005, 95937

8. Budget, internal control and information technologies

François WILLEKENS
Head of Unit
Tel. +32 229-52596, 69622

9. Simplification, communication and coordination between sites

Marie TZIRANI
Head of Unit
Tel. +32 229-58482, 59042

OFFICE FOR INFRASTRUCTURE AND LOGISTICS IN LUXEMBOURG

Bâtiment Jean Monnet
Rue Alcide de Gasperi
L-2920 Luxembourg
Tel. +352 4301-1 (operator)
Tel. +352 4301 + extension

Marian O'LEARY
Director
Tel. +352 4301-34229, 34652

1. Management of buildings and operation of installations

Robert STEINMETZ
Head of Unit
Tel. +352 4301-34481, 36243

2. Internal services and transport

Claude WILLEME
Head of Unit
Tel. +352 4301-34898, 36252

3. Social welfare infrastructure

Mariann KARCZA
Head of Unit
Tel. +352 4301-36586, 37413

4. Financial resources

Benoît MORISSET
Head of Unit
Tel. +352 4301-32458, 36071

5. Human resources — reporting and control — Health and safety

Marc SEGUINOT
Head of Unit
Tel. +352 4301-38190, 38422

6. Procurement procedures and contracts

Roman LLANSO
Head of Unit
Tel. +352 4301-32618

EUROPEAN PERSONNEL SELECTION OFFICE

Avenue de Cortenbergh 80
B-1000 Brussels
Tel. +32 229-93131
Fax +32 229-57488

Nicholas BEARFIELD
Director
Tel. +32 229-54126, 50724

Guy VAN BIESEN
Adviser
Tel. +32 229-50822, 87610

Task Force — EPSO Development Programme

Steven JOSEPH
Head of the Task Force
Tel. +32 229-68060, 63192

1. A. Competitions, selection procedures

Theo DUIVENVOORDE
Head of Unit
Tel. +32 229-94484, 69832

2. e-Selection

Alan PIOTROWSKI
Head of Unit
Tel. +32 229-88467, 88467

3. Administrative and logistical support

Ulrich SONDERMANN
Head of Unit
Tel. +32 229-85311, 56893

4. Stakeholder relations and planning

Agne MARTIKONIENE
Head of Unit
Tel. +32 229-60199, 91178

5. IT

Antonio FRIZ
Head of Unit
Tel. +32 229-59484, 96131

G. EAS — European Administrative School

David WALKER
Head of the European Administrative School (seconded)
Tel. +32 229-99300, 67515

EXTERNAL DELEGATIONS, REPRESENTATIONS AND OFFICES

In non-member countries

Afghanistan

East Wazir Akbar Khan
Kabul
Afghanistan
E-mail: delegation-afghanistan@ec.europa.eu
Website: http://www.delafg.ec.europa.eu
Tel. +873 763041236

Hansjörg KRETSCHMER
Head of Delegation
Tel. *81454

Albania

Rruga e Durresit 127-1
Laprake
Tirana
Albania
E-mail: mailto@delalb.ec.europa.eu
Tel. +355 4228320,
satellite: +871 761315832
Fax +355 4230752,
satellite: +871 1121761

Helmuth LOHAN
Head of Delegation
Tel. *80842

Algeria

Domaine Benouadah
Chemin du Val d'Hydra
El-Biar, Algiers
Algeria
E-mail: delegation-algeria@ec.europa.eu
Website: http://www.deldza.ec.europa.eu
Tel. +213 21923641
Fax +213 21923681

Laura BAEZA
Head of Delegation
Tel. +32 229-61339, 53137

Angola

Rua Rainha Jinga, 45-3º
Luanda
Angola
E-mail: delegation-Angola@ec.europa.eu
Website: http://www.delago.ec.europa.eu
Tel. +244 2391339,
satellite: +873 1246324, 1246323
Fax +244 2392531
Caixa Postal 2669
Luanda
Angola

João Gabriel FERREIRA
Head of Delegation
Tel. *80581

Argentina

Ayacucho 1537
1112 Buenos Aires
Argentina
E-mail: mailto@delarg.ec.europa.eu
Website: http://www.delarg.ec.europa.eu
Tel. +54 1148053759
Fax +54 1148011594

Gustavo MARTIN
Head of Delegation
Tel. *80994

Armenia

Raul DE LUZENBERGER MILNERNSHEIM
Head of Delegation
Tel. *81460

Australia

18, Arkana Street, Yarralumla ACT
2600 Canberra
Australia
E-mail: australia@delaus.ec.europa.eu
Website: http://www.delaus.ec.europa.eu
Tel. +61 262712777
Fax +61 262734445
PO Box 609
2600 Canberra
Australia

David DALY
Head of Delegation
Tel. +32 229-52526, 51652

Azerbaijan

Alan WADDAMS
Head of Delegation
Tel. *81921

Bangladesh

Plot 7, Road 84, Gulshan
1212 Dhaka
Bangladesh
E-mail: mailto@delbgd.ec.europa.eu
Website: http://www.eudelbangladesh.org
Tel. +880 28824730
Fax +880 28823118
PO Box No GN 6086, Gulshan
1212 Dhaka
Bangladesh

Stefan FROWEIN
Head of Delegation
Tel. *80361

Barbados

Mervue House
Marine Gardens, Hastings
Christ Church
Barbados W.I.
Bridgetown
Barbados
E-mail: delegation-barbados@ec.europa.eu
Website: http://www.delbrb.ec.europa.eu
Tel. +1246 4274362,
Direct line to the Head of Del.: +1246 4274366
Fax +1246 4277687
PO Box 654 C
Bridgetown
Barbados

Valeriano DIAZ
Head of Delegation
Tel. *80579

Benin

Av. Clozel, Bâtiment administratif
Cotonou
Benin
E-mail: mailto@delben.ec.europa.eu
Tel. +229 313099
Fax +229 315328
01 PB 910
Cotonou
Benin

Elisabeth FERET
Head of Delegation
Tel. *80517

Bolivia

Calle 15 Obrajes n° 406
La Paz
Bolivia
E-mail: delegation-bolivia@ec.europa.eu
Tel. +591 22782244
Fax +591 22784550
Casilla 10747
La Paz
Bolivia

Kenneth BELL
Head of Delegation
Tel. *80146

Bosnia and Herzegovina

Union Bank Building, 4th floor
Dubrovacka 6
Sarajevo
Bosnia and Herzegovina
E-mail: delegation-bih@ec.europa.eu
Website: http://www.delbih.ec.europa.eu
Tel. +387 33666044
Fax +387 33666037

Demetre KOURKOULAS
Head of Delegation
Tel. *81183

Botswana

Plot 758, Robinson Road
Gaborone
Botswana
E-mail: delegation-botswana@ec.europa.eu
Website: http://www.delbwa.ec.europa.eu
Tel. +267 314455
Fax +267 313626
PO Box 1253
Gaborone
Botswana

Paul MALIN
Head of Delegation
Tel. *80090

Brazil

SHIS QI 7
Bl. A, Lago Sul.
71635-050 Brasilia, DF
Brazil
E-mail: delegation-brazil@ec.europa.eu
Website: http://www.delbra.ec.europa.eu
Tel. +55 612483122
Fax +55 612480700

João PACHECO
Head of Delegation
Tel. *80462

Burkina Faso

Avenue Kwame N'Krumah,
en face de la Sonatur
Ouagadougou
Burkina Faso
E-mail: delegation-burkina-faso@ec.europa.eu
Tel. +226 307385,
Direct line to the Head of Del.: +266 308533
Fax +226 308966
BP 352
Ouagadougou
Burkina Faso

Amos TINCANI
Head of Delegation
Tel. *80095

Burundi

Avenue du 13 Octobre
Bujumbura
Burundi
E-mail: hdel@delbdi.ec.europa.eu
Tel. +257 223426,
Direct line to the Head of Del.: +257 221742
Fax +257 224612
BP 103
Bujumbura
Burundi

Alain DARTHENUCQ
Head of Delegation
Tel. *80813

Cameroon

Immeuble de Belvédère
1068 Rue Onambele Nkou
Quartier Nlongkak
Yaoundé
Cameroon
E-mail: delegation-cameroun@ec.europa.eu
Website: http://www.delcmr.ec.europa.eu
Tel. +237 2210028,
Direct line to the Head of Del.: +237 2209396
Fax +237 2202149
BP 847
Yaoundé
Cameroon

Javier PUYOL PINUELA
Head of Delegation
Tel. *80578

Canada

45 O'Connor Street, Suite 1900
K1P 1A4 Ottawa (Ontario)
Canada
E-mail: mailto@delcan.ec.europa.eu
Website: http://www.delcan.ec.europa.eu
Tel. +1 6132386464
Fax +1 6132385191

Dorian PRINCE
Head of Delegation
Tel. *80611

Cape Verde

Achada de Santo António
Praia
Cape Verde
E-mail: delegation-Cape-Verde@ec.europa.eu
Tel. +238 621393
Fax +238 621391
CP 122
Praia
Cape Verde

...

Central African Republic

Avenue Boganda
Bangui
Central African Republic
E-mail: delegation-central-african-rep@ec.europa.eu
Website: http://www.delrca.ec.europa.eu
Tel. +236 613053 (3 lines)
Fax +236 616535
BP 1298
Bangui
Central African Republic

Jean-Claude ESMIEU
Head of Delegation
Tel. *80375

Chad

Concession Caisse Coton
Route de Farcha
N'Djamena
Chad
E-mail: delegation-Tchad@ec.europa.eu
Website: http://www.deltcd.ec.europa.eu
Tel. +235 527276
Fax +235 527105
BP 552
N'Djamena
Chad

Gilles DESESQUELLES
Head of Delegation
Tel. *80062

Chile

Torre París — Av. Ricardo Lyon 222 — 3er piso
Providencia
Santiago 9
Chile
E-mail: delegation-chile@ec.europa.eu
Website: http://www.delchl.ec.europa.eu
Tel. +56 23352450
Fax +56 23351779
Casilla 10093
Santiago 9
Chile

Jaime Perez VIDAL
Head of Delegation
Tel. *80508

China

15 Dong Zhi Men Wai Dajie, Sanlitun
100600 Beijing
China
E-mail: mailto@delchn.ec.europa.eu
Website: http://www.delchn.ec.europa.eu
Tel. +86 1065324443 (7 lines)
Fax +86 1065324342

Serge ABOU
Head of Delegation
Tel. *80352

Michael PULCH
Deputy Head of Delegation
Tel. *80352

Colombia

Edificio ABN AMRO Bank, Carrera 7 No. 115-33, piso 10
94046 Santa Fe de Bogotá 8
Colombia
E-mail: delegation-colombia@ec.europa.eu
Website: http://www.delcol.ec.europa.eu
Tel. +57 16581150 (operator)
Fax +57 16581179
Ap Aéreo 94046-114
Santa Fe de Bogotá 8
Colombia

Fernando CARDESA GARCÍA
Head of Delegation
Tel. *80528

Congo

Avenue Maréchal Lyautey (face à l'ambassade d'Italie)
Brazzaville
Congo
E-mail: delegation-dem-rep-of-congo@ec.europa.eu
Website: http://www.delcod.ec.europa.eu
Tel. +242 878946690
Fax +242 8806482

Miguel AMADO
Head of Delegation
Tel. *80451

Costa Rica

Ofiplaza del Este, Edificio D, 3er piso
De la Rotonda de la Bandera, 50 m oeste
San José
Costa Rica
E-mail: mailto@delcri.ec.europa.eu
Website: http://www.delcri.ec.europa.eu
Tel. +506 2832959
Fax +506 2832960/61
Apartado 836
1007 Centro Colón
San José
Costa Rica

...
Tel. *80882

Croatia

Masarykova 1
10000 Zagreb
Croatia
E-mail: delegation-croatia@ec.europa.eu
Website: http://www.delhrv.ec.europa.eu
Tel. +385 14896500
Fax +385 14896555

Vincent DEGERT
Head of Delegation
Tel. *81059

Democratic Republic of the Congo

Immeuble BCDC, boulevard du 30 juin — Gombre
Kinshasa, Gombe
Democratic Republic of the Congo
E-mail: mailto@delcod.ec.europa.eu
Tel. +243 8841878
Fax +243 1234546 (OCPT)
BP 2699
Gombre
Democratic Republic of the Congo

Richard ZINK
Head of Delegation
Tel. *80466

Dominican Republic

Edificio Plaza J.R. piso 8º
Avenida Tiradentes esq. Roberto Pastoriza
Ensanche Naco
Santo Domingo
Dominican Republic
E-mail: delegation-dominican-rep@ec.europa.eu
Website: http://www.deldom.ec.europa.eu
Tel. +1809 2270525
Fax +1809 2270510
Aptado. postal 226-2
Santo Domingo
Dominican Republic

Maria Alicia ESCUIN SANTAOLALLA
Head of Delegation (acting)
Tel. +32 229-85245

East Timor

Juan Carlos REY SALGADO
Head of Delegation
Tel. *81949

Egypt

37 Gamaet el Dowal el Arabeya,
11th Floor, Mohandessin
Giza Cairo
Egypt
E-mail: delegation-egypt@ec.europa.eu
Website: http://www.delegy.ec.europa.eu
Tel. +20 27494680
Fax +20 27495363

Klaus-Dieter EBERMANN
Head of Delegation
Tel. *80524

Eritrea

Zone 2 Sub zone 03, Marsa Teklai 192 Street
House No 20
Asmara
Eritrea
E-mail: delegation-Eritrea@ec.europa.eu
Tel. +291 1126566
Fax +291 1126578
PO Box 5710
Asmara
Eritrea

Paola AMADEI
Head of Delegation
Tel. *81098

Ethiopia

E-mail: mailto@deleth.ec.europa.eu
Tel. +251 1612511
Direct line to the Head of Del.: 251 1613425
Fax +251 1612877
PO Box 5570
Addis Abeba
Ethiopia

Dino SINIGALLIA
Head of Delegation
Tel. *80510

Fiji

Wiepke VAN DER GOOT
Head of Delegation
Tel. *80086

Former Yugoslav Republic of Macedonia

Erwan FOUERE
Head of Delegation
Tel. *81283

Gabon

Bas de Gué-Gué
Libreville
Gabon
E-mail: eudelgab@delgab.ec.europa.eu
Website: http://www.delgab.ec.europa.eu
Tel. +241 732250,
Direct line to the Head of Del.: +241 736553
Fax +241 736554
BP 321
Libreville
Gabon

Thierry MATHISSE
Head of Delegation
Tel. *80085

Georgia

38 Nino Chkheidze St.
Tbilissi
Georgia
E-mail: mailto@delgeo.ec.europa.eu
Website: http://www.delgeo.ec.europa.eu
Tel. +995 32943763
Fax +995 32943768
Diplomatic Bag
Brussels EC Delegation
Georgia

Per EKLUND
Head of Delegation
Tel. *81022

Ghana

The Round House
81 Cantonments Road
Accra
Ghana
E-mail: delegation-ghana@ec.europa.eu
Tel. +233 21774201
Fax +233 21774154
PO Box 9505
Kotoka Int. Airport
Accra
Ghana

Filiberto CERIANI SEBREGONDI
Head of Delegation
Tel. *80483

Guinea-Bissau

Bairro da Penha
Bissau
Guinea-Bissau
E-mail: delegation-guinee-bissau@ec.europa.eu
Tel. +245 251469
Fax +245 251044
CP 359
1113 Bissau Cedex
Guinea-Bissau

Franco NULLI
Head of Delegation
Tel. *80463

Guinea

Immeuble Le Golfe, Dixinn
Conakry
Guinea
E-mail: delegation-Guinee-Conakry@ec.europa.eu
Tel. +224 13404870
BP 730
Conakry
Guinée
(via EC-Brussels)

Anna PIERGROSSI-FRASCHINI
Head of Delegation
Tel. *80516

Guyana

11, Sendall Place
Stabroek
Georgetown
Guyana
E-mail: delegation-guyana@ec.europa.eu
Website: http://www.delguy.ec.europa.eu
Tel. +592 2262667
Fax +592 2262615
PO Box 10847
Georgetown
Guyana

Geert HEIKENS
Head of Delegation
Tel. *80083

Haiti

Immeuble Hexagone — 4e étage
Angle des rues Clerveaux et Darguin
BP 15588
HT 6140 Pétion-Ville
Haiti
E-mail: delegation-haiti@ec.europa.eu
Website: http://www.delhti.ec.europa.eu
Tel. +509 22568471/72/95 to 97
Fax +509 22568473/93

Francesco GOSETTI DI STURMECK
Head of Delegation
Tel. *80082

Hong Kong

María de Los Angeles CASTILLO
Head of Delegation
Tel. *80099

India

65, Golf Links
110003 New Delhi
India
E-mail: eu@delind.ec.europa.eu
Website: http://www.eudelindia.org/
Tel. +91 1124629237
Fax +91 1124629206

Danièle SMADJA
Head of Delegation
Tel. *80490

Indonesia

Wilma Dharmala Sakti, 16th floor
Jl. Jendral Sudirman, 32
10220 Jakarta
Indonesia
E-mail: delegation-indonesia@ec.europa.eu
Website: http://www.delidn.ec.europa.eu
Tel. +62 2125546200
Fax +62 2125546201
PO Box 6454 JKPDS
10064 Jakarta
Indonesia

Julian WILSON
Head of Delegation
Tel. *80986

Iraq

Ilkka UUSITALO
Head of Delegation
Tel. *81924

Israel

Paz Tower, 15th floor
31-35 Betzalel Street
52521 Ramat Gan
Israel
E-mail: delegation-israel@ec.europa.eu
Website: http://www.eu-del.org.il
Tel. +972 36137799
Fax +972 36137770
PO Box 3513
52136 Ramat Gan
Israel

Ramiro CIBRIAN UZAL
Head of Delegation
Tel. *80724

Ivory Coast

18, rue du Dr Crozet
Abidjan-Plateau
Ivory Coast
E-mail: mailto@delciv.ec.europa.eu
Tel. +225 20318350
Fax +225 20214089
01 BP 1821
Abidjan 01
Ivory Coast

Michel ARRION
Head of Delegation
Tel. *80597

Jamaica

8, Olivier Road
Kingston 8
Jamaica
E-mail: delegation-jamaica@ec.europa.eu
Website: http://www.deljam.ec.europa.eu
Tel. +1876 9246333, 9246337
Fax +18769246339
PO Box 463
Constant Spring Road
Kingston 8
Jamaica

Marco MAZZOCCHI ALEMANNI
Head of Delegation
Tel. *80091

Japan

Europa House
9-15 Sanbancho — Chiyoda-Ku
102-0075 Tokyo
Japan
E-mail: deljapan@deljpn.ec.europa.eu
Website: http://www.jpn.ec.europa.eu
Tel. +81 332390441
Fax +81 332615194

Hugh RICHARDSON
Head of Delegation
Tel. *80614

Stefan HUBER
Deputy Head of Delegation
Tel. *80614

Silvia KOFLER
Head of Information Service
Tel. *80614

Jordan

Al Jahez Street No 15
oppo. Arab Potash Co., Shmeisani
Amman
Jordan
E-mail: delegation-jordan@ec.europa.eu
Website: http://www.deljor.ec.europa.eu
Tel. +962 65668191, 5668192
Fax +962 65686746
PO Box 926 794
Amman
Jordan

Bernard Patrick RENAULD
Head of Delegation
Tel. *80400

Kazakhstan

20A, Kazibek bi Street
480100 Almaty
Kazakhstan
E-mail: eudel@delkaz.ec.europa.eu
Website: http://www.delkaz.ec.europa.eu
Tel. +7 3272636265 (5 lines)
Fax +7 3272910749

Norbert JOUSTEN
Head of Delegation
Tel. *80511

Kenya

Union Insurance House
Ragati Road
Nairobi
Kenya
E-mail: delegation-kenya@ec.europa.eu
Tel. +254 202713020
Fax +254 202716481
PO Box 45119
Nairobi
Kenya

Eric VAN DER LINDEN
Head of Delegation
Tel. *80968

Georges ANDRÉ
Special envoy
Tel. *80968

Kosovo

Renzo DAVIDDI
Head of Delegation
Tel. *81425

Lebanon

Immeuble 490 Harbor Drive
av. Charles Helou
Saifi
BP 11
4008 Riad el Solh Beirut 1107 2150 Beirut
Lebanon
E-mail: delegation-lebanon@ec.europa.eu
Website: http://www.dellbn.ec.europa.eu
Tel. +961 1569400
Fax +961 1569415

Patrick LAURENT
Head of Delegation
Tel. *80080

Lesotho

167 Constitution Road
Maseru West
Lesotho
E-mail: mailto@dellso.ec.europa.eu
Tel. +266 22313726
Fax +266 22310193
PO Box MS 518
100 Maseru
Lesotho

Peter CHRISTIANSEN
Head of Delegation [12]
Tel. *80081

Madagascar

Tour Zital 9e étage, Ankorondrano
Antananarivo
Madagascar
E-mail: delegation-madagascar@ec.europa.eu
Website: http://www.delmdg.ec.europa.eu
Tel. +261 202224216
Fax +261 202264562
BP 746
Antananarivo
Madagascar

Jean-Claude BOIDIN
Head of Delegation
Tel. *80079

Malawi

Area 18 Roundabout
Presidential Way/Corner M1
30102
Lilongwe
Malawi
E-mail: delegation-malawi@ec.europa.eu
Website: http://www.delmvwi.ec.europa.eu
Tel. +265 1773199
Fax +265 1773534

Alessandro MARIANI
Head of Delegation
Tel. *80078

[12] Also responsible for Swaziland.

Malaysia

Menera Tan&Tan 207
Jalan Tun Razak — suite 10.01
Kuala Lumpur
Malaysia
Tel. +603 27237373
Fax +603 27237337

Vincent PIKET
Head of Delegation
Tel. *80096, *80096

Mali

Immeuble UATT
Quartier du fleuve
Bamako
Mali
E-mail: delegation-mali@ec.europa.eu
Website: http://www.delmli.ec.europa.eu
Tel. +223 2221103
Fax +223 2223670
BP 115
Bamako
Mali

Giacomo DURAZZO
Head of Delegation
Tel. *80077

Mauritania

Rue 42-163, B.P. 213
Tevragh Zeina
Nouakchott
Mauritania
E-mail: delegation-mauritania@ec.europa.eu
Tel. +222 5252724
Fax +222 5253524
BP 213
Nouakchott
Mauritania

Geza STRAMMER
Head of Delegation (acting)
Tel. *80075

Mauritius

8th floor
St. James Court Building
St Denis Street
Port Louis
Mauritius
E-mail: mailto@delmus.ec.europa.eu
Tel. +230 2071515
Fax +230 2116624
BP 1148
Port-Louis
Mauritius

Claudia WIEDEY-NIPPOLD
Head of Delegation
Tel. *80076

Mexico

Paseo de la Reforma 1675
Lomas de Chapultepec
11001 Mexico D.F.
Mexico
E-mail: mailto@delmex.ec.europa.eu
Website: http://www.delmex.ec.europa.eu
Tel. +52 5555403345
Fax +52 5555406564

Mendel GOLDSTEIN
Head of Delegation
Tel. *80363

Moldova

Cesare DE MONTIS
Head of Delegation
Tel. *80470

Montenegro

Leopold MAURER
Head of Delegation
Tel. *81930

Morocco

Riad Business Center, Aile Sud
Boulevard Er-Riad
Rabat
Morocco
E-mail: delegation-marocco@ec.europa.eu
Website: http://www.delmar.ec.europa.eu
Tel. +212 37579800
Fax +212 37579810
BP 1302
Rabat
Morocco

Bruno DETHOMAS
Head of Delegation
Tel. *80723

Mozambique

Avenida Julius Nyerere
2820 Maputo
Mozambique
E-mail: delegation-mozambique@ec.europa.eu
Tel. +258 1494949
Fax +258 1491866
CP 1306
Maputo
Mozambique

Glauco CALZUOLA
Head of Delegation
Tel. *80577

Namibia

2 Newton Street
Windhoek
Namibia
E-mail: delegation-namibia@ec.europa.eu
Website: http://www.delnam.ec.europa.eu
Tel. +264 612026224
Fax +264 612026000
PO Box 24443
Windhoek
Namibia

Elisabeth PAPE
Head of Delegation
Tel. *80074

Nicaragua

Carretera a Masaya
del Colegio Teresiano una cuadra al Este
Managua
Nicaragua
E-mail: delegation-nicaragua@ec.europa.eu
Website: http://www.delnic.org.ni
Tel. +505 2704499
Fax +505 2704484
Apartado postal 2654
Managua
Nicaragua

Marc LITVINE
Head of Delegation (acting)
Tel. *80320

Niger

Rue du Commerce
Immeuble BIA 3e étage
Niamey
Niger
E-mail: delegation-niger@ec.europa.eu
Tel. +227 732360,
Direct line to the Head of Del.: +227 734832
Fax +227 732322
BP 10388
Niamey
Niger

Hans-Peter SCHADEK
Head of Delegation
Tel. *80575

Nigeria

21st Crescent
off Constitution Avenue
Central Business District
Abuja
Nigeria
E-mail: delegation-nigeria@ec.europa.eu
Tel. +234 95244006
Fax +234 95244021
Garki
P.M.B. 280
Garki, Abuja
Nigeria

Robert VAN DER MEULEN
Head of Delegation
Tel. *80981

Norway

Haakon VII's Gate 10 (9th floor)
0161 Oslo
Norway
E-mail: delegation-norway@ec.europa.eu
Website: http://www.europakommisjonen.no
Tel. +47 22833583
Fax +47 22834055
Postboks 1643, Vika
0119 Oslo
Norway

Percy WESTERLUND
Head of Delegation ([13])
Tel. *80662

Pakistan

House No 9, Street No 88, Sector G 6/3
Islamabad
Pakistan
E-mail: delegation-pakistan@ec.europa.eu
Tel. +92 512271828
Fax +92 512822604
PO Box 1608
Islamabad
Pakistan

Johannes DE KOK
Head of Delegation
Tel. *80989

Papua New Guinea

The Lodge, 3rd floor
Bampton Street
Port Moresby
Papua New Guinea
E-mail: admin@eudelpng.org
Website: http://www.delpng.ec.europa.eu
Tel. +675 3213544
Fax +675 3217850
PO Box 76
Port Moresby
Papua New Guinea

Aldo DELL'ARICCIA
Head of Delegation ([14])
Tel. *80071

Peru

Av. Comandante Espinar 719
Miraflores
Lima 18
Peru
E-mail: delegation-peru@ec.europa.eu
Website: http://www.delper.ec.europa.eu
Tel. +51 14150800
Fax +51 14465100
Casilla Postal 18-0792
Lima 18
Peru

António CARDOSO MOTA
Head of Delegation
Tel. *80558

([13]) Also responsible for Iceland.
([14]) Also responsible for Vanuatu and the Solomon Islands.

Philippines

30/F Tower II, RCBC Plaza
6819 Ayala Ave. cor. Sen Gil Puyat
1200 Makati, Metro Manila
Philippines
E-mail: delegation-philippines@ec.europa.eu
Website: http://www.delphl.ec.europa.eu
Tel. +63 28595100
Fax +63 28595109

Alistair MACDONALD
Head of Delegation
Tel. *80403

Russia

Kadashevskaya Nab., 14/1
109017 Moscow
Russia
E-mail: delegation-russia@ec.europa.eu
Website: http://www.delrus.ec.europa.eu
Tel. +7 0957212000
Fax +7 0957212020

Marc FRANCO
Head of Delegation
Tel. *80557

Paul VANDOREN
Deputy Head of Delegation
Tel. *80557

Rwanda

Bd. Umuganda 1807
Kigali
Rwanda
E-mail: eudelrwa@delrwa.ec.europa.eu
Tel. +250 585738
Fax +250 585736
BP 515
Kigali
Rwanda

David MACRAE
Head of Delegation
Tel. *80816

Saudi Arabia

Ward Ibn khalid Street No 5, Olaya
Riyadh 11566
Saudi Arabia

Luigi NARBONE
Head of Delegation
Tel. +32 229-87321, 88654

Senegal

12, avenue Albert-Sarraut
Dakar
Senegal
E-mail: delegation-senegal@ec.europa.eu
Website: http://www.delsen.ec.europa.eu
Tel. +221 8891071
Fax +221 8236885
BP 3345
Dakar
Senegal

Gilles HERVIO
Head of Delegation
Tel. *80924

Serbia

Krunska, 73
11000 Belgrade
Serbia
E-mail: delegation-scg@ec.europa.eu
Website: http://www.delscg.ec.europa.eu
Tel. +381 113083200
Fax +381 113083201

Josep LLOVERAS
Head of Delegation
Tel. *80696

Sierra Leone

Wesley House
4, George Street
Freetown
Sierra Leone
E-mail: delegation-Sierra-Leone@ec.europa.eu
Tel. +232 22227319, 223025,
satellite: +874 762154736
Fax +232 22225212

Hans ALLDEN
Head of Delegation
Tel. *80553

Singapore

250 North Bridge Road # 38-03/04
Raffles City Tower
179101
Singapore
Tel. +65 63367919

Lars Holger STANDERTSKJOLD-NORDENSTAM
Head of Delegation
Tel. *80152

South Africa

1-2 Green Park Estate
27 George Storrar Drive
Groenkloof 0181 Pretoria
South Africa
E-mail: delegation-s-africa@ec.europa.eu
Tel. +27 124604319
Fax +27 124609923
Groenkloof 0027
PO Box 945
Pretoria
South Africa

Lodewyk BRIET
Head of Delegation
Tel. *80066

South Korea

Sean Building, 16th floor
116 Shinmoonro 1ka
Chongro-Ku
110-700 Seoul
South Korea
E-mail: mailto@delkor.ec.europa.eu
Tel. +82 27351101
Fax +82 27351211
CPO Box 911
South Korea

Brian MCDONALD
Head of Delegation

Sri Lanka

26, Sir Marcus Fernando Mawatha
Colombo 7
Sri Lanka
E-mail: mailto@dellka.ec.europa.eu
Tel. +94 112674413/14
Fax +94 112678860

Peter MAHER
Head of Delegation (acting)
Tel. *81186

Sudan

Block 1B, Plot 10
Gamhoria Street
Khartoum
Sudan
E-mail: delegation-soudan@ec.europa.eu
Tel. +249 183775054
Fax +249 183775393
PO Box 2363
Khartoum
Sudan

Carlo DE FILIPPI
Head of Delegation
Tel. *80065

Switzerland

Michael REITERER
Head of Delegation
Tel. *80068

Syria

Abou Roumaneh, Najeeb Al-Rayyes St.
Building No 3
Damascus
Syria
E-mail: mailto@delsyr.ec.europa.eu
Website: http://www.delsyr.ec.europa.eu
Tel. +963 113327640 (3 lines)
Fax +963 113320683
BP 11269
Damascus
Syria

Vassilis BONTOSOGLOU
Head of Delegation
Tel. *80402

Tanzania

Umoja House, Garden avenue
Dar es Salaam
Tanzania
E-mail: delegation-tanzania@ec.europa.eu
Tel. +255 222117473
Fax +255 222113277
PO Box 9514
Dar es Salaam
Tanzania

Timothy CLARKE
Head of Delegation
Tel. *80539

Thailand

Kian Gwan House II, 19th floor
140/1 Wireless Road
10330 Bangkok
Thailand
E-mail: delegation-thailand@ec.europa.eu
Website: http://www.deltha.ec.europa.eu
Tel. +66 23052600
Fax +66 22559113

Jean-François CAUTAIN
Head of Delegation (acting)
Tel. *80856

Togo

37, avenue Nicolas Grunitsky
Lomé
Togo
E-mail: delegation-togo@ec.europa.eu
Website: http://www.deltgo.ec.europa.eu
Tel. +228 2213662
Fax +228 2211300
BP 1657
Lomé
Togo

...
Head of Delegation

Trinidad and Tobago

The Mutual Center
16 Queen's Park West
Port of Spain
Trinidad and Tobago
E-mail: mailto@deltto.ec.europa.eu
Tel. +1868 6226628
Fax +1868 6226355
PO Box 1144
Port of Spain
Trinidad and Tobago

...

Tunisia

Immeuble Europe
Berges du lac Nord
Croisement rue du lac Mdlaren
Rue du lac Oubeira
1082 Tunis
Tunisia
E-mail: delegation-tunisia@ec.europa.eu
Website: http://www.ec.europa.eu
Tel. +216 71960330
Fax +216 71960302
BP 150
1053 Tunis
Tunisia

Adrianus KOETSENRUIJTER
Head of Delegation
Tel. *80725

Turkey

Ugur Mumcu Caddesi 88, 4th floor
06700 Gaziosmanpasa Ankara
Turkey
E-mail: delegation-turkey@ec.europa.eu
Website: http://www.deltur.ec.europa.eu
Tel. +90 3124598700
Fax +90 3124466737

Marc PIERINI
Head of Delegation
Tel. *80719

Tibor VARADI
Deputy Head of Delegation
Tel. *80719

Uganda

Crested Towers 15F
17 Hannington Road
Kampala
Uganda
E-mail: mailto@deluga.ec.europa.eu
Tel. +256 41233303
Fax +256 41233708
PO Box 5244
Kampala
Uganda

Vincent DE VISSCHER
Head of Delegation
Tel. *80731

Ukraine

Kruhlo-universitetska street, 10
01024 Kiev
Ukraine
E-mail: delegation-ukraine@ec.europa.eu
Website: http://www.delukr.ec.europa.eu
Tel. +380 443908010
Fax +380 442534547

José Manuel PINTO TEIXEIRA
Head of Delegation
Tel. +32 229-57196, 50600

United States

2300 M Street, NW
DC 20037 Washington
United States
E-mail: delegation-washington@ec.europa.eu
Website: http://www.eurunion.org
Tel. +1 2028629500
Fax +1 2024291766

John BRUTON
Head of Delegation
Tel. *80615

Angelos PANGRATIS
Deputy Head of Delegation
Tel. *80615

Uruguay

Boulevard Artigas 1300
11300 Montevideo
Uruguay
E-mail: delegation-uruguay@ec.europa.eu
Website: http://www.delury.ec.europa.eu
Tel. +598 219440101
Fax +598 219440122

Geoffrey BARRETT
Head of Delegation
Tel. +32 229-66309, 58484

Venezuela

Edificio Comisión Europea
Avenida Orinoco, Las Mercedes
1061 Caracas
Venezuela
E-mail: Delegation-Venezuela@ec.europa.eu
Website: http://www.delven.ec.europa.eu
Tel. +58 2129915133
Fax +58 2129935573
Apartado de Correos 67076
Plaza las Américas 1061-A
1060 Caracas
Venezuela

Antonio GARCIA VELAZQUEZ
Head of Delegation
Tel. *80350

Vietnam

The Metropole Centre
56 Ly Thai To Street
Hanoi
Vietnam
E-mail: delegation-vietnam@ec.europa.eu
Website: http://www.delvnm.ec.europa.eu
Tel. +84 49341300/01/02
Fax +84 49341361

Sean DOYLE
Head of Delegation
Tel. *81174

West Bank and Gaza Strip

5 George Adam Smith Street
Jerusalem
West Bank and Gaza Strip
E-mail: mailto@delwbg.ec.europa.eu
Website: http://www.delwbg.ec.europa.eu
Tel. +972 25415888
Fax +972 25415848
Mount of Olives
PO Box 22207
Jerusalem/Via Israel

Christian BERGER
Head of Delegation
Tel. +32 229-97727, 65412

Zambia

Plot 4899, Los Angeles Boulevard
Lusaka
Zambia
E-mail: Delegation-Zambia@ec.europa.eu
Website: http://www.delzmb.ec.europa.eu
Tel. +260 1251140/250711
Fax +260 1250906
PO Box 34871
Lusaka
Zambia

Derek FEE
Head of Delegation
Tel. *80537

Zimbabwe

EU
1 Norfolk Road
Mount Pleasant
Harare
Zimbabwe
E-mail: delegation-zimbabwe@ec.europa.eu
Website: http://www.delzwe.ec.europa.eu
Tel. +263 4338158-164
Fax +263 4338165
PO Box 4252
Harare
Zimbabwe

Xavier MARCHAL
Head of Delegation
Tel. *80057

To international organisations

Addis-Ababa

Koen VERVAEKE
Head of Delegation
Tel. *80510

Geneva

Rue du Grand-Pré 66
CH-1211 Geneva
E-mail: delegation-geneva@ec.europa.eu
Tel. +41 229182211
Fax +41 227342236
Case postale 107
20 Geneva

Eckart GUTH
Head of Delegation
Tel. *80607

John CLARKE
Deputy Head of Delegation
Tel. *80607

New York

222 East 41th St., 20th floor
10017 New York
United States
E-mail: delegation-new-york@ec.europa.eu
Tel. +1 2123713804
Fax +1 2127582718

Fernando VALENZUELA MARZO
Head of Delegation
Tel. *80610

Peter SCHWAIGER
Deputy Head of Delegation
Tel. *80610

Paris

(OECD, Unesco)
12 avenue d'Eylau
F-75116 Paris
E-mail: secr.eudelfra@mgn.fr
Tel. +33 144053160
Fax +33 144053179

Laurence ARGIMON-PISTRE
Head of Delegation
Tel. *80392

Rome

(FAO)
Via IV Novembre, 149
I-00187 Rome
E-mail: DelegationEC-UN-Rome@ec.europa.eu
Tel. +39 066797823
Fax +39 066797830

Luis RITTO
Head of Delegation
Tel. *80052

Vienna

(International organisations)
Argentinierstraße 26/10
A-1040 Vienna
E-mail: delegation-vienna@ec.europa.eu
Tel. +43 15058411-0
Fax +43 15058411-7

Lars-Erik LUNDIN
Head of Delegation
Tel. *81026

Community institutions, bodies and agencies

COURT OF JUSTICE OF THE EUROPEAN COMMUNITIES

Court of Justice

Boulevard Konrad Adenauer
L-2925 Luxembourg
E-mail: info@curia.europa.eu
Website: http://www.curia.europa.eu
Tel. +352 4303-1
Fax +352 4303-2600

Vassilios SKOURIS
President of the Court of Justice

Dieter KRAUS
Head of private office

Goulielmos VALASIDIS
Legal secretary

Nikolaos SORTIKOS
Legal secretary

Sarah JUND
Legal secretary

Roland MOUSTACHE
Reader of judgments

Bernard STAMM
Reader of judgments

Isabelle DOUCET
Reader of judgments

Thierry ERNIQUIN
Reader of judgments

Jean-Michel ADRIEN
Reader of judgments

Anne SCHNEIDER
Reader of judgments

Peter JANN
President of Chamber

Evelyne TICHADOU
Legal secretary

Hartmut OST
Legal secretary

Sabine LÄNGLE
Legal secretary

Christiaan W. A. TIMMERMANS
President of Chamber

Christopher VAN DER HAUWAERT
Legal secretary

James Stewart WATSON
Legal secretary

Jan INGHELRAM
Legal secretary

Allan ROSAS
President of Chamber

Caroline NAOME
Legal secretary

Sophie GRAFF-SVENNINGSEN
Legal secretary

Heidi KAILA
Legal secretary

Ann DE WOLF
Legal secretary

Koen LENAERTS
President of Chamber

Jean-Marc BINON
Legal secretary

Ludovic BERNARDEAU
Legal secretary

Piet VAN NUFFEL
Legal secretary

Eleanor SHARPSTON
First Advocate-General

Alan BAILLIE
Legal secretary

Margaret DOYIN LAWUNMI
Legal secretary

Geert DE BAERE
Legal secretary

Catherine HOWDLE
Legal secretary

Marko ILEŠIČ
President of Chamber

Jan VANHAMME
Legal secretary

Saša SEVER
Legal secretary

Alexandra RÜTH
Legal secretary

Aindrias Ó CAOIMH
President of Chamber

Bruno VAN HEES
Legal secretary

Siofra O'LEARY
Legal secretary

Henry Michael ABBOTT
Legal secretary

Jean-Claude BONICHOT
President of Chamber

Christian LAMBERT
Legal secretary

Emmanuelle BROUSSY
Legal secretary

Francis DONNAT
Legal secretary

Thomas VON DANWITZ
Judge

Ulrich FORSTHOFF
Legal secretary

Eva-Maria DERSTADT
Legal secretary

Katherina PARASCHAS
Legal secretary

Dámaso RUIZ JARABO COLOMER
Advocate-General

Antonio PEREZ VAN KAPPEL
Legal secretary

Dimitry BERBEROFF-AYUDA
Legal secretary

Ana SANTAMARIA DACAL
Legal secretary

Daniel SARMIENTO RAMIREZ-ESCUDERO
Legal secretary

Antonio TIZZANO
Judge

Bruno GENCARELLI
Legal secretary

Paolo IANNUCCELLI
Legal secretary

Massimiliano PUGLIA
Legal secretary

José Narciso DA CUNHA RODRIGUES
Judge

Timothy MILLETT
Legal secretary

Antonio José ROBALO CORDEIRO
Legal secretary

Luc WEITZEL
Legal secretary

Rosario SILVA DE LAPUERTA
Judge

Kurt RIECHENBERG
Legal secretary

Bernard CARLIER
Legal secretary

Miguel MARTINEZ GIMENO
Legal secretary

Juliane KOKOTT
Advocate-General

Christoph SOBOTTA
Legal secretary

Daniel DITTERT
Legal secretary

Thomas HENZE
Legal secretary

Ioanna DERVISOPOULOS
Legal secretary

Luis Miguel POIARES PESSOA MADURO
Advocate-General

Dominique RITLENG
Legal secretary

Francisco COSTA-CABRAL
Legal secretary

Nicholas HATZIS
Legal secretary

Ronan MCCREA
Legal secretary

Konrad SCHIEMANN
Judge

Olivier LHOEST
Legal secretary

Carsten ZATSCHLER
Legal secretary

Aleksandra MELESKO
Legal secretary

Jerzy MAKARCZYK
Judge

Catherine BROUARD-GALLET
Legal secretary

Christophe LESAUVAGE
Legal secretary

Alicja SIKORA
Legal secretary

Pranas KÜRIS
Judge

Denis D'ERSU
Legal secretary

Marie-Laure MESSE-ROTH
Legal secretary

Darius ARBACIAUSKAS
Legal secretary

Endre JUHÁSZ
Judge

Athanassios STATHOPOULOS
Legal secretary

Márton SZŰTS
Legal secretary

Thierry DE BOVIS
Legal secretary

George ARESTIS
President of Chamber

Michele TRAPANI
Legal secretary

Christina CHARALAMBOUS
Legal secretary

Juan JAUREGUI OLAGUIBEL
Legal secretary

Anthony BORG BARTHET
Judge

Katrine SAWYER
Legal secretary

Thérèse ZANKEL
Legal secretary

Jacques René ZAMMIT
Legal secretary

Jiří MALENOVSKÝ
Judge

Karen BRIET
Legal secretary

Michel ROMNICIANU
Legal secretary

David PETRLIK
Legal secretary

Ján KLUČKA
Judge

Alain SCARAMUCCI
Legal secretary

Franck MICHEL
Legal secretary

Peter PECHO
Legal secretary

Uno LÕHMUS
Judge

María Isabel ROFES i PUJOL
Legal secretary

Andrew THOMSON
Legal secretary

Liina TERAS
Legal secretary

Egils LEVITS
Judge

Claudia SCHMIDT
Legal secretary

Emmanuel FRANÇOIS
Legal secretary

Ieva FREIJA
Legal secretary

Lars BAY LARSEN
Judge

Bernard WEIER
Legal secretary

Jesper SVENNINGSEN
Legal secretary

Gianfranco GORI
Legal secretary

Paolo MENGOZZI
Advocate-General

Maria Teresa D'ALESSIO
Legal secretary

Vincent KRONENBERGER
Legal secretary

Lorenzo FEDEL
Legal secretary

József VILLÀNYI
Legal secretary

Pernilla LINDH
Judge

Françoise BLUM
Legal secretary

Jean RICHARD DE LA TOUR
Legal secretary

Pascal CARDONNEL
Legal secretary

Yves BOT
Advocate-General

Bernard CHEVALIER
Legal secretary

David MAS
Legal secretary

Maud VIEUX
Legal secretary

Véronique BEAUGRAND
Legal secretary

Ján MAZÁK
Advocate-General

Eileen SHEEHAN
Legal secretary

Martin MOSER
Legal secretary

Martina JÁNOŠIKOVÁ
Legal secretary

Milan KRISTOF
Legal secretary

Vérica TRSTENJAK
Advocate-General

Régine WINTER
Legal secretary

Werner Miguel KÜHN
Legal secretary

Jean-Christophe PUFFER-MARIETTE
Legal secretary

Maja BRKAN
Legal secretary

Alexander ARABADJIEV
Judge

Alberto ALEMANNO
Legal secretary

Alexandre KORNEZOV
Legal secretary

Camelia TOADER
Judge

Celestina IANNONE
Legal secretary

Aladar SEBENI
Legal secretary

Karim KOURI
Legal secretary

Jean-Jacques KASEL
Judge

Jean Mathias GODARD
Legal secretary

Jacques RADOUX
Legal secretary

Martine KREMER
Legal secretary

Roger GRASS
Registrar

Jean-Michel RACHET
Attaché to the Registrar

Pawel SZAJKOWSKI
Attaché to the Registrar

DEPARTMENTS OF THE COURT

Registry

Fax +352 433766

Henrik VON HOLSTEIN
Deputy Registrar

Marc-André GAUDISSART
Head of Unit

Internal Audit Unit

Javier MARTINEZ DE ARAGON

Protocol

Fax +352 4303-2030

Denise LOUTERMAN-HUBEAU
Director for Protocol and Visits
Fax +352 4303-2030

Legal Adviser for Administrative Affairs

Agostino PLACCO
Adviser

Directorate for Interpretation

Fax +352 4303-3697

Patrick TWIDLE
Director
Fax +352 4303-3697

Unit A

Marie MUTTILAINEN
Head of Unit

Unit B

Elizabeth CADE
Head of Unit

Unit C

Mohand HAMAI
Head of Unit

Press and Information Service

Fax +352 4303-2500

Juan Carlos GONZALEZ ALVAREZ
Head of Unit
Fax +352 4303-2500

Library, Research and Documentation Directorate

Fax +352 4303-2424

...
Director-General
Fax +352 4303-2424

1. Library

Fax +352 4303-2424

Nikolaos APOSTOLIDIS
Director
Fax +352 4303-2424

2. Research and Documentation

Fax +352 4303-3400

Unit A

Sabine HACKSPIEL
Head of Unit

Unit B

Philippe SINGER
Head of Division

Unit C

René BARENTS
Head of Division

Legal information

Baudoin GIELEN
Head of Unit

Translation Directorate

Fax +352 4303-2720

Alfredo CALOT ESCOBAR
Director-General
Fax +352 4303-2720

Planning and External Translation Unit

Thierry LEFÈVRE
Head of Unit

Documentary Resources and Analyses Unit

Rita ERHARD
Head of Unit

Resources and Projects Unit

Maria MUGICA ARZAMENDI
Head of Unit

Translation Tools Unit

Florent THOUVENIN
Head of Unit

Section A

José NUNES DE CARVALHO
Director

1. English Translation Unit

Susan WRIGHT
Head of Division

2. Danish Translation Unit

Jens FRAUSING
Head of Division

3. French Translation Unit

Jean-Pierre VERNIER
Head of Division

4. Greek Translation Unit

Aristides VLACHOS
Head of Division

5. Italian Translation Unit

Alberto MORELLO
Head of Division

6. Lithuanian Translation Unit

Marija ANCIUVIENE
Head of Unit

7. Maltese Translation Unit

Joseph IZZO CLARKE
Head of Unit

8. Slovakian Translation Unit

Branislav KAPALA
Head of Unit

9. Slovene Translation Unit

Silva HORVAT
Head of Unit

10. Swedish Translation Unit

Ingalill LINDBLOM
Head of Division

11. Czech Translation Unit

Martin SMEJKAL
Head of Unit

Section B

Maria Letizia LOMBARDI-LATRONICO
Director

1. German Translation Unit

Bernd ZIMMERMANN
Head of Unit

2. Bulgarian Translation Unit

...
Head of Unit

3. Spanish Translation Unit

Adolfo GUTIÉRREZ
Head of Division

4. Estonian Translation Unit

Madis VUNDER
Head of Unit

5. Finnish Translation Unit

Kari LIIRI
Head of Division

6. Hungarian Translation Unit

Rita PETRÓ
Head of Unit

7. Latvian Translation Unit

Ilona SKUJA
Head of Unit

8. Dutch Translation Unit

Christiaan VERSELE
Head of Unit

9. Polish Translation Unit

Maciej MARKIEWICZ
Head of Unit

10. Portuguese Translation Unit

Nuno FONTES NUNES
Head of Unit

11. Romanian Translation Unit

Ioana GEORGHE-BADESCU
Head of Unit

Personnel and Financial Directorate

Tel. +352 4303-1
Fax +352 4303-2600

Bernard POMMIÈS
Director-General

1. Human Resources and Personnel Administration Section

Fax +352 4303-2710

Mark RONAYNE
Director

Human Resources Unit

Claude DEROCHE
Head of Unit

Statutory Rights, Social and Medical Matters, Conditions of Work Unit

Costantinos POPOTAS
Head of Unit

In-Service Training Unit

Brigitte JANSSON
Head of Unit

Remuneration and Business Trips Unit

Paolo BRIZZI
Head of Unit

2. Budget and Accounts Directorate

Sylvain SIMONETTI
Director

3. Checking Section

Henk DEUSS
Head of Division

Infrastructure Directorate

Francis SCHAFF
Director-General

1. Buildings and Logistics Section

Fax +352 4303-2650

Marc SCHAUSS
Director

Property and Security Unit

Joachim SCHWIERS
Head of Unit

Purchases and Inventory Unit

Cornelis GEERS
Head of Unit

General Services and Rolling Stock Unit

Luis MOITINHO DE ALMEIDA
Head of Unit

Production, Publication and Diffusion of Documents Unit

...
Head of Unit

2. Information Technology Section

Reinhard KROMMES
Director

Legal and Judicial Documentation Unit

...
Head of Unit

Administration and User Support Unit

Éric DEUDON
Head of Unit

Technical Infrastructure Unit

Cinzia D'ASCANIO
Head of Unit

Court of First Instance

Boulevard Konrad Adenauer
L-2925 Luxembourg
Website: http://www.curia.europa.eu
Tel. +352 4303-1
Fax +352 4303-2600

Marc JAEGER
President of the Court of First Instance

Yves MOTTARD
Legal secretary

Johannes CONRAD
Legal secretary

Arnaud BOHLER
Legal secretary

Stefano BONI
Legal secretary

Massimo MARELLI
Legal secretary

Ellen VERDURE
Reader of judgments

Jean-Charles ENGEL
Reader of judgments

Estelle BOCQUILLON
Reader of judgments

Olivier SEGNANA
Reader of judgments

Stéphanie MAHIEU
Reader of judgments

Corentin POULLET
Reader of judgments

Virpi TIILI
President of Chamber

Nina KORJUS
Legal secretary

Marc BARENNES
Legal secretary

Aitor MONTESA LLOREDA
Legal secretary

Josef AZIZI
President of Chamber

Hanns Peter NEHL
Legal secretary

François VAN DEN BERGHE
Legal secretary

Serge PATOU
Legal secretary

Arjen MEIJ
President of Chamber

Dominique THIAVILLE
Legal secretary

Edmon OUDE ELFERINK
Legal secretary

Tristan BAUMÉ
Legal secretary

Michel VILARAS
President of Chamber

Alain BURKIC
Legal secretary

Cyrille CALLIES
Legal secretary

Ioannis NATSINAS
Legal secretary

Nicholas FORWOOD
President of Chamber

Thierry DESNEUX
Legal secretary

Ulrich KLINKE
Legal secretary

Matthew RADLEY
Legal secretary

Maria Eugénia MARTINS RIBEIRO
President of Chamber

Christophe VAHDAT
Legal secretary

Ignace MASELIS
Legal secretary

Alexandre GEULETTE
Legal secretary

Ottó CZÚCZ
President of Chamber

Katrien VERANNEMAN
Legal secretary

Viktor Stanislaw LUSZCZ
Legal secretary

Isabel GALINDO MARTIN
Legal secretary

Irena PELIKÁNOVÁ
President of Chamber

Ivo GROSS
Legal secretary

Arnaud RACLET
Legal secretary

Jan PREVRATIL
Legal secretary

Franklin DEHOUSSE
Judge

Marie-Béatrice GAVANIER
Legal secretary

Alexandre THILLIER
Legal secretary

Olivia DAVIDSON
Legal secretary

Ena CREMONA
Judge

Daniele DOMENICUCCI
Legal secretary

Dimisthenis PAPAKRIVOPOULOS
Legal secretary

Igor TACCANI
Legal secretary

Irena WISZNIEWSKA-BIAŁECKA
Judge

Stéphanie RAMET
Legal secretary

Gaëlle BONTINCK
Legal secretary

Pablo BERBEL FERNANDEZ
Legal secretary

Daniel ŠVÁBY
Judge

Susana MORENO SANCHEZ
Legal secretary

Magali ROUSSELOT
Legal secretary

Andrej STEC
Legal secretary

Vilenas VADAPALAS
Judge

Arnaldo PINTO
Legal secretary

Frédéric BARON
Legal secretary

Saulius KALEDA
Legal secretary

Küllike JÜRIMÄE
Judge

Tom GILLIAMS
Legal secretary

Cyril SARRAZIN
Legal secretary

Pascale HECKER
Legal secretary

Ingrida LABUCKA
Judge

Solvita HARBACEVICA
Legal secretary

Zaïra PENDERS
Legal secretary

Krzysztof PAWLOWSKI
Legal secretary

Savvas S. PAPASAVVAS
Judge

Kai Peter ZIEGLER
Legal secretary

Raphaël VUITTON
Legal secretary

Georgios GRYLLOS
Legal secretary

Enzo MOAVERO MILANESI
Judge

Frank HO SI FAT
Legal secretary

Giuseppe BERTOLI
Legal secretary

Jasmin BATTISTA
Legal secretary

Nils WAHL
Judge

Yolanda DE MUYNCK
Legal secretary

Leila REZKI
Legal secretary

Foad HOSEINIAN
Legal secretary

Miro PREK
Judge

Éric VANHAM
Legal secretary

Nina SAVIN-BOSSIÈRE
Legal secretary

Silvère LEFÈVRE
Legal secretary

Teodor TCHIPEV
Judge

Mattia MELLONI
Legal secretary

Dimitar STEFANOV
Legal secretary

Juan Ignacio SIGNES DE MESA
Legal secretary

Valeriu CIUCA
Judge

Valérie BAUER
Legal secretary

Jens HAMER
Legal secretary

Antonio LA PERGOLA
Legal secretary

Alfred DITTRICH
Judge

Barbara ERNST
Legal secretary

Oliver LANDWEHR
Legal secretary

Martin KRAUS-VONJAHR
Legal secretary

Santiago SOLDEVILA FRAGOSO
Judge

Nuria BERMEJO GUTIÉRREZ
Legal secretary

Eléonore VON BARDELEBEN
Legal secretary

Georges VALLINDAS
Legal secretary

Laurent TRUCHOT
Judge

Pierre ROSEREN
Legal secretary

David SIRITZKY
Legal secretary

Patrice GUIGON
Legal secretary

Sten FRIMODT NIELSEN
Judge

Michel VAN HUFFEL
Legal secretary

Gwenael MUGUET-POULLENNEC
Legal secretary

Marc BOUILLAGUET
Reader of judgments

Kevin O'HIGGINS
Judge

Olivier SPELTDOORN
Legal secretary

Yannick CARAPITO
Legal secretary

Emma-Jean HINCHY
Legal secretary

Emmanuel COULON
Registrar

Registry

Fax +352 4303-2100

Blanca PASTOR BORGOÑON
Deputy Registrar

José PALACIO GONZÁLEZ
Principal Administrator

Camilla KRISTENSEN
Administrator

Joris PLINGERS
Administrator

Katarina ANDOVA
Administrator

Katarina POCHEC
Administrator

Klotildi KANTZA
Administrator

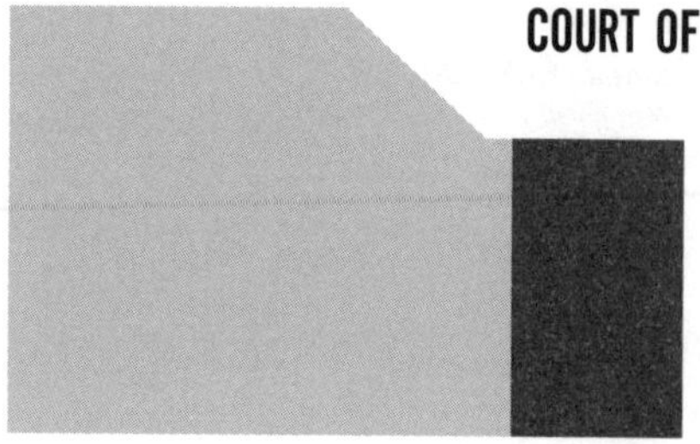

COURT OF JUSTICE OF THE EUROPEAN COMMUNITIES

Civil Service Tribunal

35 A avenue J. F. Kennedy
L-2925 Luxembourg
E-mail: tfp.greffe@curia.europa.eu
Fax +352 4303-4453

Paul J. MAHONEY
President

Nicolas MARTINEZ
Legal secretary

Anne-Géraldine CHAMBERT
Legal secretary

Laurent GRAVIÈRE
Reader of judgments

Horstpeter KREPPEL
President of Chamber

Vincent CADOR
Legal secretary

Sean VAN RAEPENBUSCH
President of Chamber

Pascal GILLIAUX
Legal secretary

Irena BORUTA
Judge

Antoine MASSON
Legal secretary

Heikki KANNINEN
Judge

Fabrice BOCQUILLON
Legal secretary

Haris TAGARAS
Judge

Eugénie CHRISTOPHE
Legal secretary

Stéphane GERVASONI
Judge

Claude CARRIER
Legal secretary

Waltraud HAKENBERG
Registrar

Roberto SCHIANO
Administrator

EUROPEAN COURT OF AUDITORS

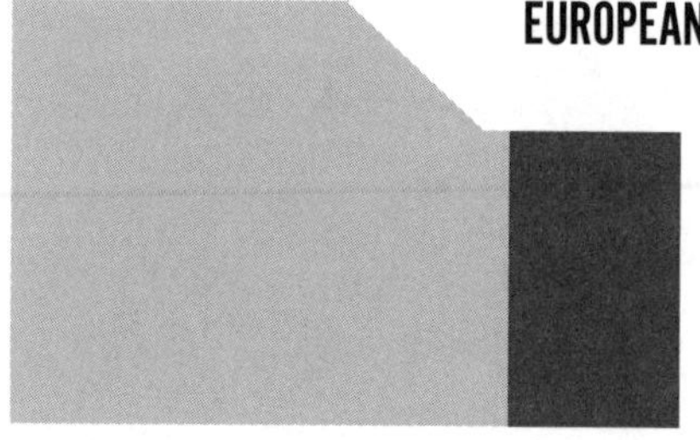

EUROPEAN COURT OF AUDITORS

Court of Auditors

12, rue Alcide De Gasperi
L-1615 Luxembourg
E-mail: euraud@eca.europa.eu
Website: http://www.eca.europa.eu
Tel. +352 4398-1
Fax +352 439342

Vítor Manuel DA SILVA CALDEIRA
President of the Court
Tel. +352 4398-45586
Fax +352 4398-46813

Manuel LOURENÇO DE OLIVEIRA
Head of private office
Tel. +352 4398-45160

Paula BETENCOURT
Attaché
Tel. +352 4398-45059

James McQUADE
Attaché
Tel. +352 4398-45906

Hubert WEBER
Member of the Court
Tel. +352 4398-45951
Fax +352 4398-46957

Joël COSTANTZER
Head of private office
Tel. +352 4398-45956

Helena PIRON-MÄKI-KORVELA
Attaché
Tel. +352 4398-45314

Maarten B. ENGWIRDA
Member of the Court
Tel. +352 4398-45236
Fax +352 4398-46202

Jan Pieter LINGEN
Head of private office
Tel. +352 4398-45746

Horst FISCHER
Attaché
Tel. +352 4398-45122

Máire GEOGHEGAN-QUINN
Member of the Court
Tel. +352 4398-45370
Fax +352 4398-46493

Gilbert JOHNSTON
Head of private office
Tel. +352 4398-45307

...
Attaché

David BOSTOCK
Member of the Court
Tel. +352 4398-45372
Fax +352 4398-46810

Peter WELCH
Head of private office
Tel. +352 4398-45275

Thomas HÄLLSTRÖM
Attaché
Tel. +352 4398-45051

Morten Louis LEVYSOHN
Member of the Court
Tel. +352 4398-45264
Fax +352 4398-46811

Hans ANDERSEN
Head of private office
Tel. +352 4398-45223

Mogens Uhd NIELSEN
Attaché
Tel. +352 4398-47655

Ioannis SARMAS
Member of the Court
Tel. +352 4398-45258
Fax +352 4398-46814

Séverin GRANDCOLAS
Head of private office
Tel. +352 4398-45441

...
Attaché

Július MOLNÁR
Member of the Court
Tel. +352 4398-47201
Fax +352 4398-48800

Christophe PERRON
Head of private office
Tel. +352 4398-47202

Vladimír CÍSAR
Attaché
Tel. +352 4398-47203

Vojko Anton ANTONČIČ
Member of the Court
Tel. +352 4398-47211
Fax +352 4398-48801

Kate HENDERSON
Head of private office
Tel. +352 4398-47213

Goranka KIRALJ
Attaché
Tel. +352 4398-47663

Gejza Zsolt HALÁSZ
Member of the Court
Tel. +352 4398-47221
Fax +352 4398-48802

Tibor TRENCSÉNYI
Head of private office
Tel. +352 4398-47222

Erika Katalin SÖVEGES
Attaché
Tel. +352 4398-47223

Jacek UCZKIEWICZ
Member of the Court
Tel. +352 4398-47251
Fax +352 4398-48805

Jacek KOLASIŃSKI
Head of private office
Tel. +352 4398-45639

Katarzyna RADECKA-MOROZ
Attaché
Tel. +352 4398-47253

Josef BONNICI
Member of the Court
Tel. +352 4398-47231
Fax +352 4398-48803

Ray CACHIA-ZAMMIT
Head of private office
Tel. +352 4398-47232

Raymund KIST
Attaché
Tel. +352 4398-47661

Irena PETRUŠKEVIČIENĖ
Member of the Court
Tel. +352 4398-47261
Fax +352 4398-48806

Peter SCHÖNBERGER
Head of private office
Tel. +352 4398-47262

Maura McELHINNEY
Attaché
Tel. +352 4398-45601

Igors LUDBORŽS
Member of the Court
Tel. +352 4398-47271
Fax +352 4398-48807

Gaston MOONEN
Head of private office
Tel. +352 4398-45716

Bernard MOYA
Attaché
Tel. +352 4398-45916

Jan KINŠT
Member of the Court
Tel. +352 4398-47281
Fax +352 4398-48808

Michael MICHOVSKY
Head of private office
Tel. +352 4398-47282

Johannes MADSEN
Attaché
Tel. +352 4398-45773

Kersti KALJULAID
Member of the Court
Tel. +352 4398-47291
Fax +352 4398-48809

Peeter LÄTTI
Head of private office
Tel. +352 4398-47292

Markku POTTONEN
Attaché
Tel. +352 4398-45969

Kikis KAZAMIAS
Member of the Court
Tel. +352 4398-47241
Fax +352 4398-48804

François OSETE
Head of private office
Tel. +352 4398-47242

Neophytos NEOPHYTOU
Attaché
Tel. +352 4398-47243

Massimo VARI
Member of the Court
Tel. +352 4398-45374
Fax +352 4398-46815

Maria Annunziata RUCIRETA
Head of private office
Tel. +352 4398-45218

...
Attaché

Juan RAMALLO MASSANET
Member of the Court
Tel. +352 4398-45592
Fax +352 4398-46818

Sabine HIERNAUX-FRITSCH
Head of private office
Tel. +352 4398-45454

Maria Belén MARTINEZ RODRIGUEZ
Attaché
Tel. +352 4398-47780

Olavi ALA-NISSILÄ
Member of the Court
Tel. +352 4398-45965
Fax +352 4398-46971

Jukka NURMIO
Head of private office
Tel. +352 4398-45390

Turo HENTILÄ
Attaché
Tel. +352 4398-45925

Lars HEIKENSTEN
Member of the Court
Tel. +352 4398-45958
Fax +352 4398-46964

Fabrice MERCADE
Head of private office
Tel. +352 4398-45486

...
Attaché

Karel PINXTEN
Member of the Court
Tel. +352 4398-45295
Fax +352 4398-46333

Gerard MADDEN
Head of private office
Tel. +352 4398-45516

Emmanuel-Douglas HELLINAKIS
Attaché
Tel. +352 4398-45032

Ovidiu ISPIR
Member of the Court
Tel. +352 4398-47121
Fax +352 4398-48812

Patrick WELDON
Head of private office
Tel. +352 4398-45335

Marilena DEMIAN
Attaché
Tel. +352 4398-47123
Fax +352 4398-48812

Nadejda SANDOLOVA
Member of the Court
Tel. +352 4398-47141
Fax +352 4398-48811

Didier LEBRUN
Head of private office
Tel. +352 4398-45704

Christina VALTCHANOVA
Attaché
Tel. +352 4398-45656

Michel CRETIN
Member of the Court
Tel. +352 4398-45203
Fax +352 4398-46817

Dirk PAUWELS
Head of private office
Tel. +352 4398-45229

Jean-Marc DANIÈLE
Attaché
Tel. +352 4398-45312

Harald NOACK
Member of the Court
Tel. +352 4398-45271
Fax +352 4398-46816

Juan Ignacio GONZÁLEZ BASTERO
Head of private office
Tel. +352 4398-45117

Dagmar FREUDENSTEIN
Attaché
Tel. +352 4398-47764

Henri GRETHEN
Member of the Court
Tel. +352 4398-45376
Fax +352 4398-46819

Martin WEBER
Head of private office
Tel. +352 4398-45151

Marc HOSTERT
Attaché
Tel. +352 4398-47711

PRESIDENCY

Supervision of the performance of the Court's work. Relations with the Community institutions. Relations with SAIs and international audit organisations. Legal matters.

Liaison Officer

Hendrik FEHR
Director
Tel. +352 4398-45503

Legal matters

Tom KENNEDY
Head of Unit
Tel. +352 4398-45766

Jean-Marie STENIER
Administrator
Tel. +352 4398-45459

Internal audit

Hélder FARIA VIEGAS
Head of Unit
Tel. +352 4398-45249

AUDIT GROUPS

Audit group I — Preservation and management of natural resources

Hubert WEBER
Dean

Július MOLNÁR
Member

Gejza Zsolt HALÁSZ
Member

Kikis KAZAMIAS
Member

Olavi ALA-NISSILÄ
Member

Michel CRETIN
Member

Edward FENNESSY
Director
Tel. +352 4398-45214

EAGF — Financial audit

Mark CRISP
Head of Unit
Tel. +352 4398-45977

EAFRD — Financial audit

Davide LINGUA
Head of Unit
Tel. +352 4398-45555

Performance Unit A

Meletios STAVRAKIS
Head of Unit
Tel. +352 4398-45261

Performance Unit B

...
Head of Unit

Performance Unit C

Michael BAIN
Head of Unit
Tel. +352 4398-45438

Fisheries, Environment, Health

José DE MIRA MENDES
Head of Unit
Tel. +352 4398-47533

Audit Group II — Structural, transport, research and energy policies

David BOSTOCK
Dean

Kersti KALJULAID
Member

Massimo VARI
Member

Ovidiu ISPIR
Member

Harald NOACK
Member

Henri GRETHEN
Member

Gabriele CIPRIANI
Director
Tel. +352 4398-45556

Peter KOEHLER
Adviser
Tel. +352 4398-45599

Structural policies — financial audit

Léon KIRSCH
Head of Unit
Tel. +352 4398-45298

Structural policies — performance audit

Alain VANSILLIETTE
Head of Unit
Tel. +352 4398-45263

Transport, research and energy — financial audit

Richard HARDY
Head of Unit
Tel. +352 4398-45625

Transport, research and energy — performance audit

Ossi LOUKO
Head of Unit
Tel. +352 4398-45546

Audit Group III — External actions

Maarten B. ENGWIRDA
Dean

Máire GEOGHEGAN-QUINN
Member

Jacek UCZKIEWICZ
Member

Jan KINŠT
Member

Karel PINXTEN
Member

Philippe FROIDURE
Director
Tel. +352 4398-45302

Cooperation with developing countries (general budget of the EU)

Bernard LOESEL
Head of Unit
Tel. +352 4398-45282

Pre-accession and neighbourhood policies

Raija PELTONEN
Head of Unit
Tel. +352 4398-45784

European Development Funds (African, Caribbean and Pacific States)

Gérald LOCATELLI
Head of Unit
Tel. +352 4398-45626

Audit Group IV —Own revenue, banking activities, administrative expenditure, community institutions and bodies, internal policies

Ioannis SARMAS
Dean

Morten Louis LEVYSOHN
Member

Irena PETRUŠKEVIČIENĖ
Member

Igors LUDBORŽS
Member

Juan RAMALLO MASSANET
Member

Nadejda SANDOLOVA
Member

Jean-Michel GAVANIER
Director
Tel. +352 4398-45428

Cornelis GROENEVELD
Head of Unit. Responsible for special tasks: Performance audit of the Leonardo programme (education).
Tel. +352 4398-45243

Revenue of the European Union

Paul STAFFORD
Head of Unit
Tel. +352 4398-45494

Administrative expenditure of the institutions of the European Union

Bertrand ALBUGUES
Head of Unit
Tel. +352 4398-45769

Internal policies of the European Union

Willem VAN DER HOOFT
Head of Unit
Tel. +352 4398-45211

Borrowing, lending and banking activities

Zacharias KOLIAS
Head of Unit
Tel. +352 4398-45907

Community agencies and other decentralised bodies

Pierre HUGÉ
Head of Unit
Tel. +352 4398-45560

CEAD Group — Coordination, communication, evaluation, assurance and development

Josef BONNICI
Member responsible for DAS, Dean

Vojko Anton ANTONČIČ
Member responsible for ADAR

Lars HEIKENSTEN
Member responsible for communication

Olavi ALA-NISSILÄ
Member

Kersti KALJULAID
Member

Jacek UCZKIEWICZ
Member

Irena PETRUŠKEVIČIENĖ
Member

Audit support and communication

Jesús LÁZARO CUENCA
Director
Tel. +352 4398-45978

Audit methodology and support

John SWEENEY
Head of Unit
Tel. +352 4398-45526

Quality control

Geoffrey SIMPSON
Head of Unit
Tel. +352 4398-45347

Communication and reports

Michel BULZ
Head of Unit
Tel. +352 4398-45250

Press Office

Géza NOVÁK
Administrator
Tel. +352 4398-45224

Audit and audit supervision — Financial compliance audit

Manfred KRAFF
Director
Tel. +352 4398-45348

Audit supervision and support for financial & compliance audit

Niels-Erik BROKOPP-SPIERMANN
Head of Unit
Tel. +352 4398-45579

Reliability of the accounts and of management representations

Ralph OTTE
Head of Unit
Tel. +352 4398-45255

ADMINISTRATIVE COMMITTEE ([1])

Members

Igors LUDBORŽS
President

Kikis KAZAMIAS

Henri GRETHEN

Jan KINŠT

Lars HEIKENSTEN

Alternate Members

Gejza Zsolt HALÁSZ

Harald NOACK

Jacek UCZKIEWICZ

Morten Louis LEVYSOHN

Vojko Anton ANTONČIČ

([1]) Responsible for all administrative questions requiring a Court decision.

Human Resources, IT and telecommunications. Finance and administration. Translation

John SPEED
Acting Secretary-General
Tel. +352 4398-45583
Fax +352 4398-46666

Denis BRUNEAU
Assistant to the Secretary-General
Tel. +352 4398-45492

John CHOMA
Assistant to the Secretary-General
Tel. +352 4398-47665

Data protection

Jan KILB
Internal Delegate
Tel. +352 4398-45562

Human resources

John SPEED
Director
Tel. +352 4398-45583

Human resources

Rose-Marie WEGNEZ
Head of Unit
Tel. +352 4398-45431

Training

Elisabeth TÜRK
Head of Unit (acting)
Tel. +352 4398-45548

Informatics and telecommunications

Magdalena CORDERO VALDAVIDA
Director
Tel. +352 4398-45007

Finance and administration

Eduardo RUIZ GARCÍA
Director
Tel. +352 4398-45620

Finance and buildings policy

Neil USHER
Head of Unit
Tel. +352 4398-45281

Administration

Vital SCHMITT
Head of Unit
Tel. +352 4398-45705

Court secretariat and library

Pilar CALVO FUENTES
Head of Unit
Tel. +352 4398-45787

Accounts

Gerhard ROSS
Head of Unit
Tel. +352 4398-45988

Protocol and visits

Raymond CLAUDEL
Head of Unit
Tel. +352 4398-45559

Translation

Ulla FALK-PETERSEN
Director
Tel. +352 4398-45530

Coordination

José ORTIZ PINTOR
Head of Unit
Tel. +352 4398-45321

Spanish/Romanian

Pilar CANO DE GARDOQUI
Head of Unit
Tel. +352 4398-45670

Danish/Czech

Dorte REMAOUN
Head of Unit
Tel. +352 4398-45582

German

Monika KRUMNAU
Head of Unit
Tel. +352 4398-45544

Greek

Androniki VLACHOU
Head of Unit
Tel. +352 4398-45576

English

Stephen HARRISON
Head of Unit
Tel. +352 4398-45532

French/Bulgarian

Alain VERKAEREN
Head of Unit
Tel. +352 4398-45512

Italian/Slovenian

Elisabetta PALLA
Head of Unit
Tel. +352 4398-45509

Latvian

Inta ŠMITE
Head of Unit
Tel. +352 4398-47618

Hungarian

Balász KASZAP
Head of Unit
Tel. +352 4398-47716

Dutch/Lithuanian

Maurice LOOS
Head of Unit
Tel. +352 4398-45573

Polish

Agata KLOPOTOWSKA
Head of Unit
Tel. +352 4398-47613

Portuguese

António CALLIXTO
Head of Unit
Tel. +352 4398-45527

Slovak

Miroslav PIKNA
Head of Unit
Tel. +352 4398-45205

Finnish/Estonian

Eija RAITTINEN
Head of Unit
Tel. +352 4398-45675

Swedish/Maltese

Carolina ASK
Head of Unit
Tel. +352 4398-45939

EUROPEAN ECONOMIC AND SOCIAL COMMITTEE

Members

BUREAU OF THE EUROPEAN ECONOMIC AND SOCIAL COMMITTEE

Presidency (1)

President

Mr Mario SEPI
President
Italie
Direttore dell'Istituto sindacale per la cooperazione allo sviluppo (ISCOS) della Confederazione italiana sindacati lavoratori (CISL)
Via Po, 21 • I-00198 Roma
Tel. +39 068473271
Fax +39 068473242
E-mail: mario.sepi@eesc.europa.eu

Vice-Presidents

Mr Seppo KALLIO
Vice-President
Suomi/Finland
Johtaja, kansainväliset asiat, Maa- ja metsätaloustuottajain Keskusliitto (MTK)
Simonkatu 6, P.O. Box 510 • FI-00101 Helsinki
Tel. +358 204132380 (direct)
Fax +358 204132408
E-mail: Seppo.Kallio@mtk.fi

Mrs Irini Ivoni PARI
Vice-President
Grèce
Μόνιμη Εκπρόσωπος του Γραφείου του ΣΕΒ (Σύνδεσμος Επιχειρήσεων και Βιομηχανιών) στις Βρυξέλλες και Μόνιμη Εκπρόσωπος του Γραφείου του ΣΕΒ στην Ένωση Ευρωπαϊκών Επιχειρήσεων (BUSINESSEUROPE - Confederation of European Business)
Avenue de Cortenbergh 168 • B-1000 Bruxelles
Tel. +32 22310053
Fax +32 22800891
E-mail: irini.pari@skynet.be

Members of the bureau

Mr Mario SEPI
President

Mr Seppo KALLIO
Vice-President

Mrs Irini Ivoni PARI
Vice-President

Mrs Milena ANGELOVA
Group I

Mr Brian CALLANAN
Group I

Mr Bryan CASSIDY
Group I

Mr Roberto CONFALONIERI
Group III

Mr Georgios DASSIS
Group II

Mrs Benedicte FEDERSPIEL
Group III

Mrs Sylvia GAUCI
Group I

Mr Hubert GHIGONIS
Group III

Mr Roman HAKEN
Group III

Mr Filip HAMRO-DROTZ
Group I

Mr Raymond HENCKS
Group II

Mr Bernardo HERNÁNDEZ BATALLER
Group III

Mr József KAPUVÁRI
Group II

Mr Armands KRAUZE
Group III

Mr Jacek KRAWCZYK
Group I

Mrs Leila KURKI
Group II

Mrs Daiva KVEDARAITĖ
Group II

Mr Andreas LOUROUTZIATIS
Group I

Mr Henri MALOSSE
Group I

Mr Staffan NILSSON
Group III

Mr Marius Eugen OPRAN
Group I

Mr Frederic Adrian OSBORN
Group III

Mrs Eve PÄÄRENDSON
Group I

Mr Krzysztof PATER
Group III

Mrs Naile PROKEŠOVÁ
Group II

Mrs Metka ROKSANDIĆ
Group II

Mr Stanisław RÓŻYCKI
Group II

Mrs María Candelas SÁNCHEZ MIGUEL
Group II

Mr Mário SOARES
Group II

Mrs Ludmilla TODOROVA
Group III

Mr János TÓTH
Group III

Mr Joost van IERSEL
Group I

Mr Tony VANDEPUTTE
Group I

Mr Dirk WESTENDORP
Group III

Mr Hans-Joachim WILMS
Group II

Mr Gustav ZÖHRER
Group II

(1) The last two years of the 13th four-year term of office (2008-2010)

Group I: Employers

Mr Henri MALOSSE
President
France
Directeur chargé des relations avec le Comité économique et social européen et le Conseil économique, social et environnemental (CESE) français à l'Assemblée des chambres françaises de commerce et d'industrie (ACFCI)
45, avenue d'Iéna - BP 3003
F-75773 Paris Cedex 16
Tel. +33 140693819
Fax +33 153571819
E-mail: h.malosse@acfci.cci.fr

Mr Paulo BARROS VALE
Vice-President
Portugal
Empresário - Dirigente da Associação Empresarial de Portugal (AEP)
Rua D. Afonso Henriques 2540
P-4425-057 Aguas Santas - Mai
Tel. +351 229773910
Fax +351 229773919
E-mail: iafe@iafe.pt

Mr Peter CLEVER
Vice-President
Deutschland
Mitglied der Hauptgeschäftsführung - Bundesvereinigung der Deutschen Arbeitgeberverbände (BDA)
Haus der Deutschen Wirtschaft
D-11054 Berlin
Tel. +49 3020331009
Fax +49 3020331015
E-mail: pc@bda-online.de

Mr Antal CSUPORT
Vice-President
Hungary
Stratégiai és Közszolgáltató Társaságok Országos Szövetsége (STRATOSZ) vezető, elismert magyarországi szociális partner, állami részvétellel működő és általános gazdasági érdekű vállalatok európai központjának tagja
Bécsi út. 3-5. III. 24. • H-1023 Budapest
Tel. +36 209386830
Fax +36 14142189
E-mail: acsuport@mail.datanet.hu

Mrs Sylvia GAUCI
Vice-President
Malta
Membru tal-Kunsill Eżekuttiv, Malta Chamber of Small and Medium Enterprises (GRTU)
Direttur ta' l-Uffiċċju Nazzjonali ta' l-Istatistika (NSO)
Direttur tal-Public Broadcasting Services Ltd.
Exchange Building - Triq ir-Repubblika
M-VLT05 Valletta
Tel. +356 21230459
Fax +356 21246925
E-mail: sylvia.gauci@grtu.net

Mrs Brenda KING
Vice-President
United Kingdom
Chief Executive, African & Caribbean Diversity - Commissioner, Women's National Commission (WNC) - Advisory Board, Hays Executive - Advisory Board, Voluntary Services Overseas (VSO)
32-36 Loman Street • UK • SE1 0EH London
Tel. +44 2079227808
Fax +44 8716613530
E-mail: brendaking@acdiversity.org
www.acdiversity.org

Mr Jacek KRAWCZYK
Vice-President
Poland
Wiceprezydent Polskiej Konfederacji Pracodawców Prywatnych (PKPP) Lewiatan
ul. Kiersnowskiego 16 • PL-03-161 Warszawa
Tel. +48 228690250
Fax +48 228690240
E-mail: jpk@fpro.pl

Mr Thomas MCDONOGH
Vice-President
Irlande
Chairman of Thomas McDonogh & Sons Ltd
Dockgate Building Dock Road • IRL • Galway
Tel. +353 1560797
Fax +353 1560792
E-mail: thomasmcdonogh@mcdonogh.eu

Mrs Eve PÄÄRENDSON
Vice-President
Estonia
Eesti Tööandjate Keskliidu (EETK) rahvusvaheliste suhete juht
Kiriku 6 • EE-10130 Tallinn
Tel. +372 6999 304
Fax +372 6999 310
E-mail: eve@employers.ee

Mr José Isaías RODRÍGUEZ GARCÍA-CARO
Vice-President
España
Miembro de la Confederación Española de Organizaciones Empresariales (CEOE)
Avenida de Europa, 27 • E-41960 Gines
Tel. +34 669010993
E-mail: jirodriguez@ceoe.es

Mr Cveto STANTIČ
Vice-President
Slovenia
Podjetnik, svetovalec Gospodarske zbornice Slovenije (GZS) in Združenja delodajalcev Slovenije
Franca Baliča 30 • SLO-5290 SI - 5290 Šempeter pri Gorici
Tel. +386 53936775
Fax +386 53936775
E-mail: cveto.stantic@gmail.com

Mrs Marie ZVOLSKÁ
Vice-President
République tchèque
Právní poradkyně a expertka v oblasti pracovního práva a sociálních věcí, Svaz českých a moravských výrobních družstev (SČMVD)
Václavské nám. 21 • CZ-113 60 Praha 1
Tel. +420 224109344
Fax +420 224228399
E-mail: zvolska@scmvd.cz

Mr Pedro ALMEIDA FREIRE
Portugal
Vice-Presidente da Confederação do Comércio e Serviços de Portugal (CCP)
Av. Dom Vasco da Gama 29
P-1449-032 Lisboa
Tel. +351 213031380
Fax +351 213031401
E-mail: freirepa@sapo.pt

Mrs Dorthe ANDERSEN
Danmark
Direktør, EU-politik - Dansk Arbejdsgiverforening (DA)
avenue de Cortenbergh 168 B-1000 Bruxelles
Fax +32 22850545
E-mail: DOA@da.dk

Mrs Milena ANGELOVA
Bulgaria
Изпълнителен директор на Асоциацията на индустриалния капитал в България (АИКБ), доктор по икономикаul. Frédéric Joliot-Curie № 20, et. 8 • BG-1113 Sofia
Tel. +359 29633752
Fax +359 29633756
E-mail: Milena.Angelova@eesc.europa.eu

Mr Michalis ANTONIOU
Cyprus
Διευθυντής του Τμήματος Εργασιακών Σχέσεων και Εργατικής Νομοθεσίας της Ομοσπονδίας Εργοδοτών & Βιομηχάνων (ΟΕΒ)
P.O. Box 21657 • CY-1511 Nicosia
Tel. +357 22665102
Fax +357 22669459
E-mail: mantsoul@cytanet.com.cy

Mr Christian ARDHE
Sverige
Direktör, EU-frågor, Svenskt Näringsliv (SN)
Rue du Luxembourg 3 • B-1000 Bruxelles
Tel. +32 25015300
Fax +32 25015320
E-mail: christian.ardhe@swedishenterprise.se

Mr Danukas ARLAUSKAS
Lithuania
Lietuvos verslo darbdavių konfederacijos (LVDK) generalinis direktorius
D. Malinausko g. 5 • LT-02001 Vilnius
Tel. +370 52385214
E-mail: danas@lvdk.w3.lt

Mr Rafael BARBADILLO LÓPEZ
España
Miembro de la Confederación Española de Organizaciones Empresariales (CEOE)
c/ Santa Cruz de Marcenado, 4
E-28015 Madrid
Tel. +34 914319864
Fax +34 914456793
E-mail: rbarbadillo@asintra.org

Mr Jean-Paul BASTIAN
France
Ancien secrétaire général adjoint de la Fédération nationale des syndicats d'exploitants agricoles (FNSEA) et vice-président de la Fédération nationale des syndicats d'exploitants agricoles (FNSEA)
6, rue des Sapins • F-67350 Bitschhoffen
Tel. +33 607793728
Fax +33 388833054
E-mail: direction@bas-rhin.chambagri.fr

Mr Nansen BEHAR
Bulgaria
Председател на Консултативния съвет на Съюза за стопанска инициатива (ССИ), член на Икономическия и социален съвет на Република България (ИСС), професор по икономика в Софийския университет
kv. Lozenets, ul. Kap. Todor Nochev № 30
BG-1407 Sofia
Tel. +359 29624836
Fax +359 29624784
E-mail: office@ssi-bg.org

Mr Jean-Marie BIOT
Belgique/België
Afgevaardigd bestuurder van de Federatie van de Chemische Industrie van België (Essenscia)
Prins Boudewijnlaan 359 • B-2650 Edegem
Tel. +32 496 593602
E-mail: jeanmarie.biot@gmail.com

Mrs Ana BONTEA
Romania
Director, Departamentul Juridic şi Dialog Social Consiliul Naţional al Întreprinderilor Private Mici şi Mijlocii din România (CNIPMMR)
Piaţa Walter Mărăcineanu, nr. 1-3, intrarea 1, etaj 1, sector 1 • RO-010155 Bucureşti
Tel. +40 213126893
Fax +40 213126608
E-mail: ana.bontea@yahoo.com

Mrs Anna BREDIMA
Grèce
Διευθύντρια του Τμήματος των Διεθνών και Ευρωπαϊκών Θεμάτων της Ένωσης Ελλήνων Εφοπλιστών (ΕΕΕ)
Akti Miaouli, 85 • GR-18 538 Pireas
Tel. +30 210 4291159
Fax +30 210 4290107
E-mail: abredima@hellasnet.gr

Mr Stéphane BUFFETAUT
France
Conseiller à l'Union des transports publics (UTP) et directeur chargé des relations avec les institutions européennes du groupe Veolia Environnement
38, avenue Kleber • F-75799 Paris Cedex 16
Tel. +33 624126042
E-mail: stephane.buffetaut@wanadoo.fr

Mr Umberto BURANI
Italie
Ex Segretario generale della Federazione bancaria europea (FBE)
Via F. Scaduto, 60 • I-00167 Roma
Tel. +39 066624615
Fax +39 066624615
E-mail: umberto.burani@eesc.europa.eu

Mr Brendan BURNS
United Kingdom
Director of Burns, Burns and Burns - Former Vice Chairman and Policy Chairman of the Federation of Small Businesses (FSB)
Killen Cottage - Killen • UK • IV9 8RQ Avoch - Ross-Shire
Tel. +44 1381622244
E-mail: Brendan.burns@eesc.europa.eu

Mr Brian CALLANAN
Irlande
Former Director of the Irish Business and Employers Confederation (IBEC)
Tullycot - Brennanstown road, Carrickmines IRL • Dublin 18
Tel. +353 12893000
E-mail: BrianCallanan2004@yahoo.co.uk

Mr Edwin CALLEJA
Malta
Ex-Direttur Ġenerali tal-Federazzjoni Maltija tal-Industrija (FOI)
Membru tal-Bord tad-Diretturi ta' Kordin Grain Terminal Company Ltd.
Misrah San Alwigi • M-BKR10 B'Kara
Tel. +356 21443544
E-mail: edwincal@maltanet.net

Mr Bryan CASSIDY
United Kingdom
Former Member of the European Parliament (1984-1999)
11 Esmond Court Thackeray Street • UK W8 5HB London
Tel. +44 2079373558
Fax +44 2079373789
E-mail: bryan.cassidy@europundit.eu
www.europundit.eu

Mr Manuel CAVALEIRO BRANDÃO
Portugal
Advogado e Consultor de Empresas - Conselho Geral da Ordem dos Advogados Portugueses (OAP)
R. São João de Brito, 605E – 1° - 1.2 • P-4100-455 Porto
Tel. +351 226052140
Fax +351 226052142
E-mail: cavaleirobrandao@opolex.pt

Mrs Lourdes CAVERO MESTRE
España
Miembro de la Confederación Española de Organizaciones Empresariales (CEOE)
C/Francisco Gervás 3 • E-28020 Madrid
Tel. +34 915674917
Fax +34 915674982
E-mail: lcavero@unesa.es

Mrs Sinne CONAN
Danmark
Leder af DI's Bruxelles-kontor
Avenue de Cortenbergh 168
B-1000 Bruxelles - Brussel
Tel. +45 33773377
Fax +32 22850555
E-mail: sbc@di.dk

Mr Bulgaria
Председател на Българска стопанска камара (БСК) - съюз на българския бизнес
ul. Alabin № 16-20 • BG-1000 Sofia
Tel. +359 29800303
Fax +359 29872604
E-mail: danev@bia-bg.com

Mr Francis DAVOUST
France
Représentant de l'artisanat français au titre de l'Union professionnelle artisanale (UPA) et de l'Assemblée permanente des chambres de métiers et de l'artisanat (APCMA) et vice-président du Conseil national des professions de l'automobile (CNPA)
24 place du Vieux-Château
F-27110 Le Neubourg
Tel. +33 608819045
Fax +33 232357667
E-mail: fdavoust@cnpa.fr

Mr Robert DE MÛELENAERE
Belgique/België
Administrateur délégué à la Confédération de la construction
Rue du Lombard 34-42 • B-1000 Bruxelles
Tel. +32 25455615
Fax +32 25455901
E-mail: robert.demuelenaere@confederationconstruction.be

Mr Dimitris DIMITRIADIS
Grèce
Α' Αντιπρόεδρος της Εθνικής Συνομοσπονδίας Ελληνικού Εμπορίου (ΕΣΕΕ)
Tsimiski Str. 75 • GR-546 22 Thessaloníki
Tel. +30 2310222268
Fax +30 2310222165
E-mail: dnd@baconsult.gr

Mr Bernd DITTMANN
Deutschland
Bereichsleiter Europa - Bundesverband der Deutschen Industrie e.V. (BIV)
Breite Strasse 29 • D-10178 Berlin
Tel. +49 3020281491
Fax +49 3020282491
E-mail: b.dittmann@bdi.eu
www.bdi.eu

Mr Tadeusz DORDA
Poland
Wiceprezydent Konfederacji Pracodawców Polskich (KPP)
ul. Frascati 12 • PL-00-483 Warszawa
Tel. +48 25 6327429-201
Fax +48 25 6327902
E-mail: tjdorda@aol.com

Mrs Vladimíra DRBALOVÁ
République tchèque
Ředitelka sekce pro mezinárodní organizace a evropské záležitosti Svazu průmyslu a dopravy ČR (SPČR)
Jankovcova 1569/2c • CZ-170 04 Praha 7
Tel. +420 234379473
Fax +420 234379463
E-mail: vdrbalova@spcr.cz

Mr Hans EKDAHL
Sverige
Handelspolitisk expert, Svenskt Näringsliv (SN)
Rue du Luxembourg, 3 • B-1000 Bruxelles
Tel. +46 705688058
Fax +46 855343099
E-mail: hans.ekdahl@svensktnaringsliv.se

Mr José María ESPUNY MOYANO
España
Miembro de la Confederación Española de Organizaciones Empresariales (CEOE)
c/ Conde de Peñalver, 35-3-B • E-28006 Madrid
Tel. +34 913095270
Fax +34 913095270
E-mail: jespunym@yahoo.es

Mr Marco FELISATI
Italie
Vicedirettore Affari europei Confindustria - Responsabile politica commerciale
Viale dell'Astronomia, 30 • I-00144 Roma
Tel. +39 065903649
Fax +39 065903277
E-mail: m.felisati@confindustria.it

Mr Kenneth FRASER
United Kingdom
Corporate adviser
Wester Clatto • UK • KY15 5UE Blebo Craigs by Cupar, Fife
Tel. +44 1334850632
Fax +44 1334850097
E-mail: kfraser@frasercorporate.co.uk

Mr Göke FRERICHS
Deutschland
Mitglied des Präsidiums im Bundesverband des Deutschen Groß- und Außenhandels e.V. (BGA)
Am Hirschsprung 11 • D-61462 Königstein im Taunus
Tel. +49 61743567
Fax +49 6174932477
E-mail: goeke.frerichs@eesc.europa.eu

Mr Vitālijs GAVRILOVS
Latvia
Latvijas Darba devēju konfederācijas (LDDK) prezidents
Latvijas Nacionālās trīspusējās sadarbības padomes līdzpriekšsēdētājs
Eiropas Biznesa konfederācijas (BUSINESSEUROPE) Prezidentu padomes loceklis
Vīlandes ielā 12-1. • LV-1010 Rīgā
Tel. +371 7225162
Fax +371 7224469
E-mail: lddk@lddk.lv
www.lddk.lv

Mr Lubomir HADJIYSKY
Bulgaria
Заместник-председател на икономическата комисия към Българския съюз на частните предприемачи "Възраждане" (БСЧП)
ul. Slavyanska № 29 • BG-1000 Sofia
Tel. +359 28468220
Fax +359 28468220
E-mail: liubomir.hadjiysky@eesc.europa.eu

Mr Filip HAMRO-DROTZ
Suomi/Finland
Kansainvälisestä viestinnästä vastaava tiedottaja, Elinkeinoelämän Keskusliitto EK
Eteläranta 10 • FI-00130 Helsinki
Tel. +358 942022363
Fax +358 96223884
E-mail: filip.hamro-drotz@ek.fi

Mr Bernard HUVELIN
France
Président d'Entreprises générales de France - Bâtiment et travaux publics (EGF-BTP), membre du bureau de la Fédération nationale des travaux publics (FNTP), de la Fédération française du bâtiment (FFB), vice-président du conseil d'administration de Vinci
Avenue de Tervueren 403 — boîte 1A
B-1150 Bruxelles
Tel. +32 27711182
Fax +32 27711182
E-mail: bmahuv@skynet.be

Mr Gerasimos KALLIGEROS
Grèce
Γενικός Γραμματέας της Πανελλήνιας Ομοσπονδίας Ξενοδόχων (ΠΟΞ)
Stadiou 22 • GR-10 564 Athènes
Tel. +30 210 3247718
Fax +30 210 3247724
E-mail: gpk@esperiahotel.com.gr

Mr Magnus KENDEL
Sverige
Direktör, Almega - forum för tjänsteföretagare
Sturegatan 11, Box 555 45 • S-10204 Stockholm
Tel. +46 87626964
Fax +46 87626948
E-mail: magnus.g.kendel@almega.se

Mr Adalbert KIENLE
Deutschland
Stellvertretender Generalsekretär des Deutschen Bauernverbands e.V. (DBV)
Claire-Waldoff-Str. 7 • D-10117 Berlin
Tel. +49 3031904276
Fax +49 3031904196
E-mail: aue.kienle@t-online.de

Mrs Waltraud KLASNIC
Österreich
Landeshauptmann a.D.
Weizer Str. 22 • A-8044 Maria Trost
Tel. +43 664300 27 07
E-mail: waltraud.klasnic@aon.at

Mr Johannes KLEEMANN
Österreich
Vorstandsmitglied der Vereinigung der Österreichischen Industrie (VÖI)
Schwarzenbergplatz 4 • A-1030 Wien
Tel. +43 171135/2535
Fax +43 171135/2411
E-mail: j.kleemann@iv-net.at

Mr Jan KLIMEK
Poland
Wiceprezes Związku Rzemiosła Polskiego (ZRP), prezes Zarządu Izby Rzemieślniczej oraz Małej i Średniej Przedsiębiorczości (IR MSP) w Katowicach
ul. Miodowa 14 • PL-00-246 Warszawa
Tel. +48 601313440
Fax +48 225044220
E-mail: jan.klimek@ir.katowice.pl

Mr Viesturs KOCIŅŠ
Latvia
Latvijas Tirdzniecības un rūpniecības kameras (LTRK) Ārējas tirdzniecības dokumentu daļas vadītājs
Kr. Valdemāra ielā 35 • LV-1010 Rīgā
Tel. +371 7225595
Fax +371 7820092
E-mail: viesturs@chamber.lv

Mr Johann KÖLTRINGER
Österreich
Hauptabteilungsleiter Österreichischer Raiffeisenverband (ÖRV) - Geschäftsführer Vereinigung Österreichischer Milchverarbeiter (VÖM)
Friedrich-Wilhelm-Raiffeisen Platz 1
A-1020 Wien
Tel. +43 121136-2558
Fax +43 121136-2559
E-mail: Johann.Koeltringer@oerv.raiffeisen.at

Mr Marek KOMOROWSKI
Poland
Radca przy Radzie Polskiej Konfederacji Pracodawców Prywatnych (PKPP)
ul. Hańczy 9 • PL-00-769 Warszawa
Tel. +48 22642 4248
Fax +48 22642 4583
E-mail: marek.komorowski@poczta.onet.pl

Mr Peter KORN
Deutschland
Leiter des Vertretung des Deutschen Industrie- und Handelskammertages (DIHK) bei der EU und des Fachbereichs Umwelt, Verbraucherpolitik und Energie
Alt Stralau 15 • D-10245 Berlin
Tel. +49 30203082200
Fax +49 30203082230
E-mail: kornpet@yahoo.com

Mr Martin KREKÁČ
Slovakia
Prezident Podnikateľskej aliancie Slovenska (PAS)
Zámocká 36 - P.O.Box 283
SK-814 99 Bratislava
Tel. +421 254436001-7
Fax +421 254436001-7
E-mail: www.alianciaPAS.sk
krekac@ajg.sk

Mr Linas LASIAUSKAS
Lithuania
Lietuvos aprangos ir tekstilės įmonių asociacijos (LATIA) prezidentas, UAB Lengvosios pramonės centras generalinis direktorius
Saltoniškių g. 29–3 • LT-08105 Vilnius
Tel. +370 52790669
E-mail: linas@latia.lt
www.latia.it

Mr Jochen LEHNHOFF
Deutschland
Mitglied des Vorstandes des Bundesverbandes der deutschen Volksbanken und Raiffeisenbanken e.V. (BVR)
Schellingstr. 4 • D-10785 Berlin
Tel. +49 302021-1200
Fax +49 302021-1902
E-mail: lehnhoff@bvr.de

Mrs Margarita LÓPEZ ALMENDÁRIZ
España
Miembro de la Confederación Española de Organizaciones Empresariales (CEOE)
Plaza Primero de Mayo, 1 Bajo • E-52004 Melilla
Tel. +34 952678295
Fax +34 952676175
E-mail: mlopez@hamelilla.com

Mrs Heidi LOUGHEED
Irlande
Head of IBEC Europe (Irish Business and Employers Confederation)
Avenue de Cortenbergh 89, Bte 2
B-1000 Bruxelles - Brussel
Tel. +32 27401431
Fax +32 25121353
E-mail: heidi.lougheed@ibec.ie

Mr Andreas LOUROUTZIATIS
Cyprus
Αντιπρόεδρος του Εμπορικού και Βιομηχανικού Επιμελητηρίου Κύπρου
10 Dimotikis Agoras - BP 40262
CY-6302 Larnaka
Tel. +357 24531320
Fax +357 24533520
E-mail: ebexltd@ebex.com.cy

Mr Vitas MAČIULIS
Lithuania
Lietuvos prekybos, pramonės ir amatų rūmų asociacijos (LPPARA) generalinis direktorius
Tumo-Vaižganto g. 9/1 • LT-01108 Vilnius
Tel. +370 52612102
Fax +370 52612112
E-mail: v.maciulis@ntgama.lt

Mr Andrzej MALINOWSKI
Poland
Prezydent Konfederacji Pracodawców Polskich (KPP)
ul. Brukselska 7 • PL-03-973 Warszawa
Tel. +48 22828-8431
Fax +48 22828- 8437
E-mail: a.malinowski@kpp.org.pl
www.kpp.org.pl

Mr Philippe MANGIN
France
Président de Coop de France et de la Confédération nationale de la mutualité, de la coopération et du crédit agricoles (CNMCCA)
Avenue des Arts 1/2, Bte 9
B-1210 Bruxelles - Brussel
Tel. +33 144175700
Fax +33 144175701
E-mail: philippe.mangin@coopdefrance.coop

Mr Mihai MANOLIU
Romania
Profesor dr. ing. - secretar general, Alianţa Confederaţiilor Patronale din România (ACPR)
Str. Mircea Eliade, nr. 2, sector 1
RO-012013 Bucureşti
Tel. +40 212316192
Fax +40 212316193
E-mail: manoliu@mailbox.ro

Mr Sandro MASCIA
Italie
Responsabile Ufficio di Bruxelles della Confederazione generale dell'agricoltura italiana (Confagricoltura)
Rue Montoyer, 31 • B-1000 Bruxelles
Tel. +32 22306732
Fax +32 22309287
E-mail: sandro.mascia@skynet.be

Mr Luís MIRA
Portugal
Secretário-Geral da Confederação dos Agricultores de Portugal (CAP)
Av. do Colégio Militar, lote 1786
P-1549-012 Lisboa
Tel. +351 217100004
Fax +351 217100012
E-mail: lmira@cap.pt

Mr André-Luc MOLINIER
France
Directeur adjoint, chargé de la coordination pour l'Europe du Mouvement des entreprises de France (MEDEF)
55, avenue Bosquet • F-75007 Paris
Tel. +33 153591673
Fax +33 153591665
E-mail: amolinier@medef.fr

Mr Peter MORGAN
United Kingdom
Partner, P.W.L. Morgan & Associates
Director of a portfolio of companies
Former Director General, Institute of Directors
Cleeves Weydown Road • UK • GU 27 1DT
Haslemere Surrey
Tel. +44 1428642757
Fax +44 01428643684
E-mail: petermorgan@cleeves2.demon.co.uk

Mr Gintaras MORKIS
Lithuania
Lietuvos pramonininkų konfederacijos (LPK) generalinio direktoriaus pavaduotojas
A. Vienuolio g. 8-304 • LT-01104 Vilnius
Tel. +370 52623801
Fax +370 52125209
E-mail: gintaras.morkis@lpk.lt

Mr Jarosław MULEWICZ
Poland
Członek Rady Organizatorów Business Centre Club (BCC)
Pl. Żelaznej Bramy 10 • PL-00-136 Warszawa
Tel. +48 228782646
Fax +48 226218420
E-mail: j.mulewicz@interia.pl

Mr Tamás NAGY
Hungary
Mezőgazdasági Szövetkezők és Termelők Országos Szövetsége (MOSZ) elnök
Istenhegyi u. 59-61 • H-1125 Budapest
Tel. +36 1332-5515
Fax +36 1332-5515
E-mail: biroagi@mosz.agrar.hu

Mrs Maria NYGREN
Sverige
Branschchef, Sveriges Hamnar
Storgatan 19 • S-11186 Stockholm
Tel. +46 87627100
Fax +46 87627110

Mr Marius Eugen OPRAN
Romania
Preşedinte Executiv, Uniunea Generală a Industriaşilor din România (UGIR - 1903)
Preşedinte, Federaţia Naţională a Patronatelor Serviciilor Publice din România (FNPSPR)
Str. Ana Davila nr. 43, sector 5 • RO-050492
Bucarest
Tel. +40 213039947
Fax +40 214118190
E-mail: marius-opran@marius-opran.net

Mr Ján ORAVEC
Slovakia
Predseda Združenia podnikateľov Slovenska (ZPS)
Cukrová 14 • SK-813 39 Bratislava
Tel. +421 905201154
Fax +421 259324343
E-mail: joravec@atlas.sk

Mr Krzysztof OSTROWSKI
Poland
Dyrektor Biura Interwencji, przedstawiciel Business Centre Club (BCC) w EKES-ie
Pl. Żelaznej Bramy 10 • PL-00-136 Warszawa
Tel. +48 225826112
Fax +48 225826116
E-mail: krzysztof.ostrowski@bcc.org.pl

Mr Ángel PANERO FLÓREZ
España
Miembro de la Confederación Española de Organizaciones Empresariales (CEOE)
Urbanizacion Atalaya, Chalet 11 • E-24010 León
Tel. +34 914116161
Fax +34 915645269
E-mail: apaneroflorez@hotmail.com

Mrs Irini Ivoni PARI
Grèce
Μόνιμη Εκπρόσωπος του Γραφείου του ΣΕΒ (Σύνδεσμος Επιχειρήσεων και Βιομηχανιών) στις Βρυξέλλες και Μόνιμη Εκπρόσωπος του Γραφείου του ΣΕΒ στην Ένωση Ευρωπαϊκών Επιχειρήσεων (BUSINESSEUROPE - Confederation of European Business)
Avenue de Cortenbergh 168 • B-1000 Bruxelles
Tel. +32 22310053
Fax +32 22800891
E-mail: irini.pari@skynet.be

Mr Jonathan PEEL
United Kingdom
Business and Trade Consultant
Sturdy Cottage - High Street - Thornborough • UK • MK148 2DF Buckingham
Tel. +44 1280816644
+44 7973528985
E-mail: jonathan@peelcomms.eu

Mrs Marja-Liisa PELTOLA
Suomi/Finland
Osastopäällikkö, Keskuskauppakamari (KKK)
P.O.Box 1000, Aleksanterinkatu 17
FI-00101 Helsinki
Tel. +358 942426200
Fax +358 9650303
E-mail: marja-liisa.peltola@chamber.fi

Mr Volker PETERSEN
Deutschland
Stellvertretender Generalsekretär des Deutschen Raiffeisenverbandes e.V. (DRV)
Adenauerallee 127 • D-53123 Bonn
Tel. +49 228106207
Fax +49 228106266
E-mail: petersen@drv.raiffeisen.de

Mr Antonello PEZZINI
Italie
Imprenditore - Rappresentante della Confederazione generale dell'industria italiana (Confindustria)
Via G. Camozzi, 70 • I-24121 Bergamo
Tel. +39 035275268
Fax +39 035235624
E-mail: antonello.pezzini@eesc.europa.eu

Mr Aurel Laurenţiu PLOŞCEANU
Romania
Preşedinte, Asociaţia Română a Antreprenorilor de Construcţii (ARACO)
Splaiul Independenţei nr. 202 A, sector 6
RO-060021 Bucarest
Tel. +40 213167896
Fax +40 213129626
E-mail: Laurentiu.Plosceanu@eesc.europa.eu

Mr Virgilio RANOCCHIARI
Italie
Dirigente d'azienda - Confederazione generale dell'industria italiana (Confindustria)
Via di Monte Savello, 30 • I-00186 Roma
Tel. +39 0648889200
Fax +39 0648889211
E-mail: virgilio.ranocchiari@fiatgroup.com

Mr Maurizio REALE
Italie
Responsabile relazioni internazionali Coldiretti
Avenue de Tervueren 27
B-1040 Bruxelles — Brussel
Tel. +39 0679819086
Fax +32 222311478
E-mail: maurizio.reale@coldiretti.it

Mr Wautier ROBYNS DE SCHNEIDAUER
Belgique/België
Directeur pour la communication, l'information et les relations internationales à Assuralia
Square de Meeûs 29 • B-1000 Bruxelles
Tel. +32 25475690
Fax +32 25475600
E-mail: wauthier.robyns@assuralia.be

Mr Claudio ROTTI
Italie
Presidente dell'Associazione italiana commercio estero (AICE) - Presidente della consulta commercio estero della Confederazione generale del commercio, del turismo, dei servizi, delle professioni e delle piccole e medie imprese (Confcommercio)
C.so Venezia, 49 • I-20121 Milano
Tel. +39 027750320 - 1
Fax +39 027750329
E-mail: www.aicebiz.com
claudio.rotti@unione.milano.it

Mrs Lena ROUSSENOVA
Bulgaria
Доцент, доктор по икономика, главен икономист на Конфедерацията на работодателите и индустриалците в България доцент в катедра "Финанси" на Университета за национално и световно стопанство, Софиябul. Al. Stamboliyski № 55
BG-1301 Sofia
Tel. +359 28842206
Fax +359 29886776
E-mail: lroussenova@ceibg.bg

Mr Jörg RUSCHE
Deutschland
Geschäftsführer des Bundesverbandes der Deutschen Binnenschifffahrt e.V. (BDB)
Dammstr. 15-17 • D-47119 Duisburg
Tel. +49 2038000630
Fax +49 2038000621
E-mail: bdb-rusche@binnenschiff.de
www.binnenschiff.de

Mr José SARTORIUS ÁLVAREZ DE BOHORQUES
España
Miembro de la Confederación Española de Organizaciones Empresariales (CEOE)
Ortega y Gasset, 29 • E-28009 Madrid
Tel. +34 915207132
Fax +34 915779208
E-mail: jsartorius@bancopopular.es

Mrs Christa SCHWENG
Österreich
Mitarbeiterin der Abteilung für Sozialpolitik und Gesundheit in der Wirtschaftskammer Österreich
Wiedner Hauptstr. 63 • A-1045 Wien
Tel. +43 590903524
Fax +43 59090 113524
E-mail: christa.schweng@wko.at

Mr David SEARS
United Kingdom
Former Deputy Director-General, British Chambers of Commerce (BCC)
3 Albany Villas • UK • BN3 2RS Hove East Sussex
Tel. +44 1273737135
Fax +44 1273207433
E-mail: searsdj@tiscali.co.uk

Mr Patrick SEYLER
Luxembourg
General Manager Government and Institutional Relations Luxembourg
Country Manager Luxembourg at ArcelorMittal, Luxembourg
19, avenue de la Liberté • L-2930 Luxembourg
Tel. +352 47922362
Fax +352 4792892362
E-mail: patrick.seyler@arcelormittal.com

Mrs Madi SHARMA
United Kingdom
Import-exporter, consultant in SMEs, entrepreneurship, CSR, training and personal development, diversity, gender equality, Board member of ITV Plc, public speaker
38 Midland Avenue - Lenton • UK
NG7 2FD Nottingham
Tel. +44 7885306711
Fax +44 115 9799333
E-mail: original.madi@tiscali.co.uk

Mr Jan SIMONS
Nederland
Voormalig voorzitter Nederlands Vervoersoverleg (NVO) - em. Professor Vervoerseconomie - Vrije Universiteit - Amsterdam
Lage Kaart 87 • B-2930 Brasschaat
Tel. +32 477266955
Fax +32 36518292
E-mail: jansimons@village.uunet.be

Mrs Ulla SIRKEINEN
Suomi/Finland
Elinkeinoelämän Keskusliiton Brysselin toimiston päällikkö (EK)
Rue de la Charité 17 • B-1210 Bruxelles
Tel. +32 22094311
Fax +32 22230805
E-mail: ulla.sirkeinen@ek.fi

Mr Dare STOJAN
Slovenia
Član Združenja delodajalcev obrtnih dejavnosti Slovenije (ZDODS)
Celovška 71 • SLO-1000 Ljubljana
Tel. +386 15830572
Fax +386 15830805
E-mail: dare.stojan@tse.si

Mr Gundars STRAUTMANIS
Latvia
Lttelecom SIA Padomes Priekšsēdētājs
Latvijas Darva Devēju Konfederācijas Padomes Loceklis
Latvijas Tirdzniecības un Rūpniecības Kameras Padomes Loceklis
Vīlandes iela 12-1 • LV-1010 Riga
Tel. +371 7055003
Fax +371 7055222
E-mail: Gundars.Strautmanis@lattelecom.lv

Mr Péter VADÁSZ
Hungary
Munkaadók és Gyáriparosok Országos Szövetsége (MGYOSZ) alelnök
Kossuth tér 6-8 • H-1055 Budapest
Tel. +36 13927838
Fax +36 13927837
E-mail: pvadasz@hungary.net

Mr Jan Willem VAN DEN BRAAK
Nederland
Permanent afgevaardigde van het Verbond van Nederlandse ondernemingen - Nederlands Christelijk Werkgeversverbond (VNO-NCW)
Archimedesstraat 5 - bus 4 • B-1000 Brussel
Tel. +32 25100880
Fax +32 25100885
E-mail: nederveen@vno-ncw.nl

Mr Joost van IERSEL
Nederland
Oud-voorzitter van de Kamer van Koophandel-Den Haag - Oud-lid van de Tweede Kamer
Bezuidenhoutseweg 12 • NL
2594 AV Den Haag
Tel. +31 703546165
Fax +31 703546165
E-mail: jviersel@planet.nl

Mr Frank van OORSCHOT
Nederland
Senior specialist Internationale Zaken, Zuidelijke Land- en Tuinbouworganisatie (ZLTO) is
Postbus 91 • NL • 5000 MA Tilburg
Tel. +31 135836233
Fax +31 135836585
E-mail: frank.van.oorschot@zlto.nl
www.zlto.nl

Mr Tony VANDEPUTTE
Belgique/België
Administrateur délégué honoraire et conseiller général de la Fédération des entreprises de Belgique (FEB)
Rue Ravenstein 4 • B-1000 Bruxelles
Tel. +32 25150823
Fax +32 25150832
E-mail: tvp@vbo-feb.be
www.feb.be

Mr Ştefan VARFALVI
Romania
Preşedinte al IMSAT.SA
Bd. Iuliu Maniu nr.7.corp B, etaj3 Sector 6
RO-061072 Bucureşti
Tel. +40 213169025
Fax +40 213163330
E-mail: stefan.varfalvi@imsat.ro

Mr János VÉRTES
Hungary
Kereskedők és Vendéglátók Országos Érdekképviseleti Szövetsége (KISOSZ)
Hegedűs Gyula u.18 • H-1136 Budapest
Tel. +36 1239 0538
Fax +36 1 239 0538
E-mail: bangkok@t-online.hu

Mr Ivan VOLEŠ
République tchèque
Zástupce tajemníka Hospodářské komory České republiky (HKČR)
Freyova 27 • CZ-190 00 Praha 9 - Vysočany
Tel. +420 724613535
Fax +420 296 646 257
E-mail: www.komora.cz
ivoles@volny.cz

Mr Josef ZBOŘIL
République tchèque
Konzultant v oblasti průmyslu papíru a celulózy, vedení podniků a životního prostředí, člen představenstva Svazu průmyslu a dopravy ČR (SPČR)
5. května 275 • CZ-381 01 Český Krumlov-Plešivec
Tel. +420 380728 901
Fax +420 380728 901
E-mail: josef.zboril@tiscali.cz

Mr Patrik ZOLTVÁNY
Slovakia
Člen výboru pre európske záležitosti a zahraničné vzťahy- Republiková únia zamestnávateľov (RÚZ)
P.O.Box 294 • SK-814 99 Bratislava
Tel. +421 254436001-7
Fax +421 254436001
E-mail: zoltvany@ajg.sk
www.ruzsr.sk

Mr Patrizio PESCI
Italie
ORGALIME (Engineering)
CEI-BOIS
ACEM-BIKE
CEMA (machines agricoles)
Avenue des Trembles 1 • B-1950 Kraainem
Tel. +39 066897123
Fax +39 066897123
E-mail: p.pesci@scarlet.be

Group II: Employees

Mr Georgios DASSIS
President
Grèce
Γραμματέας Διεθνών Σχέσεων του Ινστιτούτου Εργασίας ΓΣΕΕ-ΑΔΕΔΥ (ΙΝΕ/ΓΣΕΕ-ΑΔΕΔΥ)
Paralia Avlidas • GR-34100 Avlida
Tel. +30 6977219720
Fax +30 210 8202191
E-mail: gdassis@hol.gr

Mr Andrzej ADAMCZYK
Vice-President
Poland
Sekretarz do spraw międzynarodowych Niezależnego Samorządnego Związku Zawodowego (NSZZ) Solidarność
ul. Wały Piastowskie 24 • PL-80-855 Gdańsk
Tel. +48 583084232
Fax +48 583084482
E-mail: zagr@solidarnosc.org.pl

Mr Sandy BOYLE
Vice-President
United Kingdom
Former President UNI Finance and Uni-Europa Finance
Past President Scottish TUC
9 Learmonth Street • UK • FK1 5AG Falkirk
Tel. +44 1324626708
Fax +44 1324624910
E-mail: sandyboyle@blueyonder.co.uk

Mr Gérard DANTIN
Vice-President
France
Ancien secrétaire national de la Confédération française démocratique du travail (CFDT), ancien secrétaire général de la Fédération des mines et de la métallurgie (CFDT) et chargé de mission au service international-Europe de la CFDT
4, boulevard de la Villette
F-75955 Paris Cedex 19
Tel. +33 142038000
Fax +33 142038074
E-mail: gerard.dantin@wanadoo.fr

Mrs Anna Maria DARMANIN
Vice-President
Malta
President, Salvino Spiteri Foundation - Union Ħaddiema Magqħudin (UĦM) - Direttur tal-Bord, Foundation for Human Resource Development (FHRD) fejn tirrappreżenta lill-UĦM
'Dar Reggie Miller', Triq San Tumas • M-Floriana
Tel. +356 794 03525
Fax +356 21246091
E-mail: amdarmanin@gmail.com

Mrs Susanna FLORIO
Vice-President
Italie
Responsabile per l'Ufficio di Bruxelles della Confederazione generale italiana del lavoro - (CGIL)
Corso d'Italia, 25 • I-00199 Roma
Tel. +39 068476325
E-mail: europa.ecosoc@cgil.it

Mr Manfred SCHALLMEYER
Vice-President
Deutschland
Präsident der Internationalen Textil-, Bekleidungs- und Lederarbeitervereinigung - Beauftragter des 1. Vorsitzenden der Industriegewerkschaft Metall (IG Metall)
Minzstr. 9 • D-41466 Neuss
Tel. +49 696693-2808
Fax +49 696693-802808
E-mail: manfred.schallmeyer@igmetall.de

Mr Victor Hugo SEQUEIRA
Vice-President
Portugal
Presidente da Direcção do Sindicato dos Trabalhadores de Escritório, Comércio e Novas Tecnologias (SITESE)
Avenida Marquês de Tomar, 44-5°
P-1069-190 Lisboa
Fax +351 217934176
E-mail: Vsequeira@sitese.pt

Mrs Dana ŠTECHOVÁ
Vice-President
République tchèque
Poradkyně, oddělení pro evropské a další mezinárodní vztahy, Českomoravská konfederace odborových svazů (ČMKOS)
W. Churchilla 2 • CZ-113 59 Praha 3
Tel. +420 234462274
Fax +420 222718994
E-mail: stechova.dana@cmkos.cz

Mr Maurizio ANGELO
Italie
Presidente della Confederazione internazionale dei dirigenti e dei quadri (CIC)
Via Nazionale, 75 • I-00184 Roma
Tel. +39 0697605111
Fax +39 0697605111
E-mail: angelomau@tin.it

Mr William A. ATTLEY
Irlande
Former General Secretary of the Services, Industrial, Professional and Technical Union (SIPTU)
41 Beechwood Lawns • IRL • Rathcoole, Co. Dublin
Tel. +353 14589773
Fax +353 14589700
E-mail: wattley@eircom.net

Mrs Katarzyna BARTKIEWICZ
Poland
Ekspert do spraw integracji europejskiej Komisji Krajowej Niezależnego Samorządnego Związku Zawodowego (NSZZ) " Solidarność"
ul. Wały Piastowskie 24 • PL-80-855 Gdańsk
Tel. +48 583084413
Fax +48 58 3084244
E-mail: zagr@solidarnosc.org.pl

Mrs Laure BATUT
France
Assistante confédérale à la Confédération générale du travail - Force ouvrière (CGT-FO)
141, avenue du Maine
F-75680 Paris Cedex 134
Tel. +33 14052 8337
Fax +33 14052 8334
E-mail: lbatut@force-ouvriere.fr

Mrs Gabriele BISCHOFF
Deutschland
Bereichsleiterin für Europapolitik – DGB-Bundesvorstand
Henriette-Herz-Platz 2 • D-10178 Berlin
Tel. +49 3024060-641
Fax +49 3024060-408
E-mail: gabriele.bischoff@dgb.de

Mrs Christine BLOWER
United Kingdom
Acting General Secretary, National Union of Teachers (NUT)
Hamilton House - Mabledon Place • UK
W1H 9BD London
Tel. +44 2073886191
Fax +44 2073878458
E-mail: c.blower@nut.org.uk

Mrs Marjolijn BULK
Nederland
Beleidsmedewerker internationale Zaken, Federatie Nederlandse Vakbeweging (FNV)
Postbus 8456 • NL • 1005 AL Amsterdam
Tel. +31 205816371
Fax +31 206844541
E-mail: marjolijn.bulk@vc.fnv.nl

Mrs Marge CAREY
United Kingdom
Former President of the Union of Shop, Distributive and Allied Workers (USDAW) - Former member of the TUC General Council and Executive Committee
Banner Hey 42 - Whiston, Prescot • UK
L35 3JS Merseyside
Tel. +44 1514309834
E-mail: mc001o8758@blueyonder.co.uk

Mrs Liina CARR
Estonia
Eesti Ametiühingute Keskliidu (EAKL) välissuhete sekretär
Pärnu mnt 41a • EE-10119 Tallinn
Tel. +372 6412807
Fax +372 6412801
E-mail: liina.carr@eakl.ee

Mr Carmelo CEDRONE
Italie
Professore incaricato di "Politica economica europea'" Univ. La Sapienza Roma - Componente del "Team Europe" - Già responsabile del Dipartimento europeo ed internazionale dell'Unione italiana del lavoro (UIL) - Membro del Comitato centrale UIL
Via Lucullo, 6 • I-00187 Roma
Tel. +39 064753390
Fax +39 064753234
E-mail: cedrone@uil.it

Mr Franco CHIRIACO
Italie
Segretario generale della Federazione italiana lavoratori dell'agro-industria - Confederazione generale italiana del lavoro (FLAI-CGIL)
Via Leopoldo Serra, 31 • I-00153 Roma
Tel. +39 0658561342
Fax +39 065809021
E-mail: franco.chiriaco@flai.it

Mr Peter COLDRICK
United Kingdom
Head of Brussels Office of the Trades Union Congress (TUC)
Boulevard Roi Albert II, 5 • B-1210 Bruxelles
Tel. +32 2224 04 77
Fax +32 2224 04 79
E-mail: pcoldrick@tuc.etuc.org

Mrs Helena ČORNEJOVÁ
République tchèque
Vedoucí sociálně-ekonomického oddělení Českomoravské konfederace odborových svazů (ČMKOS)
W. Churchilla 2 • CZ-113 59 Praha 3
Tel. +420 234462 259
Fax +420 222720721
E-mail: cornejova.helena@cmkos.cz

Mr Alfredo CORREIA
Portugal
Presidente do Congresso - Sindicato dos Bancários do Norte - União Geral de Trabalhadores (UGT)
Rua Cândido dos Reis 130 - 1°
P-4050-151 Porto
Tel. +351 223398800
Fax +351 222054174
E-mail: alfredocorreia@netcabo.pt

Mr Nicholas CROOK
United Kingdom
International Officer, public sector union UNISON
Mabledon Place 1 • UK • WC 1H 9AJ London
Tel. +44 2075511219
Fax +44 2075511471
E-mail: n.crook@unison.co.uk
www.unison.org.uk

Mrs Ágnes CSER
Hungary
A Szakszervezetek Együttműködési Fóruma Értelmiségi Szakszervezeti Tömörülés (SZEF-ÉSZT) alelnöke
Nádor u. 32. • H-1051 Budapest
Tel. +36 1341-1663
Fax +36 1269-1283
E-mail: eddsz1@t-online.hu

Mr Brian CURTIS
United Kingdom
Regional Organiser, Wales and the West of England, National Union of Rail, Maritime and Transport Workers (RMT)
22 Hawthorn Road • UK • CF62 6LE Barry
Tel. +44 1446749272
Fax +44 1446749272
E-mail: curtis655@btinternet.com

Mr Petru Sorin DANDEA
Romania
Vicepreşedinte, Confederaţia Naţională Sindicală Cartel Alfa
Splaiul Independenţei, nr. 202 A, etaj 2, sector 6 • RO-060022 Bucureşti
Tel. +40 213171041
Fax +40 213123481
E-mail: dandea@cartel-alfa.ro

Mr Thomas DELAPINA
Österreich
Geschäftsführer des Beirats für Wirtschafts- und Sozialfragen
Sekretär in der Arbeiterkammer Wien
Prinz Eugen-Str. 20-22 • A-1041 Wien
Tel. +43 150165/2369
Fax +43 150165/2513
E-mail: thomas.delapina@akwien.at

Mr Olivier DERRUINE
Belgique/België
Conseiller au service d'études de la Confédération des syndicats chrétiens de Belgique (CSC)
Chaussée de Haecht 579 • B-1031 Bruxelles
Tel. +32 22463422
Fax +32 22463010
E-mail: oderruine@acv-csc.be

Mr Plamen DIMITROV
Bulgaria
Заместник-председател на Конфедерацията на независимите синдикати в България, председател на постоянната комисия на ИСС по труд, доходи, жизнено равнище и индустриални отношения, председател на управителния съвет на Колежа за работническо обучениеpl Makedoniya № 1
BG-1040 Sofia
Tel. +359 24010501
Fax +359 29877065
E-mail: pldimitrov@knsb-bg.org

Mr Ernst Erik EHNMARK
Sverige
Sakkunnig, internationella frågor, SACO, Sveriges Akademikers Centralorganisation. Sveriges Akademikers Centralorganisation Box 2206 • S-10315 Stockholm
Tel. +46 86134800
Fax +46 8247701
E-mail: ernst.erik.ehnmark@saco.se

Mr Dumitru FORNEA
Romania
Director, Departamentul de Relaţii Internaţionale al Confederaţiei Sindicale Naţionale MERIDIAN
Str. Mendeleev, nr. 36-38, sector 1
RO-010366 Bucureşti
Tel. +40 723915989
Fax +40 213168017
E-mail: international@csnmeridian.ro
www.csnmeridian.ro

Mr Pierre GENDRE
France
Assistant confédéral du secteur international-Europe de la Confédération générale du travail — Force ouvrière (CGT-FO)
141, avenue du Maine • F-75680 Paris Cedex 14
Tel. +33 140528258
Fax +33 140528202
E-mail: gendre.pierre@wanadoo.fr

Mrs Laura GONZÁLEZ DE TXABARRI ETXANIZ
España
Miembro del Comité Ejecutivo de Euskal Langileen Alkartasuna- Solidaridad de Tabajadores Vascos (ELA), responsable de relaciones internacionales
Barrainkua,13-Aptdo. 139, • E-48009 Bilbao
Tel. +34 944037760
Fax +34 944037777
E-mail: lgtxabarri@elasind.org

Mr Alexander GRAF VON SCHWERIN
Deutschland
Vereinte Dienstleistungsgewerkschaft (ver.di) im Deutschen Gewerkschaftsbund (DGB)
Mühlheimer Strasse 72-74 • D-47057 Duisburg
Tel. +49 2036044238
Fax +49 2036044239
E-mail: alex@graf-vonschwerin.de

Mr Wolfgang GREIF
Österreich
Leiter der Abteilung Europa, Konzerne und Internationale Beziehungen in der Gewerkschaft der Privatangestellten Druck, Journalismus, Papier (GPA-DJP)
Alfred-Dallinger-Platz 1 • A-1034 Wien
Tel. +43 50301-21205
Fax +43 50301-71205
E-mail: wolfgang.greif@gpa-djp.at

Mr Guy HAAZE
Belgique/België
Oud - Voorzitter van de Algemene Centrale der Liberale Vakbonden van België (ACVLB)
Slingerstraat 5 • B-9031 Gent
Tel. +32 92225751
Fax +32 92273756
E-mail: guyhaaze@yahoo.com

Mr Peder Munch HANSEN
Danmark
EU-konsulent og journalist for Landsorganisationen i Danmark (LO)
Boulevard du Roi Albert II 5, bte 24
B-1210 Bruxelles
Tel. +32 22040690
Fax +32 22035657
E-mail: munch@lo.dk

Mr Raymond HENCKS
Luxembourg
Membre du comité exécutif de la Confédération générale de la fonction publique (CGFP)
5, Aeppelwe • L-6981 Rameldange
Tel. +352 47654202
Fax +352 349319
E-mail: rhencks@pt.lu

Mrs Irīna HOMKO
Latvia
Latvijas Brīvo arodbiedrību savienības (LBAS) eksperte sociālos un veselības aizsardzības jautājumos
Bruņinieku ielā 29-31 • LV-1001 Rīgā
Tel. +371 7035903
Fax +371 7276649
E-mail: irina.homko@lbas.lv

Mr Bojan HRIBAR
Slovenia
Sekretar - Sindikat delavcev v vzgojni, izobraževalni in raziskovalni dejavnosti Slovenije (VIR)
Dalmatinova 4, p.p. 97 • SLO-1000 Ljubljana
Tel. +386 14341261
Fax +386 12317298
E-mail: Bojan.Hribar@sindikat-zsss.si

Mr Jeliazko HRISTOV
Bulgaria
Председател на Конфедерацията на независимите синдикати в България (КНСБ), доцентpl. Makedoniya № 1 • BG-1040 Sofia
Tel. +359 24010496
Fax +359 29877065
E-mail: jeliazko.hristov@eesc.europa.eu

Mr Edgardo Maria IOZIA
Italie
Segretario nazionale Unione italiana del lavoro - Credito e assicurazioni (UILCA) - Vicepresidente UNI Europa finanza
Via Lattanzio, 58 • I-00136 Roma
Tel. +39 064872132
Fax +39 06484704
E-mail: edgardo.iozia@gmail.com

Mr Giuseppe Antonio Maria IULIANO
Italie
Dipartimento Politiche internazionali della Confederazione italiana sindacati lavoratori (CISL) - Coordinatore di area - Responsabile per l'Europa centro-orientale e per l'America Latina
Via Po, 21 • I-00198 Roma
Tel. +39 068473357
Fax +39 068413782
E-mail: giuseppe.iuliano@cisl.it

Mr Minel IVAŞCU
Romania
Secretar general, Blocul Naţional Sindical (BNS)
Splaiul Independenţei, nr. 202A, etaj 4, cam. 38, sector 6 • RO-060022 Bucureşti
Tel. +40 213162801
Fax +40 213162798
E-mail: mivascu@bns.ro

Mr Thomas JANSON
Sverige
Internationell sekreterare , Tjänstemännens Centralorganisation (TCO)
Linnegatan 14 • S-11494 Stockholm
Tel. +46 8782900
Fax +46 87829108
E-mail: thomas.janson@tco.se

Mrs Maud JANSSON
Sverige
Internationell sekreterare, Landsorganisationen i Sverige (LO)
Augustendalsvägen 32 • S-13152 Nacka Strand
Tel. +46 87962616
Fax +46 87962788
E-mail: nisse.maud@telia.com

Mr Tomasz JASIŃSKI
Poland
Ekspert do spraw współpracy międzynarodowej i integracji europejskiej Ogólnopolskiego Porozumienia Związków Zawodowych (OPZZ)
ul. Kopernika 36/40 • PL-00-924 Warszawa
Tel. +48 225515525
Fax +48 228267106
E-mail: jasinski@opzz.org.pl

Mr József KAPUVÁRI
Hungary
Élelmezésipari Dolgozók Szakszervezeteinek Szövetsége (ÉDOSZ) elnök
Városligeti Fasor u. 44. • H-1068 Budapest
Tel. +36 1413-2120
Fax +36 1413-2119
E-mail: jozsef.kapuvari@eesc.europa.eu

Mr Søren KARGAARD
Danmark
Medlem af EFS' Eksekutivkomité, Funktionærernes og Tjenestemændenes Fællesråd (FTF)
Frederiksborgvej 38E • DK-4000 Roskilde
Tel. +45 33368825
Fax +45 33368880
E-mail: soka@ftf.dk

Mrs Sally Anne KINAHAN
Irlande
Assistant General Secretary - Irish Congress of Trade Unions (ICTU)
Parnell Square 31-32 • IRL • 1 Dublin
Tel. +353 18897777
Fax +353 18872012
E-mail: sallyanne.kinahan@ictu.ie

Mr Dimitris KITTENIS
Cyprus
Γενικός Γραμματέας της Συνομοσπονδίας Εργατών Κύπρου (ΣΕΚ)
1 Eleftherou Kormakiti • CY-2414 Egomi - Nicosia
Tel. +357 22849601
Fax +357 22849850
E-mail: dkittenis@gmail.com

Mrs Marie-Louise KNUPPERT
Danmark
LO-sekretær (Landsorganisationen i Danmark)
Kong Georgs Vej 31 • DK-2000 Frederiksberg
Tel. +45 35246140
E-mail: ma-lou@lo.dk

Mrs Erika KOLLER
Hungary
Független Szakszervezetek Demokratikus Ligája (LIGA) nemzetközi osztályvezető
Benczúr u. 41. • H-1068 Budapest
Tel. +36 304550923
Fax +36 13215405
E-mail: koller@liganet.hu

Mr Pēteris KRĪGERS
Latvia
Latvijas Brīvo arodbiedrību savienības (LBAS) priekšsēdētājs
Bruņinieku ielā 29-31 • LV-1001 Rīgā
Tel. +371 703 59 00
Fax +371 727 66 49
E-mail: krigers@lbas.lv

Mr Marian KRZAKLEWSKI
Poland
Członek Komisji Krajowej Niezależnego Samorządnego Związku Zawodowego (NSZZ) "Solidarność"
ul. Wały Piastowskie 24 • PL-80-855 Gdańsk
Tel. +48 583084345
Fax +48 583084367
E-mail: mkrzak@solidarnosc.org.pl
k.r.z.a.k@wp.pl

Mrs Leila KURKI
Suomi/Finland
Työllisyyspoliittinen asiantuntija - Toimihenkilökeskusjärjestö STTK ry
Mikonkatu 8 A - PL 421 • FI-00101 Helsinki
Tel. +358 400798959
Fax +358 9652367
E-mail: leila.kurki@sttk.fi

Mrs Daiva KVEDARAITĖ
Lithuania
Lietuvos profesinės sąjungos "Solidarumas" Informacinio centro direktorė
V. Mykolaičio-Putino g. 5–212 • LT-03106 Vilnius
Tel. +370 68617409
Fax +370 52133295
E-mail: daivakv@delfi.lt

Mr Algirdas Aleksandras KVEDARAVIČIUS
Lithuania
Lietuvos profesinių sąjungų konfederacijos (LPSK) pirmininko pavaduotojas - Lietuvos Respublikos trišalės tarybos narys
J. Jasinskio g. 9 • LT-01111 Vilnius
Tel. +370 52498056
Fax +370 52498078
E-mail: lpsk@takas.lt

Mr Floríval LANÇA
Portugal
Conselheiro (CGTP-IN), ex-membro da Comissão Executiva da CGTP-IN e da Direcção do Sindicato dos Metalúrgicos de Lisboa, Secretário-Geral Executivo Adjunto da Comunidade Sindical dos Países de Língua Portuguesa
Rua Almada Negreiros N° 10, Vale de Milhaços
P-2855 Corroios
Tel. +351 919354098
Fax +351 213236500
E-mail: florivalrlanca@gmail.com

Mrs An LE NOUAIL MARLIÈRE
France
Conseiller pour l'activité européenne et internationale de la Confédération générale du travail (CGT)
263, rue de Paris • F-93100 Montreuil
Tel. +33 148188496
Fax +33 148188443

Mr Christoph LECHNER
Österreich
Leiter der Abteilung Verfassungsrecht und Allgemeine und Internationale Sozialpolitik der Kammer für Arbeiter und Angestellte für Niederösterreich
Windmühlgasse 28 • A-1060 Wien
Tel. +43 6643909740
Fax +43 1588831755
E-mail: christoph.lechner@aknoe.at

Mr Georges LIAROKAPIS
France
Président de la Confédération européenne des cadres (CEC) et secrétaire de l'Instance européenne de dialogue social de l'Oréal
Passage de la Réunion • F-92400 Courbevoie
Tel. +33 147568312
Fax +33 147568277
E-mail: liarokapis@cec-managers.org

Mr Dimitar MANOLOV
Bulgaria
Вицепрезидент на Конфедерацията на труда "ПОДКРЕПА"ul. Angel Kanchev № 2
BG-1000 Sofia
Tel. +359 888531910
Fax +359 29812928
E-mail: dr_manolov@abv.bg

Mr Claus MATECKI
Deutschland
Mitglied des Geschäftsführenden Bundesvorstandes des Deutschen Gewerkschaftsbundes (DGB)
Henriette-Herz-Platz 2 - Postfach 11 03 72
D-10833 Berlin
Tel. +49 3024060299
Fax +49 3024060240
E-mail: claus.matecki@dgb.de

Mr Vladimír MATOUŠEK
République tchèque
Vedoucí mezinárodního oddělení Českomoravské konfederace odborových svazů (ČMKOS)
W. Churchilla 2 • CZ-113 59 Praha 3
Tel. +420 234 462 272
Fax +420 222 718 994
E-mail: matousek.vla@seznam.cz

Mr Jim McCUSKER
Irlande
Former General Secretary, Northern Ireland Public Service Alliance (NIPSA)
4 Taunton Avenue • UK • BT15 4AD Belfast
Tel. +44 2890371063
E-mail: jimmccusker@btinternet.com

Mrs Judy McKNIGHT
United Kingdom
Former General Secretary, National Association of Probation Officers (NAPO)
Prince of Wales Drive • UK • SW11 4HR London
Tel. +44 2076220485
Fax +44 2074984425
E-mail: judy@judymcknight.org

Mr Leon E. MEIJER
Nederland
Beleidsadviseur Europese Internationale zaken van het Christelijk Nationaal Vakverbond (CNV)
Postbus 2475 • NL • 3500 GL Utrecht
Tel. +31 307511272
Fax +31 307511109
E-mail: l.meijer@cnv.nl

Mr Juan MENDOZA CASTRO
España
Colaborador de UGT (Unión General de Trabajadores) para asuntos internacionales
Azcona 53 • E-28028 Madrid
Tel. +34 915890883
Fax +34 915897747
E-mail: jmendoza@ejb.ugt.org

Mr Janne METSÄMÄKI
Suomi/Finland
Elinkeinoasioiden päällikkö, Suomen ammattiliittojen keskusjärjestö (SAK)
PL/PO Box 157 - (Hakaniemenranta 1)
FI-00531 Helsinki
Tel. +358 207740151
Fax +358 207740231
E-mail: janne.metsamaki@sak.fi

Mr Vesselin MITOV
Bulgaria
Международен секретар на Конфедерация на труда "ПОДКРЕПА "ul. Angel Kanchev № 2
BG-1000 Sofia
Tel. +359 888417652
Fax +359 29812928
E-mail: veskom@fintech.bg
www.podkrepa.org

Mr Vladimír MOJŠ
Slovakia
Viceprezident Konfederácie odborových zväzov Slovenskej republiky (KOZ SR)
Odborárske námestie 3 • SK-815 70 Bratislava
Tel. +421 255575880
Fax +421 255423600
E-mail: mojs@kozsr.sk

Mr André MORDANT
Belgique/België
Président honoraire de la Fédération générale du travail de Belgique (FGTB)
Rue Xhovémont 130 • B-4000 Liège
Tel. +32 42266996
Fax +32 42266996
E-mail: Andre_mordant@skynet.be

Mr Juan MORENO PRECIADO
España
Responsable de la Oficina de la Confederación Sindical de Comisiones Obreras (CC OO) en Bruselas
C/Fernández de la Hoz, 12 • E-28010 Madrid
Tel. +34 630934425
Fax +34 917028175
E-mail: jmoreno@ccoo.es

Mr Wolter MULLER
Nederland
Lid algemeen bestuur van de Vakcentrale voor Middengroepen en Hoger Personeel (MHP)
Multatulilaan 12 • NL • 4103 NM Culemborg
Tel. +31 345851900
Fax +31 345851 915
E-mail: w.muller@vc-mhp.nl

Mr Lars NYBERG
Sverige
Samordnar och utreder EU-frågor, Landsorganisationen i Sverige (LO)
Barnhusgatan 18 • S-10553 Stockholm
Tel. +46 87962613
Fax +46 87962800
E-mail: lars.nyberg@lo.se

Mr Erhard OTT
Deutschland
Mitglied des ver.di-Bundesvorstandes, Ressortleiter Fachbereich Ver- und Entsorgung
Paula-Thiede-Ufer 10 • D-10179 Berlin
Tel. +49 306956 - 1700
Fax +49 306956 - 3350
E-mail: erhard.ott@verdi.de

Mrs Béatrice OUIN
France
Journaliste, chargée de mission au sein du secteur Europe et international, de la Confédération française démocratique du travail (CFDT)
Le Bourg • F-82200 Boudou
Tel. +33 601869586
E-mail: bea.ouin@wanadoo.fr

Mr Spyridon PAPASPYROS
Grèce
Πρόεδρος της Ανωτάτης Διοίκησης Ενώσεων Δημοσίων Υπαλλήλων (ΑΔΕΔΥ)
Ahelooy 11-13 • GR-15235 Vrilissia/Athens
Tel. +30 210 3246109
Fax +30 210 3246165
E-mail: spiros_61@hotmail.com

Mr Luis Miguel PARIZA CASTAÑOS
España
Secretaría de Política Internacional de la Confederación sindical de comisiones obreras (CC OO)
c/ Uribitarte, 4 • E-48001 Bilbao
Tel. +34 944241036
Fax +34 944243898
E-mail: lpariza@euskadi.ccoo.es

Mr Michael PARNIS
Malta
Deputat Segretarju-Ġenerali (Edukazzjoni u Affarijiet Internazzjonali) tal-General Workers' Union (GWU)
Avenue du Roi Albert 15
B-1082 Bruxelles - Brussel
Tel. +356 21244300
Fax +356 21234029
E-mail: mparnis@gwu.org.mt

Mr Miklós PÁSZTOR
Hungary
A Munkástanácsok Országos Szövetségének (MOSZ) elnökségi tagja, a Budapesti Corvinus Egyetem tanára, a Munkástanácsok Országos Szövetségének (MOSZ) szakértője
Szarvas Gábor utca 9/b • H-1125 Budapest
Tel. +36 209374845
Fax +36 12751445
E-mail: miklos.pasztor@uni-corvinus.hu

Mr Andreas PAVLIKKAS
Cyprus
Υπεύθυνος του Γραφείου Ερευνών και Μελετών της Παγκύπριας Εργατικής Ομοσπονδίας (ΠΕΟ)
Pancyprian Federation of Labour (PEO) - Archermou 29 • CY-21885 Nicosia
Tel. +357 22866400
Fax +357 22349382
E-mail: andreas.pavlikkas@peo.org.cy

Mr Markus PENTTINEN
Suomi/Finland
Kansainvälisten asioiden päällikkö (AKAVA)
Rautatieläisenkatu 6 • FI-00520 Helsinki
Tel. +358 407728861
Fax +358 9142595
E-mail: markus.penttinen@akava.fi

Mr Marius PETCU
Romania
Preşedinte, Confederaţia Naţionalî a Sindicatelor Libere din România Frăţia
Str. Cristian Popişteanu nr. 1-3, sector 1
RO-010024 Bucarest
Tel. +40 213124347
Fax +40 213135938
E-mail: presedinte@cnslr-fratia.ro

Mr Josly PIETTE
Belgique/België
Secrétaire général honoraire de la Confédération des syndicats chrétiens (CSC)
Rue Lulay 53 • B-4690 Glons
Tel. +32 42862474
Fax +32 43607945
E-mail: Piette.josly@teledisnet.be

Mrs Renata POLVERINI
Italie
Segretario generale dell'Unione generale del lavoro - UGL
Via Margutta, 19 • I-00187 Roma
Tel. +39 063201942
Fax +39 063201944
E-mail: segreteriapolverini@ugl.it

Mr Christos POLYZOGOPOULOS
Grèce
Πρόεδρος της Οικονομικής και Κοινωνικής Επιτροπής της Ελλάδος (Ο.Κ.Ε.)
Amvrosiou Frantzi str. 9 • GR-11 743 Athina
Tel. +30 210 9249510 12
Fax +30 210 9249515
E-mail: zsinog@inegsee.gr

Mr Konstantinos POUPAKIS
Grèce
Γενικός Γραμματέας της Γενικής Συνομοσπονδίας Εργατών Ελλάδας (ΓΣΕΕ)
Patission 69 • GR-10 434 Athens
Tel. +30 210 8202288
Fax +30 210 8202150
E-mail: gsecretary@gsee.gr

Mrs Inga PREIDIENĖ
Lithuania
Lietuvos darbo federacijos (LDF) jaunimo organizacijos pirmininko pavaduotoja
Vytauto g. 14 • LT-08118 Vilnius
Tel. +370 52312029
Fax +370 52312029
E-mail: ipreidiene@panevezys.ldrmt.lt

Mrs Naile PROKEŠOVÁ
Slovakia
Poradkyňa Konfederácie odborových zväzov Slovenskej republiky (KOZ SR) pre daňovú politiku a verejné fondy
národná koordinátorka ženskej siete ITUC
členka výboru Európskeho sociálneho fondu (ESF)
Odborárske nám. 3 • SK-815 70 Bratislava
Tel. +421 250239131
Fax +421 255423600
E-mail: prokesova@kozsr.sk

Mrs Nicole PRUD'HOMME
France
Ancienne vice-présidente de la Confédération française des travailleurs chrétiens (CFTC) et présidente d'honneur de la Caisse nationale d'allocations familiales (CNAF)
10, rue Jules Lemaître - Hall 2 • F-75012 Paris
Tel. +33 689649961
E-mail: nicoleprudhomme@orange.fr

Mr Dušan REBOLJ
Slovenia
Predsednik Konfederacije sindikatov Slovenije (KSS) Pergam in član Ekonomsko socialnega sveta (ESS) Republike Slovenije
Trg osvobodilne fronte 14 • SLO-1000 Ljubljana
Tel. +386 12310476
Fax +386 12302247
E-mail: pergam@siol.net

Mr Jean-Claude REDING
Luxembourg
Président de la Confédération syndicale indépendante du Luxembourg (OGBL) et de la Confédération générale du travail du Luxembourg (CGTL)
BP 149 • L-4002 Esch/Alzette
Tel. +352 540545-253
Fax +352 541620
E-mail: jean-claude.reding@ogbl.lu

Mrs Evelyn REGNER
Österreich
Leiterin des Österreichischen Gewerkschaftsbundes (ÖGB) Europabüro in Brüssel
Avenue de Cortenbergh 30 • B-1040 Bruxelles
Tel. +431 53444225
E-mail: evelyn.regner@oegb.at

Mr Daniel RETUREAU
France
Collaborateur B de la Confédération générale du travail (CGT) pour l'Europe et Bureau international du travail
263, rue de Paris • F-93516 Montreuil
Tel. +33 148188478
Fax +33 148188494
E-mail: dretureau@yahoo.fr

Mrs Metka ROKSANDIĆ
Slovenia
Bivša izvršna sekretarka predsedstva Zveze svobodnih sindikatov Slovenije (ZSSS)
Maistrova ulica 12 • SLO-2000 Maribor
Tel. +386 14341234
+386 22524764
Fax +386 12317298
E-mail: metka.roksandic@triera.net

Mrs Michaela ROSENBERGER
Deutschland
Stellvertretende Vorsitzende der Gewerkschaft Nahrung-Genuss-Gaststätten
Haubachstraße 61 • D-22765 Hamburg
Tel. +49 4038013 - 160
Fax +49 403892637
E-mail: hv.vorstand-rosenberger@ngg.net

Mr Stanisław RÓŻYCKI
Poland
Wiceprzewodniczący Rady Szkolnictwa Wyższego i Nauki Związku Nauczycielstwa Polskiego w Ogólnopolskim Porozumieniu Związków Zawodowych (OPZZ)
J. Smulikowskiego 6/8 • PL-00-389 Warszawa
Tel. +48 228262646
E-mail: stanislaw.rozycki@wp.pl

Mr Sabin RUSU
Romania
Secretar General, Confederaţia Sindicatelor Democratice din România (CSDR)
Piaţa Walter Mărăcineanu nr. 1-3, sector 1
RO-010155 Bucarest
Tel. +40 213156542
Fax +40 213139483
E-mail: secretariatcsdr@yahoo.com

Mr Valerio SALVATORE
Italie
Presidente della Confederazione europea dei sindacati indipendenti (CESI) - Consigliere nazionale del Sindacato nazionale autonomo lavoratori della scuola (SNALS) - Membro del consiglio generale della Confsal
Avenue de la Joyeuse Entrée 1/5 • B-1040 Bruxelles
Tel. +32 22821870
Fax +32 22821871
E-mail: valerio.salvatore@eesc.europa.eu

Mrs María Candelas SÁNCHEZ MIGUEL
España
Miembro de la Secretaría de Política Internacional de CC OO (Confederación Sindical de Comisiones Obreras) - Profesora de la Facultad de Ciencas Económicas - Universidad de Madrid
C/ Fernández de la Hoz, 12-3° • E-28010 Madrid
Tel. +34 917028120
Fax +34 917028175
E-mail: mcandelas@ccoo.es

Mr Sergio Ernesto SANTILLÁN CABEZA
España
Abogado de la Unión General de Trabajadores (UGT)
C/Hortaleza, 88 • E-28004 Madrid
Tel. +34 915897701
Fax +34 915897702
E-mail: santillan91@yahoo.es

Mr Robert SCHADECK
Luxembourg
Représentant de la Confédération des syndicats chrétiens du Luxembourg (LCGB)
7, rue Dr. Welter • L-3879 Schifflange
Tel. +352 545861
Fax +352 549036
E-mail: rschadeck@proactif.lu

Mr Mario SEPI
Italie
Direttore dell'Istituto sindacale per la cooperazione allo sviluppo (ISCOS) della Confederazione italiana sindacati lavoratori (CISL)
Via Po, 21 • I-00198 Roma
Tel. +39 068473271
Fax +39 068473242
E-mail: mario.sepi@eesc.europa.eu

Mr Martin SIECKER
Nederland
Vakbondsbestuurder - Federatie Nederlandse Vakbeweging (FNV)
Westeinde 58 A • NL • 1636 VG Schermerhorn
Tel. +31 725022506
Fax +31 725021839
E-mail: m.siecker@bg.fnv.nl

Mr Wiesław SIEWIERSKI
Poland
Przewodniczący Forum Związków Zawodowych, wiceprzewodniczący Komisji Trójstronnej
ul. Biziela 20 m. 133 • PL-85-163 Bydgoszcz
Tel. +48 523714804
Fax +48 523421871
E-mail: wieslaw.siewierski@fzz.org.pl

Mr Eugen ŠKULTÉTY
Slovakia
Viceprezident Konfederácie odborov÷ch zväzov Slovenskej republiky (KOZ SR)
Odborárske nám.3 • SK-815 70 Bratislava
Tel. +421 250239105
Fax +421 255423303
E-mail: skultety@kozsr.sk

Mr Mário SOARES
Portugal
Professor - Membro do Conselho Nacional da Confederação Geral dos Trabalhadores Portugueses - Intersindical (CGTP-IN)
Rua da Raposa, 671 • P-4415-313 Pedroso
E-mail: mario.d.soares@gmail.com

Mr Josef SUCHEL
République tchèque
Poradce Českomoravské konfederace odborových svazů (ČMKOS)
Českomalínská 43 • CZ-160 00 Praha 6
Tel. +420 606473902
Fax +420 224314881
E-mail: suchel.josef@cmkos.cz
www.icq.atlas.cz

Mr Edmund SZYNAKA
Poland
Szef Zespołu Ekspertów Forum Związków Zawodowych (FZZ)
ul. Nowowiejskiego 1 m. 110 • PL-85-869 Bydgoszcz
Tel. +48 52 3713615
Fax +48 523713615
E-mail: edmund.szynaka@neostrada.pl

Mrs Monica TAYLOR
United Kingdom
Executive Council Member, Transport and General Workers' Union (TGWU)
79 Ivyhouse Road, Kings Norton • UK Birmingham B28 8JP - West Midlands
Tel. +44 1216258485
E-mail: sisteract_mtaylor@hotmail.com

Mrs Annie van WEZEL
Nederland
Beleidsadviseur Internationale en Europese Zaken (FNV)
Box 8456 • NL • 1005 AL Amsterdam
Tel. +31 205816540
Fax +31 206844541
E-mail: annie.vanwezel@vc.fnv.nl

Mr Xavier VERBOVEN
Belgique/België
Gewezen Algemeen Secretaris van het Algemeen Belgisch Vakverbond (ABVV)
Potuitstraat 1 • B-9040 St-Amandsberg
Tel. +32 475245089

Mrs Mare VIIES
Estonia
Tallinna Tehnikaülikooli Majandusuuringute Teaduskeskuse teadur, Teenistujate Ametiliitude Keskorganisatsioon (TALO)
Kopli 101 • EE-11712 Tallinn
Tel. +372 6204031
Fax +372 6203946
E-mail: mare.viies@tv.ttu.ee

Mr Hans-Joachim WILMS
Deutschland
Stellvertretender Bundesvorsitzender der Industriegewerkschaft Bauen-Agrar-Umwelt (IG BAU)
Sültstr. 34 • D-10409 Berlin
Tel. +49 3024639300
Fax +49 3024639333
E-mail: hans-joachim.wilms@igbau.de

Mr Wilfried WOLLER
Deutschland
Gewerkschaftssekretär - Industriegewerkschaft, Bergbau, Chemie, Energie (IG/BCE)
Königsworther Platz 6 • D-30167 Hannover
Tel. +49 5117631129
Fax +49 5117631769
E-mail: wilfried.woller@igbce.de

Mr Gustav ZÖHRER
Österreich
Internationaler Sekretär der Gewerkschaft Metall - Textil - Nahrung (GMTN))
Ploesslgasse 15 • A-1041 Wien
Tel. +43 150146218
Fax +43 15014613270
E-mail: gustav.zoehrer@gmtn.at

Mr José María ZUFIAUR NARVAIZA
España
Presidente de la Fundación de Educación y Trabajo
Calle Nicolás Morales, 11-3° • E-28019 Madrid
Tel. +34 914280710
Fax +34 914723875
E-mail: jmzufiaur@labour-asociados.com

Group III: Various interests

Mr Staffan NILSSON
President
Sverige
Lantbrukare, Lantbrukarnas Riksförbund (LRF)
Björsarv 50 • S-82062 Bjuråker
Tel. +46 65331015
Fax +46 65331055
E-mail: Staffan.Nilsson@lrf.se

Mr Miklós BARABÁS
Vice-President
Hungary
Az Európa Ház igazgatója (a civil társadalom fejlesztése, partnerségek, európai együttműködés és állampolgárság)
a Magyar Gazdasági és Szociális Tanács tagja
a Nemzeti Civil Alapprogram Tanácsának tagja
Dezső u. 3. • H-1016 Budapest
Tel. +36 1356-8440
Fax +36 1356-8499
E-mail: miklos@europeanhouse.hu

Mrs Mall HELLAM
Vice-President
Estonia
Eesti Mittetulundusühingute ja Sihtasutuste Liidu (EMSL) asutaja- ja nõukogu liige
Estonia pst 5A • EE-10143 Tallinn
Tel. +372 6313791
Fax +372 6313796
E-mail: mall.hellam@eesc.europa.eu

Mr Luca JAHIER
Vice-President
Italie
Responsabile Relazioni internazionali delle ACLI (Associazioni cristiane lavoratori italiani)
Via Marcora, 18/20 • I-00153 Roma
Tel. +39 065840402
Fax +39 065840615
E-mail: luca.jahier@acli.it

Mr Richard ADAMS
United Kingdom
Consultant in social, environmental and ethical business and project development
Long Barn • UK • NE45 5LX Corbridge
Tel. +44 1434634869
E-mail: richarda@communityviewfinders.com

Mr Frank ALLEN
Irlande
Farmer - Former President of the ICMSA (Family Farm Organisation) - Former Board member, Irish Dairy Board (IDB)
The Hill Knocklong • IRL • Knocklong
Tel. +353 872449420
Fax +353 6253252
E-mail: allenfrank@eircom.net

Mrs Gunta ANČA
Latvia
Latvijas Cilvēku ar īpašām vajadzībām sadarbības organizācijas "Sustento" valdes priekšsēdētāja
Nīcgales ielā 26 • LV-1035 Rīgā
Tel. +371 7590437
Fax +371 7802546
E-mail: gunta.anca@sustento.lv

Mrs Lavinia ANDREI
Romania
Preşedinte, Fundaţia Terra Mileniul III
Bd. Mărăşeşti, nr. 86, sector 4 • RO-040256 Bucureşti
Tel. +40 213141227
Fax +40 213010333
E-mail: lavinia@terraiii.ngo.ro

Mrs Grace ATTARD
Malta
Vici President tal-Kunsill Nazzjonali tan-Nisa (NCW Malta)
Membru tal-Kummissjoni Nazzjonali għall-Promozzjoni tal-Ugwaljanza (NCPE Malta)
Membru tal-Kumitat tas-Soċjetà Ċivili tal-Kunsill Ekonomiku u Soċjali Malti (MCESD)
45, Il-Kenn Triq Emanuel Attard • M-SVR1332 Santa Venera
Tel. +356 21488391
Fax +356 21246982
E-mail: grace.attard@gmail.com

Mr Vladimír BÁLEŠ
Slovakia
Rektor slovenskej technickej univerzity v Bratislave
Prezident slovenskej rektorskej konferencie
Vazovova 5 • SK-812 43 Bratislava
Tel. +421 252497196
Fax +421 257294333
E-mail: vladimir.bales@stuba.sk

Mr Gerd BILLEN
Deutschland
Vorstand - Verbraucherzentrale Bundesverband e.V.
Markgrafenstr. 66 • D-10969 Berlin
Tel. +49 3025800510
Fax +49 3025800518
E-mail: gerd.billen@vzbv.de

Mr Jean-Michel BLOCH-LAINÉ
France
Ancien inspecteur général des finances, président d'honneur et administrateur à l'Union nationale interfédérale des œuvres et organismes privés sanitaires et sociaux (UNIOPSS)
1, rue de la Bûcherie • F-75005 Paris
Tel. +33 143251100
Fax +33 143294600
E-mail: bl.catherine@wanadoo.fr

Mr Lucien BOUIS
France
Administrateur de l'Union nationale des associations familiales (UNAF)
1, allée Evangelista Torricelli, code 24 A 68, 8e étage • F-93110 Rosny-sous-Bois
Tel. +33 148549377
Fax +33 148549377
E-mail: lbouis@wanadoo.fr

Mr Gilbert BROS
France
Vice-président de l'Assemblée permanente des chambres d'agriculture (APCA) et président de la Chambre d'agriculture de Haute-Loire
9, avenue Georges V • F-75008 Paris
Tel. +33 607392886
E-mail: gilbertbros@orange.fr

Mr Miguel Ángel CABRA DE LUNA
España
Vocal de Relaciones Internacionales de la Confederación Empresarial Española de la Economía Social (CEPES)
Sebastián Herrera, 15 • E-28012 Madrid
Tel. +34 915068890
Fax +34 915393487
E-mail: mcabradeluna@fundaciononce.es

Mr Mario CAMPLI
Italie
Direttore generale- Coordinatore politiche europee - Lega nazionale delle cooperative e mutue (Legacoop)
Via G.A. Guattani, 9 • I-00161 Roma
Tel. +39 064403147
Fax +39 0644265301
E-mail: mario.campli@eesc.europa.eu

Mr Claudio CAPPELLINI
Italie
Rappresentante dell'artigianato italiano e delle PMI - Confederazione nazionale dell'artigianato e della piccola e media impresa (CNA)
Confederazione generale italiana dell'artigianato (Confartigianato)
Via G.A. Guattani, 13 • I-00161 Roma
Tel. +39 0644188208
Fax +39 0644249518
E-mail: cappellini@cna.it

Mr Martin CHREN
Slovakia
Riaditeľ Nadácie F. A. Hayeka v Bratislave
Jašíkova 6 • SK-821 03 Bratislava
Tel. +421 248291585
Fax +421 248291243
E-mail: martin.chren@hayek.sk
http://chren.blog.sme.sk

Mrs María del Carmen COBANO SUÁREZ
España
Responsable de asuntos internacionales de la Unión de Pequeños Agricultores y Ganaderos (UPA)
c/Agustín de Betancourt, 17-3°
E-28003 Madrid
Tel. +34 915541870
Fax +34 915542621
E-mail: upa@upa.es

Mr Roberto CONFALONIERI
Italie
Segretario generale della Confederazione dei dirigenti italiani e delle alte professionalità (Confedir) - Membro del Consiglio nazionale dell'economia e del lavoro (CNEL)
Viale Achille Grandi, 15 • I-20091 Bresso (MI)
Tel. +39 026102154
Fax +39 026102054
E-mail: robconfa@libero.it

Mrs Teresa COSTA MACEDO
Portugal
Presidente da Confederação National das Associações de Família (CNAF)
rua de S. Marçal 77/79 • P-1200-419 Lisboa
Tel. +351 213242163/60
Fax +351 213460554
E-mail: mtcostamacedo@hotmail.com

Mr Hervé COUPEAU
France
Trésorier de Jeunes agriculteurs et membre de la Chambre départementale et régionale d'agriculture et du Groupe monde rural
La Garenne • F-36250 Niherne
Tel. +33 254298914
Fax +33 254298914
E-mail: coupeauh@wanadoo.fr

Mr Tomasz CZAJKOWSKI
Poland
Doradca ds. międzynarodowych Parlamentu Studentów Rzeczypospolitej Polskiej (PSRP)
ul. Szucha 24/3 • PL-02-918 Warszawa
Tel. +48 602650072
Fax +48 226252030
E-mail: tczajkowski@psrp.org.pl

Mr John DILLON
Irlande
Former President of the Irish Farmers' Association (IFA)
Killuragh - Pallasgreen • IRL • Limerick
Tel. +353 868292562
E-mail: dillon.john1@gmail.com

Mrs Rose D'SA
United Kingdom
Consultant in EU, Commonwealth and International Law - Consultant in Legal Education/Distance Learning
64 Blossom Close, Langstone • UK
NP18 2LT Newport, Gwent
Tel. +44 1633413291
Fax +44 1633413291
E-mail: rose@glacier.eclipse.co.uk

Mrs Soscha EULENBURG
Deutschland
Mitglied des Präsidiums des Deutschen Roten Kreuzes (DRK)
Carstennstr. 58 • D-12205 Berlin
Tel. +49 3085404275
Fax +49 3085404450
E-mail: soscha@eulenburg.com

Mrs Christine FAES
Belgique/België
Directeur UNIZO Internationaal vzw, Unie van Zelfstandige ondernemers
Spastraat 8 • B-1000 Brussel
Tel. +32 25526049
E-mail: christine.faes@vlaanderen.be

Mrs Benedicte FEDERSPIEL
Danmark
Chefkonsulent, Jurist, Forbrugerrådet
Fiolstraede 17 • DK-1017 København
Tel. +45 77417719
Fax +45 77417742
E-mail: bf@fbr.dk

Mr Hubert GHIGONIS
France
Vice-président de la Confédération générale des petites et moyennes entreprises (CGPME) et président de l'association Transport routier et progrès (TRP)
42, avenue Montaigne • F-75008 Paris
Tel. +33 144436252
Fax +33 144436452
E-mail: hubert-marie.ghigonis@ces.fr

Mr Panagiotis GKOFAS
Grèce
Οικονομολόγος – Μέλος του Διοικητικού Συμβουλίου της Γενικής Συνομοσπονδίας Βιοτεχνών, Επαγγελματιών και Εμπόρων (ΓΣΒΕΕ)
Manoli Gagili 13 • GR-551 32 Thessaloníki
Tel. +30 2310447943
Fax +30 2310447950
E-mail: hamodrakas@hamodrakas.gr

Mr Angelo GRASSO
Italie
Dirigente d'azienda - Membro del consiglio presidenza nazionale della Confederazione cooperative italiane (Confcooperative) e Presidente di Confcooperative di Venezia, consigliere di Camera di commercio di Venezia
Via Sabotino 46 • I-00195 Roma
Tel. +39 0415316680
Fax +39 063728513
E-mail: vsgrasso@tin.it

Mr Gerfried GRUBER
Österreich
Leiter der Abteilung EU und internationale Beziehungen
Avenue de Cortenbergh 30
B-1040 Bruxelles - Brussel
Tel. +43 1534418580
Fax +43 1534418529
E-mail: g.gruber@lk-oe.be

Mr Roman HAKEN
République tchèque
Ředitel Centra pro komunitní práci (CpKP) Střední Morava – Člen Rady vlády pro nestátní neziskové organizace – Člen výboru pro strategický a regionální rozvoj a vnější vztahy Olomouckého kraje
Palackého 30 • CZ-750 02 Přerov
Tel. +420 777793711
Fax +420 581219555
E-mail: roman.haken@cpkp.cz

Mrs Renate HEINISCH
Deutschland
Apothekerin - Repräsentantin der Bundesarbeitsgemeinschaft der Senioren-Organisationen (BAGSO) - Mitglied im Europäischen Parlament (1994-1999)
Kurpfalzstr. 37 • D-97944 Boxberg
Tel. +49 79308851
Fax +49 79308852
E-mail: info@renate-heinisch.de

Mrs Mária HERCZOG
Hungary
Család, Gyermek, Ifjúság Kiemelten Közhasznú Szervezet Kutatója
Podmaniczky utca 75. I.1
H-1064 Budapest Pf. 417
Tel. +36 30971-0923
Fax +36 1225-3525
E-mail: herczog@mail.datanet.hu

Mr Bernardo HERNÁNDEZ BATALLER
España
Secretario General de la Asociación de Usuarios de la Comunicación (AUC)
c/ Cavanilles, 29-2-D • E-28007 Madrid
Tel. +34 915016773
Fax +34 915020701
E-mail: bernardo.
hernandezbataller@batalleradvocats.es

Mr Jean François HOFFELT
Belgique/België
Secrétaire général de la Fédération belge de l'économie sociale et coopérative (Febecoop), président du Conseil national belge de la coopération et président du service externe pour la prévention et la protection au travail Arista
Rue Haute 28 • B-1000 Bruxelles
Tel. +32 25005300
Fax +32 25005397
E-mail: jf.hoffelt@skynet.be
www.febecoop.be

Mr Ludvík JÍROVEC
République tchèque
Ředitel SP Poběžovice a.s. - Předseda dozorčí rady Okresní agrární komory - Předseda dozorčí rady Okresní hospodářské komory - Člen specializované skupiny obiloviny, olejniny a proteiny při COPA-COGECA Brusel
Nadražní 350 • CZ-345 22 Poběžovice
Tel. +420 724 020 486
Fax +420 379 497 331
E-mail: ludvik@jirovec.com

Mr Tom JONES
United Kingdom
Legal Services Commissioner - Vice-President of the Wales Council for Voluntary Action (WCVA) - farmer
Plas Coch - Dolanog - Nr Welshpool • UK
SY21 OLA Powys, Wales
Tel. +44 1938810553
Fax +44 1938810005
E-mail: thjones@btconnect.com

Mr Meelis JOOST
Estonia
Eesti Puuetega Inimeste Koja (EPI Koda) välissuhete spetsialist
Ilmatari 9 • EE-51006 Tartu
Tel. +372 50 14164
Fax +372 6616628
E-mail: melis@hot.ee

Mr Seppo KALLIO
Suomi/Finland
Johtaja, kansainväliset asiat, Maa- ja metsätaloustuottajain Keskusliitto (MTK)
Simonkatu 6, P.O. Box 510 • FI-00101 Helsinki
Tel. +358 204132380 (direct)
Fax +358 204132408
E-mail: Seppo.Kallio@mtk.fi

Mr Krzysztof KAMIENIECKI
Poland
Wiceprezes Instytutu na rzecz Ekorozwoju (InE)
ul. Nabielaka 15/1 • PL-00-743 Warszawa
Tel. +48 22 8510403
Fax +48 228510400
E-mail: krzysztof.kamieniecki@eesc.europa.eu

Mrs Mette KINDBERG
Danmark
Næstformand - HK Danmark
Weidekanpsgade 8 - P. O. Box 470 • DK-0900 Copenhagen C
Tel. +45 33304857
Fax +45 33304828
E-mail: 44mki@hk.dk

Mr Charalambos KOLOKOTRONIS
Cyprus
Διευθυντής ELPASO PROPERTY & CONSULTANCIES L.T.D. Σύμβουλος – Μέλος του Διοικητικού Συμβουλίου του Συνδέσμου Προστασίας Καταναλωτών
Denousis 9 • CY-2023 Strovolos
Tel. +357 22424598
Fax +357 22424598
E-mail: charalamboskolokotronis@yahoo.gr

Mr Kostakis KONSTANTINIDIS
Cyprus
Γενικός Γραμματέας της Ένωσης Κυπρίων Αγροτών (EKA)
Androcleous 4 - P.O. Box 21409
CY-1508 Nicosia
Tel. +357 22755678
Fax +357 22768176
E-mail: eka.agroton@cytanet.com.cy

Mrs Ingrid KÖSSLER
Sverige
Ordförande, Europa Donna, Bröstcancerföreningarnas Riksorganisation (BRO)
Slottsberget 12 • S-41757 Göteborg
Tel. +46 854640532
+46 31224644
E-mail: ingrid.kossler@telia.com
www.bro.org.se

Mr Zbigniew KOTOWSKI
Poland
Doradca ds. stosunków międzynarodowych Niezależnego Samorządnego Związku Zawodowego Rolników Indywidualnych (NSZZRI) Solidarność
ul. J. Conrada 18 m. 86 • PL-01-922 Warszawa
Tel. +48 602232170
E-mail: z.kotowski@imbigs.org.pl

Mr Armands KRAUZE
Latvia
Lauksaimnieku organizāciju sadarbības padomes (LOSP) valdes priekšsēdētājs
Latvijas Biškopības biedrības (LBB) valdes priekšsēdētājs
Republikas laukums 2-320 • LV-1981 Rīga
Tel. +371 29591933
Fax +371 67027243
E-mail: krauze@strops.lv
www.losp.lv

Mr Nikolaos LIOLIOS
Grèce
Μέλος της Πανελλήνιας Συνομοσπονδίας Ενώσεων Γεωργικών Συνεταιρισμών (ΠΑΣΕΓΕΣ) – Αντιπρόεδρος της Οικονομικής και Κοινωνικής Επιτροπής της Ελλάδος
Amvrosiou Frantzi 9 • GR-117 43 Athènes
Tel. +30 210 9249510
Fax +30 210 9249515
E-mail: vpresidentC@oke-esc.eu

Mr Eugen LUCAN
Romania
Preşedinte, Asociaţia Angel
Str. Spătaru Preda, nr. 19, bloc 19, sc. 3, ap. 45, sector 5 • RO-050186 Bucureşti
Tel. +40 214238784
Fax +40 214238784
E-mail: eugensucces@yahoo.com

Mr Poul LÜNEBORG
Danmark
Konsulent, cand.jur.
Kaalundsvej 6A • DK-3520 Farum
Tel. +45 44757403
Fax +45 44950472
E-mail: poul.luneborg@mail.dk

Mrs Reine Claude MADER-SAUSSAYE
France
Présidente de l'association Consommation, logement et cadre de vie (CLCV)
17, rue Monsieur • F-75007 Paris
Tel. +33 156543224
Fax +33 143207202
E-mail: mader@clcv.org

Mrs Marzena MENDZA-DROZD
Poland
Członek Zarządu Stowarzyszenia na Rzecz Forum Inicjatyw Pozarządowych (FIP)
ul. Szpitalna 5/5 • PL-00-031 Warszawa
Tel. +48 22828 9128
Fax +48 22 828 9129
E-mail: marzena@fip.ngo.pl

Mr Arno METZLER
Deutschland
Rechtsanwalt, Hauptgeschaftsführer im Bundesverband der Freien Berufe (BFB) und Leiter des Brüsseler Büros
Reinhardtstr. 34 • D-10117 Berlin
Tel. +49 3028444421
Fax +49 3028444440
E-mail: arno.metzler@freie-berufe.de

Mrs Jane MORRICE
United Kingdom
Communications Consultant - Director, Photographic and Media Production Company, former member Northern Ireland Assembly and Deputy Speaker, former Head EC Office Northern Ireland, former BBC correspondent
Ballyholme Esplanade 18 - Co. down • UK
BT 205 LZ Bangor
Tel. +44 02891461160
E-mail: wavelength@btinternet.com

Mr Pedro NARRO
España
Director de Asuntos Europeos (ASAJA)
C/Agustín de Bethencourt 17, 2ª planta
E-28003 Madrid
Tel. +34 915336764
Fax +32 27368090
E-mail: pedro.narro@asaja.com

Mr Radu NICOSEVICI
Romania
Preşedinte, Academia de Advocacy
Bd. Republicii, nr. 9 • RO-300159 Timişoara
Tel. +40 256403840
Fax +40 256403841
E-mail:
radu@advocacy.ro
www.advocacy.ro

Mr Leif Erland NIELSEN
Danmark
Seniorkonsulent i Landbrugsrådet
Axeltorv 3 • DK-1609 København V
Tel. +45 33394511
Fax +45 33394140
E-mail: Len@Landbrug.dk

Mr Jaroslav NĚMEC
République tchèque
Ředitel Arcidiecézní charity Praha
Londýnská 44 • CZ-120 00 Praha 2
Tel. +420 603245959
Fax +420 222522352
E-mail: j.nemec@atlas.cz

Mr Martin NOSE
Slovenia
Bivši direktor Zadružne zveze Slovenije (ZZS)
Miklošičeva 4 • SLO-1000 Ljubljana
Tel. +386 41699774
Fax +386 12441370
E-mail: noski@siol.net

Mr Kaul NURM
Estonia
Eestimaa Talupidajate Keskliidu (ETKL) peadirektor
Teaduse 1 • EE-75501 Saku
Tel. +372 6041783
Fax +372 6041783
E-mail: kaul.nurm@gmail.com

Mr Jan OLSSON
Sverige
Senior rådgivare, Kooperativa Institutet (KOOPI), vice ordförande, Föreningen för kooperativ utveckling (FKU)
Körsbärsvägen 6 • S-11423 Stockholm
Tel. +46 86926078
Fax +46 86428106
E-mail: jea.olsson@telia.com

Mrs Maureen O'NEILL
United Kingdom
Associate Mowat Research Board
Member, Scottish Social Services Council
Development Director, Faith in Older People
Consultant in Charity Governance (NHS QIS)
40/5 Corstorphine Road • UK
EH12 6HS Edinburgh
Tel. +44 1313468609
E-mail: maureenponeill@yahoo.co.uk

Mr Frederic Adrian OSBORN
United Kingdom
Chair, Stakeholder Forum for our Common Future
10 The Limes - Cowbridge • UK
CF71 7BJ Vale Of Glamorgan
Tel. +44 2083407560
E-mail: osborn_derek@yahoo.co.uk

Mr Thomas PALMGREN
Suomi/Finland
Kansainväliset asiat, Suomen Yrittäjät
Arkadiankatu 31 A • FI-00100 Helsinki
Tel. +358 9229221
Fax +358 922929980
E-mail: thomas.palmgren@yrittajat.fi

Mr Jean-Paul PANZANI
France
Président de la Fédération des mutuelles de France (FMF) et membre du bureau de la Fédération nationale de la mutualité française (FNMF)
3 et 5, rue de Vincennes • F-93108 Montreuil
Tel. +33 149885218
Fax +33 149889370
E-mail: jp.panzani@wanadoo.fr

Mr Krzysztof PATER
Poland
Były wiceprzewodniczący Związku Harcerstwa Polskiego (ZHP), aktualnie wiceprzewodniczący Rady Chorągwi Stołecznej
ul. Marii Konopnickiej 6 • PL-00-491 Warszawa
Tel. +48 602212201
Fax +48 223390606
E-mail: kpater@gazeta.pl

Mr Jorge PEGADO LIZ
Portugal
Advogado
Av. da Liberdade 249 1° • P-1250-143 Lisboa
E-mail: jplizadv@hotmail.com

Mr Carlos Alberto PEREIRA MARTINS
Portugal
Presidente do Conselho Directivo do Conselho Nacional das Ordens Profissionais (CNOP)
Rua Maestro Frederico Freitas, 13, 7° E (ou a/c Belacafé) • P-1500-399 Lisboa
Tel. +351 217783119
E-mail: cpmartins@netcabo.pt

Mrs Inger PERSSON
Sverige
Ordförande, Sveriges Konsumentråd (SK)
Sveavägen 90 • S-10232 Stockholm
Tel. +46 86744300
Fax +46 86744329
E-mail: inger.persson@sverigeskonsumenter.se

Mr Heinz PETER
Österreich
Direktor der Arbeiterkammer Vorarlberg
Fridolinsgasse 2 • A-6830 Rankweil
Tel. +43 55223061212
Fax +43 55223061201
E-mail: heinz.peter@ak-vorarlberg.at

Mrs Evelyne PICHENOT
France
Membre du Conseil économique et social et environnemental (CESE) français et présidente de sa délégation pour l'Union européenne
9, place d'Iéna • F-75775 Paris Cedex 16
Tel. +33 144436038
Fax +33 144436042
E-mail: epichenot@ces.fr

Mr Cristian PÎRVULESCU
Romania
Preşedinte, Asociaţia Pro Democraţia
Decan, Facultatea de Ştiinţe Politice, Şcoala Naţională de Studii Politice şi Administrative (SNSPA)
B-dul Mareşal Al. Averescu nr. 17, (Complex social "Sf. Ecaterina") Pavilion F, et. 1, sector 1
RO-011454 Bucarest
Tel. +40 212228245
Fax +40 212228254
E-mail: crpirvulescu@yahoo.fr
www.apd.ro

Mr Primož ŠPORAR
Slovenia
Direktor Pravno-informacijskega centra nevladnih organizacij (PIC)
Povšetova 37 • SLO-1000 Ljubljana
Tel. +386 15211888
Fax +386 15401913
E-mail: primoz.sporar@pic.si
www.pic.si

Mrs Pirkko RAUNEMAA
Suomi/Finland
Kotitalous- ja kuluttajaneuvottelukunta/ KuluttajatKonsumenterna ry, hallituksen jäsen
Rannikontie 5 • FI-02780 Espoo
Tel. +358 405916231
Fax +358 405971038
E-mail: pirkko.raunemaa@pp.inet.fi

Mr Paul RECKINGER
Luxembourg
Président de la Chambre des métiers du Grand-Duché de Luxembourg
BP 1604 • L-1016 Luxembourg
Tel. +352 426767-201
Fax +352 426787
E-mail: paul.reckinger@reckinger-alfred.lu

Mr Jacques REIGNAULT
France
Vice-président délégué et président de la commission des affaires européennes et internationales de l'Union nationale des professions libérales (UNAPL)
53-57, avenue de la Division-Leclerc
F-92160 Antony
Tel. +33 142379948
Fax +33 140961024
E-mail: jacques.reignault@wanadoo.fr

Mr Lutz RIBBE
Deutschland
Direktor bei der Stiftung Europäisches Naturerbe (Euronatur)
Grabenstr. 23 • D-53359 Rheinbach
Tel. +49 22262045
Fax +49 222617100
E-mail: lutz.ribbe@euronatur.org

Mr Corrado ROSSITTO
Italie
Presidente della Confederazione italiana di unione delle professioni intellettuali (CIU) - Membro del Consiglio nazionale dell'economia e del lavoro (CNEL) - Dottore commercialista - giornalista e direttore responsabile della rivista "Professioni intellet
Via Antonio Gramsci, 34 - Int.10 • I-00197 Roma
Tel. +39 063200427
Fax +39 063225558
E-mail: c.rossitto@ciuonline.it
www.ciuonline.it

Mr Zenonas Rokus RUDZIKAS
Lithuania
Lietuvos mokslų akademijos (LMA) prezidentas, Vilniaus universiteto teorinės fizikos ir astronomijos instituto skyriaus vadovas
Gedimino pr. 3 • LT-01103 Vilnius
Tel. +370 52613651
Fax +370 52618464
E-mail: zenonas.rudzikas@eesc.europa.eu

Mr Javier SÁNCHEZ ANSÓ
España
Responsable de Relaciones Internationales, Estructuras Agrarias y Desarrollo Rural de la Comisión Ejecutiva de la Coordinadora de Organizaciones de Agricultores y Ganaderos (COAG)
C/Augustín de Bethencourt 17 5°
E-28003 Madrid
Tel. +34 91534 63 91
Fax +34 91534 65 37
E-mail: coagmadrid@coag.org

Mr Gabriel SARRÓ IPARRAGUIRRE
España
Director de la Organizacion de Productores Asociados de Grandes Atuneros Congeladores (OPAGAC)
c/Hontoria del Pinar 5 - 14°A • E-28033 Madrid
Tel. +34 913029458
Fax +34 915761222
E-mail: gabrielsarro@yahoo.es

Mr Hanns-Eberhard SCHLEYER
Deutschland
Generalsekretär des Zentralverbandes des Deutschen Handwerks (ZDH)
Mohrenstr. 20/21 • D-10117 Berlin
Tel. +49 3020619101
Fax +49 3020619104
E-mail: ducaud@zdh.de
www.zdh.de

Mr Władysław SERAFIN
Poland
Prezes Krajowego Związku Rolników, Kółek i Organizacji Rolniczych (KZRKiOR), wiceprezes Komitetu Zawodowych Organizacji Rolniczych przy UE (COPA)
al. Szucha 16 • PL-00-582 Warszawa
Tel. +48 228277555
Fax +48 228273001
E-mail: serafin@kolkarolnicze.eu

Mr Sukhdev SHARMA
United Kingdom
Chairman Southwest Yorkshire Mental Health NHS Trust
Salterhebble • UK • HX3 OPW Halifax, West Yorkshire
Tel. +44 1422222595
Fax +44 1422222420
E-mail: sukhdev.sharma@cht.nhs.uk

Mr Ionuţ SIBIAN
Romania
Director Executiv - Fundaţia pentru Dezvoltarea Societăţii Civile (FDSC)
Preşedinte - Federaţia Organizaţiilor Neguvernamentale pentru Dezvoltare şi Ajutor Umanitar (FOND)
Membru Team Europe
Fundaţia pentru Dezvoltarea Societăţii Civile - Splaiul Independenţei, nr. 2K, scara 1, etaj 4, sector 3 • RO-003099 Bucureşti
Tel. +40 213100177
Fax +40 213100180
E-mail: ionut.sibian@fdsc.ro
www.fdsc.ro

Mrs Anne-Marie SIGMUND
Österreich
Europabeauftragte des Bundeskomitees Freie Berufe Österreichs
Maria-Theresien-Str. 5/14 • A-1090 Wien
Tel. +43 15332286
Fax +43 1533228615
E-mail: sigmund@freie-berufe.at

Mr Francisco SILVA
Portugal
Secretário Geral da Confederação Nacional das Cooperativas Agrícolas e do Crédito Agrícola de Portugal (Confagri)
Rua Maria Andrade, 13 • P-1199-013 Lisboa
Tel. +351 218118015
Fax +351 218118008
E-mail: confagri@confagri.pt

Mr Algirdas ŠIUPŠINSKAS
Lithuania
Lietuvos vartotojų asociacijos (LVA) tarybos narys
Taikos 2-20 • LT-05255 Vilnius
Tel. +370 52422347
Fax +370 52619065
E-mail: algirdas.siupsinskas@eesc.europa.eu

Mr Michael SMYTH
United Kingdom
Economist - University of Ulster , Belfast
Economic Adviser to the Northern Ireland Assembly
Clanbrassil Terrace 3 • UK • BT1 80AP
Holywood - County Down - Northern Ireland
Tel. +44 2890423587
Fax +44 2890366847
E-mail: mf.smyth@ulster.ac.uk

Mrs Donka SOKOLOVA
Bulgaria
Заместник-председател на Демократичния съюз на жените в България, председател на управителния съвет на Българската асоциация на туристическите агенции (БАТА), генерален директор на "ДМ ТРАВЕЛ" ООДul. Laveleye № 15 • BG-1000 Sofia
Tel. +359 29884200
Fax +359 29814196
E-mail: www.batabg.org
sokolovadmtravel@cablebg.net

Mr Yves SOMVILLE
Belgique/België
Directeur du service d'études de la Fédération wallonne de l'agriculture (FWA)
Chaussée de Namur 47 • B-5030 Gembloux
Tel. +32 81600060
Fax +32 81600446
E-mail: fwa@fwa.be
yves.somville@fwa.be

Mr Stylianos STAIKOS
Grèce
Δικηγόρος – Μέλος του Εθνικού Συμβουλίου Καταναλωτών (ΕΣΚ)
Mavromateon 31 • GR-10 434 Athens
Tel. +30 210 8250400
Fax +30 210 8250407
E-mail: staikos-lawyer@ath.forthnet.gr

Mr Juraj STERN
Slovakia
Predseda správnej rady Slovenskej spoločnosti pre zahraničnú politiku (SFPA)
Dolnozemská cesta 1 C • SK-852 35 Bratislava 5
Tel. +421 254433151
Fax +421 254433161
E-mail: stern@sfpa.sk

Mr Frank STÖHR
Deutschland
Stellvertretender Bundesvorsitzender des dbb beamtenbund und tarifunion
Friedrichstr. 169-170 • D-10117 Berlin
Tel. +49 3040814300
Fax +49 3040814399
E-mail: stoehrfr@dbb.de

Mrs Elżbieta SZADZIŃSKA
Poland
Pełnomocnik do spraw międzynarodowych przy Federacji Konsumentów (FK)
al. Stanów Zjednoczonych 53 • PL-04-028 Warszawa
Tel. +48 228272893
Fax +48 228279059
E-mail: biuro@federacja-konsumentow.org.pl

Mrs Ludmilla TODOROVA
Bulgaria
Председател на Съвета на българските аграрни организации (СБАО)ul. Vladayska № 29, et. 1, office 1 • BG-1606 Sofia
Tel. +359 29521702
Fax +359 29521702
E-mail: ltodorova@mail.orbitel.bg

Mr János TÓTH
Hungary
Ipari Parkok Egyesülete (IPE) elnök
Hercegprímás u. 21 • H-1051 Budapest
Tel. +36 13022925
Fax +36 13022933
E-mail: bfjipest@mail.datanet.hu

Mr Pavel TRANTINA
République tchèque
Zástupce České rady dětí a mládeže (ČRDM)
Senovážné náměstí 977/24 • CZ-116 47 Praha 1
Tel. +420 602227184
Fax +420 234621541
E-mail: pavel.trantina@eesc.europa.eu

Mr Carlos TRÍAS PINTO
España
Director en la Asociación General de Consumidores (ASGECO)
Director en la Unión de Cooperativas de Consumidores y Usuarios de España (UNCCUE)
C/ Tutor 18, 3° Ex. Iz. • E-28008 Madrid
Tel. +34 675736770
Fax +34 914053997
E-mail: carlos.trias@asgeco.org

Mr Leendert Frederik van MUISWINKEL
Nederland
Oud-hoogleraar Algemene Economie, Voorzitter Raad van toezicht Oosterschelde Ziekenhuis
Donkereweg 70 - Schuddebeurs • NL 4317 NM Noordgouwe
Tel. +31 111411244
E-mail: lfmuis@zeelandnet.nl

Mr Benne van POPTA
Nederland
Directeur voor Europese Zaken en Economisch Onderzoek, MKB Nederland (Midden- en Kleinbedrijf Nederland)
Brassersplein 1 • NL • 2612 CT Delft
Tel. +31 152191235
Fax +31 152191240
E-mail: b.vanpopta@mkb.nl

Mrs Jillian van TURNHOUT
Irlande
Chief Executive, Children's Rights Alliance - Former President, National Youth Council of Ireland (NYCI)
4 Upper Mount St • IRL • Dublin 2
Tel. +353 16629400
Fax +353 16629355
E-mail: jillian@childrensrights.ie
www.childrensrights.ie

Mr Dirk WESTENDORP
Nederland
Voormalig algemeen directeur Consumentenbond (CB)
Jacqueline de Grezlaan 24 • NL • 4835 GT Breda
Tel. +31 765650717
Fax +31 765602463
E-mail: nl@dick.westendorp.nl

Mrs Josiane WILLEMS
Luxembourg
Directeur de la Centrale paysanne luxembourgeoise (CPL)
Rue de la Gare • L-7535 Mersch
Tel. +352 326464-480
Fax +352 326464-481
E-mail: jwillems@cepal.lu

Mr Gerd WOLF
Deutschland
Beauftragter der Helmholtz-Gemeinschaft Deutscher Forschungszentren (HGF)
Otto-Hahn-Str. 1 • D-52428 Jülich
Tel. +49 246154367
Fax +49 2461347283
E-mail: g.h.wolf@fz-juelich.de

Mr Plamen ZAHARIEV
Bulgaria
Председател на Националния център за социална рехабилитация (НЦСР)ul. Hristo Belchev № 8 • BG-1000 Sofia
Tel. +359 29803215
Fax +359 29803492
E-mail: plamennet@yahoo.com

Mr Christos ZEREFOS
Grèce
Καθηγητής – Πρόεδρος του Εθνικού Αστεροσκοπείου Αθηνών (ΕΑΑ)
Lofos Nimphon • GR-11 810 Athina
Tel. +30 210 3490102
Fax +30 210 3490120
E-mail: zerefos@geol.uoa.gr

No group affiliation

Mr Francesco CAVALLARO
Italie
Segretario generale della Confederazione italiana sindacati autonomi lavoratori (CISAL)
Viale Giulio Cesare, 21 • I-00192 Roma
Tel. +39 063212524
Fax +39 063212521
E-mail: gina.bossio@cisal.org

SPECIALISED SECTIONS

Section for Economic and Monetary Union and Economic and Social Cohesion

Mr Krzysztof PATER
President

Mr Panagiotis GKOFAS
Vice-President

Mr Lars NYBERG
Vice-President

Mr János VÉRTES
Vice-President

Mr Frank ALLEN

Mrs Dorthe ANDERSEN

Mr Christian ARDHE

Mr Danukas ARLAUSKAS

Mr William A. ATTLEY

Mr Rafael BARBADILLO LÓPEZ

Mr Paulo BARROS VALE

Mr Nansen BEHAR

Mr Jean-Michel BLOCH-LAINÉ

Mrs Christine BLOWER

Mrs Ana BONTEA

Mrs Marjolijn BULK

Mr Umberto BURANI

Mr Brian CALLANAN

Mr Edwin CALLEJA

Mrs Marge CAREY

Mr Bryan CASSIDY

Mr Francesco CAVALLARO

Mr Carmelo CEDRONE

Mr Martin CHREN

Mrs María del Carmen COBANO SUÁREZ

Mr Peter COLDRICK

Mr Hervé COUPEAU

Mr Tomasz CZAJKOWSKI

Mr Petru Sorin DANDEA

Mr Bojidar DANEV

Mr Gérard DANTIN

Mr Georgios DASSIS

Mr Thomas DELAPINA

Mr Olivier DERRUINE

Mr John DILLON

Mr Plamen DIMITROV

Mrs Christine FAES

Mrs Susanna FLORIO

Mr Göke FRERICHS

Mr Vitālijs GAVRILOVS

Mr Pierre GENDRE

Mr Angelo GRASSO

Mr Wolfgang GREIF

Mr Gerfried GRUBER

Mr Guy HAAZE

Mr Filip HAMRO-DROTZ

Mr Peder Munch HANSEN

Mrs Mária HERCZOG

Mrs Irīna HOMKO

Mr Bojan HRIBAR

Mr Jeliazko HRISTOV

Mr Giuseppe Antonio Maria IULIANO

Mr Ludvík JÍROVEC

Mr Meelis JOOST

Mr Gerasimos KALLIGEROS

Mr József KAPUVÁRI

Mr Søren KARGAARD

Mr Adalbert KIENLE

Mrs Mette KINDBERG

Mr Dimitris KITTENIS

Mr Viesturs KOCIŅŠ

Mr Marek KOMOROWSKI

Mr Armands KRAUZE

Mr Martin KREKÁČ

Mr Marian KRZAKLEWSKI

Mr Algirdas Aleksandras KVEDARAVIČIUS

Mr Jochen LEHNHOFF

Mrs Margarita LÓPEZ ALMENDÁRIZ

Mrs Heidi LOUGHEED

Mr Andreas LOUROUTZIATIS

Mr Eugen LUCAN

Mrs Reine Claude MADER-SAUSSAYE

Mr Henri MALOSSE

Mr Claus MATECKI

Mr Vladimír MATOUŠEK

Mrs Judy McKNIGHT

Mr Leon E. MEIJER

Mrs Marzena MENDZA-DROZD

Mr Arno METZLER

Mr Vladimír MOJŠ

Mr André-Luc MOLINIER

Mr Peter MORGAN

Mr Gintaras MORKIS

Mr Radu NICOSEVICI

Mr Kaul NURM

Mr Jan OLSSON

Mr Ján ORAVEC

Mrs Helena ČORNEJOVÁ

Mr Krzysztof OSTROWSKI

Mrs Irini Ivoni PARI

Mr Luis Miguel PARIZA CASTAÑOS

Mr Michael PARNIS

Mr Miklós PÁSZTOR

Mrs Marja-Liisa PELTOLA

Mr Markus PENTTINEN

Mr Marius PETCU

Mr Aurel Laurenţiu PLOŞCEANU

Mrs Naile PROKEŠOVÁ

Mr Maurizio REALE

Mr Dušan REBOLJ

Mr Paul RECKINGER

Mr Jean-Claude REDING

Mr Wautier ROBYNS DE SCHNEIDAUER

Mrs Lena ROUSSENOVA

Mr Valerio SALVATORE

Mr Sergio Ernesto SANTILLÁN CABEZA

Mr José SARTORIUS ÁLVAREZ DE BOHORQUES

Mr Hanns-Eberhard SCHLEYER

Mrs Christa SCHWENG

Mr Władysław SERAFIN

Mr Patrick SEYLER

Mr Wiesław SIEWIERSKI

Mr Michael SMYTH

Mrs Donka SOKOLOVA

Mr Cveto STANTIČ

Mr Frank STÖHR

Mr Gundars STRAUTMANIS

Mr János TÓTH

Mr Carlos TRÍAS PINTO

Mr Joost van IERSEL

Mr Leendert Frederik van MUISWINKEL

Mr Tony VANDEPUTTE

Mr Ştefan VARFALVI

Mrs Mare VIIES

Mr Plamen ZAHARIEV

Mrs Marie ZVOLSKÁ

Section for the Single Market, Production and Consumption

Mr Bryan CASSIDY
President

Mr Umberto BURANI
Vice-President

Mrs Anna Maria DARMANIN
Vice-President

Mr Angelo GRASSO
Vice-President

Mr Andrzej ADAMCZYK

Mrs Milena ANGELOVA

Mr Danukas ARLAUSKAS

Mrs Grace ATTARD

Mr Paulo BARROS VALE

Mr Nansen BEHAR

Mr Gerd BILLEN

Mr Jean-Marie BIOT

Mr Sandy BOYLE

Mr Brendan BURNS

Mr Miguel Ángel CABRA DE LUNA

Mr Brian CALLANAN

Mr Edwin CALLEJA

Mr Mario CAMPLI

Mrs Liina CARR

Mr Manuel CAVALEIRO BRANDÃO

Mrs Lourdes CAVERO MESTRE

Mr Franco CHIRIACO

Mr Martin CHREN

Mrs Sinne CONAN

Mr Gérard DANTIN

Mr Olivier DERRUINE

Mr Dimitris DIMITRIADIS

Mr Bernd DITTMANN

Mr Tadeusz DORDA

Mrs Rose D'SA

Mr Ernst Erik EHNMARK

Mr Hans EKDAHL

Mr José María ESPUNY MOYANO

Mrs Soscha EULENBURG

Mrs Christine FAES

Mrs Benedicte FEDERSPIEL

Mr Marco FELISATI

Mrs Sylvia GAUCI

Mr Pierre GENDRE

Mr Peder Munch HANSEN

Mrs Renate HEINISCH

Mr Raymond HENCKS

Mr Bernardo HERNÁNDEZ BATALLER

Mr Jean François HOFFELT

Mr Bojan HRIBAR

Mr Bernard HUVELIN

Mr Edgardo Maria IOZIA

Mr Algirdas ŠIUPŠINSKAS

Mr Minel IVAŞCU

Mr Thomas JANSON

Mr Gerasimos KALLIGEROS

Mr Johannes KLEEMANN

Mr Jan KLIMEK

Mr Viesturs KOCIŅŠ

Mr Charalambos KOLOKOTRONIS

Mr Marek KOMOROWSKI

Mr Kostakis KONSTANTINIDIS

Mr Zbigniew KOTOWSKI

Mr Armands KRAUZE

Mr Jacek KRAWCZYK

Mr Pēteris KRĪGERS

Mrs Leila KURKI

Mr Algirdas Aleksandras KVEDARAVIČIUS

Mr Linas LASIAUSKAS

Mr Christoph LECHNER

Mr Jochen LEHNHOFF

Mr Georges LIAROKAPIS

Mr Andreas LOUROUTZIATIS

Mrs Reine Claude MADER-SAUSSAYE

Mr Vitas MAČIULIS

Mr Vladimír MATOUŠEK

Mr Jim McCUSKER

Mr Juan MENDOZA CASTRO

Mr Arno METZLER

Mr Vesselin MITOV

Mr André-Luc MOLINIER

Mr André MORDANT

Mr Peter MORGAN

Mr Jarosław MULEWICZ

Mr Wolter MULLER

Mr Tamás NAGY

Mr Radu NICOSEVICI

Mr Martin NOSE

Mr Ján ORAVEC

Mr Thomas PALMGREN

Mr Ángel PANERO FLÓREZ

Mr Andreas PAVLIKKAS

Mr Jorge PEGADO LIZ

Mrs Marja-Liisa PELTOLA

Mrs Inger PERSSON

Mr Heinz PETER

Mr Christos POLYZOGOPOULOS

Mr Konstantinos POUPAKIS

Mr Virgilio RANOCCHIARI

Mrs Pirkko RAUNEMAA

Mr Dušan REBOLJ

Mr Paul RECKINGER

Mrs Evelyn REGNER

Mr Jacques REIGNAULT

Mr Wautier ROBYNS DE SCHNEIDAUER

Mr Claudio ROTTI

Mrs Lena ROUSSENOVA

Mr Sabin RUSU

Mrs María Candelas SÁNCHEZ MIGUEL

Mr José SARTORIUS ÁLVAREZ DE BOHORQUES

Mr Robert SCHADECK

Mr Hanns-Eberhard SCHLEYER

Mr Victor Hugo SEQUEIRA

Mr Martin SIECKER

Mr Michael SMYTH

Mrs Donka SOKOLOVA

Mr Stylianos STAIKOS

Mr Cveto STANTIČ

Mr Juraj STERN

Mr Gundars STRAUTMANIS

Mrs Elżbieta SZADZIŃSKA

Mr Pavel TRANTINA

Mr Joost van IERSEL

Mr Benne van POPTA

Mr Ştefan VARFALVI

Mr János VÉRTES

Mr Ivan VOLEŠ

Mr Dirk WESTENDORP

Mr Hans-Joachim WILMS

Mr Gerd WOLF

Section for Transport, Energy, Infrastructure and the Information Society

Mr János TÓTH
President

Mr Edgardo Maria IOZIA
Vice-President

Mr Thomas MCDONOGH
Vice-President

Mr Gerd WOLF
Vice-President

Mr Frank ALLEN

Mrs Gunta ANČA

Mrs Lavinia ANDREI

Mr Maurizio ANGELO

Mrs Milena ANGELOVA

Mr Michalis ANTONIOU

Mr Vladimír BÁLEŠ

Mr Rafael BARBADILLO LÓPEZ

Mrs Laure BATUT

Mr Lucien BOUIS

Mrs Anna BREDIMA

Mr Stéphane BUFFETAUT

Mr Claudio CAPPELLINI

Mrs Liina CARR

Mrs Lourdes CAVERO MESTRE

Mr Peter COLDRICK

Mr Roberto CONFALONIERI

Mr Antal CSUPORT

Mr Brian CURTIS

Mr Bojidar DANEV

Mrs Anna Maria DARMANIN

Mr Francis DAVOUST

Mr Robert DE MÛELENAERE

Mr Thomas DELAPINA

Mr Bernd DITTMANN

Mrs Benedicte FEDERSPIEL

Mr Dumitru FORNEA

Mr Kenneth FRASER

Mr Hubert GHIGONIS

Mr Alexander GRAF VON SCHWERIN

Mr Guy HAAZE

Mr Lubomir HADJIYSKY

Mr Peder Munch HANSEN

Mr Raymond HENCKS

Mr Bernardo HERNÁNDEZ BATALLER

Mr Bernard HUVELIN

Mr Algirdas ŠIUPŠINSKAS

Mr Minel IVAŞCU

Mr Krzysztof KAMIENIECKI

Mr Søren KARGAARD

Mr Magnus KENDEL

Mrs Brenda KING

Mr Dimitris KITTENIS

Mr Johann KÖLTRINGER

Mr Peter KORN

Mrs Ingrid KÖSSLER

Mr Jacek KRAWCZYK

Mr Martin KREKÁČ

Mr Pēteris KRĪGERS

Mr Marian KRZAKLEWSKI

Mrs Daiva KVEDARAITĖ

Mr Floríval LANÇA

Mr Linas LASIAUSKAS

Mr Georges LIAROKAPIS

Mr Nikolaos LIOLIOS

Mrs Heidi LOUGHEED

Mr Poul LÜNEBORG

Mr Vitas MAČIULIS

Mr Andrzej MALINOWSKI

Mr Mihai MANOLIU

Mr Dimitar MANOLOV

Mr Jim McCUSKER

Mr Leon E. MEIJER

Mr Janne METSÄMÄKI

Mr Luís MIRA

Mr Vladimír MOJŠ

Mr André MORDANT

Mr Juan MORENO PRECIADO

Mr Gintaras MORKIS

Mrs Jane MORRICE

Mr Staffan NILSSON

Mr Lars NYBERG

Mrs Maria NYGREN

Mr Marius Eugen OPRAN

Mr Ján ORAVEC

Mr Frederic Adrian OSBORN

Mr Krzysztof OSTROWSKI

Mr Erhard OTT

Mr Thomas PALMGREN

Mr Miklós PÁSZTOR

Mr Jorge PEGADO LIZ

Mr Carlos Alberto PEREIRA MARTINS

Mr Volker PETERSEN

Mr Antonello PEZZINI

Mrs Renata POLVERINI

Mr Christos POLYZOGOPOULOS

Mrs Inga PREIDIENĖ

Mr Virgilio RANOCCHIARI

Mr Dušan REBOLJ

Mrs Evelyn REGNER

Mr Daniel RETUREAU

Mr Lutz RIBBE

Mr Corrado ROSSITTO

Mr Stanisław RÓŻYCKI

Mr Zenonas Rokus RUDZIKAS

Mr Jörg RUSCHE

Mr Sergio Ernesto SANTILLÁN CABEZA

Mr David SEARS

Mr Victor Hugo SEQUEIRA

Mr Patrick SEYLER

Mr Wiesław SIEWIERSKI

Mr Jan SIMONS

Mrs Ulla SIRKEINEN

Mr Juraj STERN

Mr Dare STOJAN

Mr Gundars STRAUTMANIS

Mr Josef SUCHEL

Mrs Monica TAYLOR

Mr Péter VADÁSZ

Mrs Annie van WEZEL

Mr Tony VANDEPUTTE

Mr Wilfried WOLLER

Mr Josef ZBOŘIL

Mr Christos ZEREFOS

Mr Patrik ZOLTVÁNY

Section for Employment, Social Affairs and Citizenship

Mrs Leila KURKI
President

Mrs Vladimíra DRBALOVÁ
Vice-President

Mr Meelis JOOST
Vice-President

Mr Xavier VERBOVEN
Vice-President

Mr Richard ADAMS

Mr Pedro ALMEIDA FREIRE

Mrs Gunta ANČA

Mrs Dorthe ANDERSEN

Mr Maurizio ANGELO

Mr Michalis ANTONIOU

Mr Christian ARDHE

Mrs Grace ATTARD

Mr Miklós BARABÁS

Mrs Katarzyna BARTKIEWICZ

Mrs Laure BATUT

Mr Jean-Michel BLOCH-LAINÉ

Mrs Christine BLOWER

Mrs Ana BONTEA

Mrs Marjolijn BULK

Mr Miguel Ángel CABRA DE LUNA

Mr Edwin CALLEJA

Mrs Marge CAREY

Mr Manuel CAVALEIRO BRANDÃO

Mr Francesco CAVALLARO

Mr Peter CLEVER

Mr Alfredo CORREIA

Mrs Teresa COSTA MACEDO

Mr Nicholas CROOK

Mrs Ágnes CSER

Mr Tomasz CZAJKOWSKI

Mr Petru Sorin DANDEA

Mr Georgios DASSIS

Mr Francis DAVOUST

Mr Robert DE MÛELENAERE

Mr Plamen DIMITROV

Mrs Soscha EULENBURG

Mrs Susanna FLORIO

Mrs Laura GONZÁLEZ DE TXABARRI ETXANIZ

Mr Wolfgang GREIF

Mr Filip HAMRO-DROTZ

Mrs Renate HEINISCH

Mrs Mall HELLAM

Mrs Mária HERCZOG

Mr Jean François HOFFELT

Mrs Irīna HOMKO

Mr Bojan HRIBAR

Mr Luca JAHIER

Mr Thomas JANSON

Mrs Maud JANSSON

Mr Tomasz JASIŃSKI

Mr Tom JONES

Mr Søren KARGAARD

Mr Magnus KENDEL

Mrs Sally Anne KINAHAN

Mrs Mette KINDBERG

Mrs Brenda KING

Mrs Waltraud KLASNIC

Mr Jan KLIMEK

Mrs Marie-Louise KNUPPERT

Mrs Erika KOLLER

Mr Charalambos KOLOKOTRONIS

Mrs Ingrid KÖSSLER

Mr Eugen ŠKULTÉTY

Mrs Daiva KVEDARAITĖ

Mr Linas LASIAUSKAS

Mrs An LE NOUAIL MARLIÈRE

Mrs Heidi LOUGHEED

Mr Eugen LUCAN

Mr Poul LÜNEBORG

Mr Dimitar MANOLOV

Mrs Judy McKNIGHT

Mrs Marzena MENDZA-DROZD

Mr Janne METSÄMÄKI

Mrs Jane MORRICE

Mr Wolter MULLER

Mr Jaroslav NĚMEC

Mrs Maria NYGREN

Mr Jan OLSSON

Mrs Maureen O'NEILL

Mrs Helena ČORNEJOVÁ

Mrs Béatrice OUIN

Mrs Eve PÄÄRENDSON

Mr Ángel PANERO FLÓREZ

Mr Jean-Paul PANZANI

Mr Spyridon PAPASPYROS

Mrs Irini Ivoni PARI

Mr Luis Miguel PARIZA CASTAÑOS

Mr Michael PARNIS

Mr Krzysztof PATER

Mr Andreas PAVLIKKAS

Mr Jonathan PEEL

Mr Marius PETCU

Mr Antonello PEZZINI

Mrs Evelyne PICHENOT

Mr Josly PIETTE

Mr Cristian PÎRVULESCU

Mr Primož ŠPORAR

Mrs Inga PREIDIENĖ

Mrs Nicole PRUD'HOMME

Mr Paul RECKINGER

Mr Jacques REIGNAULT

Mr José Isaías RODRÍGUEZ GARCÍA-CARO

Mrs Metka ROKSANDIĆ

Mr Corrado ROSSITTO

Mr Claudio ROTTI

Mr Manfred SCHALLMEYER

Mrs Christa SCHWENG

Mr David SEARS

Mrs Madi SHARMA

Mr Sukhdev SHARMA

Mr Ionuț SIBIAN

Mrs Anne-Marie SIGMUND

Mr Mário SOARES

Mr Frank STÖHR

Mr Dare STOJAN

Mrs Elżbieta SZADZIŃSKA

Mr Edmund SZYNAKA

Mrs Dana ŠTECHOVÁ

Mr Pavel TRANTINA

Mr Péter VADÁSZ

Mr Jan Willem VAN DEN BRAAK

Mr Benne van POPTA

Mrs Jillian van TURNHOUT

Mrs Mare VIIES

Mr Plamen ZAHARIEV

Mr Gustav ZÖHRER

Mr Patrik ZOLTVÁNY

Mr José María ZUFIAUR NARVAIZA

Mrs Marie ZVOLSKÁ

Section for Agriculture, Rural Development and the Environment

Mr Hans-Joachim WILMS
President

Mr Gilbert BROS
Vice-President

Mr Adalbert KIENLE
Vice-President

Mr Martin SIECKER
Vice-President

Mr Richard ADAMS

Mr Frank ALLEN

Mrs Lavinia ANDREI

Mr Michalis ANTONIOU

Mr William A. ATTLEY

Mrs Katarzyna BARTKIEWICZ

Mr Jean-Paul BASTIAN

Mr Gerd BILLEN

Mr Jean-Marie BIOT

Mr Stéphane BUFFETAUT

Mr Brendan BURNS

Mr Franco CHIRIACO

Mrs María del Carmen COBANO SUÁREZ

Mr Roberto CONFALONIERI

Mr Hervé COUPEAU

Mr Brian CURTIS

Mrs Anna Maria DARMANIN

Mr John DILLON

Mr Tadeusz DORDA

Mr Ernst Erik EHNMARK

Mr José María ESPUNY MOYANO

Mr Kenneth FRASER

Mrs Sylvia GAUCI

Mr Hubert GHIGONIS

Mr Gerfried GRUBER

Mr Lubomir HADJIYSKY

Mr Roman HAKEN

Mr Jeliazko HRISTOV

Mr Algirdas ŠIUPŠINSKAS

Mr Ludvík JÍROVEC

Mr Tom JONES

Mr Seppo KALLIO

Mr Krzysztof KAMIENIECKI

Mr József KAPUVÁRI

Mr Dimitris KITTENIS

Mr Johann KÖLTRINGER

Mr Kostakis KONSTANTINIDIS

Mr Zbigniew KOTOWSKI

Mr Armands KRAUZE

Mr Pēteris KRĪGERS

Mr Florival LANÇA

Mr Nikolaos LIOLIOS

Mr Philippe MANGIN

Mr Sandro MASCIA

Mr Jim McCUSKER

Mr Juan MENDOZA CASTRO

Mr Luís MIRA

Mr Tamás NAGY

Mr Pedro NARRO

Mr Leif Erland NIELSEN

Mr Staffan NILSSON

Mr Martin NOSE

Mr Kaul NURM

Mr Frederic Adrian OSBORN

Mr Markus PENTTINEN

Mr Volker PETERSEN

Mr Aurel Laurenţiu PLOŞCEANU

Mrs Renata POLVERINI

Mr Primož ŠPORAR

Mr Konstantinos POUPAKIS

Mrs Pirkko RAUNEMAA

Mr Maurizio REALE

Mr Daniel RETUREAU

Mr Lutz RIBBE

Mr Stanisław RÓŻYCKI

Mr Zenonas Rokus RUDZIKAS

Mr Jörg RUSCHE

Mr Sabin RUSU

Mr Valerio SALVATORE

Mr Javier SÁNCHEZ ANSÓ

Mrs María Candelas SÁNCHEZ MIGUEL

Mr Gabriel SARRÓ IPARRAGUIRRE

Mr Robert SCHADECK

Mr Władysław SERAFIN

Mr Francisco SILVA

Mrs Ulla SIRKEINEN

Mr Yves SOMVILLE

Mr Dare STOJAN

Mrs Monica TAYLOR

Mrs Ludmilla TODOROVA

Mr Leendert Frederik van MUISWINKEL

Mr Frank van OORSCHOT

Mrs Josiane WILLEMS

Mr Wilfried WOLLER

Mr Josef ZBOŘIL

Mr Christos ZEREFOS

Mr Gustav ZÖHRER

Section for External Relations

Mr Filip HAMRO-DROTZ
President

Mr Sandy BOYLE
Vice-President

Mrs Margarita LÓPEZ ALMENDÁRIZ
Vice-President

Mr Sukhdev SHARMA
Vice-President

Mr Andrzej ADAMCZYK

Mr Pedro ALMEIDA FREIRE

Mrs Gunta ANČA

Mrs Dorthe ANDERSEN

Mrs Grace ATTARD

Mr Vladimír BÁLEŠ

Mr Miklós BARABÁS

Mr Jean-Paul BASTIAN

Mr Lucien BOUIS

Mrs Anna BREDIMA

Mr Gilbert BROS

Mr Brian CALLANAN

Mr Mario CAMPLI

Mr Claudio CAPPELLINI

Mrs Liina CARR

Mr Carmelo CEDRONE

Mr Martin CHREN

Mr Peter CLEVER

Mrs Sinne CONAN

Mr Alfredo CORREIA

Mrs Teresa COSTA MACEDO

Mr Nicholas CROOK

Mrs Ágnes CSER

Mr Antal CSUPORT

Mr John DILLON

Mr Dimitris DIMITRIADIS

Mrs Vladimíra DRBALOVÁ

Mrs Rose D'SA

Mr Hans EKDAHL

Mrs Benedicte FEDERSPIEL

Mr Marco FELISATI

Mr Dumitru FORNEA

Mr Göke FRERICHS

Mrs Sylvia GAUCI

Mr Vitālijs GAVRILOVS

Mr Panagiotis GKOFAS

Mrs Laura GONZÁLEZ DE TXABARRI ETXANIZ

Mr Alexander GRAF VON SCHWERIN

Mr Roman HAKEN

Mrs Mall HELLAM

Mrs Irīna HOMKO

Mr Giuseppe Antonio Maria IULIANO

Mr Luca JAHIER

Mrs Maud JANSSON

Mr Tomasz JASIŃSKI

Mr Meelis JOOST

Mr Seppo KALLIO

Mrs Sally Anne KINAHAN

Mrs Mette KINDBERG

Mrs Waltraud KLASNIC

Mr Johannes KLEEMANN

Mrs Marie-Louise KNUPPERT

Mr Viesturs KOCIŅŠ

Mrs Erika KOLLER

Mr Charalambos KOLOKOTRONIS

Mr Kostakis KONSTANTINIDIS

Mr Peter KORN

Mr Martin KREKÁČ

Mrs An LE NOUAIL MARLIÈRE

Mr Christoph LECHNER

Mr Andreas LOUROUTZIATIS

Mr Andrzej MALINOWSKI

Mr Henri MALOSSE

Mr Philippe MANGIN

Mr Mihai MANOLIU

Mr Sandro MASCIA

Mr Thomas MCDONOGH

Mr Vesselin MITOV

Mr Juan MORENO PRECIADO

Mr Gintaras MORKIS

Mr Jarosław MULEWICZ

Mr Pedro NARRO

Mr Leif Erland NIELSEN

Mr Jaroslav NĚMEC

Mr Martin NOSE

Mr Kaul NURM

Mrs Maureen O'NEILL

Mr Marius Eugen OPRAN

Mrs Béatrice OUIN

Mrs Eve PÄÄRENDSON

Mr Spyridon PAPASPYROS

Mr Michael PARNIS

Mr Jonathan PEEL

Mrs Marja-Liisa PELTOLA

Mr Markus PENTTINEN

Mr Carlos Alberto PEREIRA MARTINS

Mrs Inger PERSSON

Mrs Evelyne PICHENOT

Mr Josly PIETTE

Mr Cristian PÎRVULESCU

Mr Primož ŠPORAR

Mrs Inga PREIDIENĖ

Mrs Naile PROKEŠOVÁ

Mrs Nicole PRUD'HOMME

Mrs Pirkko RAUNEMAA

Mr José Isaías RODRÍGUEZ GARCÍA-CARO

Mrs Metka ROKSANDIĆ

Mr Zenonas Rokus RUDZIKAS

Mr Javier SÁNCHEZ ANSÓ

Mr Gabriel SARRÓ IPARRAGUIRRE

Mr Robert SCHADECK

Mr Patrick SEYLER

Mrs Madi SHARMA

Mr Ionuț SIBIAN

Mrs Anne-Marie SIGMUND

Mr Francisco SILVA

Mr Jan SIMONS

Mr Mário SOARES

Mr Yves SOMVILLE

Mr Stylianos STAIKOS

Mr Cveto STANTIČ

Mr Juraj STERN

Mr Josef SUCHEL

Mr Edmund SZYNAKA

Mrs Dana ŠTECHOVÁ

Mrs Ludmilla TODOROVA

Mr Jan Willem VAN DEN BRAAK

Mr Frank van OORSCHOT

Mrs Jillian van TURNHOUT

Mrs Annie van WEZEL

Mr Xavier VERBOVEN

Mr Ivan VOLEŠ

Mr Dirk WESTENDORP

Mr Patrik ZOLTVÁNY

Mr José María ZUFIAUR NARVAIZA

Consultative Commission on Industrial Change

Mr Joost van IERSEL
President

Mr Enrico GIBELLIERI
Vice-President
Italie
Esperto Siderurgia Ricercatore
via Benedetto Croce, 25 • I-01030 Vasanello
Tel. +39 0761409906
Fax +39 0761409906
E-mail: gibbs@tin.it

Mr Rumen ATANASOV
Bulgaria
Orgalime (engineering)
Kv. G. Delchev Bl. 4E • BG-1404 Sofia
Tel. +359 29633532
Fax +359 29630727
E-mail: roumen@itp.bg

Mr Stilian BALASOPULOV
Bulgaria
President of the National Union of Workers' Producers Co-operatives
Dondukov blvd. 11 • BG-1000 Sofia
Tel. +359 29805945
Fax +359 29870320
E-mail: sbalasopulov@uniontpk.com
www.uniontpk.com

Mr Patrick BAUDOUIN
France
FEM (aerospace)
17 avenue d'Issoudun • F-18020 Bourges
E-mail: patrick.baudouin@mbda-systems.com

Mr Jerzy BIELINSKI
Poland
Pro-rector for Devlopment and Financial Matters - Uniwersitet Gdanski
Ul. Bazynskiego 1a/321 • PL-80-952 Gdansk
Tel. +48 585529018
Fax +48 585522212
E-mail: rekdsrf@univ.gda.pl

Mr Peter BOOTH
United Kingdom
National Secretary - Transport & General Workers' Union - Fédération syndicale européenne (FSE-THC)
Call Lane 55 • UK • LS1 7BW Leeds
Tel. +44 1132364834
Fax +44 1132364835
E-mail: pjrbooth@btinternet.com

Mr David BREWER
United Kingdom
Director-General — COAL PRO — Confederation of UK Coal Producers
Thornes Office Park Denby Dale Road • UK • WF2 7AN Wakefield
Tel. +44 1924200802
Fax +44 1924200796
E-mail: admin@coalpro.co.uk

Mr Enrique CALVET CHAMBON
España
Chairman
Bravo Murillo 28 - 4e • E-28015 Madrid
Tel. +34 660327164
Fax +34 917293647
E-mail: ecalvetch@hotmail.com

Mr Tomasz CHRUSZCZOW
Poland
8 Mariensztat Str. • PL-00-302 Warszawa
Tel. +48 225389120
Fax +48 225389141
E-mail: tomasz.chruszczow@eesc.europa.eu

Mr Pavel ČINČERA
République tchèque
Zitavského 559 • CZ-156 00 Praha 5
Tél+420 233381546
Fax+420 233382252
E-mail: pavel.cincera@ecn.cz

Mrs Nina DHEJNE
Sverige
Jur.kand
Jungfrugatan 5 • S-11444 Stockholm
Tel. +46 86605694
Fax +46 8328600
E-mail: nina@dhejne.eu

Mr Tadeusz DONOCIK
Poland
Prezes Regionalnej Izby Gospodarczej w Katowicach - Wiceprezes Krajowej Izby Gospodarczej (KIG)
Generak Jankego 104 • PL-40-613 Katowice
Tel. +48 601180080
Fax +48 322990001
E-mail: t.donocik@onet.eu

Mrs Renata EISENVORTOVA
République tchèque
V. Rezace 315 • CZ-434 67 Most
Tél+420 476203163
Fax +420 476203727
E-mail: r.eisenvortova@czechcoal.cz

Mr Victor FERNÁNDEZ VÁZQUEZ
España
Avenide de América, 25-2e • E-28002 Madrid
Tel. +34 915897450
Fax +34 915897272
E-mail: sgeneral@fia.ugt.org

Mr Jerzy GARCZYNSKI
Poland
Ul. Kielecka Str.7 • PL-81-303 Gdynia
Tel. +48 586209501
Fax +48 586216923
E-mail: piot.gdynia@textiles.pl

Mr Bernard GAY
France
Directeur général (e.r.) de la Chambre régionale de commerce et d'industrie Nord-Pas-de-Calais
32, rue Robert Schuman • F-59139 Wattignies
Tel. +33 320960956
E-mail: bernardgay@numericable.fr

Mr Manfred GLAHE
Deutschland
Marie-Elisabeth Lüders Strasse 12 • D-97422 Schweinfurt
Tel. +49 9721476850
Fax +49 9721476851

Mr Jacques GLORIEUX
Belgique/België
Directeur
Euriscoal - Avenue des Aubépines 20B • B-1180 Bruxelles
Fax +32 23759768
E-mail: jacques.glorieux@skynet.be

Mr Jean-Luc GUIEZE
France
Chef du Département Europe
Euriscoal (Unité française de l'électricité - UFE) - 9, avenue de Friedland • F-75008 Paris
Tel. +33 147096641
E-mail: jeanlucguieze@yahoo.fr

Mrs Monika HRUŠECKÁ
Slovakia
Vedúca medzinárodného odboru OZ KOVO
Miletičova 24 • SK-815 70 Bratislava
Tel. +421 255565383
Fax +421 255565387
E-mail: hrusecka@ozkovo.sk

Mr Hans-Jürgen KERKHOFF
Deutschland
Hauptgeschäftsführer
Wirtschaftsvereinigung Stahl Sohnstrasse 65 • D-40237 Düsseldorf
Tel. +49 2116707110
Fax +49 2116707455
E-mail: hans-juergen.kerkhoff@stahl-zentrum.de

Mr Nicola KONSTANTINOU
Grèce
Secrétaire d'UNI-Europa Graphical
Avenue Sainte-Alix 57 • B-1150 Bruxelles —
Tel. +32 27325675
E-mail: nicola.konstantinou@union-network.org

Mr Jiří KUBÍČEK
République tchèque
Nám W. Churchilla 2 • CZ-113 59 Praha 3
Tel. +420 234463022
Fax +420 222715729
E-mail: JKmracek@seznam.cz

Mr Vladimir KVETAN
Slovakia
Slovak Academy of Science - Usse Sav
Sancova 56 • SK-811 05 Bratislava
Tel. +421 252497053-141
Fax +421 252495106
E-mail: vladimir.kvetan@savba.sk

Mr Göran LAGERHOLM
Sverige
CEPI (papier)
Alvägen 35 • S-19133 Sollentuna
Fax +46 8963492
E-mail: goran@mypost.se

Mr José Custódio LEIRIÃO
Portugal
Company Manager - Gestor de Empresa
Urbanização Horta do Maia, Lote 33 • P-2050-269 Azambuja
Tel. +351 917106192
Fax +351 263418310
E-mail: jleiriao@mail.telepac.pt

Mr Jörg LENNARDT
Deutschland
Geschäftsführer der ExperConsult-Gruppe und Vizepräsident des Bundesverband Deutscher Unternehmensberater BDU e.V
Martin-Schmeisser-Weg 12 • D-44227 Dortmund
Tel. +49 23175443232
Fax +49 2317544327
E-mail: joerg@lennardt.biz

Mr Hannes LEO
Österreich
Postfach 91 • A-1103 Vienna
Tel. +43 17982601-248
Fax +43 17989386
E-mail: hannes@leoon.at

Mr Godwin C MICALLEF
Malta
2 B'Kara Road • M-ATD 1216 Attard
Tel. +356 21337225
Fax +356 21332336
E-mail: gcm@keyworld.net
www.ebizfoundation.org

Mr Tautvydas MISIŪNAS
Lithuania
CEFIC (chemichals) - Commercial Director, Achema Sc.
Jonalaukio k., Ruklos sen • LT-55550 Jonavos r.
Tel. +370 34956626
+370 34956619
E-mail: alvyda@achemamc.lt

Mrs Alena NÁROVCOVÁ
République tchèque
Nám W. Churchilla 2 • CZ-113 59 Praha 3
E-mail: narovcova.alena@seznam.cz

Mrs Ingeborg NIESTROY
Nederland
European Environmental Advisory Councils - c/o Minaraad • Kliniekstraat 25, 4de verdieping; B-1070 Bruxelles
Tel. +32 25580151
E-mail: ingeborg.niestroy@eeac-net.org

Mr Ulrich PAETZOLD
Deutschland
FIEC - The European Construction Industry Ferderation
Avenue Louise 225 • B-1050 Bruxelles
Tel. +32 25145535
Fax +32 25110276
E-mail: info@fiec.eu

Mr Patrick PASSLEY
United Kingdom
ACLC Building, 9 Clarendon Road • UK • London UK N8 0DD
Tel. +44 2088887831
Fax +44 2088888133
E-mail: paralegalcharity@hotmail.com

Mr Patrizio PESCI
Italie
ORGALIME (Engineering)
CEI-BOIS
ACEM-BIKE
CEMA (machines agricoles)
Avenue des Trembles 1 • B-1950 Kraainem
Tel. +39 066897123
Fax +39 066897123
E-mail: p.pesci@scarlet.be

Mr Ion POP
Romania
Director, Strategies and International Relations - Chamber of Commerce and Industry of Romania
n° 2, Octavian Goga Blv., Sector 3 • RO-030982 Bucarest
Tel. +40 213190094
Fax +40 213190120
E-mail: ion@perfectwebware.com

Mr Gerhard ROHDE
Deutschland
Avenue de Reverdil 10 • CH-1260 Nyon
Tel. +41 223652180
Fax +41 223652121
E-mail: gerd.rohde@union-network.org

Mrs Erica SJÖLANDER
Sverige
Olof Palmes gata 11 • S-10552 Stockholm
Tel. +46 87868267
Fax +46 8218908
E-mail: erica.sjolander@ifmetall.se

Mr Peter SKYTE
United Kingdom
National Officer for the IT sector - Amicus the Union
King Street 35 - Covent garden • UK • London WC2E 8JG
Tel. +44 2074208900
Fax +44 2074208999
E-mail: peter.skyte@unitetheunion.com

Mrs Sirpa SMOLSKY
Suomi/Finland
Metallinjalostajat - Eurofer (acier)
Metallinjalostajat - Eteläranta 10 • FI-00130 Helsinki
Tel. +358 400500563
Fax +358 9624462
E-mail: sirpa.smolsky@techind.fi

Mr Gheorghe SORA
Romania
President - Federatia Nationala Sindicala Solidaritatea Metal (Cartel Alfa) - Metal 202A, sector 6, Et. 3 - CAM 14-17 • RO-060022 Bucarest
Tel. +40 213171052
Fax +40 213113575
E-mail: smetal@cartel-alfa.ro

Mr Thomas STUDENT
Deutschland
IG Bergbau, Chemie, Energie - AWI - EMCEF
Königsworther Platz 6 • D-30167 Hannover
Tel. +49 5117631383
Fax +49 5117631770
E-mail: thomas.student@igbce.de

Mr Roberto SUÁREZ SANTOS
España
CEOE - Confédération des employeurs espagnols
C/Diego de Leon, 50 • E-28006 Madrid
Tel. +34 915663401
Fax +34 914111982
E-mail: suarez@ceoe.es

Mr András SZÜCS
Hungary
Egry J.u.1 • H-1111 Budapest
Tel. +36 14631628
Fax +36 14631858
E-mail: andras.szucs@eden-online.org

Mrs Sabine TRIER
Belgique/België
Deputy General Secretary - ETF (European Transport Workers' Federation)
Rue du Midi 165 • B-1000 Bruxelles
Tel. +32 22854660
Fax +32 22800817
E-mail: s.trier@etf-europe.org

Mr Sauli VÄNTTI
Suomi/Finland
Directing Officer, telecommunication & energy, international affairs - Finnish Electrical Worker's Union
Box 747 • FI-33101 Tampere
Tel. +358 32520269
Fax +358 32520541
E-mail: sauli.vantti@sahkoliitto.fi

Mr Roland VERSTAPPEN
Luxembourg
Mittal Steel Co Ltd - Eurofer (acier)
Berkeley Square House, 7th Floor - Berkeley square • UK • London W1J 6DA
Tel. +44 2076297988
E-mail: roland.verstappen@mittalsteel.com

Mr Hans-Joachim ZIESING
Deutschland
Independant Consultant - Geschäftsführer der Arbeitsgemeinschaft Energiebilanzen e.V.
Fasanenstrasse 62 • D-10719 Berlin
Tel. +49 308913987
E-mail: hziesing@t-online.de

Mr Pedro ALMEIDA FREIRE

Mr William A. ATTLEY

Mr Miguel Ángel CABRA DE LUNA

Mr Brian CALLANAN

Mr Edwin CALLEJA

Mr Claudio CAPPELLINI

Mr Brian CURTIS

Mr Bojidar DANEV

Mr Plamen DIMITROV

Mrs Rose D'SA

Mr Dumitru FORNEA

Mr Göke FRERICHS

Mr Pierre GENDRE

Mr Bernard HUVELIN

Mr Ludvík JÍROVEC

Mr József KAPUVÁRI

Mr Dimitris KITTENIS

Mr Johannes KLEEMANN

Mr Viesturs KOCIŅŠ

Mr Marek KOMOROWSKI

Mr Armands KRAUZE

Mr Marian KRZAKLEWSKI

Mrs Leila KURKI

Mr Linas LASIAUSKAS

Mr Vladimír MATOUŠEK

Mr Martin NOSE

Mr Kaul NURM

Mr Jan OLSSON

Mr Ján ORAVEC

Mr Ángel PANERO FLÓREZ

Mr Luis Miguel PARIZA CASTAÑOS

Mr Carlos Alberto PEREIRA MARTINS

Mr Antonello PEZZINI

Mr Josly PIETTE

Mr Primož ŠPORAR

Mr Lutz RIBBE

Mr Corrado ROSSITTO

Mr Valerio SALVATORE

Mr Robert SCHADECK

Mr David SEARS

Mr Martin SIECKER

Mr Juraj STERN

Mrs Elżbieta SZADZIŃSKA

Mr János TÓTH

Mr Dirk WESTENDORP

Mr Josef ZBOŘIL

Mr Gustav ZÖHRER

Secretariat-General

Rue Belliard 99
B-1040 Brussels
E-mail: prénom.nom@eesc.europa.eu
Website: http://www.eesc.europa.eu
Tel. +32 25469011
Fax +32 25134843, 25469729, 2546 + extension

PRESIDENT'S SECRETARIAT

Andrea PIERUCCI
Head of Unit
Tel. +32 25468441
Fax +32 25469752

GROUP SECRETARIATS

Group I: Employers

Birgit FULAR
Head of Unit
Tel. +32 25469044
Fax +32 25469754

Group II: Employees

Martine VANHAMME
Head of Unit
Tel. +32 25469831
Fax +32 25469755

Group III: Various interests

Marc BEFFORT
Head of Unit
Tel. +32 25469547
Fax +32 25469756

SECRETARY-GENERAL

E-mail: prénom.nom@eesc.europa.eu

Martin WESTLAKE
Secretary-General
Tel. +32 25469226
Fax +32 25469753

Secretary-General's secretariat

Eleonora DI NICOLANTONIO
Head of Unit
Tel. +32 25469454
Fax +32 25469753

Internal audit

Freddy SMET
Head of Unit
Tel. +32 25469403
Fax +32 25469129

Communication coordination

Peter LINDVALD-NIELSEN
Head of Unit
Tel. +32 25469888
Fax +32 25469757

Press

Christian WEGER
Head of Unit (acting)
Tel. +32 25469586
Fax +32 25469764

Information

Päivi SEPPÄNEN
Head of Unit
Tel. +32 25469811
Fax +32 25469766

Visits/publications

Charis XIROUCHAKIS
Head of Unit
Tel. +32 25469984
Fax +32 25469766

Directorate A: Consultative Work

João PEREIRA DOS SANTOS
Director (acting)
Tel. +32 25469245
Fax +32 25469757

Single market, production and consumption

João PEREIRA DOS SANTOS
Head of Unit
Tel. +32 25469245
Fax +32 25468311

Transport, energy, infrastructure and the information society

Éric PONTHIEU
Head of Unit
Tel. +32 25468771
Fax +32 25469400

Agriculture, rural development and the environment

Jakob Juhler ANDERSEN
Head of Unit
Tel. +32 25469258
Fax +32 25469928

Industrial change

Pol LIEMANS
Head of Unit
Tel. +32 25468215
Fax +32 25469228

Directorate B: Consultative Work

Wolfgang JUNGK
Director
Tel. +32 25469623
Fax +32 25469762

Economic and monetary union and economic and social cohesion

Alberto ALLENDE
Head of Unit
Tel. +32 25469679
Fax +32 25468227

Employment, social affairs and citizenship

Alan HICK
Head of Unit
Tel. +32 25469302
Fax +32 25469762

External relations

Jean-François BENCE
Head of Unit
Tel. +32 25469399
Fax +32 25468241

Directorate for General Affairs

Nicolas ALEXOPOULOS
Director
Tel. +32 25469370
Fax +32 25469772

Registry, protocol, archives

Dominique-François BARETH
Head of Unit
Tel. +32 25469089
Fax +32 25469772

Relations with the institutions and the national ESCs

Vasco OLIVEIRA
Head of Unit
Tel. +32 25468181
Fax +32 25469469

Relations with civil society organisations, constitutional affairs

Patrick FEVE
Head of Unit
Tel. +32 25469616
Fax +32 25469757

Conferences/interpreting

Tatiana ADAMIŠOVÁ
Head of Unit
Tel. +32 25468110
Fax +32 25469822

Services intérieurs

Tatiana ADAMIŠOVÁ
Head of Unit (acting)
Tel. +32 25468110
Fax +32 25469822

Legal affairs

Moisés BERMEJO GARDE
Head of Unit
Tel. +32 25469814
Fax +32 25469771

Directorate for Human and Financial Resources

Martin WESTLAKE
Director (acting)
Tel. +32 25469226
Fax +32 25469198

Staff policy

Recruitment, career, training

Gerardus NIJBORG
Head of Unit
Tel. +32 25469807
Fax +32 25468251

Services de support au personnel

Anna REDSTEDT
Head of Unit
Tel. +32 25469233
Fax +32 25468130

Medical/Welfare Department

Marie-Dominique HENRY
Doctor
Tel. +32 25469597
Fax +32 25469601

Finance

Budget, service to members, payroll and allowances

Johannes KIND
Head of Unit
Tel. +32 25469111
Fax +32 25469783

Accounts

Claus BERGMAN
Head of Unit
Tel. +32 25469872
Fax +32 25469783

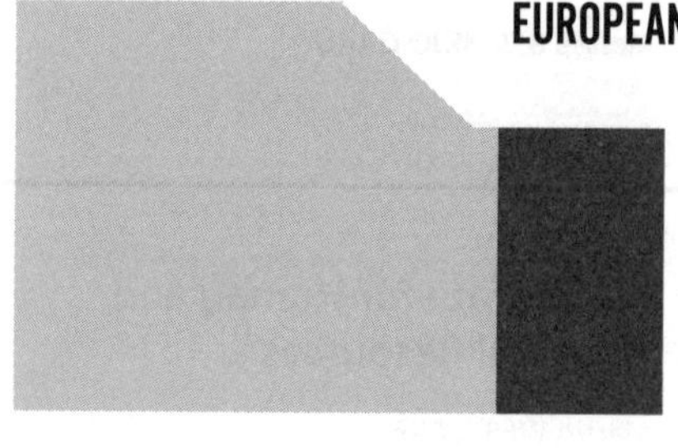

Joint Services of the European Economic and Social Committee and the Committee of the Regions

Rue Belliard 99-101
B-1040 Brussels
Website: http://www.eesc.europa.eu
Tel. +32 25469011, 25469001
Fax +32 25134893, 25469705

LOGISTICS AND TRANSLATION

Cornelius BENTVELSEN
Director
Tel. +32 25469813
Fax +32 25469705

Noëlle MATTEI
Deputy Director
Tel. +32 25469868
Fax +32 25469705

Direction

Planning/financial and contractual management

Steven PHILLIPS
Head of Unit
Tel. +32 25469461
Fax +32 25469705

Security

Antonio INCLAN GONZALEZ
Administrator
Tel. +32 25469751
Fax +32 25469705

Infrastructure

Marc DE FEU
Head of Unit
Tel. +32 25468665
Fax +32 25469080

IT and telecommunications

Niall O'HIGGINS
Head of Unit
Tel. +32 25469668
Fax +32 25469769

Printing/distribution

Jan BAUMGARTL
Head of Unit
Tel. +32 25469851
Fax +32 25469076

TRANSLATION

Gonzalo BESCÓS FERRAZ
Director
Tel. +32 22822156

Ineta STRAUTINA
Deputy Director
Tel. +32 22358243
Fax +32 22359468

Coordination of the production chain

Éric LAVIGNE
Head of Unit
Tel. +32 22822032
Fax +32 25469468

Bulgarian translation and typing

Ani DAMYANOVA
Head of Unit (acting)
Tel. +32 25469803
Fax +32 25468881

Spanish translation and transcription

Miguel PAREDES LARRUCEA
Head of Unit
Tel. +32 22359591
Fax +32 22359180

Czech translation and typing

Markéta FRANKOVÁ
Head of Unit
Tel. +32 22359742
Fax +32 22359196

Danish translation and transcription

Steen FINK-JENSEN
Head of Unit
Tel. +32 22359379
Fax +32 22359185

German translation and transcription

Giovanni DI CARLO
Head of Unit
Tel. +32 22359502
Fax +32 22359048

Estonian translation and typing

Jana KOPA
Head of Unit (acting)
Tel. +32 22359532
Fax +32 22359182

Greek translation and transcription

Nikolaos PAPANIKOLAOU
Head of Unit
Tel. +32 22359508
Fax +32 22359181

English translation and transcription

Francis PATTERSON
Head of Unit
Tel. +32 22359522
Fax +32 22359187

French translation and transcription

Joseph LONGTON
Head of Unit (acting)
Tel. +32 22359115
Fax +32 22359195

Italian translation and transcription

Eugenia PONZONI
Head of Unit
Tel. +32 22359244
Fax +32 22359188

Latvian translation and typing

Edite KRUZE
Head of Unit (acting)
Tel. +32 25468150
Fax +32 22358291

Lithuanian translation and typing

Jurate DREVINSKIENE
Head of Unit
Tel. +32 25468164
Fax +32 22358639

Hungarian translation and typing

Andras EGYEDI
Head of Unit
Tel. +32 22822463
Fax +32 22359021

Maltese translation and typing

Elgar-Paul MAGRO
Head of Unit
Tel. +32 25468471
Fax +32 22358291

Dutch translation and transcription

Francis TAILLIEN
Head of Unit
Tel. +32 22358735
Fax +32 22359183

Polish translation and typing

Izabella WISNIEWSKA-CRAVEN-GREEN
Head of Unit
Tel. +32 22358148
Fax +32 22358226

Portuguese translation and transcription

Manuel SILVEIRA
Head of Unit (acting)
Tel. +32 25469709
Fax +32 22359191

Romanian translation and typing

Gabriela VARZARU
Head of Unit (acting)
Tel. +32 25468849
Fax +32 25468885

Slovak translation and typing

Karin MIŠÁNIKOVÁ
Head of Unit
Tel. +32 25468263
Fax +32 25468651

Slovene translation and typing

Anica RANT
Head of Unit
Tel. +32 25468154
Fax +32 22358650

Finnish translation and transcription

Erja UUSITALO
Head of Unit
Tel. +32 22359051
Fax +32 22359192

Swedish translation and transcription

Pär HAMMARGREN
Head of Unit
Tel. +32 25469161
Fax +32 22359145

COMMITTEE OF THE REGIONS OF THE EUROPEAN UNION

Committee of the Regions

BUREAU OF THE COMMITTEE OF THE REGIONS

Members and alternates

Mr Luc VAN DEN BRANDE
Chairman (EPP)

Mr Michel DELEBARRE
First Vice-Chairman (PSE)

Mr Arnoldas ABRAMAVICIUS
Member (PPE)

Mr Uno ALDEGREN
Member (PSE)

Mrs Ann BESKOW
Alternate (PES)

Mr Vicente ALVAREZ ARECES
Member (PSE)

Mr Jaime RABANAL GARCIA
Alternate (PES)

Mr Knud ANDERSEN
Member (ALDE)

Mr Henrik Ringbaek MADSEN
Alternate (PES)

Mr Cristian ANGHEL
Member (ALDE)

Mr Emil PROSCAN
Alternate (ALDE)

Mr Edvins BARTKEVICS
Member (ALDE)

Mr Andris ELKSNITIS
Alternate (PPE)

Mrs Simone BEISSEL
Member (ALDE)

Mr Albert LENTZ
Alternate (PPE)

Mr Milan BELICA
Member (PPE)

JUDr. Zdenko TREBULA
Alternate (NI)

Mr Pavel BEM
Member (PPE)

Mr Roman LÍNEK
Alternate (PPE)

Mr Olivier BERTRAND
Member (PPE)

Mrs Claude DU GRANRUT
Alternate (PPE)

Mr Gabor BIHARY
Member (PSE)

Mr Gyula SZABO
Alternate (PES)

Mr Jacques BLANC
Member (PPE)

Mr Camille DE ROCCA SERRA
Alternate (PPE)

Mr Albert BORE
Member (PSE)

Mrs Jennette ARNOLD
Alternate (PES)

Mrs Mercedes BRESSO
Member (PSE)

Mr Bernard SOULAGE
Alternate (PES)

Mr Carlos CESAR
Member (PSE)

Mr Carlos Alberto Santos TUTA
Alternate (PES)

Mrs Flo CLUCAS
Member (ALDE)

Mr Guido MILANA
Alternate (ALDE)

Mr Michael COHEN
Member (PSE)

Mr Ian MICALLEF
Alternate (PPE)

Mr José CORREIA
Member (PPE)

Mr Manuel MARTINS
Alternate (PPE)

Mr Jean-Louis DESTANS
Member (PSE)

Mr Jean-Louis JOSEPH
Alternate (PES)

Mr Leonardo DOMENICI
Member (PSE)

Mr Alessandro PIETRACCI
Alternate (PES)

Mr Risto ERVELÄ
Member (ALDE)

Mr Ossi MARTIKAINEN
Alternate (ALDE)

Mr Guillermo FERNANDEZ VARA
Member (PSE)

Mrs Lucia MARTIN DOMINGUEZ
Alternate (PES)

Mr Isidoro GOTTARDO
Member (PPE)

Mr Ramón Luis VALCÁRCEL SISO
Alternate (PPE)

Mr Juan Vicente HERRERA CAMPO
Member (PPE)

Mrs María DE DIEGO DURANTEZ
Alternate (PPE)

Mr Henning JENSEN
Member (PSE)

Mr Gordon KEYMER
Member (PPE)

Sir Simon DAY
Alternate (PPE)

Mr Vladimir KISYOV
Member (PPE)

Mrs Detelina NIKOLOVA
Alternate (ALDE)

Dr Karl-Heinz KLÄR
Member (PSE)

Mrs Kerstin KIESSLER
Alternate (PES)

Mr Anders KNAPE
Member (PPE)

Mrs Catarina SEGERSTEN-LARSSON
Alternate (PPE)

Mr Risto KOIVISTO
Member (PSE)

Mrs Elina LEHTO
Alternate (PSE)

Mr Jerzy KROPIWNICKI
Member (PPE)

Mgr. Witold KROCHMAL
Alternate (UEN-EA)

Mrs Johanna MAIJ-WEGGEN
Member (PPE)

Mrs Lenie DWARSHUIS
Alternate (ALDE)

Mrs Irena MAJCEN
Member (PPE)

Mr Anton SMOLNIKAR
Alternate (PES)

Dr Ulrich MALY
Member (PSE)

Mr Helmut M. JAHN
Alternate (PPE)

Declan MCDONNELL
Member (ALDE)

Mr Denis LANDY
Alternate (PSE)

Mr Christos MESIS
Titulaire (NI)

Mr Georgios IAKOVOU
Alternate (PPE)

Mr Krasimir MIREV
Member (PSE)

Mr Hasan AZIS
Alternate (ALDE)

Mr Erwin MOHR
Member (PPE)

Mr Heinz SCHADEN
Alternate (PES)

Mr Seamus MURRAY
Member (UEN-AE)

Mr Patrick MCGOWAN
Alternate (UEN-EA)

Mr Francesco MUSOTTO
Member (PPE)

Mr Gianfranco VITAGLIANO
Alternate (PPE)

Mr Paul O'DONOGHUE
Member (UEN-AE)

Mr Milner WHITEMAN
Alternate (UEN-EA)

Mr Jan ORAVEC
Member (PPE)

Mr Andrej DURKOVSKY
Alternate (PPE)

Mr Constantin OSTAFICIUC
Member (PPE)

Mrs Veronica IONIŢĂ
Alternate (PPE)

Mr Petr OSVALD
Member (PSE)

Mr Gediminas PAVIRZIS
Member (PSE)

Mr Aidas VAISNORA
Alternate (ALDE)

Mr Michael SCHNEIDER
Member (PPE)

Mr Volker HOFF
Alternate (PPE)

Mr István SÉRTŐ-RADICS
Member (ALDE)

Mr Ferenc BENKÖ
Alternate (ALDE)

Mr Ioannis SGOUROS
Member (PSE)

Mr Christos PALEOLOGOS
Alternate (PES)

Dr Uno SILBERG
Member (UEN-AE)

Mr Teet KALLASVEE
Alternate (PPE)

Mr Gian Mario SPACCA
Member (ALDE)

Mr Vito DE FILIPPO
Alternate (ALDE)

Mr Leszek ŚWIĘTALSKI
Member (PSE)

Mr Jerzy ZAJAKAŁA
Alternate (UEN-EA)

Mr Konstantinos TATSIS
Member (PPE)

Mr Grigorios ZAFIROPOULOS
Alternate (PPE)

Dr Graham TOPE
Member (ALDE)

Mrs Linda GILLHAM
Alternate (UEN-EA)

Mr Jean-Claude VAN CAUWENBERGHE
Member (PSE)

Mr Karl-Heinz LAMBERTZ
Alternate (PES)

Mr Herwig VAN STAA
Member (PPE)

Mr Hans NIESSL
Alternate (PSE)

Mr Bas VERKERK
Member (ALDE)

Mr Antón ROMBOUTS
Alternate (PPE)

Mr Marek WOŹNIAK
Member (PPE)

Mr Brunon SYNAK
Alternate (PPE)

MEMBERS OF THE COMMITTEE

Belgium

Mr Luc VAN DEN BRANDE
Vlaams Volksvertegenwoordiger
Leuvenseweg 86 • B-1011 Bruxelles - Brussel
(Vlaams parlement)
Tel. +32 25524332
Fax +32 25524482
E-mail: luc.vandenbrande@vlaamsparlement.be

Mr Gilbert BOSSUYT
Vlaams Volksvertegenwoordiger
E. Tinelstraat, 7 • B-8930 Menen
Tel. +32 474512167
Fax +32 56512228
E-mail: Gilbert.Bossuyt@vlaamsparlement.be

Mr Jos CHABERT
Brussels parlementslid
Hollestraat 5 • B-1860 Meise
Tel. +32 22137161
Fax +32 22137160
E-mail: jchabert@bruparl.irisnet.be
http://www.bruxelles.irisnet.be

Mr Jean-François ISTASSE
Député de la Communauté française
Tel. +32 87353313
Fax +32 87351920
E-mail: jean.francois.istasse@skynet.be

Mr Patrick LACHAERT
Vlaams Volksvertegenwoordiger
Vlaams Parlement • Hundelgemsesteenweg
166/5 • B-9820 Merelbeke
Tel. +32 92306704
Fax +32 92318092
E-mail: patrick.lachaert@vlaamsparlement.be
http://merelbeke.be

Mr Karl-Heinz LAMBERTZ
Ministerpräsident der Regierung der
Deutschsprachigen Gemeinschaft
Ministeripresident der Regierung der
Deutschsprachigen Gemeinschaft
Minister für lokale Behörden • Klötzerbahn 32 •
B-4700 Eupen
Tel. +32 87596443
Fax +32 87554538
E-mail: karl-heinz.lambertz@dgov.be
www.dglive.be

Mr Michel LEBRUN
Député wallon
Tel. +32 60399686
Fax +32 60399645
E-mail: michel.lebrun@win.be

Mr Charles PICQUÉ
Ministre-président du gouvernement de la
Région Bruxelles-Capitale
Tel. +32 25063211
Fax +32 25144022
E-mail: info@picque.irisnet.be
pourbruxelles@charlespicque.be

Mr Johan SAUWENS
Vlaams Volksvertegenwoordiger
Tel. +32 089519234
Fax +32 089501100
E-mail: johan.sauwens@bilzen.be

Mr Jean-Claude VAN CAUWENBERGHE
Député wallon
Boulevard Joseph II, 50 • B-6000 Charleroi
Tel. +32 71208843
Fax +32 71331203
E-mail: vancau@brutele.be

Mr Dirk VAN MECHELEN
Ministre flamand des finances, du budget et de l'aménagement du territoire
Koning Albert II-laan 19 (Phoenixgebouw)
B-1210 Brussel
E-mail: kabinet.vanmechelen@vlaanderen.be

Bulgaria

Mr Hasan AZIS
Vice-President of the National Assembly of the Municipalities of the Republic of Bulgaria, Mayor of Kardjali
Tel. +359 36167302
Fax +359 36162968
E-mail: hasan.azis@gmail.com

Mrs Katya DOYCHEVA
Mayor of Tvarditsa
Tel. +359 45422202311
Fax +359 454404649
E-mail: oba_tv@mail.bg

Mr Vladimir KISYOV
Chair of Sofia Municipal Council
Tel. +359 29377591
Fax +359 29870855
E-mail: vkissiov@sofia.bg

Mr Krasimir MIREV
President of the National Assembly of the Municipalities of the Republic of Bulgaria, Mayor of Targovishte
Tel. +359 60168606
Fax +359 60162057
E-mail: obshtina@elnics.com

Mr Vladimir MOSKOV
Member of the management council of the NAMRB, Mayor of Gotse Delchev
Tel. +359 75160060
Fax +359 75160066
E-mail: oba@gocenet.net

Mrs Detelina NIKOLOVA
Vice-President of the National Assembly of the Municipalities of the Republic of Bulgaria, Mayor of Dobrich
Tel. +359 58600001
Fax +359 58600166
E-mail: dobrich@dobrich.org

Mrs Penka Nedelkova PENKOVA
Mayor of Lom, Vice-Chairman of the management council of the NAMBR
Tel. +359 97169101
Fax +359 97166026
E-mail: obshtina.lom@mail.bg

Mr Guner Fariz SERBEST
Mayor of Stambolovo, member of the management council of the NAMRB
Tel. +359 3721234
Fax +359 3721463
E-mail: kmet_stambolovo@dir.bg

Mr Georgi Ivanov SLAVOV
Mayor of Yambol municipality
Tel. +359 46662266
Fax +359 46662247
E-mail: kmet@obshtinayambol.org

Mrs Dora Ilieva YANKOVA
Mayor of Smolian municipality, Chairman of the management council of the NAMRB
Tel. +359 30162662
Fax +359 30162435
E-mail: smolyan_mayor@abv.bg

Mr Bojidar Ivanov YOTOV
Mayor of Ruse
Tel. +359 82826100
Fax +359 82834413
E-mail: mayor@elits.rousse.bg

Mr Zlatko ZHIVKOV
Vice-Chairman of the management council of the NAMRB, Mayor of Montana
Tel. +359 96300400
Fax +359 96300401
E-mail: mayor@montana.bg

Czech Republic

Mr Pavel BEM
Lord Mayor of the Capital City of Prague, president of the delegation (Primátor hlavního města Prahy, vedoucí delegace)
Tel. +420 236002266
Fax +420 236003402
E-mail: pavel.bem@cityofprague.cz

Bc. Ondřej BENEŠÍK
Member of the Regional Assembly of Zlínský kraj (Člen zastupitelstva Zlínského kraje)
Tel. +420 577043149
Fax +420 577043124
E-mail: ondrej.benesik@kr-zlinsky.cz

Mr Jiří BYTEL
Mayor of the Municipality of Velká Hleďsebe, Karlovarský kraj (Starosta obce Velká Hleďsebe, Karlovarský kraj)
Tel. +420 354624328
E-mail: Hledsebe@iol.cz

Mr Jan KUBATA
Mayor of the City of Ústí nad Labem
Tel. +420 475210867
Fax +420 475211503
E-mail: jan.kubata@mag-ul.cz

Mrs Helena LANGŠÁDLOVÁ
Vice-Mayor of the Municipality of Černošice
Tel. +420 251640328
Fax +420 251640328
E-mail: mesto-cernosice@tiscali.cz

Ing. Roman LÍNEK
Deputy of the President of the Regional Council of Pardubický kraj (Náměstek hejtmana Pardubického kraje)
Tel. +420 466026118
Fax +420 466611215
E-mail: roman.linek@pardubickykraj.cz

Ing. Petr OSVALD
Member of the town assembly of the City of Plzeň, Plzeňský kraj (Člen zastupitelstva města Plzeň, Plzeňský kraj)
Tel. +420 378032075
Fax +420 378032024
E-mail: osvald@mmp.plzen-city.cz

Mr Juraj THOMA
Mayor of the City of České Budějovice
Tel. +420 386802901
Fax +420 386802951
E-mail: thomaj@c-budejovice.cz

Denmark

Mr Knud ANDERSEN
Regionnsrådsmedlem
Danish Regions • Square de Meeûs 1 • B-1000 Bruxelles - Brussel
Tel. +45 35298100
Fax +45 35298300
E-mail: cor@regioner.dk

Mr Per BØDKER ANDERSEN
Borgmester, Kolding Kommune
Square de Meeûs 1, 4e • B-1000 Bruxelles
Tel. +32 25501260
Fax +32 25501272
E-mail: international.relations@kl.dk

Mrs Mona HEIBERG
Borgerrepræsentant, Københavns Kommune
Tel. +32 25501260
Fax +32 25501272
E-mail: international.relations@kl.dk

Mr Henning JENSEN
Borgmester
Square de Meeûs 1, 4e • B-1000 Bruxelles
Tel. +32 25501260
Fax +32 25501272
E-mail: international.relations@kl.dk

Mrs Helene LUND
Byrådsmedlem
Square de Meeûs 1, 4e • B-1000 Bruxelles
Tel. +32 25501260
Fax +32 25501272
E-mail: international.relations@kl.dk

Mr Henrik Ringbæk MADSEN
Regionsrådsmedlem
Tel. +45 35298100
Fax +45 35298300
E-mail: cor@regioner.dk

Mr Jens Jørgen NYGAARD
Viceborgmester, Egedal Kommune
Ledoje Bygade 26 ‡ DK-2765 Smørum
E-mail: jens.jorgen.nygaard@egekom.dk

Mr Karsten Uno PETERSEN
Regionsrådsmedlem
Tel. +45 35298100
Fax +45 35298300
E-mail: cor@regioner.dk

Germany

Mr Dietmar BROCKES
Mitglied des Landtages, Nordrhein-Westfalen
Tel. +49 02118842750
+49 02118843608
E-mail: brockes-adr@landtag.nrw.de

Mr Hermann DINKLA
Mitglied des Landtages, Niedersachsen
Tel. +49 497591020
Fax +49 4975910222
E-mail: dinkla@t-online.de

Mr Uwe DÖRING
Minister für Justiz, Arbeit und Europa des Landes Schleswig-Holstein
Tel. +49 4319883700
Fax +49 4319883805
E-mail: uwe.doering@jumi.landsh.de

Mr Wolfgang GIBOWSKI
Staatssekretär, Bevollmächtigter des Landes Niedersachsen beim Bund
Tel. +49 030726291502
Fax +49 030726291509
E-mail: wolfgang.gibowski@stk.niedersachsen.de

Mr Rolf HARLINGHAUSEN
Mitglied des Europaausschusses der Hamburgischen Bürgerschaft
Tel. +49 40428311532
Fax +49 40428311653
E-mail: internationales@bk.hamburg.de

Dr Gerd HARMS
Bevollmächtigter des Landes Brandenburg für Bundes- und Europaangelegenheiten und Staatssekretär in der Staatskanzlei
Tel. +49 3318661496
Fax +49 3318661469
E-mail: petra.schmietendorf@stk.brandenburg.de
kathrin.rahn@eulv.brandenburg.de

Mrs Monika HELBIG
Bevollmächtigte des Landes Berlin
Büro des Landes Berlin • Av. Michel Ange 71 • B-1000 Bruxelles
Tel. +32 27380070
Fax +32 27324746
E-mail: renate.voelpel@lvbe.verwalt-berlin.de

Mr Volker HOFF
Hessen Minister for Federal and European Affaires and Commissioner of the Land of Hessen to the Federation
Tel. +49 611323660
Fax +49 611323696
E-mail: volker.hoff@stk.hessen.de

Mr Helmut M. JAHN
Landrat des Hohenlohekreises
Tel. +49 794018200
Fax +49 794018370
E-mail: helmut.m.jahn@hohenlohekreis.de

Mr Werner Heinrich JOSTMEIER
Mitglied des Landtages, Nordrhein-Westfalen
Tel. +49 02118842346
Fax +49 02118843341
E-mail: jostmeier@landtag.nrw.de

Dr Kerstin KIESSLER
Staatsrätin, Mitglied des Bremer Senats, Bevollmächtige der Freien Hansestadt Bremen beim Bund und für Europa
Landesvertretung der Freien Hansestadt Bremen • Hiroshimastrasse 24 • D-10785 Berlin
Tel. +49 3026930117
Fax +49 3026930175
E-mail: Kerstin.Kiessler@lvhb.bremen.de

Dr Karl-Heinz KLÄR
Bevollmächtigter des Landes Rheinland-Pfalz beim Bund und für Europa
Vertretung des Landes Rheinland-Pfalz beim Bund • In den Ministergärten 6 • D-10117 Berlin
Tel. +49 30726291100
Fax +49 30726291200
E-mail: kklaer@lv.rlp.de

Mrs Uta-Maria KUDER
Justizministerin Mecklenburg-Vorpommern
Tel. +49 3855881731
Fax +49 3855881079
E-mail: katrin.hilthorst@stk.mv-regierung.de

Mr Reinhard LOSKE
Senator für Umwelt, Bau, Verkehr und Europa der Freien Hansestadt Bremen
Tel. +49 4213612227
Fax +49 4213614565
E-mail: frank.steffe@umwelt.bremen.de

Dr Ulrich MALY
Oberbürgermeister des Stadt Nürnberg
Tel. +49 09112315001
Fax +49 09112315013
E-mail: obm@stadt.nuernberg.de

Prof. Ursula MÄNNLE
Mitglied des Landtages
Tel. +49 08941262634
Fax +49 08941261634
E-mail: adr-mitglied@bayern.Landtag.de

Mrs Emilia MÜLLER
Staatsministerin für Bundes- und Europaangelegenheiten in der Bayrischen Staatskanzlei
Bayerische Staatskanzlei, Franz-Josef-Strauß-Ring 1, D-80539 München, Allemagne
Tel. +49 89 21.65.25.13
Fax +49 89 21.65.35.13
E-mail: thorsten.hemming@stk.bayern.de

Mr Karl RAUBER
Mitglied des Landtages des Saarlandes
Minister für Bundes- und Europaangelegenheiten und Chef der Staatskanzlei
c/o Vertretung des Saarlandes bei der EU • Avenue de la Renaissance 46 • B-1000 Bruxelles - Brussel
Tel. +32 27430790
Fax +32 27327370
E-mail: c.geib@eu.saarland.de
http://www.saarland.de

Prof. Dr. Wolfgang REINHART
Minister für Bundes- und Europaangelegenheiten des Landes Baden-Württemberg
Tel. +49 7112153360
Fax +49 7112153510
E-mail: nicola.schelling@stm.bwl.de

Dr Michael SCHNEIDER
Staatsekretär, Bevollmächtigter des Landes Sachsen-Anhalt beim Bund
Vertretung des Landes Sachsen-anhalt beim Bund • Luisenstrasse 18 • D-10117 Berlin
Tel. +49 3024345880
Fax +49 3024345847
E-mail: michael.schneider@lv.stk.sachsen-anhalt.de

Mr Peter STRAUB
Mitglied des Landtages von Baden-Württemberg
c/o Herrn Hönle • Konrad-Adenauer-Str. 3 • D-70173 Stuttgart
Tel. +49 7112063208
Fax +49 7112063299
E-mail: reinhard.hoenle@landtag-bw.de

Mr Hans-Josef VOGEL
Bürgermeister der Stadt Arnsberg
Tel. +49 029322011246
Fax +49 029322011498
E-mail: buergermeister@arnsberg.de

Mr Hermann WINKLER
Mitglied des Landtages
Tel. +32 22358730
Fax +32 22358722
E-mail: adr@bxl.sk.sachsen.de

Dr Klaus ZEH
Minister für Bundes- und Europaangelegenheiten und Chef der Staatskanzlei, Mitglied des Thüringer Landtags
Tel. +49 3613792830
Fax +49 3613792832
E-mail: adr@tsk.thueringen.de

Estonia

Mr Väino HALLIKMÄGI
Member of Pärnu Town Council
Tel. +372 56652801
Fax +372 4425972
E-mail: vaino.hallikmagi@mail.ee

Mr Mihkel JUHKAMI
Chairman of Rakvere Town Council
Tel. +372 3225885
Fax +372 3225871
E-mail: Mihkel.Juhkami@mail.ee

Ph.D. Saima KALEV
Mayor of Jõgeva
Tel. +372 7766572
Fax +372 7766570
E-mail: saima@jogevavv.ee

Mr Teet KALLASVEE
Member of the council of Haapsalu
Tel. +372 4725300
Fax +372 4725310
E-mail: teet@tennis.ee

Mr Kurmet MÜÜRSEPP
Member of Antsla Municipality Council
Tel. +372 7857304
Fax +372 7857307
E-mail: kurmet@urvaste.werro.ee

Dr Uno SILBERG
Chairman of Kose Municipality Council
Tel. +372 5065533
Fax +372 6484928
E-mail: uno.silberg.001@mail.ee

Mr Toomas VITSUT
Chairman of Tallinn
Tel. +372 6943211
Fax +372 6943249
E-mail: Toomas.Vitsut@tallinnlv.ee

Ireland

Mr Cathal CROWE
Member of Clare County Council
Tel. +353 871368882
E-mail: cathalcrowe@yahoo.ie

Mr Michael FITZGERALD
Member of South Tipperary County Council
Tel. +353 6272136
E-mail: cllrmichael.Fitzgerald@southtippcoco.ie

Mrs Constance HANNIFFY
Member of Offaly County Council
Doon
Ballinahown, Co. Offaly • IRL • Athlone, Co. Westmeath
Tel. +353 906430106
Fax +353 906430057
E-mail: connieh@iol.ie

Cllr John LAHART
Member of South Dublin County Council
6 Orlagh Grange, Scholarstown Road, Rathfarnham, ‡ IRL ‡ Dublin
Tel. +353 14939608
E-mail: jlahart@sdublincoco.ie

Mr Denis LANDY
Member of South Tipperary County Council
Tel. +353 51641641
E-mail: cllrdenis.landy@southtippcoco.ie

Mr Declan MCDONNELL
Member of Galway City Council
Tara Grove, Monivea Road 4 • IRL • Galway
Tel. +353 91753770
Fax +353 91764786
E-mail: declanpmcdonnell@eircom.net

Mr Patrick MCGOWAN
Member of Donegal County Council
Tel. +353 876868438
E-mail: patrick.mcgowan@donegalcoco.ie

Mr Seamus MURRAY
Member of Meath County Council
c/o Johnatan Murray • Cullentra • IRL
Longwood, Co. Meath
Tel. +353 469555189
Fax +353 469021463
E-mail: smurray@members.meathcoco.ie

Mr Paul O'DONOGHUE
Member of Kerry County Council
Tel. +353 669761186
Fax +353 669761847
E-mail: jpodonoghuek@eircom.net

Greece

Mr Andreas FOURAS
Mayor of Patras
Tel. +30 2610966207
Fax +30 2610623562
E-mail: afouras@patras.gr

Mr Nikitas KAKLAMANIS
Mayor of Athens
Tel. +30 2103310861
Fax +30 2103722308
E-mail: christaki@cityofathens.gr

Mr Páris KOUKOULÓPOULOS
Maire de Kozani - Président de KEDKE
Dimarchos Kozanis - Proedros KEDKE
Pl. Níkis 1 • GR-501 00 Kozáni
Tel. +30 246105031112
Fax +30 2461050325
E-mail: dimarkoz@otenet.gr

Mr Chrístos PALEOLÓGOS
Conseiller municipal de Livadia
Dimotikos Symvoulos Dimou Livadias
Fidipidou 11 • GR-22 100 Livadiá
Tel. +30 2261025091
Fax +30 2261023349
E-mail: cpalogos@otenet.gr

Mr Georgios PAPASTERGIOU
Prefect of Pieria
Tel. +23 51351260
Fax +23 51020036
E-mail: nomarxis@pieria.gr

Mr Panayotis PSOMIADIS
Prefect of Thessaloniki
Tel. +30 2310409877
Fax +30 2310409896
E-mail: grnom@nath.gr

Mrs Evangelia SCHOINARAKI-ILIAKI
Prefect of Heraklion
Tel. +30 2810342584
Fax +30 2810342588
E-mail: shinarak@otenet.gr

Mr Ioannis SGOUROS
Préfet d'Athènes
Nomarchis Athinon
Tel. +30 2106914145
Fax +30 2106984182
E-mail: nomath10@otenet.gr

Mr Konstantinos TATSIS
Président de l'autorité préfectorale élargie de Dramas-Kavalas-Xanthis
Proedros Dievrimenis N.A. Dramas-Kavalas-Xanthis
Tel. +30 25412507001
Fax +30 2541350730
E-mail: pref-dkx@otenet.gr

Mr Dimitrios TSIGKOUNIS
Mayor of Leonidio (Arcadia)
Tel. +30 275736020
Fax +30 2757360214
E-mail: leonidio@otenet.gr

Mr Konstantinos TZATZANIS
Counsellor, Prefecture of Piraeus
Tel. +30 2104194000
Fax +30 2104194290
E-mail: tza@central.tee.gr

Mr Grigorios ZAFIROPOULOS
Mayor of Chalandri (Athens)
Tel. +30 2106860730
Fax +30 2106860735
E-mail: mayor@halaydri.gr

Spain

Mrs Esperanza AGUIRRE GIL DE BIEDMA
Presidenta de la Comunidad de Madrid
Tel. +34 915801592
Fax +34 913103750
E-mail: nuria.rosa@madrid.org

Mr Vicente ALVAREZ ARECES
Presidente del Gobierno del Principado de Asturias
Principado de Asturias • C/Suárez de la Riva, s/n • E-33071 Oviedo
Tel. +34 985106786
Fax +34 985106784
E-mail: vaareces@princast.es
http://www.princast.es/

Mr Francesc ANTICH I OLIVER
Presidente del Gobierno de la Comunidad Autónoma Islas Baleares
Llotja de Mar 3 • E-07012 Palma de Mallorca
Tel. +34 971784126
Fax +34 971784208
E-mail: president@caib.es
http://www.caib.es

Mrs Rita BARBERÁ NOLLA
Alcaldesa de Valencia
Tel. +34 963516994
Fax +34 963529795
E-mail: informacion@ayto-valencia.es

Mr José María BARREDA FONTES
Presidente de la Junta de Comunidades de Castilla-La Mancha
Tel. +34 925267600
Fax +34 925267619
E-mail: jmbarreda@jccm.es

Mr Francisco CAMPS ORTIZ
Presidente de la Comunidad Autónoma de la Región de Valencia
Tel. +34 963866100
Fax +34 963863597
E-mail: fayos_sus@gva.es

Mr Pedro CASTRO VÁZQUEZ
Alcalde de Getafe (Madrid)
Tel. +34 913643701
Fax +34 913655482

Mr Manuel CHAVES GONZÁLEZ
Presidente de la Junta de Andalucía
Palacio de San Telmo • Calle Manuel Siurot, s/n (Casa Rosa) • E-41071 Sevilla
Tel. +34 955035500
Fax +34 955035221
E-mail: manuel.chaves@juntadeandalucia.es

Mr Guillermo FERNÁNDEZ VARA
Presidente de la Junta de Extremadura
Tel. +34 924008251
Fax +34 924008285
E-mail: presidente@prs.juntaex.es

Mrs Dolores GOROSTIAGA SAIZ
Vicepresidenta del Gobierno de Cantabria z Consejera de Empleo y Bienestar Social
Tel. +34 942207226
Fax +34 942207224
E-mail: gorostiaga_md@gobcantabria.es

Mr Jordi HEREU I BOHER
Mayor of the City of Barcelona
Tel. +34 934027881
Fax +34 934027877
E-mail: asabartes@bcn.cat

Mr Juan Vicente HERRERA CAMPO
Presidenta de la Junta de Castilla y León
Plaza de Castille y León 1 • E-47008 Valladolid
Tel. +34 983411121
Fax +34 983411269
E-mail: hersagma@jcyl.es

Mr Juan José IBARRETXE MARKUARTU
Presidente del Gobierno Vasco
Palacio de Ajuria-Enea • Navarra 2 • E-01007 Vitoria-Gasteiz
Tel. +34 945017900
Fax +34 945017830
E-mail: Sofia-Orue@ej-gv.es
http://www.euskadi.net/home/menu800_i.htm#

Mr Marcelino IGLESIAS RICOU
Presidente de la Comunidad autónoma de Aragón
Paseo de María Agustín 36 • E-50071 Zaragoza
Tel. +34 976714013
Fax +34 976714136
E-mail: ctabuenca@aragon.es

Mr José MONTILLA AGUILERA
Presidente de la Generalitat de Cataluña
Tel. +34 934024819
Fax +34 934024821
E-mail: gbpresident.presidencia@gencat.net

Mr Emilio PÉREZ TOURIÑO
Presidente de la Xunta de Galicia
Tel. +34 981541215
Fax +34 981541219
E-mail: secre.presidente@xunta.es

Mr Paulino RIVERO BAUTE
Presidente de la Comunidad Autónoma de Canarias
Plaza Dr Rafael O'Shanahan, N 1, E-35071 Las Palmas de Gran Canaria
Tel. +34 928452100
Fax +34 928452144

Mr Alberto RUIZ-GALLARDON JIMENEZ
Alcalde de Madrid
Tel. +34 915880022
Fax +34 915882475
E-mail: cestudios@munimadrid.es

Mr Pedro SANZ ALONSO
Presidente del Gobierno de La Rioja
Vara del Rey, 3 • E-26071 Logroño
Tel. +34 941291114
Fax +34 941291223
E-mail: presidente@larioja.org

Mr Miguel SANZ SESMA
Presidente del Gobierno de Navarra
Avda. San Ignacio 1 • E-31002 Pamplona
Tel. +34 848427011
Fax +34 848427776
E-mail: secretarias.presidente@cfnavarra.es

Mr Ramón Luis VALCÁRCEL SISO
Presidente de la Comunidad autónoma de la Región de Murcia
s/n Palacio de San Esteban • C/. Acisclo Díaz • E-30071 Murcia
Tel. +34 968368600
Fax +34 968293477
E-mail: mdolores.alarcon3@carm.es

France

Mr Alfred ALMONT
Conseiller municipal de Schoelcher
Villa Beausite - enclos - 97 route de Terreville
F-97233 Schoelcher
Tel. +596 596521217
Fax +596 596762401
E-mail: aalmont@assemblee-nationale.fr

Mr Olivier BERTRAND
Conseiller municipal de Saint-Sylvain de Bellegarde
Rimareix • F-23190 Saint-Sylvain-Bellegarde
Tel. +33 555676682
Fax +33 555676682
E-mail: olivier.bertrand230@orange.fr

Mr Jacques BLANC
Conseiller régional du Languedoc-Roussillon
Chemin des Clauzes • F-48500 La Canourgue Cedex 2
Tel. +33 466328255
Fax +33 466329188
E-mail: jacques.blanc21@wanadoo.fr

Mr Jean-Paul BORÉ
Premier vice-président du Conseil régional du Languedoc-Roussillon
Tel. +33 673287291
Fax +33 467229460
E-mail: jp-bore@wanadoo.fr

Mr Bruno BOURG-BROC
Maire de Châlons en Champagne
Tel. +33 326693802
Fax +33 326693894
E-mail: cabinet.mairie@chalons-en-champagne.net

Mrs Claudette BRUNET-LECHENAULT
Vice-président du Conseil général de Saône-et-Loire
Fax +33 685912717
E-mail: claudette.blc@wanadoo.fr

Mr Camille DE ROCCA SERRA
Président de l'Assemblée de Corse
Tel. +33 495516427
Fax +33 495516590
E-mail: camille.deroccaserra@ct-corse.fr

Mr Michel DELEBARRE
Maire de Dunkerque
Hôtel de Ville • Place Charles Valentin • F-59140 Dunkerque Cedex
Tel. +33 328262633
Fax +33 328262863
E-mail: PES-Secretariat@cor.europa.eu
abourdon@ville-dunkerque.fr

Mr Jean-Louis DESTANS
Président du Conseil général de l'Eure
Tel. +33 232315009
Fax +33 232315099
E-mail: jeanlouis.destans@cg27.fr

Mrs Claude DU GRANRUT
Conseiller régional de Picardie
8, rue de la Montagne-Saint-Aignan BP166
F-60300 Senlis Cedex
Tel. +33 344531996
Fax +33 344535097
E-mail: claudedugranrut@orange.fr

Mr Pierre HUGON
Vice-président du Conseil général de Lozère
101, avenue du 11 Novembre BP24 • F-48000 MENDE CEDEX
Tel. +33 466650064
Fax +33 466496623
E-mail: p.hugon@cg48.fr

Mr Jean-Louis JOSEPH
Maire de la Bastidonne
Mairie • Hôtel de ville • F-84120 La Bastidonne
Tel. +33 491575338
Fax +33 491575318
E-mail: jeanlouisjoseph@wanadoo.fr

Mr Jean-Yves LE DRIAN
Président du Conseil régional de Bretagne
Tel. +33 299271338
Fax +33 299271437
E-mail: v.laurent@region-bretagne.fr

Mr Alain LE VERN
Président du Conseil régional de Haute-Normandie
5, rue Robert-Schuman • F-76174 Rouen
Tel. +33 235525906
Fax +33 235525773
E-mail: alain.levern@cr-haute-normandie.fr

Mr Philippe LEROY
Président du Conseil général de Moselle
Tel. +33 387375757
Fax +33 387375707

Mr Jean-Jacques LOZACH
Président du Conseil général de Creuse
Tel. +33 544302314
Fax +33 555522855
E-mail: president@cg23.fr

Mr Pierre MAILLE
Président du Conseil général du Finistère
Tel. +33 298762398
Fax +33 298762013
E-mail: pierre.maille2@cg29.fr

Mr Daniel PERCHERON
Président du Conseil régional du Nord-Pas-de-Calais
Tel. +33 328825030
Fax +33 328825900
E-mail: d.rousseau@nordpasdecalais.fr

Mr Jean-Vincent PLACÉ
Conseiller régional d'Ile-de-France
Tel. +33 153856945
Fax +33 153856949
E-mail: jean-vincent.place@wanadoo.fr

Mr Jean PRORIOL
Conseiller régional d'Auvergne
Tel. +33 140637315
Fax +33 140637951
E-mail: jproriol.assemblee@wanadoo.fr

Mr Christophe ROUILLON
Maire de Coulaines
Tel. +33 243743518
Fax +33 243743542
E-mail: christopherouillon@wanadoo.fr

Mr Alain ROUSSET
Président du Conseil régional d'Aquitaine
Tel. +33 557570202
Fax +33 556247280
E-mail: arousset@aquitaine.fr

Mr René SOUCHON
Président du Conseil régional d'Auvergne
Tel. +33 608803812
E-mail: s.chanet@cr-auvergne.fr

Mr Bernard SOULAGE
Premier vice-président du Conseil régional de Rhône-Alpes
2, impasse du Tramier BP19 • F-38240 Meylan
Tel. +33 476418397
Fax +33 476418397
E-mail: b.soulage@wanadoo.fr
http://www.cr-rhone-alpes.fr

Italy

Mr Antonio BASSOLINO
Presidente della Regione Campania
Regione Campania • Av. de Cortenbergh 60 • B-1000 Bruxelles - Brussel
Tel. +32 27379189
Fax +32 27379199
E-mail: dario.gargiulo@regione.campania.it

Dott. Enrico BORGHI
Consigliere comunale di Vogogna (VB)
c/o Uncem • Via Palestro 30 • I-00186 Roma
Tel. +39 064441381
Fax +39 064441621
E-mail: e.borghi@uncem.net

Mrs Mercedes BRESSO
Presidente della Regione Piemonte
Piazza Castello 165 • I-10122 Torino
Tel. +39 0114321600
Fax +39 0114323848
E-mail: presidente@regione.piemonte.it

Mr Claudio BURLANDO
Presidente della Regione Liguria
Tel. +39 0105488890
Fax +39 0105373812
E-mail: anna.costantini@regione.liguria.it

Mr Luciano CAVERI
Consigliere regionale/Presidente della Regione Valle d'Aosta
Tel. +39 0165273764
Fax +39 0165273303
E-mail: presidenza@regione.vda.it

Mrs Maria Luisa COPPOLA
Consigliere regionale - Assessore, Regione Veneto
Tel. +39 0412792827
Fax +39 0412792856
E-mail: ass.bilancio@regione.veneto.it

Mr Ottaviano DEL TURCO
Presidente della Regione Abruzzo
Tel. +32 26262850
Fax +32 26262859
E-mail: ottaviano.delturco@regione.abruzzo.it

Mr Leonardo DOMENICI
Mayor of Florence, Sindaco del comune di Firenze
Via dei Prefetti 46, I-00186 Roma, Italia
Tel. +39 0668009237
Fax +39 0668009222
E-mail: p.manna@anci.it

Mr Luis DURNWALDER
Consigliere regionale/Presidente Provincia autonoma di Bolzano
Landhaus • Crispistr. 3 • I-39100 Bozen
Tel. +39 0471412222
Fax +39 0471992299
E-mail: presidente@provincia.bz.it

Mr Isidoro GOTTARDO
Consigliere comunale di Sacile (PN)
Secretariat PPE bureau 7050 • Rue Belliard 101 • B-1040 Bruxelles - Brussel
Tel. +39 0403773102
Fax +39 0403773180
E-mail: presidente@forzaitalia-fvg.com

Mr Agazio LOIERO
Presidente della Regione Calabria
Tel. +39 0961368776
Fax +39 0961858253
E-mail: v.falcone@regcal.it

Mr Piero MARRAZZO
Presidente della Regione Lazio
Tel. +39 0651685334
Fax +39 0651685455
E-mail: presidente@regione.lazio.it

Mr Claudio MARTINI
Presidente della Regione Toscana
c/o Regione Toscana • Via Cavour 18 • I-50129 Firenze
Tel. +39 055215425
Fax +39 055212820
E-mail: claudiomartini@regione.toscana.it

Mrs Sonia MASINI
Presidente della Provincia di Reggio Emilia
Tel. +39 0522444138
+39 0522444174
Fax +39 0522444108
E-mail: presidenza@mbox.provincia.re.it
c.manicardi@mbox.provincia.re.it

Mr Giuseppe MICARELLI
Sindaco del Comune di Capodimonte
Municipio di Capodimonte, I-01010 Capodimonte, Italie
Tel. +39 0761870043
Fax +39 0761871206
E-mail: sindaco@comune.capodimonte.vt.it

Mr Guido MILANA
Consigliere comunale di Olevano
Tel. +39 0669941905
Fax +39 066790319
E-mail: gmilana@regione.lazio.it

Mr Graziano Ernesto MILIA
President of the Province of Cagliari
Tel. +39 0704092013
Fax +39 0704092230
E-mail: presidente@provincia-cagliari.it

Mr Francesco MUSOTTO
Deputato dell'Assemblea Regionale Siciliana, Assemblea regionale Siciliana
Piazza del Parlamento 1
I-90134 Palermo, Italie
Tel. +39 0916114696
Fax +39 0916127042
E-mail: info@eurodevelopment.it

Mr Roberto PELLA
Consigliere provinciale di Biella
Vice-sindaco Valdengo
Via Libertà 41 • I-13855 Valdengo
Tel. +39 3355450686
Fax +39 015881375
E-mail: robertopella@libero.it

Mr Vito SANTARSIERO
Sindaco di Potenza
Tel. +39 097137475
Fax +39 097137475
E-mail: ancibasilicata@ancibasilicata.191.it

Dr Renato SORU
Presidente della Regione Sardegna
Tel. +39 0706067000
Fax +39 070272485
E-mail: presidente@regione.sardegna.it

Mr Gian Mario SPACCA
Presidente della Regione Marche
Tel. +39 07180623287
Fax +39 0718062422
E-mail: segreteria.presidenza@regione.marche.it

Mr Nichi VENDOLA
Presidente della Regione Puglia
Tel. +39 0805522021
Fax +39 0805406035
E-mail: presidente@regione.puglia.it

Mrs Marta VINCENZI
Maire de la commune de Gênes
Tel. +39 105572200
Fax +39 102459941
E-mail: gabsindaco@comune.genova.it

Cyprus

Mr Spiros ELENODOROU
President (Proedros) of the Community Council of Oroklini
Tel. +357 24815280
Fax +357 24636817
E-mail: anetel@cytanet.com.cy

Mr Savvas ELIOFOTOU
Mayor of Strovolos
Tel. +357 99620350
Fax +357 22314043
E-mail: seliofotou@strovolos.org.cy

Mr Georgios GEORGIOU
Mayor (Dimarchos) of Kato Polemidia
Tel. +357 25821382
Fax +357 25395632
E-mail: polemidiamunicipal@cytanet.com.cy

Mr Georgios IAKOVOU
President (Proedros) of the Community Council of Agii Trimithias
Tel. +357 22832470
Fax +357 22835054
E-mail: trimithi@cytanet.com.cy
www.agioitrimithias.com.cy

Mrs Eleni LOUCAIDES
Conseiller municipal de Nicosie
Tel. +357 99619000
Fax +357 22762626
E-mail: eloucaidou@logosnet.cy.net

Mr Christos MESIS
Mayor (Dimarchos) of Mesa Yitonia
Tel. +357 25723597
Fax +357 25723744
E-mail: mesa.yitonia.municipality@cytanet.com.cy

Latvia

Mr Edvins BARTKEVICS
Ogres novada domes priekšsēdētājs (Chairman of Ogre Amalgamated Municipality Council)
Tel. +371 5071163
Fax +371 5071161
E-mail: edvinsb@oic.lv

Mr Andris ELKSNĪTIS
Dobeles pilsētas domes priekšsēdētājs (Chairman of Dobele Town Council)
Tel. +371 3722009
Fax +371 3722463
E-mail: dome@dobele.lv

Mr Edmunds KRASTIŅŠ
Rīgas pilsētas domes deputāts (Councillor of Rīga City Council)
Tel. +371 7026120
Fax +371 7026018
E-mail: edmunds.krastins@riga.lv

Mr Guntars KRIEVIŅŠ
Liepājas pilsētas domes deputāts (Councillor of Liepāja City Council)
Tel. +371 3427605
Fax +371 3480252
E-mail: authority@lsez.lv

Mr Aleksandrs LIELMEŽS
Mālpils pagasta padomes priekšsēdētājs (Chairman of Mālpils Rural Municipality Council)
Tel. +371 7970900
Fax +371 7925342
E-mail: aleksandrs@malpils.lv

Mr Tālis PUĶĪTIS
Siguldas novada domes priekšsēdētājs (Chairman of Sigulda Amalgamated Municipality Council)
Tel. +371 7970844
Fax +371 7971371
E-mail: talis.pukitis@sigulda.lv

Mrs Indra RASSA
Présidente du Conseil de district de Saldus et présidente du Conseil municipal de Nīgrande
Tel. +371 63807901
Fax +371 63807910
E-mail: i.rassa@saldus.lv

Lithuania

Mr Arnoldas ABRAMAVIČIUS
Zarasai District Municipality Council (member)
Tel. +370 38650401
Fax +370 38650402
E-mail: meras@zarasai.lt

Mr Antanas GUSTAITIS
Prienai District Municipal Council (member, mayor)
Tel. +370 31961100
Fax +370 31961199
E-mail: agustaitis@prienai.lt

Mr Raimundas JAKUTIS
Šiauliai District Municipal Council (member)
Tel. +370 41523888
Fax +370 41523886
E-mail: grazulas@takas.lt

Mr Ričardas MALINAUSKAS
Druskininkai Municipal Council (member, mayor)
Tel. +370 31355355
Fax +370 31355376
E-mail: meras@druskininkai.lt

Mr Gediminas PAVIRŽIS
Member of the Council of Vilnius district municipality
Tel. +370 52487898
Fax +370 52487478
E-mail: g.pavirzis@ubig.lt

Mrs Stasė SKUTULIENĖ
Member of Šilutė District Municipality Council
Tel. +371 68501831
Fax +371 44152474
E-mail: vicemer@pamarys.lt

Mr Aidas VAISNORA
Kazlų Rūda Municipal Council (member, mayor)
Tel. +370 34396100
Fax +370 34395276
E-mail: avaisnora@is.lt

Mr Vytautas VIGELIS
Švenčioniai District Municipal Council (member, mayor)
Tel. +370 38766364
Fax +370 38766365
E-mail: meras@svencionys.lt

Luxembourg

Mrs Simone BEISSEL
Membre du conseil communal de la ville de Luxembourg
Rue Laurent, 7 • L-1919 Luxembourg
Tel. +352 691632723
Fax +352 26201445
E-mail: sbeissel@chd.lu
http://www.luxembourg-city.lu/

Mrs Agnès DURDU
Membre du conseil communal de la commune de Wincrange
Administration communale • Maison n°47 • L-9752 Hamiville
Tel. +352 994366
Fax +352 26914047
E-mail: durdur@pt.lu

Mr Albert LENTZ
Membre du conseil communal de la commune de Mersch
20, rue Ad. Bouvart • L-7519 Mersch
Tel. +352 328387
Fax +352 320741
E-mail: lentza@pt.lu

Mr Paul-Henri MEYERS
Membre du conseil communal de la ville de Luxembourg
1, Auguste Trémont • L-2624 Luxembourg
Tel. +352 474282
Fax +352 466466
E-mail: pmeyers@chd.lu
http://www.luxembourg-city.lu/

Mr Marc SCHAEFER
Member of Vianden municipal council
Tel. +352 834178
Fax +352 834178
E-mail: marcsch@pt.lu

Mr Romain SCHNEIDER
Membre du conseil communal de la ville de Wiltz
Réimerwée 10 • L-9681 ROULLINGEN
Tel. +352 95993936
Fax +352 95993936
E-mail: schniggi@chd.lu
http://www.wiltz.lu/

Hungary

Mr Ferenc BENKÖ
Tiszaladány polgármestere
Tel. +36 47552140
+36 47352835
Fax +36 47352835
E-mail: benkof@tiszaladany.hu

Mr Gabor BIHARY
Member of Budapest General Assembly
Tel. +36 204668471
Fax +36 13271795
E-mail: biharyg@t-online.hu

Dr György GÉMESI
Gödöllö polgármestere
Tel. +36 28529179
Fax +36 28529255
E-mail: gemesi@godollo.hu

Dr Gyorgy IPKOVICH
Szombathely Megyei Jogú Város polgármestere
Tel. +36 94520125
Fax +36 94313172
E-mail: ipkovich@szombathely.hu

Mr Árpád MOLNÁR
Balatonszabadi polgármestere (Mayor of Balatonszabadi)
Tel. +36 702186538
E-mail: molnararpad@hotmail.com

Mr Sándor NAGY
Kistelek polgármestere
Tel. +36 62598102
Fax +36 62598101
E-mail: polgarmester@kistelek.hu

Mr István SÉRTŐ-RADICS
Uszka polgármestere
Tel. +36 44378250
Fax +36 44578051
E-mail: stephen2@axelero.hu

Mr Gyula SZABO
Parlamenti képviselö, Heves Megyei Közgyülés tagja
Tel. +36 204668138
Fax +36 14415306
E-mail: gyula.szabo@parlament.hu

Mr András SZALAY
Representative of the Settlement Veszprém
Tel. +36 704574634
Fax +36 88549268
E-mail: szalay.andras@gov.veszprem.hu

Mr Zoltán VARGA
Békés Megyei Közgyülés elnöke
Tel. +36 66441156
Fax +36 66441609
E-mail: zoltan.varga@parlament.hu

Dr Ferenc WEKLER
Mecseknádasd polgármestere
Tel. +36 72463047
Fax +36 72463033
E-mail: kosz@kosz.hu

Malta

Mrs Claudette ABELA BALDACCHINO
Deputy Mayor, Qrendi Local Council
Tel. +356 79420707
Fax +356 21240717
E-mail: claudette.baldacchino@super1.com
claudette.baldacchino@gmail.com

Mr Michael COHEN
Mayor, Kalkara Local Council
Tel. +356 79478921
Fax +356 21665566
E-mail: cohen@di-ve.com

Mr Frederick CUTAJAR
Mayor of Santa Lucija
Tel. +356 21826190
Fax +356 21666622
E-mail: frederick.cutajar@gov.mt
www.santalucija.gov.mt

Mr Noel FORMOSA
Mayor, San Lawrenz Local Council
Tel. +356 99475948
Fax +356 21563656
E-mail: noel.a.formosa@gov.mt

Mr Ian MICALLEF
Councillor, Gzira Local Council
Tel. +356 79470191
Fax +356 21446427
E-mail: imicallef@waldonet.net.mt

The Netherlands

Mr Rob BATS
Gedeputeerde in de provincie Drenthe
Tel. +31 592365453
Fax +31 592365765
E-mail: j.h.bats@drenthe.nl

Mrs Lenie DWARSHUIS-VAN DE BEEK
Gedeputeerde van de provincie Zuid-Holland
Tel. +31 704417087
Fax +31 704417992
E-mail: secrdwarshuis@pzh.nl

Mr Léon FRISSEN
Commissaris der Koningin in de provincie Limburg
Tel. +31 433897002
Fax +31 433618575
E-mail: ljpm.frissen@prvlimburg.nl

Mr Henk KOOL
Wethouder te Den Haag
Tel. +31 703532650
Fax +31 703532479
E-mail: h.p.m.kool@denhaag.nl

Mrs Rinske KRUISINGA
Gedeputeerde van de provincie Noord-Holland
Tel. +31 235144248
Fax +31 235144073
E-mail: secr.kruisinga@noord-holland.nl

Mr Cor LAMERS
Burgemeester van Houten
Tel. +31 0306392700
Fax +31 0306392680
E-mail: bestuurssecretariaat@houten.nl

Mrs Johanna MAIJ-WEGGEN
Commissaris der Koningin in de provincie Noord-Brabant
Tel. +31 736812150
Fax +31 736808558
E-mail: istegeman@brabant.nl

Mr Ivo OPSTELTEN
Burgemeester van de gemeente Rotterdam
Stadhuis Rotterdam
Coolsingel 40
NL-3011 AD Rotterdam
Tél +31 104896998
Fax +31 104897149
E-mail: c.lange@obr.rotterdam.nl

Mr Antón ROMBOUTS
Burgemeester van de gemeente 's-Hertogenbosch
Postbus 12345 • NL • 5200 GZ 's-Hertogenbosch
Tel. +31 736155888
Fax +31 736155300
E-mail: dinl@s-hertogenbosch.nl

Dr Co VERDAAS
Gedeputeerde in de provincie Gelderland
Tel. +31 263599035
Fax +31 263599093
E-mail: j.verdaas@gs.gelderland.nl

Mr Bas VERKERK
Burgemeester van Delft
Gemeente Delft • M. Nijhofflaan 2 • NL • 2624 Delft
Tel. +31 152602424
Fax +31 152602364
E-mail: bverkerk@delft.nl

Mr Ruud VREEMAN
Burgemeester van de gemeente Tilburg
Tel. +31 135429000
Fax +31 135429396
E-mail: ruud.vreeman@tilburg.nl

Austria

Gabriele BURGSTALLER
Landeshauptfrau von Salzburg
Chiemseehof, Stiege 1 • A-5010 Salzburg
Tel. +43 66280425001
Fax +43 66280425010
E-mail: burgstaller@salzburg.gv.at
http://www.land-sbg.gv.at

Mr Gerhard DÖRFLER
Landeshauptmann, Kärnten
Arnulfplatz 1, A-9020 Klagefurt am Wörthersee, A-9020 Klagenfurt, Austria
Tél +43 5053622601
Fax +43 5053622600
E-mail: gerhard.doerfler@knt.gv.at

Mrs Marianne FÜGL
Vizebürgermeisterin, Marktgemeinde Traisen
Tel. +43 6645854413
Fax +43 274231305420
E-mail: mfuegl@gvvnoe.at

Dr Michael HÄUPL
Landeshauptmann von Wien
Rathaus • A-1082 Wien
Tel. +43 1400081111
Fax +43 140007110
E-mail: michael.haeupl@wien.gv.at

Mr Erwin MOHR
Bürgermeister, Marktgemeinde Wolfurt
Tel. +43 6643382325
Fax +43 55746840811
E-mail: erwin.mohr@wolfurt.at

Mr Hans NIESSL
Landeshauptmann von Burgenland
Verbingundgsbüro des Landes Burgenland zur EU z. Hd. Andrea M. KRAINER • Europaplatz 1 • A-7000 Eisenstadt
Tel. +43 26826002499
Fax +43 26826002499
E-mail: hans.niessl@bgld.gv.at

Dr Erwin PRÖLL
Landeshauptmann von Niederösterreich
Landeshausplatz 1 • A-3109 St. Pölten
Tel. +43 2742900512000
Fax +43 2742900513030
E-mail: lh.proell@noel.gv.at

Dr Josef PÜHRINGER
Landeshauptman von Oberösterreich
Klosterstr. 7 • A-4021 Linz
Tel. +43 732772011100
Fax +43 732772011790
E-mail: lh.puehringer@ooe.gv.at

Dr Herbert SAUSGRUBER
Landeshauptman von Vorarlberg
Landhaus • Römerstr. 15 • A-6900 Bregenz
Tel. +43 557451120090
Fax +43 557451120000
E-mail: herbert.sausgruber@vorarlberg.at

Mr Heinz SCHADEN
Bürgermeister der Stadt Salzburg
Tel. +43 66280722520
Fax +43 66280722398
E-mail: buergermeister@stadt-salzburg.at

Mr Herwig VAN STAA
Präsident des Tiroler Landtages
Eduard-Wallnöfer-Platz 3 • A-6020 Innsbruck
Tel. +43 5125082002
Fax +43 5125082005
E-mail: h.vanstaa@tirol.gv.at

Franz VOVES
Landeshauptmann von Steiermark
Steiermark büro - Avenue de Tervuren 82-84 • B-1040 Bruxelles - Brussel
Tel. +32 27320361
Fax +32 27321263
E-mail: steiermark-office@stmk.gv.at

Poland

Mr Jacek CZERNIAK
Przewodniczący Sejmiku województwa lubelskiego (président du Parlement de la voïvodie de Lublin)
Tel. +48 0814416614
Fax +48 0814416615
E-mail: czerniakjacek@wp.pl

Mr Adam Sebastian JARUBAS
Marshall of the Świĕtokrzyskie voivodship
Tel. +48 604420310
Fax +48 413446045
E-mail: marszalek@sejmik.kielce.pl

Mr Lech JAWORSKI
Councillor of the city of Warszawa
Tel. +48 609500322
Fax +48 228181783
E-mail: ljaworski@warszawa.um.gov.pl

Mr Maciej KOBYLIŃSKI
Prezydent miasta
Tel. +48 598424220
Fax +48 598423583
E-mail: prezydent@um.slupsk.pl

Mgr. Witold KROCHMAL
Burmistrz miasta
Tel. +48 713892429
Fax +48 713893070
E-mail: burmistrz@wolow.pl

Mr Jerzy KROPIWNICKI
Prezydent miasta
Tel. +48 426384115
Fax +48 426384124
E-mail: prezydentmiasta@uml.lodz.pl

Mr Marek NAWARA
Marshall of the Małopolskie voivodship
Tel. +48 126160124
Fax +48 122859410
E-mail: marek.nawara@umwm.pl

Mr Jacek PROTAS
Marshall of the Warmińsko-Mazurskie voivodship
Tel. +48 0895219100
Fax +48 0895219109
E-mail: marszalek@warmia.mazury.pl

Mr Józef SEBESTA
Marshall of the Opolskie voivodship
Tel. +48 775416510
Fax +48 775416512
E-mail: marszalek@umwo.opole.pl

Mr Bogusław ŚMIGIELSKI
Marszalek województwa sląskiego (Maréchal de la Voïvodie de Silésie)
Tel. +48 322553534
Fax +48 322519999
E-mail: marszal@silesia-region.pl

Mr Adam STRUZIK
Marszałek województwa
Tel. +48 225979104
Fax +48 225979290
E-mail: a.struzik@mazovia.pl

Mr Brunon SYNAK
Przewodniczący sejmiku
Tel. +48 583077543
Fax +48 58305116
E-mail: przewodniczacy@woj-pomorskie.pl

Dr Stanisław SZWABSKI
Chairman of the municipality of Gdynia
Tel. +48 586688023
Fax +48 586208772
E-mail: s.szwabski@gdynia.pl

Mgr. Marek TRAMŚ
Councillor of the Polkowice poviat
Tel. +48 767461502
Fax +48 767461501
E-mail: marektrams@op.pl

Mgr. Ludwik Kajetan WĘGRZYN
Councillor of the Bochnia poviat
Tel. +48 146122552
Fax +48 146125949
E-mail: lw@zpp.pl

Mr Leszek ŚWIĘTALSKI
Wójt gminy
Tel. +48 748452220
Fax +48 748452266
E-mail: wojt@starebogaczowice.ug.gov.pl
lswietalski@zgwrp.org.pl

Mr Marek WOŹNIAK
Marszałek województwa
Tel. +48 618541988
Fax +48 618541717
E-mail: marszalek@umww.pl

Mr Tadeusz WRONA
President of the city of Częstochowa
Tel. +48 343682552
Fax +48 343651361
E-mail: prezydent@czestochowa.um.gov.pl

Mr Jerzy ZAJAKAŁA
Wójt gminy
Tel. +48 566788217
Fax +48 566788219
E-mail: jzajakala@zgwrp.org.pl

Portugal

Mr José Luís CARNEIRO
Presidente da Câmara Municipal de Baião
Tel. +351 255540500
Fax +351 255540510
E-mail: jlcarneiro@cm-baiao.pt

Mr Carlos Manuel Martins do Vale CÉSAR
Presidente do Governo Regional dos Açores
Palácio de Santana • Rua José Jacóme Corrêa • P-9500 Ponta Delgada
Tel. +351 296301000
Fax +351 296628890
E-mail: maeirobotelho@pg.raa.pt

Mr José CORREIA
Presidente da Câmara Municipal de Tavira
Praça da República • P-8800-951 Tavira
Tel. +351 281320515
Fax +351 281324752
E-mail: presidente@cm-tavira.pt

Mr Rui Fernando DA SILVA RIO
Presidente da Câmara Municipal do Porto
Tel. +351 222097092
Fax +351 222097078
E-mail: dmri@cm-porto.pt

Mr Alberto João JARDIM
Presidente do Governo Regional da Madeira
Quinta da Vigia • Avenida do Infante, 1 • P-9004-547 Funchal
Tel. +351 291214660
Fax +351 291222827
E-mail: gabimprensa.presidencia@gov-madeira.pt

Dr Manuel do Nascimento MARTINS
Presidente da Câmara Municipal de Vila Real
Avenida Carvalho Araújo • P-5000-657 Vila Real
Tel. +351 259308100
Fax +351 259308161
E-mail: ri@cm-vilareal.pt

Mr Carlos Alberto PINTO
Presidente da Câmara Municipal da Covilhã
Praça do Município • P-6200-151 Covilhá
Tel. +351 275330600
Fax +351 275330633
E-mail: info@cm-covilha.pt

Mr Joaquim Moreira RAPOSO
Presidente da Câmara Municipal da Amadora
Av. Movimento das Forças Armadas • P-2700-595 Amadora
Tel. +351 214369000
Fax +351 214922082
E-mail: gab.presidente.cma@mail.telepac.pt
www.cm-amadora.pt

Mr Carlos Manuel RODRIGUES PINTO DE SÁ
Presidente da Câmara Municipal de Montemor-o-Novo
Largo Paços do Concelho • P-7050-127 Montemor-o-Novo
Tel. +351 266898100
Fax +351 266896617
E-mail: Cpintosa@mail.telepac.pt

Mr Fernando de Carvalho RUAS
Presidente da Câmara Municipal de Viseu
Praça da República • P-3504-501 Viseu
Tel. +351 232429572
Fax +351 232427427
E-mail: presidencia@cmviseu.pt

Mr Francisco MESQUITA MACHADO
Presidente da Câmara Municipal de Braga
Praça do Município • P-4704-514 Braga
Tel. +351 253613380
Fax +351 253613387
E-mail: gab.presidencia@cm-braga.pt

Mr Carlos Alberto Santos TUTA
Presidente da Câmara Municipal de Monchique
Câmara Municipal de Monchique • Travessa Da Portela • P-8550-470 Monchique
Tel. +351 282910200
Fax +351 282912810
E-mail: presidente@cm-monchique.pt

Romania

Mr Cristian ANGHEL
Maire, mairie de la municipalité Baia Mare
Tel. +40 262213824
Fax +40 262212332
E-mail: cristian_anghel@baiamarecity.ro

Mr Decebal ARNĂUTU
Mayor of Târgu-Neamţ town
Tel. +40 751040004
Fax +40 233790508
E-mail: primar@primariatgneamt.ro

Mr Gheorghe BUNEA STANCU
President of Brăila County Council
Tél: +40 239619945
Fax: +40 239611765
E-mail: gheorghe_bunea@cjbraila.ro

Mr Mircea COSMA
President of Prahova County Council
Tel. +40 244514820
Fax +40 244596669
E-mail: presedinte@cjph.ro

Mr Emil DRĂGHICI
Maire, mairie de la commune Vulcana Băi
Tel. +40 744329838
Fax +40 245230904
E-mail: primar@vulcanabai.ro

Mr Gheorghe FALCĂ
Mayor of Arad municipality
Tel. +40 257250603
Fax +40 257253842
E-mail: gfalca@yahoo.com

Mr Răducu George FILIPESCU
Président, conseil départemental Călăraşi
Tel. +40 242331591
Fax +40 242331609
E-mail: cicalarasi@calarasi.ro

Mrs Veronica IONIŢĂ
Maire, mairie de la commune Gorgota
Tel. +40 745157946
Fax +40 244474041
E-mail: primar@gorgota.ro

Mrs Edita Emoke LOKODI
Présidente, conseil départemental Mureş
Tel. +40 265261904
Fax +40 265268718
E-mail: lokodi@cjmures.ro

Mr Alin Adrian NICA
Maire, mairie de la commune Dudeştii Noi
Tel. +40 256378020
Fax +40 256378294
E-mail: alinnica@yahoo.com

Mr Constantin OSTAFICIUC
Président, conseil départemental Timiş
Tel. +40 256406323
Fax +40 256406301
E-mail: constantin.ostaficiuc@cjtimis.ro

Mr Tudor PENDIUC
Maire, mairie de la municipalité Piteşti
Tel. +40 248220088
Fax +40 248212166
E-mail: primar@primariapitesti.ro

Mr Ion PRIOTEASA
President of Dolj County Council
Tel. +40 251418650
Fax +40 251408241
E-mail: ion.prioteasa@cjdolj.ro

Mr Emil PROSCAN
Maire, mairie de la ville Mizil
Tel. +40 244250027
Fax +40 244251120
E-mail: primaria@primaria-mizil.ro

Mr Vasile SAVA
Mayor of Ţăndărei town
Tel. +40 243273529
Fax +40 243273552
E-mail: primaria.tandarei@yahoo.com

Slovenia

Mr Aleš ČERIN
Podžupan Mestne občine Ljubljana
E-mail: ales.cerin@ljubljana.si

Mrs Irena MAJCEN
Županja Občine Slovenska Bystrica
Tel. +386 41673147
Fax +386 28181141
E-mail: mira.kresnik@slov-bistrica.si

Mr Franci ROKAVEC
Župan Občine Litija
Tel. +386 015690001
Fax +386 018963460
E-mail: franci.rokavec@litijo.si

Mr Anton SMOLNIKAR
Mayor of the Municipality of Kamnik
Tel. +386 18318117
Fax +386 18318119
E-mail: zupan@kamnik.si

Mr Robert SMRDELJ
Mayor of the Municipality of Pivka
Tel. +386 57210100
Fax +386 57210102
E-mail: zupan@pivka.si

Mrs Jasmina VIDMAR
Članica občinskega sveta Mestne občine Maribor
Tel. +386 41791003
E-mail: jasmina@skupnostobcin.si

Mr Franci VOVK
Župan Občine Dolenjske Toplice
Tel. +386 41408555
Fax +386 73854190
E-mail: zupan.dtoplice@siol.net

Slovakia

Ing. Vladimír BAJAN
Predseda Bratislavského samosprávneho kraja (Président de la région autonome de Bratislava)
Tel. +421 248264151
Fax +421 248264397
E-mail: predseda@region-bsk.sk

Mr Milan BELICA
President of the Nitra Self-governing Region (Predseda Nitrianskeho samosprávneho kraja)
Tel. +421 376534344
Fax +421 376566536
E-mail: predseda@unsk.sk

Mr Juraj BLANÁR
President of the Žilina Self-governing Region (Predseda Žilinského samosprávneho kraja)
Tel. +421 415032700
Fax +421 415032702
E-mail: predseda@zask.sk

MUDr. Peter CHUDÍK
President of the Prešov Self-governing Region (Predseda Prešovského samosprávneho kraja)
Tel. +421 517460401
Fax +421 517712524
E-mail: predseda@vucpo.sk

Ing. Andrej ĎURKOVSKÝ
Primátor hlavného mesta SR - Bratislavy
Tel. +421 259356555
E-mail: primatorba@bratislava.sk

Ing. František KNAPÍK
Primátor mesta Košice
Tel. +421 556419212
Fax +421 556419104
E-mail: primator@kosice.sk

Mr Ján ORAVEC
Mayor of the City of Štúrovo (Primátor mesta Štúrovo)
Tel. +421 367511073
Fax +421 367511472
E-mail: primator@sturovo.sk

JUDr. Zdenko TREBULA
President of the Košice Self-governing Region (Predseda Košického samosprávneho kraja)
Tel. +421 557268113
Fax +421 557268119
E-mail: vuc@kosice.regionet.sk

Ing. István ZACHARIAŠ
Primátor mesta Moldava nad Bodvou
Tel. +421 554880211
Fax +421 554603221
E-mail: zacharias.istvan@moldava.sk

Finland

Mr Risto ERVELÄ
Varsinais-Suomen liiton maakuntavaltuuston puheenjohtaja
Sauvontie 11 • FI-21570 Sauvo
Tel. +358 500130550
Fax +358 22312036
E-mail: risto.ervela@keskusta.fi

Mrs Pauliina HAIJANEN
Varsinais-Suomen liiton maakuntahallituksen jäsen
Koulukatu 7 • FI-23500 Uusikaupunki
Tel. +358 400723952
Fax +358 28414472
E-mail: pauliina@haijanen.fi

Mr Risto KOIVISTO
Pirkanmaan liiton maakuntahallituksen puheenjohtaja
Laaksotie 1 B 23 • FI-33960 Pirkkala
Tel. +358 505526115
Fax +358 331342391
E-mail: risto.koivisto@pirkkala.fi

Mr Veikko KUMPUMÄKI
Lapin liiton maakuntavaltuuston jäsen
Tel. +358 405472496
Fax +358 016259679
E-mail: veikko.kumpumaki@kemi.fi

Mr Antti LIIKKANEN
Rovaniemen kaupunginvaltuuston jäsen
Tel. +358 400692548
E-mail: antti.liikkanen@rovaniemi.fi

Mrs Britt LUNDBERG
Landskapsregeringsledamot
Tel. +358 1825000
Fax +358 1825381
E-mail: britt.lundberg@regeringen.ax

Mr Jyrki MYLLYVIRTA
Mayor of Lahti
City of Lahti • Harjukatu 31 • FI - Lahti
Tel. +358 151942000
Fax +358 151942040
E-mail: Jyrki.Myllyvirta@lahti.fi

Sweden

Mr Uno ALDEGREN
Ordförande i regionstyrelsen, Skåne läns landsting
Region Skåne ‡ S-29189 Kristianstad
Tel. +46 44133262
Fax +46 44133347
E-mail: uno.aldegren@skane.se

Mrs Kristina ALVENDAL
Tel. +46 850829005
Fax +46 850829997
E-mail: kristina.alvendal@stadshuset.stockholm.se

Mrs Ann BESKOW
Orsa kommun
Orsa Kommun • Jarnvagsgatan 23F • S-79430 Orsa
Tel. +46 25040572
E-mail: ann.beskow@orsa.se

Mrs Lotta HÅKANSSON HARJU
Järfälla kommun
Tel. +46 704808596
E-mail: lotta.hakansson@jarfalla.se

Mr Kent JOHANSSON
Västra Götalands läns landsting
Regionalstyrelsen, Residenset • S-46280 Vänersborg
Tel. +46 521275718
Fax +46 521275720
E-mail: kent.johansson@vgregion.se

Mr Anders KNAPE
Karlstads kommun
Sveriges Kommuner och Landsting, Hornsgatan 20 • S-11882 Stockholm
Tel. +46 54295131
Fax +46 54295099
E-mail: Anders.Knape@skl.se

Mr Paul LINDQUIST
Lidingö kommun
Lidingo Stad, Stockholmsvagen 50
S-18182 Lidingö, Suède
Tel. +46 87313050
Fax +46 87313592
E-mail: paul.lindquist@lidingo.se

Mrs Mona-Lisa NORRMAN
Ledamot i landstingsfullmäktige, Jämtlands läns landsting
Jämtlands läns landsting, Box 602 • S-83223 Frösön
Tel. +46 63147554
Fax +46 63147515
E-mail: monalisa.norrman@jll.se

Mr Ilmar REEPALU
Malmö kommun
Tel. +46 40341002
Fax +46 40237300
E-mail: ilmar.reepalu@malmo.se

Mrs Catarina SEGERSTEN-LARSSON
Värmlands läns landsting
Nyponstigen 15 • S-66535 Kil
Tel. +46 54614132
Fax +46 54614057
E-mail: catarina.segersten.larsson@moderat.se
eskebol@hotmail.com

Mrs Annelie STARK
Vätra Götalands läns landsting
Västra Götalandsregionen, Regionens hus
Regiostyrelsen • S-46280 Vänersborg
Tel. +46 521275732
Fax +46 521275760
E-mail: anneli.stark@vgregion.se

Mrs Maria WALLHAGER NECKMAN
Stockholms läns landsting
Tel. +46 87374191
Fax +46 87374470
E-mail: maria.wallhager@politik.sll.se

United Kingdom

Cllr Doris ANSARI
Member of Cornwall County Council
Tel. +44 1872274846
E-mail: dansari@cornwall.gov.uk

Mrs Jennette ARNOLD
Member of London Assembly
City Hall, The Queen's Walk • UK • SEI 2AA London
Tel. +44 2079834357
Fax +44 2079835874
E-mail: jennette.arnold@london.gov.uk

Cllr Paula BAKER
Member of Basingstoke and Deane Council
Tel. +44 1256771219
Fax +44 1256773130
E-mail: cllr. paula.baker@basingstoke.gov.uk

Mr Albert BORE
Member of Birmingham City Council
The Council House • Victoria Square • UK
B1 1BB Birmingham
Tel. +44 1213032496
Fax +44 1213032787
E-mail: albert.bore@birmingham.gov.uk

Mr Keith BROWN
Member of the Scottish Parliament
The Scottish Parliament • UK • EH99 1SP
Edinburgh
Tel. +44 1259743005
Fax +44 1259743768
E-mail: keith.brown.msp@scottish.parliament.uk
http://www.clacksweb.org.uk

Mrs Christine CHAPMAN
Member of the National Assembly of Wales
E-mail: christine.chapman@wales.gov.uk

Mrs Flo CLUCAS
Member of Liverpool City Council
Hunts Cross Avenue 209 • UK • L25 9NB
Liverpool
Tel. +44 1512252601
Fax +44 1512252983
E-mail: flo.clucas@liverpool.gov.uk

Sir Simon DAY
Member of Devon County Council
County Hall • Topsham • UK • EX2 4QD Exeter
Tel. +44 1392382000
Fax +44 1392382286
E-mail: simon.day@devon.gov.uk

Cllr Linda GILLHAM
Member of Runnymede Borough Council
Tel. +44 1932564834
Fax +44 1932569672
E-mail: cllr.linda.gillham@runnymede.gov.uk

Cllr Martin HEATLEY
Member of Warwickshire County Council
Tel. +44 2476382547
Fax +44 2476382547
E-mail: cllrheatley@warwickshire.gov.uk

Mr Gordon KEYMER
Member of Tandridge District Council
Courtlands Rockfield Road • UK • RH8 0EJ
Oxted
Tel. +44 1883 717363
Fax +44 1883 717363
E-mail: gordon@gckeymer.freeserve.co.uk

Mr Roger KNOX
Member Services
East Lothian Council - John Muir House
Haddington EH41 3HA
E-mail: rknox@eastlothian.gov.uk

Cllr Iain MALCOLM
Member of South Tyneside Council
Tel. +44 1914562019
Fax +44 1914562019
E-mail: cllr.iain.malcolm@southtyneside.gov.uk

Cllr Corrie MCCHORD
Member of Stirling Council
Viewforth • UK • FK8 2ET Stirling
Tel. +44 1786 443378
Fax +44 1786 442636
E-mail: mcchordc@stirling.gov.uk

Mrs Irene OLDFATHER
Member of the Scottish Parliament
10 Willow Gardens, Stanecastle, Ayrshire • UK •
KA11 1QY Irvine
Tel. +44 1294313078
Fax +44 1294313605
E-mail: irene.oldfather.msp@scottish.parliament.uk

Cllr Stephen PARNABY
Member of East Riding of Yorkshire Council
Tel. +44 1482393220
E-mail: councillor.parnaby@eastriding.gov.uk

Cllr David PARSONS
Member of Leicestershire County Council
Tel. +44 1162390869
Fax +44 1162392675
E-mail: dparsons@leics.gov.uk

Cllr Edwin POOTS
Member of Lisburn City Council
E-mail: edwin.poots@niassembly.gov.uk

Cllr Dave QUAYLE
Member of Trafford Metropolitan Borough Council
Tel. +44 1619124199
E-mail: dave.quayle@trafford.gov.uk

Dr Graham TOPE
Member of London Borough of Sutton
88 The Gallop • UK • Sutton
Tel. +44 2087707269
Fax +44 2086428595
E-mail: Graham.Tope@sutton.gov.uk

Cllr Keith WALTERS
Member of Cambridgeshire County Council
Tel. +44 1223717228
Fax +44 1223717561
E-mail: keith.walters@cambridgeshire.gov.uk

Cllr Dave WILCOX
Member of Derbyshire County Council
Tel. +44 1457853415
E-mail: dave.wilcox@debyshire.gov.uk

ALTERNATE MEMBERS

Belgium

Mr Maurice BAYENET
Député wallon
Tel. +32 81259572
Fax +32 81230945
E-mail: mbayenet@skynet.be

Mr Ludwig CALUWE
Membre du Parlement flamand
Fax +32 36672782
E-mail: ludwig@caluwe.be

Mr Bart CARON
Vlaams Volksvertegenwoordiger
Tel. +32 25524616
Fax +32 25524476
E-mail: Bart.caron@vlaamsparlement.be

Mrs Julie DE GROOTE
Député de la Communauté française
Tel. +32 25125425
Fax +32 25140928
E-mail: j.degroote@brutele.be

Mr Claude DESAMA
Bourgmestre de Verviers
Tel. +32 87325201
Fax +32 87 325354
E-mail: claude.desama@verviers.be

Mr Eloi GLORIEUX
Vlaams Volksvertegenwoordiger
Vlaams Parlement • Leuvenseweg 86 • B-1011
Bruxelles - Brussel
Tel. +32 475982093
+32 25524197
Fax +32 25524431
E-mail: Eloi.glorieux@vlaamsparlement.be

Mrs Evelyne HUYTEBROECK
Ministre de l'environnement, de l'énergie, du tourisme et de l'aide aux personnes du gouvernement de la Région de Bruxelles-Capitale

Mr Stefaan PLATTEAU
Burgemeester van Dilbeek
Boslaan 28 • B-1700 St-Ulriks-Kapelle
Tel. +32 24662558
Fax +32 24662558
E-mail: Stefaan.platteau@dilbeek.be

Mr Jan ROEGIERS
Vlaams Volksvertegenwoordiger
Tel. +32 25524251
Fax +32 25524465
E-mail: Jan.roegiers@vlaamsparlement.be

Mr Pascal SMET
Minister van de Brusselse Hoofdstedelijke regering
Tel. +32 25171272
Fax +32 25115464
E-mail: psmet@smet.irisnet.be

Mr René THISSEN
Député de la Communauté française
Tel. +32 475783185
Fax +32 80670152
E-mail: rene.thissen@skynet.be

Mr Marc VAN DEN ABEELEN
Vlaams Volksvertegenwoordiger
Tel. +32 38879401
Fax +32 38879401
E-mail: thedes@pandora.be

Bulgaria

Mr Ivo Kirilov ANDONOV
Mayor of Silistra, member of the management council of the NAMRB
Tel. +359 86824243
Fax +359 86823343
E-mail: mayor@silistra.bg

Mr Ivan ASPARUHOV
Member of BD of the National Assembly of the Municipalities of the Republic of Bulgaria, Mayor of Mezdra
Tel. +359 91092621
Fax +359 91092523
E-mail: mezdra@mail.bg

Mr Stanislav BLAGOV
Mayor of Svishtov
Tel. +359 63160854
Fax +359 63160504
E-mail: obshtina@svishtov.com

Mr Pavel Iliev DIMITROV
Municipal councillor, Varna
Tel. +359 052653138
Fax +359 052658464
E-mail: gerb_vn@mail.bg

Mr Shukran IDRIZ
Mayor of Kirkovo
Tel. +359 36792016
Fax +359 36792140
E-mail: oba_kirkovo@kardjali.net
oba_kirkovo@infotel.bg

Mr Krasimir Blagoev KOSTOV
Mayor of Shumen
Tel. +359 54800810
Fax +359 54876902
E-mail: mayor@shoumen.bg

Mr Veselin Petrov LICHEV
Mayor of Sopot
Tel. +359 886888852
Fax +359 31347660
E-mail: vessopot@abv.bg

Mr Emil Hristov NAIDENOV
Mayor of Gorna Malina
Tel. +359 7152320
Fax +359 7152252
E-mail: kmet@gornamalina.net

Mr Rumen Georgiev RASHEV
Mayor of Veliko Turnovo, Member of the management council of the NAMRB
Tel. +359 62619304
Fax +359 62627997
E-mail: rashev@vt.bia-bg.com

Mr Mithat TABAKOV
Mayor of Dulovo
Tel. +359 8553000
Fax +359 8553020
E-mail: dulovokmet@abv.bg

Mr Svetlin Genov TANCHEV
Mayor of Stara Zagora
Tel. +359 42600105
Fax +359 42601103
E-mail: mayor@city.starazagora.net

Mr Naiden ZELENOGORSKI
Mayor of Pleven
Tel. +359 64800700
Fax +359 64844230
E-mail: mayor@pleven.bg

Czech Republic

Mrs Jana ČERMÁKOVÁ
Vice-Mayor of the Municipality of Proboštov
Tel. +420 417560035
Fax +420 774137161
E-mail: sekretariat@ouprobostov.cz

Ing. Ivana ČERVINKOVÁ
Mayor of the City of Kostelec nad Orlicí, Královéhradecký kraj (Starostka města Kostelec nad Orlicí, Královehradecký kraj)
Tel. +420 494337267
Fax +420 494321295
E-mail: ivana.cervinkova@muko.cz

Ing. Pavel HORÁK
Deputy President of the Olomouc Region, Olomoucký kraj
Tel. +420 585508850
Fax +420 585508832
E-mail: p.horak@kr-olomoucky.cz

Mrs Sylva KOVÁČIKOVÁ
Mayor of the City of Bílovec
Tel. +420 603426797
Fax +420 556414205
E-mail: starosta@bilovec.cz

Mrs Ivana STRÁSKÁ
Vice-Mayor of the City of Milevsko
Tel. +420 382504124
+420 382521879
E-mail: posta@milevsko-mesto.cz

Mr Tomáš ÚLEHLA
Statutární město Zlín
Náměstí Míru 12, ‡ CZ-76140 Zlin
Tel. +420 577630736
Fax +420 577432911
E-mail: tomasulehla@muzlin.cz

Denmark

Mrs Lykke DEBOIS
Regionsrådsmedlem
Tel. +32 25501280
Fax +32 25501275
E-mail: cor@regioner.dk

Mr Jens Christian GJESING
Borgmester, Haderslev Kommune
Tel. +32 25501260
Fax +32 25501272
E-mail: international.relations@kl.dk

Mr Jens Arne HEDEGAARD
Borgmester, Brønderslev Kommune
Tel. +32 25501260
Fax +32 25501272
E-mail: international.relations@kl.dk

Mrs Anna Margrethe KAALUND
Byrådsmedlem (Town Councillor), Viborg Kommune
Tel. +32 25501260
Fax +32 25501272
E-mail: international.relations@kl.dk

Mrs Tove LARSEN
Formand for sammenlægningsudvalget, Aabenraa Kommune
Local Government Denmark • Square de Meeûs 1 • B-1000 Bruxelles
Tel. +32 25501260
Fax +32 25501272
E-mail: international.relations@kl.dk

Mr Bent LARSEN
Regionsrådsmedlem
Tel. +32 25501280
Fax +32 25501275
E-mail: cor@regioner.dk

Mr Erik NIELSEN
Borgmester, Rødovre Kommune
Tel. +32 25501260
Fax +32 25501272
E-mail: international.relations@kl.dk

Mr Søren SALLING
Regionsrådsmedlem
Tel. +32 25501280
Fax +32 25501275
E-mail: cor@regioner.dk

Mr Jens STENBÆK
Viceborgmester (Deputy Mayor), Holbæk Kommune
Square de Meeùs 1 ‡ B-1000 Bruxelles

Germany

Mr Peter Harry CARSTENSEN
Ministerpräsident des Landes Schleswig-Holstein
Tel. +49 4319882000
Fax +49 4319881960
E-mail: peter.harry.carstensen@stk.landsh.de

Dr Karl DÖHLER
Mitglied des Landtages des Freistaates Bayern
Tel. +49 08941262318
Fax +49 08941261318
E-mail: karl.doehler@t-online.de

Mr Roland HEINTZE
Mitglied der Hamburger Bürgerschaft
Bürgerschaftskanzlei ‡ C 200
Schmiedestrasse 2
D-20095 Hamburg

Mr Norbert KARTMANN
Mitglied des Landtages, Hessen
Tel. +49 611350200
Fax +49 611350435
E-mail: c.reitzmann@ltg.hessen.de

Mr Guido KOSMEHL
Mitglied des Landtages, Sachsen-Anhalt
Tel. +49 03915606106
Fax +49 03915606006
E-mail: info@kosmehl-mdl.de

Dr Hermann KUHN
Mitglied der Bremischen Bürgerschaft (Landtag)
Tel. +49 4215974721
Fax +49 4213011250
E-mail: hermann.kuhn@gruene-bremen.de

Mrs Helma KUHN-THEIS
Mitglied des Landtages des Saarlandes
Landtag des Saarlandes • Franz-Josef-Röder Strasse 7 • D-66119 Saarbruecken
Tel. +49 6815002294
Fax +49 6815002519
E-mail: b.klenner@cdu-fraktion-saar.de
http://www.saarland.de

Mr Wolfram KUSCHKE
Mitglied des Landtages, Nordrhein-Westfalen
Tel. +49 02118842585
Fax +49 02118843194
E-mail: wolfram.kuschke@landtag.nrw.de

Mr Clemens LINDEMANN
Landrat des Saarpfalz-Kreises
Tel. +49 06841104203
Fax +49 06841104200
E-mail: Clemens.Lindemann@saarpfalz-kreis.de

Mr Winfried MACK
Mitglied des Landtages von Baden-Württemberg
Tel. +49 07112063959
Fax +49 0711206314959
E-mail: Winfried.Mack@cdu.landtag-bw.de

Mrs Manuela MAHNKE
Mitglied der Bremischen Bürgerschaft (Landtag)
Tel. +49 04713089381
Fax +49 04713086559
E-mail: manuela.mahnke@spd-online.de

Martina MICHELS
Mitglied des Abgeordnetenhauses von Berlin
Tel. +32 27380070
Fax +32 27324746
E-mail: renate.voelpel@skzl.verwalt-berlin.de

Prof. Dr. Georg MILBRADT
Ministerpräsident des Freistaates Sachsen, Mitglied des Landtages
Tel. +32 22358730
Fax +32 22358722
E-mail: adr@bxl.sk.sachsen.de

Mrs Nicole MORSBLECH
Mitglied des Landtages, Rheinland-Pfalz
Tel. +49 061312083017
Fax +49 061312084047
E-mail: nicole@morsblech.de

Mr Detlef MÜLLER
Mitglied des Landtages von Mecklenburg-Vorpommern
Tel. +49 3855881731
Fax +49 3855881079
E-mail: doris.junewitz@stk.mv-regierung.de

Mr Günther H. OETTINGER
Ministerpräsident von Baden-Württemberg
Tel. +49 07112153360
E-mail: anita.wochner@stm.bwl.de

Mrs Barbara RICHSTEIN
Mitglied des Landtags von Brandenburg
Landtag Brandenburg • Am Havelblick 6 • D-14473 Potsdam
Tel. +49 3319661435
Fax +49 3319661406
E-mail: barbara.richstein@lt-cdu-fraktion.brandenburg.de

Mr Roland RIESE
Mitglied des Niedersächsischen Landtages
Tel. +49 4921993577
Fax +49 4921993579
E-mail: riese-fdp@online.de

Mrs Petra ROTH
Oberbürgermeisterin der Stadt Frankfurt
Stadt Frankfurt am Main • Römerberg 23 • D-60275 Frankfurt
Tel. +49 6921233100
Fax +49 6921237893
E-mail: petra.roth@stadt-frankfurt.de
burero-oberbuergermeisterin@stadt-frankfurt.de

Mr Michael SCHROEREN
Mitglied des Landtages, Nordrhein-Westfalen
Tel. +49 02118842976
Fax +49 02118843179
E-mail: michael.schroeren@landtag.nrw.de

Mr Fritz SCHRÖTER
Mitglied des Landtages, Freistaat Thüringen
Thüringer Landtag • Eisenbahnstr. 4 • D-04626 SCHMÖLLN
Tel. +49 3449123654
Fax +49 3449161108
E-mail: fritz.schroeter@t-online.de

Mr Günter THUM
Mitglied des Rates der Stadt Rheine
Vorsitzender des Europaausschusses des Dt. Städte- und Gemeindebundes
Tel. +49 05971986619
Fax +49 05971986620
E-mail: gthum@gmx.de

Mr Christian WULFF
Ministerpräsident des Landes Niedersachsen
Tel. +49 5116901
Fax +49 5116838
E-mail: christian.wulff@stk.niedersachsen.de

Estonia

Mrs Urve ERIKSON
Chairman of Tudulinna Municipality Council
Tel. +372 3370327
Fax +372 3370327
E-mail: urve@ivol.ee

Mr Kaido KAASIK
Mayor of Valjala
Valjala Municipality government
Tel. +372 4549532
+372 5082677
E-mail: kaido.kaasik@valjala.ee

Mr Aivar KALDJÄRV
Mayor of Võnnu
Võnnu Municipality government
Tel. +372 5049905
Fax +372 7492342
E-mail: aivar678@gmail.com

Mrs Kersti KÕOSAAR
Mayor of Võru
Tel. +372 5086822
Fax +372 7850902
E-mail: kersti.koosaar@vorulinn.ee

Mr Edgar SAVISAAR
Mayor of Tallinn
Tel. +372 6404100
Fax +372 6404103
E-mail: edgar.savisaar@tallinnlv.ee

Mrs Sirje TOBRELUTS
Mayor of Laheda
Laheda Municipality government
Tel. +372 7929380
Fax +372 7929380
E-mail: sirjeT@laheda.ee

Mr Ivar UNT
Mayor of Varga
Tel. +37 284217
E-mail: ivar.unt@mail.ee

Greece

Mr Dimitrios DRAKOS
Prefect of Messinia
Tel. +30 2107468703
Fax +30 2107796016
E-mail: enae@otenet.gr

Mr Dimitrios KALOGEROPOULOS
Mayor of Aigaleo (Athens)
Tel. +30 2105315667
Fax +30 2105315669
E-mail: egaleo@egaleo.gr

Mr Loukas KATSAROS
Prefet de Larissa
Nomarchis Larissas
Tel. +30 24105975523
Fax +30 2410536289
E-mail: nomarxis@larissa.gr

Mr Miltiadis KLAPAS
Maire de Preveza
Dimarchos Prevezas
Tel. +30 2682022212
Fax +30 2682027553

Mr Konstantinos KONTOYORGOS
Prefect of Evritania
Tel. +30 2237080208
Fax +30 2237080210
www.nomeyryt@otenet.gr

Mr Georgios KOTRONIAS
Maire de Lamia
Dimarchos Lamieon
Tel. +30 2231022314
Fax +30 2241031435

Mr Giannis KOURAKIS
Maire d'Héraklion - Crète (Dimarchos Hirakleiou-Kritis)
Tel. +30 2810399399
Fax +30 2810227180

Mr Polidoros LAMBRINOUDIS
Préfet de Chios
Nomarchis Chiou
Tel. +30 2271044200
Fax +30 2271040718
E-mail: ds_nadrios@yahoo.com

Mr Giannis MACHAIRIDIS
Préfet du Dodécanèse
Nomarchis Dodekanissou
Tel. +30 2241046502
Fax +30 2241046531
E-mail: nom@nad.gr

Mr Panagiotis OIKONOMIDIS
Maire d'Arta
Dimarchos Artas
Tel. +30 2681028336
Fax +30 2681027274

Mr Dimitris PREVEZANOS
Counsellor, Municipality of Shiathos (Magnissia)
Tel. +30 2427021500
Fax +30 2427021500
E-mail: diprev@in.gr

Mr Spyridon SPYRIDON
Counsellor, Prefecture of Athens - Piraeus
Tel. +30 2104125745
Fax +30 2104125745
E-mail: sspyridon@gmail.com
http://www.spyridon.gr

Spain

Mrs Rosa AGUILAR RIVERO
Alcaldesa de Córdoba
C/Capitulares 1 • E-14071 CORDOBA
Tel. +34 957499910
Fax +34 957485805
E-mail: alcaldia@ayuncordoba.es

Mr Iñaki AGUIRRE ARIZMENDI
Secretario General de Acción Exterior, Comunidad Autónoma del País Vasco
Navarra 2, E-1007 Vitoria-Gasteiz, Espagne
E-mail: accion-exterior@ej-gv.es

Mr Gabriel AMER AMER
Delegado del Gobierno de las Islas Baleares en Bruselas
Tel. +32 22231410
Fax +32 22232524
E-mail: delegat@skynet.be

Mrs María Luisa ARAÚJO CHAMORRO
Consejera de Economia y Hacienda de la Junta de Comunidades de Castilla-La Mancha
Junta de Comunidades de Castilla-la-Mancha - Edificio El Nuncio • Calle Real 14 • E-45071 Toledo
Tel. +34 925266501
Fax +34 925266531
E-mail: mlaraujo@jccm.es

Mrs Elsa CASAS CABELLO
Comisionada de Acción Exterion, Comunidad Autónoma de Canarias
Tel. +34 922476538
Fax +34 922476959
E-mail: comisionado.accionexterior@gobiernodecanarias.org

Mr Alberto CATALÁN HIGUERAS
Consejero de Relaciones Institucionales y Portavoz del Gobierno, Comunidad Foral de Navarra
Avda. San Ignacio 1, E-31002 Pamplona, Espagne
Tel. +34 848427682
Fax +34 848427810
E-mail: acatalah@navarra.es

Mrs María DE DIEGO DURANTEZ
Directora General Relaciones Institucionales y Acción Exterior, Comunidad Autónoma Castilla y León

Mr Francisco DE LA TORRE PRADOS
Alcalde de Málaga
E-mail: alcaldia@malaga.eu

Mr Emilio DEL RÍO SANZ
Consejero de Presidencia y Acción Exterior del Gobierno de La Rioja
Gobierno Autónomo de la Rioja • Vara del Rey, 3 • E-26071 Logroño
Tel. +34 941291121
Fax +34 941291224
E-mail: consejero.presidencia@larioja.org

Mrs Paz FERNANDEZ FELGUEROSO
Alcaldesa de Gijón (Asturias)
Plaza Mayor 1 • E-33201 Gijon
Tel. +34 985181108
Fax +34 985181194
E-mail: alcadia@gijon.es

Mr Julio César FERNÁNDEZ MATO
Secretario General de Relaciones Exteriores, Comunidad Autónoma de Galicia
Tel. +34 981541002
Fax +34 981541003
E-mail: sunioneu@xunta.es

Mr Alberto GARCÍA CERVIÑO
Director General de Asuntos Europeos y Cooperación al Desarrollo
Tel. +34 942208544
E-mail: garcia_alb@gobcantabria.es

Mr Antonio GONZÁLEZ TEROL
Director General de Asuntos Europeos, Comunidad Autónoma de Madrid
Tel. +34 915804294
Fax +34 915804292
E-mail: antonio.gonzalezt@madrid.org

Mr Francisco Javier LEÓN DE LA RIVA
Alcalde de Valladolid
Plaza Mayor 1 • E-47071 Valladolid
Tel. +34 983426101
Fax +34 983343351
E-mail: 010@ava.es

Mrs Lucía MARTÍN DOMÍNGUEZ
Directora General de Acción Exterior, Comunidad Autónoma de Extremadura
Tel. +34 924003906
E-mail: lucia.martin@prs.juntaex.es

Mrs Esther MONTERRUBIO VILLAR
Comisionada para las Relaciones Exteriores del Gobierno de Aragón, Comunidad Autonóma de Aragón
E-mail: emonterrubio@aragon.es

Mr Juan Antonio MORALES RODRÍGUEZ
Director General de Relaciones Institucionales y Acción Exterior, Murcia
Tel. +34 968366539
Fax +34 968362163
E-mail: juanantonio.morales@carm.es

Mr Enrique OJEDA VILA
Secretario General de Acción Exterior, Andalucía
E-mail: enrique.ojeda.vila@juntadeandalucia.es

Mr Jaime RABANAL GARCÍA
Consejero de Economía y Asuntos Europeos, Comunidad Autónoma del Principado de Asturias
Tel. +34 985105801
Fax +34 985105455
E-mail: jaimerg@princast.es

Mr Vicente RAMBLA MOMPLET
Vicepresidente Primero y Consejero de Presidencia Comunidad Valenciana
Tel. +34 963425750
Fax +34 963425798
E-mail: grino_pil@gva.es

Mrs Anna TERRÓN I CUSÍ
Secretaria para la Unión Europea del Gobierno de Cataluña
Tel. +32 22310330
Fax +32 22302110
E-mail: annaterron@gencat.cat

France

Mr Jacques AUXIETTE
Président du Conseil régional des Pays-de-la-Loire
Tel. +33 228205512
Fax +33 228205023
E-mail: jacques.auxiette@paysdelaloire.fr

Mr Jean-Paul BACHY
Président du Conseil régional de Champagne-Ardenne
Conseil Régional • 5, rue de Jéricho • F-51037 Châlons-en-Champagne Cedex
Tel. +33 326708909
Fax +33 326706680
E-mail: jpredont@cr-champagne-ardenne.fr

Mr Pierre BERTRAND
Vice-président du Conseil général du Bas-Rhin
Tel. +33 388548787
Fax +33 388542795
E-mail: s.hauck@mairie-wissembourg.fr

Mr Philippe BODARD
Maire de Mûrs-Érigné
Hôtel de Ville BP15 • F-49610 Mûrs-Érigné
Tel. +33 241797880
Fax +33 241459508
E-mail: secretariat.du.maire@ville-murs-erigne.fr

Mrs Martine CALDEROLI-LOTZ
Conseiller régional d'Alsace
3, rue Grandidier • F-67000 Strasbourg
Tel. +33 388212308
Fax +33 388211390
E-mail: avocats.calderoli.decot.faure@wanadoo.fr

Mrs Anne-Marie COMPARINI
Conseiller régional de Rhône-Alpes
78, route de Paris BP19 • F-69751 Charbonnières-les-Bains
Tel. +33 472594000
Fax +33 472594511
E-mail: anne-marie@comparini.net
amcomparini@assemblee-nationale.fr
http://www.cr-rhone-alpes.fr

Mr Jean-Michel DACLIN
Adjoint au maire de Lyon
Tel. +33 472105121
Fax +33 472105145
E-mail: jean-michel.daclin@mairie-lyon.fr

Mrs Nassimah DINDAR
Président du Conseil général de la Réunion
Tel. +33 262903030
+33 262903999
E-mail: dgs@cg974.fr

Mrs Rose-Marie FALQUE
Maire d'Azerailles
E-mail: direction@adm54.asso.fr

Mr Christian FAVIER
Président du Conseil général du Val-de-Marne
Avenue du Général-de-Gaulle • F-94011 Créteil Cedex
Tel. +33 143997002
Fax +33 143997006
E-mail: ginette.moreau@cg94.fr

Mr Jean-Jacques FRITZ
Conseiller régional de la Région d'Alsace

Mr Claude GEWERC
Président du Conseil régional de Picardie
Tel. +33 322973737
Fax +33 322973900
E-mail: claude.gewerc@picardie.fr

Mr Antoine KARAM
Président du Conseil régional de Guyane
108, avenue du Général-de-Gaulle • F-97300 Cayenne Cedex
Tel. +594 292020
Fax +594 319522
E-mail: doc.crg@nplus.gf

Mrs Mireille LACOMBE
Conseiller général du Puy-de-Dôme
Hôtel du département • 24, rue St. Esprit • F-63033 Clermont-Ferrand Cedex 1
Tel. +33 473422011
Fax +33 473422000
E-mail: mirlacombe@aol.com
http://www.puydedome.com/

Mrs Claudine LEDOUX
Maire de Charleville-Mézières
Tel. +33 471744107
E-mail: mairie@mairie-charlevillemezieres.fr

Mr Martin MALVY
Président du Conseil régional du Midi-Pyrénées
Tel. +33 561335247
Fax +33 561335284
E-mail: karen.piotrowsky@cr-mip.fr

Mr Denis MERVILLE
Maire de Sainneville
Mairie • F-76430 Saineville
Tel. +33 235209007
Fax +33 235557891
E-mail: mairie-sainneville-sur-seine@wanadoo.fr

Mrs Anne-Marie MONTCHAMP
Conseiller régional d'Ile-de-France
Tel. +33 153856804
E-mail: marianne.montchamp@iledefrance.fr

Mr Michel NEUGNOT
Conseiller régional de Bourgogne
14, rue de la Fontaignotte • F-21140 Semur-en-Auxois
Tel. +33 607487845
Fax +33 380970626
E-mail: Neugnot-Michel@wanadoo.fr

Mrs Rachel PAILLARD
Maire de Bouzy
Place de la mairie
F-51150 Bouzy
Tel. +33 326577070
Fax +33 326577070
E-mail: mairie-bouzy@wanadoo.fr

Mrs Gisèle STIEVENARD
Vice-président du Conseil général de Paris
Tel. +33 142764040
Fax +33 142765343
E-mail: gisele.stievenard@paris.fr

Mrs Elisabeth THEVENON-DURANTIN
Conseiller régional d'Auvergne
Tel. +33 683102335
Fax +33 473318490
E-mail: info10@tiscali.fr

Mr Jean-Louis TOURENNE
Président du Conseil général d'Ille-et-Vilaine
E-mail: jean-louis.tourenne@wanadoo.fr

Mr Michel VAUZELLE
Président du Conseil régional de Provence-Alpes-Côte d'Azur
Tel. +33 491575057
Fax +33 491575151
E-mail: jristori@regionpaca.fr

Ireland

Mr Terry BRENNAN
Member of Louth County Council
Louth County Council • Ghan Road • IRL • Carlingford, Co. Louth
Tel. +353 872942956
Fax +353 4232211
E-mail: terry.brennan@mail.esb.ie

Mrs Veronica CAWLEY
Member of Sligo County Council
Tel. +353 876494723
E-mail: Cawley.veronica@itsligo.ie

Mr Peter COYLE
Member of Fingal County Council
Tel. +353 872837160
E-mail: Peter.coyle@fingalcoco.ie

Mr Pat DORAN
Member of Wicklow County Council
Tel. +353 5526249

Mrs Michelle MULHERIN
Member of Mayo County Council
Tel. +353 9671935
E-mail: cllr.michelle@oceanfree.net

Mr John PENDER
Member of Carlow County Council
Grangeview, Friarstown • IRL • Carlow
Tel. +353 868538696
E-mail: johnpender@oceanfree.net
http://www.countycarlow.ie/
http://www.fiannafail.ie/

Mrs Noreen RYAN
Member of Limerick County Council
Lacka, Castleconnell • IRL • Limerick
Tel. +353 872458144
Fax +353 61377308
E-mail: noreenryan@limerickcoco.ie
http://www.limerickcoco.ie/
http://www.fiannafail.ie/

Mrs Mary SHIELDS
Member of Cork City Council
Tel. +353 214544486
E-mail: mshields@corkcity.ie

Mr Barney STEELE
Member of Longford County Council
Tel. +353 906432407
E-mail: barneysteele@longfordcoco.ie

Italy

Mr Alvaro ANCISI
Consigliere comunale di Ravenna
Via S. Alberto 134/A • I-48100 Ravenna
Tel. +39 3385622839
Fax +39 544482532
E-mail: grulistara@comune.ra.it

Mr Antonino ANGELO
Consigliere provinciale di Palermo
Tel. +39 3204319718
Fax +39 0916250570
E-mail: info@urps.it

Mrs Carmela CASILE
Consiegliere comunale del Comune di Giaveno (Torino)
Tel. +39 0119376911
E-mail: carmelacasile@aliceposta.it

Mr Francesco CROCETTO
Consigliere provinciale di Potenza
Tel. +39 0971417303
Fax +39 0971417210
E-mail: crocetto@crocetto.it

Mr Vito DE FILIPPO
Presidente della Regione Basilicata
Tel. +39 0971668250
Fax +39 0971668191
E-mail: presgiun@regione.basilicata.it

Mr Flavio DELBONO
Consigliere regionale/Vice Presidente della Regione Emilia Romagna
Viale A. Moro 52 • I-40127 Bologna
Tel. +39 0516395700
Fax +39 0516395388
E-mail: fdelbono@regione.emilia-romagna.it

Mr Vicenzo GIULIANO
Consigliere provinciale di Potenza
Tel. +39 3356395791
Fax +39 0971417361
E-mail: vincenzogiuliano@tim.it

Mr Franco IACOP
Consigliere della Regione Friuli Venezia Giulia
Tel. +39 3358230515
Fax +39 0432857967
E-mail: franco.iacop@regione.fvg.it

Mrs Maria Rita LORENZETTI
Presidente della Regione Umbria
C.so Vannucci 96 • I-06100 Perugia
Tel. +39 0755043501
+39 0755043502
Fax +39 0755043530
E-mail: prgiunta@regione.umbria.it

Mr Mario MAGNANI
Consigliere regionale/Presidente del Consiglio Regione Trentino Alto Adige
Tel. +39 461201201
Fax +39 461201045
E-mail: presidenza.tn@consiglio.regione.taa.it

Mr Oreste PASTORELLI
Consigliere provinciale di Rieti
Via Selci 1 • I-02044 Gavignano Sabino
Tel. +39 0668307666
Fax +39 0668307659
E-mail: orestepastorelli@virgilio.it

Prof. Alessandro PIETRACCI
Consigliere comunale di Trento
Tel. +39 0461983891
Fax +39 0461934506
E-mail: alessandro.pietracci@tin.it

Mr Guido RHODIO
Sindaco di Squillace (CZ)
Via G.Rhodio 4 • I-88069 Squillace
Tel. +39 0961912040
Fax +39 0961912159
E-mail: rhodi@libero.it

Mr Massimo ROSSI
Presidente della Provincia Ascoli Piceno
Tel. +39 0736277
Fax +39 0736250006
E-mail: massimo.rossi@provincia.ap.it

Mr Savino Antonio SANTARELLA
Sindaco di Candela (FG)
Tel. +39 0885653669
Fax +39 0885653995
E-mail: sindacocandela@libero.it

Mr Marco SCALVINI
Sindaco di Bagolino (BS)
Tel. +39 0365904011
Fax +39 0365903117
E-mail: uesegreteria@comune.bagolino.bs.it

Mrs Linetta SERRI
Consigliere comunale di Armungia (CA)
Via Sassari 48 • I-09123 Cagliari
Tel. +39 070666798
Fax +39 070660486
E-mail: linetta.serri@tiscali.it

Mr Giovanni SPERANZA
Sindaco del Comune di Lamezia Terme
Tel. +39 0968207226
Fax +39 0968207353
E-mail: sindaco@comune.lamezia-terme.cr.it

Mr Renzo TONDO
Presidente della Regione Friuli Venezia Giulia
Tel. +39 0403773703
Fax +39 0403773702
E-mail: presidente@regione.fvg.it

Mr Giuseppe VARACALLI
Member of the Municipal Council of Gerace
Tel. +39 3483825974
Fax +39 0964356384
E-mail: pinovaracalli@libero.it

Mr Gianfranco VITAGLIANO
Assessore della Regione Molise
Tel. +39 0874429301
Fax +39 0874429304
E-mail: vitagliano@regione.molise.it

Mr Sante ZUFFADA
Consigliere della Regione Lombardia
Tel. +39 3356264804
Fax +39 0267482488
E-mail: info@zuffada.it

Cyprus

Mr Kyriakos CHATZITTOFIS
Mayor (Dimarchos) of Agios Athanasios
Tel. +357 25720049
Fax +357 25725010
E-mail: demos.agios.athanasios@cytanet.com.cy

Mr Costas HADJIKAKOU
Municipal Councillor of Famagusta
Tel. +357 99628600
Fax +357 22755686
E-mail: haccos@cytanet.com.cy

Mr Nikos KALLIS
President (Proedros) of the Community Council of Zoopigi
Tel. +357 25542510
Fax +357 25352858
E-mail: cuc@cytanet.com.cy

Mr Ioannis LAZARIDES
President of the Community Council of Psimolofou

Mr Andreas MOISEOS
Mayor of Larnaca

Mr Charalampos PITTAS
Mayor (Dimarchos) of Morphou
Tel. +357 22447333
Fax +357 22762015
E-mail: dimosmorphou@cytanet.com.cy

Latvia

Mrs Ligita GINTERE
Chairman of Jaunpils Local Municipality
Tel. +371 29246217
Fax +371 3107068
E-mail: ligitag@tuzums.parus.lv

Mrs Nellija KLEINBERGA
Skrundas pilsēta ar lauku teritoriju, priekšsēdētāja (Chairman of Skrunda Town Council with Rural Territory)
Tel. +371 6444311
Fax +371 3350452
E-mail: nellija@skrunda.lv

Mr Valdis LIEPIŅŠ
Rīgas pilsētas domes deputāts (Councillor of Rīga City Council)
Tel. +371 6307002
Fax +371 7508540
E-mail: bci@apollo.lv

Mr Jānis NEIMANIS
Chairman of Grobina Town Municipality
Tel. +371 29287260
Fax +371 3490171
E-mail: janis.dome@apollo.lv

Mr Jānis RAŠČEVSKIS
Président du conseil de district de Jēkabpils et président du conseil municipal de Sauka
E-mail: jekabpils@jekabpils-rp.lv

Mr Andris VAIVODS
Līvānu novada domes priekšsēdētājs (Chairman of Līvāni Amalgamated Municipality Council)
Tel. +371 5307260
Fax +371 5307255
E-mail: andris@livani.lv

Mr Jānis VĪTOLIŅŠ
Ventspils pilsētas domes priekšsēdētāja 1. vietnieks (1st Deputy Chairman of Ventspils City Council)
Tel. +371 3601105
Fax +371 3601118
E-mail: janis.vitolins@ventspils.gov.lv

Lithuania

Mr Povilas ŽAGUNIS
Panevėžys District Municipal Council (member, mayor)
Tel. +370 45582943
Fax +370 45582975
E-mail: zagunis@panrs.lt

Mr Valdemaras JASEVIČIUS
Šilalė district Municipal Council (member, mayor)
Tel. +370 44976111
Fax +370 44976118
E-mail: makost@centras.lt

Mr Donatas KAUBRYS
Telšiai District Municipal Council (member)
Tel. +370 44476272
Fax +370 44452505
E-mail: donatas.kaubrys@dovirma.lt

Mr Andrius KUPČINSKAS
Mayor of Kaunas city municipality
Tel. +370 37426058
Fax +370 37423409
E-mail: meras@kaunas.lt

Mr Vytautas RAČKAUSKAS
Visaginas City Municipal Council (member, mayor)
Tel. +370 68666605
Fax +370 38631286
E-mail: meras@visaginas.lt

Mr Liudvikas ŽUKAUSKAS
Skuodas District Municipal Council (member, mayor)
Tel. +370 44073933
Fax +370 44073984
E-mail: liudvikaszukauskas@ktv.satela.lt

Mr Zenonas ULKĖ
Šakiai District Municipal Council (member)
Tel. +370 34560750
Fax +370 34542468
E-mail: z.ulke@gsm.lt

Mr Kěstutis VAITUKAITIS
Elektrėnai Municipal Council (member, mayor)
Tel. +370 52858000
Fax +370 52858005
E-mail: kestutis.v@is.lt

Luxembourg

Mr Roby BIWER
Membre du conseil communal de la commune de Bettembourg
Tel. +352 518080-1
Fax +352 518080-601
E-mail: roby.biwer@bettembourg.lu

Mr Fernand ETGEN
Membre du conseil communal de la commune de Feulen
30, route d'Arlon • L-9180 Oberfeulen
Tel. +352 691817550
Fax +352 817908
E-mail: etgen@pt.lu

Mr Gusty GRAAS
Member of Bettembourg municipal council
Tel. +352 518113
Fax +352 26510913
E-mail: ggraas@chd.lu

Mr Norbert HAUPERT
Membre du conseil communal de la commune de Mondercange
Tel. +352 551538
Fax +352 572140
E-mail: nhaupert@chd.lu

Mrs Lydia MUTSCH
Membre du conseil communal de la commune d'Esch-sur-Alzette
54, rue Bourgrund • L-4039 Esch-sur-Alzette
Tel. +352 549573
Fax +352 547383555
E-mail: lydia.mutsch@villeesch.lu
http://www.esch.lu/

Mrs Martine STEIN-MERGEN
Membre du conseil communal de la ville de Luxembourg
Fax +352 26200298
E-mail: mmergen@chd.lu

Hungary

Mr Béla CSÉCSEI
Budapest VIII. kerület polgármestere
Tel. +36 14592200
Fax +36 13331597
E-mail: miklosr@jozsefvaros.hu

Mr Attila JÓSZAI
önkormányzati képviselö, Szigetszenmiklós
Tel. +36 204668216
Fax +36 17885345
E-mail: attila.joszai@uni-corvinus.hu

Mrs Karolyne KOCSIS
önkormányzati képviselö, Dunapataj
Tel. +36 209420650
Fax +36 78425072
E-mail: julia@emitelnet.hu

Mr Levente MAGYAR
Member of the General Assembly of Jász-Nagykun-Szolnok

Mrs Helga MIHÁLYI
Member of the General Assembly of Borsod-Abaúj-Zemplén
E-mail: mszpmisk@mail.olh.hu

Mr Csaba MOLNÁR
Member of the General Assembly of Gyÿr-Moson-Sopron
E-mail: elnok@nydrft.hu

Mr Zoltán NAGY
önkormányzati képviselö, Komárom Város Önkormányzata
Tel. +36 34541302
Fax +36 302121211
E-mail: zoltan.nagy@komarom.hu

Mr József PAIZS
Szigetvár polgármestere
Tel. +36 73514304
Fax +36 73311923
E-mail: onkormanyzat@szigetvar.hu

Mr Loránd SZABÓ
Dombóvár polgármestere
Tel. +36 74564500
Fax +36 74564501
E-mail: polgarmester@dombovar.hu

Mr Imre SZAKÁCS
Györ-Moson-Sopron Megyei Közgyülés tagja
Tel. +36 96522201
Fax +36 96522220
E-mail: iszakacs@gymsmo.hu

Mrs Kata TŰTTÖ
Member of the General Assembly of Capital

Mr László VÉCSEY
Mayor of Szada

Malta

Mrs Joan AGIUS
Deputy Mayor, Zejtun Local Coucil
Tel. +356 99424517
Fax +356 21663939
E-mail: joanagius@global.net.mt

Mrs Doris BORG
Deputy Mayor, Birkirkara Local Council
Tel. +356 19891722
Fax +356 21446427
E-mail: doris_borg@hotmail.com

Mr Joseph CORDINA
Councillor, Xaghra Local Council
Tel. +356 79559999
Fax +356 21557185
E-mail: corjoe@vol.net.mt

Mr Malcolm MIFSUD
Moyor, Pietá Local Council
Tel. +356 99472747
Fax +356 25402747
E-mail: mmifsud@gmtd.net

Mrs Maria NATOLI
Tel. +356 21562193
E-mail: mayan@onvol.net

The Netherlands

Mr Joop BINNEKAMP
Gedeputeerde in de provincie Utrecht
Tel. +31 302583666
Fax +31 302583121
E-mail: j.binnekamp@provincie-utrecht.nl

Mr Henk BLEKER
Gedeputeerde van de provincie Groningen
Tel. +31 503164007
Fax +31 503185615
E-mail: h.bleker@provinciegroningen.nl

Mr Dick BUURSINK
Gedeputeerde in de provincie Overijssel
Tel. +31 622601486
Fax +31 384254855
E-mail: d.buursink@overijssel.nl

Mr Job COHEN
Burgemeester van Amsterdam

Mr Rik DE LANGE
Wethouder van Zutphen
E-mail: r.delange@zutphen.nl

Mrs Rinda DEN BESTEN
Wethouder van Utrecht
Tel. +31 302861110
Fax +31 302861475
E-mail: r.den.besten@utrecht.nl

Drs. Harry DIJKSMA
Gedeputeerde van de provincie Flevoland
Visarenddreef 1 • NL • 8232 PH Lelystad
Tel. +31 320265667
Fax +31 320265654
E-mail: dijksma@flevoland.nl
http://www.flevoland.nl

Mrs Ellie FRANSSEN
Wethouder te Voerendaal

Mr Sjoerd GALEMA
Gedeputeerde in de provincie Fryslân

Mr Hans KOK
Burgemeester van Hof van Twente
De Höfte 7, Goor-Hof van Twente NL-7471 Goor
Tel. +31 547858585
Fax +31 547858586
E-mail: h.kok@hofvantwente.nl

Mrs Carla PEIJS
Commissaris der Koningin in de provincie Zeeland
Tel. +31 118631312
Fax +31 118631316
E-mail: kmh.peijs@zeeland.nl

Austria

Mrs Renate BRAUNER
Vizebürgermeisterin der Stadt Wien und stellvertretende Landeshauptfrau
Tel. +43 1400081200
Fax +43 140009981200

Mr Gebhard HALDER
Präsident des Vorarlberger Landtages
Tel. +43 557451130000
Fax +43 557451130095
E-mail: landtag@vorarlberg.at

Markus LINHART
Bürgermeister der Stadt Bregenz
Tel. +43 55744103000
Fax +43 557447476
E-mail: buergermeister@bregenz.at

Dr Josef MARTINZ
Landesrat
Tel. +43 5053622701
Fax +43 5053622700
E-mail: josef.martinz@ktn.gv.at

Johanna MIKL-LEITNER
Landesträtin
Tel. +43 2742900512600
Fax +43 2742900512650
E-mail: lr.mikl-leitner@noel.gv.at

Mr Johannes PEINSTEINER
Bürgermeister, Marktgemeinde St. Wolfgang
Tel. +43 6642102320
Fax +43 613830224
E-mail: office@rollermax.at

Mr Günther PLATTER
Landeshauptmann
Tel. +43 5125082002
Fax +43 5125082005
E-mail: buero.lh.platter@tirol.gv.at

Mr Walter PRIOR
Präsident des Burgenländischen Landtages
Verbindungsbüro des Landes Burgenland zur EU • Avenue Edmond Mesens 7A • B-1040 Bruxelles - Brussel
Tel. +43 26826002448
Fax +43 26826002050
E-mail: walter.prior@bgld-landtag.at

Prof. Dr. Franz SCHAUSBERGER
Beauftragter des Landes Salzburg für den Ausschuss der Regionen
Institut der Regionen Europas • Franz-Josef-Kai 1 • A-5020 Salzburg
Tel. +43 6628432885050
Fax +43 6628432885017
E-mail: schausberger@salzburg.gv.at
www.ire.or.at

Mr Hermann SCHÜTZENHÖFER
Landeshauptmann-Stellvertreter von Steiermark
Tel. +43 3168778700
Fax +43 3168778704
E-mail: hermann.schuetzenhoefer@stmk.gv.at

Mr Viktor SIGL
Landesrat
Tel. +43 732772015100
Fax +43 732772011792
E-mail: lr.sigl@ooe.gv.at

Dr Elisabeth VITOUCH
Gemeinderätin der Stadt Wien
Tel. +43 17137388
E-mail: vitouch@aon.at

Poland

Mr Adam BANASZAK
Councillor of the Sejmik of the Kujawsko-Pomorskie voivodship
Tel. +48 501625997
E-mail: adam.banaszak@poczta.onet.pl

Mr Jan BROŃ
Mayor of the city of Oleśnica
Tel. +48 692495696
Fax +48 717982108
E-mail: janbrons@wp.pl

Mr Konstanty DOMBROWICZ
Prezydent miasta
Tel. +48 525858358
Fax +48 525858301
E-mail: k.dombrowics@um.bydgoszcz.pl

Mr Lech DYMARSKI
Chairman of the Sejmik of the Wielkopolskie voivodship

Mr Jan DZIUBIŃSKI
President of the city of Tarnobrzeg

Mr Robert GODEK
Starosta of the Strzyzów poviat
Tel. +48 0172765000
Fax +48 0172765000
E-mail: starosta@strzyzow.com.pl

Mr Michał KARALUS
Councillor of the Pleszew poviat
Tel. +48 627429652
Fax +48 927429652
E-mail: powiat.pleszew@poczta.fm

Mrs Marzena KĔMPIŃSKA
Councillor of the Świecie poviat
Tel. +48 523332110
Fax +48 523332163
E-mail: promocja@powiat.swiecki.lo.pl

Mr Józef KOTYŚ
Councillor of the Sejmik of the Opolskie voivodship
Tel. +48 775416522
Fax +48 775416520
E-mail: j.kotys@umwo.opole.pl

Mr Tadeusz KOWALCZYK
Chairman of the Sejmik of the Świĕtokrzyskie voivodship
Tel. +48 603860860
Fax +48 413443096
E-mail: tadeusz.kowalczyk@sejmik.kielce.pl

Mr Lucjan KUŹNIAR
Radny Sejmiku województwa Podkarpackiego
Tel. +48 178501790
Fax +48 178501790
E-mail: sejmik@podkarpackie.pl

Mr Andrzej KUNT
Burmistrz miasta
Tel. +48 957278100
Fax +48 957278102
E-mail: burmistrz@kostrzyn.um.gov.pl

Mr Mirosław LECH
Wójt gminy
Tel. +48 857229185
Fax +48 857229180
E-mail: korycin@kki.net.pl

Mr Andrzej MATUSIEWICZ
Chairman of the Sejmik of the Podkarpackie voivodship
Grunwaldzka 15, Przewodniczacy Sejmiku Wojewodztwa Podkarpackiego
Pl-35-959 Rzeszów
Tel. +48 178501790
Fax +48 178501791

Mr Marek OLSZEWSKI
Wójt gminy
Tel. +48 566782128
Fax +48 566782122
E-mail: molszewski@zgwrp.org.pl

Mrs Ewa PANASIUK
Councillor of the Sejmik of the Lubelskie voivodship

Mr Czesław SOBIERAJSKI
Councillor of the Sejmik of the Śląskie voivodship
Tel. +48 0324237172
Fax +48 322564276
E-mail: c.sobierajski@silesia-region.pl

Mr Robert SOSZYŃSKI
Chairman of the Sejmik of the Mazowieckie voivodship
Tel. +48 226956616
Fax +48 226202707
E-mail: r.soszynski@mazovia.pl

Mr Tadeusz TRUSKOLASKI
President of the city of Białystok
Str. Stonimska 1
PL-15-950 Białystok
Tel. +48 858696002
Fax +48 858696265
E-mail: prezydent@um.bialystok.pl

Mr Dariusz WRÓBEL
Burzmistr Opola Lubelskiego (Maire d'Opole Lubelskie)
Tel. +48 818272045
Fax +48 818272835
E-mail: burmistrz@opolelubelskie.pl

Portugal

Mr Américo AFONSO PEREIRA
Presidente da Câmara Municipal de Vinhais
Tel. +351 273770300
Fax +351 273771108
E-mail: geral@cm-vinhais.pt

Mr António Manuel Leitão BORGES
Presidente da Câmara Municipal de Resende
Tel. +351 916139974
Fax +351 254877039
E-mail: presidente@cm-resende.pt

Dr Aníbal Reis COSTA
Presidente da Câmara Municipal de Ferreira do Alentejo
Tel. +351 284739250
Fax +351 966924232
E-mail: anibalreiscosta@cm-ferreira-alentejo.pt
www.cm-ferreira-alentejo.pt

Mr João Carlos CUNHA E SILVA
Vice-Presidente do Governo Regional da Madeira
Arriaga • P-9004 527 Funchal
Tel. +351 291234039
Fax +351 291232102
E-mail: gab.vp@gov-madeira.pt

Mr Joaquim Carlos DIAS VALENTE
Presidente da Câmara Municipal da Guarda
Tel. +351 271220226
E-mail: presidente@mun_guarda.pt

Mr Manuel Joaquim Barata FREXES
Presidente da Câmara Municipal do Fundão
Tel. +351 968340340
Fax +351 275779078
E-mail: manuel.frexes@netvisao.pt

Mr Pedro Namorado LANCHA
Presidente da Câmara Municipal de Fronteira
Tel. +351 245600070
Fax +351 245600099
E-mail: presidente@cm-fronteira.pt

Mr Jaime Carlos MARTA SOARES
Presidente da Câmara Municipal de Vila Nova de Poiares
Tel. +351 239420850
+351 239421800
E-mail: cmvnp@mail.telepac.pt

Mr Vítor Manuel Chaves de Caro PROENÇA
Presidente da Câmara Municipal de Santiago do Cacém
Praça do Municipio • P-7540-136 Santiago de Cacém
Tel. +351 269829400
Fax +351 269829498
E-mail: cmsc.bib@mail.telepac.pt

Mr Paulo Ramalheira TEIXEIRA
Presidente da Câmara Municipal de Castelo de Paiva
Câmara Municipal Castelo de Paiva • Largo do Conde • P-4550-102 Castelo de Paiva
Tel. +351 255689500
Fax +351 255699660
E-mail: paulo_ramalheira@hotmail.com

Romania

Mr Silvian CIUPERCĂ
President of Ialomiţa County Council
Tel. +40 243232000
Fax +40 243230250
E-mail: cjj@cicnet.ro

Mr Árpád Szabolcs CSEHI
President of Satu Mare County Council
Tel. +40 261716994
Fax +40 261710651
E-mail: consiliu@cjsm.ro

Mr Liviu Nicolae DRAGNEA
Président, conseil départemental Teleorman
Tel. +40 247311201
Fax +40 247312494
E-mail: dragnea@cictelnet.ro

Mr Alexandru DRĂGAN
Maire, mairie de la commune de Taşca
Tel. +40 233255.023
Fax +40 233255.083
E-mail: alexandredragan@yahoo.fr

Mr Dumitru ENACHE
Maire, mairie de la commune de Stejaru
Tel. +40 240564809
Fax +40 240564833
E-mail: enachedumitru1964@yahoo.com

Mr Péter FERENC
Mayor of Sovata town
Tel. +40 744538782
Fax +40 265570524
E-mail: pferenc@szovata.ro

Mr Gheorghe FLUTUR
President of Suceava County Council
Str. Stefan cel Mare nr.36
RO Suceava - jud. Sudeava

Mrs Mariana MIRCEA
Tel. + 40 241238030
Fax + 40 241237733
E-mail: marianamircea@yahoo.com

Mr Mircea Ioan MOLOŢ
President of Hunedoara County Council
Tel. +40 254211624
Fax +40 254230030
E-mail: mircea.ioan.molot@cjhunedoara.ro

Ing. Mircia MUNTEAN
Maire, mairie de la municipalité de Deva
Tel. +40 744611449
Fax +40 254226176
E-mail: primar@primariadeva.ro

Mr Gheorghe NICHITA
Mayor of Iasi
Tel. +40 232211215
Fax +40 232211200
E-mail: gheorghe.nichita@primaria-iasi.ro

Mr Marian OPRIŞAN
President of Vrancea County Council

Mr George SCRIPCARU
Mayor of Braşov municipality

Mr Adrian Ovidiu TEBAN
Mayor of Cugir town

Mrs Ioana TRIFOI
Maire, mairie de la commune de Botiza
Tel. +40 262334019
Fax +40 262334030
E-mail: it54@artelecom.net

Slovenia

Mr Štefan ČELAN
Mayor of the City Municipality of Ptuj
Tel. +386 27482999
Fax +386 27482998
E-mail: stefan.celan@ptuj.si

Mr Siniša GRMOVŠEK
Local Councillor of the Municipality of Bovec
Tel. +386 53841900
Fax +386 53841915
E-mail: grmovsek_sinisa@yahoo.com

Mrs Breda ŠKRJANEC
Local Councillor of the Municipality of Grosuplje
Tel. +386 17888750
Fax +386 17888764
E-mail: breda.skrjanec@mglc-lj.si

Mr Branko LEDINEK
Mayor of the Municipality of Rače - Fram
Tel. +386 41663910
Fax +386 26096018
E-mail: branko.ledinek@race-fram.com

Mr Jure MEGLIČ
Podžupan Občine Tržič
Tel. +386 41386688
Fax +386 45955341
E-mail: jure.meglic@fov.uni-mb.si

Mr Blaž MILAVEC
Župan Občine Sodražica
E-mail: zupan@sodrazica.si

Mr Antón ŠTIHEC
Župan Mestne občine Murska Sobota
E-mail: urad.zupana@murska-sobota.si

Slovakia

Ing. PhD Ján BLCHÁČ
Primátor mesta Liptovský Mikuláš
Tel. +421 445565201
E-mail: j.blchac@mikulas.sk

Mr Remo CICUTTO
Mayor of the City of Piešťany (Primátor mesta Piešťany)
Tel. +421 337765301
Fax +421 337765333
E-mail: sekretariat@piestany.sk

JUDr. Pavel HAGYARI
Primátor mesta Prešov
Tel. +421 513100101
+421 517734809
E-mail: primator@presov.sk

Mgr. art. Andrej HRNČIAR
Primátor mesta Martin
Tel. +421 434204175
E-mail: hrnciar@martin.sk

Mrs Božena KOVÁČOVÁ
Mayor of Janova Lehota village (Starostka obce Janova Lehota)
Tel. +421 456726261
Fax +421 456726262
E-mail: janovalehota@stonline.sk

Ing. Tibor MIKUŠ
President of the Trnava Self-governing Region (Predseda Trnavského samosprávneho kraja)
Tel. +421 335933310
Fax +421 335933318
E-mail: predseda@trnava-vuc.sk

Mr Milan MURGAŠ
Predseda Banskobystrického samosprávneho kraja (président de la région autonome de Banská Bystrica)
Tel. +421 484325600
Fax +421 484323515
E-mail: milan.murgas@vucbb.sk

Mr Jozef PETUŠÍK
Mayor of Dolný Lopašov village (Starosta obce Dolný Lopašov)
Tel. +421 337794102
E-mail: obecdlopasov@kios.sk

Mr Pavol SEDLÁČEK
President of the Trenčín Self-governing Region (Predseda Trenčianskeho samosprávneho kraja)
Tel. +421 327411421
Fax +421 327446174
E-mail: predseda@tsk.sk

Finland

Mr Markus AALTONEN
Seinäjoen kaupunginvaltuuston jäsen
Vuorenmaanrinne 10C • FI-60220 Seinäjoki
Tel. +358 407504940
Fax +358 64141627
E-mail: markus.aaltonen@kolumbus.fi
http://www.seinajoki.fi

Mrs Carina AALTONEN
Lagtingsledamot
Tel. +358 01825561
Fax +358 01813302
E-mail: carina.aaltonen@lagtinget.ax

Mrs Minerva KROHN
Uudenmaan liiton maakuntahallituksen jäsen
Tel. +358 0505884244
E-mail: minerva.krohn@kolumbus.fi

Mrs Martina MALMBERG
Présidente du conseil municipal d'Inkoo

Mr Markku MARKKULA
Uudenmaan liiton maakuntavaltuuston jäsen
Tel. +358 94514000
Fax +358 94514490
E-mail: markku.markkula@dipoli.tkk.fi

Mr Ossi MARTIKAINEN
Pohjois-Savon liiton maakuntavaltuuston jäsen
Kuopiontie 84 • FI-73100 Lapinlahti
Tel. +358 405926769
Fax +358 17731066
E-mail: ossi.martikainen@pp1.inet.fi
omartika@nettilinja.fi

Mrs Lea SAUKKONEN
Helsingin kaupunginvaltuuston varajäsen
Tel. +358 0919293340
E-mail: lea.saukkonen@fmi.fi

Mrs Irja SOKKA
Member of Kuopio city council
Tel. +358 106024267
Fax +358 106024211
E-mail: irja.sokka@te-keskus.fi

Heini UTUNEN ZIV
Jyväskylän kaupunginvaltuuston jäsen
Tel. +358 400878769
Fax +358 14214448
E-mail: heini.utunenziv@jkl.fi
http://www.heiniutunen.net

Sweden

Mr Carl Fredrik GRAF
Halmstads kommun
Tel. +46 35137304
Fax +46 35137308
E-mail: carlfredrik.graf@halmstad.se

Mrs Susanna HABY
Göteborgs kommun
Tel. +46 313680040
Fax +46 31134880
E-mail: susanna.haby@stadshuset.goteborg.se

Mr Tore HULT
Alingsås kommun
Tel. +46 706750708
Fax +46 322616730
E-mail: tore.hult@alingsas.se

Mr Bernth JOHNSON
Blekinge läns landsting
Landstinget Blekinge • S-37181 Karlskrona
Tel. +46 455731092
Fax +46 45580005
E-mail: bernth.johnson@ltblekinge.se

Mrs Ewa-May KARLSSON
Vindelns kommun
Tel. +46 93314013
Fax +46 93314003
E-mail: ewa-may.karlsson@vindeln.se

Mrs Agneta LIPKIN
Norrbottens läns landsting
Hummelsvagen 6
S-95250 Kalix-Nyborg

Mr Kenth LÖVGREN
Gävle kommun
Tel. +46 704140714
E-mail: kenth.lovgren@gavle.se

Mr Jens NILSSON
Östersunds kommun • The Town Hall • S-83182 Östersund
Tel. +46 706539754
Fax +46 63144200
E-mail: jens.nilsson@ostersund.se

Mrs Ingela NYLUND WATZ
Stockholms läns landsting
Tel. +46 87374150
Fax +46 86536650
E-mail: ingela.nylund-watz@politik.sll.se

Mrs Yoomi RENSTRÖM
Ovanåkers kommun
Tel. +46 706063005
E-mail: yoomi.renstrom@ovanaker.se

Mr Rolf SÄLLRYD
Kronobergs läns landsting
Tel. +46 47032012
Fax +46 470588530
E-mail: rs@kristdemokraterna.se

Mr Carl Johan SONESSON
Skåne läns landsting
Tel. +946 105083233
E-mail: carljohan.sonesson@moderat.se

United Kingdom

Cllr Robert BRIGHT
Mandate of Newport City Council
Tel. +44 1633232121
E-mail: bob.bright@newport.gov.uk

Mr Ted BROCKLENBANK
Member of the Scottish Parliament
E-mail: ted.brocklenbank.msp@scottish.parliament.uk

Cllr Katrina BULL
Member of Nottingham City Council
Tel. +44 1158460507
E-mail: katrina.bull@nottinghamcity.gov.uk

Cllr Feryat DEMIRCI
Member of London Borough of Hackney
E-mail: feryat.demirci@hackney.gov.uk

Mrs Nerys EVANS
Member of the National Assembly of Wales
E-mail: nerys.evans@wales.gov.uk

Cllr Graham GARVIE
Member of Scottish Borders Council
Tel. +44 1835825155
E-mail: ggarvie@scotborders.gov.uk

Joan HANHAM
Member of Royal Borough of Kensington and Chelsea
Town Hall • Horton Street • UK
London W8 7MX
Fax +44 2079378692
+44 2073613105
E-mail: cgsbl@rbkc.gov.uk

Cllr Doreen HUDDART
Member of Newcastle-upon-Tyne City Council
Tel. +44 1912401084144
E-mail: dorhud@btinternet.com

Cllr Cindy HUGHES
Member of Darlington Borough Council
Tel. +44 1325388020

Cllr Syeda KHATUN
Member of Sandwell Metropolitan Borough Council
Tel. +44 1215576766
Fax +44 121 5577137
E-mail: Asha12@btconnect.com

Cllr Mohammad MASOOD
Member of Bradford City Council
Tel. +44 7789774141
E-mail: mohammad.masood@bradford.gov.uk

Cllr Jim MCCABE
Member of North Lanarkshire Council
Tel. +44 1698302226
Fax +44 1698302462
E-mail: mccabej@northlan.gov.uk

Mrs Allison MCINNES
Member of the Scottish Parliament
E-mail: alison.mcinnes.msp@scottish.parliament.uk

Cllr Peter MOORE
Member of Sheffield City Council
Town Hall • UK • S1 2HH Sheffield
Tel. +44 1142726444
Fax +44 1142735003
E-mail: sangimoore@aol.com

Cllr Maurice MORROW
Member of Dungannon and South Tyrone Borough Council
25 Ranfurly Heights • UK
Dungannon BT71 6PL

Cllr Kathy POLLARD
Member of Suffolk County Council
Tel. +44 1473313036
E-mail: kathy.pollard@suffolkcc.gov.uk

Cllr David SHAKESPEARE
Member of Buckinghamshire County Council
Bucks County Council, County Hall • UK
HP2 1UD Aylesbury
Tel. +44 1296395000
Fax +44 1296383441
E-mail: dshakespeare@buckscc.gov.uk
http://www.southeast-ra.gov.uk
http://www.buckscc.gov.uk

Cllr Bernice SWIFT
Member of Fermanagh District Council
E-mail: bernice.swift@sinn-fein.ie

Cllr Sharon TAYLOR
Member of Stevenage Borough Council
Tel. +44 1438367884
Fax +44 1438242228
E-mail: sharon.taylor@stevenage.gov.uk

Cllr Kay TWITCHEN
Member of Essex County Council
Tel. +44 1702585164
Fax +44 1702585164
E-mail: cllr.kay.twitchen@essexcc.gov.uk

Cllr Sir Ron WATSON
Member of Sefton Metropolitan Borough Council
7 Carnoustie Close, Oxford Road, Birkdale • UK • PR8 2FB Southport
Tel. +44 1704565574
Fax +44 1519342060
E-mail: conservatives@sefton.gov.uk

Cllr Milner WHITEMAN
Member of Bridgnorth District Council
Arlescott Farm • UK • TF12 5BG Broseley, Shropshire
Tel. +44 1952727340
Fax +44 1952728832
E-mail: cllr.mwhiteman@bridgnorth-dc.gov.uk

COMMISSIONS OF THE COMMITTEE OF THE REGIONS

Commission for Territorial Cohesion Policy

Dr Michael SCHNEIDER
President

Mr Arnoldas ABRAMAVIČIUS

Mr Vicente ALVAREZ ARECES

Mr Cristian ANGHEL

Cllr Doris ANSARI

Mr Decebal ARNĂUTU

Mr Edvins BARTKEVICS

Mr Antonio BASSOLINO

Mr Juraj BLANÁR

Mr Albert BORE

Mr Bruno BOURG-BROC

Mrs Mercedes BRESSO

Mr Robert BRIGHT

Mrs Claudette BRUNET-LECHENAULT

Mr José Luís CARNEIRO

Mr Luciano CAVERI

Mr Manuel CHAVES GONZÁLEZ

Mrs Flo CLUCAS

Mr Michael COHEN

Mr José CORREIA

Mr Cathal CROWE

Mr Michel DELEBARRE

Mr Camille DE ROCCA SERRA

Mr Hermann DINKLA

Mr Leonardo DOMENICI

Mrs Agnès DURDU

Mr Răducu George FILIPESCU

Mr Noel FORMOSA

Dr György GÉMESI

Mr Isidoro GOTTARDO

Mr Antanas GUSTAITIS

Mrs Pauliina HAIJANEN

Mr Väino HALLIKMÄGI

Mr Rolf HARLINGHAUSEN

Dr Michael HÄUPL

Mr Jens Arne HEDEGAARD

Mrs Mona HEIBERG

Mr Juan Vicente HERRERA CAMPO

Mr Georgios IAKOVOU

Mr Marcelino IGLESIAS RICOU

Mr Gordon KEYMER

Mr Vladimir KISYOV

Mr Anders KNAPE

Mr Roger KNOX

Mr Maciej KOBYLIŃSKI

Mr Guntars KRIEVIŅŠ

Mgr. Witold KROCHMAL

Mr Jerzy KROPIWNICKI

Mrs Rinske KRUISINGA

Mr Jan KUBATA

Cllr John LAHART

Mr Michel LEBRUN

Mr Jean-Yves LE DRIAN

Mr Philippe LEROY

Mr Reinhard LOSKE

Mrs Eleni LOUCAIDES

Mr Henrik Ringbæk MADSEN

Dr Ulrich MALY

Mr Patrick MCGOWAN

Mr Krasimir MIREV

Mr Árpád MOLNÁR

Mr Vladimir MOSKOV

Mr Francesco MUSOTTO

Mr Alin Adrian NICA

Mr Hans NIESSL

Mrs Detelina NIKOLOVA

Mrs Mona-Lisa NORRMAN

Mr Constantin OSTAFICIUC

Ing. Petr OSVALD

Mr Chrístos PALEOLÓGOS

Cllr Stephen PARNABY

Mr Emilio PÉREZ TOURIÑO

Mr Carlos Alberto PINTO

Dr Erwin PRÖLL

Mr Panayotis PSOMIADIS

Mrs Indra RASSA

Mr Karl RAUBER

Mr Ilmar REEPALU

Mr Paulino RIVERO BAUTE

Mr Alain ROUSSET

Mr Romain SCHNEIDER

Mr István SÉRTŐ-RADICS

Dr Uno SILBERG

Mr Anton SMOLNIKAR

Mr Robert SMRDELJ

Dr Renato SORU

Mr Bernard SOULAGE

Mr Leszek ŚWIETALSKI

Dr Stanisław SZWABSKI

Mr Krzysztof SZYMAŃSKI

Mr Konstantinos TATSIS

JUDr. Zdenko TREBULA

Mr Dimitrios TSIGKOUNIS

Mr Carlos Alberto Santos TUTA

Mr Ramón Luis VALCÁRCEL SISO

Mr Jean-Claude VAN CAUWENBERGHE

Mr Luc VAN DEN BRANDE

Mr Dirk VAN MECHELEN

Mr Herwig VAN STAA

Dr Co VERDAAS

Mr Bas VERKERK

Mr Vytautas VIGELIS

Mrs Marta VINCENZI

Mr Toomas VITSUT

Mr Hans-Josef VOGEL

Mrs Maria WALLHAGER NECKMAN

Mr Hermann WINKLER

Mr Tadeusz WRONA

Ing. István ZACHARIAŠ

Commission for Economic and Social Policy

Mrs Constance HANNIFFY
President

Mrs Claudette ABELA BALDACCHINO

Mrs Esperanza AGUIRRE GIL DE BIEDMA

Mr Alfred ALMONT

Mrs Kristina ALVENDAL

Mr Decebal ARNĂUTU

Ing. Vladimír BAJAN

Mr José María BARREDA FONTES

Mr Rob BATS

Mrs Simone BEISSEL

Mr Milan BELICA

Bc. Ondřej BENEŠÍK

Mrs Ann BESKOW

Mr Gabor BIHARY

Mr Albert BORE

Dott. Enrico BORGHI

Mr Gilbert BOSSUYT

Mr Dietmar BROCKES

Mr Keith BROWN

Mr Gheorghe BUNEA STANCU

Mr Claudio BURLANDO

Mrs Christine CHAPMAN

Mrs Flo CLUCAS

Mrs Maria Luisa COPPOLA

Mr Frederick CUTAJAR

Mr Jacek CZERNIAK

Mr Rui Fernando DA SILVA RIO

Sir Simon DAY

Mr Camille DE ROCCA SERRA

Mr Jean-Louis DESTANS

Mr Hermann DINKLA

Mr Gerhard DÖRFLER

Mrs Katya DOYCHEVA

Mr Andrej DURKOVSKY

Mr Spiros ELENODOROU

Mr Savvas ELIOFOTOU

Mr Léon FRISSEN

Mrs Marianne FÜGL

Mrs Dolores GOROSTIAGA SAIZ

Dr Gerd HARMS

Mrs Mona HEIBERG

Mrs Monika HELBIG

Mr Jordi HEREU I BOHER

Mr Juan Vicente HERRERA CAMPO

Mr Juan José IBARRETXE MARKUARTU

Dr Gyorgy IPKOVICH

Mr Adam Sebastian JARUBAS

Dr Karl-Heinz KLÄR

Mr Henk KOOL

Mr Páris KOUKOULÓPOULOS

Mr Edmunds KRASTIŅŠ

Mr Guntars KRIEVIŅŠ

Mgr. Witold KROCHMAL

Mr Jan KUBATA

Mrs Uta-Maria KUDER

Mr Veikko KUMPUMÄKI

Mr Karl-Heinz LAMBERTZ

Mr Denis LANDY

Mr Philippe LEROY

Mr Alain LE VERN

Mr Paul LINDQUIST

Mrs Helene LUND

Mr Henrik Ringbæk MADSEN

Mrs Irena MAJCEN

Mr Ričardas MALINAUSKAS

Mrs Sonia MASINI

Mr Declan MCDONNELL

Mr Giuseppe MICARELLI

Mr Jyrki MYLLYVIRTA

Cllr David PARSONS

Mr Gediminas PAVIRŽIS

Mr Tudor PENDIUC

Mr Daniel PERCHERON

Mr Charles PICQUÉ

Cllr Edwin POOTS

Mr Ion PRIOTEASA

Mr Jean PRORIOL

Mr Emil PROSCAN

Mr Panayotis PSOMIADIS

Cllr Dave QUAYLE

Mr Carlos Manuel RODRIGUES PINTO DE SÁ

Mr Alain ROUSSET

Mr Fernando de Carvalho RUAS

Mr Vito SANTARSIERO

Mr Pedro SANZ ALONSO

Dr Herbert SAUSGRUBER

Mr Romain SCHNEIDER

Mrs Catarina SEGERSTEN-LARSSON

Mr Guner Fariz SERBEST

Dr Uno SILBERG

Mrs Stasė SKUTULIENĖ

Mr Francisco MESQUITA MACHADO

Mr Gian Mario SPACCA

Mr Peter STRAUB

Mr Leszek ŚWIĔTALSKI

Mr Krzysztof SZYMAŃSKI

Mr Konstantinos TATSIS

Mr Juraj THOMA

Mgr. Marek TRAMŚ

Mr Dimitrios TSIGKOUNIS

Mrs Kata TŰTTÖ

Mr Dirk VAN MECHELEN

Mr Zoltán VARGA

Mr Toomas VITSUT

Franz VOVES

Mr Franci VOVK

Mr Ruud VREEMAN

Mgr. Ludwik Kajetan WĔGRZYN

Mrs Dora Ilieva YANKOVA

Mr Zlatko ZHIVKOV

Commission for Sustainable Development

Mr Jerzy ZAJAKAŁA
President

Mr Uno ALDEGREN

Mr Cristian ANGHEL

Mr Francesc ANTICH I OLIVER

Mr Hasan AZIS

Cllr Paula BAKER

Mr José María BARREDA FONTES

Mr Edvins BARTKEVICS

Mr Ferenc BENKÖ

Mr Olivier BERTRAND

Mr Juraj BLANÁR

Mr Jacques BLANC

Mr Per BØDKER ANDERSEN

Mr Jean-Paul BORÉ

Dott. Enrico BORGHI

Mr Gilbert BOSSUYT

Mr Dietmar BROCKES

Mr Claudio BURLANDO

Mr Jiří BYTEL

Mr Francisco CAMPS ORTIZ

Mr José Luís CARNEIRO

Mr Michael COHEN

Mr José CORREIA

Mr Mircea COSMA

Sir Simon DAY

Mr Gerhard DÖRFLER

Mr Uwe DÖRING

Mr Emil DRĂGHICI

Mrs Agnès DURDU

Ing. Andrej ĎURKOVSKÝ

Mr Luis DURNWALDER

Mrs Lenie DWARSHUIS-VAN DE BEEK

Mr Spiros ELENODOROU

Mr Michael FITZGERALD

Mr Noel FORMOSA

Mrs Marianne FÜGL

Mr Georgios GEORGIOU

Mr Wolfgang GIBOWSKI

Cllr Linda GILLHAM

Cllr Martin HEATLEY

Mrs Veronica IONIȚĂ

Mr Helmut M. JAHN

Mr Raimundas JAKUTIS

Mr Henning JENSEN

Mr Kent JOHANSSON

Mr Jean-Louis JOSEPH

Mr Nikitas KAKLAMANIS

Ph.D. Saima KALEV

Mr Teet KALLASVEE

Mr Páris KOUKOULÓPOULOS

Mr Jerzy KROPIWNICKI

Mrs Uta-Maria KUDER

Mr Patrick LACHAERT

Mr Cor LAMERS

Mr Michel LEBRUN

Mr Albert LENTZ

Mr Aleksandrs LIELMEŽS

Mr Antti LIIKKANEN

Mrs Edita Emoke LOKODI

Mr Jean-Jacques LOZACH

Mrs Britt LUNDBERG

Mrs Johanna MAIJ-WEGGEN

Mr Pierre MAILLE

Mr Ričardas MALINAUSKAS

Mr Piero MARRAZZO

Cllr Corrie MCCHORD

Mr Patrick MCGOWAN

Mr Giuseppe MICARELLI

Mr Guido MILANA

Mr Erwin MOHR

Mr Vladimir MOSKOV

Mrs Emilia MÜLLER

Mr Seamus MURRAY

Mr Marek NAWARA

Mrs Mona-Lisa NORRMAN

Mrs Irene OLDFATHER

Mr Georgios PAPASTERGIOU

Mr Roberto PELLA

Mrs Penka Nedelkova PENKOVA

Mr Emilio PÉREZ TOURIÑO

Mr Karsten Uno PETERSEN

Cllr Edwin POOTS

Mr Jean PRORIOL

Mr Jacek PROTAS

Dr Josef PÜHRINGER

Mr Tālis PUĶĪTIS

Mr Ilmar REEPALU

Prof. Dr. Wolfgang REINHART

Mr Carlos Manuel RODRIGUES PINTO DE SÁ

Mr Franci ROKAVEC

Mr Christophe ROUILLON

Mr Fernando de Carvalho RUAS

Mr Pedro SANZ ALONSO

Mr Miguel SANZ SESMA

Mr Johan SAUWENS

Mr Józef SEBESTA

Mrs Stasė SKUTULIENĖ

Mr Georgi Ivanov SLAVOV

Mr Bogusław ŚMIGIELSKI

Mr Robert SMRDELJ

Mr René SOUCHON

Mr Adam STRUZIK

Mr Gyula SZABO

Mr Juraj THOMA

Mr Konstantinos TZATZANIS

Mr Ramón Luis VALCÁRCEL SISO

Mr Zoltán VARGA

Mr Nichi VENDOLA

Mr Ruud VREEMAN

Dr Ferenc WEKLER

Cllr Dave WILCOX

Ing. István ZACHARIAŠ

Commission for Culture and Education

Dr Gerd HARMS
President

Mrs Claudette ABELA BALDACCHINO

Mr Alfred ALMONT

Mr Vicente ALVAREZ ARECES

Mrs Jennette ARNOLD

Ing. Vladimír BAJAN

Cllr Paula BAKER

Mrs Rita BARBERÁ NOLLA

Mrs Simone BEISSEL

Mr Milan BELICA

Mr Pavel BEM

Mrs Ann BESKOW

Mr Robert BRIGHT

Mr Pedro CASTRO VÁZQUEZ

Mr Luciano CAVERI

Mr Carlos Manuel Martins do Vale CÉSAR

Mr Jos CHABERT

Mr Cathal CROWE

Mr Rui Fernando DA SILVA RIO

Mrs Katya DOYCHEVA

Mrs Claude DU GRANRUT

Mr Luis DURNWALDER

Mrs Lenie DWARSHUIS-VAN DE BEEK

Mr Savvas ELIOFOTOU

Mr Gheorghe FALCĂ

Mr Guillermo FERNÁNDEZ VARA

Mr Andreas FOURAS

Mr Georgios GEORGIOU

Dr Michael HÄUPL

Mr Jens Arne HEDEGAARD

Mrs Monika HELBIG

Mr Jordi HEREU I BOHER

Mrs Veronica IONIŢĂ

Mr Jean-François ISTASSE

Mr Raimundas JAKUTIS

Mr Adam Sebastian JARUBAS

Mr Lech JAWORSKI

Mr Henning JENSEN

Mr Kent JOHANSSON

Mr Jean-Louis JOSEPH

Mr Werner Heinrich JOSTMEIER

Mr Mihkel JUHKAMI

Dr Kerstin KIESSLER

Mr Roger KNOX

Mr Risto KOIVISTO

Mr Henk KOOL

Mr Veikko KUMPUMÄKI

Mr Karl-Heinz LAMBERTZ

Mrs Helena LANGŠÁDLOVÁ

Mr Jean-Yves LE DRIAN

Mr Alain LE VERN

Mr Aleksandrs LIELMEŽS

Mr Agazio LOIERO

Mrs Edita Emoke LOKODI

Mr Jean-Jacques LOZACH

Mr Pierre MAILLE

Cllr Iain MALCOLM

Prof. Ursula MÄNNLE

Dr Manuel do Nascimento MARTINS

Mr Paul-Henri MEYERS

Mr Ian MICALLEF

Mr Guido MILANA

Mr Seamus MURRAY

Mr Kurmet MÜÜRSEPP

Mr Jyrki MYLLYVIRTA

Mr Sándor NAGY

Mr Marek NAWARA

Mrs Detelina NIKOLOVA

Mr Paul O'DONOGHUE

Mr Ján ORAVEC

Cllr David PARSONS

Mr Roberto PELLA

Mr Karsten Uno PETERSEN

Mr Jean-Vincent PLACÉ

Mr Emil PROSCAN

Dr Josef PÜHRINGER

Mr Joaquim Moreira RAPOSO

Mrs Indra RASSA

Mr Karl RAUBER

Mr Antón ROMBOUTS

Mr Alberto RUIZ-GALLARDON JIMENEZ

Mr Vito SANTARSIERO

Mr Miguel SANZ SESMA

Mr Vasile SAVA

Mr Heinz SCHADEN

Mrs Evangelia SCHOINARAKI-ILIAKI

Mr Ioannis SGOUROS

Mr Anton SMOLNIKAR

Dr Renato SORU

Mrs Annelie STARK

Mr Brunon SYNAK

Mr Gyula SZABO

Mr András SZALAY

Dr Co VERDAAS

Mrs Jasmina VIDMAR

Mr Vytautas VIGELIS

Mr Hans-Josef VOGEL

Mrs Maria WALLHAGER NECKMAN

Cllr Keith WALTERS

Dr Ferenc WEKLER

Mr Marek WOŹNIAK

Mrs Dora Ilieva YANKOVA

Mr Bojidar Ivanov YOTOV

Mr Grigorios ZAFIROPOULOS

Mr Jerzy ZAJAKAŁA

Dr Klaus ZEH

Commission for Constitutional Affairs and European Governance

Mr Claudio MARTINI
President

Mr Arnoldas ABRAMAVIČIUS

Mrs Esperanza AGUIRRE GIL DE BIEDMA

Mrs Kristina ALVENDAL

Mr Knud ANDERSEN

Cllr Doris ANSARI

Mrs Rita BARBERÁ NOLLA

Mr Antonio BASSOLINO

Mr Rob BATS

Mr Olivier BERTRAND

Mr Per BØDKER ANDERSEN

Mrs Mercedes BRESSO

Mr Keith BROWN

Mrs Claudette BRUNET-LECHENAULT

Mr Jiří BYTEL

Mr Pedro CASTRO VÁZQUEZ

Mr Aleš ČERIN

Mr Carlos Manuel Martins do Vale CÉSAR

Mrs Christine CHAPMAN

MUDr. Peter CHUDÍK

Mr Michael COHEN

Mrs Maria Luisa COPPOLA

Mr Mircea COSMA

Mr Jacek CZERNIAK

Mr Michel DELEBARRE

Mr Emil DRĂGHICI

Mrs Claude DU GRANRUT

Mr Andris ELKSNĪTIS

Mr Risto ERVELÄ

Mr Gheorghe FALCĂ

Mr Guillermo FERNÁNDEZ VARA

Mr Răducu George FILIPESCU

Mr Léon FRISSEN

Dr György GÉMESI

Cllr Linda GILLHAM

Mrs Dolores GOROSTIAGA SAIZ

Mrs Lotta HÅKANSSON HARJU

Mrs Constance HANNIFFY

Mr Pierre HUGON

Mr Georgios IAKOVOU

Mr Juan José IBARRETXE MARKUARTU

Dr Gyorgy IPKOVICH

Mr Helmut M. JAHN

Mr Alberto João JARDIM

Mr Lech JAWORSKI

Mr Werner Heinrich JOSTMEIER

Mr Nikitas KAKLAMANIS

Ph.D. Saima KALEV

Dr Karl-Heinz KLÄR

Ing. František KNAPÍK

Mr Risto KOIVISTO

Mr Edmunds KRASTIŅŠ

Cllr John LAHART

Mr Paul LINDQUIST

Ing. Roman LÍNEK

Mr Agazio LOIERO

Mr Reinhard LOSKE

Mrs Britt LUNDBERG

Mrs Sonia MASINI

Cllr Corrie MCCHORD

Mr Declan MCDONNELL

Mr Christos MESIS

Mr Paul-Henri MEYERS

Mr Ian MICALLEF

Mr Graziano Ernesto MILIA

Mr Erwin MOHR

Mr Árpád MOLNÁR

Mr José MONTILLA AGUILERA

Mrs Emilia MÜLLER

Mr Kurmet MÜÜRSEPP

Mr Sándor NAGY

Mr Jens Jørgen NYGAARD

Mrs Irene OLDFATHER

Mr Ján ORAVEC

Ing. Petr OSVALD

Cllr Stephen PARNABY

Mr Gediminas PAVIRŽIS

Mrs Penka Nedelkova PENKOVA

Mr Daniel PERCHERON

Mr Charles PICQUÉ

Mr Carlos Alberto PINTO

Mr Jean-Vincent PLACÉ

Mr Joaquim Moreira RAPOSO

Mr Franci ROKAVEC

Dr Herbert SAUSGRUBER

Mr Johan SAUWENS

Mr Vasile SAVA

Mr Marc SCHAEFER

Dr Michael SCHNEIDER

Mrs Evangelia SCHOINARAKI-ILIAKI

Mr Józef SEBESTA

Mr Georgi Ivanov SLAVOV

Mr Bogusław ŚMIGIELSKI

Mrs Annelie STARK

Mr Peter STRAUB

Dr Graham TOPE

Mgr. Marek TRAMŚ

Mr Konstantinos TZATZANIS

Mr Aidas VAISNORA

Mr Jean-Claude VAN CAUWENBERGHE

Mr Luc VAN DEN BRANDE

Mr Herwig VAN STAA

Mr Bas VERKERK

Mrs Marta VINCENZI

Mr Tadeusz WRONA

Mr Bojidar Ivanov YOTOV

Mr Grigorios ZAFIROPOULOS

Dr Klaus ZEH

Mr Zlatko ZHIVKOV

Commission for External Relations

Mr István SÉRTŐ-RADICS
President

Mr Uno ALDEGREN

Mr Knud ANDERSEN

Mr Francesc ANTICH I OLIVER

Mrs Jennette ARNOLD

Mr Hasan AZIS

Mr Pavel BEM

Bc. Ondřej BENEŠÍK

Mr Ferenc BENKÖ

Mr Gabor BIHARY

Mr Jacques BLANC

Mr Jean-Paul BORÉ

Mr Bruno BOURG-BROC

Mr Gheorghe BUNEA STANCU

Gabriele BURGSTALLER

Mr Francisco CAMPS ORTIZ

Mr Aleš ČERIN

Mr Jos CHABERT

Mr Manuel CHAVES GONZÁLEZ

MUDr. Peter CHUDÍK

Mr Frederick CUTAJAR

Mr Jean-Louis DESTANS

Mr Leonardo DOMENICI

Mr Uwe DÖRING

Mr Andris ELKSNĪTIS

Mr Risto ERVELÄ

Mr Michael FITZGERALD

Mr Andreas FOURAS

Mr Wolfgang GIBOWSKI

Mr Isidoro GOTTARDO

Mr Antanas GUSTAITIS

Mrs Pauliina HAIJANEN

Mrs Lotta HÅKANSSON HARJU

Mr Väino HALLIKMÄGI

Mr Rolf HARLINGHAUSEN

Cllr Martin HEATLEY

Mr Pierre HUGON

Mr Marcelino IGLESIAS RICOU

Mr Jean-François ISTASSE

Mr Alberto João JARDIM

Mr Mihkel JUHKAMI

Mr Teet KALLASVEE

Mr Gordon KEYMER

Dr Kerstin KIESSLER

Mr Vladimir KISYOV

Mr Anders KNAPE

Ing. František KNAPÍK

Mr Maciej KOBYLIŃSKI

Mrs Rinske KRUISINGA

Mr Patrick LACHAERT

Mr Cor LAMERS

Mr Denis LANDY

Mrs Helena LANGŠÁDLOVÁ

Mr Albert LENTZ

Mr Antti LIIKKANEN

Mrs Eleni LOUCAIDES

Mrs Helene LUND

Mrs Johanna MAIJ-WEGGEN

Cllr Iain MALCOLM

Dr Ulrich MALY

Prof. Ursula MÄNNLE

Mr Piero MARRAZZO

Mr Claudio MARTINI

Dr Manuel do Nascimento MARTINS

Mr Christos MESIS

Mr Ian MICALLEF

Mr Graziano Ernesto MILIA

Mr Krasimir MIREV

Mr José MONTILLA AGUILERA

Mr Francesco MUSOTTO

Mr Alin Adrian NICA

Mr Hans NIESSL

Mr Jens Jørgen NYGAARD

Mr Paul O'DONOGHUE

Mr Constantin OSTAFICIUC

Mr Chrístos PALEOLÓGOS

Mr Georgios PAPASTERGIOU

Mr Tudor PENDIUC

Mr Ion PRIOTEASA

Mr Jacek PROTAS

Mr Tālis PUĶĪTIS

Cllr Dave QUAYLE

Prof. Dr. Wolfgang REINHART

Mr Paulino RIVERO BAUTE

Mr Antón ROMBOUTS

Mr Christophe ROUILLON

Mr Alberto RUIZ-GALLARDON JIMENEZ

Mr Heinz SCHADEN

Mr Marc SCHAEFER

Mrs Catarina SEGERSTEN-LARSSON

Mr Guner Fariz SERBEST

Mr Ioannis SGOUROS

Mr Francisco MESQUITA MACHADO

Mr René SOUCHON

Mr Bernard SOULAGE

Mr Gian Mario SPACCA

Mr Adam STRUZIK

Mr Brunon SYNAK

Mr András SZALAY

Dr Stanisław SZWABSKI

Dr Graham TOPE

JUDr. Zdenko TREBULA

Mr Carlos Alberto Santos TUTA

Mr Aidas VAISNORA

Mr Nichi VENDOLA

Mrs Jasmina VIDMAR

Cllr Keith WALTERS

Mgr. Ludwik Kajetan WĘGRZYN

Cllr Dave WILCOX

Mr Hermann WINKLER

Mr Marek WOŹNIAK

Secretariat-General of the Committee of the Regions

Rue Belliard 101
B-1040 Brussel/Bruxelles
Website: http://www.cor.europa.eu
Tel. +32 22822211
Fax +32 22822325

POLITICAL GROUP SECRETARIATS

Group of the European People's Party (PPE)

Heinz-Peter KNAPP
Head of Unit
Tel. +32 22822221
Fax +32 22822329

Paul WILLEMS
Administrator
Tel. +32 22822308
Fax +32 22822329

Simone BRUSADIN
Administrator
Tel. +32 22822091
Fax +32 22822329

Inès ROSETA
Administrator
Tel. +32 22822247
Fax +32 22822329

Vasileios ANTONIOU
Administrator
Tel. +32 22822388
Fax +32 22822329

Group of the Party of European Socialists (PSE)

Jordi HARRISON
Head of Unit
Tel. +32 22822312
Fax +32 22822318

Olga FOTINOU
Administrator
Tel. +32 22822086
Fax +32 22822069

Justus SCHÖNLAU
Administrator
Tel. +32 22822227
Fax +32 22822069

Julien DE RIDDER
Administrator
Tel. +32 2282-2309
Fax +32 2282-2318

Chiara MALAGODI
Administrator
Tel. +32 2282-2243
Fax +32 2282-2180

Group of Alliance of Liberals and Democrats for Europe (ALDE)

Sean O'CURNEEN
Head of Unit
Tel. +32 22822226
Fax +32 22822331

Johanna LINDBLOM
Administrator
Tel. +32 22822238
Fax +32 22822331

Marcus SCHEUREN
Administrator
Tel. +32 2282-2281
Fax +32 2282-2331

Union for Europe of the Nations — European Alliance (UEN-EA)

Michael O'CONCHUIR
Administrator
Tel. +32 22822251
Fax +32 22822334

Bogna RODZIEWICZ
Administrator
Tel. +32 22822158
Fax +32 22822334

CHAIRMAN'S PRIVATE OFFICE

Guido DUMON
Head of Private Office
Tel. +32 22822323
Fax +32 22822318

Matthieu HORNUNG
Administrator
Tel. +32 22822578
Fax +32 22822069

Filippo TERRUSO
Administrator
Tel. +32 22822291
Fax +32 22822329

Anna SCHADE
Administrator
Tel. +32 22822523

SECRETARIAT-GENERAL

Gerhard STAHL
Secretary-General
Tel. +32 22822005
Fax +32 22822007

Reinhold GNAN
Head of Private Office
Tel. +32 22822335
Fax +32 22822180

Serafino NARDI
Administrator
Tel. +32 22822508
Fax +32 22822180

Pavla DANISOVA
Administrator
Tel. +32 2282-2011
Fax +32 2282-2180

Advisers to the Secretary General

Hans-Jürgen SCHMEHR
Adviser
Tel. +32 22822527
Fax +32 22822150

INTERNAL AUDIT SERVICE

Pascale VAN OUTRYVE D'YDEWALLE
Head of Unit
Tel. +32 22822456
Fax +32 22822150

Barbara MASOTTI
Administrator
Tel. +32 22822398
Fax +32 22822150

Unit for Forward Planning

Béatrice TAULEGNE
Head of Unit
Tel. +32 22822175
Fax +32 22822442

Gianluca SPINACI
Administrator
Tel. +32 22822541
Fax +32 22822442

Isabelle DIRKX
Administrator
Tel. +32 22822513
Fax +32 22822442

Hendrik THEUNISSEN
Administrator
Tel. +32 22822110
Fax +32 22822150

Till HOFFSTADT
Administrator
Rue Belliard 101
B-1040 Brussels
E-mail: till.hoffstadt@cor.europa.eu
Tel. +32 25469353
Fax +32 22822442

DIRECTORATE A – ADMINISTRATION AND FINANCE

Pedro CERVILLA
Director (acting)
Tel. +32 22822189
Fax +32 22822118

Budget/Finance Unit

Peder JAKOBSSON
Head of Unit
Tel. +32 22822055
Fax +32 22822332

Elmars KRONBERGS
Administrator
Tel. +32 22822592
Fax +32 22359922

Sylvain YLIEFF
Administrator
Tel. +32 22822591
Fax +32 22822332

Éric LEURQUIN
Administrator
Tel. +32 22822286
Fax +32 22359922

Unit for Recruitment and careers

Claudine KESTELOOT
Head of Unit
Tel. +32 22829422
Fax +32 22822013

Svetlozar ANDREEV
Administrator
Fax +32 22822013

Thierry FIRMIN
Administrator
Tel. +32 22822076
Fax +32 22822013

François FILIPEK
Administrator
Tel. +32 25468486
Fax +32 22822013

Unit for Working conditions, rights and training

Tom HAENEBALCKE
Head of Unit
Tel. +32 22822228
Fax +32 22822118

Katerina PINTOVA
Administrator
Tel. +32 22822048
Fax +32 22822118

Joanna LINDBERG
Administrator
Tel. +32 22822370

Elena TACHKALOVA
Doctor
Tel. +32 25469597
Fax +32 25469601/2822118

General Administration Unit

Sybren SINGELSMA
Head of Unit
Tel. +32 22829362
Fax +32 22822213

Pierre GILLES
Administrator
Tel. +32 22822501
Fax +32 22822213

Florence WALLERAND
Administrator
Tel. +32 22822048
Fax +32 22822213

Marcin SZCZEPANSKI
Administrator
Tel. +32 25468667
Fax +32 22822213

Malgorzata KOWALIK
Administrator
Tel. +32 22822563
Fax +32 22822213

DIRECTORATE B – MEMBERS SERVICE AND REGISTRY

Steen ILLEBORG
Director
Tel. +32 22822184
Fax +32 22822072

Thierry CASTILLON
Deputy Director
Tel. +32 22822203
Fax +32 22822321

Legal Service

Juan Carlos CAÑOTO ARGÜELLES
Head of Unit
Fax +32 22823334

Sophie BACHOTET
Administrator
Tel. +32 22822181
Fax +32 22823334

Petra CANDELLIER
Administrator
Tel. +32 22822196
Fax +32 22823334

Internal Services

Caroline BOUQUEREL
Head of Unit
Tel. +32 25469019
Fax +32 22822265

Piotr Pawel ZAJACZKOWSKI
Administrator
Tel. +32 22822401
Fax +32 22822265

Registry, services to members, national delegations

Stergios BANIOTOPOULOS
Head of Unit
Tel. +32 22822186
Fax +32 22822119

Alina VASILE
Administrator
Tel. +32 25468820
Fax +32 22822119

Dimitrios KATSANIDIS
Administrator
Tel. +32 25469703
Fax +32 22822119

Saskia BELJAARS-VERHOEVEN
Administrator
Tel. +32 22822315
Fax +32 22822119

Péter HÓRVATH
Administrator
Tel. +32 22822157
Fax +32 22822119

Holger BENZING
Administrator
Tel. +32 22822511
Fax +32 22822119

Monika WEYMANN
Administrator
Tel. +32 22822509
Fax +32 22822119

DIRECTORATE C – CONSULTATIVE WORKS

Lucio GUSSETTI
Director
Tel. +32 22822512
Fax +32 22822515

Michael COLLINS
Deputy Director
Tel. +32 22822105
Fax +32 22822515

Unit Commissions 1 CONST, COTER, DEVE)

Marie-Claire NEILL-COWPER
Head of Unit
Tel. +32 22822185
Fax +32 22822113

Commission on Constitutional Affairs and European Governance (CONST)

Simona ARDOVINO
Administrator
Tel. +32 22822464
Fax +32 22822326

Delphine BOURDIN
Administrator
Tel. +32 22822346
Fax +32 22822326

Commission for Economic and Social Policy (DEVE)

Helene MORAUT
Administrator
Tel. +32 22822161
Fax +32 22822074

Jens ZVIRGZDGRAUDS
Administrator
Tel. +32 22822137
Fax +32 22822074

Carsten BRAUNS
Administrator
Tel. +32 22822585
Fax +32 22822074

Commission for Territorial Cohesion (COTER)

Carole LABBE
Administrator
Tel. +32 22822191
Fax +32 22822113

Pablo CORNIDE
Administrator
Tel. +32 22822266
Fax +32 22822113

Christof KIENEL
Administrator
Tel. +32 22822521
Fax +32 22822113

Unit Commissions 2 (RELEX, EDUC, ECOS)

Silke TÖNSHOFF
Head of Unit
Tel. +32 22822455
Fax +32 22822326

Commission for External Relations and Decentralised Cooperation (RELEX)

Judith BÜRGER
Administrator
Tel. +32 22822172
Fax +32 22822070

Branislav STANICEK
Administrator
Tel. +32 22822471
Fax +32 22822070

Victor TILEA
Administrator
Tel. +32 22822395
Fax +32 22822070

Commission for Culture, Education and Research (EDUC)

Anna KÀDÀR
Administrator
Tel. +32 22822028
Fax +32 22822088

Alexander POPOV
Administrator
Tel. +32 22022351
Fax +32 22822088

Commission for Economic and Social Policy (ECOS)

Robert RÖNSTROM
Administrator
Tel. +32 22822192
Fax +32 25469061

Wojciech DYBA
Administrator
Tel. +32 22822565
Fax +32 25469061

Karina SULEIMANOVA
Administrator
Tel. +32 22822478
Fax +32 25469061

Unit 3 Networks and subsidiarity

Elisa GAROSI
Head of Unit
Tel. +32 22822246
Fax +32 22822087

Emmanouil DARDOUFAS
Administrator
Tel. +32 22822502
Fax +32 22822087

Andrea FORTI
Administrator
Tel. +32 22822084
Fax +32 22822087

Krzysztof NOWACZEK
Administrator
Tel. +32 22822590
Fax +32 22822087

Bernard CHANE KUNE
Administrator
Tel. +32 22822394
Fax +32 22822087

Doris SPICKENREUTHER
Administrator
Tel. +32 22822391
Fax +32 22822087

Unit 4 Studies and legislative planning

Kyriakos TSIRIMIAGOS
Head of Unit
Tel. +32 22822122
Fax +32 22822330

Maria KETSETZI
Administrator
Tel. +32 22822064
Fax +32 22822330

DIRECTORATE D – COMMUNICATION, PRESS AND PROTOCOL

Laurent THIEULE
Director
Tel. +32 22822199
Fax +32 22822329

Lambrini YALAMBOUKIDOU
Deputy Director
Tel. +32 22822154
Fax +32 22822338

Unit 1'Media, Communication, Association'

Christian GSODAM
Head of Unit
Tel. +32 22822121
Fax +32 22822329

Alina Mihaela VASILE
Administrator
Tel. +32 22822123
Fax +32 22822329

Athénaïs CAZALIS DE FONDOUCE
Administrator
Tel. +32 22822447
Fax +32 22822329

Peter VERLINDEN
Administrator
Tel. +32 22822170
Fax +32 22822119

Ioan-Petru VASCAN
Administrator
Tel. +32 22822285
Fax +32 22822329

Unit for Events

Wolfgang PETZOLD
Head of Unit
Fax +32 22822338

Boris ESSENDER
Administrator
Tel. +32 22822390
Fax +32 22822338

Klaus HULLMANN
Administrator
Tel. +32 22822124
Fax +32 22822338

Unit for Administration, Budget, Editions

Pierre-Alexis FERAL
Head of Unit
Tel. +32 22822205
Fax +32 22822329

Luisa DOMENICHELLI
Administrator
Tel. +32 22822025
Fax +32 22822329

Carolyn LEFFLER-ROTH
Administrator
Tel. +32 22822117
Fax +32 22822329

COMMITTEE OF THE REGIONS

Joint Services of the Committee of the Regions and of the European Economic and Social Committee

Rue Montoyer 92-102
B-1000 Brussels
Rue Belliard 68
B-1000 Brussel/Bruxelles
Tel. +32 2235 + extension
Fax +32 2235 + extension

DIRECTORATE E – TRANSLATION

Gonzalo BESCÓS FERRAZ
Director
Tel. +32 22822156

Ineta STRAUTINA
Deputy Director
Tel. +32 25468243

Translation coordination

Éric LAVIGNE
Head of Unit
Tel. +32 22822032
Fax +32 25469076

Bulgarian translation

Ani DAMYANOVA
Head of Unit
Tel. +32 25469803
Fax +32 25468882

Spanish translation

Miguel PAREDES LARRUCEA
Head of Unit
Tel. +32 22359591
Fax +32 22359180

Czech translation

Markéta FRANKOVÁ
Head of Unit
Tel. +32 25469742
Fax +32 25469190

Danish translation

Steen FINK-JENSEN
Head of Unit
Tel. +32 25469379
Fax +32 25468185

German translation

Giovanni DI CARLO
Head of Unit
Tel. +32 25469502
Fax +32 25468653

Estonian translation

Jana KOPA
Head of Unit
Tel. +32 25468497
Fax +32 25469182

Greek translation

Nikolaos PAPANIKOLAOU
Head of Unit
Tel. +32 25469508
Fax +32 25469181

English translation

Francis PATTERSON
Head of Unit
Tel. +32 25469522
Fax +32 25469187

French translation

Joseph LONGTON
Head of Unit
Tel. +32 25469115
Fax +32 25469182

Italian translation

Eugenia PONZONI
Head of Unit
Tel. +32 25469244
Fax +32 22359188

Latvian translation

Edite KRUZE
Head of Unit
Fax +32 25468640

Lithuanian translation

Jurate DREVINSKIENE
Head of Unit
Tel. +32 25468164
Fax +32 25468639

Hungarian translation

Andras EGYEDI
Head of Unit
Tel. +32 22822463
Fax +32 25469021

Maltese translation

Elgar-Paul MAGRO
Head of Unit
Tel. +32 25468471
Fax +32 22358291

Dutch translation

Francis TAILLEU
Head of Unit
Tel. +32 25468735
Fax +32 25469183

Polish translation

Izabella WISNIEWSKA-CRAVEN-GREEN
Head of Unit
Tel. +32 25468148
Fax +32 25468226

Portuguese translation

Manuel SILVEIRA
Head of Unit
Tel. +32 25469709
Fax +32 25469186

Romanian translation

Gabriela VARZARU
Head of Unit
Tel. +32 25468849
Fax +32 25468885

Slovak translation

Karin MIŠÁNIKOVÁ
Head of Unit
Tel. +32 25468263
Fax +32 25468651

Slovene translation

Anica RANT
Head of Unit
Tel. +32 25468154
Fax +32 25468650

Finnish translation

Erja UUSITALO
Head of Unit
E-mail: 546 90 71
Tel. +32 25469051
Fax 322

Swedish translation

Pär HAMMARGREN
Head of Unit
Tel. +32 25469161
Fax +32 25469145

DIRECTORATE F – LOGISTICS

Direction

Cornelius BENTVELSEN
Director
Tel. +32 25469813
Fax +32 25469705

Noëlle MATTEI
Deputy Director
Tel. +32 25469868
Fax +32 25469705

Pedro ASSUNCAO
Administrator
Tel. +32 22822272
Fax +32 22359922

Programming/financial and contractual management

Steven PHILLIPS
Head of Unit
Tel. +32 25469461
Fax +32 25469705

Infrastructures

Marc DE FEU
Head of Unit
Tel. +32 25468665
Fax +32 25469080

Sandra MACCANTI
Administrator
Tel. +32 25469825
Fax +32 25469080

IT and telecommunications

Niall O'HIGGINS
Head of Unit
Tel. +32 25469668
Fax +32 25469769

Jean Marc DEBRUE
Administrator
Tel. +32 25469515
Fax +32 22359922

Jean-Pierre MORANT
Administrator
Tel. +32 25469045
Fax +32 22359922

Printing/Diffusion

Jan BAUMGARTL
Head of Unit
Tel. +32 25469851
Fax +32 25469076

Security

Antonio INCLAN GONZALEZ
Administrator
Tel. +32 25469751
Fax +32 25469705

EUROPEAN INVESTMENT BANK

European Investment Bank

98-100, boulevard Konrad Adenauer
L-2950 Luxembourg
E-mail: info@eib.org
Website: http://www.bei.org
Tel. +352 4379-1
Fax +352 437704

MANAGEMENT COMMITTEE

Philippe MAYSTADT
President of the Bank and Chairman of the Board of Directors

Philippe de FONTAINE VIVE CURTAZ
Vice-President

Simon BROOKS
Vice-President

Carlos da SILVA COSTA
Vice-President

Matthias KOLLATZ-AHNEN
Vice-President

Eva SREJBER
Vice-President

Marta GAJĚCKA
Vice-President

Dario SCANNAPIECO
Vice-President

Plutarchos SAKELLARIS
Vice-President

GENERAL SECRETARIAT AND LEGAL AFFAIRS

Alfonso QUEREJETA
Secretary General and General Counsel of Legal Affairs

Interinstitutional Affairs

Dominique de CRAYENCOUR
Director

Guido PRUD'HOMME

Ferdinand SASSEN

Governing Bodies, Secretariat, Protocol

Hugo WOESTMANN
Director

Linguistic Services

Kenneth PETERSEN

Legal Affairs

Community and Financial Affairs, Lending Operations outside Europe

Marc DUFRESNE
Deputy General Counsel

Jean-Philippe MINNAERT
Data Protection Officer

Financial Issues

Nicola BARR
Associate Director

Institutional and Staff Issues

Carlos GÓMEZ DE LA CRUZ

Mediterranean (FEMIP), Africa, Caribbean, Pacific — Investment Facility, Asia and Latin America

Regan WYLIE-OTTE
Associate Director

Lending Operations in Europe

Gerhard HÜTZ
Director

Gian Domenico SPOTA

Operational Policy, New Financial Instruments

José María FERNÁNDEZ MARTÍN

Adriatic Sea, South-Eastern Europe

Manfredi TONCI OTTIERI
Associate Director

United Kingdom, Ireland, Baltic States, Denmark, Finland, Sweden, EFTA Countries

Patrick Hugh CHAMBERLAIN
Associate Director

France, Belgium, Netherlands, Luxembourg

Pierre ALBOUZE

Central Europe, Poland, Russia, Eastern Neighbours

Emeram BINDER

Spain, Portugal

Ignacio LACORZANA

Maria SHAW-BARRAGAN

STRATEGY AND CORPORATE CENTRE

Rémy JACOB
Director General
Financial Controller and Chief Information Officer

Financial Control

Frank TASSONE

Resource Management and Coordination

Geneviève DEWULF

Strategy and Management Control

Jürgen MOEHRKE
Director

Groupe de travail 'Réforme des méthodes et processus'

Theoharry GRAMMATIKOS
Associate Director

Groupe de travail 'IFRS' (Normes internationales d'information financière)

Henricus SEERDEN

Economic and Financial Studies

Éric PERÉE
Associate Director

Groupe de travail 'Réforme des méthodes et processus'

Theoharry GRAMMATIKOS
Associate Director

Groupe de travail 'IFRS' (Normes internationales d'information financière)

Henricus SEERDEN

Budget, Analytics and Partnerships

Janette FOSTER

Strategy and Processes

Claudio PASQUI

Corporate Responsibility Policies

Felismino ALCARPE

Communication

Gill TUDOR
Spokesperson and Director

Press Office

Rainer SCHLITT

Public Information and Relations with Civil Society

Yvonne BERGHORST

Information Offices

Paris Office

Henry MARTY-GAUQUIÉ
Director

London Office

Adam MC DONAUGH

Berlin Office

Paul Gerd LÖSER

Rome Office

Marco SANTARELLI

Madrid Office

Mercedes SENDÍN DE CÁCERES

Brussels Office

Nicholas ANTONOVICS

Information Technology

Derek BARWISE
Director

Administration and Risk Applications

Simon NORCROSS

Finance and Lending Applications

Jean-Yves PIRNAY

Operations and Client Services

...

Technical Support and Architecture

...

Buildings, Logistics and Documentation

Patricia TIBBELS
Director

Facilities Management

Enzo UNFER

Purchasing and Administrative Services

Gudrun LEITHMANN-FRÜH

Documentation and Records Management

...

DIRECTORATE FOR OPERATIONS IN THE EUROPEAN UNION AND CANDIDATE COUNTRIES

Thomas HACKETT
Director General

Operations Support

Simon BARNES
Chief Operational Coordinator

Coordination

Dietmar DUMLICH

Information Systems and Applications

Thomas FAHRTMANN

Business Support

Patrick BOEUF

JESSICA

Eugenio LEANZA

Gianni CARBONARO

European PPP Expertise Centre

Nicholas JENNETT

Action for Growth Instruments

Thomas BARRETT
Director

Trans European Networks

Jukka LUUKKANEN

Ale Jan GERCAMA

Knowledge Economy (i2i)

Heinz OLBERS

Environment, Energy and Advisory

Christopher KNOWLES
Associate Director

James RANAIVOSON

Western Europe

Laurent de MAUTORT
Director

i2i and Corporates

Robert SCHOFIELD

Project Finance

Cheryl FISHER
Associate Director

Public Sector and Utilities

Jean-Christophe CHALINE

Implementation

Peter JACOBS

Spain, Portugal

Carlos GUILLE
Director

Spain — Infrastructure

Luca LAZZAROLI

Spain — Banks and Corporates

Fernando DE LA FUENTE
Associate Director

Madrid office

Angel FERRERO

Portugal

Miguel MORGADO

Lisbon Office

Alexandra ALMEIDA

Implementation

Rui Artur MARTINS

Central Europe

Joachim LINK
Director

Germany — Infrastructure, Energy and Promotional Banks

Peggy NYLUND-GREEN
Associate Director

Germany — Banks and Corporates

Anita FUERSTENBERG-LUCIUS

Austria, Czech Republic, Hungary, Slovakia — Infrastructure and Promotional Banks

Jean VRLA

Austria, Czech Republic, Hungary, Slovakia — Banks and Corporates

Paolo MUNINI

Vienna Office

Emanuel MARAVIC
Director

Adriatic Sea

Romualdo MASSA BERNUCCI
Director

Italy, Malta — Infrastructure

Antonello RICCI

Flavio SCHIAVO CAMPO de GREGORIO

Italy, Malta — Banks and Corporates

Marguerite MCMAHON

Slovenia, Croatia, Western Balkans

Dominique COURBIN

South-East Europe

Jean-Christophe LALOUX
Director

Greece

Themistoklis KOUVARAKIS

Athens Office

Fotini KOUTZOUKOU

Bulgaria, Romania, Cyprus

Cormac MURPHY

Bucharest Office

Götz VON THADDEN

Turkey

Bruno DENIS

Ankara Office

...

Istanbul Office

Alain TERRAILLON

Baltic Sea

Tilman SEIBERT
Director

Poland

Kim KREILGAARD

Warsaw Office

Michal LUBIENIECKI

Baltic States, Denmark, Finland, Sweden, EFTA Countries

Michael O'HALLORAN

Helsinki Office

Jaani PIETIKAINEN

DIRECTORATE FOR OPERATIONS OUTSIDE THE EUROPEAN UNION AND CANDIDATE COUNTRIES

Martin CURWEN
Director General (acting)

Matthias ZÖLLNER
Conseiller de direction pour les activités en matière de changements climatiques

Development Economics Advisory Service

Matthias ZÖLLNER
Conseiller de direction pour les activités en matière de changements climatiques

Daniel OTTOLENGHI
Chief Development Economist
Associate Director

Bernard ZILLER

Europe's Neighbour and Partner Countries

Claudio CORTESE
Director

Alain NADEAU

Maghreb

Bernard GORDON

Rabat Office

René PEREZ

Tunis Office

Diederick ZAMBON

Near East

Javier GUTIÉRREZ DEGENÈVE

Cairo Office

Jane MACPHERSON

Eastern Europe, Southern Caucasus and Russia

Constantin SYNADINO

Umberto DEL PANTA

Special Operations

Angus MACRAE

Africa, Caribbean, Pacific — Investment Facility

Martin CURWEN
Director

West Africa and Sahel

Gustaaf HEIM

Dakar Office

Jack REVERSADE

Central and East Africa

Flavia PALANZA
Associate Director

Nairobi Office

Carmelo COCUZZA

Southern Africa and Indian Ocean

Serge-Arno KLÜMPER

Tshwane (Pretoria) Office

David WHITE

Caribbean and Pacific

David CRUSH

Fort-de-France Office

Anthony WHITEHOUSE

Sydney Office

Jean-Philippe DE JONG

Resources and Development

Tassilo HENDUS
Associate Director

Portfolio Management, Policy

Catherine COLLIN

Asia and Latin America

Francisco de PAULA COELHO
Director

Latin America

Alberto BARRAGÁN

Asia

Philippe SZYMCZAK

TRANSACTION MANAGEMENT AND RESTRUCTURING DEPARTMENT

Klaus TRÖMEL
Director

Counterpart and Contract Monitoring and Review

Stefano BOTTANI

Restructuring, Refinancing and Repackaging

Volkmar BRUHN-LÉON

FINANCE DIRECTORATE

Bertrand de MAZIÈRES
Director General

Coordination and Financial Policies

Éric LAMARCQ

Investor Relations and Marketing

Peter MUNRO

Financial Engineering and Advisory Services

Guido BICHISAO

Capital Markets

Barbara BARGAGLI PETRUCCI
Director

Euro

Carlos FERREIRA DA SILVA

Aldo ROMANI

Europe (excluding euro), Africa

Richard TEICHMEISTER

Thomas SCHROEDER

America, Asia, Pacific

Eila KREIVI

Sandeep DHAWAN

Treasury

Anneli PESHKOFF
Director

Liquidity Management

Francis ZEGHERS

Timothy O'CONNELL

Asset and Liability Management

Jean-Dominique POTOCKI

Nicola SANTINI

Portfolio Management

...

Planning and Settlement of Operations

Elisabeth MATIZ
Director

Back-Office Loans and Operational Lending Support

Eleonore FIGNOLET

Back Office Treasury

Cynthia LAVALLÉ

Back Office Borrowings

Antonio VIEIRA

Systems and Procedures

Lorenzo CICCHELLI

PROJECTS DIRECTORATE

Grammatiki TSINGOU-PAPADOPETROU
Director General

Sustainable Development

Peter CARTER
Associate Director

Resources Management

Béatrice LAURY

Quality Management

Maj THEANDER

Project Development and Implementation Support

Hugh GOLDSMITH

Innovation and Competitiveness

Constantin CHRISTOFIDIS
Director

Manufacturing and Industry (R&D)

Gunnar MUENT

ICT and e-Economy

Harald GRUBER

Human Capital

John DAVIS

Maria Luisa FERREIRA

Services and SMEs, Agroindustry (including Biofuels)

Hans-Harald JAHN

Pedro OCHOA

Rüdiger SCHMIDT

Campbell THOMSON

Transport and Energy

Christopher HURST
Director

Nigel HALL

Road and Rail

Matthew ARNDT

Air and Sea

José Luis ALFARO
Associate Director

Klaus HEEGE

Energy Generation and Networks

François TREVOUX

Josef WELTERMANN

Energy Efficiency and Renewables

Juan ALARIO
Associate Director

Convergence and Environment

Guy CLAUSSE
Director

Water and Environmental Protection

José FRADE
Deputy Director

Michel DECKER

Programme Lending

Eugenia KAZAMAKI-OTTERSTEN

Urban Transport and other Urban Infrastructure

Mateo TURRÓ CALVET
Associate Director

Mario AYMERICH

Development Projects, New Initiatives, Solid Waste

Stephen WRIGHT
Associate Director

Eberhard GSCHWINDT

Philippe GUINET

JASPERS

Patrick WALSH
Director

Agustin AURÍA
Associate Director

Operations Management

Norbert HAHN

Vienna Office

Axel HÖRHAGER

Bucharest Office

Nicos YIAMBIDES

Warsaw Office

Michael MAJEWSKI

Water and Wastewater

Eckart TRONNIER

Ports, Airports and Railways

Alan LYNCH

RISK MANAGEMENT DIRECTORATE

Pierluigi GILIBERT
Director General

Coordination and Support

Juliette LENDARO

Pierre TYCHON

Credit Risk

Per JEDEFORS
Director

Corporates, Public, Infrastructure

Stuart ROWLANDS
Associate Director

Project and Structured Finance

Paolo LOMBARDO

Financial Institutions and Securitisations

Per DE HAAS

Financial and Operational Risks

Alain GODARD
Director

ALM and Market Risk Management

Giancarlo SARDELLI

Vincent THUNUS

Derivatives

Luis GONZALEZ-PACHECO

Operational Risk

Antonio ROCA IGLESIAS

INSPECTORATE GENERAL

Jan Willem VAN DER KAAIJ
Inspector-General

Siward DE VRIES
Fraud Investigations Unit

Internal Audit

Ciaran HOLLYWOOD

Operations Evaluation

Alain SÈVE
Associate Director

Gavin DUNNETT

Ivory Lorena YONG-PROTZEL

Werner SCHMIDT

EIB GROUP COMPLIANCE OFFICE

...
Chief Compliance Officer

Francesco MANTEGAZZA
Deputy Chief

HUMAN RESOURCES DEPARTMENT

Michel GRILLI
Director

Jean-Philippe BIRCKEL

Leena LAHTI

Administration and Management Systems

Carlo MORI

Catherine ALBRECHT

Staffing

Luis GARRIDO

Internal Communication

Alain JAVEAU

People Development and Organisation Management

Barbara BALKE
Directeur adjoint

Ute PIEPER-SECKELMANN

Well-being and Work/Life Balance

René CHRISTENSEN

REPRESENTATION ON BOARD OF DIRECTORS OF EUROPEAN BANK FOR RECONSTRUCTION AND DEVELOPMENT

Terence BROWN
Administrateur

Walter CERNOIA
Administrateur suppléant
Conseiller spécial auprès du Président de la BEI

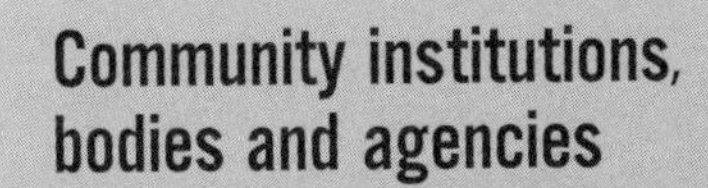

EUROPEAN INVESTMENT FUND

96, boulevard Konrad Adenauer
L-2968 Luxembourg
Luxembourg
E-mail: info@eif.org
Website: http://www.eif.org
Tel. +352 426688-1
Fax +352 426688-200

Chief Executive

Richard PELLY

Deputy Chief Executive

Jean-Marie MAGNETTE

EUROPEAN CENTRAL BANK

European Central Bank

Eurotower
Kaiserstrasse 29
D-60311 Frankfurt am Main
Website: http://www.ecb.europa.eu
Tel. +49 691344-0
Fax +49 6913446000

EXECUTIVE BOARD OF THE EUROPEAN CENTRAL BANK

Jean-Claude TRICHET
President of the ECB

Lucas D. PAPADEMOS
Vice-President of the ECB

Lorenzo BINI SMAGHI
Board Member of the ECB

José Manuel GONZÁLEZ-PÁRAMO
Board Member of the ECB

Jürgen STARK
Board Member of the ECB

Gertrude TUMPEL-GUGERELL
Board Member of the ECB

GOVERNING COUNCIL

Jean-Claude TRICHET
President of the ECB

Lucas D. PAPADEMOS
Vice-President of the ECB

Lorenzo BINI SMAGHI
Board Member of the ECB

José Manuel GONZÁLEZ-PÁRAMO
Board Member of the ECB

Jürgen STARK
Board Member of the ECB

Gertrude TUMPEL-GUGERELL
Board Member of the ECB

Michael C. BONELLO
Central Bank of Malta

Vítor Manuel RIBEIRO CONSTÂNCIO
Banco de Portugal

Mario DRAGHI
Banca d'Italia

Miguel FERNÁNDEZ ORDÓÑEZ
Banco de España

John HURLEY
Central Bank & Financial Services Authority of Ireland

Marko KRANJEC
Banka Slovenije

Erkki LIIKANEN
Suomen Pankki - Finlands Bank

Yves MERSCH
Banque Centrale du Luxembourg

Ewald NOWOTNY
Österreichische Nationalbank

Christian NOYER
Banque de France

Athanasios ORPHANIDES
Kentriki Trapeza tis Kiprou
Central Bank of Cyprus

Georgios PROVOPOULOS
Trapeza tis Ellados
Bank of Greece

Guy QUADEN
Nationale Bank van België
Banque Nationale de Belgique

Ivan ŠRAMKO
Národná banka Slovenska

Axel A. WEBER
Deutsche Bundesbank

Nout WELLINK
De Nederlandsche Bank

GENERAL COUNCIL

Jean-Claude TRICHET
President of the ECB

Lucas D. PAPADEMOS
Vice-President of the ECB

Nils BERNSTEIN
Danmarks Nationalbank

Michael C. BONELLO
Central Bank of Malta

Vítor Manuel RIBEIRO CONSTÂNCIO
Banco de Portugal

Mario DRAGHI
Banca d'Italia

Miguel FERNÁNDEZ ORDÓÑEZ
Banco de España

John HURLEY
Central Bank & Financial Services Authority of Ireland

Stefan INGVES
Sveriges Riksbank

Mugur ISĂRESCU
Banca Națională a României

Ivan ISKROV
Balgarska Narodna Banka
Bulgarian National Bank

Mervyn KING
Bank of England

Marko KRANJEC
Banka Slovenije

Erkki LIIKANEN
Suomen Pankki
Finlands Bank

Andres LIPSTOK
Eesti Pank

Yves MERSCH
Banque Centrale du Luxembourg

Ewald NOWOTNY
Österreichische Nationalbank

Christian NOYER
Banque de France

Athanasios ORPHANIDES
Kentriki Trapeza tis Kiprou
Central Bank of Cyprus

Georgios PROVOPOULOS
Trapeza tis Ellados
Bank of Greece

Guy QUADEN
Nationale Bank van België
Banque Nationale de Belgique

Ilmārs RIMŠĒVIČS
Latvijas bankas

Reinoldijus ŠARKINAS
Lietuvos bankas

András SIMOR
Magyar Nemzeti Bank

Sławomir SKRZYPEK
Narodowy Bank Polski

Ivan ŠRAMKO
Národná banka Slovenska

Zdeněk TŮMA
Česká Národní Banka

Axel A. WEBER
Deutsche Bundesbank

Nout WELLINK
De Nederlandsche Bank

DIRECTORATE-GENERAL ADMINISTRATION

Gerald GRISSE
Director General

Administrative Services Division

Jesper DELEURAN
Head of Division

Premises Division

Günter FLOHR
Head of Division

Security Division

Erich NIEDERDORFER
Head of Division

Internal finance Directorate

Ian INGRAM
Director

Accounting Division

Manfred STRIEGL
Head of Division

Financial Reporting and Policy Division

Denis BLENCK
Head of Division

Banknotes Directorate

Ton ROOS
Director

Currency management

Thomas SCHWEIKART
Head of Division

Currency development

Brian DENNIS
Head of Division

Communications Directorate

Elisabeth ARDAILLON-POIRIER
Director

Press and Information Division

Regina SCHÜLLER
Head of Division

Publishing, Events and Protocol Division

Helga MEISTER
Head of Division

Counsel to the Executive Board

Christian THIMANN
Counsellor to the President and Co-ordinator of the Counsel to the Executive Board

ECB Permanent Representation in Washington D.C.

Georges PINEAU
Permanent Representative

DIRECTORATE-GENERAL ECONOMICS

Wolfgang SCHILL
Director General

Philippe MOUTOT
Deputy Director General

Fiscal Policies Division

Ad VAN RIET
Head of Division

Economic Developments Directorate

Hans-Joachim KLÖCKERS
Director

Euro Area Macroeconomic Developments Division

José MARÍN ARCAS
Head of Division

EU Countries Division

Klaus MASUCH
Head of Division

External Developments Division

Filippo DI MAURO
Head of Division

Monetary Policy Directorate

Philippe MOUTOT
Director

Capital Markets and Financial Structure Division

Francesco DRUDI
Head of Division

Monetary Policy Stance Division

Huw PILL
Head of Division

Monetary Policy Strategy Division

Massimo ROSTAGNO
Head of Division

Financial Stability and Supervision Directorate

Mauro GRANDE
Director

Financial Stability Division

John FELL
Head of Division

Financial Supervision Division

Panagiotis STROUZAS
Head of Division

DIRECTORATE-GENERAL HUMAN RESOURCES, BUDGET AND ORGANISATION

Koenraad DE GEEST
Director General

Berend VAN BAAK
Deputy Director General

Recruitment and Compensation Division

Sören BEIER
Head of Division

Human Resources Policies and Staff Relations Division

Manfred KOCH
Head of Division

Budget and Projects Division

Claudia BOCK-VALOTTA
Head of Division

Organisational Planning Division

Emily WITT
Head of Division

Risk Management Division

Ulrich BINDSEIL
Head of division a.i.

DIRECTORATE-GENERAL INFORMATION SYSTEMS

Hans-Gert PENZEL
Director General

François LAURENT
Deputy Director-General

IT Management Functions Divisison

François LAURENT
Head of Division

IT Operations and Support Division

Jean-Luc GÉRARDY
Head of Division

IT Projects Directorate

Magi CLAVÉ
Director

Alessandro BONARA
IT Portfolio Manager

Paul CHURCH
IT Portfolio Manager

Magnus FRIED
IT Portfolio Manager

Andreas HAKE
IT Portfolio Manager

Christian REYNDERS
IT Portfolio Manager

Internal Audit Directorate

Klaus GRESSENBAUER
Director

Audit Services Division

Jan WAPPEROM
Head of Division

Audit Missions Division

Eric VERMEIR
Head of Division

INTERNATIONAL AND EUROPEAN RELATIONS

Frank MOSS
Director General

Gilles NOBLET
Deputy Director-General

International Policy Analysis and Emerging Markets Division

Marcel FRATZSCHER
Head of Division

EU Institutions and Fora Division

Theodor MARTENS
Head of Division

EU Neighbouring Regions Division

Francesco MAZZAFERRO
Head of Division

DIRECTORATE-GENERAL LEGAL SERVICES

Antonio SÁINZ DE VICUÑA
Director General

Legal Advice Division

Chiara ZILIOLI
Head of Division

Lawyer-Linguists Division

Mikael STENSTRÖM
Head of Division

DIRECTORATE-GENERAL MARKET OPERATIONS

Francesco PAPADIA
Director General

Paul MERCIER
Deputy Director General

Werner STUDENER
Deputy Director General

Back Office Division

Harm METSELAAR
Head of Division

Front Office Division

Holger NEUHAUS
Head of Division

Investment Division

Roberto SCHIAVI
Head of Division

Market Operations Analysis Division

Michel STUBBE
Head of Division

Market Operation Systems Division

Matthew LAPPER
Head of Division

DIRECTORATE-GENERAL PAYMENT SYSTEMS AND MARKET INFRASTRUCTURE

Jean-Michel GODEFFROY
Director General

Daniela RUSSO
Deputy Director-General

Oversight Division

Niall MERRIMAN
Head of Division

TARGET Division

Hans-Dieter BECKER
Head of Division

Division 'TARGET2 — Securities Division'

Marc BAYLE
Head of Division

Market Infrastructure Division

Wiebe RUTTENBERG
Head of Division

DIRECTORATE-GENERAL RESEARCH

Frank SMETS
Director General

Huw PILL
Deputy Director-General

Monetary Policy Research Division

Gabriel FAGAN
Head of Division

Econometric Modelling Division

Günter COENEN
Head of Division

Financial Research Division

Philipp HARTMANN
Head of Division

DIRECTORATE-GENERAL SECRETARIAT AND LANGUAGE SERVICES

Pierre VAN DER HAEGEN
Director General

Klaus RIEMKE
Deputy Director-General

Secretariat Division

Roman SCHREMSER
Head of Division

Language Services Division

Sarah JOHNS
Head of Division

DIRECTORATE-GENERAL STATISTICS

Steven KEUNING
Director General

Werner BIER
Deputy Director-General

Euro Area Accounts and Economic Statistics Division

Gabriel QUIRÓS
Head of Division

External Statistics Division

Francis GROSS
Head of Division

Monetary, Financial Institutions and Markets Statistics Division

Jean-Marc ISRAËL
Head of Division

Statistical Information Management and User Services Division

Gérard SALOU
Head of Division

Statistics Development and Coordination Division

Caroline WILLEKE
Head of Division

Community institutions, bodies and agencies

EUROPEAN OMBUDSMAN

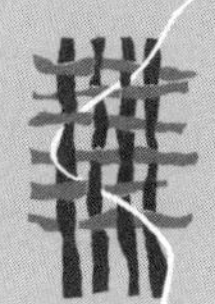

1 av. du Président Robert Schuman
CS 30403
F-67001 Strasbourg Cedex
E-mail: eo@ombudsman.europa.eu
Website:
http://www.ombudsman.europa.eu
Tel. +33 3881-72313
Fax +33 3881-79062

EUROPEAN OMBUDSMAN

P. Nikiforos DIAMANDOUROS
European Ombudsman
Tel. +33 3881-72313

SECRETARIAT OF THE EUROPEAN OMBUDSMAN

Ian HARDEN
Secretary-General
Tel. +33 3881-72384

Nicholas CATEPHORES
Adviser to the European Ombudsman
Tel. +33 3881-12383

Administration and Finance Department

João SANT'ANNA
Head of the Administration and Finance Department (ad interim)
Tel. +33 3881-75346

Administration and Personnel Unit

Alessandro DEL BON
Head of the Unit Administration and Personnel
Tel. +33 3881-72382
Fax +33 3881-79062

Budgetary and Financial Unit

Loïc JULIEN
Head of the Budgetary and Financial Unit
Tel. +33 3881-76779

Communication Unit

Ben HAGARD
Head of the Communication Unit
Tel. +33 3881-72424

Dace PICOT
Communication Officer
Tel. +33 3881-74080

Media, Enterprise and Civil Society Unit

Rosita AGNEW
Head of the Media, Enterprise and Civil Society Unit
Tel. +32 22842542

Gundi GADESMANN
Media and External Relations Officer
Tel. +32 22842609

Legal Department

João SANT'ANNA
Head of the Legal Department
Tel. +33 3881-75346

Christopher MILNES
Lawyer Linguist
Tel. +33 3881-72977

Legal Unit A

Gerhard GRILL
Head of the Legal Unit
Tel. +33 3881-72423

Violetta DIMOVA
Legal officer
Tel. +33 3881-72563

Bernard HOFSTÖTTER
Legal officer
Tel. +33 3881-78105

Vukašin LONČAREVIĆ
Legal officer
Tel. +33 3881-64915

Wiebke PANKAUKE
Legal officer
Tel. +33 3881-72402

Olivier VERHEECKE
Principal legal adviser
Tel. +32 22842003

Legal Unit B

Peter BONNOR
Head of Legal Unit (ad interim)
Tel. +33 3881-72541

Daniel KOBLENCZ
Legal officer
Tel. +32 22843831

Sevon TEA
Legal officer
Tel. +32 22842180

Legal Unit C

Marta HIRSCH-ZIEMBIŃSKA
Head of the Legal Unit
Tel. +33 3881-72746

Benita BROMS
Principal legal adviser
Tel. +32 22842543

Juliano FRANCO
Legal officer
Tel. +33 3881-72151

Marjorie FUCHS
Legal officer
Tel. +33 3881-74078

Raluca TRASCA
Legal officer
Tel. +33 3881-73108

Branislav URBANIČ
Legal officer
Tel. +33 3881-72714

Legal Unit D

Fergal Ó REGAN
Head of the Legal Unit
Tel. +33 3881-76784

Elodie BELFY
Legal officer
Tel. +32 22843901

José MARTÍNEZ ARAGÓN
Principal legal adviser
Tel. +33 3881-72401

Tina NILSSON
Legal officer
Tel. +32 22841417

Ida PALUMBO
Legal officer
Tel. +33 3881-72385

Complaints-Handling Sector

Peter BONNOR
Chef du secteur

EUROPEAN DATA PROTECTION SUPERVISOR

Bureaux: rue Montoyer 63 — 6th and 7th floor
Postal address:
Rue Wiertz 60
B-1047 Brussel/Bruxelles
E-mail: edps@edps.europa.eu
Tel. +32 22831900
Fax +32 22831950

EUROPEAN DATA PROTECTION SUPERVISOR

Peter Johan HUSTINX
EDPS
Tel. +32 22831901

Giovanni BUTTARELLI
Assistant Supervisor
Tel. +32 22831902

Supervision

Rosa BARCELÓ
Administrator/Legal Officer

Zsuzsanna BELENYESSY
Administrator/Legal Officer

Isabelle CHATELIER
Administrator/Legal Officer

Ėva DIMOVNĖ KERESZTES
Administrator/Legal Officer

Thomas GREMEL
Supervision Assistant

Delphine HAROU
Supervision Assistant

Xanthi KAPSOSIDERI
Supervision Assistant

Kim Thien LÊ
Secretariat assistant

Sylvie LONGRÉE
Supervision Assistant

Jaroslaw LOTARSKI
Administrator/Legal Officer

Sophie LOUVEAUX
Administrator/Legal Officer

Maria Veronica PEREZ ASINARI
Administrator/Legal Officer

Tereza STRUNCOVA
Administrator/Legal Officer

Political affairs

Andrea BEACH
Secretariat assistant

Laurent BESLAY
Administrator/Technology Officer

Athena BOURKA
National expert/Legal Adviser

Katarzyna CUADRAT-GRZYBOWSKA
Administrator/Legal Officer

Manuel GARCIA SANCHEZ
National expert/Legal Adviser

Bénédicte HAVELANGE
Administrator/Legal Officer

Hielke HIJMANS
Administrator/Legal Officer

Herke KRANENBORG
Administrator/Legal Officer

Anne-Christine LACOSTE
Administrator/Legal Officer

Francisco Javier MOLEÓN GARCIA
Documentation Assistant

Alfonso SCIROCCO
Administrator/Legal Officer

Michaël VANFLETEREN
Administrator/Legal Officer

Information

Martine BLONDEAU
Documentation Assistant

Nathalie VANDELLE
Administrator/Press Officer

Personnel, Budget and Administration

Monique LEENS-FERRANDO
Head of Unit
Tel. +32 22831903

Giuseppina LAURITANO
Administrator/Vocational training/Audit and Data Protection Officer

Anne LEVECQUE
Human Resources Assistant (Staff matters)

Vittorio MASTROJENI
Human Resources Assistant (Trainees, SNE)

Tonny MATHIEU
Administrator/Finance and Budget

Anne-Françoise REYNDERS
Human Resources Assistant (Social Activities)

Raja ROY
Financial and Accounting Assistant

Maria SANCHEZ LOPEZ
Financial and Accounting Assistant

Community institutions, bodies and agencies

AGENCIES AND OTHER BODIES

Community agencies

COMMUNITY FISHERIES CONTROL AGENCY (CFCA)

CFCA — Community Fisheries Control Agency
Edificio Odriozola
Avenida García Barbón 4
E-36201 Vigo
E-mail: cfca@ec.europa.eu
Website: http://www.cfca.europa.eu
Tel. +34 986120610
Fax +34 886125237

The primary role of the Community Fisheries Control Agency is to organise coordination and cooperation between national control and inspection activities so that the rules of the common fisheries policy (CFP) are respected and applied effectively. European Union governments agreed to establish the Agency in the 2002 CFP reform as part of the drive to install a culture of compliance within the fisheries sector across Europe. In April 2005, they adopted the necessary legislation.

The work of the Agency has clear added value. It will contribute to a level playing field for the fishing industry so that obligations are observed and everyone in the sector is treated equally, wherever they might be operating. Secondly, it will contribute towards sustainable fisheries by enhancing compliance with existing conservation and management measures to the benefit of present and future generations.

Working together

As an independent executive body, the Agency works closely with the European Commission, Member States, regional advisory councils and, where appropriate, third parties such as regional fisheries organisations. Each has a particular role to play in making sure that the EU fisheries policy operates in the most sustainable manner possible.

The common fisheries policy requires that Member States ensure effective control, inspection and enforcement of the rules and cooperate with each other and third countries in achieving this. This involves coordinating activities on land and in Community and international waters and where fishing takes place in third country waters, as appropriate.

The creation of the Agency is designed to enhance this cooperation and to ensure that legislation is implemented in a systematic, uniform and effective way. Pooling separate efforts should overcome shortcomings which may arise because of the different resources and priorities national authorities allocate to their own controls and inspections. Uniform inspection procedures by national inspectors will also make it possible to document all cases of non-compliance in a transparent manner.

Enforcing CFP rules remains the full responsibility of Member States. Each is obliged to follow up on all cases of non-compliance discovered by its own inspectors and, where appropriate, Community inspectors, and to impose deterrent sanctions according to national rules and procedures.

The way national monitoring arrangements are organised illustrates the clear added value the Agency can bring to a coherent and consistent application of CFP rules at European level. Member States are responsible for applying the rules on their own territory, in waters under their sovereignty and for fishing vessels flying their flag, irrespective of their zone of activity. Until the Agency arrived, there was no systematic coordination of national surveillance and inspection operations in Community waters. This meant that control and enforcement activities were fragmented. Indeed, the frequency and efficiency of controls varied from country to country and fishery to fishery, thus undermining effective and uniform application of CFP rules. The picture is further complicated by the fact that in most Member States monitoring and implementation of the CFP are under the responsibility of several authorities — fisheries inspection services, coastguards, the navy, customs or police. Some have a national remit, others regional, and some have additional non-fishery responsibilities as well.

International role

The Agency's remit is not confined to control and operational cooperation of fishing control by the Member States in Community waters, although these are its first priority, stretching as they do from the Black Sea in the east to the Atlantic in the west and the Baltic Sea in the north to the Mediterranean in the south. In principle, its mission covers zones wherever European vessels fish.

The Union is obliged by a number of international agreements and by its participation in Regional Fisheries Organisations to carry out controls and inspections on vessels operating outside EU waters. This is especially true for the North-East Atlantic Fisheries Commission (NEAFC) and the Northwest Atlantic Fisheries Organisation (NAFO).

One of the Agency's tasks may, if deemed appropriate, be to coordinate Member States' surveillance and inspection activities in more distant waters, not just in the North Atlantic, but as far afield as the Pacific and South Atlantic.

Harm KOSTER
Director
E-mail: harm.koster@cfca.europa.eu
Tel. +34 986120611

Aurelio CRESPO
Secretary General
E-mail: Aurelio.crespo@cfca.europa.eu
Tel. +34 986120614

Unit A — Administration and Resources

Niall MCHALE
Head of Unit
E-mail: Niall.MCHALE@cfca.europa.eu
Tel. +34 986120618

Unit C — Operational Coordination

Pedro GALACHE
Head of Unit
E-mail: pedro.galache@cfca.europa.eu
Tel. +34 986120633

EUROPEAN UNION AGENCY FOR FUNDAMENTAL RIGHTS (FRA)

Schwarzenbergplatz 11
A-1040 Vienna
E-mail: info@fra.europa.eu
Website: http://www.fra.europa.eu
Tel. +43 15803060
Fax +43 158030699

The European Union is based on principles of freedom, democracy, respect for human rights and fundamental freedoms, and the rule of law. It has a Charter of Fundamental Rights which reflects the rights common to the constitutional traditions and international obligations of its Member States. It is important that greater knowledge and awareness of these rights and issues related to them inform EU action. The European Union Agency for Fundamental Rights (FRA) has been set up to contribute to that process.

The Agency will provide assistance and expertise relating to fundamental rights, in line with Community law, to Community institutions and bodies and Member States. It will achieve this via the principal tasks of data collection, improving comparability and reliability of data, research and analysis, cooperation with international organisations, national specialised bodies and civil society, and raising public awareness of fundamental rights. It will get the results out in the form of conclusions and opinions to policymakers, stakeholders and those who implement policy and take action at the key levels of the EU and its Member States. The goal is to build respect and promotion of fundamental rights as part of the value system and culture of the EU.

The Agency will also lay great stress on engaging actively with a variety of groups and the wider public through the organisation of events, the hosting of seminars and workshops, the use of new technology and the publication of targeted materials. These activities will aim to highlight the relevance and importance of fundamental rights to all within the EU.

The European Union Agency for Fundamental Rights was established through Council Regulation (EC) No 168/2007 of 15 February 2007 and builds on the work of the former European Monitoring Centre on Racism and Xenophobia (EUMC). The Agency was launched on 1 March 2007 and has its seat in Vienna, Austria.

Morten KJAERUM
Director
E-mail: directorate@fra.europa.eu
Tel. +43 158030652, 653
Fax +43 158030699

Administration

Constantinos MANOLOPOULOS
Head of Department
E-mail: constantinos.manolopoulos@fra.europa.eu
Tel. +43 158030810
Fax +43 158030691

Human Resources and Planning

...
Head of Department
E-mail: personnel@fra.europa.eu
Tel. +43 158030670
Fax +43 158030699

Research and Data Collection

Ioannis DIMITRAKOPOULOS
Head of Unit
E-mail: ioannis.dimitrakopoulos@fra.europa.eu
Tel. +43 158030622
Fax +43 158030692

Freedoms and Justice

...
Head of Department
Tel. +43 158030629
Fax +43 158030692

Communication and Awareness Raising

...
E-mail: info@fra.europa.eu
Tel. +43 158030671
Fax +43 158030691

External Relations and Networking

John KELLOCK
Head of Unit
E-mail: john.kellock@fra.europa.eu
Tel. +43 158030632
Fax +43 158030693

EUROPEAN NETWORK AND INFORMATION SECURITY AGENCY (ENISA)

Science and Technology Park of Crete (ITE)
Vassilika Vouton, 700 13 Heraklion

P.O. Box 1309
71001 Crete
E-mail: info@enisa.europa.eu
Website: http://www.enisa.europa.eu
Tel. +30 2810391280
Fax +30 2810391410

ENISA was established through Regulation (EC) No 460/2004 of the European Parliament and of the Council of 10 March 2004 establishing a European Network and Information Security Agency. ENISA aims at assisting the Commission and the Member States, and indirectly cooperating with the business community, with regard to network and information security. The purpose of ENISA is the smooth functioning of the EU internal market. To meet its objectives ENISA additionally:

— collects and analyses data on security incidents in Europe and emerging risks;
— promotes risk assessment and risk management methods;
— facilitates awareness-raising and cooperation by developing public–private partnerships.

Further information about ENISA can be obtained at http://www.enisa.europa.eu

Andrea PIROTTI
Executive Director
E-mail: andrea.pirotti@enisa.europa.eu
Tel. +30 2810391284
Fax +30 2810391410

Administration

Andreas MITRAKAS
Head of Department
E-mail: andreas.mitrakas@enisa.europa.eu
Tel. +30 2810391280
Fax +30 2810391410

Technical Department

Steve PURSER
Head of Department
Tel. +30 2810391356
Fax +30 2810391895

Cooperation and Support Department

Ronald DE BRUIN
Head of Department
E-mail: ronald.de-bruin@enisa.europa.eu
Tel. +30 2810391369
Fax +30 2810391408

EUROPEAN AVIATION SAFETY AGENCY (EASA)

PO Box 10 12 53
D-50452 Cologne
E-mail: communications@easa.europa.eu
Website: http://www.easa.europa.eu
Tel. +49 22189990000
Fax +49 22189990999
Ottoplatz 1
D-50679 Cologne

Air transport is one of the safest modes of travel. It is also the fastest growing. That is why the European Union decided on a common initiative to keep air transport safe and sustainable, allowing for growth and improved safety. It is called the European Aviation Safety Agency.

The European Aviation Safety Agency promotes the highest common standards of safety and environmental protection in civil aviation in Europe and worldwide. It is the centrepiece of a new regulatory system which provides for a single European market in the aviation industry.

The main tasks of the Agency currently include:

- rulemaking: drafting aviation safety legislation and providing technical advice to the European Commission and to the Member States;
- inspections, training and standardisation programmes to ensure uniform implementation of European aviation safety legislation in all Member States;
- safety and environmental type-certification of aircraft, engines and parts;
- approving design organisations worldwide, and organisations responsible for production and maintenance located outside the territory of the Member States, or inside the EU on request of Member States;
- coordination of the EU SAFA programme (safety assessment of foreign aircraft) regarding the safety of foreign aircraft using Community airports;
- data collection, analysis and research to improve aviation safety.

By 2010, the Agency will be in charge of authorisations for third-country (non-EASA country) operators wishing to operate in the EU.

Further responsibilities for the safety of airports, air traffic management and air navigation systems, as well as a global regulatory approach to environmental protection are planned for the following years.

Based in Cologne, Germany, the Agency employs some 500 professionals from across Europe. It will continue to recruit highly qualified specialists and administrators in the next years as it consolidates its position as Europe's centre of excellence in aviation safety.

Patrick GOUDOU
Executive Director
E-mail: communications@easa.europa.eu

Management Board

Michael SMETHERS
Chairman

Maxime COFFIN
Vice Chairman

Communications

Daniel HÖLTGEN
Head of Communications
E-mail: daniel.hoeltgen@easa.europa.eu
Tel. +49 221899902002
Fax +49 221899902502

Rulemaking

Jules KNEEPKENS
Rulemaking Director
E-mail: jules.kneepkens@easa.europa.eu
Website: http://www.easa.europa.eu
Tel. +49 22189990000
Fax +49 22189990999

Certification

Norbert LOHL
Certification Director
E-mail: norbert.lohl@easa.europa.eu
Website: http://www.easa.europa.eu
Tel. +49 22189990000
Fax +49 22189990999

Quality and standardisation

Francesco BANAL
Quality and Standardisation Director
E-mail: francesco.banal@easa.europa.eu
Website: http://www.easa.europa.eu
Tel. +49 22189990000
Fax +49 22189990999

Finance and business services

Luc VANHEEL
Finance and Business Services (acting)
E-mail: luc.vanheel@easa.europa.eu
Website: http://www.easa.europa.eu
Tel. +49 22189990000
Fax +49 22189990999

EUROPEAN MEDICINES AGENCY (EMEA)

7 Westferry Circus
Canary Wharf
London E14 4HB
United Kingdom
E-mail: mail@emea.europa.eu
Website: http://www.emea.europa.eu
Tel. +44 2074188400
Fax +44 2074188416

The European Medicines Agency (EMEA) is a decentralised body of the European Union with headquarters in London. Its main responsibility is the protection and promotion of public and animal health, through the evaluation and supervision of medicines for human and veterinary use.

The EMEA is responsible for the scientific evaluation of applications for European marketing authorisation for medicinal products (centralised procedure). Under this procedure, companies submit one single marketing authorisation application to the EMEA.

All medicinal products for human and animal use derived from biotechnology and other high-technology processes must be approved via the centralised procedure. The same applies to all human medicines intended for the treatment of HIV/AIDS, cancer, diabetes and neurodegenerative diseases, and for all designated medicines intended for the treatment of rare diseases. Similarly, all veterinary medicines intended for use as performance enhancers in order to promote the growth of treated animals or to increase yields from treated animals have to go through the centralised procedure.

For medicinal products that do not fall under any of these categories, companies can submit an application for a centralised marketing authorisation to the EMEA, provided the medicinal product constitutes a significant therapeutic, scientific or technical innovation or the product is in any other respect in the interests of patient or animal health.

The safety of medicines is monitored constantly by the Agency through a pharmaco-vigilance network. The EMEA takes appropriate action if adverse drug reaction reports suggest changes to the benefit–risk balance of a medicinal product. For veterinary medicinal products the Agency has the responsibility to establish safe limits for medicinal residues in food of animal origin.

The Agency also has a role in stimulating innovation and research in the pharmaceutical sector. The EMEA gives scientific advice and protocol assistance to companies for the development of new medicinal products. It publishes guidelines on quality, safety and efficacy testing requirements. A dedicated office established in 2005 provides special assistance to small and medium-sized enterprises (SMEs).

In 2001, the Committee for Orphan Medicinal Products (COMP) was established, charged with reviewing designation applications from persons or companies who intend to develop medicines for rare diseases (so-called 'orphan drugs'). The Committee on Herbal Medicinal Products (HMPC) was established in 2004 and provides scientific opinions on traditional herbal medicines. The Paediatric Committee (PDCO) was established in July 2007 and provides scientific opinions on medicines for children.

The Agency brings together the scientific resources of over 40 national competent authorities in 30 EU and EEA-EFTA countries in a network of over 4 000 European experts. It contributes to the European Union's international activities through its work with the European Pharmacopoeia, the World Health Organization, and the ICH and VICH trilateral (EU, Japan and US) conferences on harmonisation, among other international organisations and initiatives.

The EMEA is headed by the Executive Director and had a secretariat of 481 staff members in 2008. The Management Board is the supervisory body of the EMEA, responsible, in particular, for budgetary matters.

The Agency is also involved in referral procedures relating to medicinal products that are approved or under consideration by Member States.

Management Board

Pat O'MAHONY
Chair

Lisette TIDDENS-ENGWIRDA
Vice Chair

Birthe BYSKOV HOLM
Vice Chair

Committee for Medicinal Products for Human Use (CHMP)

Éric ABADIE
Chair

Tomas SALMONSON
Vice Chair

Committee for Medicinal Products for Veterinary Use (CVMP)

Gérard MOULIN
Chair

Anja HOLM
Vice Chair

Committee for Orphan Medicinal Products (COMP)

Kerstin WESTERMARK
Chair

Committee on Herbal Medicinal Products (HMPC)

Konstantin KELLER
Chair

Ioanna CHINOU
Vice-Chair

Pediatric Committee (PDCO)

Daniel BRASSEUR
Chair

Gérard PONS
Vice-Chair

Secretariat

7 Westferry Circus
Canary Wharf
London E14 4HB
United Kingdom
E-mail: mail@emea.europa.eu
Tel. +44 2074188400
Fax +44 2074188416

Thomas LÖNNGREN
Executive Director
E-mail: thomas.lonngren@emea.europa.eu
Tel. +44 2074188406, 8415

Executive support

Martin HARVEY ALLCHURCH
Head of Sector
E-mail: martin.harvey@emea.europa.eu
Tel. +44 2074188699

Legal Sector

Vincenzo SALVATORE
Head of Sector
E-mail: vincenzo.salvatore@emea.europa.eu
Tel. +44 2075237290

Integrated quality management and audit

...
Head of Sector

Hans-Georg EICHLER
Senior Medical Officer
E-mail: hans-georg.eichler@emea.europa.eu
Tel. +44 2075237491

1. Administration

Andreas POTT
Head of Unit
E-mail: andreas.pott@emea.europa.eu
Tel. +44 2074188405, 75237033

Personnel and budget

Frances NUTTALL
Head of Sector
E-mail: frances.nuttall@emea.europa.eu
Tel. +44 2074188475

Infrastructure services

Sara MENDOSA
Head of Sector
E-mail: sara.mendosa@emea.europa.eu
Tel. +44 2074188403

Accounting

Gerard O'MALLEY
Head of Sector
E-mail: gerard.omalley@emea.europa.eu
Tel. +44 2074188466

2. Pre-authorisation evaluation of medicines for human use

Patrick LE COURTOIS
Head of Unit
E-mail: patrick.lecourtois@emea.europa.eu
Tel. +44 2074188649, 75237074

Scientific advice and orphan drugs

Agnès SAINT-RAYMOND
Head of Sector
E-mail: agnes.saint-raymond@emea.europa.eu
Tel. +44 2075237017

Spiros VAMVAKAS
Deputy Head of Sector (acting)
E-mail: spiros.vamvakas@emea.europa.eu
Tel. +44 2075237006

Quality of medicines

John PURVES
Head of Sector
E-mail: john.purves@emea.europa.eu
Tel. +44 2074188402

Safety and efficacy of medicines

Xavier LURIA OLLER
Head of Sector
E-mail: xavier.luria@emea.europa.eu
Tel. +44 2074188512

Marisa PAPALUCA AMATI
Deputy Head of Sector (acting)
E-mail: marisa.papaluca@emea.europa.eu
Tel. +44 2074188436

3. Post-authorisation evaluation of medicines for human use

Noël WATHION
Head of Unit
E-mail: noel.wathion@emea.europa.eu
Tel. +44 2074188592, 74188550

Regulatory affairs and organisational support

Anthony HUMPHREYS
Head of Sector
E-mail: anthony.humphreys@emea.europa.eu
Tel. +44 2074188583

Pharmacovigilance and risk management

Peter ARLETT
Head of Sector
Tel. +44 2075237108

Sabine BROSCH
Deputy Head of Sector (acting)
E-mail: sabine.brosch@emea.europa.eu
Tel. +44 2074188569

Post-authorisation safety and efficacy of medicines

Noël WATHION
Tel. +44 2074188592

Medical Information

Isabelle MOULON
Head of Sector
E-mail: isabelle.moulon@emea.europa.eu
Tel. +44 2074188443

4. Veterinary medicines and inspections

David MACKAY
Head of Unit
E-mail: david.mackay@emea.europa.eu
Tel. +44 2074188413

Veterinary marketing authorisation procedures

Jill ASHLEY-SMITH
Head of Sector
E-mail: jill.ashley@emea.europa.eu
Tel. +44 2074188646

Mélanie LEIVERS
Head of Area (acting)
E-mail: melanie.leivers@emea.europa.eu
Tel. +44 2074188535

Safety of veterinary medicines

Kornelia GREIN
Head of Sector
E-mail: kornelia.grein@emea.europa.eu
Tel. +44 2074188432

Inspections

...
Head of Sector

5. Communications and networking

Hans-Georg WAGNER
Head of Unit
E-mail: hans-georg.wagner@emea.europa.eu
Tel. +44 2075237079, 74188506

Document management and publishing

Béatrice FAYL
Head of Sector
E-mail: beatrice.fayl@emea.europa.eu
Tel. +44 2074188426

Meeting management and conferences

Sylvie BÉNÉFICE
Head of Sector
E-mail: sylvie.benefice@emea.europa.eu
Tel. +44 2074188651

Project management

Tim BUXTON
Head of Sector
E-mail: tim.buxton@emea.europa.eu
Tel. +44 2074188631

Information technology

David DRAKEFORD
Head of Sector
E-mail: david.drakeford@emea.europa.eu
Tel. +44 2074188599

Riccardo ETTORE
Deputy Head of Sector (acting)
E-mail: riccardo.ettore@emea.europa.eu
Tel. +44 2074188469

EUROPEAN CHEMICALS AGENCY (ECHA)

Annankatu 18
P.O. Box 400
00121 Helsinki
Finland
E-mail: info@echa.europa.eu
Website: http://echa.europa.eu
Tel. +358 9686180
Fax +358 968618210

The European Chemicals Agency (ECHA), located in Helsinki, Finland, was established by the REACH regulation and was set up on 1 June 2007. It manages the registration, evaluation, authorisation and restriction processes for chemical substances. In addition, ECHA carries out work on technical, scientific and administrative aspects of REACH and contributes to the consistent implementation of the regulation across the European Union. ECHA started to accept pre-registrations, registrations, inquiries and PPORD notifications after one year of preparations, on 1 June 2008.

The mission of the ECHA is to:
— manage and coordinate the registration, evaluation, authorisation and restriction processes under REACH to ensure consistency in chemicals management across the EU;
— provide the Member States and the institutions of the Community with scientific and technical advice on chemicals covered by the regulation;
— manage IT-based guidance documents, tools and databases;
— run a helpdesk for registrants and coordinate national helpdesks;
— make information on chemicals publicly available on the Agency website.

One of the tasks of the Agency is to provide sufficient information and guidance to companies — especially small and medium-sized enterprises — on how to comply with REACH requirements. To this end, the Agency operates a multilingual website. The website serves as a single access point for general information on chemicals, REACH guidance documents and other tools which help companies to comply with the new legislation.

The Management Board of the Agency is composed of the representatives of the EU Member States, three EEA countries, the European Parliament, the European Commission and three members representing industry, trade unions and NGOs.

The activities of the Committee for Risk Assessment (RAC), the Committee for Socio-economic Analysis (SEAC), the Member State Committee (MSC) and the Forum for Exchange of Information on Enforcement are crucial for the effective implementation of REACH.

Geert DANCET
Executive Director
Annankatu 18
P.O. Box 400
00121 Helsinki
Finland
E-mail: executive-director@echa.europa.eu

Operations

Andreas HERDINA
Director of Cooperation

Jef MAES
Director of Resources

Jukka MALM
Director of Assessment

Christel MUSSET
Director of Procedures and Processes

Management Board

Thomas JAKL
Chairman of the Management Board
Annankatu 18
P.O. Box 400
00121 Helsinki
Suomi/Finland
E-mail: mb-secretariat@echa.europa.eu

Antonello LAPALORCIA
Deputy Chairman of the Management Board

Committee for risk assessment

Sharon MUNN
President

Committee for socio-economic analysis

Leena YLÄ-MONONEN
President (acting)

Member State committee

Anna-Liisa SUNDQUIST
President

Forum for exchange of information on enforcement

Ulrike KOWALSKI
President

Joop BLENKERS
Deputy President

Nikolay SAVOV
Deputy President

Board of Appeal

P.O. Box 400
00121 Helsinki
Suomi/Finland
E-mail: appeal@echa.europa.eu

...
President

Henricus SPAAS
Technically qualified member

...
Legally qualified member

Sari HAUKKA
Registrar

EUROPEAN AGENCY FOR THE MANAGEMENT OF OPERATIONAL COOPERATION AT THE EXTERNAL BORDERS (FRONTEX)

Rondo ONZ 1
PL-00-124 Warsaw
E-mail: frontex@frontex.europa.eu
Website: http://www.frontex.europa.eu
Tel. +48 225449500
Fax +48 225449501

The European Agency for the Management of Operational Cooperation at the External Borders of the Member States of the European Union (Frontex) strengthens border security by ensuring the coordination of Member States' actions in the implementation of Community measures relating to the management of the external borders.

Frontex:
- coordinates Member States' operational cooperation for the management of the EU's external borders;
- assists Member States in the training of national border guards/establishes common training standards;
- carries out risk analyses;
- follows research relevant for the control and surveillance of external borders;
- assists Member States when increased technical and operational assistance at external borders is needed;
- provides Member States with the necessary support in organising joint return operations.

Ilkka LAITINEN
Executive Director

Gil ARIAS
Deputy Executive Director

Michał PARZYSZEK
Spokesperson
E-mail: pr@frontex.europa.eu
Tel. +48 225449532

Izabella COOPER
Spokesperson
E-mail: pr@frontex.europa.eu
Tel. +48 225449535

EUROPEAN AGENCY FOR SAFETY AND HEALTH AT WORK (OSHA)

Gran Vía 33
E-48009 Bilbao
E-mail: information@osha.europa.eu
Website: http://osha.europa.eu
Tel. +34 944794360
Fax +34 944794383

Safety and health at work is one of the European Union's most important and challenging policy areas. Statistics show that every five seconds a worker in the EU is involved in a work-related accident, and every three-and-a-half minutes someone in the EU dies from work-related causes.

Workers need to be made aware of the risks that they face and how to deal with them. Employers need to know what they must do to keep their employees safe and how to do it. But occupational safety and health (OSH) issues are complex and diverse. Dealing with them effectively and equitably is more than individual organisations or Member States can manage alone.

That is why the European Agency for Safety and Health at Work was set up in 1996. We collect, analyse and communicate OSH-related information across the EU. Our mission is to make Europe's workplaces safer, healthier and more productive, by promoting a culture of risk prevention.

Located in Bilbao, Spain, EU-OSHA has a dedicated staff of OSH specialists and a network of partners in all Member States and beyond. At the national level we are represented by a network of focal points, which are typically the lead OSH organisations in their country. These focal points work with government, employers' and workers' representatives, providing information and advice to support agency initiatives. They also manage the national agency websites, organise European campaign events in the individual Member States, and nominate representatives to expert groups, which provide advice to EU-OSHA in their own field of expertise.

Safety and health is an ethical issue, a basic human right, but it is also about company productivity and competitiveness, making Europe a safer, healthier and more productive place to work.

Károly GYÖRGY
Chair of the Governing Board

Jukka TAKALA
Director
E-mail: takala@osha.europa.eu
Tel. +34 944794374

Jukka TAKALA
Head of Network Secretariat Unit
E-mail: takala@osha.europa.eu
Tel. +34 944794374

Working Environment Information Unit

Terence TAYLOR
Head of Unit
E-mail: taylor@osha.europa.eu
Tel. +34 944794670

Risk Observatory Unit

Eusebio RIAL GONZÁLEZ
Head of Unit
E-mail: rial@osha.europa.eu
Tel. +34 944793538

Communication and Promotion Unit

Andrew SMITH
Head of Unit
E-mail: smith@osha.europa.eu
Tel. +34 944795733

Resource and Service Centre

Françoise MURILLO
Head of Unit
E-mail: murillo@osha.europa.eu
Tel. +34 944794361

EUROPEAN MARITIME SAFETY AGENCY (EMSA)

Av. Dom Joao II, lote 1.06.2.5
P-1998-001 Lisbon
Website: http://www.emsa.europa.eu
Tel. +351 211209200
Fax +351 211209210

The European Maritime Safety Agency (EMSA) started its activities in 2003. It provides the Commission and EU Member States with technical and scientific assistance. The Agency facilitates cooperation between Member States and helps them to correctly apply EU legislation in the field of maritime safety and the prevention of pollution by ships. By pooling their resources, Member States can achieve economies of scale, e.g. in creating and managing a European Long Range Identification and Tracking (LRIT) Data Centre, working around the clock, or in assessing classification societies and maritime training centres throughout the world.

By having at its disposal an oil pollution response fleet, covering all European waters, EMSA delivers added value to national administrations which are tasked with protecting the marine environment. Sophisticated tools such as satellite imagery also allow the Agency to spot oil spills dumped accidentally or deliberately, and to quickly inform concerned Member States.

Brian WADSWORTH
Chairman of the Administrative Board

Willem DE RUITER
Executive Director

Bureau of the Executive Director

Manuela TOMASSINI
Policy Adviser

Michel METZGER
Accounting Officer

James WOOD
Assistant to the Director

Department A — Corporate Services

Human resources and communication

Jacob TERLING
Head of Unit

Legal and financial affairs

Joachim MENZE
Head of Unit

Operations support

Steve DEIGHTON
Head of Unit

Department B — Implementation

Safety assessments and inspections

Michael HUNTER
Head of Unit

Ship Safety

Marine environment, training and statistics

Henrik RINGBOM
Head of Unit

Department C — Operations

Pollution preparedness and response

Bernd BLUHM
Head of Unit

Vessel traffic and reporting services

Lazaros AICHMALOTIDIS
Head of Unit

Satellite-based monitoring services

Leendert BAL
Head of Unit

EUROPEAN ENVIRONMENT AGENCY (EEA)

Kongens Nytorv 6
DK-1050 Copenhagen
E-mail: eea@eea.europa.eu
Website: http://eea.europa.eu
Tel. +45 33367100
Fax +45 33367199

The European Environment Agency (EEA) is the EU body dedicated to providing sound and independent information on the environment. It is an important information source for those involved in developing, adopting, implementing and evaluating environmental policy, as well as for the general public.

Its aim is to help the EU and member countries make informed decisions about improving the environment, integrating environmental considerations into economic policies and moving towards sustainability.

To do this, it provides a wide range of information and assessments. This covers the state of the environment and trends in it, together with pressures on the environment and the economic and social driving forces behind them. It also covers policies and their effectiveness. The EEA tries to identify possible future trends and problems using scenarios and other techniques.

A major source of information is the European environment information and observation network (Eionet). The EEA is responsible for developing the network and coordinating its activities. To do this, it works closely with the national focal points, typically national environment agencies and environment ministries in the member countries. They are responsible for coordinating national networks involving about 300 institutions in all.

To support data collection, management and analysis the EEA has established and works closely with five European topic centres covering water, air and climate change, nature protection and biodiversity, waste and material flows, and the terrestrial environment.

The EEA also works closely with other European and international institutions such as the Statistical Office (Eurostat), the Joint Research Centre of the European Commission, the United Nations Environment Programme (UNEP) and the World Health Organisation (WHO).

The EEA and Eionet were established by Council Regulation (EEC) No 1210/90 of 7 May 1990 with later amendments (1999, 2003). The Agency is located in Copenhagen and by 2007 had a staff of approximately 150. Membership is open to countries that are not members of the European Union. The EEA has 32 member countries: 27 EU Member States together with Iceland, Liechtenstein, Norway (European Economic Area countries), Switzerland and Turkey.

Management Board

Lars-Erik LILJELUND
Chair
Swedish Environmental Protection Agency
Blekholmsterrassen 36
S-106 48 Stockholm
E-mail: lars-erik.liljelund@naturvardsverket.se
Tel. +46 86981508
Fax +46 86981080

EEA Scientific Committee

László SOMLYÓDY
Chair
Budapest University of Technology and Economics
Department of Sanitary and Environmental Engineering
Műegyetem rkp. 3. 3 Budapest
Hungary

Executive Director's Office

Jacqueline MCGLADE
Executive Director
E-mail: Jacqueline.McGlade@eea.europa.eu

Gordon MCINNES
Deputy Director
E-mail: Gordon.McInnes@eea.europa.eu

Communication and corporate affairs

Marion NIELSEN-HANNERUP
Head of Programme
E-mail: Marion.Hannerup@eea.europa.eu

Administrative services

Gordon MCINNES
Head of Programme
E-mail: Gordon.McInnes@eea.europa.eu

Information and data services

Sigfus BJARNASON
Head of Programme
E-mail: Sigfus.Bjarnason@eea.europa.eu

Biodiversity, spatial analysis and scenarios

Colin MARTIN
Head of Programme

Environmental assessment

Jeff HUNTINGTON
Head of Programme
E-mail: Jeff.Huntington@eea.europa.eu

Strategic knowledge and innovation

David Andrew STANNERS
Head of Programme
E-mail: David.Stanners@eea.europa.eu

EUROPEAN RAILWAY AGENCY (ERA)

160 Boulevard Henri Harpignies
BP 20392
F-59300 Valenciennes
E-mail: Directorate-info@era.europa.eu
Website: http://www.era.europa.eu
Tel. +33 327096500
Fax +33 327334065

The European Railway Agency was established by Regulation (EC) No 881/2004 which describes its organisation, tasks and working methods. The Agency is located in Valenciennes, Lille.

The objective of the Agency is to contribute, on technical matters, to the implementation of Community legislation aimed at improving the competitive position of the railway sector (by enhancing the level of interoperability of railway systems) and to developing a common approach to safety on the European railway system, in order to contribute to creating a European railway area without frontiers and guaranteeing a high level of safety.

The Agency does not have any regulatory powers. It submits opinions and recommendations to the European Commission which, in accordance with the safety and interoperability directives, transforms them into decisions applicable in the Member States of the European Union. The Agency may send technical opinions to the European Commission or Member States' committees at their request or on its own initiative.

The Agency is governed by an Administrative Board composed of one representative of each Member State, four representatives of the Commission, and of six representatives of the railway sector (the latter are not entitled to vote). The Agency is managed by its Executive Director and is financed by the budget of the European Union. The Executive Director is appointed by the Administrative Board.

Michael HARTING
Chairman of the Administrative Board

Marcel VERSLYPE
Executive Director
E-mail: marcel.verslype@era.europa.eu

Richard LOCKETT
Strategy and Research Adviser
E-mail: richard.lockett@era.europa.eu

Accountancy

Catherine PONCIN
E-mail: catherine.poncin@era.europa.eu

Communications and Public Relations

Thorsten HAHN
E-mail: thorsten.hahn@era.europa.eu
Tel. +33 327096595
Fax +33 327096695

Economic Evaluation Unit

Airy MAGNIEN
Head of Unit
E-mail: airy.magnien@era.europa.eu

ERTMS

Pio GUIDO
Head of Unit
E-mail: pio.guido@era.europa.eu

Interoperability

Jean-Charles PICHANT
Head of Unit
E-mail: jean-charles.pichant@era.europa.eu

Safety

Anders LÜNDSTROM
Head of Unit
E-mail: anders.lundstrom@era.europa.eu

Administration

Zografia PYLORIDOU
Head of Unit (acting)
E-mail: zografia.pyloridou@era.europa.eu

EUROPEAN GNSS SUPERVISORY AUTHORITY (GSA)

Rue de la Loi, 56
B-1049 Brussels
E-mail: info@gsa.europa.eu
Tel. +32 22971616
Fax +32 22967238

By developing a new generation of global navigation satellite systems (GNSS), Europe is opening new doors for high-technology industry development, job creation and economic growth.

With Europe in the driver's seat, Galileo has the potential to become a cornerstone of the global radio navigation positioning system of the future. Given the strategic nature of European satellite positioning and navigation programmes — which include both EGNOS and Galileo — and the need to ensure that essential public interests in this field are adequately defended and represented, the European GNSS Supervisory Authority (GSA) was established to manage the public interests and to be the regulatory authority for the European GNSS programmes, while laying the foundations for a fully sustainable and economically viable system.

The GSA:
— manages the European satellite navigation programmes, controls the use of funds, and manages the related R & D activities;
— is responsible for matters related to the right to use the frequencies necessary for the operation of the systems, certification of the components, and their safety and security;
— will be the licensing authority vis-à-vis the concession holders responsible for the operations and service provision of Galileo and ensure contract compliance;
— owns the assets created or developed under the Galileo and EGNOS programmes.

Pedro PEDREIRA
Executive Director

EUROPEAN FOOD SAFETY AUTHORITY (EFSA)

Largo N. Palli, 5A
I-43100 Parma
E-mail: info@efsa.europa.eu
Website: http://www.efsa.europa.eu
Tel. +39 0521036111
Fax +39 0521036110

The European Food Safety Authority (EFSA) was established and funded by the European Community as an independent agency in 2002 following a series of food crises that caused the European public to voice concerns about food safety and the ability of regulatory authorities to fully protect consumers.

In close collaboration with national authorities and in open consultation with its stakeholders, EFSA provides objective scientific advice on all matters with a direct or indirect impact on food and feed safety, including animal health and welfare and plant protection. EFSA is also consulted on nutrition in relation to Community legislation.

EFSA's work falls into two areas: risk assessment and risk communication. In particular, EFSA's risk assessments provide risk managers (EU institutions with political accountability, i.e. the European Commission, European Parliament and Council) with a sound scientific basis for defining policy-driven legislative or regulatory measures required to ensure a high level of consumer protection with regard to food and feed safety. EFSA communicates to the public in an open and transparent way on all matters within its remit.

Collection and analysis of scientific data, identification of emerging risks and scientific support to the Commission, particularly in a food crisis, are also part of EFSA's mandate, as laid down in the founding Regulation (EC) No 178/2002 of 28 January 2002.

Management Board

Patrick WALL
Chair

Bart SANGSTER
Vice Chair

Diána BANATI
Vice Chair

Executive Director

Catherine GESLAIN-LANÉELLE
Executive Director
E-mail: catherine.geslain-laneelle@efsa.europa.eu

Administration

Alexandrine MAVIEL-SONET
Director of Administration
E-mail: alexandrine.maviel-sonet@efsa.europa.eu

Science

Herman B.W.M. KOËTER
Director of Science
E-mail: Herman.Koeter@efsa.europa.eu

Riitta Liisa MAIJALA
Head of Risk Assessment Department
E-mail: riitta-liisa.maijala@efsa.europa.eu

Hubert DELUYKER
Head of Scientific Cooperation and Assistance Department
E-mail: hubert.deluyker@efsa.europa.eu

Communications

Anne-Laure GASSIN
Director of Communications
E-mail: anne-laure.gassin@efsa.europa.eu

TRANSLATION CENTRE FOR THE BODIES OF THE EUROPEAN UNION (CDT)

Bâtiment Nouvel Hémicycle
1, rue du Fort Thüngen
L-1499 Luxembourg
E-mail: cdt@cdt.europa.eu
Website: http://www.cdt.europa.eu
Tel. +352 421711-1 (operator)
Tel. 421711 + extension
Fax +352 421711-220

The Translation Centre for the Bodies of the European Union was set up in 1994 to provide the translation services required by the specialised decentralised agencies of the European Union. The Centre also provides services to the Community institutions and bodies which have their own translation service, in order to absorb any peaks in their workload.

The Centre's mission also has an interinstitutional dimension. Above all, it is closely involved in the work of the Interinstitutional Committee for Translation and Interpreting, the purpose of which is to help achieve economies of scale in the Community translation system by rationalising and pooling working methods and tools. Such cooperation also contributes to the undertaking of large-scale projects, such as the creation of IATE (InterActive Terminology for Europe), a terminology database for the European Union.

The Centre is based in Luxembourg and is governed by a Management Board comprising representatives of all its clients, the Member States and the European Commission. It is financed mainly by payments from the agencies, offices and institutions for translation services provided. The Centre's publications and documents can be downloaded free of charge directly from its website (www.cdt.europa.eu).

The Translation Centre for the Bodies of the European Union was established by Council Regulation (EC) No 2965/94 of 28 November 1994 (OJ L 314, 7.12.1994), last amended by Council Regulation (EC) No 1645/03 of 18 June 2003 (OJ L 245, 29.9.2003).

Karl-Johan LÖNNROTH
Chairman of the Administrative Board
Director-General, Directorate-General for Translation of the European Commission

Gailė DAGILIENĖ
Director
E-mail: Gaile.Dagiliene@cdt.europa.eu
Tel. +352 421711-200

Direction

Catherine STEINMETZ
Director's Assistant
E-mail: Catherine.Steinmetz@cdt.europa.eu
Tel. +352 421711-213

Maurice VAN WEYENBERG
Director's Advisor
E-mail: Maurice.Van_Weyenberg@cdt.europa.eu
Tel. +352 421711-363

Alessandra POLITI
Internal Auditor — Integrated Audit and Quality Group
E-mail: alessandra.politi@cdt.europa.eu
Tel. +352 421711-490

Translation Department

Marie-Anne FERNÁNDEZ
Head of Department
E-mail: Marie-Anne.Fernandez_Suarez@cdt.europa.eu
Tel. +352 421711-202

Pablo ELORZA
Deputy Head
E-mail: Pablo.Elorza@cdt.europa.eu
Tel. +352 421711-250

Denis DECHANDON
Head of Group
Linguistic Group - Slavonic and Greek Language
E-mail: Denis.Dechandon@cdt.europa.eu
Tel. +352 421711-295

Mauro BUBNIC
Head of Group
Linguistic Group - Germanic Language
E-mail: Mauro.Bubnic@cdt.europa.eu
Tel. +352 421711307

Tamara FERLUSCA
Head of Group
Linguistic Group - Romance and Mediterranean Language
E-mail: Tamara.Ferlusca@cdt.europa.eu
Tel. +352 421711-382

Sona TAVODOVA
Head of Group
Linguistic Group - Finno-Ugric and Baltic Language
E-mail: Sona.Tavodova@cdt.europa.eu
Tel. +352 421711264

Translation Support Department

Dieter RUMMEL
Head of Department
E-mail: Dieter.Rummel@cdt.europa.eu
Tel. +352 421711284

Demand Management Section

Marcus ANGIONI
Head of Section
E-mail: marcus.angioni@cdt.europa.eu
Tel. +352 421711233

Documentation and Terminology Section

...
Head of Section

Freelance Management Section

Jacky NAZAC
Head of Section
E-mail: Jacky.Nazac@cdt.europa.eu
Tel. +352 421711399

Administration Department

Marie-Anne FERNÁNDEZ
Head of Department (acting)
E-mail: Marie-Anne.Fernandez_Suarez@cdt.europa.eu
Tel. +352 421711202

Facilities and Security Group

Didier MARCHESIN
Head of Group
E-mail: didier.marchesin@cdt.europa.eu
Tel. +352 421711214

Legal Affairs Section

Guy HELLINCKX
Head of Section
E-mail: Guy.Hellinckx@cdt.europa.eu
Tel. +352 421711266

Finance Section

...
Accounting Officer

Human Resources Section

Silvana MIGGIANO
Head of Section
E-mail: Silvana.Miggiano@cdt.europa.eu
Tel. +352 421711-335

Computer Department

Benoît VITALE
Head of Department
E-mail: Benoit.Vitale@cdt.europa.eu
Tel. +352 421711-374

Infrastructure Section

Pascal DUFOUR
Head of Section
E-mail: Pascal.Dufour@cdt.europa.eu
Tel. +352 421711-224

Helpdesk Section

Marc MARÉCHAL
Head of Section
E-mail: Marc.Marechal@cdt.europa.eu
Tel. +352 421711-277

Development Section

Salvatore SANFILIPPO
Head of Section
E-mail: Salvatore.Sanfilippo@cdt.europa.eu
Tel. +352 421711-325

General Affairs Department

Benoît VITALE
Head of Department (acting)

Project Management Office

Interinstitutional and Public Relations Group

Client Coordination Section

Stephanie BUSSE
Head of Section
E-mail: Stephanie.Busse@cdt.europa.eu
Tel. +352 421711-389

EUROPEAN CENTRE FOR DISEASE PREVENTION AND CONTROL (ECDC)

Tomtebodavägen 11A
Karolinska Campus
171 83 Stockholm
E-mail: info@ecdc.europa.eu
Website: http://ecdc.europa.eu
Tel. +46 858601000
Fax +46 858601001

The European Centre for Disease Prevention and Control is an EU agency tasked with reinforcing Europe's defences against infectious disease by identifying, assessing and communicating current and emerging threats to human health. In carrying out its mission, ECDC works closely with national disease-control organisations, EU-level authorities and international organisations, encouraging cooperation and the pooling of knowledge. Key areas of activities are providing scientific advice, strengthening Europe-wide disease surveillance, supporting preparedness and response to disease outbreaks, training, country support and health communication. ECDC became operational in May 2005 and has its headquarters in Stockholm. The Centre will have about 300 staff by the end of 2009.

For further information about ECDC, please consult our website at www.ecdc.europa.eu or contact our information centre at info@ecdc.europa.eu or +46 8 58601616.

For information about our scientific journal *(Eurosurveillance)*, please see http://www.eurosurveillance.org or contact eurosurveillance@ecdc.europa.eu.

For enquiries concerning other scientific publications of ECDC, please contact publications@ecdc.europa.eu.

Zsuzsanna JAKAB
Director

Director's Office

Maarit KOKKI
Director's Cabinet Coordinator

...
Country Relations Officer

Arun NANDA
Advisor and WHO Liaison Officer

John O'TOOLE
External Relations Officer

Corinne SKARSTEDT
Governance Officer

Helena HOLLAND
Personal Assistant to the Director

Scientific Advice

Johan GIESECKE
Scientific in chief and Head of Unit of the Scientific Council

Piotr KRAMARZ
Deputy Head of Unit

Piotr KRAMARZ
Head of Section 'Evidence base for prevention and control'

Amanda OZIN-HOFSÄSS
Head of Section 'Scientific and technical advice (Knowledge services)'

Jan SEMENZA
Head of Section 'Future threats and determinants'

Health and Communication

Karl EKDAHL
Head of Unit

Ben DUNCAN
Spokesperson and Media Relations Officer

Ines STEFFENS
Head of Scientific Publications Section and Managing Editor of Eurosurveillance

Karl EKDAHL
Editor-in-Chief for Eurosurveillance

Paulo MOREIRA
Head of Unit (acting)

Ines STEFFENS
Head of Section 'Managing Editor for Eurosurveillance'

Jouko RAATIKAINEN
Head of Section 'Web Services'

Preparedness and Response

Denis COULOMBIER
Head of Unit

Massimo CIOTTI
Deputy Head of Unit

Pedro ARIAS BOHIGAS
Head of Section 'Epidemic intelligence and EOC'

Arnold BOSMAN
Head of Section 'Epidemiological Training'

Evelyn DEPOORTERE
Head of Section 'Outbreak Preparedness and Support'

Administrative Services

...
Head of Unit

Theo ORFANOS
Head of Section 'Finance and Accounting'

Clemencia WIDLUND
Head of Section 'Missions, Meetings and Logistics'

Surveillance unit

Andrea AMMON
Head of Unit

Andrew AMATO-GAUCI
Head of Unit (acting)

Andrew AMATO-GAUCI
Head of Section 'Disease specific surveillance'

Edward VAN STRATEN
Head of Section 'Data management and general surveillance'

Disease Programmes

Angus NICOLL
Programme Coordinator 'influenza'

Davide MANISSERO
Programme Coordinator 'tuberculosis'

Pierluigi LOPALCO
Programme Coordinator 'vaccine-preventable diseases and invasive bacterial infections'

Marita VAN DE LAAR
Programme Coordinator 'HIV, STI and blood-borne viruses'

Dominique MONNET
Programme Coordinator 'antimicrobial resistance and healthcare-associated infections'

Johanna TAKKINEN
Programme Coordinator 'food and waterborne diseases and zoonoses'

Katrin LEITMEYER
Programme Coordinator 'emerging and vector-borne diseases'

EUROPEAN CENTRE FOR THE DEVELOPMENT OF VOCATIONAL TRAINING (CEDEFOP)

Europe 123
GR-55102 Thessaloniki
E-mail: info@cedefop.europa.eu
Website: http://www.cedefop.europa.eu
Interactive website:
http://www.trainingvillage.gr
Tel. +30 2310490111
Fax +30 2310490049
PO Box 22427 Pylea
GR-57001 Thessaloniki

The European Union (EU), its Member States and social partners are committed to making Europe's education and training systems the best in the world.

Cedefop (the European Centre for the Development of Vocational Training), as the EU's agency supporting policy development in vocational education and training, provides the expertise to help them achieve that aim.

Cedefop supports policy development and helps strengthen European cooperation in vocational education and training policy by providing applied research, policy analysis, support for developing European tools and approaches, encouraging mutual and peer learning and effective communication. Cedefop was founded in 1975 by Council Regulation (EEC) 337/75.

Cedefop's priorities for 2009-11 provide the focus for its activities. They are:
— informing European VET policies
— interpreting European trends in and challenges for skills, competences and learning
— assessing VET's benefits
— raising the profile of VET.

Cedefop's web portal www.cedefop.europa.eu provides information on its activities for vocational education and training policy-makers, researchers. Cedefop's web portal provides:
— news on training developments (briefing notes, newsletters, press releases);
— information on Cedefop's conferences and events;
— access to bibliographical database and information on vocational education and training systems in Europe;
— summaries of Cedefop's activities and networks (ReferNet, Skillsnet, etc.);
— access to Europass and study visits;
— information about Cedefop and about working with us (vacancies, calls for tender, etc.).

Most of Cedefop's publications can also be downloaded at Cedefop's bookshop. Cedefop publications cover a range of issues, including:
— vocational education and training policy
— vocational education and training research
— future skill needs
— learning outcomes
— European qualifications framework
— validation of informal and non-formal learning
— teachers and trainers.

Juan MENÉNDEZ-VALDÉS
Chairman of the Administrative Board

Aviana BULGARELLI
Director
E-mail: aviana.bulgarelli@cedefop.europa.eu
Tel. +30 2310490140

Christian F. LETTMAYR
Deputy Director
E-mail: christian.lettmayr@cedefop.europa.eu
Tel. +30 2310490169

Eleonora SCHMID
Assistant to the Director
E-mail: lore.schmid@cedefop.europa.eu
Tel. +30 2310490027

Internal Audit

Michael KEMMER
Internal Auditor
E-mail: michael.kemmer@cedefop.europa.eu
Tel. +30 2310490038

Area Research and Policy Analysis

Manfred TESSARING
Head of Area
E-mail: manfred.tessaring@cedefop.europa.eu
Tel. +30 2310490151

Area-Enhanced Cooperation in VET and Lifelong Learning (LLL)

Mara BRUGIA
Head of Area
E-mail: mara.brugia@cedefop.europa.eu
Tel. +30 2310490125

Communication, Information and Dissemination

Gerd Oskar BAUSEWEIN
Head of Area
E-mail: Gerd-Oskar.Bausewein@cedefop.europa.eu
Tel. +30 2310490288

Area Resources

Thierry BERNARD-GUELE
Head of Area
E-mail: thierry.bernard-guele@cedefop.europa.eu
Tel. +30 2310490062

Legal Advisor

Miriam FUCHS
E-mail: miriam.fuchs@cedefop.europa.eu
Tel. +30 2310490061

Human Resources

Ginette MANDERSCHEID
Head of Service
E-mail: ginette.manderscheid@cedefop.europa.eu
Tel. +30 2310490072

Finance and Procurement

George PARASKEVAIDIS
Head of Service
E-mail: georgios.paraskevaidis@cedefop.europa.eu
Tel. +30 2310490145

Accountancy

Stephen TEMKOW
E-mail: stephen.temkow@cedefop.europa.eu
Tel. +30 2310490013

ICT and Facilities

Lazaros TOSSOUNIDIS
Head of Service
E-mail: lazaros.tossounidis@cedefop.europa.eu
Tel. +30 2310490176

Brussels Office

Office 4/67 Tour Madou
Place Madou 1
B-1210 Saint-Josse-Ten-Noode Brussels
Tel. +32 22991093
Fax +32 22921891

Jens BJØRNÅVOLD
Service Manager
E-mail: jens.bjornavold@cedefop.europa.eu
Tel. +32 22991093

FUSION FOR ENERGY (EUROPEAN JOINT UNDERTAKING FOR ITER AND THE DEVELOPMENT OF FUSION ENERGY)

calle Josep Pla, 2
Torres Diagonal Litoral
Building B3, 8th floor
E-08019 Barcelona
E-mail: info@f4e.europa.eu
Website: http://fusionforenergy.europa.eu
Tel. +34 933201800
Fax +34 933201851

The 'Fusion for Energy' joint undertaking was set up in 2007. With a 4 billion euro budget for the first ten years, its task is to work with European industry and research organisations on the development and manufacturing of hi-tech components for the ITER fusion project.

Drawing on Fusion for Energy's pool of collective expertise, Europe can become world leader in the construction of demonstration fusion reactors. The members of the Joint Undertaking are the 27 EU countries, Euratom (represented by the European Commission) and Switzerland.

The aims of Fusion for Energy are:
— to provide Europe's contribution to the ITER fusion demonstration device to be built in Cadarache, France;
— to prepare for the next generation of more advanced demonstration fusion reactors (DEMO);
— to lead the EU's cooperation with Japan on fusion ('broader approach' agreement).

Structure:
A Director (chief executive officer) is responsible for day-to-day management. Each member of Fusion for Europe is represented on the Governing Board. The Governing Board is assisted by an Executive Committee (e.g. to approve the awarding of contracts). On technical and scientific matters, the Governing Board and Director are advised by a technical advisory panel.

Didier GAMBIER
Director

EUROPEAN TRAINING FOUNDATION (ETF)

Villa Gualino
Viale Settimio Severo, 65
I-10133 Turin
E-mail: info@etf.europa.eu
Website: http://www.etf.europa.eu
Tel. +39 0116302222
Fax +39 0116302200

The European Training Foundation (ETF) is an agency of the European Union (EU) established to help countries surrounding the EU — partner countries — to reform their education and training systems, and so bring out the full potential of their people.

The ETF is funded from the European Union's external relations programmes. All its activities are designed to maximise the investment in education and training reform in partner countries, in line with EU external relations policies.

The ETF believes that a holistic approach to learning — one that encompasses every aspect of education and training throughout an individual's lifetime — is the best way to help transition economies increase their prosperity, create sustainable growth and encourage social inclusion.

The ETF regards education and training as part of one, complete learning system. It helps its partner countries to modernise their education and training systems — equipping their people with the knowledge, skills and wider competences to take part in dynamic economies and societies.

Training used to be about helping people acquire specific skills for the labour market. Education, too, was treated as a series of separate stages from childhood to adulthood.

In today's fast-changing world, such limited approaches are no longer sustainable — especially when it comes to tackling the enormous social and economic challenges the partner countries often face.

The ETF works on projects in partner countries to reform vocational education, training and employment systems.

On a broader level, the ETF:
— provides information, advice and help to the European Community in developing human resources policies in partner countries;
— supports relevant stakeholders in partner countries to build capacity in human resources development;
— helps deliver Community assistance to stakeholders in partner countries;
— encourages networking and the sharing of information, experience and good practice, both between the European Union and partner countries, and among partner countries.

The ETF works with the following countries surrounding the EU in the context of the EU's external relations programmes.
— The European neighbourhood policy offers a privileged relationship based on a mutual commitment to common values. It applies to the EU's immediate neighbours by land or sea: Algeria, Armenia, Azerbaijan, Belarus, Egypt, Georgia, Israel, Jordan, Lebanon, Moldova, Morocco, Syria, Tunisia, Ukraine and the Palestinian territories. A similar partnership also exists for Russia.
— The enlargement process helps countries transform in readiness for joining the EU. Currently these are Albania, Bosnia and Herzegovina, Croatia, Kosovo, the former Yugoslav Republic of Macedonia, Montenegro, Serbia and Turkey.
— The ETF also works with development countries in Central Asia, specifically Kazakhstan, Kyrgyzstan, Tajikistan, Turkmenistan and Uzbekistan.

Odile QUINTIN
Chair of the Governing Board

David LIPMAN
Representative of the European Commission

Timo SUMMA
Representative of the European Commission

Muriel DUNBAR
Director
E-mail: muriel.dunbar@etf.europa.eu

Operations Department

Peter GREENWOOD
E-mail: peter.greenwood@etf.europa.eu

External Communication

Bent SØRENSEN
E-mail: bent.sorensen@etf.europa.eu

Planning, Monitoring and Evaluation

Xavier MATHEU DE CORTADA
E-mail: xavier.matheu-de-cortada@etf.europa.eu

Administration Department

Olivier RAMSAYER
E-mail: olivier.ramsayer@etf.europa.eu

EUROPEAN FOUNDATION FOR THE IMPROVEMENT OF LIVING AND WORKING CONDITIONS (EUROFOUND)

Wyattville Road
Loughlinstown
Dublin 18
Ireland
E-mail: postmaster@eurofound.europa.eu
Website: http://www.eurofound.europa.eu
Tel. +353 12043100
Fax +353 12826456

Eurofound is a European Union body set up in 1975 to contribute to the planning and establishment of better living and working conditions in Europe. It provides findings, knowledge and advice, from independent and comparative research, to governments, employers, trade unions and the European Commission.

Eurofound organises its work around three core areas of expertise, with a focus on the following issues:

— industrial relations and working conditions (including work organisation, time issues in the workplace, flexibility, monitoring of changes in working conditions, employee participation in decision-making);
— living conditions (issues that affect the everyday lives of Europe's citizens, including the balance between work and family life, the provision of social public services and promoting integration into employment);
— anticipation and management of change (industrial change and corporate restructuring, supply of labour in changing labour markets).

Eurofound research reports can be downloaded free of charge from the website or ordered online (www.eurofound.europa.eu). Eurofound has a tripartite Governing Board, made up representatives from public authorities (governments and the European Commission), employer organisations and trade unions.

Herman FONCK
Chairperson of the Governing Board

Jorma KARPPINEN
Director
E-mail: jka@eurofound.europa.eu

...
Deputy Director

Eberhard KÖHLER
Advisor to the Directorate
E-mail: emk@eurofound.europa.eu

Liaison office, Brussels

Sylvie JACQUET
Head of Office
E-mail: sja@eurofound.europa.eu

1. Research programmes

Employment and Competitiveness

Donald STORRIE
Coordinator (acting)
E-mail: dst@eurofound.europa.eu

Industrial Relations and Workplace Development

Stavroula DEMETRIADES
Coordinator
E-mail: std@eurofound.europa.eu

Living Conditions and Quality of Life

Robert ANDERSON
Coordinator
E-mail: rma@eurofound.europa.eu

Monitoring and Surveys

Agnès PARENT-THIRION
Coordinator
E-mail: apt@eurofound.europa.eu

2. Information and communication

Mary MCCAUGHEY
Head of Information and Communication
E-mail: mcu@eurofound.europa.eu

Communication Products

Barbara GERSTENBERGER
Head of Communication Products
E-mail: bge@eurofound.europa.eu

Customer Relations

Catherine PRESTON
Customer Relations Manager
E-mail: cpr@eurofound.europa.eu

Press Office

Måns MÅRTENSSON
Press Officer
E-mail: mma@eurofound.europa.eu

3. Administrative and research support services

Administration and Finance

Markus GRIMMEISEN
Head of Administration and Finance
E-mail: mgr@eurofound.europa.eu

Human Resources

Raymond COMERFORD
Head of Human Resources
E-mail: rac@eurofound.europa.eu

Information and Communication Technologies

Jim HALPENNY
Head of Information Technologies
E-mail: jim@eurofound.europa.eu

Operational Support Unit

Mattanja DE BOER
Head of Operations
E-mail: mdb@eurofound.europa.eu

EUROPEAN MONITORING CENTRE FOR DRUGS AND DRUG ADDICTION (EMCDDA)

Palacete Mascarenhas
Rua da Cruz de Santa
Apolónia, 23–25
P-1149-045 Lisbon
E-mail: info@emcdda.europa.eu
Website: http://www.emcdda.europa.eu
Tel. +351 218113000
Fax +351 218131711

The European Monitoring Centre for Drugs and Drug Addiction (EMCDDA) is the hub of drug-related information in the European Union. Its role is to gather, analyse and disseminate factual, objective, reliable and comparable information on drugs and drug addiction and, in so doing, provide its audiences with a sound and evidence-based picture of the drug phenomenon at European level.

Among the Centre's target groups are policy-makers, who use this information to help formulate coherent national and Community drug strategies.

Professionals and researchers working in the drugs field and, more broadly, the European media and general public are also served.

At the heart of the Centre's work is the task of improving the comparability of drug information across Europe and devising the methods and tools required to achieve this. As a result of efforts to date, countries can now view how they fit into the wider European picture and examine common problems and goals.

A key feature of the drug phenomenon is its shifting, dynamic nature, and tracking new developments is a central task of the EMCDDA. The Centre obtains information primarily from the Reitox network, a group of focal points in each of the 27 EU Member States, Norway, the candidate countries to the EU and at the European Commission. The*Annual report on the state of the drugs problem in the European Union and Norway (Annual report on the state of the drugs problem in Europe)* and an online*Statistical bulletin* offer a yearly overview of the latest European drug situation and trends. Online country situation summaries provide a rich pool of national drug-related data.

The EMCDDA works on the assumption that sound information is the key to an effective strategy on drugs. Although the Centre cannot propose any kind of policy model, it is now making a clear impact on decision-making through its analyses, instruments and standards.

Marcel REIMEN
Chairman of the Management Board

Ralf LÖFSTEDT
Vice-Chairman of the Management Board

Wolfgang GÖTZ
Director
E-mail: Wolfgang.Goetz@emcdda.europa.eu

Directorate

Gonçalo FELGUEIRAS
Assistant to the Director
E-mail: Goncalo.Felgueiras@emcdda.europa.eu

Monika BLUM
Assistant to the Management Board
E-mail: Monika.Blum@emcdda.europa.eu

Epidemiology, crime and markets

Paul GRIFFITHS
Head of Unit
E-mail: Paul.Griffiths@emcdda.europa.eu

Interventions, law and policies

Roland SIMON
Head of Unit
E-mail: Roland.Simon@emcdda.europa.eu

Reitox and international cooperation

Alexis GOOSDEEL
Head of Unit
E-mail: Alexis.Goosdeel@emcdda.europa.eu

Scientific partners and documentation

Margareta NILSON
Head of Unit
E-mail: Margareta.Nilson@emcdda.europa.eu

Communication

Rosemary DE SOUSA
Head of Unit
E-mail: Rosemary.de.Sousa@emcdda.europa.eu

Information and communication technologies

Pedro RIBEIRO
Head of Unit
E-mail: Pedro.Ribeiro@emcdda.europa.eu

Administration

Dante STORTI
Head of Unit
E-mail: Dante.Storti@emcdda.europa.eu

COMMUNITY PLANT VARIETY OFFICE (CPVO)

3, bd du Maréchal Foch
BP 10121
F-49101 Angers Cedex 02
E-mail: cpvo@cpvo.europa.eu
Website: http://www.cpvo.europa.eu
Tel. +33 241256400
Fax +33 241256410

Council Regulation (EC) No 2100/94 of 27 July 1994 established a system of Community plant variety rights as the sole and exclusive form of Community industrial property rights for new plant varieties. The system is administered by the Community Plant Variety Office (CPVO). The CPVO is a self-financing Community body with legal personality, which came into being on 27 April 1995. Since August 1997, the CPVO has been based in Angers (France).

The CPVO decides on applications for Community plant variety rights on the basis of a formal examination and a technical examination of the candidate variety. A Community plant variety right is valid for 25 or 30 years, depending on the species. The rights are valid in all 27 Member States of the EU. Since 1995, the CPVO has received more than 33 000 applications and has granted more than 23 500 titles of protection.

The CPVO is managed by its President, assisted by a Vice-President, both appointed by the Council of the EU. It consists of two units, the Technical Unit and the Finance and Administration Unit, supported by IT, personnel and legal services. The CPVO is supervised by an Administrative Council comprising one representative of each Member State and of the European Commission, and their alternates. A Board of Appeal is responsible for deciding on appeals against decisions of the CPVO. A right of appeal against a decision of the board lies with the Court of First Instance and subsequently the Court of Justice.

Bart KIEWIET
President

Carlos GODINHO
Vice-Chair

Martin EKVAD
Head of the Legal Service

Dirk THEOBALD
Head of the Technical Unit

Thomas WOLLERSEN
Head of the Administration and Finance Unit

Management Board

Jože ILERŠIČ
Chair

Udo VON KRÖCHER
Vice Chair

OFFICE FOR HARMONIZATION IN THE INTERNAL MARKET (TRADE MARKS AND DESIGNS) (OHIM)

Avenida de Europa, 4
E-03008 Alicante
E-mail: information@oami.europa.eu
Website: http://www.oami.europa.eu
Tel. +34 965139100, 96513 + extension
Fax +34 965131344

The OHIM is the official authority carrying out the procedures for the Community trade marks since 1996 and for the Community registered design from 2003. These intellectual property rights are valid in all the countries of the EU.

Trade marks and designs belong to the world of private company law. The OHIM is both an agency of the European Community and an industrial property office with its technical function being the registration of industrial property rights.

As a service agency, the Office has to place its clients, that is to say the businesses that file their trade marks and their designs with the OHIM, at the centre of the overall mechanism of the Office and it has to provide them with the best service at the best price.
The Community trade mark and the Community registered design are the gateway to a single market. Their unitary nature means that formalities and management can be kept simple: a single application, a single administrative centre and a single file to be managed.

A uniform law applies to trade marks and designs, thereby providing strong and unique protection throughout the European Union. The simplification results in considerably reduced costs as compared with the overall costs of national registration in all countries of the European Union.

The size of the OHIM today, the speed at which it has grown and the way it became self-financing from its second year of operation are proof of the success of the system at the service of the single market.

Chairman of the Administrative Board

Martti ENÄJÄRVI

Chairman of the Budget Committee

Robert ULLRICH

President of the Office for Harmonisation in the Internal Market (Trade Marks and Designs)

Wubbo de BOER

Vice-President

Peter LAWRENCE

Boards of Appeal

Paul MAIER
Chair

First Board of Appeal

Theophilos MARGELLOS
Chair

Second Board of Appeal

Tomás DE LAS HERAS LORENZO
Chair

Third Board of Appeal

Theophilos MARGELLOS
Chair

Fourth Board of Appeal

Detlef SCHENNEN
Chair

Industrial-property policy

Vincent O'REILLY
Chair

Designs

Peter RODINGER
Chair

Finance

Peter LAWRENCE
Chair

General affairs and external relations

João MIRANDA DE SOUSA
Director

Human resources

Peter LAWRENCE
Director

Information technologies and facilities management

Marc VANAEKEN
Director

Quality management

Juan Ramón RUBIO MUÑOZ
Director

Cancelling trade marks

Beate SCHMIDT
Director

Trade marks

Hans JAKOBSEN
Director

Industrial property litigation

Oreste MONTALTO
Director

'Common foreign and security policy' agencies

EUROPEAN DEFENCE AGENCY (EDA)

Rue des Drapiers 17–23
B-1050 Brussels
E-mail: info@eda.europa.eu
Website: http://www.eda.europa.eu
Tel. +32 25042800
Fax +32 25042815

The European Defence Agency was established under a Joint Action of the Council of Ministers of 12 July, 2004, 'to support the Member States and the Council in their effort to improve European defence capabilities in the field of crisis management and to sustain the European security and defence policy as it stands now and develops in the future'.

The Agency's tasks are to:
— work for a more comprehensive and systematic approach to defining and meeting the capability needs of ESDP;
— promote more effective use of defence R & T resources in Europe;
— promote equipment collaborations, both to contribute to defence capabilities and as catalysts for further restructuring of the European defence industry;
— work for an internationally competitive European defence equipment market and a strong defence technological and industrial base.

These functions all relate to improving Europe's defence performance, by promoting coherence in place of fragmentation. The Agency's comparative advantage is its ability to tie its different agendas together, so as to realise their synergies. Its special position allows it to develop uniquely relevant analyses and proposals across the range of its activities.

The European Defence Agency is an agency of the European Union and therefore under the direction and authority of the Council, which issues guidelines to and receives reports from High Representative Javier Solana as Head of the Agency.

Overall control and guidance is exercised by the Steering Board, which is chaired by Solana. It is made up of Defence Ministers from the participating Member States (all EU members except Denmark) and a member of the European Commission. In addition to ministerial meetings at least twice a year, the Steering Board also meets at the level of national armaments directors, R & T directors and in capabilities formation. The EDA is managed by a staff headed by the Chief Executive, Alexander Weis.

Alexander WEIS
Chief Executive

Carlo MAGRASSI
Deputy Chief Executive

Adam SOWA
Deputy Chief Executive

Media and communication

Malgorzata ALTERMAN
Head of Unit

Planning and policy

Dick ZANDEE
Head of Unit

Capabilities

Jonathan MULLIN
Director

Research and technology

Bertrand DE CORDOUE
Director

Armaments

Jukka JUUSTI
Director

Industry and market

Ulf HAMMARSTRÖM
Director

Corporate services

Franco BALDI
Director

EUROPEAN UNION SATELLITE CENTRE (EUSC)

Apdo de Correos 511
E-28850 Torrejon de Ardoz (Madrid)
E-mail: info@eusc.europa.eu
Tel. +34 916786000
Fax +34 916786006

The EU Satellite Centre supports the decision-making of the European Union by providing geospatial intelligence products and services in the context of the common foreign and security policy and, in particular, the European security and defence policy, primarily through the analysis of data from Earth observation satellites.

Under the supervision of the Political and Security Committee and the operational direction of the EU Secretary-General/High Representative, Javier Solana, the EUSC is a decentralised agency of the EU that responds to requests from different users: the Council of the European Union, Member States, the European Commission, third states [1] and international organisations such as the UN or NATO.

The Centre provides early warning of potential crises to decision-makers in order to enable timely, diplomatic, economic and humanitarian measures, including generic planning for intervention. Examples of activities that the EUSC supports are:
— European security and defence policy operations;

— arms control and non proliferation treaty verification;
— countering terrorism;
— humanitarian aid missions;
— contingency planning of peacekeeping missions;
— countering crime;
— general security surveillance.

In response to task requests, the EUSC produces geospatial analysis reports. These range from brief descriptions for rapid response requirements to detailed studies on complex areas and installations. Furthermore, the Centre offers specialised training to image analysts from Member States.

The EUSC cooperates with national and international institutions in the field of space. It participates in the 'global monitoring for environment and security' programme (GMES) and works closely with the European Defence Agency, the European Commission and the European Space Agency, as well as other institutions and international organisations.

(¹) Third states are non-EU European NATO members and other countries which are candidates for accession to the EU.

Frank ASBECK
Director

Tomaž LOVRENČIČ
Deputy Director

Operations Division

Adriano BAPTISTA
Head of Division

Operations Support Division

Brian ROUTLEDGE
Head of Division

Administration and Personnel Division

Jean-Baptiste TAUPIN
Head of Division (acting)

Technical Division

Brian ROUTLEDGE
Head of Division (acting)

Finance Section

Javier ROC
Head of Section

Brussels Office

Benedict ENGELEN
Brussels Point of Contact

EUROPEAN UNION INSTITUTE FOR SECURITY STUDIES (ISS)

43, avenue du Président Wilson
F-75775 Paris Cedex 16
E-mail: info@iss.europa.eu
Tel. +33 156891930
Fax +33 156891931

The European Union Institute for Security Studies (ISS) was set up in 2002 based on a Council Joint Action on 20 July 2001, (OJ L 200, 25 July 2001). Its aim is to help create a common European security culture, to support the strategic debate by providing the best possible interface between European decision-makers and the diverse circles of non-official specialists.

The Institute's activities are directed towards data analysis and recommendations necessary for EU policymaking. Consequently, the Institute contributes to the development of the EU's common foreign and security policy (CFSP) by executing several main tasks:
— organising research and debate on key security and defence issues that are of importance to the European Union;
— bringing together academics, officials, experts and decision-makers from the EU Member States, other European countries, the United States and Canada in order to provide a forward-looking analysis on defence issues for the EU's Council of Ministers and the High Representative for the EU's common foreign and security policy (CFSP);
— developing a transatlantic dialogue on all security issues among the countries of Europe, the United States and Canada in order to raise the profile of the transatlantic relationship and enrich both sides' approaches to security issues;
— offering fellowships in order to expand its network of contacts and synergies with national think tanks.

Visiting fellowships are given to junior academics from all European countries, while senior visiting fellowships are granted to well-known experts. The Institute has an autonomous status and intellectual freedom, which means that it does not represent or defend any particular national interest. Its activities look collectively and from a 'thinking European' point of view at issues that are normally dealt separately by each Member State, allowing for constructive criticism on the EU's current security and defence policy (ESDP).

Alvaro DE VASCONCELOS
Director

'Police and judicial cooperation in criminal matters' agencies

CEPOL – EUROPEAN POLICE COLLEGE

CEPOL Secretariat
CEPOL House
Bramshill, Hook
RG27 0JW Hampshire
United Kingdom
E-mail: secretariat@cepol.europa.eu
Website: http://www.cepol.europa.eu
Tel. +44 01256602668
Fax +44 01256602996

The European Police College (CEPOL) is the European agency tasked with organising training for senior police officers in Member States of the European Union. CEPOL brings together senior police officers across Europe to encourage cross-border cooperation in the fight against crime and maintenance of public security and law and order.

CEPOL began operating in 2001 and became an EU agency on 1 January 2006 (Council Decision 2005/681/JHA of 20 September 2005). CEPOL has an annual budget of 8.8 million euro (2009) funded by the European Communities.

CEPOL operates as a network where the activities — courses, seminars, conferences and meetings — are implemented in and by Member States, mainly by the national senior police training colleges.

CEPOL organises between 80–100 courses, seminars and conferences per year on key topics relevant to police forces in Europe, as well as carries out specialised projects such as the CEPOL/Agis exchange programme for senior officers and trainers and the Euromed police II project for Meda countries.

CEPOL also focuses on developing common curricula to harmonise training programmes, combating cross-border crime through specialist training; disseminating best practice and research findings; providing training for trainers; providing training for police authorities in candidate countries; and providing a state-of-the-art electronic network for sharing knowledge and best practice.

In 2008, over 2 000 senior police officers attended CEPOL activities and more than 750 experts, lecturers and trainers contributed to its activities. A vast majority of the experts, lecturers and trainers were senior police officers, who together with the participants, form a competent and experienced network for future European police cooperation.

The agency cooperates with a wide range of partners, including other law enforcement agencies such as Europol and Interpol. CEPOL has working agreements with non-EU countries Iceland, Norway and Switzerland and has built relationships with other non-EU countries and different universities and research institutes.

CEPOL's secretariat, headed by Director Ulf Göransson, is based at Bramshill in the United Kingdom, and provides the network with administrative, budgetary and logistical support. The 20-plus staff members carry out the day-to-day work within two units: the Programme Unit and the Administration Unit together with the eight staff members working on the projects.

The acronym CEPOL is French and stands for*collège européen de police*: European Police College, in English.

Ulf GORANSSON
Director
E-mail: director@cepol.europa.eu

Brenda SCOTT
Senior Secretary
E-mail: brenda.scott@cepol.europa.eu

Marcel CHOURRY
Head of Programme
E-mail: marcel.chourry@cepol.europa.eu

Theo BREKELMANS
Programme Coordinator
E-mail: theo.brekelmans@cepol.europa.eu

Joanne BARNETT
Communications Officer
E-mail: joanne.barnett@cepol.europa.eu

Anja VAN BRABANT
Accounting Officer
E-mail: anja.vanbrabant@cepol.europa.eu

Gabriella KAES
Human Resources Officer
E-mail: gabriella.kaes@cepol.europa.eu

Pierre ANTONMATTEI
Euromed Police II Project Manager
E-mail: pierre.antonmattei@cepol.europa.eu

Yordanka MINKOVA
CEPOL/Agis Exchange Programme Project Manager
E-mail: yordanka.minkova@cepol.europa.eu

EUROPEAN JUDICIAL COOPERATION UNIT (EUROJUST)

2500 BD La Haye
B.P.16183
Netherlands
E-mail: info@eurojust.europa.eu
Website: http://www.eurojust.europa.eu
Tel. +31 704125000
Fax +31 704125005

Eurojust is a European Union body established in 2002 to enhance the effectiveness of the competent authorities within Member States when they are dealing with the investigation and prosecution of serious cross-border and organised crime.

Eurojust stimulates and improves the coordination of investigations and prosecutions in the Member States. It improves cooperation between the competent authorities of the Member States, in particular by facilitating the execution of international mutual legal assistance and the implementation of extradition requests. It also supports the competent authorities of the

Member States in rendering their investigations and prosecutions more effective.

Eurojust fulfils a unique role as a permanent body in the European legal area. Its mission is to enhance the development of Europe-wide cooperation on criminal justice cases. This means that Eurojust is a key interlocutor with the European institutions such as the Parliament, the Council and the Commission. This role also provides Eurojust with a mission to be a privileged partner with Liaison Magistrates, the European Judicial Network and organisations such as the European Police Office (Europol) and the European Anti-Fraud Office (OLAF). Eurojust is a legal melting-pot from which subsequent developments to strengthen the European judicial area will be defined.

The College of Eurojust is composed of 27 national members, one nominated by each EU Member State. The national members are senior, experienced prosecutors or judges. Some national members are supported by deputies and assistants (see website).

José Luís LOPES DA MOTA
President of the College and National Member for Portugal

Raivo SEPP
Vice-President and Estonian National Member

Michèle CONINSX
Vice-President and Belgian National Member

Diana ALONSO BLAS
Data Protection Officer
Tel. +31 704125510

...
Head of Unit - Human Resources
Tel. +31 704125550

Elizabeth GAVIN
Head of Budget and Finance
Tel. +31 704125650

Catherine DEBOYSER
Head of the Legal Service
Tel. +31 704125591

Jon BROUGHTON
Head of Management Information Systems
Tel. +31 704125680

Fatima Adélia PIRES MARTINS
EJN Secretary
Tel. +31 704125575

Jacques VOS
Head of Security and General Services and of Events
Tel. +31 704125730

Jacques VOS
Administrative director (acting)

Joannes THUY
Head of Service 'Press and Public Relations'
E-mail: jthuy@eurojust.europa.eu
Tel. +31 704125508
Fax +31 704125005

EUROPEAN POLICE OFFICE (EUROPOL)

Raamweg 47
Den Haag
Netherlands
Postbus 90850
2509 LW Den Haag
Nederland
Website: http://www.europol.europa.eu
Tel. +31 703025000
Fax +31 703025896

Mission

Europol is the European Union law enforcement organisation that handles criminal intelligence. Its aim is to improve the effectiveness of, and cooperation between, the competent authorities of the Member States in preventing and combating serious international organised crime. The mission of Europol is to make a significant contribution to the European Union's law enforcement action against organised crime and terrorism, with an emphasis on targeting criminal organisations.

Mandate

Europol supports the law enforcement activities of the Member States mainly against:
— illicit drug trafficking;
— illicit immigration networks;
— terrorism;
— illicit vehicle trafficking;
— trafficking in human beings including child pornography;
— forgery of money (counterfeiting of the euro) and other means of payment;
— trafficking in radioactive and nuclear substances;
— money laundering.

This applies where an organised criminal structure is involved and two or more Member States are affected.

Based on the Council decision of 6 December 2001 the mandate of Europol was extended, as of 1 January 2002, to deal with the serious forms of international crime listed in the Annex to the Europol Convention, such as environmental crime, organised robbery, illicit trade in cultural goods, and product piracy.

Other main priorities for Europol include crime against persons, financial crime and cybercrime.

Europol supports Member States by:
— facilitating the exchange of information, in accordance with national law, between Europol liaison officers (ELOs). ELOs are seconded to Europol by the Member States as representatives of their national law enforcement agencies;
— providing operational analysis in support of Member States' operations;
— generating strategic reports (e.g. threat assessments) and crime analysis on the basis of information and intelligence supplied by Member States and third parties;
— providing expertise and technical support for investigations and operations carried out within the EU, under the supervision and the legal responsibility of the Member States concerned.

Europol is also active in promoting crime analysis and harmonisation of investigative techniques within the Member States.

Max-Peter RATZEL
Director

1. Information management and technology

Eugenio ORLANDI
Deputy Director

2. Serious crime

Mariano SIMANCAS
Deputy Director

3. Corporate governance

Michel QUILLÉ
Deputy Director

Management Board

Management Board Secretariat

Alfredo NUNZI
Secretary

Financial Controller

Aat van der MEER

Joint Supervisory Body

David SMITH
Chair

Joint Audit Committee

Jan KINŠT

Executive agencies

EUROPEAN RESEARCH COUNCIL EXECUTIVE AGENCY (ERC)

COV2
B-1049 Brussels
E-mail: rtd-erc-info@ec.europa.eu
Website: http://erc.europa.eu

The European Research Council (ERC) is part of the EU's Seventh Research Framework Programme (FP7). It is set up by the European Commission to support investigator-driven frontier research and was established in February 2007 on the basis of the FP7 IDEAS specific programme, with a total budget of 7.5 billion Euro (2007–13).

Its main aim is to stimulate scientific excellence in Europe by supporting and encouraging the very best, truly creative scientists, scholars and engineers, who are invited to submit their individual proposals in any field of research. The ERC consists of an independent Scientific Council and an Executive Agency acting on behalf of the European Commission. The ERC Scientific Council defines the scientific strategy and methodologies, whereas the ERC Executive Agency implements and applies these strategies and methodologies in the management and operations of the ERC funding activities in the legal context of FP7.

The ERC Executive Agency was formally established in December 2007 and is expected to be fully operational in 2009. Until then, a dedicated service of the European Commission has the task of building up the operational capacities and managing ERC activities. The ERC operates transparently with autonomy and integrity which is guaranteed by the European Commission, to which it is accountable. The European Commission assumes final responsibility for the execution of FP7 and its budget.

The ERC Executive Agency manages the following tasks.
- Execute the annual work programme, as defined by the ERC Scientific Council and adopted by the Commission
- Implement calls for proposals, in accordance with the work programme
- Provide information and support to applicants
- Organise peer review evaluation
- Establish and manage grant agreements, in accordance with the EU's financial regulation
- Provide assistance to the ERC Scientific Council.

Jack METTHEY
Director ad interim

TRANS-EUROPEAN TRANSPORT NETWORK EXECUTIVE AGENCY (TEN-T EA)

Square du Frère Orban 10
B-1049 Brussels
E-mail (for general questions):
TENT-AGENCY@ec.europa.eu
E-mail (for questions concerning human resources): TREN-TENT-HR@ec.europa.eu
Website: http://ec.europa.eu/tentea

An effective trans-European transport network benefits all European citizens by allowing more efficient and more environmental friendly transport, while re-enforcing economic and social cohesion across the continent at the same time. Envisioning such a network, the European Commission's TEN-T programme dedicates financial support towards the realisation of important transport infrastructure projects — in line with the overreaching goal of European competitiveness, job creation and cohesion.

With these ambitions in mind, the Trans-European Transport Network Executive Agency (TEN-T EA) was created by the European Commission in 2006. Based in Brussels, the Agency's mission is to provide an efficient and effective service in realising the technical and financial implementation of the TEN-T programme.

The Agency is in charge of all open TEN-T projects under the funding scheme 2000–06 and 2007–13. The projects represent all transport modes — air, rail, road, and maritime/sea — plus logistics and intelligent transport systems, and involves all EU Member States.

Its status as an executive agency, means that although independent, the TEN-T EA is closely linked with its parent, the Directorate-General for Energy and Transport (DG TREN). DG TREN deals with all policy-making issues related to the TEN-T programme, while the Agency exists to execute the programme's specific tasks with a limited duration (31 December 2015).

Responsible for defining policy, the European Commission (DG TREN):
- makes political decisions regarding the TEN-T programme;
- defines strategy, objectives and priority areas of action;
- takes final financing decisions;
- monitors and supervises the Agency.

Turning policy into action, TEN-T EA:
- implements the TEN-T programme on behalf of the European Commission and under its responsibility;
- efficiently manages the entire project lifecycle, including organising calls and evaluations and giving support to Member States;
- prepares financing decisions;
- provides key feedback to the European Commission.

The Agency's key stakeholders are the Member States, which are the beneficiaries of the TEN-T project funding. Its work aims to benefit these stakeholders by:
- using new project management techniques and IT tools (GIS, statistical data);
- simplifying administrative procedures;

— reducing payment delays and reaction time on requests;
— increasing the types of services available (expertise in financial engineering, transport engineering) and targeting the flow of information to project promoters, Member States and the Commission;
— focusing on public–private partnerships;
— improving the visibility for EU support to infrastructure projects through dissemination activities.

The Agency's multinational team includes specialists experienced in financial and project management, transport engineering and legal affairs. To provide a fully effective service, the Agency will expand to 99 staff members, reaching its maximum in early 2009.

Dirk BECKERS
Director

Resources

Marcos ROMAN PARRA
Head of Unit

Unit 'Road and Rail'

Ioannis GIOGKARAKIS ARGYROPOULOS
Head of Unit

Unit 'Air, Waterborne Transport, Logistics Innovation and Co-modality'

Christopher NORTH
Head of Unit

Unit 'Technical & Financial Engineering, GIS and Monitoring'

...
Head of Unit

EDUCATION, AUDIOVISUAL AND CULTURE EXECUTIVE AGENCY (EACEA)

Avenue du Bourget 1
B-1140 Brussels
E-mail: eacea-info@ec.europa.eu
Tel. +32 22991111

The Education, Audiovisual and Culture Executive Agency (EACEA), located in Brussels, started work on 1 January 2006. Its mission is to implement certain strands of more than 15 programmes and actions funded by the Community in the areas of education and training: (lifelong learning, Erasmus mundus/ external cooperation), active citizenship (Europe for citizens), youth (youth in action), audiovisual (media 2007) and culture (culture 2007).

Bringing these programmes together under the same roof enables coordinated management and the provision of a full service to programme beneficiaries. Since 2008, the mandate of the Agency has been widened to include the Eurydice network, which is responsible for the collection, analysis and dissemination of information on education systems.

While the Agency has its own legal identity, it operates under the supervision of three Commission directorates-general: Education and Culture (EAC), Information Society Audiovisual and Media (INFSO) and the Europe Aid Cooperation Office (AIDCO), which remain responsible for programming, evaluation and for policy elaboration.

The Agency is responsible for most aspects of the programme management, including the drafting of calls for proposals, project selection, signature of project agreements, financial management, project monitoring (interim and final reports), communicating with beneficiaries and on-site project inspections.

The strands managed by the Agency are all centralised and support technical projects, and in no way involve making political decisions.

In 2009, the Agency will see an extension of its mandate in the field of external cooperation with the arrival of the Tempus programme and the management of education projects funded through bilateral agreements with Australia, Japan, New Zealand, and South Korea, in the framework of the 'industrialised countries instrument education cooperation' programme.

Gilbert GASCARD
Director
Tel. +32 22950017
Fax +32 22921325

P1 — Lifelong learning: Comenius, Minerva, ICT and languages

Brian HOLMES
Head of Unit
Tel. +32 22987979
Fax +32 22921324

P2 — Lifelong learning: Erasmus, Jean Monnet

Ralf RAHDERS
Head of Unit
Tel. +32 22988371
Fax +32 22921326

P3 — Lifelong learning: Leonardo da Vinci and studies, indicators and dissemination, Grundtvig

Monika HOLIK
Head of Unit
Tel. +32 22961655
Fax +32 22921327

P4 — Erasmus Mundus and external cooperation

Joachim FRONIA
Head of Unit
Tel. +32 22967899
Fax +32 22921328

P5 — Culture

Corinne MIMRAN
Head of Unit (acting)
Tel. +32 22953371

P6 — Youth

Antonios KOSMOPOULOS
Head of Unit
Tel. +32 22986814
Fax +32 22921330

P7 — Citizenship

Philippe COVA
Head of Unit
Tel. +32 22967717
Fax +32 22962389

P8 — Media

Constantin DASKALAKIS
Head of Unit
Tel. +32 22984302
Fax +32 22921332

P9 — Eurydice

David HUGHES
Head of Unit
Tel. +32 22994168
Fax +32 22921971

P10 — Tempus

Klaus HAUPT
Head of Unit

R1 — Human Resources, Administration, IT, Communication

...
Head of Unit
Tel. +32 229-64774
Fax +32 229-21333

R2 — Finance, Accounting, Programming

Hubert COUSIN
Head of Unit
Tel. +32 229-96377
Fax +32 229-21334

EXECUTIVE AGENCY FOR COMPETITION AND INNOVATION (EACI)

EACI Commission européenne
Tour Madou
Place Madou 1
B-1049 Brussels
E-mail: eaci-enquiries@ec.europa.eu
Website: http://ec.europa.eu/eaci
EACI Commission européenne
Square Orban 10
B-1049 Brussels
Energy, transport, environment, competitiveness, innovation — Europe today is up against extraordinary challenges but also great opportunities.

Whether it is about promoting smart energy use and 'renewables', creating markets for eco-innovative technology, switching to more sustainable freight transport, or getting better information to SMEs, environmental improvement and commercial success can actually work together.

In order to efficiently deliver high-quality European programmes and initiatives in these areas, the European Commission has set up the Executive Agency for Competitiveness & Innovation (EACI) to manage on its behalf three EU funding schemes ('intelligent energy — Europe', Marco Polo, eco-innovation) and the Enterprise Europe Network.

Our team includes both European Commission officials and professionals from the private sector. They all share a commitment to the European way of linking competitiveness and innovation with environmental protection and a cleaner energy future.

Patrick LAMBERT
Director
Tel. +32 22950531

Unit R — Resources

Guido DE CLERCQ
Head of Unit
Tel. +32 22955096

Unit 1 — IEE Renewable Energy

William GILLETT
Head of Unit
Tel. +32 22995676

Unit 2 — IEE Energy Efficiency

Vincent BERRUTTO
Head of Unit
Tel. +32 22968642

Unit 3 — Enterprise Europe Network Animation

Martine DISS
Head of Unit
Tel. +32 22961494

Unit 4 — Enterprise Europe Network — Project Management

José PUIGPELAT VALLS
Head of Unit

Unité 5 — Market Replication — Eco-Innovation — Intelligent Energy

Beatriz YORDI AGUIRRE
Head of Unit
Tel. +32 22953970

Unit 6 — Marco Polo

Patrick VANKERCKHOVEN
Head of Unit
Tel. +32 22963882

RESEARCH EXECUTIVE AGENCY (REA)

B-1049 Brussels
Belgique/België
E-mail: REA-INFO@ec.europa.eu

The Research Executive Agency, located in Brussels, was created in December 2007. Managing over 6.5 billion euro for the period 2007-2013, it started its work in 2008, and should become fully independent in 2009. The REA works with the four Directorates-General for Research, Enterprise, Information Society and Media and Energy and Transport.

The evaluation of proposals and the management of projects are at the heart of research support. The Research Executive Agency will carry out these evaluation and management processes for a large part of the current research framework programme — FP7. With increasing research budgets, dedicating facilities and services to these tasks is at the core of the framework programme. These dedicated facilities and services will enable us to improve the delivery of support to the research community.

The REA's tasks will be to:
- manage the Marie-Curie fellowships and related grants;
- manage specific research grant agreements for the benefit of small and medium sized enterprises;
- manage multi-partner projects in the field of space research;
- manage multi-partner projects in the field of security research;
- operate the proposal reception and evaluation facility in the Covent Garden building in central Brussels;
- operate a 'one-stop shop' helpdesk for enquiries about FP7;
- It will operate the unique registration facility for project partners to reduce the amount of paperwork involved in project management.

Graham STROUD
Director

EXECUTIVE AGENCY FOR HEALTH AND CONSUMERS (EAHC)

L-2920 Luxembourg
Luxembourg
E-mail: eahc@ec.europa.eu
Website: http://ec.europa.eu/eahc/
Tel. +352 430132015
Fax +352 430130359

The Executive Agency for Health and Consumers (formerly the Public Health Executive Agency) was created on 1 January 2005 to support implementation of EU public health programme.

In 2008, the Agency's lifetime was prolonged until 31 December 2015, and the tasks expanded to include actions in the field of consumer protection and training for safer food. The EAHC new mandate includes implementation of the EU health programme, consumer programme and the 'better training for safer food' initiative.

The Agency performs the tasks entrusted to it by the European Commission, and it works closely with Directorate-General for Health and Consumers. The EAHC manages relations with some 2 200 beneficiaries involved in more than 200 projects in the field of health; it has about 40 staff members based in Luxembourg.

Luc BRIOL
Director

OFFICIAL DIRECTORY OF THE EUROPEAN UNION

© PHOTODISK/GETTY IMAGE

General index of names

General index of names

General index of names

A

B

C

D

E

F

G

H

I

J

K

L

M

N

O

P

Q

R

S

T

U

V

W

X

Y

Z

European Commission

Official Directory of the European Union

Luxembourg: Office for Official Publications of the European Communities

2009 — XL, 488 pp. — 21 x 29,7 cm

ISBN 978-92-78-40601-1

Price (excluding VAT) in Luxembourg: EUR 25.00